List of Elements with Their Symbols and Atomic Weights

Element	Symbol	Atomic Number	Atomic Weight
Actinium	Ac	89	227.03[a]
Aluminum	Al	13	26.981538
Americium	Am	95	243.06[a]
Antimony	Sb	51	121.760
Argon	Ar	18	39.948
Arsenic	As	33	74.92160
Astatine	At	85	209.99[a]
Barium	Ba	56	137.327
Berkelium	Bk	97	247.07[a]
Beryllium	Be	4	9.012182
Bismuth	Bi	83	208.98038
Bohrium	Bh	107	264.12[a]
Boron	B	5	10.811
Bromine	Br	35	79.904
Cadmium	Cd	48	112.411
Calcium	Ca	20	40.078
Californium	Cf	98	251.08[a]
Carbon	C	6	12.0107
Cerium	Ce	58	140.116
Cesium	Cs	55	132.90545
Chlorine	Cl	17	35.453
Chromium	Cr	24	51.9961
Cobalt	Co	27	58.933200
Copernicium	Cn	112	285
Copper	Cu	29	63.546
Curium	Cm	96	247.07[a]
Darmstadtium	Ds	110	281.15[a]
Dubnium	Db	105	262.11[a]
Dysprosium	Dy	66	162.50
Einsteinium	Es	99	252.08[a]
Erbium	Er	68	167.259
Europium	Eu	63	151.964
Fermium	Fm	100	257.10[a]
Fluorine	F	9	18.9984032
Francium	Fr	87	223.02[a]
Gadolinium	Gd	64	157.25
Gallium	Ga	31	69.723
Germanium	Ge	32	72.64
Gold	Au	79	196.96655

Element	Symbol	Atomic Number	Atomic Weight
Hafnium	Hf	72	178.49
Hassium	Hs	108	269.13[a]
Helium	He	2	4.002602[a]
Holmium	Ho	67	164.93032
Hydrogen	H	1	1.00794
Indium	In	49	114.818
Iodine	I	53	126.90447
Iridium	Ir	77	192.217
Iron	Fe	26	55.845
Krypton	Kr	36	83.80
Lanthanum	La	57	138.9055
Lawrencium	Lr	103	262.11[a]
Lead	Pb	82	207.2
Lithium	Li	3	6.941
Lutetium	Lu	71	174.967
Magnesium	Mg	12	24.3050
Manganese	Mn	25	54.938049
Meitnerium	Mt	109	268.14[a]
Mendelevium	Md	101	258.10[a]
Mercury	Hg	80	200.59
Molybdenum	Mo	42	95.94
Neodymium	Nd	60	144.24
Neon	Ne	10	20.1797
Neptunium	Np	93	237.05[a]
Nickel	Ni	28	58.6934
Niobium	Nb	41	92.90638
Nitrogen	N	7	14.0067
Nobelium	No	102	259.10[a]
Osmium	Os	76	190.23
Oxygen	O	8	15.9994
Palladium	Pd	46	106.42
Phosphorus	P	15	30.973761
Platinum	Pt	78	195.078
Plutonium	Pu	94	244.06[a]
Polonium	Po	84	208.98[a]
Potassium	K	19	39.0983
Praseodymium	Pr	59	140.90765
Promethium	Pm	61	145[a]
Protactinium	Pa	91	231.03588
Radium	Ra	88	226.03[a]

Element	Symbol	Atomic Number	Atomic Weight
Radon	Rn	86	222.02[a]
Rhenium	Re	75	186.207[a]
Rhodium	Rh	45	102.90550
Roentgenium	Rg	111	272.15[a]
Rubidium	Rb	37	85.4678
Ruthenium	Ru	44	101.07
Rutherfordium	Rf	104	261.11[a]
Samarium	Sm	62	150.36
Scandium	Sc	21	44.955910
Seaborgium	Sg	106	266[a]
Selenium	Se	34	78.96
Silicon	Si	14	28.0855
Silver	Ag	47	107.8682
Sodium	Na	11	22.989770
Strontium	Sr	38	87.62
Sulfur	S	16	32.065
Tantalum	Ta	73	180.9479
Technetium	Tc	43	98[a]
Tellurium	Te	52	127.60
Terbium	Tb	65	158.92534
Thallium	Tl	81	204.3833
Thorium	Th	90	232.0381
Thulium	Tm	69	168.93421
Tin	Sn	50	118.710
Titanium	Ti	22	47.867
Tungsten	W	74	183.84
Uranium	U	92	238.02891
Vanadium	V	23	50.9415
Xenon	Xe	54	131.293
Ytterbium	Yb	70	173.04
Yttrium	Y	39	88.90585
Zinc	Zn	30	65.39
Zirconium	Zr	40	91.224
*b			284[a]
*b			289[a]
*b			288[a]
*b			292[a]
*b			294[a]
*b		118	294[a]

[a] Mass of longest-lived or most important isotope.
[b] The names of elements 113 and above have not yet been decided.

Brown • LeMay • Bursten • Murphy • Woodward

Chemistry: The Central Science

Custom Edition for the University of Victoria

**University
of Victoria**

Taken from:
Chemistry: The Central Science, Twelfth Edition
by Theodore L. Brown, H. Eugene LeMay, Jr., Bruce E. Bursten, Catherine J. Murphy,
and Patrick M. Woodward

Cover image courtesy of Shutterstock.com

Taken from:

Chemistry: The Central Science, Twelfth Edition
by Theodore L. Brown, H. Eugene LeMay, Jr., Bruce E. Bursten, Catherine J. Murphy, and Patrick M. Woodward
Copyright © 2012, 2009, 2006, 2003, 2000, 1997, 1994, 1991, 1988, 1985, 1981, 1977 by Pearson
Education, Inc.
Published by Prentice Hall
Upper Saddle River, New Jersey 07458

This special edition published in cooperation with Pearson Learning Solutions.

Pearson Learning Solutions, 501 Boylston Street, Suite 900, Boston, MA 02116
A Pearson Education Company
www.pearsoned.com

Printed in Canada

 13 14 15 XXXX 16 15 14

000200010270730398

MHB/AM

PEARSON   ISBN 10: 1-256-16927-7
ISBN 13: 978-1-256-16927-7

To our students,
whose enthusiasm and curiosity
have often inspired us,
and whose questions and suggestions
have sometimes taught us.

BRIEF CONTENTS

CONTENTS

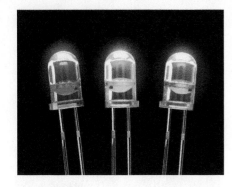

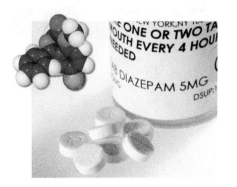

4 MOLECULAR GEOMETRY AND BONDING THEORIES   110

5 INTERMOLECULAR FORCES   154

6 THE CHEMISTRY OF LIFE: ORGANIC AND BIOLOGICAL CHEMISTRY 176

7 SOLIDS AND MODERN MATERIALS 208

8 GASES 232

9 CHEMISTRY OF THE ENVIRONMENT 274

10 THERMOCHEMISTRY 308

11 LIQUIDS 356

12 CHEMICAL EQUILIBRIUM 376

13 CHEMICAL THERMODYNAMICS 416

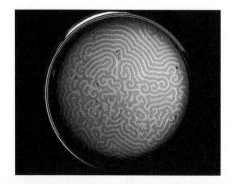

14 CHEMICAL KINETICS 458

Appendices

CHEMICAL APPLICATIONS AND ESSAYS

◢ CHEMISTRY PUT TO WORK

◢ A CLOSER LOOK

◢ CHEMISTRY AND LIFE

◢ STRATEGIES IN CHEMISTRY

PREFACE

TO THE STUDENT

Chemistry: The Central Science, **Twelfth Edition,** has been written to introduce you to modern chemistry. As authors, we have, in effect, been engaged by your instructor to help you learn chemistry. Based on the comments of students and instructors who have used this book in its previous editions, we believe that we have done that job well. Of course, we expect the text to continue to evolve through future editions. We invite you to write to tell us what you like about the book so that we will know where we have helped you most. Also, we would like to learn of any shortcomings so that we might further improve the book in subsequent editions. Our addresses are given at the end of the Preface.

Advice for Learning and Studying Chemistry

Learning chemistry requires both the assimilation of many concepts and the development of analytical skills. In this text we have provided you with numerous tools to help you succeed in both tasks. If you are going to succeed in your chemistry course, you will have to develop good study habits. Science courses, and chemistry in particular, make different demands on your learning skills than do other types of courses. We offer the following tips for success in your study of chemistry:

Don't fall behind! As the course moves along, new topics will build on material already presented. If you don't keep up in your reading and problem solving, you will find it much harder to follow the lectures and discussions on current topics. Experienced teachers know that students who read the relevant sections of the text *before* coming to a class learn more from the class and retain greater recall. "Cramming" just before an exam has been shown to be an ineffective way to study any subject, chemistry included. So now you know. How important to you in this competitive world is a good grade in chemistry?

Focus your study. The amount of information you will be expected to learn can sometimes seem overwhelming. It is essential to recognize those concepts and skills that are particularly important. Pay attention to what your instructor is emphasizing. As you work through the **Sample Exercises** and homework assignments, try to see what general principles and skills they employ. Use the **What's Ahead** feature at the beginning of each chapter to help orient yourself to what is important in each chapter. A single reading of a chapter will simply not be enough for successful learning of chapter concepts and problem-solving skills. You will need to go over assigned materials more than once. Don't skip the **Give It Some Thought** and **Go Figure** features, **Sample Exercises**, and **Practice Exercises**. They are your guides to whether you are learning the material. The **Key Skills** and **Key Equations** at the end of the chapter should help you focus your study.

Keep good lecture notes. Your lecture notes will provide you with a clear and concise record of what your instructor regards as the most important material to learn. Using your lecture notes in conjunction with this text is the best way to determine which material to study.

Skim topics in the text before they are covered in lecture. Reviewing a topic before lecture will make it easier for you to take good notes. First read the **What's Ahead** points and the end-of-chapter **Summary**; then quickly read through the chapter, skipping Sample Exercises and supplemental sections. Paying attention to the titles of sections and subsections gives you a feeling for the scope of topics. Try to avoid thinking that you must learn and understand everything right away.

After lecture, carefully read the topics covered in class. As you read, pay attention to the concepts presented and to the application of these concepts in the Sample Exercises. Once you think you understand a Sample Exercise, test your understanding by working the accompanying Practice Exercise.

Learn the language of chemistry. As you study chemistry, you will encounter many new words. It is important to pay attention to these words and to know their meanings or the entities to which they refer. Knowing how to identify chemical substances from their names is an important skill; it can help you avoid painful mistakes on examinations. For example, "chlorine" and "chloride" refer to very different things.

Attempt the assigned end-of-chapter exercises. Working the exercises selected by your instructor provides necessary practice in recalling and using the essential ideas of the chapter. You cannot learn merely by observing; you must be a participant. In particular, try to resist checking the *Student-Solutions Manual* (if you have one) until you have made a sincere effort to solve the exercise yourself. If you get stuck on an exercise, however, get help from your instructor, your teaching assistant, or another student. Spending more than 20 minutes on a single exercise is rarely effective unless you know that it is particularly challenging.

Use online resources. Some things are more easily learned by discovery, and others are best shown in three dimensions. If your instructor has included MasteringChemistry with your book, take advantage of the unique tools it provides to get the most out of your time in chemistry.

The bottom line is to work hard, study effectively, and use the tools available to you, including this textbook. We want to help you learn more about the world of chemistry and why chemistry is the central science. If you really learn chemistry, you can be the life of the party, impress your friends and parents, and . . . well, also pass the course with a good grade.

THEODORE L. BROWN received his Ph.D. from Michigan State University in 1956. Since then, he has been a member of the faculty of the University of Illinois, Urbana-Champaign, where he is now Professor of Chemistry, Emeritus. He served as Vice Chancellor for Research, and Dean of The Graduate College, from 1980 to 1986, and as Founding Director of the Arnold and Mabel Beckman Institute for Advanced Science and Technology from 1987 to 1993. Professor Brown has been an Alfred P. Sloan Foundation Research Fellow and has been awarded a Guggenheim Fellowship. In 1972 he was awarded the American Chemical Society Award for Research in Inorganic Chemistry and received the American Chemical Society Award for Distinguished Service in the Advancement of Inorganic Chemistry in 1993. He has been elected a Fellow of the American Association for the Advancement of Science, the American Academy of Arts and Sciences, and the American Chemical Society.

H. EUGENE LEMAY, JR., received his B.S. degree in Chemistry from Pacific Lutheran University (Washington) and his Ph.D. in Chemistry in 1966 from the University of Illinois, Urbana-Champaign. He then joined the faculty of the University of Nevada, Reno, where he is currently Professor of Chemistry, Emeritus. He has enjoyed Visiting Professorships at the University of North Carolina at Chapel Hill, at the University College of Wales in Great Britain, and at the University of California, Los Angeles. Professor LeMay is a popular and effective teacher, who has taught thousands of students during more than 40 years of university teaching. Known for the clarity of his lectures and his sense of humor, he has received several teaching awards, including the University Distinguished Teacher of the Year Award (1991) and the first Regents' Teaching Award given by the State of Nevada Board of Regents (1997).

BRUCE E. BURSTEN received his Ph.D. in Chemistry from the University of Wisconsin in 1978. After two years as a National Science Foundation Postdoctoral Fellow at Texas A&M University, he joined the faculty of The Ohio State University, where he rose to the rank of Distinguished University Professor. In 2005, he moved to the University of Tennessee, Knoxville, as Distinguished Professor of Chemistry and Dean of the College of Arts and Sciences. Professor Bursten has been a Camille and Henry Dreyfus Foundation Teacher-Scholar and an Alfred P. Sloan Foundation Research Fellow, and he is a Fellow of both the American Association for the Advancement of Science and the American Chemical Society. At Ohio State he has received the University Distinguished Teaching Award in 1982 and 1996, the Arts and Sciences Student Council Outstanding Teaching Award in 1984, and the University Distinguished Scholar Award in 1990. He received the Spiers Memorial Prize and Medal of the Royal Society of Chemistry in 2003, and the Morley Medal of the Cleveland Section of the American Chemical Society in 2005. He was President of the American Chemical Society for 2008. In addition to his teaching and service activities, Professor Bursten's research program focuses on compounds of the transition-metal and actinide elements.

CATHERINE J. MURPHY received two B.S. degrees, one in Chemistry and one in Biochemistry, from the University of Illinois, Urbana-Champaign, in 1986. She received her Ph.D. in Chemistry from the University of Wisconsin in 1990. She was a National Science Foundation and National Institutes of Health Postdoctoral Fellow at the California Institute of Technology from 1990 to 1993. In 1993, she joined the faculty of the University of South Carolina, Columbia, becoming the Guy F. Lipscomb Professor of Chemistry in 2003. In 2009 she moved to the University of Illinois, Urbana-Champaign, as the Peter C. and Gretchen Miller Markunas Professor of Chemistry. Professor Murphy has been honored for both research and teaching as a Camille Dreyfus Teacher-Scholar, an Alfred P. Sloan Foundation Research Fellow, a Cottrell Scholar of the Research Corporation, a National Science Foundation CAREER Award winner, and a subsequent NSF Award for Special Creativity. She has also received a USC Mortar Board Excellence in Teaching Award, the USC Golden Key Faculty Award for Creative Integration of Research and Undergraduate Teaching, the USC Michael J. Mungo Undergraduate Teaching Award, and the USC Outstanding Undergraduate Research Mentor Award. Since 2006, Professor Murphy has served as a Senior Editor for the Journal of Physical Chemistry. In 2008 she was elected a Fellow of the American Association for the Advancement of Science. Professor Murphy's research program focuses on the synthesis and optical properties of inorganic nanomaterials, and on the local structure and dynamics of the DNA double helix.

PATRICK M. WOODWARD received B.S. degrees in both Chemistry and Engineering from Idaho State University in 1991. He received a M.S. degree in Materials Science and a Ph.D. in Chemistry from Oregon State University in 1996. He spent two years as a postdoctoral researcher in the Department of Physics at Brookhaven National Laboratory. In 1998, he joined the faculty of the Chemistry Department at The Ohio State University where he currently holds the rank of Professor. He has enjoyed visiting professorships at the University of Bordeaux in France and the University of Sydney in Australia. Professor Woodward has been an Alfred P. Sloan Foundation Research Fellow and a National Science Foundation CAREER Award winner. He currently serves as an Associate Editor to the Journal of Solid State Chemistry and as the director of the Ohio REEL program, an NSF-funded center that works to bring authentic research experiments into the laboratories of first- and second-year chemistry classes in 15 colleges and universities across the state of Ohio. Professor Woodward's research program focuses on understanding the links between bonding, structure, and properties of solid-state inorganic functional materials.

A GUIDE TO USING THIS TEXT

■ *Chemistry: The Central Science*, AP* Edition has been the leader in AP chemistry for decades. Now, its unrivaled problems, scientific accuracy, and clarity have been upheld and are woven seamlessly with each new feature. Every word and piece of art has been scrutinized for effectiveness by all five authors, and many revisions are based on student performance data gathered through MasteringChemistry.®

Visualizing concepts makes chemistry accessible

Chemistry is by nature an abstract subject. First, it relies on a symbolic language based on chemical formulas and equations. Second, it is based on the behavior of atoms and molecules—particles far too small to see. By presenting chemistry visually, the authors help you to "see" the chemistry you need to learn and increase your success in the course and on the AP exam.

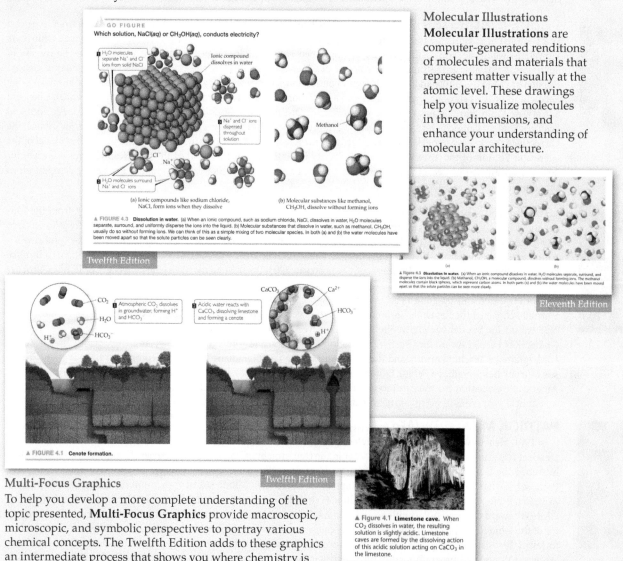

Molecular Illustrations

Molecular Illustrations are computer-generated renditions of molecules and materials that represent matter visually at the atomic level. These drawings help you visualize molecules in three dimensions, and enhance your understanding of molecular architecture.

Multi-Focus Graphics

To help you develop a more complete understanding of the topic presented, **Multi-Focus Graphics** provide macroscopic, microscopic, and symbolic perspectives to portray various chemical concepts. The Twelfth Edition adds to these graphics an intermediate process that shows you where chemistry is occurring in problem solving.

▲ Figure 4.1 **Limestone cave.** When CO_2 dissolves in water, the resulting solution is slightly acidic. Limestone caves are formed by the dissolving action of this acidic solution acting on $CaCO_3$ in the limestone.

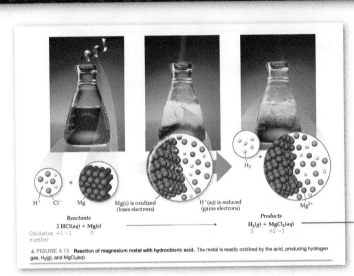

Reactants

$2\,HCl(aq) + Mg(s)$

Oxidation $+1\ -1$ 0
number

$Mg(s)$ is oxidized
(loses electrons)

$H^+(aq)$ is reduced
(gains electrons)

Products

$H_2(g) + MgCl_2(aq)$

0 $+2\ -1$

▲ FIGURE 4.13 **Reaction of magnesium metal with hydrochloric acid.** The metal is readily oxidized by the acid, producing hydrogen gas, $H_2(g)$, and $MgCl_2(aq)$.

Macro to Micro Art

These illustrations offer three parts: a macroscopic image (what you can see with your eyes); a molecular image (what the molecules are doing); and a symbolic representation (how chemists represent the process with symbols and equations).

A new intermediate step has been added, showing where chemistry occurs in the problem-solving process.

A focus on relevance makes chemistry meaningful

Chemistry occurs all around us, throughout every day. Recognizing the importance of chemistry in your daily life can improve your understanding of chemical concepts.

CHEMISTRY PUT TO WORK

Antacids

Your stomach secretes acids to help digest foods. These acids, which include hydrochloric acid, contain about 0.1 mol of H^+ per liter of solution. The stomach and digestive tract are normally protected from the corrosive effects of stomach acid by a mucosal lining. Holes can develop in this lining, however, allowing the acid to attack the underlying tissue, causing painful damage. These holes, known as ulcers, can be caused by the secretion of excess acids or by a weakness in the digestive lining. Studies indicate, however, that many ulcers are caused by bacterial infection. Between 10 and 20% of Americans suffer from ulcers at some point in their lives. Many others experience occasional indigestion or heartburn due to digestive acids entering the esophagus.

We can address the problem of excess stomach acid in two ways: (1) removing the excess acid or (2) decreasing the production of acid. Substances that remove excess acid are called *antacids*, whereas those that decrease acid production are called *acid inhibitors*. ◄ FIGURE 4.10 shows several common over-the-counter antacids, which usually contain hydroxide, carbonate, or bicarbonate ions (▼ TABLE 4.4). Antiulcer drugs, such as Tagamet® and Zantac®, are acid inhibitors. They act on acid-producing cells in the lining of the stomach. Formulations that control acid in this way are now available as over-the-counter drugs.

RELATED EXERCISE: 4.95

▲ FIGURE 4.10 **Antacids.** These products all serve as acid-neutralizing agents in the stomach.

TABLE 4.4 • Some Common Antacids

Commercial Name	Acid-Neutralizing Agents
Alka-Seltzer®	$NaHCO_3$
Amphojel®	$Al(OH)_3$
Di-Gel®	$Mg(OH)_2$ and $CaCO_3$
Milk of Magnesia	$Mg(OH)_2$
Maalox®	$Mg(OH)_2$ and $Al(OH)_3$
Mylanta®	$Mg(OH)_2$ and $Al(OH)_3$
Rolaids®	$NaAl(OH)_2CO_3$
Tums®	$CaCO_3$

Chemistry Put to Work and Chemistry and Life

Chemistry's connection to world events, scientific discoveries, and medical breakthroughs are showcased in **Chemistry and Life** and **Chemistry Put to Work** features throughout the text.

CHEMISTRY AND LIFE

DRINKING TOO MUCH WATER CAN KILL YOU

For a long time dehydration was considered a potential danger for people engaged in extended vigorous activity. Thus, athletes were encouraged to drink lots of water while engaged in active sport. The trend toward extensive hydration has spread throughout society, so that today many people carry water bottles everywhere and dutifully keep well hydrated.

In some circumstances, however, drinking too much water is a greater danger than not drinking enough. Excess water consumption can lead to *hyponatremia*, a condition in which the concentration of sodium ion in the blood is too low. In the past decade at least four marathon runners have died from hyponatremia-related trauma, and dozens more have become seriously ill. For example, a first-time marathoner named Hillary Bellamy, running in the Marine Corps marathon in 2003, collapsed near mile 22 and died the next day. One physician who treated her said that she died from hyponatremia-induced brain swelling, the result of drinking too much water before and during the race.

The normal blood sodium level is 135 to 145 mM (*millimolar*). When that level drops to 125 mM, dizziness and confusion set in. A concentration below 120 mM can be critical. Dangerously low levels can occur in any active athlete who is sweating out salt (NaCl) at the same time that excessive amounts of NaCl-free water are being drunk to compensate for water loss. The condition affects women more than men because of differences in body composition and patterns of metabolism. Drinking a sport drink that contains some electrolytes helps to prevent hyponatremia.

RELATED EXERCISES: 4.63, 4.64

CONCEPTUAL UNDERSTANDING BRINGS CHEMISTRY TO LIFE

The authors help you achieve a deeper understanding of concepts through a variety of learning aids, including **Give it Some Thought** and NEW! **Go Figure** questions.

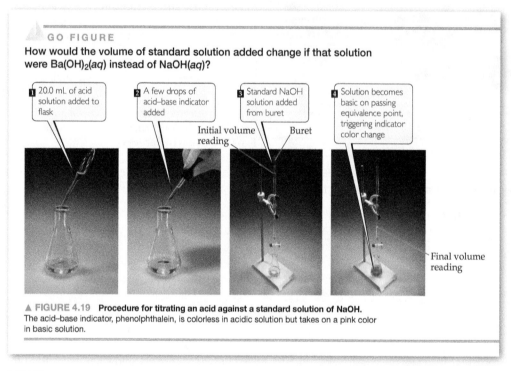

◢ GO FIGURE

How would the volume of standard solution added change if that solution were Ba(OH)₂(aq) instead of NaOH(aq)?

1. 20.0 mL of acid solution added to flask
2. A few drops of acid–base indicator added
3. Standard NaOH solution added from buret
4. Solution becomes basic on passing equivalence point, triggering indicator color change

Initial volume reading Buret

Final volume reading

▲ FIGURE 4.19 **Procedure for titrating an acid against a standard solution of NaOH.** The acid–base indicator, phenolphthalein, is colorless in acidic solution but takes on a pink color in basic solution.

NEW! Go Figure questions
Go Figure questions encourage you to stop and analyze the artwork in the text, for conceptual understanding. "Voice Balloons" in selected figures help you break down and understand the components of the image. These questions are also available in MasteringChemistry.

 GIVE IT SOME THOUGHT

What is the principal reason we must consider the uncertainty principle when discussing electrons and other subatomic particles but not when discussing our macroscopic world?

Give It Some Thought (GIST) questions
These informal, sharply focused exercises give you opportunities to test whether you are "getting it" as you read along. We've increased the number of GIST questions in the Twelfth Edition.

PROBLEM-SOLVING SKILLS HELP YOU SUCCEED IN YOUR COURSE

A consistent problem-solving process is incorporated throughout, so you'll always know where to go when solving problems.

Analyze/Plan/Solve/Check
This four-step problem-solving method helps you understand what you are being asked to solve, to plan how you will solve each problem, to work your way through the solution, and to check your answers. This method is introduced in Chapter 3 and reinforced throughout the book.

Dual-Column Problem-Solving Strategies
Found in Selected Sample Exercises, these strategies explain the thought process involved in each step of a mathematical calculation using a unique layout for clarity. They help you develop a conceptual understanding of those calculations.

SAMPLE EXERCISE 5.6 | **Measuring ΔH Using a Coffee-Cup Calorimeter**

When a student mixes 50 mL of 1.0 *M* HCl and 50 mL of 1.0 *M* NaOH in a coffee-cup calorimeter, the temperature of the resultant solution increases from 21.0 °C to 27.5 °C. Calculate the enthalpy change for the reaction in kJ/mol HCl, assuming that the calorimeter loses only a negligible quantity of heat, that the total volume of the solution is 100 mL, that its density is 1.0 g/mL, and that its specific heat is 4.18 J/g-K.

SOLUTION

Analyze Mixing solutions of HCl and NaOH results in an acid–base reaction:

$$HCl(aq) + NaOH(aq) \longrightarrow H_2O(l) + NaCl(aq)$$

We need to calculate the heat produced per mole of HCl, given the temperature increase of the solution, the number of moles of HCl and NaOH involved, and the density and specific heat of the solution.

Plan The total heat produced can be calculated using Equation 5.23. The number of moles of HCl consumed in the reaction must be calculated from the volume and molarity of this substance, and this amount is then used to determine the heat produced per mol HCl.

Solve

Because the total volume of the solution is 100 mL, its mass is $\quad$ $(100 \text{ mL})(1.0 \text{ g/mL}) = 100 \text{ g}$

The temperature change is $\quad$ $\Delta T = 27.5\,°C - 21.0\,°C = 6.5\,°C = 6.5 \text{ K}$

Using Equation 5.23, we have $\quad$ $q_{rxn} = -C_s \times m \times \Delta T$

$\quad = -(4.18 \text{ J/g-K})(100 \text{ g})(6.5 \text{ K}) = -2.7 \times 10^3 \text{ J} = -2.7 \text{ kJ}$

Because the process occurs at constant pressure, $\quad$ $\Delta H = q_P = -2.7 \text{ kJ}$

To express the enthalpy change on a molar basis, we use the fact that the number of moles of HCl is given by the product of the volume (50 mL = 0.050 L) and concentration (1.0 *M* = 1.0 mol/L) of the HCl solution: $\quad$ $(0.050 \text{ L})(1.0 \text{ mol/L}) = 0.050 \text{ mol}$

Thus, the enthalpy change per mole of HCl is $\quad$ $\Delta H = -2.7 \text{ kJ}/0.050 \text{ mol} = -54 \text{ kJ/mol}$

Check ΔH is negative (exothermic), which is expected for the reaction of an acid with a base and evidenced by the fact that the reaction causes the temperature of the solution to increase. The magnitude of the molar enthalpy change seems reasonable.

PRACTICE EXERCISE

When 50.0 mL of 0.100 *M* AgNO₃ and 50.0 mL of 0.100 *M* HCl are mixed in a constant-pressure calorimeter, the temperature of the mixture increases from 22.30 °C to 23.11 °C. The temperature increase is caused by the following reaction:

$$AgNO_3(aq) + HCl(aq) \longrightarrow AgCl(s) + HNO_3(aq)$$

Calculate ΔH for this reaction in kJ/mol AgNO₃, assuming that the combined solution has a mass of 100.0 g and a specific heat of 4.18 J/g °C.
Answer: −68,000 J/mol = −68 kJ/mol

STRATEGIES IN CHEMISTRY

PROBLEM SOLVING

Practice is the key to success in solving problems. As you practice, you can improve your skills by following these steps:

Step 1: Analyze the problem. Read the problem carefully. What does it say? Draw a picture or diagram that will help you to visualize the problem. Write down both the data you are given and the quantity you need to obtain (the unknown).

Step 2: Develop a plan for solving the problem. Consider a possible path between the given information and the unknown. What principles or equations relate the known data to the unknown?

Recognize that some data may not be given explicitly in the problem; you may be expected to know certain quantities (such as Avogadro's number) or look them up in tables (such as atomic weights). Recognize also that your plan may involve either a single step or a series of steps with intermediate answers.

Step 3: Solve the problem. Use the known information and suitable equations or relationships to solve for the unknown. Dimensional analysis ⇔ (Section 1.6) is a useful tool for solving a great number of problems. Be careful with significant figures, signs, and units.

Step 4: Check the solution. Read the problem again to make sure you have found all the solutions asked for in the problem. Does your answer make sense? That is, is the answer outrageously large or small or is it in the ballpark? Finally, are the units and significant figures correct?

Strategies in Chemistry
Strategies in Chemistry teach ways to analyze information and organize thoughts, helping to improve your problem-solving and critical-thinking abilities.

UPDATED END-OF-CHAPTER MATERIALS BOOST YOUR COMPREHENSION

Unique to the Twelfth Edition, the end-of-chapter materials have been updated and streamlined based on student performance data gathered through MasteringChemistry. Only content that has proven to increase student comprehension of fundamental concepts has been retained.

CHAPTER SUMMARY AND KEY TERMS

INTRODUCTION AND SECTION 3.1 The study of the quantitative relationships between chemical formulas and chemical equations is known as **stoichiometry**. One of the important concepts of stoichiometry is the law of conservation of mass, which states that the total mass of the products of a chemical reaction is the same as the total mass of the reactants. The same numbers of atoms of each type are present before and after a chemical reaction. A balanced **chemical equation** shows equal numbers of atoms of each element on each side of the equation. Equations are balanced by placing coefficients in front of the chemical formulas for the **reactants** and **products** of a reaction, *not* by changing the subscripts in chemical formulas.

SECTION 3.2 Among the reaction types described in this chapter are (1) **combination reactions**, in which two reactants combine to form one product; (2) **decomposition reactions**, in which a single reactant forms two or more products; and (3) **combustion reactions** in oxygen, in which a hydrocarbon or related compound reacts with O_2 to form CO_2 and H_2O.

SECTION 3.3 Much quantitative information can be determined from chemical formulas and balanced chemical equations by using atomic weights. The **formula weight** of a compound equals the sum of the atomic weights of the atoms in its formula. If the formula is a molecular formula, the formula weight is also called the **molecular weight**. Atomic weights and formula weights can be used to determine the elemental composition of a compound.

SECTION 3.4 A mole of any substance is **Avogadro's number** (6.02×10^{23}) of formula units of that substance. The mass of a **mole** of atoms, molecules, or ions (the **molar mass**) equals the formula weight of that material expressed in grams. The mass of one molecule of H_2O, for example, is 18 amu, so the mass of 1 mol of H_2O is 18 g. That is, the molar mass of H_2O is 18 g/mol.

SECTION 3.5 The empirical formula of any substance can be determined from its percent composition by calculating the relative number of moles of each atom in 100 g of the substance. If the substance is molecular in nature, its molecular formula can be determined from the empirical formula if the molecular weight is also known.

SECTIONS 3.6 AND 3.7 The mole concept can be used to calculate the relative quantities of reactants and products in chemical reactions. The coefficients in a balanced equation give the relative numbers of moles of the reactants and products. To calculate the number of grams of a product from the number of grams of a reactant, first convert grams of reactant to moles of reactant. Then use the coefficients in the balanced equation to convert the number of moles of reactant to moles of product. Finally, convert moles of product to grams of product.

A **limiting reactant** is completely consumed in a reaction. When it is used up, the reaction stops, thus limiting the quantities of products formed. The **theoretical yield** of a reaction is the quantity of product calculated to form when all of the limiting reactant reacts. The actual yield of a reaction is always less than the theoretical yield. The **percent yield** compares the actual and theoretical yields.

Summary with Key Terms
These list all of the chapter's boldfaced items, organized by section in order of appearance, with page references. Definitions are found in the Glossary.

Key Equations
The **Key Equations** section lists each of the key equations and important quantitative relationships from the chapter.

KEY EQUATIONS

- $E_{el} = \dfrac{\kappa Q_1 Q_2}{d}$ [8.4]   The potential energy of two interacting charges

- $\mu = Qr$ [8.11]   The dipole moment of two charges of equal magnitude but opposite sign, separated by a distance r

- $\Delta H_{rxn} = \Sigma$(bond enthalpies of bonds broken) $-$ [8.12]   The enthalpy change as a function of bond enthalpies for Σ(bond enthalpies of bonds formed)   reactions involving gas-phase molecules

KEY SKILLS

- Write Lewis symbols for atoms and ions. (Section 8.1)
- Understand lattice energy and be able to arrange compounds in order of increasing lattice energy based on the charges and sizes of the ions involved. (Section 8.2)
- Use atomic electron configurations and the octet rule to write Lewis structures for molecules to determine their electron distribution. (Section 8.3)
- Use electronegativity differences to identify nonpolar covalent, polar covalent, and ionic bonds. (Section 8.4)
- Calculate charge separation in diatomic molecules based on the experimentally measured dipole moment and bond distance. (Section 8.4)
- Calculate formal charges from Lewis structures and use those formal charges to identify the dominant Lewis structure for a molecule or ion. (Section 8.5)
- Recognize molecules where resonance structures are needed to describe the bonding. (Section 8.6)
- Recognize exceptions to the octet rule and draw accurate Lewis structures even when the octet rule is not obeyed. (Section 8.7)
- Understand the relationship between bond type (single, double, and triple), bond strength (or enthalpy), and bond length. (Section 8.8)
- Use bond enthalpies to estimate enthalpy changes for reactions involving gas-phase reactants and products. (Section 8.8)

Key Skills
The **Key Skills** section in each chapter lists the fundamental concepts you should comprehend.

VISUALIZING CONCEPTS

4.1 Which of the following schematic drawings best describes a solution of Li₂SO₄ in water (water molecules not shown for simplicity)? [Section 4.1]

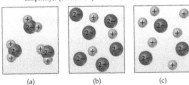

(a)   (b)   (c)

4.2 Aqueous solutions of three different substances, AX, AY, and AZ, are represented by the three accompanying diagrams. Identify each substance as a strong electrolyte, weak electrolyte, or non-electrolyte. [Section 4.1]

AX   AY   AZ

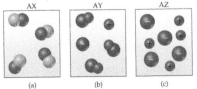

(a)   (b)   (c)

4.3 Use the molecular representations shown here to classify each compound as either a nonelectrolyte, a weak electrolyte, or a strong electrolyte. [Sections 4.1 and 4.3]

(a)   (b)   (c)

See inside back cover for element color scheme.

4.4 A 0.1 M solution of acetic acid, CH₃COOH, causes the light-bulb in the apparatus of Figure 4.2 to glow about as brightly as a 0.001 M solution of HBr. How do you account for this fact? [Section 4.1]

4.5 You are presented with a white solid and told that due to careless labeling it is not clear if the substance is barium chloride, lead chloride, or zinc chloride. When you transfer the solid to a beaker and add water, the solid dissolves to give a clear solution. Next a Na₂SO₄(aq) solution is added and a white precipitate forms. What is the identity of the unknown white solid? [Section 4.2]

4.6 We have seen that ions in aqueous solution are stabilized by the attractions between the ions and the water molecules. Why then do some pairs of ions in solution form precipitates? [Section 4.2]

4.7 Which of the following ions will *always* be a spectator ion in a precipitation reaction? (a) Cl⁻, (b) NO₃⁻, (c) NH₄⁺, (d) S²⁻, (e) SO₄²⁻. Explain briefly. [Section 4.2]

4.8 The labels have fallen off three bottles containing powdered samples of metals; one contains zinc, one lead, and the other platinum. You have three solutions at your disposal: 1 M sodium nitrate, 1 M nitric acid, and 1 M nickel nitrate. How could you use these solutions to determine the identities of each metal powder? [Section 4.4]

4.9 Explain how a redox reaction involves electrons in the same way that a neutralization reaction involves protons. [Sections 4.3 and 4.4]

4.10 If you want to double the concentration of a solution, how could you do it? [Section 4.5]

Visualizing Concepts

Visualizing Concepts exercises begin the end-of-chapter exercises and ask you to consider concepts through the use of models, graphs, and other visual materials. These help you develop a conceptual understanding of the key ideas in the chapter. Additional conceptual exercises are found among the end-of-chapter exercises.

EXERCISES

VISUALIZING CONCEPTS

8.1 For each of these Lewis symbols, indicate the group in the periodic table in which the element X belongs: [Section 8.1]

(a) ·Ẍ·   (b) ·X·   (c) :Ẍ·

8.2 Illustrated are four ions—A, B, X, and Y— showing their relative ionic radii. The ions shown in red carry positive charges: a

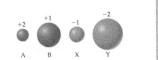

+2   +1   −1   −2
A   B   X   Y

Exercises

End-of-Chapter Exercises are grouped by topic and presented in matched pairs based on data gathered from MasteringChemistry, giving you multiple opportunities to test each concept.

ADDITIONAL EXERCISES

6.75 Consider the two waves shown here, which we will consider to represent two electromagnetic radiations:
(a) What is the wavelength of wave A? Of wave B?
(b) What is the frequency of wave A? Of wave B?
(c) Identify the regions of the electromagnetic spectrum to which waves A and B belong.

A

B

← 1.6 × 10⁻⁷ m →

Additional Exercises
Additional Exercises follow the paired exercises and are not categorized, because many of these exercises draw on multiple concepts from within the chapter.

INTEGRATIVE EXERCISES

6.97 Microwave ovens use microwave radiation to heat food. The energy of the microwaves is absorbed by water molecules in food and then transferred to other components of the food. (a) Suppose that the microwave radiation has a wavelength of 11.2 cm. How many photons are required to heat 200 mL of coffee from 23 °C to 60 °C? (b) Suppose the microwave's power is 900 W (1 Watt = 1 joule-second). How long would you have to heat the coffee in part (a)?

6.98 The stratospheric ozone (O₃) layer helps to protect us from harmful ultraviolet radiation. It does so by absorbing ultraviolet light and falling apart into an O₂ molecule and an oxygen atom, a process known as photodissociation.

$$O_3(g) \longrightarrow O_2(g) + O(g)$$

Use the data in Appendix C to calculate the enthalpy change for this reaction. What is the maximum wavelength a photon can have if it is to possess sufficient energy to cause this dissociation? In what portion of the spectrum does this wavelength occur?

Integrative Exercises

Included among the exercises at the end of Chapters 1–14 **Integrative Exercises** connect concepts for the current chapter with those from previous chapters. These help you gain a deeper understanding of how chemistry fits together and serve as an overall review of key concepts.

[4.114] The newest US standard for arsenate in drinking water, mandated by the Safe Drinking Water Act, required that by January 2006, public water supplies must contain no greater than 10 parts per billion (ppb) arsenic. If this arsenic is present as arsenate, AsO₄³⁻, what mass of sodium arsenate would be present in a 1.00-L sample of drinking water that just meets the standard? Parts per billion is defined on a mass basis as

$$ppb = \frac{g\ solute}{g\ solution} \times 10^9.$$

Bracketed Challenge Problems

The **Bracketed Challenge Problems** have been revised based on student performance data gathered through MasteringChemistry reflecting the difficulty of the problem.

PERSONALIZED COACHING AND FEEDBACK AT YOUR FINGERTIPS

MasteringChemistry is the most effective, widely used online tutorial, homework and assessment system for chemistry. It helps instructors maximize class time with customizable, easy-to-assign, and automatically graded assessments that motivate students to learn outside of class and arrive prepared for lecture. These assessments can easily be customized and personalized by instructors to suit their individual teaching style. To learn more, visit **www.masteringchemistry.com**

Student Tutorials
MasteringChemistry is the only system to provide instantaneous feedback specific to the most-common wrong answers. Students can submit an answer and receive immediate, error-specific feedback. Simpler sub-problems—"hints"—are provided upon request.

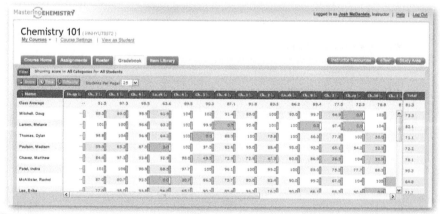

Gradebook
MasteringChemistry is the only system to capture the step-by-step work of each student in class, including wrong answers submitted, hints requested, and time taken on every step. This data powers an unprecedented gradebook.

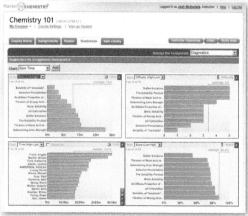

Student Performance Snapshot
This screen provides your favorite weekly diagnostics. With a single click, charts summarize the most difficult problems, vulnerable students, grade distribution, and even score improvement over the course.

EXTEND LEARNING
BEYOND THE CLASSROOM

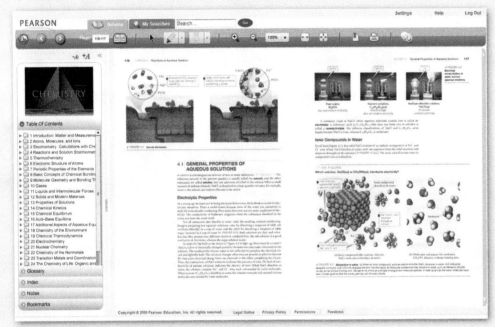

Pearson eText

The eText gives students access to the text whenever and wherever they can access the Internet. The eText pages look exactly like the printed text, and include powerful interactive and customization features.

Students can:

- Create notes, highlight text in different colors, create book marks, zoom, click hyperlinked words and phrases to view definitions, and view in single-page or two-page format.

- Link directly to associated media files, enabling them to view an animation as they read the text.

- Perform a full-text search and save or export notes.

Instructors can share their notes and highlights with students, and can also hide chapters that they do not want students to read.

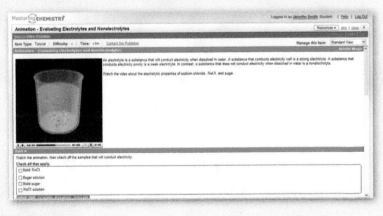

NEW! Visualizations

These new tutorials enable you to make connections between real-life phenomena and the underlying chemistry that explains such phenomena. The tutorials increase your understanding of chemistry and clearly illustrate cause-and-effect relationships.

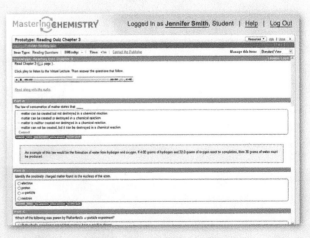

NEW! Reading Quizzes

Chapter-specific quizzes and activities focus on important, hard-to-grasp chemistry concepts.

1

THE GLASS TUBES OF NEON LIGHTS contain various gases that can be excited by electricity. Light is produced when electrically excited atoms return to their lowest-energy states.

orbitals. The orbitals can be described in a shorthand notation using *quantum numbers*.

1.6 REPRESENTATIONS OF ORBITALS
We consider the three-dimensional shapes of orbitals and how they can be represented by graphs of electron density.

1.7 MANY-ELECTRON ATOMS
We recognize that the energy levels for an atom with one electron are altered when the atom contains multiple electrons. Each electron has a quantum-mechanical property called *spin*. The *Pauli exclusion principle* states that no two electrons in an atom can have the same four quantum numbers (three for the orbital and one for the spin). Therefore, an orbital can hold a maximum of two electrons.

1.8 ELECTRON CONFIGURATIONS
We learn that knowing orbital energies as well as some fundamental characteristics of electrons described by *Hund's rule* allows us to determine how electrons are distributed in an atom (*electron configurations*).

1.9 ELECTRON CONFIGURATIONS AND THE PERIODIC TABLE
We observe that the electron configuration of an atom is related to the location of the element in the periodic table.

ELECTRONIC STRUCTURE OF ATOMS

WHAT HAPPENS WHEN SOMEONE switches on a neon light? Electrons in the neon atoms are excited to a higher energy by electricity. An electron can remain in a higher-energy state for only a very short time, and it emits light when it returns to a lower energy. The resulting glow is explained by one of the most revolutionary discoveries of the twentieth century—the *quantum theory*, which explains much of the behavior of electrons in atoms.

In this chapter we explore the quantum theory and its importance in chemistry. We begin by looking at the nature of light and how our description of light was changed by the quantum theory. We will explore some of the tools used in *quantum mechanics*, the "new" physics that had to be developed to describe atoms correctly. We will then use the quantum theory to describe the arrangements of electrons in atoms—what we call the **electronic structure** of atoms. The electronic structure of an atom refers to the number of electrons in the atom as well as their distribution around the nucleus and their energies. We will see that the quantum description of the electronic structure of atoms helps us to understand the arrangement of the elements in the periodic table—why, for example, helium and neon are both unreactive gases, whereas sodium and potassium are both soft, reactive metals.

▲ FIGURE 1.1 **Water waves.** The movement of a boat through the water forms waves that move away from the boat.

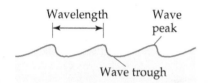

▲ FIGURE 1.2 **Water waves.** The *wavelength* is the distance between two adjacent peaks or two adjacent troughs.

GO FIGURE

If wave (a) has a wavelength of 1.0 m and a frequency of 3.0 × 10⁸ cycles/s, what are the wavelength and frequency of wave (b)?

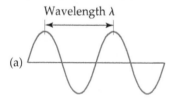
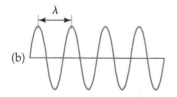

▲ FIGURE 1.3 **Electromagnetic waves.** Like water waves, electromagnetic radiation can be characterized by a wavelength. Notice that the shorter the wavelength, λ, the higher the frequency, ν. The wavelength in (b) is half as long as that in (a), and the frequency of the wave in (b) is therefore twice as great as the frequency in (a).

1.1 | THE WAVE NATURE OF LIGHT

Much of our present understanding of the electronic structure of atoms has come from analysis of the light either emitted or absorbed by substances. To understand electronic structure, therefore, we must first learn about light. The light we see with our eyes, *visible light,* is one type of **electromagnetic radiation**. Because electromagnetic radiation carries energy through space, it is also known as *radiant energy.*

There are many types of electromagnetic radiation in addition to visible light. These different types—radio waves that carry music to our radios, infrared radiation (heat) from a glowing fireplace, X-rays—may seem very different from one another, but they all share certain fundamental characteristics.

All types of electromagnetic radiation move through a vacuum at 3.00×10^8 m/s, the *speed of light.* All have wavelike characteristics similar to those of waves that move through water. Water waves are the result of energy imparted to the water, perhaps by the dropping of a stone or the movement of a boat on the water surface (◄ **FIGURE 1.1**). This energy is expressed as the up-and-down movements of the water.

A cross section of a water wave (◄ **FIGURE 1.2**) shows that it is *periodic,* which means that the pattern of peaks and troughs repeats itself at regular intervals. The distance between two adjacent peaks (or between two adjacent troughs) is called the **wavelength**. The number of complete wavelengths, or *cycles,* that pass a given point each second is the **frequency** of the wave.

Just as with water waves, we can assign a frequency and wavelength to electromagnetic waves, as illustrated in ◄ **FIGURE 1.3**. These and all other wave characteristics of electromagnetic radiation are due to the periodic oscillations in the intensities of the electric and magnetic fields associated with the radiation.

The speed of water waves can vary depending on how they are created—for example, the waves produced by a speedboat travel faster than those produced by a rowboat. In contrast, all electromagnetic radiation moves at the same speed, 3.00×10^8 m/s, the speed of light. As a result, the wavelength and frequency of electromagnetic radiation are always related in a straightforward way. If the wavelength is long, fewer cycles of the wave pass a given point per second, and so the frequency is low. Conversely, for a wave to have a high frequency, it must have a short wavelength. This inverse relationship between the frequency and wavelength of electromagnetic radiation is expressed by the equation

$$c = \lambda\nu \qquad\qquad [1.1]$$

where c is the speed of light, λ (lambda) is wavelength, and ν (nu) is frequency.

Why do different types of electromagnetic radiation have different properties? Their differences are due to their different wavelengths. ► **FIGURE 1.4** shows the various types of electromagnetic radiation arranged in order of increasing wavelength, a display called the *electromagnetic spectrum.* Notice that the wavelengths span an enormous range. The wavelengths of gamma rays are comparable to the diameters of atomic nuclei, whereas the wavelengths of radio waves can be longer than a football field. Notice also that visible light, which corresponds to wavelengths of about 400 to 750 nm (4×10^{-7} m to 7×10^{-7} m), is an extremely small portion of the electromagnetic spectrum. The unit of length chosen to express wavelength depends on the type of radiation, as shown in ▼ **TABLE 1.1**.

TABLE 1.1 • Common Wavelength Units for Electromagnetic Radiation			
Unit	**Symbol**	**Length (m)**	**Type of Radiation**
Angstrom	Å	10^{-10}	X-ray
Nanometer	nm	10^{-9}	Ultraviolet, visible
Micrometer	μm	10^{-6}	Infrared
Millimeter	mm	10^{-3}	Microwave
Centimeter	cm	10^{-2}	Microwave
Meter	m	1	Television, radio
Kilometer	km	1000	Radio

GO FIGURE

How do the wavelength and frequency of an X-ray compare with those of the red light from a neon sign?

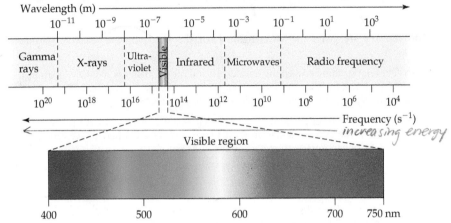

◀ **FIGURE 1.4   The electromagnetic spectrum.** Wavelengths in the spectrum range from very short gamma rays to very long radio waves.

Frequency is expressed in cycles per second, a unit also called a *hertz* (Hz). Because it is understood that cycles are involved, the units of frequency are normally given simply as "per second," which is denoted by s^{-1} or /s. For example, a frequency of 820 kilohertz (kHz), a typical frequency for an AM radio station, could be written as 820 kHz, 820,000 Hz, 820,000 s^{-1}, or 820,000/s.

SAMPLE EXERCISE 1.1   **Concepts of Wavelength and Frequency**

Two electromagnetic waves are represented in the margin. **(a)** Which wave has the higher frequency? **(b)** If one wave represents visible light and the other represents infrared radiation, which wave is which?

SOLUTION

(a) The lower wave has a longer wavelength (greater distance between peaks). The longer the wavelength, the lower the frequency ($\nu = c/\lambda$). Thus, the lower wave has the lower frequency, and the upper wave has the higher frequency.

(b) The electromagnetic spectrum (Figure 1.4) indicates that infrared radiation has a longer wavelength than visible light. Thus, the lower wave would be the infrared radiation.

PRACTICE EXERCISE

If one of the waves in the margin represents blue light and the other red light, which is which?

Answer: The expanded visible-light portion of Figure 1.4 tells you that red light has a longer wavelength than blue light. The lower wave has the longer wavelength (lower frequency) and would be the red light.

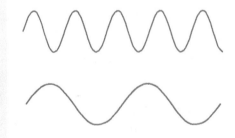

A CLOSER LOOK

THE SPEED OF LIGHT

How do we know that light has a finite speed and does not move infinitely fast?

During the late 1600s, the Danish astronomer Ole Rømer (1644–1710) measured the orbits of several of Jupiter's moons. These moons move much faster than our own—they have orbits of 1–7 days and are eclipsed by Jupiter's shadow at every revolution. Over many months, Rømer measured discrepancies of up to 10 minutes in the times of these orbits. He reasoned that the discrepancies occurred because Jupiter was farther from Earth at different times of the year. Thus, light from the Sun, which reflected off Jupiter and ultimately to his telescope, had farther to travel at different times of the year, implying that light travels at a finite speed. Rømer's data led to the first estimate of the speed of light, 3.5×10^8 m/s.

Since Rømer's time, increasingly sophisticated techniques have been used to measure the speed of light. For example, in 1927, A. A. Michelson (1852–1931) set up a rotating mirror at the top of Mount Wilson in California. The mirror bounced light to the top of Mount San Antonio, 22 miles away, where another mirror bounced the light back to Mount Wilson. Michelson was able to change the speed of the rotating mirror and measure small displacements in the position of the reflected spot. The value for the speed of light (in air) based on this experiment was $2.9980 \pm 0.0002 \times 10^8$ m/s. The main source of error was the distance between the mirrors, which was measured within a fifth of an inch in 22 miles.

By 1975, the measured value was even more precise, $2.99792458 \pm 0.00000004 \times 10^8$ m/s (in vacuum), the error being mostly due to the uncertainty in the length of the meter. In 1983, the meter was redefined based on the distance that light travels in vacuum in one second. As a result, the value for the speed of light became a fixed, exact quantity, $c = 2.99792458 \times 10^8$ m/s.

SAMPLE EXERCISE 1.2   **Calculating Frequency from Wavelength**

The yellow light given off by a sodium vapor lamp used for public lighting has a wavelength of 589 nm. What is the frequency of this radiation?

SOLUTION

Analyze We are given the wavelength, λ, of the radiation and asked to calculate its frequency, ν.

Plan The relationship between the wavelength and the frequency is given by Equation 1.1. We can solve for ν and use the values of λ and c to obtain a numerical answer. (The speed of light, c, is a fundamental constant whose value is 3.00×10^8 m/s.)

Solve Solving Equation 1.1 for frequency gives $\nu = c/\lambda$. When we insert the values for c and λ, we note that the units of length in these two quantities are different. We can convert the wavelength from nanometers to meters, so the units cancel:

$$\nu = \frac{c}{\lambda} = \left(\frac{3.00 \times 10^8 \text{ m/s}}{589 \text{ nm}} \right)\left(\frac{1 \text{ nm}}{10^{-9} \text{ m}} \right) = 5.09 \times 10^{14} \text{ s}^{-1}$$

Check The high frequency is reasonable because of the short wavelength. The units are proper because frequency has units of "per second," or s^{-1}.

PRACTICE EXERCISE

(a) A laser used in eye surgery to fuse detached retinas produces radiation with a wavelength of 640.0 nm. Calculate the frequency of this radiation. (b) An FM radio station broadcasts electromagnetic radiation at a frequency of 103.4 MHz (megahertz; 1 MHz = 10^6 s^{-1}). Calculate the wavelength of this radiation. The speed of light is 2.998×10^8 m/s to four significant digits.

Answers: (a) 4.688×10^{14} s^{-1}, (b) 2.899 m

 GIVE IT SOME THOUGHT

Our bodies are penetrated by X-rays but not by visible light. Is this because X-rays travel faster than visible light?

1.2 | QUANTIZED ENERGY AND PHOTONS

Although the wave model of light explains many aspects of its behavior, this model cannot explain several phenomena. Three of these are particularly pertinent to our understanding of how electromagnetic radiation and atoms interact: (1) the emission of light from hot objects (referred to as *blackbody radiation* because the objects studied appear black before heating), (2) the emission of electrons from metal surfaces on which light shines (the *photoelectric effect*), and (3) the emission of light from electronically excited gas atoms (*emission spectra*). We examine the first two phenomena here and the third in Section 1.3.

Hot Objects and the Quantization of Energy

When solids are heated, they emit radiation, as seen in the red glow of an electric stove burner or the bright white light of a tungsten lightbulb. The wavelength distribution of the radiation depends on temperature; a red-hot object, for instance, is cooler than a yellowish or white-hot one (◀ FIGURE 1.5). During the late 1800s, a number of physicists studied this phenomenon, trying to understand the relationship between the temperature and the intensity and wavelength of the emitted radiation. The prevailing laws of physics could not account for the observations.

In 1900 a German physicist named Max Planck (1858–1947) solved the problem by assuming that energy can be either released or absorbed by atoms only in discrete "chunks" of some minimum size. Planck gave the name **quantum** (meaning "fixed amount") to the smallest quantity of energy that can be emitted or absorbed as electromagnetic radiation. He proposed that the energy, E, of a single quantum equals a constant times the frequency of the radiation:

$$E = h\nu \qquad\qquad [1.2]$$

▲ **GO FIGURE**

Which area in the photograph corresponds to the highest temperature?

▲ **FIGURE 1.5   Color and temperature.** The color and intensity of the light emitted by a hot object, such as this pour of molten steel, depend on the temperature of the object.

Potential energy of person walking up steps increases in stepwise, quantized manner

Potential energy of person walking up ramp increases in uniform, continuous manner

◄ FIGURE 1.6   **Quantized versus continuous change in energy.**

The constant h is called **Planck's constant** and has a value of 6.626×10^{-34} joule-second (J-s).

According to Planck's theory, matter can emit and absorb energy only in whole-number multiples of $h\nu$, such as $h\nu$, $2h\nu$, $3h\nu$, and so forth. If the quantity of energy emitted by an atom is $3h\nu$, for example, we say that three quanta of energy have been emitted (*quanta* being the plural of *quantum*). Because the energy can be released only in specific amounts, we say that the allowed energies are *quantized*—their values are restricted to certain quantities. Planck's revolutionary proposal that energy is quantized was proved correct, and he was awarded the 1918 Nobel Prize in Physics for his work on the quantum theory.

If the notion of quantized energies seems strange, it might be helpful to draw an analogy by comparing a ramp and a staircase (▲ FIGURE 1.6). As you walk up a ramp, your potential energy increases in a uniform, continuous manner. When you climb a staircase, you can step only *on* individual stairs, not *between* them, so that your potential energy is restricted to certain values and is therefore quantized.

If Planck's quantum theory is correct, why are its effects not obvious in our daily lives? Why do energy changes seem continuous rather than quantized, or "jagged"? Notice that Planck's constant is an extremely small number. Thus, a quantum of energy, $h\nu$, is an extremely small amount. Planck's rules regarding the gain or loss of energy are always the same, whether we are concerned with objects on the scale of our ordinary experience or with microscopic objects. With everyday objects, however, the gain or loss of a single quantum of energy is so small that it goes completely unnoticed. In contrast, when dealing with matter at the atomic level, the impact of quantized energies is far more significant.

GO FIGURE

Why is it necessary to carry out this experiment in an evacuated chamber?

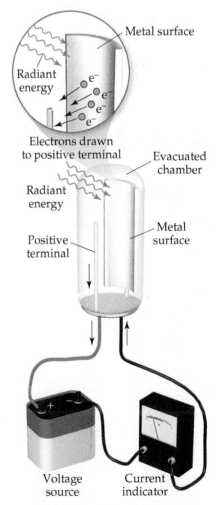

Metal surface

Radiant energy

Electrons drawn to positive terminal

Radiant energy

Positive terminal

Evacuated chamber

Metal surface

Voltage source

Current indicator

▲ FIGURE 1.7   **The photoelectric effect.**

GIVE IT SOME THOUGHT

Calculate the energy (to one significant figure) of one quantum of electromagnetic radiation whose frequency is 5×10^{-3} s^{-1}. Can this radiation produce a burst of energy $E = 5 \times 10^{-36}$ J? Why or why not?

The Photoelectric Effect and Photons

A few years after Planck presented his quantum theory, scientists began to see its applicability to many experimental observations. In 1905, Albert Einstein (1879–1955) used Planck's theory to explain the **photoelectric effect** (► FIGURE 1.7). Light shining on a clean metal surface causes the surface to emit electrons. A minimum frequency of light, different for different metals, is required for the emission of electrons. For example, light with a frequency of 4.60×10^{14} s^{-1} or greater causes cesium metal to emit electrons, but light of lower frequency has no effect.

To explain the photoelectric effect, Einstein assumed that the radiant energy striking the metal surface behaves like a stream of tiny energy packets. Each packet, which is like a "particle" of energy, is called a **photon**. Extending Planck's quantum theory,

Einstein deduced that each photon must have an energy equal to Planck's constant times the frequency of the light:

$$\text{Energy of photon} = E = h\nu \qquad [1.3]$$

Thus, radiant energy itself is quantized.

Under the right conditions, photons striking a metal surface can transfer their energy to electrons in the metal. A certain amount of energy—called the *work function*—is required for the electrons to overcome the attractive forces holding them in the metal. If the photons striking the metal have less energy than the work function, the electrons do not acquire sufficient energy to escape from the metal, even if the light beam is intense. If the photons have energy greater than the work function of the particular metal, however, electrons are emitted. The intensity (brightness) of the light is related to the number of photons striking the surface per unit time but not to the energy of each photon. Einstein won the Nobel Prize in Physics in 1921 for his explanation of the photoelectric effect.

To better understand what a photon is, imagine you have a light source that produces radiation of a single wavelength. Further suppose that you could switch the light on and off faster and faster to provide ever-smaller bursts of energy. Einstein's photon theory tells us that you would eventually come to the smallest energy burst, given by $E = h\nu$. This smallest burst consists of a single photon of light.

SAMPLE EXERCISE 1.3   **Energy of a Photon**

Calculate the energy of one photon of yellow light that has a wavelength of 589 nm.

SOLUTION

Analyze Our task is to calculate the energy, E, of a photon, given $\lambda = 589$ nm.

Plan We can use Equation 1.1 to convert the wavelength to frequency: $\nu = c/\lambda$

We can then use Equation 1.3 to calculate energy: $E = h\nu$

Solve The frequency, ν, is calculated from the given wavelength, as shown in Sample Exercise 1.2:

$$\nu = c/\lambda = 5.09 \times 10^{14}\ \text{s}^{-1}$$

The value of Planck's constant, h, is given both in the text and in the table of physical constants on the inside back cover of the text, and so we can easily calculate E:

$$E = (6.626 \times 10^{-34}\ \text{J-s})(5.09 \times 10^{14}\ \text{s}^{-1}) = 3.37 \times 10^{-19}\ \text{J}$$

Comment If one photon of radiant energy supplies 3.37×10^{-19} J, then one mole of these photons will supply

$$(6.02 \times 10^{23}\ \text{photons/mol})(3.37 \times 10^{-19}\ \text{J/photon})$$
$$= 2.03 \times 10^{5}\ \text{J/mol}$$

PRACTICE EXERCISE

(a) A laser emits light that has a frequency of $4.69 \times 10^{14}\ \text{s}^{-1}$. What is the energy of one photon of this radiation? (b) If the laser emits a pulse containing 5.0×10^{17} photons of this radiation, what is the total energy of that pulse? (c) If the laser emits 1.3×10^{-2} J of energy during a pulse, how many photons are emitted?

Answers: (a) 3.11×10^{-19} J, (b) 0.16 J, (c) 4.2×10^{16} photons

---

The idea that the energy of light depends on its frequency helps us understand the diverse effects of different kinds of electromagnetic radiation. For example, because of the high frequency (short wavelength) of X-rays (Figure 1.4), X-ray photons cause tissue damage and even cancer. Thus, signs are normally posted around X-ray equipment warning us of high-energy radiation.

Although Einstein's theory of light as a stream of photons rather than a wave explains the photoelectric effect and a great many other observations, it also poses a dilemma. Is light a wave, or is it particle-like? The only way to resolve this dilemma is to adopt what might seem to be a bizarre position: We must consider that light possesses both wave-like and particle-like characteristics and, depending on the situation, will behave more like waves or more like particles. We will soon see that this dual nature of light is also a characteristic trait of matter.

◢ GIVE IT SOME THOUGHT

Which has more energy, a photon of infrared light or a photon of ultraviolet light?

1.3 | LINE SPECTRA AND THE BOHR MODEL

The work of Planck and Einstein paved the way for understanding how electrons are arranged in atoms. In 1913, the Danish physicist Niels Bohr (▶ FIGURE 1.8) offered a theoretical explanation of *line spectra*, another phenomenon that had puzzled scientists during the nineteenth century.

Line Spectra

A particular source of radiant energy may emit a single wavelength, as in the light from a laser. Radiation composed of a single wavelength is *monochromatic*. However, most common radiation sources, including lightbulbs and stars, produce radiation containing many different wavelengths and is *polychromatic*. A **spectrum** is produced when radiation from such sources is separated into its component wavelengths, as shown in ▶ FIGURE 1.9. The resulting spectrum consists of a continuous range of colors—violet merges into indigo, indigo into blue, and so forth, with no blank spots. This rainbow of colors, containing light of all wavelengths, is called a **continuous spectrum**. The most familiar example of a continuous spectrum is the rainbow produced when raindrops or mist acts as a prism for sunlight.

Not all radiation sources produce a continuous spectrum. When a high voltage is applied to tubes that contain different gases under reduced pressure, the gases emit different colors of light (▶ FIGURE 1.10). The light emitted by neon gas is the familiar red-orange glow of many "neon" lights, whereas sodium vapor emits the yellow light characteristic of some modern streetlights. When light coming from such tubes is passed through a prism, only a few wavelengths are present in the resultant spectra (▼ FIGURE 1.11). Each colored line in such spectra represents light of one wavelength. A spectrum containing radiation of only specific wavelengths is called a **line spectrum**.

When scientists first detected the line spectrum of hydrogen in the mid-1800s, they were fascinated by its simplicity. At that time, only four lines at wavelengths of 410 nm (violet), 434 nm (blue), 486 nm (blue-green), and 656 nm (red) were observed (Figure 1.11). In 1885, a Swiss schoolteacher named Johann Balmer showed that the wavelengths of these four lines fit an intriguingly simple formula that relates the wavelengths to integers. Later, additional lines were found in the ultraviolet and infrared regions of hydrogen's line spectrum. Soon Balmer's equation was extended to a more general one, called the *Rydberg equation*, which allows us to calculate the wavelengths of all the spectral lines of hydrogen:

$$\frac{1}{\lambda} = (R_H)\left(\frac{1}{n_1^2} - \frac{1}{n_2^2}\right) \qquad [1.4]$$

In this formula λ is the wavelength of a spectral line, R_H is the *Rydberg constant* $(1.096776 \times 10^7 \text{ m}^{-1})$, and n_1 and n_2 are positive integers, with n_2 being larger

▲ FIGURE 1.8 **Quantum giants.** Niels Bohr (right) with Albert Einstein. Bohr (1885–1962) made major contributions to the quantum theory and was awarded the Nobel Prize in Physics in 1922.

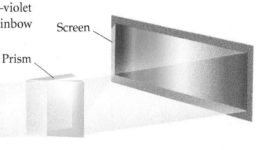

Screen

Prism

Slit

Light source

▲ FIGURE 1.9 **Creating a spectrum.** A continuous visible spectrum is produced when a narrow beam of white light is passed through a prism. The white light could be sunlight or light from an incandescent lamp.

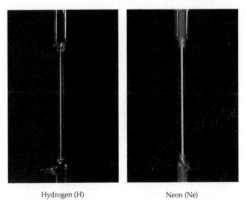

Hydrogen (H)   Neon (Ne)

▲ FIGURE 1.10 **Atomic emission of hydrogen and neon.** Different gases emit light of different characteristic colors when an electric current is passed through them.

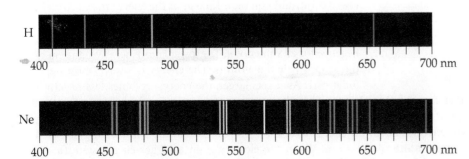

H

400   450   500   550   600   650   700 nm

Ne

400   450   500   550   600   650   700 nm

▲ FIGURE 1.11 **Line spectra of hydrogen and neon.**

than n_1. How could the remarkable simplicity of this equation be explained? It took nearly 30 more years to answer this question.

Bohr's Model

To explain the line spectrum of hydrogen, Bohr assumed that electrons in hydrogen atoms move in circular orbits around the nucleus, but this assumption posed a problem. According to classical physics, a charged particle (such as an electron) moving in a circular path should continuously lose energy. As an electron loses energy, therefore, it should spiral into the positively charged nucleus. This behavior, however, does not happen—hydrogen atoms are stable. So how can we explain this apparent violation of the laws of physics? Bohr approached this problem in much the same way that Planck had approached the problem of the nature of the radiation emitted by hot objects: He assumed that the prevailing laws of physics were inadequate to describe all aspects of atoms. Furthermore, he adopted Planck's idea that energies are quantized.

Bohr based his model on three postulates:

1. Only orbits of certain radii, corresponding to certain specific energies, are permitted for the electron in a hydrogen atom.
2. An electron in a permitted orbit is in an "allowed" energy state. An electron in an allowed energy state does not radiate energy and, therefore, does not spiral into the nucleus.
3. Energy is emitted or absorbed by the electron only as the electron changes from one allowed energy state to another. This energy is emitted or absorbed as a photon that has energy $E = h\nu$.

GIVE IT SOME THOUGHT

Before reading further about Bohr's model, speculate as to how it explains the fact that hydrogen gas emits a line spectrum (Figure 1.11) rather than a continuous spectrum.

The Energy States of the Hydrogen Atom

Starting with his three postulates and using classical equations for motion and for interacting electrical charges, Bohr calculated the energies corresponding to the allowed orbits for the electron in the hydrogen atom. Ultimately, the calculated energies fit the formula

$$E = (-hcR_H)\left(\frac{1}{n^2}\right) = (-2.18 \times 10^{-18}\,\text{J})\left(\frac{1}{n^2}\right) \qquad [1.5]$$

where h, c, and R_H are Planck's constant, the speed of light, and the Rydberg constant, respectively. The integer n, which can have whole-number values of $1, 2, 3, \ldots \infty$, is called the *principal quantum number*. Each orbit corresponds to a different value of n, and the radius of the orbit gets larger as n increases. Thus, the first allowed orbit (the one closest to the nucleus) has $n = 1$, the next allowed orbit (the one second closest to the nucleus) has $n = 2$, and so forth. The electron in the hydrogen atom can be in any allowed orbit, and Equation 1.5 tells us the energy the electron has in each allowed orbit.

Note that the energies of the electron given by Equation 1.5 are negative for all values of n. The lower (more negative) the energy is, the more stable the atom is. The energy is lowest (most negative) for $n = 1$. As n gets larger, the energy becomes less negative and therefore increases. We can liken the situation to a ladder in which the rungs are numbered from the bottom. The higher one climbs (the greater the value of n), the higher the energy. The lowest-energy state ($n = 1$, analogous to the bottom rung) is called the **ground state** of the atom. When the electron is in a higher-energy state ($n = 2$ or higher), the atom is said to be in an **excited state**. ◀ FIGURE 1.12 shows the energy of the electron in a hydrogen atom for several values of n.

GO FIGURE

If the transition of an electron from the $n = 3$ state to the $n = 2$ state results in emission of visible light, is the transition from the $n = 2$ state to the $n = 1$ state more likely to result in the emission of infrared or ultraviolet radiation?

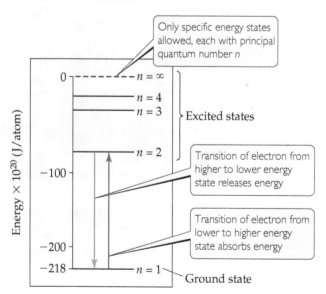

▲ FIGURE 1.12 **Energy states in the hydrogen atom.** Only states for $n = 1$ through $n = 4$ and $n = \infty$ are shown. Energy is released or absorbed when an electron moves from one energy state to another.

What happens to the orbit radius and the energy as n becomes infinitely large? The radius increases as n^2, so when $n = \infty$ the electron is completely separated from the nucleus, and the energy of the electron is zero:

$$E = (-2.18 \times 10^{-18}\ \text{J})\left(\frac{1}{\infty^2}\right) = 0$$

The state in which the electron is removed from the nucleus is called the reference, or zero-energy, state of the hydrogen atom.

In his third postulate, Bohr assumed that the electron can "jump" from one allowed orbit to another by either absorbing or emitting photons whose radiant energy corresponds exactly to the energy difference between the two orbits. The electron must absorb energy in order to move to a higher-energy state (higher value of n). Conversely, radiant energy is emitted when the electron jumps to a lower-energy state (lower value of n).

If the electron jumps from an initial state of energy E_i to a final state of energy E_f, the change in energy is

$$\Delta E = E_f - E_i = E_{\text{photon}} = h\nu \qquad [1.6]$$

Bohr's model of the hydrogen atom states, therefore, that only the specific frequencies of light that satisfy Equation 1.6 can be absorbed or emitted by the atom.

Substituting the energy expression in Equation 1.5 into Equation 1.6 and recalling that $\nu = c/\lambda$, we have

$$\Delta E = h\nu = \frac{hc}{\lambda} = (-2.18 \times 10^{-18}\ \text{J})\left(\frac{1}{n_f^2} - \frac{1}{n_i^2}\right) \qquad [1.7]$$

where n_i and n_f are the principal quantum numbers of the initial and final states of the atom, respectively. If n_f is smaller than n_i, the electron moves closer to the nucleus and ΔE is a negative number, indicating that the atom releases energy. For example, if the electron moves from $n_i = 3$ to $n_f = 1$, we have

$$\Delta E = (-2.18 \times 10^{-18}\ \text{J})\left(\frac{1}{1^2} - \frac{1}{3^2}\right) = (-2.18 \times 10^{-18}\ \text{J})\left(\frac{8}{9}\right) = -1.94 \times 10^{-18}\ \text{J}$$

Knowing the energy of the emitted photon, we can calculate either its frequency or its wavelength. For the wavelength, we have

$$\lambda = \frac{c}{\nu} = \frac{hc}{\Delta E} = \frac{(6.626 \times 10^{-34}\ \text{J-s})(3.00 \times 10^8\ \text{m/s})}{1.94 \times 10^{-18}\ \text{J}} = 1.02 \times 10^{-7}\ \text{m}$$

We have not included the negative sign of the energy in this calculation because wavelength and frequency are always reported as positive quantities. The direction of energy flow is indicated by saying that a photon of wavelength 1.02×10^{-7} m has been *emitted*.

If we solve Equation 1.7 for $1/\lambda$ and replace $(-2.18 \times 10^{-18}\ \text{J})$ by its equivalent, hcR_H from Equation 1.5, we find that Equation 1.7 derived from Bohr's theory corresponds to the Rydberg equation, Equation 1.4, which was obtained using experimental data:

$$\frac{1}{\lambda} = \frac{-hcR_H}{hc}\left(\frac{1}{n_f^2} - \frac{1}{n_i^2}\right) = R_H\left(\frac{1}{n_i^2} - \frac{1}{n_f^2}\right)$$

Thus, the existence of discrete spectral lines can be attributed to the quantized jumps of electrons between energy levels.

GIVE IT SOME THOUGHT

As the electron in a hydrogen atom jumps from the $n = 3$ orbit to the $n = 7$ orbit, does it absorb energy or emit energy?

SAMPLE EXERCISE 1.4 **Electronic Transitions in the Hydrogen Atom**

Using Figure 1.12, predict which of these electronic transitions produces the spectral line having the longest wavelength: $n = 2$ to $n = 1$, $n = 3$ to $n = 2$, or $n = 4$ to $n = 3$.

SOLUTION

The wavelength increases as frequency decreases ($\lambda = c/\nu$). Hence, the longest wavelength will be associated with the lowest frequency. According to Planck's equation, $E = h\nu$, the lowest frequency is associated with the lowest energy. In Figure 1.12 the energy levels (horizontal lines) that are closest together represents the smallest energy change. Thus, the $n = 4$ to $n = 3$ transition produces the longest wavelength (lowest frequency) line.

PRACTICE EXERCISE

Indicate whether each of the following electronic transitions emits energy or requires the absorption of energy: **(a)** $n = 3$ to $n = 1$; **(b)** $n = 2$ to $n = 4$.

Answers: **(a)** emits energy, **(b)** requires absorption of energy

Limitations of the Bohr Model

Although the Bohr model explains the line spectrum of the hydrogen atom, it cannot explain the spectra of other atoms, except in a crude way. Bohr also avoided the problem of why the negatively charged electron would not just fall into the positively charged nucleus by simply assuming it would not happen. Furthermore, there is a problem with describing an electron merely as a small particle circling the nucleus. As we will see in Section 1.4, the electron exhibits wavelike properties, a fact that any acceptable model of electronic structure must accommodate. As it turns out, the Bohr model was only an important step along the way toward the development of a more comprehensive model. What is most significant about Bohr's model is that it introduces two important ideas that are also incorporated into our current model:

1. *Electrons exist only in certain discrete energy levels, which are described by quantum numbers.*

2. *Energy is involved in the transition of an electron from one level to another.*

We will now start to develop the successor to the Bohr model, which requires that we take a closer look at the behavior of matter.

1.4 | THE WAVE BEHAVIOR OF MATTER

In the years following the development of Bohr's model for the hydrogen atom, the dual nature of radiant energy became a familiar concept. Depending on the experimental circumstances, radiation appears to have either a wave-like or a particle-like (photon) character. Louis de Broglie (1892–1987), who was working on his Ph.D. thesis in physics at the Sorbonne in Paris, boldly extended this idea. If radiant energy could, under appropriate conditions, behave as though it were a stream of particles (photons), could matter, under appropriate conditions, possibly show the properties of a wave?

De Broglie suggested that an electron moving about the nucleus of an atom behaves like a wave and therefore has a wavelength. He proposed that the wavelength of the electron, or of any other particle, depends on its mass, m, and on its velocity, v:

$$\lambda = \frac{h}{mv} \qquad [1.8]$$

(where h is Planck's constant). The quantity mv for any object is called its **momentum**. De Broglie used the term **matter waves** to describe the wave characteristics of material particles.

Because de Broglie's hypothesis is applicable to all matter, any object of mass m and velocity v would give rise to a characteristic matter wave. However, Equation 1.8 indicates that the wavelength associated with an object of ordinary size, such as a golf ball, is so tiny as to be completely unobservable. This is not so for an electron because its mass is so small, as we see in Sample Exercise 1.5.

SAMPLE EXERCISE 1.5   **Matter Waves**

What is the wavelength of an electron moving with a speed of 5.97×10^6 m/s? The mass of the electron is 9.11×10^{-31} kg.

SOLUTION

Analyze We are given the mass, m, and velocity, v, of the electron, and we must calculate its de Broglie wavelength, λ.

Plan The wavelength of a moving particle is given by Equation 1.8, so λ is calculated by inserting the known quantities h, m, and v. In doing so, however, we must pay attention to units.

Solve Using the value of Planck's constant, $h = 6.626 \times 10^{-34}$ J-s

we have the following:

$$\lambda = \frac{h}{mv}$$

$$= \frac{(6.626 \times 10^{-34} \text{ J-s})}{(9.11 \times 10^{-31} \text{ kg})(5.97 \times 10^6 \text{ m/s})}\left(\frac{1 \text{ kg-m}^2/\text{s}^2}{1 \text{ J}}\right)$$

$$= 1.22 \times 10^{-10} \text{ m} = 0.122 \text{ nm} = 1.22 \text{ Å}$$

Comment By comparing this value with the wavelengths of electromagnetic radiation shown in Figure 1.4, we see that the wavelength of this electron is about the same as that of X-rays.

PRACTICE EXERCISE

Calculate the velocity of a neutron whose de Broglie wavelength is 500 pm. The mass of a neutron is given in the table inside the back cover of the text.
Answer: 7.92×10^2 m/s

A few years after de Broglie published his theory, the wave properties of the electron were demonstrated experimentally. When X-rays pass through a crystal, an interference pattern results that is characteristic of the wavelike properties of electromagnetic radiation. This phenomenon is called X-ray *diffraction*. As electrons pass through a crystal, they are similarly diffracted. Thus, a stream of moving electrons exhibits the same kinds of wave behavior as X-rays and all other types of electromagnetic radiation.

The technique of electron diffraction has been highly developed. In the electron microscope, for instance, the wave characteristics of electrons are used to obtain images at the atomic scale. This microscope is an important tool for studying surface phenomena at very high magnifications (▶ FIGURE 1.13). Electron microscopes can magnify objects by 3,000,000 times (×), far more than can be done with visible light (1000×), because the wavelength of the electrons is so much smaller than the wavelengths of visible light.

▲ FIGURE 1.13   **Electrons as waves.** The white dots in this transmission electron micrograph indicate the tops of columns of atoms.

GIVE IT SOME THOUGHT

A baseball pitcher throws a fastball that moves at 95 miles per hour. Does that moving baseball generate matter waves? If so, can we observe them?

The Uncertainty Principle

The discovery of the wave properties of matter raised some new and interesting questions. Consider, for example, a ball rolling down a ramp. Using the equations of classical physics, we can calculate, with great accuracy, the ball's position, direction of motion, and speed at any instant. Can we do the same for an electron, which exhibits wave properties? A wave extends in space and its location is not precisely defined. We might therefore anticipate that it is impossible to determine exactly where an electron is located at a specific instant.

The German physicist Werner Heisenberg (▶ FIGURE 1.14) proposed that the dual nature of matter places a fundamental limitation on how precisely we can know both the location and

◀ FIGURE 1.14   **Werner Heisenberg (1901–1976).** During his postdoctoral assistantship with Niels Bohr, Heisenberg formulated his famous uncertainty principle. At 32 he was one of the youngest scientists to receive a Nobel Prize.

the momentum of an object at a given instant. The limitation becomes important only when we deal with matter at the subatomic level (that is, with masses as small as that of an electron). Heisenberg's principle is called the **uncertainty principle**. When applied to the electrons in an atom, this principle states that it is impossible for us to know simultaneously both the exact momentum of the electron and its exact location in space.

Heisenberg mathematically related the uncertainty in position, Δx, and the uncertainty in momentum, $\Delta(mv)$, to a quantity involving Planck's constant:

$$\Delta x \cdot \Delta(mv) \geq \frac{h}{4\pi} \qquad [1.9]$$

A brief calculation illustrates the dramatic implications of the uncertainty principle. The electron has a mass of 9.11×10^{-31} kg and moves at an average speed of about 5×10^6 m/s in a hydrogen atom. Let's assume that we know the speed to an uncertainty of 1% [that is, an uncertainty of $(0.01)(5 \times 10^6 \text{ m/s}) = 5 \times 10^4$ m/s] and that this is the only important source of uncertainty in the momentum, so that $\Delta(mv) = m\,\Delta v$. We can use Equation 1.9 to calculate the uncertainty in the position of the electron:

$$\Delta x \geq \frac{h}{4\pi m \Delta v} = \left(\frac{6.626 \times 10^{-34} \text{ J-s}}{4\pi(9.11 \times 10^{-31} \text{ kg})(5 \times 10^4 \text{ m/s})} \right) = 1 \times 10^{-9} \text{ m}$$

Because the diameter of a hydrogen atom is about 1×10^{-10} m, the uncertainty in the position of the electron in the atom is an order of magnitude greater than the size of the atom. Thus, we have essentially no idea where the electron is located in the atom. On the other hand, if we were to repeat the calculation with an object of ordinary mass, such as a tennis ball, the uncertainty would be so small that it would be inconsequential. In that case, m is large and Δx is out of the realm of measurement and therefore of no practical consequence.

De Broglie's hypothesis and Heisenberg's uncertainty principle set the stage for a new and more broadly applicable theory of atomic structure. In this approach, any attempt to define precisely the instantaneous location and momentum of the electron is abandoned. The wave nature of the electron is recognized, and its behavior is described in terms appropriate to waves. The result is a model that precisely describes the energy of the electron while describing its location not precisely but rather in terms of probabilities.

A CLOSER LOOK

MEASUREMENT AND THE UNCERTAINTY PRINCIPLE

Whenever any measurement is made, some uncertainty exists. Our experience with objects of ordinary dimensions, such as balls or trains or laboratory equipment, indicates that using more precise instruments can decrease the uncertainty of a measurement. In fact, we might expect that the uncertainty in a measurement can be made indefinitely small. However, the uncertainty principle states that there is an actual limit to the accuracy of measurements. This limit is not a restriction on how well instruments can be made; rather, it is inherent in nature. This limit has no practical consequences when dealing with ordinary-sized objects, but its implications are enormous when dealing with subatomic particles, such as electrons.

To measure an object, we must disturb it, at least a little, with our measuring device. Imagine using a flashlight to locate a large rubber ball in a dark room. You see the ball when the light from the flashlight bounces off the ball and strikes your eyes. When a beam of photons strikes an object of this size, it does not alter its position or momentum to any practical extent. Imagine, however, that you wish to locate an electron by similarly bouncing light off it into some detector. Objects can be located to an accuracy no greater than the wavelength of the radiation used. Thus, if we want an accurate position measurement for an electron, we must use a short wavelength. This means that photons of high energy must be employed. The more energy the photons have, the more momentum they impart to the electron when they strike it, which changes the electron's motion in an unpredictable way. The attempt to measure accurately the electron's position introduces considerable uncertainty in its momentum; the act of measuring the electron's position at one moment makes our knowledge of its future position inaccurate.

Suppose, then, that we use photons of longer wavelength. Because these photons have lower energy, the momentum of the electron is not so appreciably changed during measurement, but its position will be correspondingly less accurately known. This is the essence of the uncertainty principle: *There is an uncertainty in simultaneously knowing either the position or the momentum of the electron that cannot be reduced beyond a certain minimum level.* The more accurately one is known, the less accurately the other is known. Although we can never know the exact position and momentum of the electron, we can talk about the probability of its being at certain locations in space. In Section 1.5 we introduce a model of the atom that provides the probability of finding electrons of specific energies at certain positions in atoms.

RELATED EXERCISES: 1.47 and 1.48

◢ **GIVE IT SOME THOUGHT**

What is the principal reason we must consider the uncertainty principle when discussing electrons and other subatomic particles but not when discussing our macroscopic world?

1.5 | QUANTUM MECHANICS AND ATOMIC ORBITALS

In 1926 the Austrian physicist Erwin Schrödinger (1887–1961) proposed an equation, now known as Schrödinger's wave equation, that incorporates both the wave-like behavior of the electron and its particle-like behavior. His work opened a new approach to dealing with subatomic particles, an approach known as *quantum mechanics* or *wave mechanics*. The application of Schrödinger's equation requires advanced calculus, and so we will not be concerned with its details. We will, however, qualitatively consider the results Schrödinger obtained because they give us a powerful new way to view electronic structure. Let's begin by examining the electronic structure of the simplest atom, hydrogen.

Schrödinger treated the electron in a hydrogen atom like the wave on a plucked guitar string (▼ **FIGURE 1.15**). Because such waves do not travel in space, they are called *standing waves*. Just as the plucked guitar string produces a standing wave that has a fundamental frequency and higher overtones (harmonics), the electron exhibits a lowest-energy standing wave and higher-energy ones. Furthermore, just as the overtones of the guitar string have *nodes*, points where the amplitude of the wave is zero, so do the waves characteristic of the electron.

Solving Schrödinger's equation for the hydrogen atom leads to a series of mathematical functions called **wave functions** that describe the electron in an atom. These wave functions are usually represented by the symbol ψ (lowercase Greek letter *psi*). Although the wave function has no direct physical meaning, the square of the wave function, ψ^2, provides information about the electron's location when it is in an allowed energy state.

For the hydrogen atom, the allowed energies are the same as those predicted by the Bohr model. However, the Bohr model assumes that the electron is in a circular orbit of some particular radius about the nucleus. In the quantum mechanical model, the electron's location cannot be described so simply.

According to the uncertainty principle, if we know the momentum of the electron with high accuracy, our simultaneous knowledge of its location is very uncertain. Thus, we cannot hope to specify the exact location of an individual electron around the

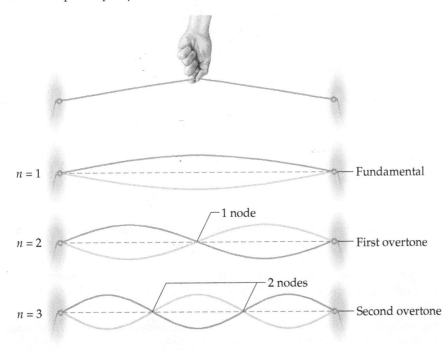

$n = 1$ — Fundamental

1 node

$n = 2$ — First overtone

2 nodes

$n = 3$ — Second overtone

◀ **FIGURE 1.15 Standing waves in a vibrating string.**

Where in the figure is the region of highest electron density?

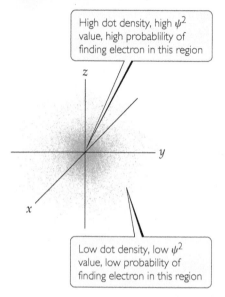

High dot density, high ψ^2 value, high probability of finding electron in this region

Low dot density, low ψ^2 value, low probability of finding electron in this region

▲ **FIGURE 1.16 Electron-density distribution.** This rendering represents the probability, ψ^2, of finding the electron in a hydrogen atom in its ground state. The origin of the coordinate system is at the nucleus.

nucleus. Rather, we must be content with a kind of statistical knowledge. We therefore speak of the *probability* that the electron will be in a certain region of space at a given instant. As it turns out, the square of the wave function, ψ^2, at a given point in space represents the probability that the electron will be found at that location. For this reason, ψ^2 is called either the **probability density** or the **electron density**.

One way of representing the probability of finding the electron in various regions of an atom is shown in ◄ **FIGURE 1.16**, where the density of the dots represents the probability of finding the electron. The regions with a high density of dots correspond to relatively large values for ψ^2 and are therefore regions where there is a high probability of finding the electron. Based on this representation, we often describe atoms as consisting of a nucleus surrounded by an electron cloud.

Orbitals and Quantum Numbers

The solution to Schrödinger's equation for the hydrogen atom yields a set of wave functions called **orbitals**. Each orbital has a characteristic shape and energy. For example, the lowest-energy orbital in the hydrogen atom has the spherical shape illustrated in Figure 1.16 and an energy of -2.18×10^{-18} J. Note that an *orbital* (quantum mechanical model, which describes electrons in terms of probabilities, visualized as "electron clouds") is not the same as an *orbit* (Bohr model, which visualizes the electron moving in a physical orbit, like a planet around a star). The quantum mechanical model does not refer to orbits because the motion of the electron in an atom cannot be precisely determined (Heisenberg uncertainty principle).

The Bohr model introduced a single quantum number, n, to describe an orbit. The quantum mechanical model uses three quantum numbers, n, l, and m_l, which result naturally from the mathematics used, to describe an orbital.

1. The *principal quantum number, n,* can have positive integral values 1, 2, 3, ... As n increases, the orbital becomes larger, and the electron spends more time farther from the nucleus. An increase in n also means that the electron has a higher energy and is therefore less tightly bound to the nucleus. For the hydrogen atom, $E_n = -(2.18 \times 10^{-18} \text{ J})(1/n^2)$, as in the Bohr model.

2. The second quantum number—the *angular momentum quantum number, l*—can have integral values from 0 to $(n - 1)$ for each value of n. This quantum number defines the shape of the orbital. The value of l for a particular orbital is generally designated by the letters s, p, d, and f,* corresponding to l values of 0, 1, 2, and 3:

Value of l	0	1	2	3
Letter used	s	p	d	f

3. The *magnetic quantum number, m_l,* can have integral values between $-l$ and l, including zero. This quantum number describes the orientation of the orbital in space, as we discuss in Section 1.6.

Notice that because the value of n can be any positive integer, an infinite number of orbitals for the hydrogen atom are possible. At any given instant, however, the electron in a hydrogen atom is described by only one of these orbitals—we say that the electron *occupies* a certain orbital. The remaining orbitals are *unoccupied* for that particular state of the hydrogen atom.

GIVE IT SOME THOUGHT

What is the difference between an *orbit* in the Bohr model of the hydrogen atom and an *orbital* in the quantum mechanical model?

The collection of orbitals with the same value of n is called an **electron shell**. All the orbitals that have $n = 3$, for example, are said to be in the third shell. The set of

*The letters come from the words *sharp, principal, diffuse,* and *fundamental*, which were used to describe certain features of spectra before quantum mechanics was developed.

TABLE 1.2 • Relationship among Values of *n*, *l*, and *m$_l$* through *n* = 4

n	Possible Values of *l*	Subshell Designation	Possible Values of *m$_l$*	Number of Orbitals in Subshell	Total Number of Orbitals in Shell
1	0	1*s*	0	1	1
2	0	2*s*	0	1	
	1	2*p*	1, 0, −1	3	4
3	0	3*s*	0	1	
	1	3*p*	1, 0, −1	3	
	2	3*d*	2, 1, 0, −1, −2	5	9
4	0	4*s*	0	1	
	1	4*p*	1, 0, −1	3	
	2	4*d*	2, 1, 0, −1, −2	5	
	3	4*f*	3, 2, 1, 0, −1, −2, −3	7	16

orbitals that have the same *n* and *l* values is called a **subshell**. Each subshell is designated by a number (the value of *n*) and a letter (*s*, *p*, *d*, or *f*, corresponding to the value of *l*). For example, the orbitals that have *n* = 3 and *l* = 2 are called 3*d* orbitals and are in the 3*d* subshell.

▲ TABLE 1.2 summarizes the possible values of *l* and *m$_l$* for values of *n* through *n* = 4. The restrictions on possible values give rise to the following very important observations:

1. The shell with principal quantum number *n* consists of exactly *n* subshells. Each subshell corresponds to a different allowed value of *l* from 0 to (*n* − 1). Thus, the first shell (*n* = 1) consists of only one subshell, the 1*s* (*l* = 0); the second shell (*n* = 2) consists of two subshells, the 2*s* (*l* = 0) and 2*p* (*l* = 1); the third shell consists of three subshells, 3*s*, 3*p*, and 3*d*, and so forth.

2. Each subshell consists of a specific number of orbitals. Each orbital corresponds to a different allowed value of *m$_l$*. For a given value of *l*, there are (2*l* + 1) allowed values of *m$_l$*, ranging from −*l* to +*l*. Thus, each *s* (*l* = 0) subshell consists of one orbital; each *p* (*l* = 1) subshell consists of three orbitals; each *d* (*l* = 2) subshell consists of five orbitals, and so forth.

3. The total number of orbitals in a shell is *n*², where *n* is the principal quantum number of the shell. The resulting number of orbitals for the shells—1, 4, 9, 16—are related to a pattern seen in the periodic table: We see that the number of elements in the rows of the periodic table—2, 8, 18, and 32—equals twice these numbers. We will discuss this relationship further in Section 1.9.

▶ FIGURE 1.17 shows the relative energies of the hydrogen atom orbitals through *n* = 3. Each box represents an orbital, and orbitals of the same subshell, such as the three 2*p* orbitals, are grouped together. When the electron occupies the lowest-energy orbital (1*s*), the hydrogen atom is said to be in its *ground state*. When the electron occupies any other orbital, the atom is in an *excited state*. (The electron can be excited to a higher-energy orbital by absorption of a photon of appropriate energy.) At ordinary temperatures, essentially all hydrogen atoms are in the ground state.

◢ **GIVE IT SOME THOUGHT**

Notice in Figure 1.17 that the energy difference between the *n* = 1 and *n* = 2 levels is much greater than the energy difference between the *n* = 2 and *n* = 3 levels. How does Equation 1.5 explain this trend?

◢ **GO FIGURE**

If the fourth shell (the *n* = 4 energy level) were shown, how many subshells would it contain? How would they be labeled?

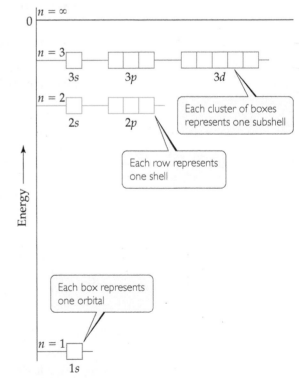

n = 1 shell has one orbital
n = 2 shell has two subshells composed of four orbitals
n = 3 shell has three subshells composed of nine orbitals

▲ **FIGURE 1.17 Energy levels in the hydrogen atom.**

SAMPLE EXERCISE 1.6   **Subshells of the Hydrogen Atom**

(a) Without referring to Table 1.2, predict the number of subshells in the fourth shell, that is, for $n = 4$. (b) Give the label for each of these subshells. (c) How many orbitals are in each of these subshells?

Analyze and Plan   We are given the value of the principal quantum number, n. We need to determine the allowed values of l and m_l for this given value of n and then count the number of orbitals in each subshell.

SOLUTION

There are four subshells in the fourth shell, corresponding to the four possible values of l (0, 1, 2, and 3).

These subshells are labeled $4s$, $4p$, $4d$, and $4f$. The number given in the designation of a subshell is the principal quantum number, n; the letter designates the value of the angular momentum quantum number, l: for $l = 0$, s; for $l = 1$, p; for $l = 2$, d; for $l = 3$, f.

There is one $4s$ orbital (when $l = 0$, there is only one possible value of m_l: 0). There are three $4p$ orbitals (when $l = 1$, there are three possible values of m_l: 1, 0, −1). There are five $4d$ orbitals (when $l = 2$, there are five allowed values of m_l: 2, 1, 0, −1, −2). There are seven $4f$ orbitals (when $l = 3$, there are seven permitted values of m_l: 3, 2, 1, 0, −1, −2, −3).

PRACTICE EXERCISE

(a) What is the designation for the subshell with $n = 5$ and $l = 1$? (b) How many orbitals are in this subshell? (c) Indicate the values of m_l for each of these orbitals.
Answers: (a) $5p$; (b) 3; (c) 1, 0, −1

1.6 | REPRESENTATIONS OF ORBITALS

So far we have emphasized orbital energies, but the wave function also provides information about an electron's probable location in space. Let's examine the ways in which we can picture orbitals because their shapes help us visualize how the electron density is distributed around the nucleus.

The s Orbitals

We have already seen one representation of the lowest-energy orbital of the hydrogen atom, the $1s$ (Figure 1.16). The first thing we notice about the electron density for the $1s$ orbital is that it is *spherically symmetric*—in other words, the electron density at a given distance from the nucleus is the same regardless of the direction in which we proceed from the nucleus. All of the other s orbitals ($2s$, $3s$, $4s$, and so forth) are also spherically symmetric and centered on the nucleus.

Recall that the l quantum number for the s orbitals is 0; therefore, the m_l quantum number must be 0. Thus, for each value of n, there is only one s orbital.

So how do s orbitals differ as the value of n changes? One way to address this question is to look at the **radial probability function**, also called the *radial probability density*, which is defined as the probability that we will find the electron at a specific distance from the nucleus.

▶ FIGURE 1.18 shows the radial probability density for the $1s$, $2s$, and $3s$ orbitals of hydrogen as a function of r, the distance from the nucleus. Three features of these graphs are noteworthy: the number of peaks, the number of points at which the probability function goes to zero (called **nodes**), and how spread out the distribution is, which gives a sense of the size of the orbital.

For the $1s$ orbital, we see that the probability rises rapidly as we move away from the nucleus, maximizing at about 0.5 Å. Thus, when the electron occupies the $1s$ orbital, it is *most likely* to be found this distance from the nucleus.* Notice also that in the $1s$ orbital the probability of finding the electron at a distance greater than about 3 Å from the nucleus is essentially zero.

---

*In the quantum mechanical model, the most probable distance at which to find the electron in the $1s$ orbital is actually 0.529 Å, the same as the radius of the orbit predicted by Bohr for $n = 1$. The distance 0.529 Å is often called the Bohr radius.

⚠ **GO FIGURE**

How many maxima would you expect to find in the radial probability function for the 4s orbital of the hydrogen atom? How many nodes would you expect in this function?

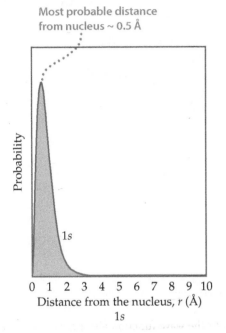

Most probable distance from nucleus ~ 0.5 Å

1s

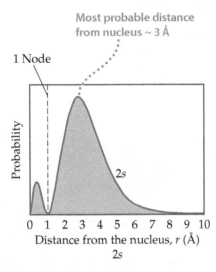

Most probable distance from nucleus ~ 3 Å

1 Node

2s

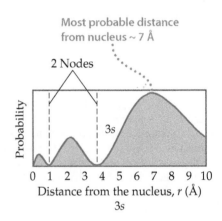

Most probable distance from nucleus ~ 7 Å

2 Nodes

3s

▲ **FIGURE 1.18 Radial probability distributions for the 1s, 2s, and 3s orbitals of hydrogen.** These graphs of the radial probability function plot probability of finding the electron as a function of distance from the nucleus. As n increases, the most likely distance at which to find the electron (the highest peak) moves farther from the nucleus.

Comparing the radial probability distributions for the 1s, 2s, and 3s orbitals reveals three trends:

1. *The number of peaks increases with increasing* n, *with the outermost peak being larger than inner ones.*

2. *The number of nodes increases with increasing* n.

3. *The electron density becomes more spread out with increasing* n.

One widely used method of representing orbital *shape* is to draw a boundary surface that encloses some substantial portion, say 90%, of the electron density for the orbital. This type of drawing is called a *contour representation*, and the contour representations for the *s* orbitals are spheres (▼ **FIGURE 1.19**). All the orbitals have the same shape, but they differ in size, becoming larger as *n* increases, reflecting the fact that the electron density becomes more spread out as *n* increases. Although the details of how

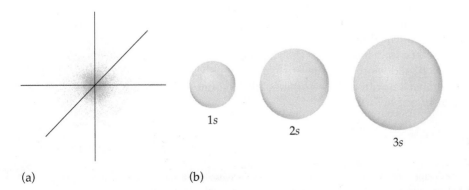

(a)

(b)

1s

2s

3s

◀ **FIGURE 1.19 Comparison of the 1s, 2s, and 3s orbitals.** (a) Electron-density distribution of a 1s orbital. (b) Contour representions of the 1s, 2s, and 3s orbitals. Each sphere is centered on the atom's nucleus and encloses the volume in which there is a 90% probability of finding the electron.

A CLOSER LOOK

PROBABILITY DENSITY AND RADIAL PROBABILITY FUNCTIONS

According to quantum mechanics, we must describe the position of the electron in the hydrogen atom in terms of probabilities. The information about the probability is contained in the wave functions, ψ, obtained from Schrödinger's equation. The square of the wave function, ψ^2, called either the probability density or the electron density, as noted earlier, gives the probability that the electron is at any *point* in space. Because s orbitals are spherically symmetric, the value of ψ for an s electron depends only on its distance from the nucleus, r. Thus, the probability density can be written as $[\psi(r)]^2$, where $\psi(r)$ is the value of ψ at r. This function $[\psi(r)]^2$ gives the probability density for any point located a distance r from the nucleus.

The radial probability function, which we used in Figure 1.18, differs from the probability density. The radial probability function equals the *total* probability of finding the electron at all the points at any distance r from the nucleus. In other words, to calculate this function, we need to "add up" the probability densities $[\psi(r)]^2$ over all points located a distance r from the nucleus. ▶ FIGURE 1.20 compares the probability density at a point ($[\psi(r)]^2$) with the radial probability function.

Let's examine the difference between probability density and radial probability function more closely. ▶ FIGURE 1.21 shows plots of $[\psi(r)]^2$ as a function of r for the 1s, 2s, and 3s orbitals of the

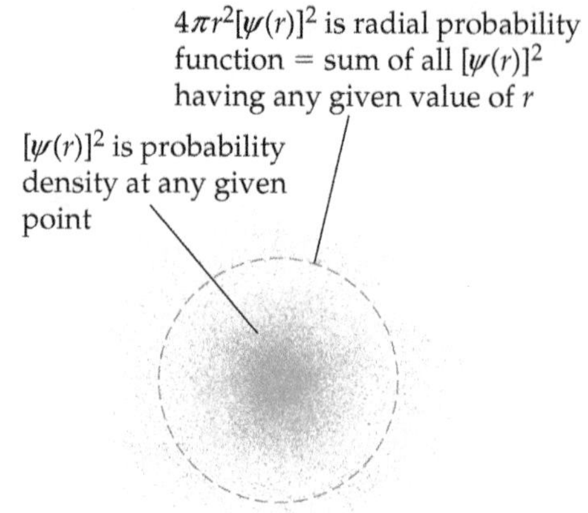

$4\pi r^2[\psi(r)]^2$ is radial probability function = sum of all $[\psi(r)]^2$ having any given value of r

$[\psi(r)]^2$ is probability density at any given point

▲ FIGURE 1.20 **Comparing probability density $[\psi(r)]^2$ and radial probability function $4\pi r^2[\psi(r)]^2$.**

electron density varies within a given contour representation are lost in these representations, this is not a serious disadvantage. For qualitative discussions, the most important features of orbitals are shape and relative size, which are adequately displayed by contour representations.

The *p* Orbitals

The distribution of electron density for a 2p orbital is shown in ▶ FIGURE 1.22(a). The electron density is not distributed spherically as in an s orbital. Instead, the density is concentrated in two regions on either side of the nucleus, separated by a node at the nucleus. We say that this dumbbell-shaped orbital has two *lobes*. Recall that we are making no statement of how the electron is moving within the orbital. Figure 1.22(a) portrays only the *averaged* distribution of the electron density in a 2p orbital.

Beginning with the $n = 2$ shell, each shell has three p orbitals. Recall that the l quantum number for p orbitals is 1. Therefore, the magnetic quantum number m_l can have three possible values: -1, 0, and $+1$. Thus, there are three 2p orbitals, three 3p orbitals, and so forth, corresponding to the three possible values of m_l. Each set of p orbitals has the dumbbell shapes shown in Figure 1.22(a) for the 2p orbitals. For each value of n, the three p orbitals have the same size and shape but differ from one another in spatial orientation. We usually represent p orbitals by drawing the shape and orientation of their wave functions, as shown in Figure 1.22(b). It is convenient to label these as the p_x, p_y, and p_z orbitals. The letter subscript indicates the Cartesian axis along which the orbital is oriented.* Like s orbitals, p orbitals increase in size as we move from 2p to 3p to 4p, and so forth.

---

*We cannot make a simple correspondence between the subscripts (x, y, and z) and the allowed m_l values (1, 0, and -1). To explain why this is so is beyond the scope of an introductory text.

hydrogen atom. You will notice that these plots look distinctly differ-ent from the radial probability functions shown in Figure 1.18.

As shown in Figure 1.20, the collection of points a distance r from the nucleus is the surface of a sphere of radius r. The probabil-ity density at each point on that spherical surface is $[\psi(r)]^2$. To add up all the individual probability densities requires calculus and so is beyond the scope of this text. However, the result of that calculation tells us that the radial probability function is the probability density, $[\psi(r)]^2$, multiplied by the surface area of the sphere, $4\pi r^2$:

$$\text{Radial probability function} = 4\pi r^2[\psi(r)]^2$$

Thus, the plots of radial probability function in Figure 1.18 are equal to the plots of $[\psi(r)]^2$ in Figure 1.21 multiplied by $4\pi r^2$. The fact that $4\pi r^2$ increases rapidly as we move away from the nucleus makes the two sets of plots look very different from each other. For example, the plot of $[\psi(r)]^2$ for the 3s orbital in Figure 1.21 shows that the function generally gets smaller the farther we go from the nucleus. But when we multiply by $4\pi r^2$, we see peaks that get larger and larger as we move away from the nucleus (Figure 1.18).

The radial probability functions in Figure 1.18 provide us with the more useful information because they tell us the probability of finding the electron at *all* points a distance r from the nucleus, not just one particular point.

RELATED EXERCISES: 1.50, 1.59, 1.60, and 1.91

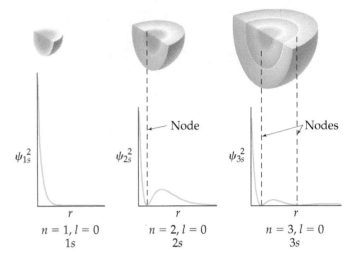

▲ **FIGURE 1.21** **Probability density $[\psi(r)]^2$ in the 1s, 2s, and 3s orbitals of hydrogen.**

▲ GO FIGURE

(a) Note on the left that the color is deep pink in the interior of each lobe but fades to pale pink at the edges. What does this change in color repre-sent? (b) What label is applied to the 2p orbital aligned along the x axis?

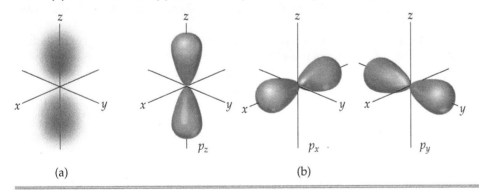

(a)   (b)

◀ FIGURE 1.22   **The p orbitals.**
(a) Electron-density distribution of a 2p orbital.
(b) Contour representations of the three p orbitals. The subscript on the orbital label indicates the axis along which the orbital lies.

The d and f Orbitals

When n is 3 or greater, we encounter the d orbitals (for which $l = 2$). There are five $3d$ orbitals, five $4d$ orbitals, and so forth because in each shell there are five possible values for the m_l quantum number: $-2, -1, 0, 1$, and 2. The different d orbitals in a given shell have different shapes and orientations in space, as shown in ▶ **FIGURE 1.23**. Four of the d-orbital contour representations have a "four-leaf clover" shape, and each lies primarily in a plane. The d_{xy}, d_{xz}, and d_{yz} lie in the xy, xz, and yz planes, respectively, with the lobes oriented *between* the axes. The lobes of the $d_{x^2-y^2}$ orbital also lie in the xy plane, but the lobes lie *along* the x and y axes. The d_{z^2} orbital looks very different from the other four: It has two lobes along the z axis and a "doughnut" in the xy plane. Even though the d_{z^2} orbital looks different from the other d orbitals, it has the same energy as the other four

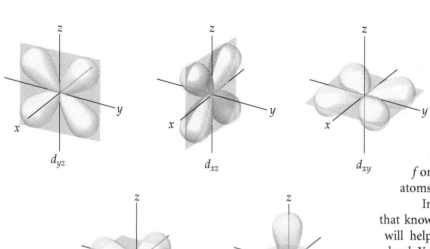

d_{yz} d_{xz} d_{xy}

$d_{x^2-y^2}$ d_{z^2}

▲ **FIGURE 1.23** **Contour representations of the five *d* orbitals.**

d orbitals. The representations in Figure 1.23 are commonly used for all *d* orbitals, regardless of principal quantum number.

When *n* is 4 or greater, there are seven equivalent *f* orbitals (for which *l* = 3). The shapes of the *f* orbitals are even more complicated than those of the *d* orbitals and are not presented here. As you will see in the next section, however, you must be aware of *f* orbitals as we consider the electronic structure of atoms in the lower part of the periodic table.

In many instances later in the text you will find that knowing the number and shapes of atomic orbitals will help you understand chemistry at the molecular level. You will therefore find it useful to memorize the shapes of the *s*, *p*, and *d* orbitals shown in Figures 1.19, 1.22, and 1.23.

1.7 | MANY-ELECTRON ATOMS

One of our goals in this chapter has been to determine the electronic structures of atoms. So far, we have seen that quantum mechanics leads to an elegant description of the hydrogen atom. This atom, however, has only one electron. How does our description change when we consider an atom with two or more electrons (a *many-electron atom*)? To describe such an atom, we must consider the nature of orbitals and their relative energies as well as how the electrons populate the available orbitals.

Orbitals and Their Energies

We can describe the electronic structure of a many-electron atom in terms of orbitals like those of the hydrogen atom. Thus, we continue to designate orbitals as ls, $2p_x$, and so forth. Further, these orbitals have the same general shapes as the corresponding hydrogen orbitals.

Although the shapes of the orbitals of a many-electron atom are the same as those for hydrogen, the presence of more than one electron greatly changes the energies of the orbitals. In hydrogen the energy of an orbital depends only on its principal quantum number, *n* (Figure 1.17). For instance, the 3s, 3p, and 3d subshells all have the same energy. In a many-electron atom, however, the electron–electron repulsions cause the various subshells in a given shell to be at different energies, as shown in ◀ **FIGURE 1.24**.

To explain this fact, we must consider the forces between the electrons and how these forces are affected by the shapes of the orbitals. We will, however, forgo this analysis until Chapter 2.

The important idea is this: *In a many-electron atom, for a given value of n, the energy of an orbital increases with increasing value of l.* For example, notice in Figure 1.24 that the *n* = 3 orbitals increase in energy in the order 3s < 3p < 3d. Notice also that all orbitals of a given subshell (such as the five 3d orbitals) have the same energy as one another. Orbitals with the same energy are said to be **degenerate**.

Figure 1.24 is a *qualitative* energy-level diagram; the exact energies of the orbitals and their spacings differ from one atom to another.

◢ GO FIGURE

Not all of the orbitals in the *n* = 4 shell are shown in this figure. Which subshells are missing?

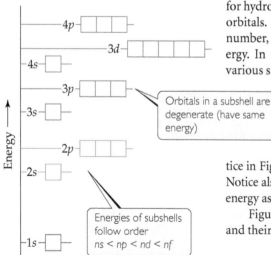

Energy →

4p ☐☐☐

3d ☐☐☐☐☐

4s ☐

3p ☐☐☐

3s ☐

Orbitals in a subshell are degenerate (have same energy)

2p ☐☐☐

2s ☐

Energies of subshells follow order
ns < *np* < *nd* < *nf*

1s ☐

▲ **FIGURE 1.24** **General energy ordering of orbitals for a many-electron atom.**

▲ GIVE IT SOME THOUGHT
a. How may orbitals have the principal quantum number *n* = 3?
b. In a many-electron atom, what are the relative energies of these orbitals?

Electron Spin and the Pauli Exclusion Principle

We have now seen that we can use hydrogen-like orbitals to describe many-electron atoms. What, however, determines which orbitals the electrons occupy? That is, how do the electrons of a many-electron atom populate the available orbitals? To answer this question, we must consider an additional property of the electron.

When scientists studied the line spectra of many-electron atoms in great detail, they noticed a very puzzling feature: Lines that were originally thought to be single were actually closely spaced pairs. This meant, in essence, that there were twice as many energy levels as there were "supposed" to be. In 1925 the Dutch physicists George Uhlenbeck and Samuel Goudsmit proposed a solution to this dilemma. They postulated that electrons have an intrinsic property, called **electron spin**, that causes each electron to behave as if it were a tiny sphere spinning on its own axis.

By now it probably does not surprise you to learn that electron spin is quantized. This observation led to the assignment of a new quantum number for the electron, in addition to n, l, and m_l, which we have already discussed. This new quantum number, the **spin magnetic quantum number**, is denoted m_s (the subscript s stands for *spin*). Two possible values are allowed for m_s, $+\frac{1}{2}$ or $-\frac{1}{2}$, which was first interpreted as indicating the two opposite directions in which the electron can spin. A spinning charge produces a magnetic field. The two opposite directions of spin therefore produce oppositely directed magnetic fields (▶ FIGURE 1.25).* These two opposite magnetic fields lead to the splitting of spectral lines into closely spaced pairs.

Electron spin is crucial for understanding the electronic structures of atoms. In 1925 the Austrian-born physicist Wolfgang Pauli (1900–1958) discovered the principle that governs the arrangements of electrons in many-electron atoms. The **Pauli exclusion principle** states that *no two electrons in an atom can have the same set of four quantum numbers* n, l, m$_l$, *and* m$_s$. For a given orbital, the values of n, l, and m_l are fixed. Thus, if we

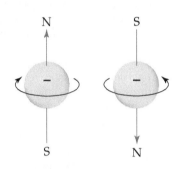

▲ FIGURE 1.25 **Electron spin.** The electron behaves as if it were spinning about an axis, thereby generating a magnetic field whose direction depends on the direction of spin. The two directions for the magnetic field correspond to the two possible values for the spin quantum number, m_s.

A CLOSER LOOK

EXPERIMENTAL EVIDENCE FOR ELECTRON SPIN

Even before electron spin had been proposed, there was experimental evidence that electrons had an additional property that needed explanation. In 1921, Otto Stern and Walter Gerlach succeeded in separating a beam of electrically neutral atoms into two groups by passing them through a nonhomogeneous magnetic field (▶ FIGURE 1.26).

Let's assume they used a beam of hydrogen atoms (in actuality, they used silver atoms, which contain just one unpaired electron). We would normally expect electrically neutral atoms to be unaffected by a magnetic field. However, the magnetic field arising from the electron's spin interacts with the magnet's field, deflecting the atom from its straight-line path. As shown in Figure 1.26, the magnetic field splits the beam in two, suggesting that there are two (and only two) equivalent values for the electron's magnetic field. The Stern–Gerlach experiment could be readily interpreted once it was realized that there are exactly two values for the spin of the electron. These values produce equal magnetic fields that are opposite in direction.

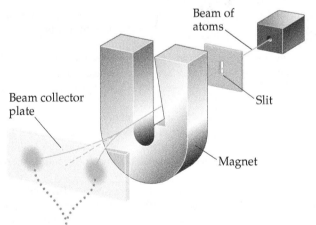

Atoms having unpaired electron with spin quantum number $m_s = +1/2$ deflect in one direction; those having unpaired electron with $m_s = -1/2$ deflect in opposite direction

▲ FIGURE 1.26 **The Stern–Gerlach experiment.**

---

*The electron has both particle-like and wave-like properties. Thus, the picture of an electron as a spinning charged sphere is, strictly speaking, just a useful pictorial representation that helps us understand the two directions of magnetic field that an electron can possess.

CHEMISTRY AND LIFE

NUCLEAR SPIN AND MAGNETIC RESONANCE IMAGING

A major challenge facing medical diagnosis is seeing inside the human body. Until recently, this was accomplished primarily by using X-rays to image human bones, muscles, and organs. However, there are several drawbacks to using X-rays for medical imaging. First, X-rays do not give well-resolved images of overlapping physiological structures. Moreover, because damaged or diseased tissue often yields the same image as healthy tissue, X-rays frequently fail to detect illness or injuries. Finally, X-rays are high-energy radiation that can cause physiological harm, even in low doses.

During the 1980s, a technique called *magnetic resonance imaging* (MRI) moved to the forefront of medical imaging technology. The foundation of MRI is a phenomenon called nuclear magnetic resonance (NMR), which was discovered in the mid-1940s. Today NMR has become one of the most important spectroscopic methods used in chemistry. It is based on the observation that, like electrons, the nuclei of many elements possess an intrinsic spin. Like electron spin, nuclear spin is quantized. For example, the nucleus of ^{1}H has two possible magnetic nuclear spin quantum numbers, $+\frac{1}{2}$ and $-\frac{1}{2}$. The hydrogen nucleus is the most common one studied by NMR.

A spinning hydrogen nucleus acts like a tiny magnet. In the absence of external effects, the two spin states have the same energy. However, when the nuclei are placed in an external magnetic field, they can align either parallel or opposed (antiparallel) to the field, depending on their spin. The parallel alignment is lower in energy than the antiparallel one by a certain amount, ΔE (▶ FIGURE 1.27). If the nuclei are irradiated with photons having energy equal to ΔE, the spin of the nuclei can be "flipped," that is, excited from the parallel to the antiparallel alignment. Detection of the flipping of nuclei between the two spin states leads to an NMR spectrum. The radiation used in an NMR experiment is in the radiofrequency range, typically 100 to 900 MHz, which is far less energetic per photon than X-rays.

Because hydrogen is a major constituent of aqueous body fluids and fatty tissue, the hydrogen nucleus is the most convenient one for study by MRI. In MRI a person's body is placed in a strong magnetic field. By irradiating the body with pulses of radiofrequency radiation and using sophisticated detection techniques, medical technicians can image tissue at specific depths in the body, giving pictures with spectacular detail (▶ FIGURE 1.28). The ability to sample at different depths allows the technicians to construct a three-dimensional picture of the body.

MRI has none of the disadvantages of X-rays. Diseased tissue appears very different from healthy tissue, resolving overlapping structures at different depths in the body is much easier, and the radio frequency radiation is not harmful to humans in the doses used. The technique has had such a profound influence on the modern practice of medicine that Paul Lauterbur, a chemist, and Peter Mansfield, a physicist, were awarded the 2003 Nobel Prize in Physiology or

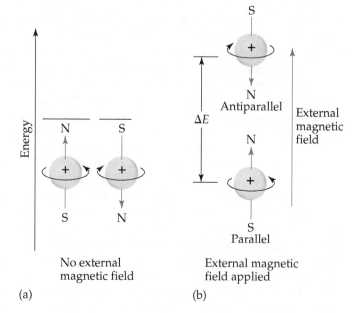

(a) No external magnetic field

(b) External magnetic field applied

▲ FIGURE 1.27 **Nuclear spin.** Like electron spin, nuclear spin generates a small magnetic field and has two allowed values. (a) In the absence of an external magnetic field, the two spin states have the same energy. (b) When an external magnetic field is applied, the spin state in which the spin direction is parallel to the direction of the external field is lower in energy than the spin state in which the spin direction is antiparallel to the field direction. The energy difference, ΔE, is in the radio frequency portion of the electromagnetic spectrum.

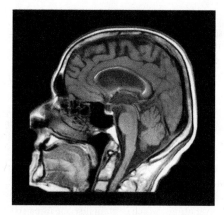

▲ FIGURE 1.28 **MRI image.** This image of a human head, obtained using magnetic resonance imaging, shows a normal brain, airways, and facial tissues.

Medicine for their discoveries concerning MRI. The major drawback of this technique is expense: The current cost of a new MRI instrument for clinical applications is over $1.5 million.

RELATED EXERCISE: 1.93

want to put more than one electron in an orbital *and* satisfy the Pauli exclusion principle, our only choice is to assign different m_s values to the electrons. Because there are only two such values, we conclude that *an orbital can hold a maximum of two electrons and they must have opposite spins*. This restriction allows us to index the electrons in an atom, giving their quantum numbers and thereby defining the region in space where each electron is most likely to be found. It also provides the key to understanding the structure of the periodic table of the elements.

1.8 | ELECTRON CONFIGURATIONS

Armed with knowledge of the relative energies of orbitals and the Pauli exclusion principle, we are in a position to consider the arrangements of electrons in atoms. The way electrons are distributed among the various orbitals of an atom is called the **electron configuration** of the atom.

The most stable electron configuration—the ground state—is that in which the electrons are in the lowest possible energy states. If there were no restrictions on the possible values for the quantum numbers of the electrons, all the electrons would crowd into the ls orbital because it is the lowest in energy (Figure 1.24). The Pauli exclusion principle tells us, however, that there can be at most two electrons in any single orbital. Thus, *the orbitals are filled in order of increasing energy, with no more than two electrons per orbital*. For example, consider the lithium atom, which has three electrons. (Recall that the number of electrons in a neutral atom equals its atomic number.) The ls orbital can accommodate two of the electrons. The third one goes into the next lowest energy orbital, the 2s.

We can represent any electron configuration by writing the symbol for the occupied subshell and adding a superscript to indicate the number of electrons in that subshell. For example, for lithium we write $ls^2 2s^1$ (read "ls two, 2s one"). We can also show the arrangement of the electrons as

$$\text{Li} \quad \boxed{\uparrow\downarrow} \quad \boxed{\uparrow}$$
$$\quad\quad\quad 1s \qquad 2s$$

In this representation, which we call an *orbital diagram,* each orbital is denoted by a box and each electron by a half arrow. A half arrow pointing up ($\uparrow$) represents an electron with a positive spin magnetic quantum number ($m_s = +\frac{1}{2}$) and a half arrow pointing down ($\downarrow$) represents an electron with a negative spin magnetic quantum number ($m_s = -\frac{1}{2}$). This pictorial representation of electron spin, which corresponds to the directions of the magnetic fields in Figure 1.25, is quite convenient.

Electrons having opposite spins are said to be *paired* when they are in the same orbital ($\uparrow\downarrow$). An *unpaired electron* is one not accompanied by a partner of opposite spin. In the lithium atom the two electrons in the 1s orbital are paired and the electron in the 2s orbital is unpaired.

Hund's Rule

Consider now how the electron configurations of the elements change as we move from element to element across the periodic table. Hydrogen has one electron, which occupies the 1s orbital in its ground state:

$$\text{H} \quad \boxed{\uparrow} \quad : 1s^1$$
$$\quad\quad\quad 1s$$

The choice of a spin-up electron here is arbitrary; we could equally well show the ground state with one spin-down electron. It is customary, however, to show unpaired electrons with their spins up.

TABLE 1.3 • Electron Configurations of Several Lighter Elements

Element	Total Electrons	Orbital Diagram 1s	2s	2p			3s	Electron Configuration
Li	3	↑↓	↑					$1s^2 2s^1$
Be	4	↑↓	↑↓					$1s^2 2s^2$
B	5	↑↓	↑↓	↑				$1s^2 2s^2 2p^1$
C	6	↑↓	↑↓	↑	↑			$1s^2 2s^2 2p^2$
N	7	↑↓	↑↓	↑	↑	↑		$1s^2 2s^2 2p^3$
Ne	10	↑↓	↑↓	↑↓	↑↓	↑↓		$1s^2 2s^2 2p^6$
Na	11	↑↓	↑↓	↑↓	↑↓	↑↓	↑	$1s^2 2s^2 2p^6 3s^1$

The next element, helium, has two electrons. Because two electrons with opposite spins can occupy the same orbital, both of helium's electrons are in the $1s$ orbital:

$$\text{He} \quad \boxed{↑↓} \; : \; 1s^2$$

$$1s$$

The two electrons present in helium complete the filling of the first shell. This arrangement represents a very stable configuration, as is evidenced by the chemical inertness of helium.

The electron configurations of lithium and several elements that follow it in the periodic table are shown in ▲ TABLE 1.3. For the third electron of lithium, the change in principal quantum number from $n = 1$ for the first two electrons to $n = 2$ for the third electron represents a large jump in energy and a corresponding jump in the average distance of the electron from the nucleus. In other words, it represents the start of a new shell occupied with electrons. As you can see by examining the periodic table, lithium starts a new row of the table. It is the first member of the alkali metals (group 1A).

The element that follows lithium is beryllium; its electron configuration is $1s^2 2s^2$ (Table 1.3). Boron, atomic number 5, has the electron configuration $1s^2 2s^2 2p^1$. The fifth electron must be placed in a $2p$ orbital because the $2s$ orbital is filled. Because all the three $2p$ orbitals are of equal energy, it does not matter which $2p$ orbital we place this fifth electron in.

With the next element, carbon, we encounter a new situation. We know that the sixth electron must go into a $2p$ orbital. However, does this new electron go into the $2p$ orbital that already has one electron or into one of the other two $2p$ orbitals? This question is answered by **Hund's rule**, which states that *for degenerate orbitals, the lowest energy is attained when the number of electrons having the same spin is maximized.* This means that electrons occupy orbitals singly to the maximum extent possible and that these single electrons in a given subshell all have the same spin magnetic quantum number. Electrons arranged in this way are said to have *parallel spins*. For a carbon atom to achieve its lowest energy, therefore, the two $2p$ electrons must have the same spin. For this to happen, the electrons must be in different $2p$ orbitals, as shown in Table 1.3. Thus, a carbon atom in its ground state has two unpaired electrons.

Similarly, for nitrogen in its ground state, Hund's rule requires that the three $2p$ electrons singly occupy each of the three $2p$ orbitals. This is the only way that all three electrons can have the same spin. For oxygen and fluorine, we place four and five electrons, respectively, in the $2p$ orbitals. To achieve this, we pair up electrons in the $2p$ orbitals, as we will see in Sample Exercise 1.7.

Hund's rule is based in part on the fact that electrons repel one another. By occupying different orbitals, the electrons remain as far as possible from one another, thus minimizing electron–electron repulsions.

SAMPLE EXERCISE 1.7   **Orbital Diagrams and Electron Configurations**

Draw the orbital diagram for the electron configuration of oxygen, atomic number 8. How many unpaired electrons does an oxygen atom possess?

SOLUTION

Analyze and Plan Because oxygen has an atomic number of 8, each oxygen atom has 8 electrons. Figure 1.24 shows the ordering of orbitals. The electrons (represented as arrows) are placed in the orbitals (represented as boxes) beginning with the lowest-energy orbital, the $1s$. Each orbital can hold a maximum of two electrons (the Pauli exclusion principle). Because the $2p$ orbitals are degenerate, we place one electron in each of these orbitals (spin-up) before pairing any electrons (Hund's rule).

Solve Two electrons each go into the $1s$ and $2s$ orbitals with their spins paired. This leaves four electrons for the three degenerate $2p$ orbitals. Following Hund's rule, we put one electron into each $2p$ orbital until all three orbitals have one electron each. The fourth electron is then paired up with one of the three electrons already in a $2p$ orbital, so that the orbital diagram is

$$\boxed{\uparrow\downarrow}\quad\boxed{\uparrow\downarrow}\quad\boxed{\uparrow\downarrow}\,\boxed{\uparrow}\,\boxed{\uparrow}$$
$$1s\qquad 2s\qquad\quad 2p$$

The corresponding electron configuration is written $1s^2 2s^2 2p^4$. The atom has two unpaired electrons.

PRACTICE EXERCISE

(a) Write the electron configuration for phosphorus, element 15. **(b)** How many unpaired electrons does a phosphorus atom possess?
Answers: **(a)** $1s^2 2s^2 2p^6 3s^2 3p^3$, **(b)** three

Condensed Electron Configurations

The filling of the $2p$ subshell is complete at neon (Table 1.3), which has a stable configuration with eight electrons (an *octet*) in the outermost occupied shell. The next element, sodium, atomic number 11, marks the beginning of a new row of the periodic table. Sodium has a single $3s$ electron beyond the stable configuration of neon. We can therefore abbreviate the electron configuration of sodium as

$$\text{Na:}\quad [\text{Ne}]3s^1$$

The symbol [Ne] represents the electron configuration of the ten electrons of neon, $1s^2 2s^2 2p^6$. Writing the electron configuration as $[\text{Ne}]3s^1$ focuses attention on the outermost electron of the atom, which is the one largely responsible for how sodium behaves chemically.

We can generalize what we have just done for the electron configuration of sodium. In writing the *condensed electron configuration* of an element, the electron configuration of the nearest noble-gas element of lower atomic number is represented by its chemical symbol in brackets. For lithium, for example, we write

$$\text{Li:}\quad [\text{He}]2s^1$$

We refer to the electrons represented by the bracketed symbol as the *noble-gas core* of the atom. More usually, these inner-shell electrons are referred to as the **core electrons**. The electrons given after the noble-gas core are called the *outer-shell electrons*. The outer-shell electrons include the electrons involved in chemical bonding, which are called the **valence electrons**. For the elements with atomic number of 30 or less, all of the outer-shell electrons are valence electrons. By comparing the condensed electron configurations of lithium and sodium, we can appreciate why these two elements are so

1A

| 3 |
| Li |
| [He]2s¹ |

| 11 |
| Na |
| [Ne]3s¹ |

| 19 |
| K |
| [Ar]4s¹ |

| 37 |
| Rb |
| [Kr]5s¹ |

| 55 |
| Cs |
| [Xe]6s¹ |

| 87 |
| Fr |
| [Rn]7s¹ |

Alkali
metals

▲ FIGURE 1.29 **The outer-shell electron configurations of the alkali metals (group 1A in the periodic table).**

similar chemically. They have the same type of electron configuration in the outermost occupied shell. Indeed, all the members of the alkali metal group (1A) have a single s valence electron beyond a noble-gas configuration (◀ FIGURE 1.29).

Transition Metals

The noble-gas element argon ($1s^22s^22p^63s^23p^6$) marks the end of the row started by sodium. The element following argon in the periodic table is potassium (K), atomic number 19. In all its chemical properties, potassium is clearly a member of the alkali metal group. The experimental facts about the properties of potassium leave no doubt that the outermost electron of this element occupies an s orbital. But this means that the electron with the highest energy has *not* gone into a $3d$ orbital, which we might expect it to do. Because the $4s$ orbital is lower in energy than the $3d$ orbital (Figure 1.24), the condensed electron configuration of potassium is

$$K: \quad [Ar]4s^1$$

Following the complete filling of the $4s$ orbital (this occurs in the calcium atom), the next set of orbitals to be filled is the $3d$. (You will find it helpful as we go along to refer often to the periodic table on the front inside cover.) Beginning with scandium and extending through zinc, electrons are added to the five $3d$ orbitals until they are completely filled. Thus, the fourth row of the periodic table is ten elements wider than the two previous rows. These ten elements are known as either **transition elements** or **transition metals**. Note the position of these elements in the periodic table.

In writing the electron configurations of the transition elements, we fill orbitals in accordance with Hund's rule—we add them to the $3d$ orbitals singly until all five orbitals have one electron each and then place additional electrons in the $3d$ orbitals with spin pairing until the shell is completely filled. The condensed electron configurations and the corresponding orbital diagram representations of two transition elements are as follows:

		4s		3d				
Mn:	$[Ar]4s^23d^5$ or $[Ar]$	↑↓		↑	↑	↑	↑	↑
Zn:	$[Ar]4s^23d^{10}$ or $[Ar]$	↑↓		↑↓	↑↓	↑↓	↑↓	↑↓

Once all the $3d$ orbitals have been filled with two electrons each, the $4p$ orbitals begin to be occupied until the completed octet of outer electrons ($4s^24p^6$) is reached with krypton (Kr), atomic number 36, another of the noble gases. Rubidium (Rb) marks the beginning of the fifth row. Refer again to the periodic table on the front inside cover. Notice that this row is in every respect like the preceding one, except that the value for n is greater by 1.

⊿ **GIVE IT SOME THOUGHT**

Based on the structure of the periodic table, which becomes occupied first, the $6s$ orbital or the $5d$ orbitals?

The Lanthanides and Actinides

The sixth row of the periodic table begins with one electron in the $6s$ orbital of cesium (Cs) and two electrons in the $6s$ orbital of barium (Ba). Notice, however, that the periodic table then has a break, with elements 57–70 placed below the main portion of the table. This break point is where we begin to encounter a new set of orbitals, the $4f$.

There are seven degenerate $4f$ orbitals, corresponding to the seven allowed values of m_l, ranging from 3 to −3. Thus, it takes 14 electrons to fill the $4f$ orbitals completely. The 14 elements corresponding to the filling of the $4f$ orbitals are known as either the **lanthanide elements** or the **rare earth elements**. These elements are set below the other elements to avoid making the periodic table unduly wide. The properties of the lanthanide elements are all quite similar, and these elements occur together in nature. For many years it was virtually impossible to separate them from one another.

Because the energies of the $4f$ and $5d$ orbitals are very close to each other, the electron configurations of some of the lanthanides involve $5d$ electrons. For example, the elements lanthanum (La), cerium (Ce), and praseodymium (Pr) have the following electron configurations:

$$[Xe]6s^2 5d^1 \quad [Xe]6s^2 5d^1 4f^1 \quad [Xe]6s^2 4f^3$$
Lanthanum   Cerium   Praseodymium

Because La has a single $5d$ electron, it is sometimes placed below yttrium (Y) as the first member of the third series of transition elements; Ce is then placed as the first member of the lanthanides. Based on their chemistry, however, La can be considered the first element in the lanthanide series. Arranged this way, there are fewer apparent exceptions to the regular filling of the $4f$ orbitals among the subsequent members of the series.

After the lanthanide series, the third transition element series is completed by the filling of the $5d$ orbitals, followed by the filling of the $6p$ orbitals. This brings us to radon (Rn), heaviest of the known noble-gas elements.

The final row of the periodic table begins by filling the $7s$ orbitals. The **actinide elements**, of which uranium (U, element 92) and plutonium (Pu, element 94) are the best known, are then built up by completing the $5f$ orbitals. The actinide elements are radioactive, and most of them are not found in nature.

1.9 | ELECTRON CONFIGURATIONS AND THE PERIODIC TABLE

We just saw that the electron configurations of the elements correspond to their locations in the periodic table. Thus, elements in the same column of the table have related outer-shell (valence) electron configurations. As ▶ TABLE 1.4 shows, for example, all 2A elements have an ns^2 outer configuration, and all 3A elements have an $ns^2 np^1$ outer configuration, with the value of n increasing as we move down each column.

As shown in ▼ FIGURE 1.30, the periodic table can be divided into four blocks based on the filling order of orbitals. On the left are *two* blue columns of elements. These elements, known as the alkali metals (group 1A) and alkaline earth metals (group 2A), are those in which the valence s orbitals are being filled. These two columns make up the s block of the periodic table.

On the right is a block of *six* pink columns that comprises the p block, where the valence p orbitals are being filled. The s block and the p block elements together are the **representative elements**, sometimes called the **main-group elements**.

The orange block in Figure 1.30 has *ten* columns containing the transition metals. These are the elements in which the valence d orbitals are being filled and make up the d block.

TABLE 1.4
Electron Configurations of Group 2A and 3A Elements

Group 2A

Be	$[He]2s^2$
Mg	$[Ne]3s^2$
Ca	$[Ar]4s^2$
Sr	$[Kr]5s^2$
Ba	$[Xe]6s^2$
Ra	$[Rn]7s^2$

Group 3A

B	$[He]2s^2 2p^1$
Al	$[Ne]3s^2 3p^1$
Ga	$[Ar]3d^{10}4s^2 4p^1$
In	$[Kr]4d^{10}5s^2 5p^1$
Tl	$[Xe]4f^{14}5d^{10}6s^2 6p^1$

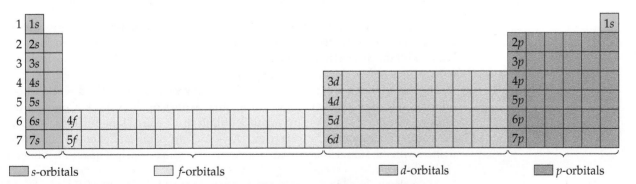

☐ s-orbitals   ☐ f-orbitals   ☐ d-orbitals   ☐ p-orbitals

▲ **FIGURE 1.30 Regions of the periodic table.** The order in which electrons are added to orbitals is read left to right beginning in the top left corner.

The elements in the two tan rows containing *14* columns are the ones in which the valence *f* orbitals are being filled and make up the *f* block. Consequently, these elements are often referred to as the ***f*-block metals**. In most tables, the *f* block is positioned below the periodic table to save space:

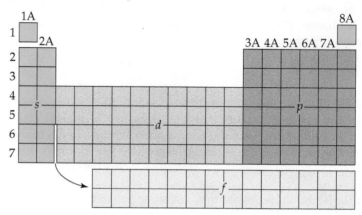

The number of columns in each block corresponds to the maximum number of electrons that can occupy each kind of subshell. Recall that 2, 6, 10, and 14 are the numbers of electrons that can fill the *s, p, d,* and *f* subshells, respectively. Thus, the *s* block has 2 columns, the *p* block has 6, the *d* block has 10, and the *f* block has 14. Recall also that l*s* is the first *s* subshell, 2*p* is the first *p* subshell, 3*d* is the first *d* subshell, and 4*f* is the first *f* subshell, as Figure 1.30 shows. Using these facts, you can write the electron configuration of an element based merely on its position in the periodic table.

Let's use the periodic table to write the electron configuration of selenium (Se, element 34). We first locate Se in the table and then move backward from it through the table, from element 34 to 33 to 32 and so forth, until we come to the noble gas that precedes Se. In this case, the noble gas is argon, Ar, element 18. Thus, the noble-gas core for Se is [Ar]. Our next step is to write symbols for the outer electrons. We do this by moving across period 4 from K, the element following Ar, to Se:

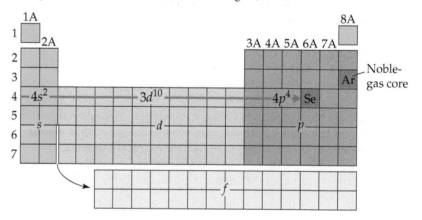

Because K is in the fourth period and the *s* block, we begin with the 4*s* electrons, meaning our first two outer electrons are written $4s^2$. We then move into the *d* block, which begins with the 3*d* electrons. (The principal quantum number in the *d* block is always one less than that of the preceding elements in the *s* block, as seen in Figure 1.30.) Traversing the *d* block adds ten electrons, $3d^{10}$. Finally we move into the *p* block, whose principal quantum number is always the same as that of the *s* block. Counting the squares as we move across the *p* block to Se tells us that we need four electrons, $4p^4$. The electron configuration for Se is therefore $[Ar]4s^2 3d^{10} 4p^4$. This configuration can also be written with the subshells arranged in order of increasing principal quantum number: $[Ar]3d^{10}4s^2 4p^3$.

As a check, we add the number of electrons in the [Ar] core, 18, to the number of electrons we added to the 4*s*, 3*d*, and 4*p* subshells. This sum should equal the atomic number of Se, 34: 18 + 2 + 10 + 4 = 34.

SAMPLE EXERCISE 1.8 **Electron Configurations for a Group**

What is the characteristic valence electron configuration of the group 7A elements, the halogens?

SOLUTION

Analyze and Plan We first locate the halogens in the periodic table, write the electron configurations for the first two elements, and then determine the general similarity between the configurations.

Solve The first member of the halogen group is fluorine (F, element 9). Moving backward from F, we find that the noble-gas core is [He]. Moving from He to the element of next higher atomic number brings us to Li, element 3. Because Li is in the second period of the s block, we add electrons to the $2s$ subshell. Moving across this block gives $2s^2$. Continuing to move to the right, we enter the p block. Counting the squares to F gives $2p^5$. Thus, the condensed electron configuration for fluorine is

$$\text{F:} \quad [\text{He}]2s^2 2p^5$$

The electron configuration for chlorine, the second halogen, is

$$\text{Cl:} \quad [\text{Ne}]3s^2 3p^5$$

From these two examples, we see that the characteristic valence electron configuration of a halogen is $ns^2 np^5$, where n ranges from 2 in the case of fluorine to 6 in the case of astatine.

PRACTICE EXERCISE

Which family of elements is characterized by an $ns^2 np^2$ electron configuration in the outermost occupied shell?

Answer: group 4A

SAMPLE EXERCISE 1.9 **Electron Configurations from the Periodic Table**

(a) Based on its position in the periodic table, write the condensed electron configuration for bismuth, element 83. **(b)** How many unpaired electrons does a bismuth atom have?

SOLUTION

(a) Our first step is to write the noble-gas core. We do this by locating bismuth, element 83, in the periodic table. We then move backward to the nearest noble gas, which is Xe, element 54. Thus, the noble-gas core is [Xe].

Next, we trace the path in order of increasing atomic numbers from Xe to Bi. Moving from Xe to Cs, element 55, we find ourselves in period 6 of the s block. Knowing the block and the period identifies the subshell in which we begin placing outer electrons, $6s$. As we move through the s block, we add two electrons: $6s^2$.

As we move beyond the s block, from element 56 to element 57, the curved arrow below the periodic table reminds us that we are entering the f block. The first row of the f block corresponds to the $4f$ subshell. As we move across this block, we add 14 electrons: $4f^{14}$.

With element 71, we move into the third row of the d block. Because the first row of the d block is $3d$, the second row is $4d$ and the third row is $5d$. Thus, as we move through the ten elements of the d block, from element 71 to element 80, we fill the $5d$ subshell with ten electrons: $5d^{10}$.

Moving from element 80 to element 81 puts us into the p block in the $6p$ subshell. (Remember that the principal quantum number in the p block is the same as in the s block.) Moving across to Bi requires 3 electrons: $6p^3$. The path we have taken is

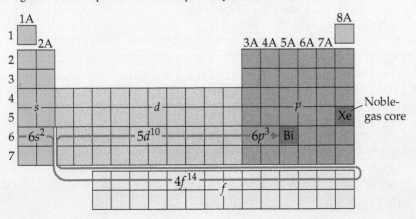

Putting the parts together, we obtain the condensed electron configuration: $[Xe]6s^2 4f^{14} 5d^{10} 6p^3$. This configuration can also be written with the subshells arranged in order of increasing principal quantum number: $[Xe]4f^{14} 5d^{10} 6s^2 6p^3$.

Finally, we check our result to see if the number of electrons equals the atomic number of Bi, 83: Because Xe has 54 electrons (its atomic number), we have $54 + 2 + 14 + 10 + 3 = 83$. (If we had 14 electrons too few, we would realize that we have missed the f block.)

(b) We see from the condensed electron configuration that the only partially occupied subshell is $6p$. The orbital diagram representation for this subshell is

In accordance with Hund's rule, the three $6p$ electrons occupy the three $6p$ orbitals singly, with their spins parallel. Thus, there are three unpaired electrons in the bismuth atom.

PRACTICE EXERCISE

Use the periodic table to write the condensed electron configuration for **(a)** Co (element 27), **(b)** Te (element 52).

Answers: **(a)** $[Ar]4s^2 3d^7$ or $[Ar]3d^7 4s^2$, **(b)** $[Kr]5s^2 4d^{10} 5p^4$ or $[Kr]4d^{10} 5s^2 5p^4$

▼ **FIGURE 1.31** gives, for all the elements, the ground-state electron configurations for the valence electrons. You can use this figure to check your answers as you practice writing electron configurations. We have written these configurations with orbitals

▲ **FIGURE 1.31** Valence electron configurations of the elements.

listed in order of increasing principal quantum number. As we saw in Sample Exercise 1.9, the orbitals can also be listed in order of filling, as they would be read off the periodic table.

Figure 1.31 allow us to reexamine the concept of *valence electrons*. Notice, for example, that as we proceed from Cl ($[Ne]3s^2 3p^5$) to Br ($[Ar]3d^{10}4s^2 4p^5$) we add a complete subshell of $3d$ electrons to the electrons beyond the [Ar] core. Although the $3d$ electrons are outer-shell electrons, they are not involved in chemical bonding and are therefore not considered valence electrons. Thus, we consider only the $4s$ and $4p$ electrons of Br to be valence electrons. Similarly, if we compare the electron configurations of Ag (element 47) and Au (element 79), we see that Au has a completely full $4f^{14}$ subshell beyond its noble-gas core, but those $4f$ electrons are not involved in bonding. In general, *for representative elements we do not consider the electrons in completely filled* d *or* f *subshells to be valence electrons, and for transition elements we do not consider the electrons in a completely filled* f *subshell to be valence electrons.*

Anomalous Electron Configurations

The electron configurations of certain elements appear to violate the rules we have just discussed. For example, Figure 1.31 shows that the electron configuration of chromium (element 24) is $[Ar]3d^5 4s^1$ rather than the $[Ar]3d^4 4s^2$ configuration we might expect. Similarly, the configuration of copper (element 29) is $[Ar]3d^{10}4s^1$ instead of $[Ar]3d^9 4s^2$.

This anomalous behavior is largely a consequence of the closeness of the $3d$ and $4s$ orbital energies. It frequently occurs when there are enough electrons to form precisely half-filled sets of degenerate orbitals (as in chromium) or a completely filled d subshell (as in copper). There are a few similar cases among the heavier transition metals (those with partially filled $4d$ or $5d$ orbitals) and among the f-block metals. Although these minor departures from the expected are interesting, they are not of great chemical significance.

  GIVE IT SOME THOUGHT

The elements Ni, Pd, and Pt are all in the same group. By examining the electron configurations for these elements in Figure 1.31, what can you conclude about the relative energies of the nd and $(n + 1)s$ orbitals for this group?

SAMPLE INTEGRATIVE EXERCISE   **Putting Concepts Together**

Boron, atomic number 5, occurs naturally as two isotopes, ^{10}B and ^{11}B, with natural abundances of 19.9% and 80.1%, respectively. **(a)** In what ways do the two isotopes differ from each other? Does the electronic configuration of ^{10}B differ from that of ^{11}B? **(b)** Draw the orbital diagram for an atom of ^{11}B. Which electrons are the valence electrons? **(c)** Indicate three major ways in which the $1s$ electrons in boron differ from its $2s$ electrons. **(d)** Elemental boron reacts with fluorine to form BF_3, a gas. Write a balanced chemical equation for the reaction of solid boron with fluorine gas. **(e)** ΔH_f° for $BF_3(g)$ is -1135.6 kJ/mol. Calculate the standard enthalpy change in the reaction of boron with fluorine. **(f)** When BCl_3, also a gas at room temperature, comes into contact with water, the two react to form hydrochloric acid and boric acid, H_3BO_3, a very weak acid in water. Write a balanced net ionic equation for this reaction.

SOLUTION

(a) The two isotopes of boron differ in the number of neutrons in the nucleus. ∞∞ (Sections 2.3 and 2.4) Each of the isotopes contains five protons, but ^{10}B contains five neutrons, whereas ^{11}B contains six neutrons. The two isotopes of boron have identical electron configurations, $1s^2 2s^2 2p^1$, because each has five electrons.

(b) The complete orbital diagram is

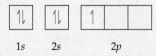

The valence electrons are the ones in the outermost occupied shell, the $2s^2$ and $2p^1$ electrons. The $1s^2$ electrons constitute the core electrons, which we represent as [He] when we write the condensed electron configuration, $[He]2s^2 2p^1$.

(c) The 1s and 2s orbitals are both spherical, but they differ in three important respects: First, the 1s orbital is lower in energy than the 2s orbital. Second, the average distance of the 2s electrons from the nucleus is greater than that of the 1s electrons, so the 1s orbital is smaller than the 2s. Third, the 2s orbital has one node, whereas the 1s orbital has no nodes (Figure 1.18).

(d) The balanced chemical equation is

$$2\ B(s)\ +\ 3\ F_2(g)\ \longrightarrow\ 2\ BF_3(g)$$

(e) $\Delta H° = 2(-1135.6) - [0 + 0] = -2271.2$ kJ. The reaction is strongly exothermic.

(f) $BCl_3(g) + 3\ H_2O(l) \longrightarrow H_3BO_3(aq) + 3\ H^+(aq) + 3\ Cl^-(aq)$. Note that because H_3BO_3 is a very weak acid, its chemical formula is written in molecular form.

CHAPTER SUMMARY AND KEY TERMS

INTRODUCTION AND SECTION 1.1 The **electronic structure** of an atom describes the energies and arrangement of electrons around the atom. Much of what is known about the electronic structure of atoms was obtained by observing the interaction of light with matter. Visible light and other forms of **electromagnetic radiation** (also known as radiant energy) move through a vacuum at the speed of light, $c = 3.00 \times 10^8$ m/s. Electromagnetic radiation has both electric and magnetic components that vary periodically in wavelike fashion. The wave characteristics of radiant energy allow it to be described in terms of **wavelength**, λ, and **frequency**, ν, which are interrelated: $c = \lambda\nu$.

SECTION 1.2 Planck proposed that the minimum amount of radiant energy that an object can gain or lose is related to the frequency of the radiation: $E = h\nu$. This smallest quantity is called a **quantum** of energy. The constant h is called **Planck's constant**: $h = 6.626 \times 10^{-34}$ J-s. In the quantum theory, energy is quantized, meaning that it can have only certain allowed values. Einstein used the quantum theory to explain the **photoelectric effect**, the emission of electrons from metal surfaces when exposed to light. He proposed that light behaves as if it consists of quantized energy packets called **photons**. Each photon carries energy, $E = h\nu$.

SECTION 1.3 Dispersion of radiation into its component wavelengths produces a **spectrum**. If the spectrum contains all wavelengths, it is called a **continuous spectrum**; if it contains only certain specific wavelengths, the spectrum is called a **line spectrum**. The radiation emitted by excited hydrogen atoms forms a line spectrum.

Bohr proposed a model of the hydrogen atom that explains its line spectrum. In this model the energy of the electron in the hydrogen atom depends on the value of a quantum number, n. The value of n must be a positive integer $(1, 2, 3, \ldots)$, and each value of n corresponds to a different specific energy, E_n. The energy of the atom increases as n increases. The lowest energy is achieved for $n = 1$; this is called the **ground state** of the hydrogen atom. Other values of n correspond to **excited states**. Light is emitted when the electron drops from a higher-energy state to a lower-energy state; light is absorbed to excite the electron from a lower energy state to a higher one. The frequency of light emitted or absorbed is such that $h\nu$ equals the difference in energy between two allowed states.

SECTION 1.4 De Broglie proposed that matter, such as electrons, should exhibit wavelike properties. This hypothesis of **matter waves** was proved experimentally by observing the diffraction of electrons. An object has a characteristic wavelength that depends on its momentum, mv: $\lambda = h/mv$. Discovery of the wave properties of the electron led to Heisenberg's **uncertainty principle**, which states that there is an inherent limit to the accuracy with which the position and momentum of a particle can be measured simultaneously.

SECTION 1.5 In the quantum mechanical model of the hydrogen atom, the behavior of the electron is described by mathematical functions called **wave functions**, denoted with the Greek letter ψ. Each allowed wave function has a precisely known energy, but the location of the electron cannot be determined exactly; rather, the probability of it being at a particular point in space is given by the **probability density**, ψ^2. The **electron density** distribution is a map of the probability of finding the electron at all points in space.

The allowed wave functions of the hydrogen atom are called **orbitals**. An orbital is described by a combination of an integer and a letter, corresponding to values of three quantum numbers. The *principal quantum number, n,* is indicated by the integers 1, 2, 3, ... This quantum number relates most directly to the size and energy of the orbital. The *angular momentum quantum number, l,* is indicated by the letters s, p, d, f, and so on, corresponding to the values of 0, 1, 2, 3, ... The l quantum number defines the shape of the orbital. For a given value of n, l can have integer values ranging from 0 to $(n - 1)$. The *magnetic quantum number, m_l,* relates to the orientation of the orbital in space. For a given value of l, m_l can have integral values ranging from $-l$ to l, including 0. Subscripts can be used to label the orientations of the orbitals. For example, the three $3p$ orbitals are designated $3p_x$, $3p_y$, and $3p_z$, with the subscripts indicating the axis along which the orbital is oriented.

An **electron shell** is the set of all orbitals with the same value of n, such as $3s$, $3p$, and $3d$. In the hydrogen atom all the orbitals in an electron shell have the same energy. A **subshell** is the set of one or more orbitals with the same n and l values; for example, $3s$, $3p$, and $3d$ are each subshells of the $n = 3$ shell. There is one orbital in an s subshell, three in a p subshell, five in a d subshell, and seven in an f subshell.

SECTION 1.6 Contour representations are useful for visualizing the shapes of the orbitals. Represented this way, s orbitals appear as spheres that increase in size as n increases. The **radial probability function** tells us the probability that the electron will be found at a certain distance from the nucleus. The wave function for each p orbital has two lobes on opposite sides of the nucleus. They are oriented along the x, y, and z axes. Four of the d orbitals appear as shapes with four lobes around the nucleus; the fifth one, the d_{z^2} orbital, is represented as two lobes along the z axis and a "doughnut" in the xy plane. Regions in which the wave function is zero are called **nodes**. There is zero probability that the electron will be found at a node.

SECTION 1.7 In many-electron atoms, different subshells of the same electron shell have different energies. For a given value of n, the energy of the subshells increases as the value of l increases: $ns<np<nd<nf$. Orbitals within the same subshell are **degenerate**, meaning they have the same energy.

Electrons have an intrinsic property called **electron spin**, which is quantized. The **spin magnetic quantum number**, m_s, can have two possible values, $+\frac{1}{2}$ and $-\frac{1}{2}$, which can be envisioned as the two directions of an electron spinning about an axis. The **Pauli exclusion principle** states that no two electrons in an atom can have the same values for n, l, m_l, and m_s. This principle places a limit of two on the number of electrons that can occupy any one atomic orbital. These two electrons differ in their value of m_s.

SECTIONS 1.8 AND 1.9 The **electron configuration** of an atom describes how the electrons are distributed among the orbitals of the atom. The ground-state electron configurations are generally obtained by placing the electrons in the atomic orbitals of lowest possible energy with the restriction that each orbital can hold no more than two electrons. When electrons occupy a subshell with more than one degenerate orbital, such as the $2p$ subshell, **Hund's rule** states that the lowest energy is attained by maximizing the number of electrons with the same electron spin. For example, in the ground-state electron configuration of carbon, the two $2p$ electrons have the same spin and must occupy two different $2p$ orbitals.

Elements in any given group in the periodic table have the same type of electron arrangements in their outermost shells. For example, the electron configurations of the halogens fluorine and chlorine are $[He]2s^2 2p^5$ and $[Ne]3s^2 3p^5$, respectively. The outer-shell electrons are those that lie outside the orbitals occupied in the next lowest noble-gas element. The outer-shell electrons that are involved in chemical bonding are the **valence electrons** of an atom; for the elements with atomic number 30 or less, all the outer-shell electrons are valence electrons. The electrons that are not valence electrons are called **core electrons**.

The periodic table is partitioned into different types of elements, based on their electron configurations. Those elements in which the outermost subshell is an s or p subshell are called the **representative** (or **main-group**) elements. The alkali metals (group 1A), halogens (group 7A), and noble gases (group 8A) are representative elements. Those elements in which a d subshell is being filled are called the **transition elements** (or **transition metals**). The elements in which the $4f$ subshell is being filled are called the **lanthanide** (or **rare earth**) **elements**. The **actinide elements** are those in which the $5f$ subshell is being filled. The lanthanide and actinide elements are collectively referred to as the **f-block metals**. These elements are shown as two rows of 14 elements below the main part of the periodic table. The structure of the periodic table, summarized in Figure 1.30, allows us to write the electron configuration of an element from its position in the periodic table.

KEY SKILLS

- Calculate the wavelength of electromagnetic radiation given its frequency or its frequency given its wavelength. (Section 1.1)

- Order the common kinds of radiation in the electromagnetic spectrum according to their wavelengths or energy. (Section 1.1)

- Explain what photons are and be able to calculate their energies given either their frequency or wavelength. (Section 1.2)

- Explain how line spectra relate to the idea of quantized energy states of electrons in atoms. (Section 1.3)

- Calculate the wavelength of a moving object. (Section 1.4)

- Explain how the uncertainty principle limits how precisely we can specify the position and the momentum of subatomic particles such as electrons. (Section 1.4)

- Relate the quantum numbers to the number and type of orbitals and recognize the different orbital shapes. (Section 1.5)

- Interpret radial probability function graphs for the orbitals. (Section 1.6)

- Draw an energy-level diagram for the orbitals in a many-electron atom and describe how electrons populate the orbitals in the ground state of an atom, using the Pauli exclusion principle and Hund's rule. (Section 1.8)

- Use the periodic table to write condensed electron configurations and determine the number of unpaired electrons in an atom. (Section 1.9)

KEY EQUATIONS

- $c = \lambda \nu$ [1.1]   light as a wave: c = speed of light (3.00×10^8 m/s), λ = wavelength in meters, ν = frequency in s^{-1}

- $E = h\nu$ [1.2]   light as a particle (photon): E = energy of photon in joules, h = Planck's constant (6.626×10^{-34} J-s), ν = frequency in s^{-1} (same frequency as previous formula)

- $\lambda = h/mv$ [1.8]   matter as a wave: λ = wavelength, h = Planck's constant, m = mass of object in kg, v = speed of object in m/s

- $\Delta x \cdot \Delta(mv) \geq \dfrac{h}{4\pi}$ [1.9]   Heisenberg's uncertainty principle. The uncertainty in position (Δx) and momentum [$\Delta(mv)$] of an object cannot be zero; the smallest value of their product is $h/4\pi$

EXERCISES

VISUALIZING CONCEPTS

1.1 Consider the water wave shown here. **(a)** How could you measure the speed of this wave? **(b)** How would you determine the wavelength of the wave? **(c)** Given the speed and wavelength of the wave, how could you determine the frequency of the wave? **(d)** Suggest an independent experiment to determine the frequency of the wave. [Section 1.1]

1.2 A popular kitchen appliance produces electromagnetic radiation with a frequency of 2450 MHz. With reference to Figure 1.4, answer the following: **(a)** Estimate the wavelength of this radiation. **(b)** Would the radiation produced by the appliance be visible to the human eye? **(c)** If the radiation is not visible, do photons of this radiation have more or less energy than photons of visible light? **(d)** Propose the identity of the kitchen appliance. [Section 1.1]

1.3 The following diagrams represent two electromagnetic waves. Which wave corresponds to the higher-energy radiation? Explain. [Section 1.2]

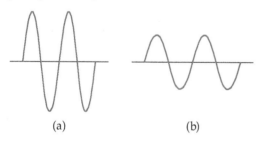

(a)   (b)

1.4 As shown in the accompanying photograph, an electric stove burner on its highest setting exhibits an orange glow. **(a)** When the burner setting is changed to low, the burner continues to produce heat but the orange glow disappears. How can this observation be explained with reference to one of the fundamental observations that led to the notion of quanta? **(b)** Suppose that the energy provided to the burner could be increased beyond the highest setting of the stove. What would we expect to observe with regard to visible light emitted by the burner? [Section 1.2]

1.5 The familiar phenomenon of a rainbow results from the diffraction of sunlight through raindrops. **(a)** Does the wavelength of light increase or decrease as we proceed outward from the innermost band of the rainbow? **(b)** Does the frequency of light increase or decrease as we proceed outward? **(c)** Suppose that instead of sunlight, the visible light from a hydrogen discharge tube (Figure 1.10) was used as the light source. What do you think the resulting "hydrogen discharge rainbow" would look like? [Section 1.3]

1.6 A certain quantum mechanical system has the energy levels shown in the diagram below. The energy levels are indexed by a single quantum number n that is an integer. **(a)** As drawn, which quantum numbers are involved in the transition that requires the most energy? **(b)** Which quantum numbers are involved in the transition that requires the least energy? **(c)** Based on the drawing, put the following in order of increasing wavelength of the light absorbed or emitted during the transition: (*i*) $n = 1$ to $n = 2$; (*ii*) $n = 3$ to $n = 2$; (*iii*) $n = 2$ to $n = 4$; (*iv*) $n = 3$ to $n = 1$. [Section 1.3]

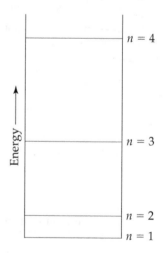

1.7 Consider a fictitious one-dimensional system with one electron. The wave function for the electron, drawn at the top of the next page, is $\psi(x) = \sin x$ from $x = 0$ to $x = 2\pi$. **(a)** Sketch the probability density, $\psi^2(x)$, from $x = 0$ to $x = 2\pi$. **(b)** At what value or values of x will there be the greatest probability of finding the electron? **(c)** What is the probability that the electron will be found at $x = \pi$? What is such a point in a wave function called? [Section 1.5]

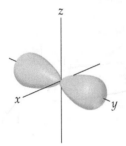

1.8 The contour representation of one of the orbitals for the $n = 3$ shell of a hydrogen atom is shown below. **(a)** What is the quantum number l for this orbital? **(b)** How do we label this orbital? **(c)** How would you modify this sketch to show the analogous orbital for the $n = 4$ shell? [Section 1.6]

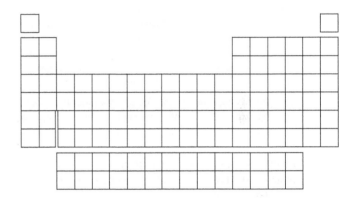

1.9 The drawing below shows part of the orbital diagram for an element. **(a)** As drawn, the drawing is *incorrect*. Why? **(b)** How would you correct the drawing without changing the number of electrons? **(c)** To which group in the periodic table does the element belong? [Section 1.8]

1.10 State where in the periodic table these elements appear:
  (a) elements with the valence-shell electron configuration ns^2np^5
  (b) elements that have three unpaired p electrons
  (c) an element whose valence electrons are $4s^24p^1$
  (d) the d-block elements

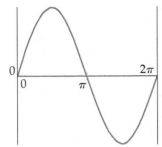

THE WAVE NATURE OF LIGHT (section 1.1)

1.11 What are the basic SI units for **(a)** the wavelength of light, **(b)** the frequency of light, **(c)** the speed of light?

1.12 **(a)** What is the relationship between the wavelength and the frequency of radiant energy? **(b)** Ozone in the upper atmosphere absorbs energy in the 210–230-nm range of the spectrum. In what region of the electromagnetic spectrum does this radiation occur?

1.13 Label each of the following statements as true or false. For those that are false, correct the statement. **(a)** Visible light is a form of electromagnetic radiation. **(b)** Ultraviolet light has longer wavelengths than visible light. **(c)** X-rays travel faster than microwaves. **(d)** Electromagnetic radiation and sound waves travel at the same speed.

1.14 Determine which of the following statements are false and correct them. **(a)** The frequency of radiation increases as the wavelength increases. **(b)** Electromagnetic radiation travels through a vacuum at a constant speed, regardless of wavelength. **(c)** Infrared light has higher frequencies than visible light. **(d)** The glow from a fireplace, the energy within a microwave oven, and a foghorn blast are all forms of electromagnetic radiation.

1.15 Arrange the following kinds of electromagnetic radiation in order of increasing wavelength: infrared, green light, red light, radio waves, X-rays, ultraviolet light.

1.16 List the following types of electromagnetic radiation in order of increasing wavelength: **(a)** the gamma rays produced by a radioactive nuclide used in medical imaging; **(b)** radiation from an FM radio station at 93.1 MHz on the dial; **(c)** a radio signal from an AM radio station at 680 kHz on the dial; **(d)** the yellow light from sodium vapor streetlights; **(e)** the red light of a light-emitting diode, such as in a calculator display.

1.17 **(a)** What is the frequency of radiation that has a wavelength of 10 μm, about the size of a bacterium? **(b)** What is the wavelength of radiation that has a frequency of 5.50×10^{14} s^{-1}? **(c)** Would the radiations in part (a) or part (b) be visible to the human eye? **(d)** What distance does electromagnetic radiation travel in 50.0 μs?

1.18 **(a)** What is the frequency of radiation whose wavelength is 5.0×10^{-5} m? **(b)** What is the wavelength of radiation that has a frequency of 2.5×10^{8} s^{-1}? **(c)** Would the radiations in part (a) or part (b) be detected by an X-ray detector? **(d)** What distance does electromagnetic radiation travel in 10.5 fs?

1.19 An argon ion laser emits light at 532 nm. What is the frequency of this radiation? Using Figure 1.4, predict the color associated with this wavelength.

1.20 It is possible to convert radiant energy into electrical energy using photovoltaic cells. Assuming equal efficiency of conversion, would infrared or ultraviolet radiation yield more electrical energy on a per-photon basis?

QUANTIZED ENERGY AND PHOTONS (section 1.2)

1.21 If human height were quantized in one-foot increments, what would happen to the height of a child as she grows up?

1.22 Einstein's 1905 paper on the photoelectric effect was the first important application of Planck's quantum hypothesis. Describe Planck's original hypothesis, and explain how Einstein made use of it in his theory of the photoelectric effect.

1.23 (a) Calculate the energy of a photon of electromagnetic radiation whose frequency is 6.75×10^{12} s^{-1}. (b) Calculate the energy of a photon of radiation whose wavelength is 322 nm. (c) What wavelength of radiation has photons of energy 2.87×10^{-18} J?

1.24 (a) A red laser pointer emits light with a wavelength of 650 nm. What is the frequency of this light? (b) What is the energy of one of these photons? (c) The laser pointer emits light because electrons in the material are excited (by a battery) from their ground state to an upper excited state. When the electrons return to the ground state, they lose the excess energy in the form of 650 nm photons. What is the energy gap between the ground state and excited state in the laser material?

1.25 (a) Calculate and compare the energy of a photon of wavelength 3.3 μm with that of wavelength 0.154 nm. (b) Use Figure 1.4 to identify the region of the electromagnetic spectrum to which each belongs.

1.26 An AM radio station broadcasts at 1010 kHz, and its FM partner broadcasts at 98.3 MHz. Calculate and compare the energy of the photons emitted by these two radio stations.

1.27 One type of sunburn occurs on exposure to UV light of wavelength in the vicinity of 325 nm. (a) What is the energy of a photon of this wavelength? (b) What is the energy of a mole of these photons? (c) How many photons are in a 1.00 mJ burst of this radiation? (d) These UV photons can break chemical bonds in your skin to cause sunburn—a form of radiation damage. If the 325-nm radiation provides exactly the energy to break an average chemical bond in the skin, estimate the average energy of these bonds in kJ/mol.

1.28 The energy from radiation can be used to cause the rupture of chemical bonds. A minimum energy of 941 kJ/mol is required to break the nitrogen–nitrogen bond in N_2. What is the longest wavelength of radiation that possesses the necessary energy to break the bond? What type of electromagnetic radiation is this?

1.29 A diode laser emits at a wavelength of 987 nm. (a) In what portion of the electromagnetic spectrum is this radiation found? (b) All of its output energy is absorbed in a detector that measures a total energy of 0.52 J over a period of 32 s. How many photons per second are being emitted by the laser?

1.30 A stellar object is emitting radiation at 3.55 mm. (a) What type of electromagnetic spectrum is this radiation? (b) If a detector is capturing 3.2×10^8 photons per second at this wavelength, what is the total energy of the photons detected in one hour?

1.31 Molybdenum metal must absorb radiation with a minimum frequency of 1.09×10^{15} s^{-1} before it can eject an electron from its surface via the photoelectric effect. (a) What is the minimum energy needed to eject an electron? (b) What wavelength of radiation will provide a photon of this energy? (c) If molybdenum is irradiated with light of wavelength of 120 nm, what is the maximum possible kinetic energy of the emitted electrons?

1.32 Sodium metal requires a photon with a minimum energy of 4.41×10^{-19} J to emit electrons. (a) What is the minimum frequency of light necessary to emit electrons from sodium via the photoelectric effect? (b) What is the wavelength of this light? (c) If sodium is irradiated with light of 405 nm, what is the maximum possible kinetic energy of the emitted electrons? (d) What is the maximum number of electrons that can be freed by a burst of light whose total energy is 1.00 μJ ?

BOHR'S MODEL; MATTER WAVES (sections 1.3 and 1.4)

1.33 Explain how the existence of line spectra is consistent with Bohr's theory of quantized energies for the electron in the hydrogen atom.

1.34 (a) In terms of the Bohr theory of the hydrogen atom, what process is occurring when excited hydrogen atoms emit radiant energy of certain wavelengths and only those wavelengths? (b) Does a hydrogen atom "expand" or "contract" as it moves from its ground state to an excited state?

1.35 Is energy emitted or absorbed when the following electronic transitions occur in hydrogen: (a) from $n = 4$ to $n = 2$, (b) from an orbit of radius 2.12 Å to one of radius 8.46 Å, (c) an electron adds to the H$^+$ ion and ends up in the $n = 3$ shell?

1.36 Indicate whether energy is emitted or absorbed when the following electronic transitions occur in hydrogen: (a) from $n = 2$ to $n = 6$, (b) from an orbit of radius 4.76 Å to one of radius 0.529 Å, (c) from the $n = 6$ to the $n = 9$ state.

1.37 (a) Using Equation 1.5, calculate the energy of an electron in the hydrogen atom when $n = 2$ and when $n = 6$. Calculate the wavelength of the radiation released when an electron moves from $n = 6$ to $n = 2$. (b) Is this line in the visible region of the electromagnetic spectrum? If so, what color is it?

1.38 (a) Calculate the energies of an electron in the hydrogen atom for $n = 1$ and for $n = \infty$. How much energy does it require to move the electron out of the atom completely (from $n = 1$ to $n = \infty$), according to Bohr? Put your answer in kJ/mol. (b) The energy for the process H + energy $\rightarrow$ H$^+$ + e$^-$ is called the ionization energy of hydrogen. The experimentally determined value for the ionization energy of hydrogen is 1310 kJ/mol. How does this compare to your calculation?

1.39 The visible emission lines observed by Balmer all involved $n_f = 2$. (a) Explain why only the lines with $n_f = 2$ were observed in the visible region of the electromagnetic spectrum. (b) Calculate the wavelengths of the first three lines in the Balmer series—those for which $n_i = 3$, 4, and 5—and identify these lines in the emission spectrum shown in Figure 1.11.

1.40 The Lyman series of emission lines of the hydrogen atom are those for which $n_f = 1$. (a) Determine the region of the electromagnetic spectrum in which the lines of the Lyman series are observed. (b) Calculate the wavelengths of the first three lines in the Lyman series—those for which $n_i = 2$, 3, and 4.

1.41 One of the emission lines of the hydrogen atom has a wavelength of 93.8 nm. (a) In what region of the electromagnetic spectrum is this emission found? (b) Determine the initial and final values of n associated with this emission.

1.42 The hydrogen atom can absorb light of wavelength 2626 nm. **(a)** In what region of the electromagnetic spectrum is this absorption found? **(b)** Determine the initial and final values of n associated with this absorption.

1.43 Use the de Broglie relationship to determine the wavelengths of the following objects: **(a)** an 85-kg person skiing at 50 km/hr, **(b)** a 10.0-g bullet fired at 250 m/s, **(c)** a lithium atom moving at 2.5×10^5 m/s, **(d)** an ozone (O_3) molecule in the upper atmosphere moving at 550 m/s.

1.44 Among the elementary subatomic particles of physics is the muon, which decays within a few nanoseconds after formation. The muon has a rest mass 206.8 times that of an electron. Calculate the de Broglie wavelength associated with a muon traveling at a velocity of 8.85×10^5 cm/s.

1.45 Neutron diffraction is an important technique for determining the structures of molecules. Calculate the velocity of a neutron needed to achieve a wavelength of 0.955 Å. (Refer to the inside cover for the mass of the neutron).

1.46 The electron microscope has been widely used to obtain highly magnified images of biological and other types of materials. When an electron is accelerated through a particular potential field, it attains a speed of 8.95×10^6 m/s. What is the characteristic wavelength of this electron? Is the wavelength comparable to the size of atoms?

1.47 Using Heisenberg's uncertainty principle, calculate the uncertainty in the position of **(a)** a 1.50-mg mosquito moving at a speed of 1.40 m/s if the speed is known to within ± 0.01 m/s; **(b)** a proton moving at a speed of $(5.00 \pm 0.01) \times 10^4$ m/s. (The mass of a proton is given in the table of fundamental constants in the inside cover of the text.)

1.48 Calculate the uncertainty in the position of **(a)** an electron moving at a speed of $(3.00 \pm 0.01) \times 10^5$ m/s, **(b)** a neutron moving at this same speed. (The masses of an electron and a neutron are given in the table of fundamental constants in the inside cover of the text.) **(c)** What are the implications of these calculations to our model of the atom?

QUANTUM MECHANICS AND ATOMIC ORBITALS (sections 1.5 and 1.6)

1.49 **(a)** Why does the Bohr model of the hydrogen atom violate the uncertainty principle? **(b)** In what way is the description of the electron using a wave function consistent with de Broglie's hypothesis? **(c)** What is meant by the term *probability density*? Given the wave function, how do we find the probability density at a certain point in space?

1.50 **(a)** According to the Bohr model, an electron in the ground state of a hydrogen atom orbits the nucleus at a specific radius of 0.53 Å. In the quantum mechanical description of the hydrogen atom, the most probable distance of the electron from the nucleus is 0.53 Å. Why are these two statements different? **(b)** Why is the use of Schrödinger's wave equation to describe the location of a particle very different from the description obtained from classical physics? **(c)** In the quantum mechanical description of an electron, what is the physical significance of the square of the wave function, ψ^2?

1.51 **(a)** For $n = 4$, what are the possible values of l? **(b)** For $l = 2$, what are the possible values of m_l? **(c)** If m_l is 2, what are the possible values for l?

1.52 How many possible values for l and m_l are there when **(a)** $n = 3$; **(b)** $n = 5$?

1.53 Give the numerical values of n and l corresponding to each of the following orbital designations: **(a)** $3p$, **(b)** $2s$, **(c)** $4f$, **(d)** $5d$.

1.54 Give the values for n, l, and m_l for **(a)** each orbital in the $2p$ subshell, **(b)** each orbital in the $5d$ subshell.

1.55 Which of the following represent impossible combinations of n and l: **(a)** $1p$, **(b)** $4s$, **(c)** $5f$, **(d)** $2d$?

1.56 For the table that follows, write which orbital goes with the quantum numbers. Don't worry about x, y, z subscripts. If the quantum numbers are not allowed, write "not allowed."

n	l	m_l	Orbital
2	1	-1	$2p$ (example)
1	0	0	
3	-3	2	
3	2	-2	
2	0	-1	
0	0	0	
4	2	1	
5	3	0	

1.57 Sketch the shape and orientation of the following types of orbitals: **(a)** s, **(b)** p_z, **(c)** d_{xy}.

1.58 Sketch the shape and orientation of the following types of orbitals: **(a)** p_x, **(b)** d_{z^2}, **(c)** $d_{x^2-y^2}$.

1.59 **(a)** What are the similarities and differences between the $1s$ and $2s$ orbitals of the hydrogen atom? **(b)** In what sense does a $2p$ orbital have directional character? Compare the "directional" characteristics of the p_x and $d_{x^2-y^2}$ orbitals. (That is, in what direction or region of space is the electron density concentrated?) **(c)** What can you say about the average distance from the nucleus of an electron in a $2s$ orbital as compared with a $3s$ orbital? **(d)** For the hydrogen atom, list the following orbitals in order of increasing energy (that is, most stable ones first): $4f$, $6s$, $3d$, $1s$, $2p$.

1.60 **(a)** With reference to Figure 1.18, what is the relationship between the number of nodes in an s orbital and the value of the principal quantum number? **(b)** Identify the number of nodes; that is, identify places where the electron density is zero, in the $2p_x$ orbital; in the $3s$ orbital. **(c)** What information is obtained from the radial probability functions in Figure 1.18? **(d)** For the hydrogen atom, list the following orbitals in order of increasing energy: $3s$, $2s$, $2p$, $5s$, $4d$.

MANY-ELECTRON ATOMS AND ELECTRON CONFIGURATIONS (sections 1.7–1.9)

1.61 For a given value of the principal quantum number, n, how do the energies of the s, p, d, and f subshells vary for **(a)** hydrogen, **(b)** a many-electron atom?

1.62 **(a)** The average distance from the nucleus of a $3s$ electron in a chlorine atom is smaller than that for a $3p$ electron. In light of this fact, which orbital is higher in energy? **(b)** Would you expect it to require more or less energy to remove a $3s$ electron from the chlorine atom, as compared with a $2p$ electron? Explain.

1.63 **(a)** What experimental evidence is there for the electron having a "spin"? **(b)** Draw an energy-level diagram that shows the relative energetic positions of a $1s$ orbital and a $2s$ orbital. Put two electrons in the $1s$ orbital. **(c)** Draw an arrow showing the excitation of an electron from the $1s$ to the $2s$ orbital.

1.64 **(a)** State the Pauli exclusion principle in your own words. **(b)** The Pauli exclusion principle is, in an important sense, the key to understanding the periodic table. Explain.

1.65 What is the maximum number of electrons that can occupy each of the following subshells: **(a)** $3p$, **(b)** $5d$, **(c)** $2s$, **(d)** $4f$?

1.66 What is the maximum number of electrons in an atom that can have the following quantum numbers: **(a)** $n = 2$, $m_s = -\frac{1}{2}$, **(b)** $n = 5$, $l = 3$; **(c)** $n = 4$, $l = 3$, $m_l = -3$; **(d)** $n = 4, l = 0, m_l = 0$?

1.67 **(a)** What are "valence electrons"? **(b)** What are "core electrons"? **(c)** What does each box in an orbital diagram represent? **(d)** What quantity is represented by the half arrows in an orbital diagram?

1.68 For each element, indicate the number of valence electrons, core electrons, and unpaired electrons in the ground state: **(a)** carbon, **(b)** phosphorus, **(c)** neon.

1.69 Write the condensed electron configurations for the following atoms, using the appropriate noble-gas core abbreviations: **(a)** Cs, **(b)** Ni, **(c)** Se, **(d)** Cd, **(e)** U, **(f)** Pb.

1.70 Write the condensed electron configurations for the following atoms and indicate how many unpaired electrons each has: **(a)** Mg, **(b)** Ge, **(c)** Br, **(d)** V, **(e)** Y, **(f)** Lu.

1.71 Identify the specific element that corresponds to each of the following electron configurations and indicate the number of unpaired electrons for each: **(a)** $1s^2 2s^2$, **(b)** $1s^2 2s^2 2p^4$, **(c)** $[Ar]4s^1 3d^5$, **(d)** $[Kr]5s^2 4d^{10} 5p^4$.

1.72 Identify the group of elements that corresponds to each of the following generalized electron configurations and indicate the number of unpaired electrons for each:
   (a) [noble gas] $ns^2 np^5$
   (b) [noble gas] $ns^2 (n - 1)d^2$
   (c) [noble gas] $ns^2 (n - 1)d^{10} np^1$
   (d) [noble gas] $ns^2 (n - 2)f^6$

1.73 What is wrong with the following electron configurations for atoms in their ground states? **(a)** $1s^2 2s^2 3s^1$, **(b)** $[Ne]2s^2 2p^3$, **(c)** $[Ne]3s^2 3d^5$.

1.74 The following electron configurations represent excited states. Identify the element, and write its ground-state condensed electron configuration. **(a)** $1s^2 2s^2 3p^2 4p^1$, **(b)** $[Ar]3d^{10} 4s^1 4p^4 5s^1$, **(c)** $[Kr]4d^6 5s^2 5p^1$.

ADDITIONAL EXERCISES

1.75 Consider the two waves shown here, which we will consider to represent two electromagnetic radiations:
   (a) What is the wavelength of wave A? Of wave B?
   (b) What is the frequency of wave A? Of wave B?
   (c) Identify the regions of the electromagnetic spectrum to which waves A and B belong.

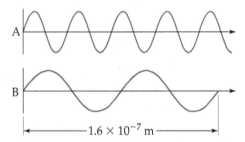

1.76 If you put 120 volts of electricity through a pickle, the pickle will smoke and start glowing orange-yellow. The light is emitted because sodium ions in the pickle become excited; their return to the ground state results in light emission. **(a)** The wavelength of this emitted light is 589 nm. Calculate its frequency. **(b)** What is the energy of 0.10 mole of these photons? **(c)** Calculate the energy gap between the excited and ground states for the sodium ion. **(d)** If you soaked the pickle for a long time in a different salt solution, such as strontium chloride, would you still observe 589-nm light emission? Why or why not?

1.77 Certain elements emit light of a specific wavelength when they are burned. Historically, chemists used such emission wavelengths to determine whether specific elements were present in a sample. Characteristic wavelengths for some of the elements are given in the following table:

Ag	328.1 nm	Fe	372.0 nm
Au	267.6 nm	K	404.7 nm
Ba	455.4 nm	Mg	285.2 nm
Ca	422.7 nm	Na	589.6 nm
Cu	324.8 nm	Ni	341.5 nm

(a) Determine which elements emit radiation in the visible part of the spectrum. **(b)** Which element emits photons of highest energy? Of lowest energy? **(c)** When burned, a sample of an unknown substance is found to emit light of frequency $6.59 \times 10^{14} \ s^{-1}$. Which of these elements is probably in the sample?

1.78 In June 2004, the Cassini–Huygens spacecraft began orbiting Saturn and transmitting images to Earth. The closest distance between Saturn and Earth is 746 million miles. What is the minimum amount of time it takes for the transmitted signals to travel from the spacecraft to Earth?

1.79 The rays of the Sun that cause tanning and burning are in the ultraviolet portion of the electromagnetic spectrum. These rays are categorized by wavelength. So-called UV-A radiation has wavelengths in the range of 320–380 nm, whereas UV-B radiation has wavelengths in the range of 290–320 nm. **(a)** Calculate the frequency of light that has a wavelength of 320 nm. **(b)** Calculate the energy of a mole of 320-nm photons. **(c)** Which are more energetic, photons of UV-A radiation or photons of UV-B radiation? **(d)** The UV-B radiation from the Sun is considered a greater cause of sunburn in humans than is UV-A radiation. Is this observation consistent with your answer to part (c)?

1.80 The watt is the derived SI unit of power, the measure of energy per unit time: 1 W = 1 J-s. A semiconductor laser in a CD player has an output wavelength of 780 nm and a power level of 0.10 mW. How many photons strike the CD surface during the playing of a CD 69 minutes in length?

1.81 Carotenoids are yellow, orange, and red pigments synthesized by plants. The observed color of an object is not the color of light it absorbs but rather the complementary color, as described by a color wheel such as the one shown here. On this wheel, complementary colors are across from each other. **(a)** Based on this wheel, what color is absorbed most strongly if a plant is orange? **(b)** If a particular carotenoid absorbs photons at 455 nm, what is the energy of the photon?

1.82 A photocell is a device used to measure the intensity of light. In a certain experiment, when light of wavelength 630 nm is directed onto the photocell, electrons are emitted at the rate of 2.6×10^{-12} C/s (coulombs per second). Assume that each photon that impinges on the photocell emits one electron. How many photons per second are striking the photocell? How much energy per second is the photocell absorbing?

1.83 In an experiment to study the photoelectric effect, a scientist measures the kinetic energy of ejected electrons as a function of the frequency of radiation hitting a metal surface. She obtains the following plot. The point labeled "ν_0" corresponds to light with a wavelength of 680 nm. (a) What is the value of ν_0 in s^{-1}? (b) What is the value of the work function of the metal in units of kJ/mol of ejected electrons? (c) What happens when the metal is irradiated with light of frequency less than ν_0? (d) Note that when the frequency of the light is greater than ν_0, the plot shows a straight line with a nonzero slope. Why is this the case? (e) Can you determine the slope of the line segment discussed in part (d)? Explain.

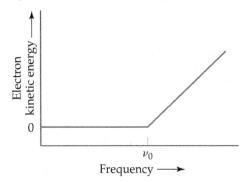

1.84 The human retina has three types of receptor cones, each sensitive to a different range of wavelengths of visible light, as shown in this figure (the colors are merely to differentiate the three curves from one another; they do not indicate the actual colors represented by each curve):

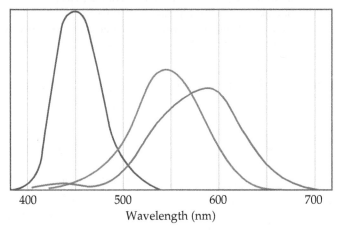

(a) Estimate the energies of photons with wavelengths at the maximum for each type of cone. (b) The color of the sky is due to scattering of solar light by the molecules of the atmosphere. Lord Rayleigh was one of the first to study scattering of this kind. He showed that the amount of scattering for very small particles such as molecules is inversely proportional to the fourth power of the wavelength. Estimate the ratio of the scattering efficiency of light at the wavelength of the maximum for the "blue" cones, as compared with that for the "green" cones. (c) Explain why the sky appears blue even though all wavelengths of solar light are scattered by the atmosphere.

1.85 The series of emission lines of the hydrogen atom for which $n_f = 3$ is called the *Paschen series*. (a) Determine the region of the electromagnetic spectrum in which the lines of the Paschen series are observed. (b) Calculate the wavelengths of the first three lines in the Paschen series—those for which $n_i = 4, 5,$ and 6.

1.86 When the spectrum of light from the Sun is examined in high resolution in an experiment similar to that illustrated in Figure 1.9, dark lines are evident. These are called Fraunhofer lines, after the scientist who studied them extensively in the early nineteenth century. Altogether, about 25,000 lines have been identified in the solar spectrum between 2950 Å and 10,000 Å. The Fraunhofer lines are attributed to absorption of certain wavelengths of the Sun's "white" light by gaseous elements in the Sun's atmosphere. (a) Describe the process that causes absorption of specific wavelengths of light from the solar spectrum. (b) To determine which Fraunhofer lines belonged to a given element, say neon, what experiments could a scientist conduct here on Earth?

[1.87] Bohr's model can be used for hydrogen-like ions—ions that have only one electron, such as He^+ and Li^{2+}. (a) Why is the Bohr model applicable to He^+ ions but not to neutral He atoms? (b) The ground-state energies of H, He^+, and Li^{2+} are tabulated as follows:

Atom or ion	H	He+	Li2+
Ground-state energy	-2.18×10^{-18} J	-8.72×10^{-18} J	-1.96×10^{-17} J

By examining these numbers, propose a relationship between the ground-state energy of hydrogen-like systems and the nuclear charge, Z. (c) Use the relationship you derive in part (b) to predict the ground-state energy of the C^{5+} ion.

[1.88] An electron is accelerated through an electric potential to a kinetic energy of 18.6 keV. What is its characteristic wavelength? [*Hint*: Recall that the kinetic energy of a moving object is $E = \frac{1}{2}mv^2$, where m is the mass of the object and v is the speed of the object.]

1.89 In the television series *Star Trek*, the transporter beam is a device used to "beam down" people from the *Starship Enterprise* to another location, such as the surface of a planet. The writers of the show put a "Heisenberg compensator" into the transporter beam mechanism. Explain why such a compensator (which is entirely fictional) would be necessary to get around Heisenberg's uncertainty principle.

1.90 Which of the quantum numbers governs (a) the shape of an orbital, (b) the energy of an orbital, (c) the spin properties of the electron, (d) the spatial orientation of the orbital?

[1.91] Consider the discussion of radial probability functions in "A Closer Look" in Section 1.6. (a) What is the difference between the probability density as a function of r and the radial probability function as a function of r? (b) What is the significance of the term $4\pi r^2$ in the radial probability functions for the s orbitals? (c) Based on Figures 1.18 and 1.21, make sketches of what you think the probability density as a function of r and the radial probability function would look like for the $4s$ orbital of the hydrogen atom.

[1.92] For orbitals that are symmetric but not spherical, the contour representations (as in Figures 1.22 and 1.23) suggest where nodal planes exist (that is, where the electron density is zero). For example, the p_x orbital has a node wherever $x = 0$. This equation is satisfied by all points on the yz plane, so this plane is called a nodal plane of the p_x orbital. (a) Determine the nodal plane of the p_z orbital. (b) What are the two nodal planes of the d_{xy} orbital? (c) What are the two nodal planes of the $d_{x^2-y^2}$ orbital?

[1.93] The "Chemistry and Life" box in Section 1.7 described the techniques called NMR and MRI. (a) Instruments for obtaining MRI data are typically labeled with a frequency, such as 600 MHz. Why do you suppose this label is relevant to the experiment? (b) What is the value of ΔE in Figure 1.27 that would correspond to the absorption of a photon of radiation with frequency 450 MHz? (c) In general, the stronger the magnetic field, the greater the information obtained from an NMR or MRI experiment. Why do you suppose this is the case?

1.94 Suppose that the spin quantum number, m_s, could have *three* allowed values instead of two. How would this affect the number of elements in the first four rows of the periodic table?

1.95 Using the periodic table as a guide, write the condensed electron configuration and determine the number of unpaired electrons for the ground state of (a) Si, (b) Zn, (c) Zr, (d) Sn, (e) Ba, (f) Tl.

1.96 Scientists have speculated that element 126 might have a moderate stability, allowing it to be synthesized and characterized. Predict what the condensed electron configuration of this element might be.

INTEGRATIVE EXERCISES

1.97 Microwave ovens use microwave radiation to heat food. The energy of the microwaves is absorbed by water molecules in food and then transferred to other components of the food. (a) Suppose that the microwave radiation has a wavelength of 11.2 cm. How many photons are required to heat 200 mL of coffee from 23 °C to 60 °C? (b) Suppose the microwave's power is 900 W (1 Watt = 1 joule-second). How long would you have to heat the coffee in part (a)?

1.98 The stratospheric ozone (O_3) layer helps to protect us from harmful ultraviolet radiation. It does so by absorbing ultraviolet light and falling apart into an O_2 molecule and an oxygen atom, a process known as photodissociation.

$$O_3(g) \longrightarrow O_2(g) + O(g)$$

Use the data in Appendix C to calculate the enthalpy change for this reaction. What is the maximum wavelength a photon can have if it is to possess sufficient energy to cause this dissociation? In what portion of the spectrum does this wavelength occur?

1.99 The discovery of hafnium, element number 72, provided a controversial episode in chemistry. G. Urbain, a French chemist, claimed in 1911 to have isolated an element number 72 from a sample of rare earth (elements 58–71) compounds. However, Niels Bohr believed that hafnium was more likely to be found along with zirconium than with the rare earths. D. Coster and G. von Hevesy, working in Bohr's laboratory in Copenhagen, showed in 1922 that element 72 was present in a sample of Norwegian zircon, an ore of zirconium. (The name hafnium comes from the Latin name for Copenhagen, *Hafnia*). (a) How would you use electron configuration arguments to justify Bohr's prediction? (b) Zirconium, hafnium's neighbor in group 4B, can be produced as a metal by reduction of solid $ZrCl_4$ with molten sodium metal. Write a balanced chemical equation for the reaction. Is this an oxidation-reduction reaction? If yes, what is reduced and what is oxidized? (c) Solid zirconium dioxide, ZrO_2, is reacted with chlorine gas in the presence of carbon. The products of the reaction are $ZrCl_4$ and two gases, CO_2 and CO in the ratio 1:2. Write a balanced chemical equation for the reaction. Starting with a 55.4-g sample of ZrO_2, calculate the mass of $ZrCl_4$ formed, assuming that ZrO_2 is the limiting reagent and assuming 100% yield. (d) Using their electron configurations, account for the fact that Zr and Hf form chlorides MCl_4 and oxides MO_2.

1.100 (a) Account for formation of the following series of oxides in terms of the electron configurations of the elements and the discussion of ionic compounds K_2O, CaO, Sc_2O_3, TiO_2, V_2O_5, CrO_3. (b) Name these oxides. (c) Consider the metal oxides whose enthalpies of formation (in kJ mol^{-1}) are listed here.

Oxide	$K_2O(s)$	$CaO(s)$	$TiO_2(s)$	$V_2O_5(s)$
ΔH_f°	−363.2	−635.1	−938.7	−1550.6

Calculate the enthalpy changes in the following general reaction for each case:

$$M_nO_m(s) + H_2(g) \longrightarrow nM(s) + mH_2O(g)$$

(You will need to write the balanced equation for each case and then compute ΔH°.) (d) Based on the data given, estimate a value of ΔH_f° for $Sc_2O_3(s)$.

1.101 The first 25 years of the twentieth century were momentous for the rapid pace of change in scientists' understanding of the nature of matter. (a) How did Rutherford's experiments on the scattering of α particles by a gold foil set the stage for Bohr's theory of the hydrogen atom? (b) In what ways is de Broglie's hypothesis, as it applies to electrons, consistent with J. J. Thomson's conclusion that the electron has mass? In what sense is it consistent with proposals preceding Thomson's work that the cathode rays are a wave phenomenon?

[1.102] The two most common isotopes of uranium are ^{235}U and ^{238}U. (a) Compare the number of protons, the number of electrons, and the number of neutrons in atoms of these two isotopes. (b) Using the periodic table in the front inside cover, write the electron configuration for a U atom. (c) Compare your answer to part (b) to the electron configuration given in Figure 1.31. How can you explain any differences between these two electron configurations? (d) ^{238}U undergoes radioactive decay to ^{234}Th. How many protons, electrons, and neutrons are gained or lost by the ^{238}U atom during this process? (e) Examine the electron configuration for Th in Figure 1.31. Are you surprised by what you find? Explain.

1.103 Imagine sunlight falling on three square areas. One is an inert black material. The second is a photovoltaic cell surface, which converts radiant energy into electricity. The third is an area on a green tree leaf. Draw diagrams that show the energy conversions in each case. How are these three examples related to the idea of sustainable energy sources?

WHAT'S AHEAD

2.1 DEVELOPMENT OF THE PERIODIC TABLE
We begin our discussion with a brief history of the periodic table.

2.2 EFFECTIVE NUCLEAR CHARGE
We next explore the many properties of atoms that depend on the net attraction of the outer electrons to the nucleus and on the average distance of those electrons from the nucleus. The net positive charge of the nucleus experienced by the outer electrons is called the *effective nuclear charge*.

2.3 SIZES OF ATOMS AND IONS
We explore the relative sizes of atoms and ions, both of which follow trends that are related to their placement in the periodic table.

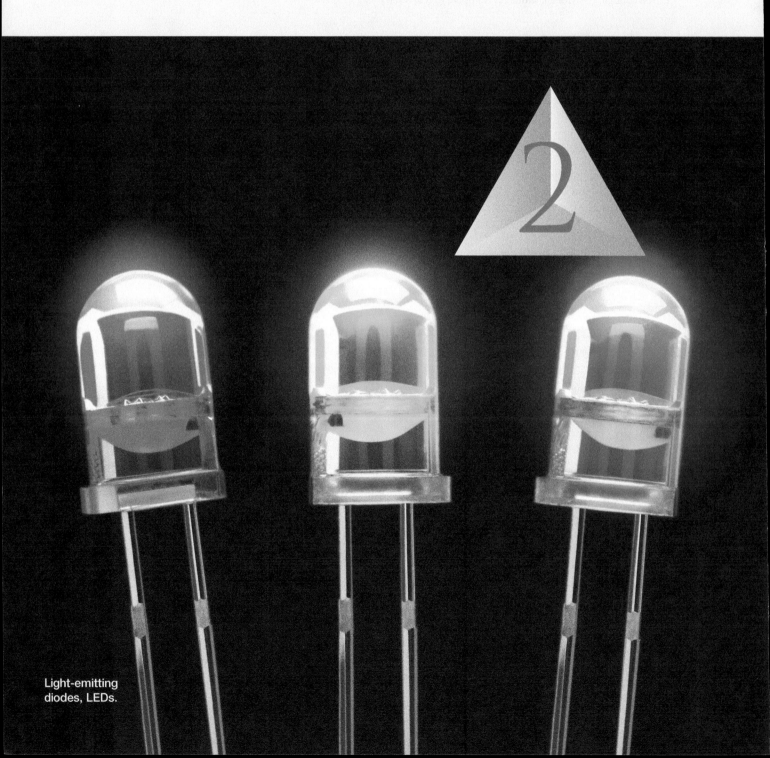

Light-emitting diodes, LEDs.

2.4 IONIZATION ENERGY
We next encounter the *ionization energy* required to remove one or more electrons from an atom. The periodic trends in ionization energy depend on variations in effective nuclear charge and atomic radii.

2.5 ELECTRON AFFINITIES
Next we examine periodic trends in the energy released when an electron is added to an atom.

PERIODIC PROPERTIES OF THE ELEMENTS

THE BRILLIANT COLORS OF light-emitting diodes (LEDs) arise from the composition of the materials from which they are made. The LEDs shown here are compounds of gallium and aluminum mixed with nitrogen, phosphorus, and arsenic. GaN, GaP, and GaAs can make solid solutions with each other and with AlN,

AlP, and AlAs; the composition of each solid solution dictates the wavelength of light emitted by a given LED. Because these elements are in groups 3A and 5A, we say that LEDs are composed of "3-5" materials.

As we saw in Chapter 1, the periodic nature of the periodic table arises from repeating patterns in the electron configurations of the elements. Elements in the same column contain the same number of electrons in their **valence orbitals**, which are the occupied orbitals that hold the electrons involved in bonding. For example, O ([He]$2s^2 2p^4$) and S ([Ne]$3s^2 3p^4$) are both in group 6A. The similarity of the electron distribution in their valence *s* and *p* orbitals leads to similarities in the properties of these two elements. When we compare elemental O and elemental S, however, it is apparent that they exhibit differences as well, not the least of which is that at room temperature oxygen is a colorless gas but sulfur is a yellow solid. One major difference between O and S atoms is that the outermost electrons of O are in the second shell, whereas those of S are in the third shell. Thus, electron configurations can be used to explain differences as well as similarities in the properties of elements.

In this chapter we explore how some of the important properties of elements change as we move across a row or down a column of the periodic table. In many cases the trends in a row or column allow us to predict the physical and chemical properties of the elements.

2.1 | DEVELOPMENT OF THE PERIODIC TABLE

The discovery of chemical elements has been ongoing since ancient times (▼ FIGURE 2.1). Certain elements, such as gold (Au), appear in nature in elemental form and were thus discovered thousands of years ago. In contrast, some elements, such as technetium (Tc), are radioactive and intrinsically unstable. We know about them only because of technology developed during the twentieth century.

The majority of elements readily form compounds and, consequently, are not found in nature in their elemental form. For centuries, therefore, scientists were unaware of their existence. During the early nineteenth century, advances in chemistry made it easier to isolate elements from their compounds. As a result, the number of known elements more than doubled from 31 in 1800 to 63 by 1865.

As the number of known elements increased, scientists began classifying them. In 1869, Dmitri Mendeleev in Russia and Lothar Meyer in Germany published nearly identical classification schemes. Both scientists noted that similar chemical and physical properties recur periodically when the elements are arranged in order of increasing atomic weight. Scientists at that time had no knowledge of atomic numbers. Atomic weights, however, generally increase with increasing atomic number, so both Mendeleev and Meyer fortuitously arranged the elements in proper sequence. Although Mendeleev and Meyer came to essentially the same conclusion about the periodicity of elemental properties, Mendeleev is given credit for advancing his ideas more vigorously and stimulating new work. His insistence that elements with similar characteristics be listed in the same column forced him to leave blank spaces in his table. For example, both gallium (Ga) and germanium (Ge) were unknown to Mendeleev. He boldly predicted their

GO FIGURE

Which row of the periodic table contains the most recently discovered elements? Can you suggest a reason?

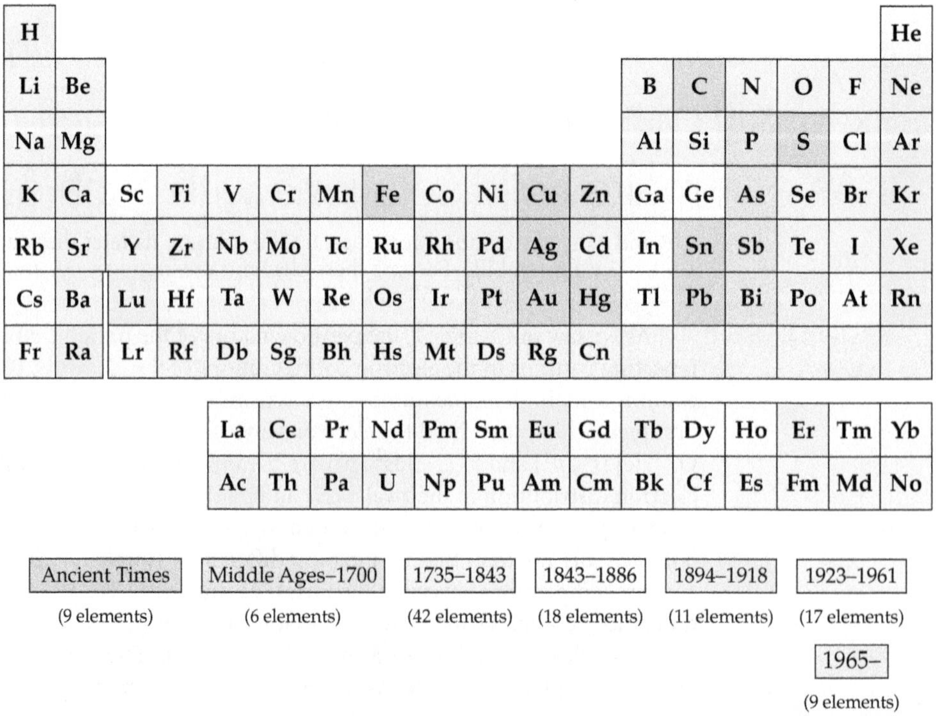

▶ FIGURE 2.1 Discovering the elements.

TABLE 2.1 • Comparison of the Properties of Eka-Silicon Predicted by Mendeleev with the Observed Properties of Germanium		
Property	Mendeleev's Predictions for Eka-Silicon (made in 1871)	Observed Properties of Germanium (discovered in 1886)
Atomic weight	72	72.59
Density (g/cm³)	5.5	5.35
Specific heat (J/g-K)	0.305	0.309
Melting point (°C)	High	947
Color	Dark gray	Grayish white
Formula of oxide	XO_2	GeO_2
Density of oxide (g/cm³)	4.7	4.70
Formula of chloride	XCl_4	$GeCl_4$
Boiling point of chloride (°C)	A little under 100	84

existence and properties, referring to them as *eka-aluminum* ("under" aluminum) and *eka-silicon* ("under" silicon), respectively, after the elements under which they appeared in his table. When these elements were discovered, their properties closely matched those predicted by Mendeleev, as shown in ▲ TABLE 2.1.

In 1913, two years after Rutherford proposed the nuclear model of the atom, English physicist Henry Moseley (1887–1915) developed the concept of atomic numbers. Bombarding different elements with high-energy electrons, Moseley found that each element produced X-rays of a unique frequency and that the frequency generally increased as the atomic mass increased. He arranged the X-ray frequencies in order by assigning a unique whole number, called an *atomic number,* to each element. Moseley correctly identified the atomic number as the number of protons in the nucleus of the atom.

The concept of atomic number clarified some problems in the periodic table of Moseley's day, which was based on atomic weights. For example, the atomic weight of Ar (atomic number 18) is greater than that of K (atomic number 19), yet the chemical and physical properties of Ar are much more like those of Ne and Kr than like those of Na and Rb. However, when the elements are arranged in order of increasing atomic number, rather than increasing atomic weight, Ar and K appear in their correct places in the table. Moseley's studies also made it possible to identify "holes" in the periodic table, which led to the discovery of previously unknown elements.

GIVE IT SOME THOUGHT

Arranging the elements by atomic weight leads to an order slightly different from that in a modern periodic table, where the arrangement is by atomic number. Why does this happen? Looking at the periodic table on the inside front cover, can you find an example other than Ar and K where the order of the elements would be different if the elements were arranged in order of increasing atomic weight?

2.2 | EFFECTIVE NUCLEAR CHARGE

Many properties of atoms depend on electron configuration and on how strongly the outer electrons in the atoms are attracted to the nucleus. Coulomb's law tells us that the strength of the interaction between two electrical charges depends on the magnitudes of the charges and on the distance between them. Thus, the attractive force between an electron and the nucleus depends on the magnitude of the nuclear charge and on the average distance between the nucleus and the electron. The force increases as the nuclear charge increases and decreases as the electron moves farther from the nucleus.

Sodium nucleus
contains 11 protons (11$^+$)

Valence electron (3s)

e$^-$

Each of the 11 electrons is
attracted to positively
charged nucleus

10$^-$

Sodium atoms contains 10 core
electrons (10$^-$) that screen the 3s
valence electron

▲ **FIGURE 2.2 Effective nuclear
charge.** The effective nuclear charge
experienced by the valence electron in a
sodium atom depends mostly on the 11+
charge of the nucleus and the 10− charge
of the core electrons.

In a many-electron atom, each electron is simultaneously
attracted to the nucleus and repelled by the other electrons. In general,
there are so many electron–electron repulsions that we cannot
analyze the situation exactly. We can, however, estimate the attractive
force between any one electron and the nucleus by considering
how the electron interacts with the *average* environment created by
the nucleus and the other electrons in the atom. We treat each electron
as though it were moving in the net electric field created by the
nucleus and the electron density of the other electrons. We view this
net electric field as if it results from a single positive charge located
at the nucleus, called the **effective nuclear charge**, Z_{eff}. The effective
nuclear charge acting on an electron in an atom is smaller than
the *actual* nuclear charge ($Z_{eff} < Z$) because the effective nuclear
charge includes the effect of the other electrons in the atom.

In any many-electron atom, the inner electrons partially *screen* outer electrons from
the attraction of the nucleus, and the relationship between Z_{eff} and the number of protons
in the nucleus Z is

$$Z_{eff} = Z - S \qquad [2.1]$$

where S is a positive number called the *screening constant*. It represents the portion of
the nuclear charge that is screened from a valence electron by the other electrons in the
atom. Because core electrons are most effective at screening a valence electron from the
nucleus, *the value of S is usually close to the number of core electrons in an atom.* (Electrons
in the same valence shell do not screen one another very effectively, but they do
affect the value of S slightly; see "A Closer Look: Effective Nuclear Charge.")

Let's look at the Na atom to see what to expect for the magnitude of Z_{eff}. Sodium has
the electron configuration [Ne]3s^1. The nuclear charge is $Z = 11+$, and there are 10 core
electrons ($1s^2 2s^2 2p^6$). We therefore expect S to equal 10 and the 3s electron to experience
an effective nuclear charge of $Z_{eff} = 11 - 10 = 1+$ (◀ **FIGURE 2.2**). The situation is
more complicated, however, because the 3s electron has a small probability of being closer
to the nucleus, in the region occupied by
the core electrons. ∞(Section 1.6)
Thus, there is a probability that this electron
experiences a greater attraction than
our simple $S = 10$ model suggests. This
greater attraction turns out to increase the
value of Z_{eff} for the 3s electron in Na from
our expected $Z_{eff} = 1+$ to $Z_{eff} = 2.5+$. In
other words, the fact that the 3s electron
spends some small amount of time close
to the nucleus changes the value of S in
Equation 2.1 from 10 to 8.5.

The notion of effective nuclear charge
also explains an important effect we noted
in Section 1.7: For a many-electron atom,
the energies of orbitals with the same n
value increase with increasing l value. For
example, in the carbon atom, electron configuration
$1s^2 2s^2 2p^2$, the energy of the 2p
orbital ($l = 1$) is higher than that of the 2s
orbital ($l = 0$) even though both orbitals
are in the $n = 2$ shell (Figure 1.24). This
difference in energies is due to the radial
probability functions for the orbitals
(◀ **FIGURE 2.3**). The greater attraction
between the 2s electron and the nucleus

GO FIGURE

Which orbital has more electron
density near the nucleus, 2s or 2p?

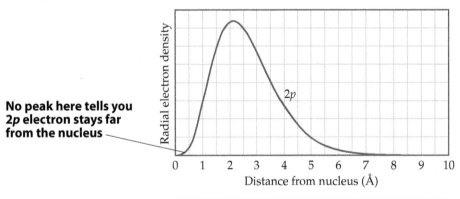

No peak here tells you
2p electron stays far
from the nucleus

2p

Radial electron density

Distance from nucleus (Å)

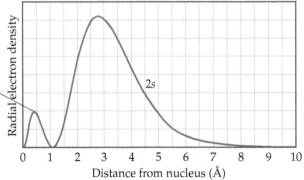

This peak tells you the
2s electron spends some
time close to nucleus

2s

Radial electron density

Distance from nucleus (Å)

▲ **FIGURE 2.3   2s and 2p radial
probability functions.**

leads to a lower energy for the 2s orbital than for the 2p orbital. The same reasoning explains
the general trend in orbital energies ($ns < np < nd$) in many-electron atoms.

Finally, let's examine trends in valence-electron Z_{eff} values. *The effective nuclear charge increases from left to right across any period of the periodic table.* Although the number of core electrons stays the same across the period, the number of protons increases. The valence electrons added to counterbalance the increasing nuclear charge screen one another ineffectively. Thus, Z_{eff} increases steadily. For example, the core electrons of lithium ($1s^2 2s^1$) screen the $2s$ valence electron from the $3+$ nucleus fairly efficiently. Consequently, the valence electron experiences an effective nuclear charge of roughly $3 - 2 = 1+$. For beryllium ($1s^2 2s^2$) the effective nuclear charge experienced by each valence electron is larger because here the $1s$ electrons screen a $4+$ nucleus, and each $2s$ electron only partially screens the other. Consequently, the effective nuclear charge experienced by each $2s$ electron is about $4 - 2 = 2+$.

A CLOSER LOOK

EFFECTIVE NUCLEAR CHARGE

To get a sense of how effective nuclear charge varies as both nuclear charge and number of electrons increase, consider ▼ FIGURE 2.4. Although the details of how the Z_{eff} values in the graph were calculated are beyond the scope of our discussion, the trends are instructive.

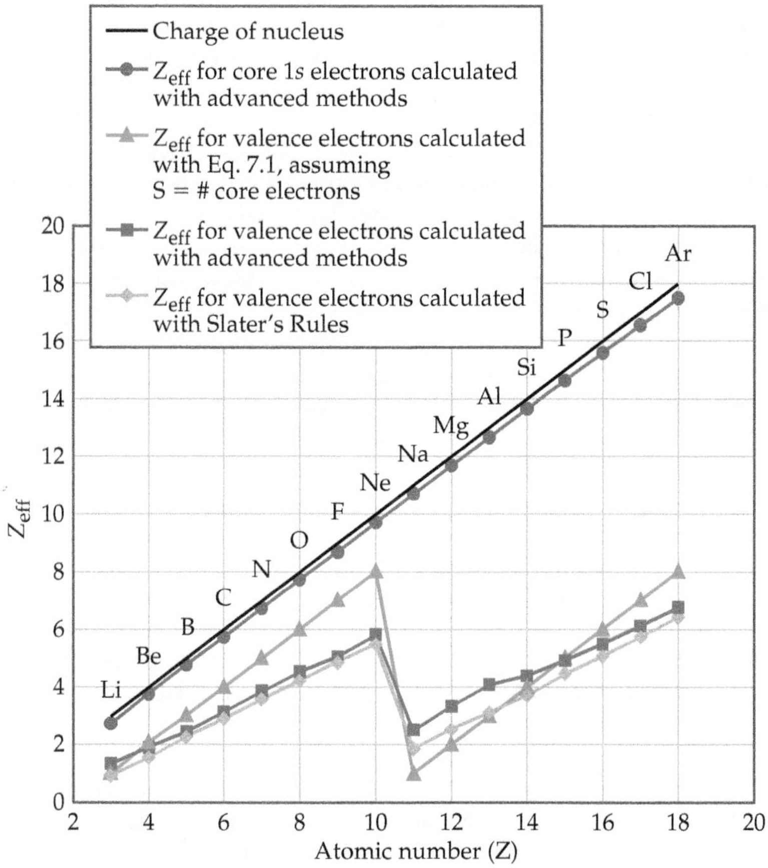

The effective nuclear charge felt by the outermost electrons is smaller than that felt by inner electrons because of screening by the inner electrons. In addition, the effective nuclear charge felt by the outermost electrons does not increase as steeply with increasing atomic number because the valence electrons make a small but non-negligible contribution to the screening constant S. The most striking feature associated with the Z_{eff} value for the outermost electrons is the sharp drop between the last period 2 element (Ne) and the first period 3 element (Na). This drop reflects the fact that the core electrons are much more effective than the valence electrons at screening the nuclear charge.

Because Z_{eff} can be used to understand many physically measurable quantities, it is desirable to have a simple method for estimating it. The value of Z in Equation 2.1 is known exactly, so the challenge boils down to estimating the value of S. In the text, we estimated S by assuming that each core electron contributes 1.00 to S and the outer electrons contribute nothing. A more accurate approach was developed by John Slater, however, and we can use his approach if we limit ourselves to elements that do not have electrons in d or f subshells.

Electrons for which the principal quantum number n is larger than the value of n for the electron of interest contribute 0 to the value of S. Electrons with the same value of n as the electron of interest contribute 0.35 to the value of S. Electrons for which n is 1 less than n for the electron of interest contribute 0.85, while those with even smaller values of n contribute 1.00. For example, consider fluorine, which has the ground-state electron configuration $1s^2 2s^2 2p^5$. For a valence electron in fluorine, Slater's rules tell us that $S = (0.35 \times 6) + (0.85 \times 2) = 3.8$. (Slater's rules ignore the contribution of an electron to itself in screening; therefore, we consider only six $n = 2$ electrons, not all seven). Thus, $Z_{eff} = Z - S = 9 - 3.8 = 5.2+$.

Values of Z_{eff} estimated using the simple method outlined in the text, as well as those estimated with Slater's rules, are plotted in Figure 2.4. While neither of these methods exactly replicate the values of Z_{eff} obtained from more sophisticated calculations, both methods effectively capture the periodic variation in Z_{eff}. While Slater's approach is more accurate, the method outlined in the text does a reasonably good job of estimating Z_{eff} despite its simplicity. For our purposes, therefore, we can assume that the screening constant S in Equation 2.1 is roughly equal to the number of core electrons.

- ── Charge of nucleus
- ──●── Z_{eff} for core $1s$ electrons calculated with advanced methods
- ──▲── Z_{eff} for valence electrons calculated with Eq. 7.1, assuming S = # core electrons
- ──■── Z_{eff} for valence electrons calculated with advanced methods
- ──◆── Z_{eff} for valence electrons calculated with Slater's Rules

▲ **FIGURE 2.4** **Variations in effective nuclear charge for period 2 and period 3 elements.** Moving from one element to the next in the periodic table, the increase in Z_{eff} felt by the innermost ($1s$) electrons (red circles) closely tracks the increase in nuclear charge Z (black line) because these electrons are not screened. The results of several methods to calculate Z_{eff} for valence electrons are shown in other colors.

RELATED EXERCISES: 2.11, 2.12, 2.13, 2.14, 2.34, 2.35, 2.84, 2.85

Going down a column, the effective nuclear charge experienced by valence electrons changes far less than it does across a period. For example, we would expect the effective nuclear charge experienced by the valence electrons in lithium and sodium to be about the same, roughly $3 - 2 = 1+$ for lithium and $11 - 10 = 1+$ for sodium. In fact, however, effective nuclear charge increases slightly as we go down a column because the more diffuse core electron cloud is less able to screen the valence electrons from the nuclear charge. In the case of the alkali metals, Z_{eff} increases from 1.3+ for lithium, to 2.5+ for sodium, to 3.5+ for potassium.

GIVE IT SOME THOUGHT

Which would you expect to experience a greater effective nuclear charge, a 2*p* electron of a Ne atom or a 3*s* electron of a Na atom?

2.3 | SIZES OF ATOMS AND IONS

We often think of atoms as hard, spherical objects. According to the quantum mechanical model, however, atoms do not have sharply defined boundaries at which the electron distribution becomes zero. ∞ (Section 1.5) Nevertheless, we can define atomic size in several ways, based on the distances between atoms in various situations.

Imagine a collection of argon atoms in the gas phase. When two of these atoms collide with each other, they ricochet apart like colliding billiard balls. This ricocheting happens because the electron clouds of the colliding atoms cannot penetrate each other to any significant extent. The shortest distance separating the two nuclei during such collisions is twice the radii of the atoms. We call this radius the *nonbonding atomic radius* or the *van der Waals* radius (◄ FIGURE 2.5).

In molecules, an attractive interaction exists between any two adjacent atoms in the molecule, leading to a chemical bond between the atoms. We discuss bonding in Chapter 3. For now, we only need to realize that this attractive interaction brings the two atoms closer together than they would be in a nonbonding collision where the atoms ricochet apart. We can define an atomic radius based on the distance separating the nuclei when two atoms are bonded to each other, shown as distance *d* in Figure 2.5. The **bonding atomic radius** for any atom in a molecule is equal to half of the nucleus-to-nucleus distance *d*. Note from Figure 2.5 that the bonding atomic radius (also known as the *covalent radius*) is shorter than the nonbonding atomic radius. Unless otherwise noted, we mean the bonding atomic radius when we speak of the "size" of an atom.

Scientists have developed a variety of techniques for measuring the distances separating nuclei in molecules. From observations of these distances in many molecules, each element can be assigned a bonding atomic radius. For example, in the I_2 molecule, the distance separating the nuclei is observed to be 2.66 Å, which means the bonding atomic radius of an iodine atom is (2.66 Å)/2 = 1.33 Å.* Similarly, the distance separating adjacent carbon nuclei in diamond (a three-dimensional solid network of carbon atoms) is 1.54 Å; thus, the bonding atomic radius of carbon is 0.77 Å. The bonding atomic radii of other elements can be similarly defined (► FIGURE 2.6). (For helium and neon, the bonding atomic radii must be estimated because there are no known compounds of these elements.)

Knowing atomic radii allows us to estimate bond lengths in molecules. For example, the Cl—Cl bond length in Cl_2 is 1.99 Å, so a bonding atomic radius of 0.99 Å is assigned to Cl. In CCl_4 the measured length of the C—Cl bond is 1.77 Å, very close to the sum (0.77 + 0.99 Å) of the bonding atomic radii of C and Cl.

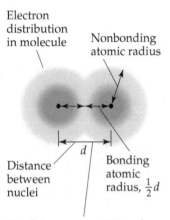

Electron distribution in molecule

Nonbonding atomic radius

Distance between nuclei

Bonding atomic radius, $\frac{1}{2}d$

Nuclei cannot get any closer to each other because of electron–electron repulsion

▲ FIGURE 2.5 **Distinction between nonbonding and bonding atomic radii within a molecule.**

---

*Remember: The angstrom (1 Å = 10^{-10} m) is a convenient metric unit for atomic measurements of length. It is not an SI unit. The most commonly used SI unit for atomic measurements is the picometer (1 pm = 10^{-12} m; 1 Å = 100 pm).

GO FIGURE

Which part of the periodic table (top/bottom, left/right) has the elements with the largest atoms?

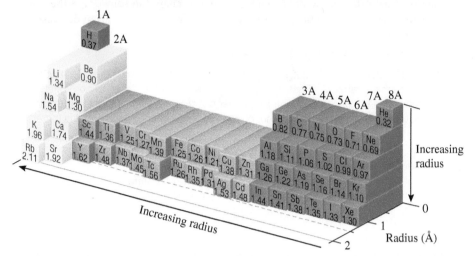

◀ **FIGURE 2.6**   **Trends in bonding atomic radii for periods 1 through 5.**

SAMPLE EXERCISE 2.1   **Bond Lengths in a Molecule**

Natural gas used in home heating and cooking is odorless. Because natural gas leaks pose the danger of explosion or suffocation, various smelly substances are added to the gas to allow detection of a leak. One such substance is methyl mercaptan, CH_3SH. Use Figure 2.6 to predict the lengths of the C—S, C—H, and S—H bonds in this molecule.

SOLUTION

Analyze and Plan   We are given three bonds and told to use Figure 2.6 for bonding atomic radii. We will assume that each bond length is the sum of the bonding atomic radii of the two atoms involved.

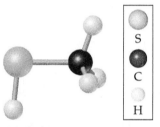

Methyl mercaptan

Solve

C—S bond length = bonding atomic radius of C + bonding atomic radius of S

$$= 0.77 Å + 1.02 Å = 1.79 Å$$

C—H bond length = $0.77 Å + 0.37 Å = 1.14 Å$

S—H bond length = $1.02 Å + 0.37 Å = 1.39 Å$

Check   The experimentally determined bond lengths are C—S = 1.82 Å, C—H = 1.10 Å, and S—H = 1.33 Å. (In general, the lengths of bonds involving hydrogen show larger deviations from the values predicted from bonding atomic radii than do bonds involving larger atoms.)

Comment   Notice that our estimated bond lengths are close but not exact matches to the measured bond lengths. Bonding atomic radii must be used with some caution in estimating bond lengths.

PRACTICE EXERCISE

Using Figure 2.6, predict which is longer, the P—Br bond in PBr_3 or the As—Cl bond in $AsCl_3$.

Answer: P—Br

Periodic Trends in Atomic Radii

Figure 2.6 shows two interesting trends:

1. Within each group, bonding atomic radius tends to increase from top to bottom. This trend results primarily from the increase in the principal quantum number (n) of the outer electrons. As we go down a column, the outer electrons have a greater probability of being farther from the nucleus, causing the atomic radius to increase.

2. Within each period, bonding atomic radius tends to decrease from left to right. The major factor influencing this trend is the increase in effective nuclear charge Z_{eff} across a period. The increasing effective nuclear charge steadily draws the valence electrons closer to the nucleus, causing the bonding atomic radius to decrease.

GIVE IT SOME THOUGHT

In Section 2.2 we said that Z_{eff} generally increases when you move down a column of the periodic table, whereas in Chapter 1 we saw that the "size" of an orbital increases as the principal quantum number n increases. With respect to atomic radii, do these trends work together or against each other? Which effect is larger?

SAMPLE EXERCISE 2.2 | **Atomic Radii**

Referring to a periodic table, arrange (as much as possible) the atoms $_{15}P$, $_{16}S$, $_{33}As$, and $_{34}Se$ in order of increasing size. (Atomic numbers are given to help you locate the atoms quickly in the table.)

SOLUTION

Analyze and Plan We are given the chemical symbols for four elements and told to use their relative positions in the periodic table to predict the relative size of their atomic radii. We can use the two periodic trends just described to help with this problem.

Solve P and S are in the same period, with S to the right of P. Therefore, we expect the radius of S to be smaller than that of P because radii decrease as we move across a period. Likewise, the radius of Se is expected to be smaller than that of As. As is directly below P, and Se is directly below S. We expect, therefore, the radius of P to be smaller than that of As and the radius of S to be smaller than that of Se. Thus, so far we can say $S < P, P < As, S < Se, Se < As$. We can therefore conclude that S has the smallest radius and As has the largest radius and so can write $S < ? < ? < As$.

Our two periodic trends for atomic size do not supply enough information to allow us to determine whether P or Se (represented by the two question marks) has the larger radius, however. Going from P to Se in the periodic table, we move down (radius tends to increase) and to the right (radius tends to decrease). In Figure 2.6 we see that the radius of Se is greater than that of P. If you examine the figure carefully, you will discover that for the s- and p-block elements the increase in radius moving down a column tends to be the greater effect. There are exceptions, however.

Check From Figure 2.6, we have $S(1.02\,\text{Å}) < P(1.06\,\text{Å}) < Se(1.16\,\text{Å}) < As(1.19\,\text{Å})$.

Comment Note that the trends we have just discussed are for the s- and p-block elements. Figure 2.6 shows that the transition elements do not show a regular decrease moving across a period.

PRACTICE EXERCISE

Arrange $_{11}Na$, $_{4}Be$, and $_{12}Mg$ in order of increasing atomic radius.
Answer: $Be < Mg < Na$

Periodic Trends in Ionic Radii

Just as bonding atomic radii can be determined from interatomic distances in molecules, ionic radii can be determined from interatomic distances in ionic compounds. Like the size of an atom, the size of an ion depends on its nuclear charge, the number of electrons it possesses, and the orbitals in which the valence electrons reside. When a cation is formed from a neutral atom, electrons are removed from the occupied atomic orbitals that are the most spatially extended from the nucleus. Also, the number of electron–electron repulsions is reduced. Therefore, *cations are smaller than their parent atoms* (▶ FIGURE 2.7). The opposite is true of anions. When electrons are added to an atom to form an anion, the increased electron–electron repulsions cause the electrons to spread out more in space. Thus, *anions are larger than their parent atoms.*

GO FIGURE

How do cations of the same charge change in radius as you move down a column in the periodic table?

Group 1A	Group 2A	Group 3A	Group 6A	Group 7A
Li^+ 0.90	Be^{2+} 0.59	B^{3+} 0.41	O^{2-} 1.26	F^- 1.19
Li 1.34	Be 0.90	B 0.82	O 0.73	F 0.71
Na^+ 1.16	Mg^{2+} 0.86	Al^{3+} 0.68	S^{2-} 1.70	Cl^- 1.67
Na 1.54	Mg 1.30	Al 1.18	S 1.02	Cl 0.99
K^+ 1.52	Ca^{2+} 1.14	Ga^{3+} 0.76	Se^{2-} 1.84	Br^- 1.82
K 1.96	Ca 1.24	Ga 1.26	Se 1.16	Br 1.14
Rb^+ 1.66	Sr^{2+} 1.32	In^{3+} 0.94	Te^{2-} 2.07	I^- 2.06
Rb 2.11	Sr 1.92	In 1.44	Te 1.35	I 1.33

= cation   = anion   = neutral atom

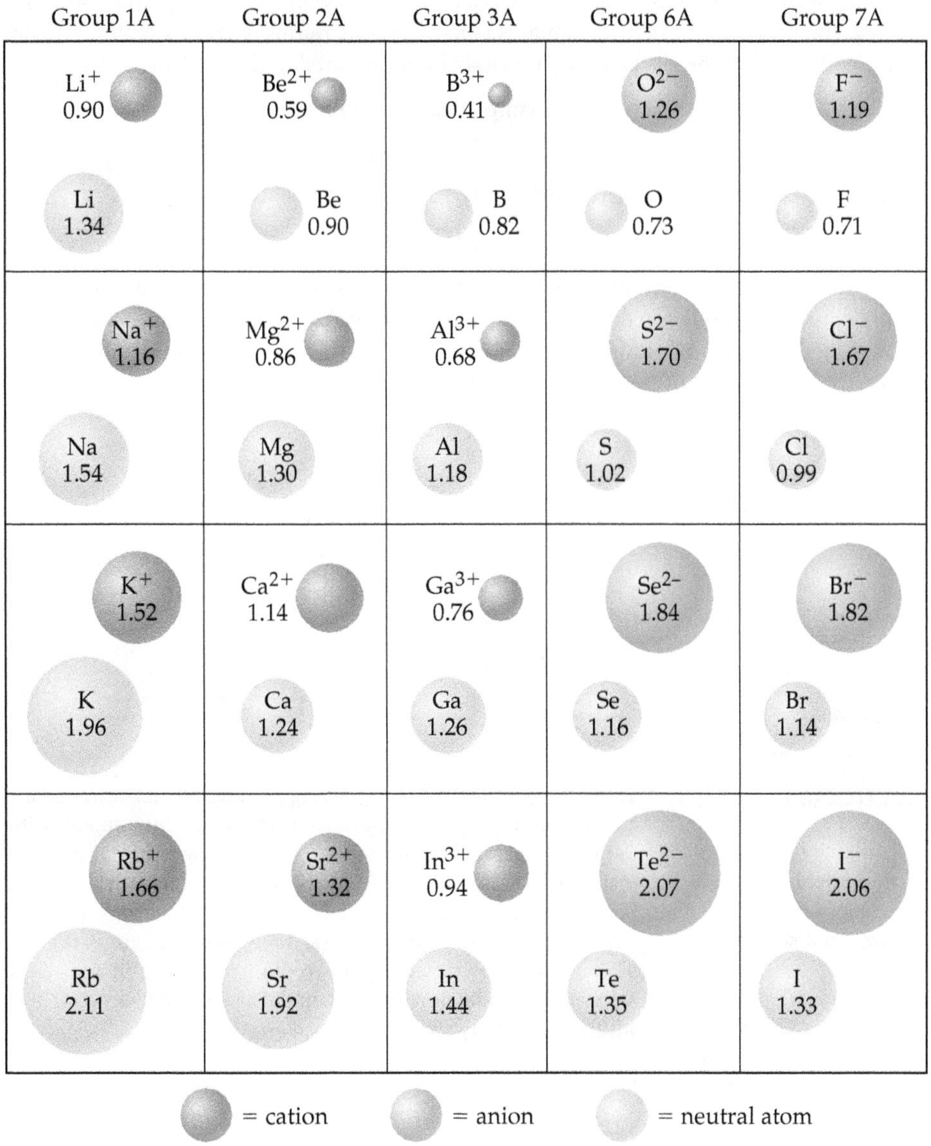

▲ FIGURE 2.7 **Cation and anion size.** Radii, in angstroms, of atoms and their ions for five groups of representative elements.

For ions carrying the same charge, ionic radius increases as we move down a column in the periodic table (Figure 2.7). In other words, as the principal quantum number of the outermost occupied orbital of an ion increases, the radius of the ion increases.

SAMPLE EXERCISE 2.3   **Atomic and Ionic Radii**

Arrange Mg^{2+}, Ca^{2+}, and Ca in order of decreasing radius.

SOLUTION

Cations are smaller than their parent atoms, and so $Ca^{2+} <$ Ca. Because Ca is below Mg in group 2A, Ca^{2+} is larger than Mg^{2+}. Consequently, Ca > Ca^{2+} > Mg^{2+}.

PRACTICE EXERCISE

Which of the following atoms and ions is largest: S^{2-}, S, O^{2-}?
Answer: S^{2-}

An **isoelectronic series** is a group of ions all containing the same number of electrons. For example, each ion in the isoelectronic series O^{2-}, F^-, Na^+, Mg^{2+}, Al^{3+} has 10 electrons. In any isoelectronic series we can list the members in order of increasing atomic number; therefore, nuclear charge increases as we move through the series. Because the number of electrons remains constant, ionic radius decreases with increasing nuclear charge as the electrons are more strongly attracted to the nucleus:

$$\longleftarrow \text{Increasing nuclear charge} \longrightarrow$$

O^{2-}	F^-	Na^+	Mg^{2+}	Al^{3+}
1.26 Å	1.19 Å	1.16 Å	0.86 Å	0.68 Å

$$\longleftarrow \text{Decreasing ionic radius} \longrightarrow$$

Notice the positions and atomic numbers of these elements in the periodic table. The nonmetal anions precede the noble gas Ne in the table. The metal cations follow Ne. Oxygen, the largest ion in this isoelectronic series, has the lowest atomic number, 8. Aluminum, the smallest of these ions, has the highest atomic number, 13.

CHEMISTRY PUT TO WORK

Ion Movement Powers Electronics

Ionic size plays a major role in determining the properties of devices that rely on movement of ions. "Lithium ion" batteries are everywhere—cell phones, iPods, laptop computers—and so let's see how a lithium ion battery works.

A fully charged battery spontaneously produces an electric current and, therefore, power when its positive and negative electrodes are connected in an electrical circuit. The positive electrode is called the anode, and the negative electrode is called the cathode. The materials used for the electrodes in lithium ion batteries are under intense development. Currently the anode material is graphite, a form of carbon, and the cathode is most frequently $LiCoO_2$, lithium cobalt oxide (▶ FIGURE 2.8). Between anode and cathode is a *separator,* a solid material that allows lithium ions, but not electrons, to pass through.

When the battery is being charged by an external source, lithium ions migrate from the cathode to the anode where they insert between the layers of carbon atoms. Lithium ions are smaller and lighter than most other elements, which means that many can fit between the layers. When the battery discharges and its electrodes are properly connected, it is energetically favorable for the lithium ions to move from anode to cathode. In order to maintain charge balance, electrons simultaneously migrate from anode to cathode through an external circuit, thereby producing electricity.

At the cathode, lithium ions then insert in the oxide material. Again, the small size of lithium ions is an advantage. For every lithium ion that inserts into the lithium cobalt oxide cathode, a Co^{4+} ion is reduced to a Co^{3+} by an electron that has traveled through the external circuit.

The ion migration and the changes in structure that result when lithium ions enter and leave the electrode materials are complicated.

Teams all over the world are trying to discover new cathode and anode materials that will easily accept and release lithium ions without falling apart over many repeated cycles. New separator materials that allow for faster lithium ion passage are also under development. Some research groups are looking at using sodium ions instead of lithium ions because sodium is far more abundant on Earth than lithium; new materials that allow sodium ion insertion and release are therefore under development. In the next decade we expect great advances in battery technology based on chemistry.

RELATED EXERCISE: 2.64

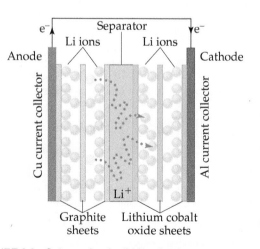

▲ FIGURE 2.8 **Schematic of a lithium ion battery.**

SAMPLE EXERCISE 2.4   **Ionic Radii in an Isoelectronic Series**

Arrange the ions K^+, Cl^-, Ca^{2+}, and S^{2-} in order of decreasing size.

SOLUTION

This is an isoelectronic series, with all ions having 18 electrons. In such a series, size decreases as nuclear charge (atomic number) increases. The atomic numbers of the ions are S 16, Cl 17, K 19, Ca 20. Thus, the ions decrease in size in the order $S^{2-} > Cl^- > K^+ > Ca^{2+}$.

PRACTICE EXERCISE

In the isoelectronic series Rb^+, Sr^{2+}, Y^{3+}, which ion is largest?
Answer: Rb^+

2.4 | IONIZATION ENERGY

The ease with which electrons can be removed from an atom or ion has a major impact on chemical behavior. The **ionization energy** of an atom or ion is the minimum energy required to remove an electron from the ground state of the isolated gaseous atom or ion. The *first ionization energy*, I_1, is the energy needed to remove the first electron from a neutral atom. For example, the first ionization energy for the sodium atom is the energy required for the process

$$Na(g) \longrightarrow Na^+(g) + e^- \qquad [2.2]$$

The *second ionization energy*, I_2, is the energy needed to remove the second electron, and so forth, for successive removals of additional electrons. Thus, I_2 for the sodium atom is the energy associated with the process

$$Na^+(g) \longrightarrow Na^{2+}(g) + e^- \qquad [2.3]$$

The greater the ionization energy, the more difficult it is to remove an electron.

Variations in Successive Ionization Energies

Notice in ▼ TABLE 2.2 that ionization energies for a given element increase as successive electrons are removed: $I_1 < I_2 < I_3$, and so forth. This trend exists because with each successive removal, an electron is being pulled away from an increasingly more positive ion, requiring increasingly more energy.

 GIVE IT SOME THOUGHT

Light can be used to ionize atoms and ions. Which of the two processes shown in Equations 2.2 and 2.3 requires shorter-wavelength radiation?

A second important feature shown in Table 2.2 is the sharp increase in ionization energy that occurs when an inner-shell electron is removed. For example, consider silicon, $1s^2 2s^2 2p^6 3s^2 3p^2$. The ionization energies increase steadily from 786 kJ/mol to

TABLE 2.2 • Successive Values of Ionization Energies, *I*, for the Elements Sodium through Argon (kJ/mol)						
Element	I_1	I_2	I_3	I_4	I_5	I_6	I_7
Na	496	4562	(inner-shell electrons)				
Mg	738	1451	7733				
Al	578	1817	2745	11,577			
Si	786	1577	3232	4356	16,091		
P	1012	1907	2914	4964	6274	21,267	
S	1000	2252	3357	4556	7004	8496	27,107
Cl	1251	2298	3822	5159	6542	9362	11,018
Ar	1521	2666	3931	5771	7238	8781	11,995

4356 kJ/mol for the four electrons in the 3s and 3p subshells. Removal of the fifth electron, which comes from the 2p subshell, requires a great deal more energy: 16,091 kJ/mol. The large increase occurs because the 2p electron is much more likely to be found close to the nucleus than are the four $n = 3$ electrons and, therefore, the 2p electron experiences a much greater effective nuclear charge than do the 3s and 3p electrons.

GIVE IT SOME THOUGHT

Which would you expect to be greater, I_1 for a boron atom or I_2 for a carbon atom?

Every element exhibits a large increase in ionization energy when one of its inner electrons is removed. This observation supports the idea that only the outermost electrons are involved in the sharing and transfer of electrons that give rise to chemical bonding and reactions. The inner electrons are too tightly bound to the nucleus to be lost from the atom or even shared with another atom.

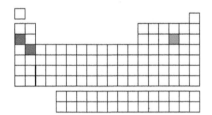

SAMPLE EXERCISE 2.5 | **Trends in Ionization Energy**

Three elements are indicated in the periodic table in the margin. Which one has the largest second ionization energy?

SOLUTION

Analyze and Plan The locations of the elements in the periodic table allow us to predict the electron configurations. The greatest ionization energies involve removal of core electrons. Thus, we should look first for an element with only one electron in the outermost occupied shell.

Solve The red box represents Na, which has one valence electron. The second ionization energy of this element is associated, therefore, with the removal of a core electron. The other elements indicated, S (green) and Ca (blue), have two or more valence electrons. Thus, Na should have the largest second ionization energy.

Check A chemistry handbook gives these I_2 values: Ca 1145 kJ/mol, S 2252 kJ/mol, Na 4562 kJ/mol.

PRACTICE EXERCISE

Which has the greater third ionization energy, Ca or S?

Answer: Ca

Periodic Trends in First Ionization Energies

▶ FIGURE 2.9 shows, for the first 54 elements, the trends we observe in first ionization energy as we move from one element to another in the periodic table. The important trends are as follows:

1. I_1 generally increases as we move across a period. The alkali metals show the lowest ionization energy in each period, and the noble gases show the highest. There are slight irregularities in this trend that we will discuss shortly.

2. I_1 generally decreases as we move down any column in the periodic table. For example, the ionization energies of the noble gases follow the order He > Ne > Ar > Kr > Xe.

3. The s- and p-block elements show a larger range of I_1 values than do the transition-metal elements. Generally, the ionization energies of the transition metals increase slowly from left to right in a period. The f-block metals (not shown in Figure 2.9) also show only a small variation in the values of I_1.

In general, smaller atoms have higher ionization energies. The same factors that influence atomic size also influence ionization energies. The energy needed to remove an electron from the outermost occupied shell depends on both the effective nuclear charge and the average distance of the electron from the nucleus. Either increasing the effective nuclear charge or decreasing the distance from the nucleus increases the attraction

GO FIGURE

Which has a larger first ionization energy, Ar or As? Why?

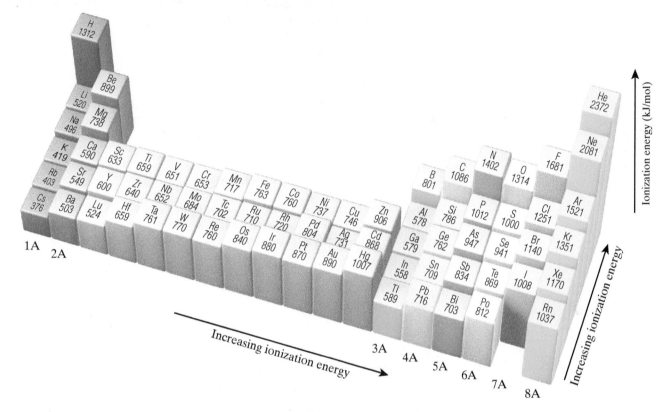

▲ **FIGURE 2.9**   **Trends in first ionization energies of the elements.**

between the electron and the nucleus. As this attraction increases, it becomes more difficult to remove the electron and, thus, the ionization energy increases. As we move across a period, there is both an increase in effective nuclear charge and a decrease in atomic radius, causing the ionization energy to increase. As we move down a column, the atomic radius increases while the effective nuclear charge increases rather gradually. Thus, the attraction between the nucleus and the electron decreases, causing the ionization energy to decrease.

The irregularities in a given period are subtle but still readily explained. For example, the decrease in ionization energy from beryllium ($[He]2s^2$) to boron ($[He]2s^2 2p^1$), shown in Figure 2.9, occurs because the third valence electron of B must occupy the $2p$ subshell, which is empty for Be. Recall that the $2p$ subshell is at a higher energy than the $2s$ subshell (Figure 1.24). The decrease in ionization energy when moving from nitrogen ($[He]2s^2 2p^3$) to oxygen ($[He]2s^2 2p^4$) is because of the repulsion of paired electrons in the p^4 configuration (▶ **FIGURE 2.10**). Remember that according to Hund's rule, each electron in the p^3 configuration resides in a different p orbital, which minimizes the electron–electron repulsion among the three $2p$ electrons. ∞ (Section 1.8)

GO FIGURE

Explain why it is easier to remove a $2p$ electron from an oxygen atom than from a nitrogen atom.

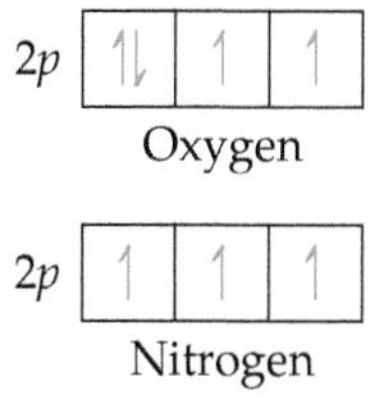

$2p$ | ↑↓ | ↑ | ↑ |
Oxygen

$2p$ | ↑ | ↑ | ↑ |
Nitrogen

▲ **FIGURE 2.10**   **$2p$ orbital filling in nitrogen and oxygen.**

SAMPLE EXERCISE 2.6   **Periodic Trends in Ionization Energy**

Referring to a periodic table, arrange the atoms Ne, Na, P, Ar, K in order of increasing first ionization energy.

SOLUTION

Analyze and Plan We are given the chemical symbols for five elements. To rank them according to increasing first ionization energy, we need to locate each element in the periodic table. We can then use their relative positions and the trends in first ionization energies to predict their order.

Solve Ionization energy increases as we move left to right across a period and decreases as we move down a group. Because Na, P, and Ar are in the same period, we expect I_1 to vary in the order Na < P < Ar. Because Ne is above Ar in group 8A, we expect Ar < Ne. Similarly, K is directly below Na in group 1A, and so we expect K < Na.

From these observations, we conclude that the ionization energies follow the order

$$K < Na < P < Ar < Ne$$

Check The values shown in Figure 2.9 confirm this prediction.

PRACTICE EXERCISE

Which has the lowest first ionization energy, B, Al, C, or Si? Which has the highest?

Answer: Al lowest, C highest

Electron Configurations of Ions

When electrons are removed from an atom to form a cation, they are always removed first from the occupied orbitals having the largest principal quantum number, n. For example, when one electron is removed from a lithium atom ($1s^2 2s^1$), it is the $2s^1$ electron:

$$Li\ (1s^2 2s^1) \Longrightarrow Li^+\ (1s^2) + e^-$$

Likewise, when two electrons are removed from Fe ($[Ar]3d^6 4s^2$), the $4s^2$ electrons are the ones removed:

$$Fe\ ([Ar]3d^6 4s^2) \Longrightarrow Fe^{2+}\ ([Ar]3d^6) + 2e^-$$

If an additional electron is removed, forming Fe^{3+}, it comes from a $3d$ orbital because all the orbitals with $n = 4$ are empty:

$$Fe^{2+}\ ([Ar]3d^6) \Longrightarrow Fe^{3+}\ ([Ar]3d^5) + e^-$$

It may seem odd that $4s$ electrons are removed before $3d$ electrons in forming transition-metal cations. After all, in writing electron configurations, we added the $4s$ electrons before the $3d$ ones. In writing electron configurations for atoms, however, we are going through an imaginary process in which we move through the periodic table from one element to another. In doing so, we are adding both an electron to an orbital and a proton to the nucleus to change the identity of the element. In ionization, we do not reverse this process because no protons are being removed.

If there is more than one occupied subshell for a given value of n, the electrons are first removed from the orbital with the highest value of l. For example, a tin atom loses its $5p$ electrons before it loses its $5s$ electrons:

$$Sn\ ([Kr]4d^{10}5s^2 5p^2) \Longrightarrow Sn^{2+}\ ([Kr]4d^{10}5s^2) + 2e^- \Longrightarrow Sn^{4+}\ ([Kr]4d^{10}) + 4e^-$$

Electrons added to an atom to form an anion are added to the empty or partially filled orbital having the lowest value of n. For example, an electron added to a fluorine atom to form the F^- ion goes into the one remaining vacancy in the $2p$ subshell:

$$F\ (1s^2 2s^2 2p^5) + e^- \Longrightarrow F^-\ (1s^2 2s^2 2p^6)$$

 GIVE IT SOME THOUGHT

Do Cr^{3+} and V^{2+} have the same or different electron configurations?

SAMPLE EXERCISE 2.7 | **Electron Configurations of Ions**

Write the electron configuration for **(a)** Ca^{2+}, **(b)** Co^{3+}, and **(c)** S^{2-}.

SOLUTION

Analyze and Plan We are asked to write electron configurations for three ions. To do so, we first write the electron configuration of each parent atom, then remove or add electrons to form the ions. Electrons are first removed from the orbitals having the highest value of n. They are added to the empty or partially filled orbitals having the lowest value of n.

Solve

(a) Calcium (atomic number 20) has the electron configuration $[Ar]4s^2$. To form a 2+ ion, the two outer electrons must be removed, giving an ion that is isoelectronic with Ar:

$$Ca^{2+}: [Ar]$$

(b) Cobalt (atomic number 27) has the electron configuration $[Ar]3d^74s^2$. To form a 3+ ion, three electrons must be removed. As discussed in the text, the $4s$ electrons are removed before the $3d$ electrons. Consequently, the electron configuration for Co^{3+} is

$$Co^{3+}: [Ar]3d^6$$

(c) Sulfur (atomic number 16) has the electron configuration $[Ne]3s^23p^4$. To form a 2− ion, two electrons must be added. There is room for two additional electrons in the $3p$ orbitals. Thus, the S^{2-} electron configuration is

$$S^{2-}: [Ne]3s^2\,3p^6 = [Ar]$$

Comment Remember that many of the common ions of the *s*- and *p*-block elements, such as Ca^{2+} and S^{2-}, have the same number of electrons as the closest noble gas.

PRACTICE EXERCISE

Write the electron configuration for (a) Ga^{3+}, (b) Cr^{3+}, and (c) Br^-.

Answers: (a) $[Ar]3d^{10}$, (b) $[Ar]3d^3$, (c) $[Ar]3d^{10}4s^24p^6 = [Kr]$

2.5 | ELECTRON AFFINITIES

The first ionization energy of an atom is a measure of the energy change associated with removing an electron from the atom to form a cation. For example, the first ionization energy of $Cl(g)$, 1251 kJ/mol, is the energy change associated with the process

$$Ionization\ energy:\ Cl(g) \longrightarrow Cl^+(g) + e^- \qquad \Delta E = 1251\ \text{kJ/mol} \qquad [2.4]$$
$$[Ne]3s^23p^5 \qquad [Ne]3s^23p^4$$

The positive ionization energy means that energy must be put into the atom to remove the electron.

Most atoms can also gain electrons to form anions. The energy change that occurs when an electron is added to a gaseous atom is called the **electron affinity** because it measures the attraction, or *affinity*, of the atom for the added electron. For most atoms, energy is released when an electron is added. For example, the addition of an electron to a chlorine atom is accompanied by an energy change of −349 kJ/mol, the negative sign indicating that energy is released during the process. We therefore say that the electron affinity of Cl is −349 kJ/mol.*

$$Electron\ affinity:\ Cl(g) + e^- \longrightarrow Cl^-(g) \qquad \Delta E = -349\ \text{kJ/mol} \qquad [2.5]$$
$$[Ne]3s^23p^5 \qquad [Ne]3s^23p^6$$

It is important to understand the difference between ionization energy and electron affinity: Ionization energy measures the ease with which an atom *loses* an electron, whereas electron affinity measures the ease with which an atom *gains* an electron.

The greater the attraction between an atom and an added electron, the more negative the atom's electron affinity. For some elements, such as the noble gases, the electron affinity has a positive value, meaning that the anion is higher in energy than are the separated atom and electron:

$$Ar(g) + e^- \longrightarrow Ar^-(g) \qquad \Delta E > 0 \qquad [2.6]$$
$$[Ne]3s^23p^6 \qquad [Ne]3s^23p^64s^1$$

---

*Two sign conventions are used for electron affinity. In most introductory texts, including this one, the thermodynamic sign convention is used: A negative sign indicates that addition of an electron is an exothermic process, as in the electron affinity for chlorine, −349 kJ/mol. Historically, however, electron affinity has been defined as the energy released when an electron is added to a gaseous atom or ion. Because 349 kJ/mol is released when an electron is added to $Cl(g)$, the electron affinity by this convention would be +349 kJ/mol.

GO FIGURE

Which of the groups shown here has the most negative electron affinities? Why does this make sense?

1A								8A
H −73	2A	3A	4A	5A	6A	7A		**He** >0
Li −60	**Be** >0	**B** −27	**C** −122	**N** >0	**O** −141	**F** −328		**Ne** >0
Na −53	**Mg** >0	**Al** −43	**Si** −134	**P** −72	**S** −200	**Cl** −349		**Ar** >0
K −48	**Ca** −2	**Ga** −30	**Ge** −119	**As** −78	**Se** −195	**Br** −325		**Kr** >0
Rb −47	**Sr** −5	**In** −30	**Sn** −107	**Sb** −103	**Te** −190	**I** −295		**Xe** >0

▲ **FIGURE 2.11** Electron affinity in kJ/mol for selected *s*- and *p*-block elements.

The fact that the electron affinity is positive means that an electron will not attach itself to an Ar atom; the Ar⁻ ion is unstable and does not form.

◀ **FIGURE 2.11** shows the electron affinities for the *s*- and *p*-block elements of the first five periods. Notice that the trends are not as evident as they are for ionization energy. The halogens, which are one electron shy of a filled *p* subshell, have the most-negative electron affinities. By gaining an electron, a halogen atom forms a stable anion that has a noble-gas configuration (Equation 2.5). The addition of an electron to a noble gas, however, requires that the electron reside in a higher-energy subshell that is empty in the atom (Equation 2.6). Because occupying a higher-energy subshell is energetically unfavorable, the electron affinity is highly positive. The electron affinities of Be and Mg are positive for the same reason; the added electron would reside in a previously empty *p* subshell that is higher in energy.

The electron affinities of the group 5A elements are also interesting. Because these elements have half-filled *p* subshells, the added electron must be put in an orbital that is already occupied, resulting in larger electron–electron repulsions. Consequently, these elements have electron affinities that are either positive (N) or less negative than the electron affinities of their neighbors to the left (P, As, Sb). Recall that in Section 2.4 we saw a discontinuity in the trends for first ionization energy for the same reason.

Electron affinities do not change greatly as we move down a group (Figure 2.11). For F, for instance, the added electron goes into a 2*p* orbital, for Cl a 3*p* orbital, for Br a 4*p* orbital, and so forth. As we proceed from F to I, therefore, the average distance between the added electron and the nucleus steadily increases, causing the electron–nucleus attraction to decrease. However, the orbital that holds the outermost electron is increasingly spread out, so that as we proceed from F to I, the electron–electron repulsions are also reduced. As a result, the reduction in the electron–nucleus attraction is counterbalanced by the reduction in electron–electron repulsions.

 GIVE IT SOME THOUGHT

What is the relationship between the value for the first ionization energy of a Cl⁻(*g*) ion and the electron affinity of Cl(*g*)?

CHAPTER SUMMARY AND KEY TERMS

INTRODUCTION AND SECTION 2.1 The periodic table was first developed by Mendeleev and Meyer on the basis of the similarity in chemical and physical properties exhibited by certain elements. Moseley established that each element has a unique atomic number, which added more order to the periodic table. We now recognize that elements in the same column of the periodic table have the same number of electrons in their **valence orbitals**. This similarity in valence electronic structure leads to the similarities among elements in the same group. The differences among elements in the same group arise because their valence orbitals are in different shells.

SECTION 2.2 Many properties of atoms are due to the average distance of the outer electrons from the nucleus and to the **effective nuclear charge** experienced by these electrons. The core electrons are very effective in screening the outer electrons from the full charge of the nucleus, whereas electrons in the same shell do not screen each other effectively. As a result, the effective nuclear charge experienced by valence electrons increases as we move left to right across a period.

SECTION 2.3 The size of an atom can be gauged by its **bonding atomic radius**, based on measurements of the distances separating atoms in their chemical compounds. In general, atomic radii increase as we go down a column in the periodic table and decrease as we proceed left to right across a row.

Cations are smaller than their parent atoms; anions are larger than their parent atoms. For ions of the same charge, size increases going down a column of the periodic table. An **isoelectronic series** is a series of ions that has the same number of electrons. For such a series, size decreases with increasing nuclear charge as the electrons are attracted more strongly to the nucleus.

SECTION 2.4 The first **ionization energy** of an atom is the minimum energy needed to remove an electron from the atom in the gas phase, forming a cation. The second ionization energy is the energy needed to remove a second electron, and so forth. Ionization energies show a sharp increase after all the valence electrons have been removed because of the much higher effective nuclear charge experienced by the core electrons. The first ionization energies of the elements show periodic trends that are opposite those seen for atomic radii, with smaller atoms having higher first ionization energies. Thus, first ionization energies decrease as we go down a column and increase as we proceed left to right across a row.

We can write electron configurations for ions by first writing the electron configuration of the neutral atom and then removing or adding the appropriate number of electrons. Electrons are removed first from the orbitals with the largest value of *n*. If there are two valence orbitals with the same value of *n* (such as 4*s* and 4*p*), then the electrons are lost first from the orbital with a higher value of *l* (in this case, 4*p*). Electrons are added to orbitals in the reverse order.

SECTION 2.5   The **electron affinity** of an element is the energy change upon adding an electron to an atom in the gas phase, forming an anion. A negative electron affinity means that the anion is stable; a positive electron affinity means that the anion is not stable relative to the separated atom and electron, in which case its exact value cannot be measured. In general, electron affinities become more negative as we proceed from left to right across the periodic table. The halogens have the most-negative electron affinities. The electron affinities of the noble gases are positive because the added electron would have to occupy a new, higher-energy subshell.

KEY SKILLS

- Understand the meaning of effective nuclear charge, Z_{eff}, and how Z_{eff} depends on nuclear charge and electron configuration. (Section 2.2)
- Use the periodic table to predict the trends in atomic radii, ionic radii, ionization energy, and electron affinity. (Sections 2.2, 2.3, 2.4, and 2.5)
- Explain how the radius of an atom changes upon losing electrons to form a cation or gaining electrons to form an anion. (Section 2.3)
- Be able to write the electron configurations of ions. (Section 2.3)
- Explain how the ionization energy changes as we remove successive electrons. Recognize the jump in ionization energy that occurs when the ionization corresponds to removing a core electron. (Section 2.4)
- Understand how irregularities in the periodic trends for electron affinity can be related to electron configuration. (Section 2.5)

KEY EQUATIONS

- $Z_{eff} = Z - S$ [2.1]   Estimating effective nuclear charge

EXERCISES

VISUALIZING CONCEPTS

2.1 We can draw an analogy between the attraction of an electron to a nucleus and seeing a lightbulb—in essence, the more nuclear charge the electron "sees," the greater the attraction. **(a)** Within this analogy, discuss how the screening by core electrons is analogous to putting a frosted-glass lampshade between the lightbulb and your eyes, as shown in the illustration. **(b)** Explain how we could mimic moving to the right in a row of the periodic table by changing the wattage of the lightbulb. **(c)** How would you change the wattage of the bulb and/or the frosted glass to mimic the effect of moving down a column of the periodic table? [Section 2.2]

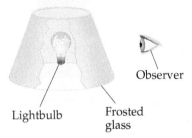

Observer

Lightbulb   Frosted glass

2.2 If you look up the radius of the sulfur atom in this book, you will find just one number: 1.02 Å. However, if you look deeper into the chemical literature, you can find another number for the radius of a sulfur atom: the nonbonding radius of 1.80 Å. This is a very large difference! Explain. [Section 2.3]

2.3 Consider the A_2X_4 molecule depicted here, where A and X are elements. The A—A bond length in this molecule is d_1, and the four A—X bond lengths are each d_2. **(a)** In terms of d_1 and d_2, how could you define the bonding atomic radii of atoms A and X? **(b)** In terms of d_1 and d_2, what would you predict for the X—X bond length of an X_2 molecule? [Section 2.3]

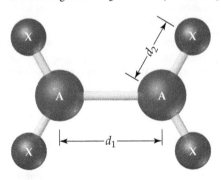

2.4 Make a simple sketch of the shape of the main part of the periodic table, as shown. **(a)** Ignoring H and He, write a single straight arrow from the element with the smallest bonding atomic radius to the element with the largest. **(b)** Ignoring H and He, write a single straight arrow from the element with the smallest first ionization energy to the element with the largest. **(c)** What significant observation can you make from the arrows you drew in parts (a) and (b)? [Sections 2.3 and 2.4]

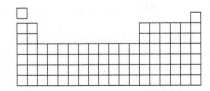

2.5 In the chemical process called *electron transfer*, an electron is transferred from one atom or molecule to another. A simple electron transfer reaction is

$$A(g) + A(g) \longrightarrow A^+(g) + A^-(g)$$

In terms of the ionization energy and electron affinity of atom A, what is the energy change for this reaction? For a representative nonmetal such as chlorine, is this process exothermic? For a representative metal such as sodium, is this process exothermic? [Sections 2.4 and 2.5]

PERIODIC TABLE; EFFECTIVE NUCLEAR CHARGE (sections 2.1 and 2.2)

2.6 Explain the structure of the periodic table—two columns on the left, a block of ten for the transition metals, a block of six on the right, and a pair of 14-member rows below, with reference to the orbitals we discussed in Chapter 1.

2.7 The prefix *eka-* comes from the Sanskrit word for "one." Mendeleev used this prefix to indicate that the unknown element was one place away from the known element that followed the prefix. For example, *eka-silicon*, which we now call germanium, is one element below silicon. Mendeleev also predicted the existence of *eka-manganese,* which was not experimentally confirmed until 1937 because this element is radioactive and does not occur in nature. Based on the periodic table shown in Figure 2.1, what do we now call the element Mendeleev called *eka-manganese*?

2.8 You might have expected that the elements would have been discovered in order of their relative abundance in the Earth's crust, but this is not the case. Suggest a general reason.

2.9 (a) Moseley's experiments on X-rays emitted from atoms led to the concept of atomic numbers. Where exactly do these X-rays come from? Draw an energy-level diagram to explain. (b) Why are chemical and physical properties of the elements more closely related to atomic number than they are to atomic weight?

2.10 (a) What is meant by the term *effective nuclear charge*? (b) How does the effective nuclear charge experienced by the valence electrons of an atom vary going from left to right across a period of the periodic table?

2.11 (a) How is the concept of effective nuclear charge used to simplify the numerous electron–electron repulsions in a many-electron atom? (b) Which experiences a greater effective nuclear charge in a Be atom, the $1s$ electrons or the $2s$ electrons? Explain.

2.12 Detailed calculations show that the value of Z_{eff} for the outermost electrons in Na and K atoms is 2.51+ and 3.49+, respectively. (a) What value do you estimate for Z_{eff} experienced by the outermost electron in both Na and K by assuming core electrons contribute 1.00 and valence electrons contribute 0.00 to the screening constant? (b) What values do you estimate for Z_{eff} using Slater's rules? (c) Which approach gives a more accurate estimate of Z_{eff}? (d) Does either method of approximation account for the gradual increase in Z_{eff} that occurs upon moving down a group? (e) Predict Z_{eff} for the outermost electrons in the Rb atom based on the calculations for Na and K.

2.13 Detailed calculations show that the value of Z_{eff} for the outermost electrons in Si and Cl atoms is 4.29+ and 6.12+, respectively. (a) What value do you estimate for Z_{eff} experienced by the outermost electron in both Si and Cl by assuming core electrons contribute 1.00 and valence electrons contribute 0.00 to the screening constant? (b) What values do you estimate for Z_{eff} using Slater's rules? (c) Which approach gives a more accurate estimate of Z_{eff}? (d) Which method of approximation more accurately accounts for the steady increase in Z_{eff} that occurs upon moving left to right across a period? (e) Predict Z_{eff} for a valence electron in P, phosphorus, based on the calculations for Si and Cl.

2.14 Which will experience the greater effective nuclear charge, the electrons in the $n = 3$ shell in Ar or the $n = 3$ shell in Kr? Which will be closer to the nucleus? Explain.

2.15 Arrange the following atoms in order of increasing effective nuclear charge experienced by the electrons in the $n = 3$ electron shell: K, Mg, P, Rh, and Ti. Explain the basis for your order.

ATOMIC AND IONIC RADII (section 2.3)

2.16 (a) Because an exact outer boundary cannot be measured or even calculated for an atom, how are atomic radii determined? (b) What is the difference between a bonding radius and a nonbonding radius? (c) For a given element, which one is larger? (d) If a free atom reacts to become part of a molecule, would you say that the atom gets smaller or larger?

2.17 (a) Why does the quantum mechanical description of many-electron atoms make it difficult to define a precise atomic radius? (b) When nonbonded atoms come up against one another, what determines how closely the nuclear centers can approach?

2.18 Tungsten has the highest melting point of any metal in the periodic table: 3422 °C. The distance between W atoms in tungsten metal is 2.74 Å. (a) What is the atomic radius of a tungsten atom in this environment? (This radius is called the *metallic radius.*) (b) If you put tungsten metal under high pressure, predict what would happen to the distance between W atoms.

2.19 Based on the radii presented in Figure 2.6, predict the distance between Si atoms in solid silicon. How does this compare to the distance between the C atoms in diamond, which has the same structure as solid silicon?

2.20 Estimate the As—I bond length from the data in Figure 2.6, and compare your value to the experimental As—I bond length in arsenic triiodide, AsI_3, 2.55 Å.

2.21 The experimental Bi—I bond length in bismuth triiodide, BiI_3, is 2.81 Å. Based on this value and data in Figure 2.6, predict the atomic radius of Bi.

2.22 How do the sizes of atoms change as we move (a) from left to right across a row in the periodic table, (b) from top to bottom in a group in the periodic table? (c) Arrange the following atoms in order of increasing atomic radius: O, Si, I, Ge.

2.23 (a) Among the nonmetallic elements, the change in atomic radius in moving one place left or right in a row is smaller than the change in moving one row up or down. Explain these observations. **(b)** Arrange the following atoms in order of increasing atomic radius: Si, Al, Ge, Ga.

2.24 Using only the periodic table, arrange each set of atoms in order from largest to smallest: **(a)** K, Li, Cs; **(b)** Pb, Sn, Si; **(c)** F, O, N.

2.25 Using only the periodic table, arrange each set of atoms in order of increasing radius: **(a)** Ba, Ca, Na; **(b)** Sn, Sb, As; **(c)** Al, Be, Si.

2.26 True or False: **(a)** Cations are larger than their corresponding neutral atoms. **(b)** Li^+ is smaller than Li. **(c)** Cl^- is bigger than I^-.

2.27 Explain the following variations in atomic or ionic radii: **(a)** $I^- > I > I^+$, **(b)** $Ca^{2+} > Mg^{2+} > Be^{2+}$, **(c)** $Fe > Fe^{2+} > Fe^{3+}$.

2.28 In the reaction

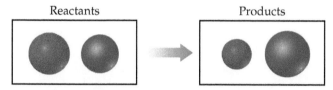

Reactants   Products

which sphere represents a metal and which represents a nonmetal? Explain your answer.

2.29 Which of these spheres represents F, which represents Br, and which represents Br^-?

2.30 **(a)** What is an isoelectronic series? **(b)** Which neutral atom is isoelectronic with each of the following ions: Ga^{3+}, Zr^{4+}, Mn^{7+}, I^-, Pb^{2+}?

2.31 Identify at least two ions that have the following ground-state electron configurations: **(a)** [Ar]; **(b)** $[Ar]3d^5$; **(c)** $[Kr]5s^2 4d^{10}$.

2.32 Some ions do not have a corresponding neutral atom that has the same electron configuration. For each of the following ions, identify the neutral atom that has the same number of electrons and determine if this atom has the same electron configuration. If such an atom does not exist, explain why. **(a)** Cl^-, **(b)** Sc^{3+}, **(c)** Fe^{2+}, **(d)** Zn^{2+}, **(e)** Sn^{4+}.

2.33 Consider the isoelectronic ions F^- and Na^+. **(a)** Which ion is smaller? **(b)** Using Equation 2.1 and assuming that core electrons contribute 1.00 and valence electrons contribute 0.00 to the screening constant, S, calculate Z_{eff} for the 2p electrons in both ions. **(c)** Repeat this calculation using Slater's rules to estimate the screening constant, S. **(d)** For isoelectronic ions, how are effective nuclear charge and ionic radius related?

2.34 Consider the isoelectronic ions Cl^- and K^+. **(a)** Which ion is smaller? **(b)** Using Equation 2.1 and assuming that core electrons contribute 1.00 and valence electrons contribute nothing to the screening constant, S, calculate Z_{eff} for these two ions. **(c)** Repeat this calculation using Slater's rules to estimate the screening constant, S. **(d)** For isoelectronic ions, how are effective nuclear charge and ionic radius related?

2.35 Consider S, Cl, and K and their most common ions. **(a)** List the atoms in order of increasing size. **(b)** List the ions in order of increasing size. **(c)** Explain any differences in the orders of the atomic and ionic sizes.

2.36 For each of the following sets of atoms and ions, arrange the members in order of increasing size: **(a)** Se^{2-}, Te^{2-}, Se; **(b)** Co^{3+}, Fe^{2+}, Fe^{3+}; **(c)** Ca, Ti^{4+}, Sc^{3+}; **(d)** Be^{2+}, Na^+, Ne.

2.37 In the ionic compounds LiF, NaCl, KBr, and RbI, the measured cation–anion distances are 2.01 Å (Li–F), 2.82 Å (Na–Cl), 3.30 Å (K–Br), and 3.67 Å (Rb–I), respectively. **(a)** Predict the cation–anion distance using the values of ionic radii given in Figure 2.7. **(b)** Calculate the difference between the experimentally measured ion–ion distances and the ones predicted from Figure 2.7. Assuming we have an accuracy of 0.04 Å in the measurement, would you say that the two sets of ion–ion distances are the same or not? **(c)** What estimates of the cation–anion distance would you obtain for these four compounds using *bonding atomic radii*? Are these estimates as accurate as the estimates using ionic radii?

IONIZATION ENERGIES; ELECTRON AFFINITIES (sections 2.4 and 2.5)

2.38 Write equations that show the processes that describe the first, second, and third ionization energies of an aluminum atom. Which process would require the least amount of energy?

2.39 Write equations that show the process for **(a)** the first two ionization energies of lead and **(b)** the fourth ionization energy of zirconium.

2.40 Identify each statement as true or false. If it is false, rewrite it so that it is true: **(a)** Ionization energies are always negative quantitites. **(b)** Oxygen has a larger first ionization energy than fluorine. **(c)** The second ionization energy of an atom is always greater than its first ionization energy.

2.41 **(a)** Why does Li have a larger first ionization energy than Na? **(b)** The difference between the third and fourth ionization energies of scandium is much larger than the difference between the third and fourth ionization energies of titanium. Why? **(c)** Why does Li have a much larger second ionization energy than Be?

2.42 **(a)** What is the general relationship between the size of an atom and its first ionization energy? **(b)** Which element in the periodic table has the largest ionization energy? Which has the smallest?

2.43 **(a)** What is the trend in first ionization energies as one proceeds down the group 7A elements? Explain how this trend relates to the variation in atomic radii. **(b)** What is the trend in first ionization energies as one moves across the fourth period from K to Kr? How does this trend compare with the trend in atomic radii?

2.44 Based on their positions in the periodic table, predict which atom of the following pairs will have the smaller first ionization energy: **(a)** Cl, Ar; **(b)** Be, Ca; **(c)** K, Co; **(d)** S, Ge; **(e)** Sn, Te.

2.45 For each of the following pairs, indicate which element has the smaller first ionization energy: **(a)** Ti, Ba; **(b)** Ag, Cu; **(c)** Ge,

Cl; (d) Pb, Sb. (In each case use electron configuration and effective nuclear charge to explain your answer.)

2.46 Write the electron configurations for the following ions: (a) Fe^{2+}, (b) Hg^{2+}, (c) Mn^{2+}, (d) Pt^{2+}, (e) P^{3-}.

2.47 Write electron configurations for the following ions, and determine which have noble-gas configurations: (a) Cr^{3+}, (b) N^{3-}, (c) Sc^{3+}, (d) Cu^{2+}, (e) Tl^{+}, (f) Au^{+}.

2.48 Find three examples of ions in the periodic table that have an electron configuration of nd^8 ($n = 3, 4, 5...$).

2.49 Find three atoms in the periodic table whose ions have an electron configuration of nd^6 ($n = 3, 4, 5...$).

2.50 The first ionization energy and electron affinity of Ar are both positive values. (a) What is the significance of the positive value in each case? (b) What are the units of electron affinity?

2.51 If the electron affinity for an element is a negative number, does it mean that the anion of the element is more stable than the neutral atom? Explain.

2.52 Although the electron affinity of bromine is a negative quantity, it is positive for Kr. Use the electron configurations of the two elements to explain the difference.

2.53 What is the relationship between the ionization energy of an anion with a 1− charge such as F^- and the electron affinity of the neutral atom, F?

2.54 Consider the first ionization energy of neon and the electron affinity of fluorine. (a) Write equations, including electron configurations, for each process. (b) These two quantities will have opposite signs. Which will be positive, and which will be negative? (c) Would you expect the **magnitudes** of these two quantities to be equal? If not, which one would you expect to be larger? Explain your answer.

2.55 Write an equation for the process that corresponds to the electron affinity of the Mg^{+} ion. Also write the electron configurations of the species involved. What is the magnitude of the energy change in the process? [*Hint:* The answer is in Table 2.2.]

ADDITIONAL EXERCISES

2.56 Consider the stable elements through lead ($Z = 82$). In how many instances are the atomic weights of the elements in the reverse order relative to the atomic numbers of the elements? What is the explanation for these cases?

[2.57] We saw in Chapter 1 that the probability of finding an electron in three-dimensional space depends on what orbital it is in. Look back at Figures 1.19 and 1.22, which show the radial probability distribution functions for the s orbitals and contour plots of the 2p orbitals, respectively. (a) Which orbitals, 2s or 2p, have more electron density at the nucleus? (b) How would you modify Slater's rules to adjust for the difference in electronic penetration of the nucleus for the 2s and 2p orbitals?

2.58 (a) If the core electrons were totally effective at screening the valence electrons and the valence electrons provided no screening for each other, what would be the effective nuclear charge acting on the 3s and 3p valence electrons in P? (b) Repeat these calculations using Slater's rules. (c) Detailed calculations indicate that the effective nuclear charge is 5.6+ for the 3s electrons and 4.9+ for the 3p electrons. Why are the values for the 3s and 3p electrons different? (d) If you remove a single electron from a P atom, which orbital will it come from? Explain.

2.59 The size of an atomic nucleus is on the order of 10^{-15} m. If two protons were able to make a bond, what would you predict the bond length to be?

2.60 As we move across a period of the periodic table, why do the sizes of the transition elements change more gradually than those of the representative elements?

2.61 In the series of group 5A hydrides, of general formula MH_3, the measured bond distances are P—H, 1.419 Å; As—H, 1.519 Å; Sb—H, 1.707 Å. (a) Compare these values with those estimated by use of the atomic radii in Figure 2.6. (b) Explain the steady increase in M—H bond distance in this series in terms of the electronic configurations of the M atoms.

2.62 Elements in group 7A in the periodic table are the halogens; elements in group 6A are called the chalcogens. (a) What is the most common oxidation state of the chalcogens compared to the halogens? Can you suggest an explanation for the difference? (b) For each of the following periodic properties, state whether the halogens or the chalcogens have larger values: atomic radii; ionic radii of the most common oxidation state; first ionization energy; second ionization energy.

2.63 Note from the following table that the increase in atomic radius in moving from Zr to Hf is smaller than in moving from Y to La. Suggest an explanation for this effect.

Atomic Radii (Å)

Sc	1.44	Ti	1.36
Y	1.62	Zr	1.48
La	1.69	Hf	1.50

[2.64] (a) Which ion is smaller, Co^{3+} or Co^{4+}? (b) In a lithium ion battery that is discharging to power a device, for every Li^+ that inserts into the lithium cobalt oxide electrode, a Co^{4+} ion must be reduced to a Co^{3+} ion in order to balance charge. Using the *CRC Handbook of Chemistry and Physics* or other standard reference, find the ionic radii of Li^+, Co^{3+}, and Co^{4+}. Order these ions from smallest to largest. (c) Will the lithium cobalt electrode expand or contract as lithium ions are inserted? (d) Lithium is not nearly as abundant as sodium. If sodium ion batteries were developed that function as lithium ion ones, do you think "sodium cobalt oxide" would still work as the electrode material? Explain. (e) If you don't think cobalt would work as the redox-active partner ion in the sodium version of the electrode, suggest an alternative metal ion and explain your reasoning.

[2.65] The ionic substance strontium oxide, SrO, forms from the reaction of strontium metal with molecular oxygen. The arrangement of the ions in solid SrO is analogous to that in solid NaCl.

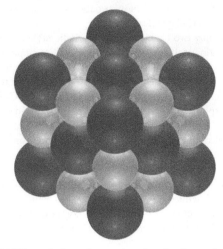

(a) Write a balanced equation for the formation of SrO(s) from its elements. (b) Based on the ionic radii in Figure 2.7, predict the length of the side of the cube in the figure (the distance from the center of an atom at one corner to the center of an atom at a neighboring corner). (c) The density of SrO is 5.10 g/cm^3. Given your answer to part (b), how many formula units of SrO are contained in the cube shown here?

2.66 Explain the variation in ionization energies of carbon, as displayed in this graph:

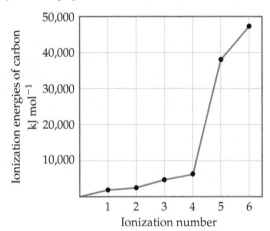

2.67 Group 4A elements have much more negative electron affinities than their neighbors in groups 3A and 5A (see Figure 2.11). Suggest an explanation.

2.68 (a) Use orbital diagrams to illustrate what happens when an oxygen atom gains two electrons. (b) Why does O^{3-} not exist?

[2.69] Use electron configurations to explain the following observations: (a) The first ionization energy of phosphorus is greater than that of sulfur. (b) The electron affinity of nitrogen is lower (less negative) than those of both carbon and oxygen. (c) The second ionization energy of oxygen is greater than the first ionization energy of fluorine. (d) The third ionization energy of manganese is greater than those of both chromium and iron.

2.70 The electron affinities, in kJ/mol, for the group 1B and group 2B metals are

Cu −119	Zn > 0
Ag −126	Cd > 0
Au −223	Hg > 0

(a) Why are the electron affinities of the group 2B elements greater than zero? (b) Why do the electron affinities of the group 1B elements become more negative as we move down the group? [Hint: Examine the trends in the electron affinity of other groups as we proceed down the periodic table.]

2.71 Hydrogen is an unusual element because it behaves in some ways like the alkali metal elements and in other ways like nonmetals. Its properties can be explained in part by its electron configuration and by the values for its ionization energy and electron affinity. (a) Explain why the electron affinity of hydrogen is much closer to the values for the alkali elements than for the halogens. (b) Is the following statement true? "Hydrogen has the smallest bonding atomic radius of any element that forms chemical compounds." If not, correct it. If it is, explain in terms of electron configurations. (c) Explain why the ionization energy of hydrogen is closer to the values for the halogens than for the alkali metals. (d) The hydride ion is H^-. Write out the process corresponding to the first ionization energy of hydride. (e) How does the process you wrote in part (d) compare to the process for the electron affinity of elemental hydrogen?

[2.72] The first ionization energy of the oxygen molecule is the energy required for the following process:

$$O_2(g) \longrightarrow O_2^+(g) + e^-$$

The energy needed for this process is 1175 kJ/mol, very similar to the first ionization energy of Xe. Would you expect O_2 to react with F_2? If so, suggest a product or products of this reaction.

2.73 The elements of group 4A—carbon, silicon, germanium, tin, and lead—go from nonmetal through metalloid to metal as we go down the column. (a) Predict the order of melting temperature from highest to lowest in this group and justify your logic. (b) Using the *CRC Handbook of Chemistry and Physics* or other resource, look up the melting points of these elements. How accurate was your prediction?

2.74 Zinc in its 2+ oxidation state is an essential metal ion for life. Zn^{2+} is found bound to many proteins that are involved in biological processes, but unfortunately Zn^{2+} is hard to detect by common chemical methods. Therefore, scientists who are interested in studying Zn^{2+}-containing proteins will frequently substitute Cd^{2+} for Zn^{2+}, since Cd^{2+} is easier to detect. (a) On the basis of the properties of the elements and ions discussed in this chapter and their positions in the periodic table, describe the pros and cons of using Cd^{2+} as a Zn^{2+} substitute. (b) Proteins that speed up (catalyze) chemical reactions are called *enzymes*. Many enzymes are required for proper metabolic reactions in the body. One problem with using Cd^{2+} to replace Zn^{2+} in enzymes is that Cd^{2+} substitution can decrease or even eliminate enzymatic activity. Can you suggest a different metal ion that might replace Zn^{2+} in enzymes instead of Cd^{2+}? Justify your answer.

[**2.75**] A historian discovers a nineteenth-century notebook in which some observations, dated 1822, were recorded on a substance thought to be a new element. Here are some of the data recorded in the notebook: "Ductile, silver-white, metallic looking. Softer than lead. Unaffected by water. Stable in air. Melting point: 153 °C. Density: 7.3 g/cm³. Electrical conductivity: 20% that of copper. Hardness: About 1% as hard as iron. When 4.20 g of the unknown is heated in an excess of oxygen, 5.08 g of a white solid is formed. The solid could be sublimed by heating to over 800 °C." (**a**) Using information in the text and the *CRC Handbook of Chemistry and Physics,* and making allowances for possible variations in numbers from current values, identify the element reported. (**b**) Write a balanced chemical equation for the reaction with oxygen. (**c**) Judging from Figure 2.1, might this nineteenth-century investigator have been the first to discover a new element?

2.76 In April 2010, a research team reported that they had made Element 112. The report has yet to be confirmed. Write out Element 117's ground-state electron configuration, and estimate values for its first ionization energy, electron affinity, atomic size, and common oxidation state based on its position in the periodic table.

2.77 The only two elements in the periodic table that are technologically useful semiconductors are silicon and germanium. Integrated circuits in computer chips today are based on silicon. Compound semiconductors are also used in the electronics industry. Examples are gallium arsenide, GaAs; gallium phosphide, GaP; cadmium sulfide, CdS; cadium selenide, CdSe. (**a**) What is the relationship between the compound semiconductors' compositions and the positions of their elements on the periodic table relative to Si and Ge? (**b**) Workers in the semiconductor industry refer to "II-VI" and "III-V" materials, using Roman numerals; can you identify which compound semiconductors are II-VI and which are III-V? (**c**) Suggest other compositions of compound semiconductors based on the positions of their elements in the periodic table.

INTEGRATIVE EXERCISES

[**2.78**] Moseley established the concept of atomic number by studying X-rays emitted by the elements. The X-rays emitted by some of the elements have the following wavelengths:

Element	Wavelength (Å)
Ne	14.610
Ca	3.358
Zn	1.435
Zr	0.786
Sn	0.491

(**a**) Calculate the frequency, ν, of the X-rays emitted by each of the elements, in Hz. (**b**) Using the appropriate graphing program on your computer, plot the square root of ν versus the atomic number of the element. What do you observe about the plot? (**c**) Explain how the plot in part (b) allowed Moseley to predict the existence of undiscovered elements. (**d**) Use the result from part (b) to predict the X-ray wavelength emitted by iron. (**e**) A particular element emits X-rays with a wavelength of 0.980 Å. What element do you think it is?

[**2.79**] (**a**) Write the electron configuration for Li, and estimate the effective nuclear charge experienced by the valence electron. (**b**) The energy of an electron in a one-electron atom or ion equals $(-2.18 \times 10^{-18} \text{ J})\left(\dfrac{Z^2}{n^2}\right)$ where Z is the nuclear charge and n is the principal quantum number of the electron. Estimate the first ionization energy of Li. (**c**) Compare the result of your calculation with the value reported in Table 2.4 and explain the difference. (**d**) What value of the effective nuclear charge gives the proper value for the ionization energy? Does this agree with your explanation in (c)?

[**2.80**] One way to measure ionization energies is ultraviolet photoelectron spectroscopy (UPS, or just PES), a technique based on the photoelectric effect. ∞ (Section 1.2) In PES, monochromatic light is directed onto a sample, causing electrons to be emitted. The kinetic energy of the emitted electrons is measured. The difference between the energy of the photons and the kinetic energy of the electrons corresponds to the energy needed to remove the electrons (that is, the ionization energy). Suppose that a PES experiment is performed in which mercury vapor is irradiated with ultraviolet light of wavelength 58.4 nm. (**a**) What is the energy of a photon of this light in eV? (**b**) Write an equation that shows the process corresponding to the first ionization energy of Hg. (**c**) The kinetic energy of the emitted electrons is measured to be 10.75 eV. What is the first ionization energy of Hg in kJ/mol? (**d**) Using Figure 2.9, determine which of the halogen elements has a first ionization energy closest to that of mercury.

2.81 Mercury in the environment can exist in oxidation states 0, +1, and +2. One major question in environmental chemistry research is how to best measure the oxidation state of mercury in natural systems; this is made more complicated by the fact that mercury can be reduced or oxidized on surfaces differently than it would be if it were free in solution. XPS, X-ray photoelectron spectroscopy, is a technique related to PES (see Exercise 2.80), but instead of using ultraviolet light to eject valence electrons, X-rays are used to eject core electrons. The energies of the core electrons are different for different oxidation states of the element. In one set of experiments, researchers examined mercury contamination of minerals in water. They measured the XPS signals that corresponded to electrons ejected from mercury's 4f orbitals at 105 eV, from an X-ray source that provided 1253.6 eV of energy. The oxygen on the mineral surface gave emitted electron energies at 531 eV, corresponding to the 1s orbital of oxygen. Overall the researchers concluded that oxidation states were +2 for Hg and −2 for O. (**a**) Calculate the wavelength of the X-rays used in this experiment. (**b**) Compare the energies of the 4f electrons in mercury and the 1s electrons in oxygen from these data to the first ionization energies of mercury and oxygen from the data in this chapter. (**c**) Write out the ground-state electron configurations for Hg^{2+} and O^{2-}; which electrons are the valence electrons in each case? (**d**) Use Slater's rules to estimate Z_{eff} for the 4f and valence electrons of Hg^{2+} and O^{2-}; assume for this purpose that all the inner electrons with $(n - 3)$ or less screen a full +1.

2.82 Consider the gas-phase transfer of an electron from a sodium atom to a chlorine atom:

$$Na(g) + Cl(g) \longrightarrow Na^+(g) + Cl^-(g)$$

(a) Write this reaction as the sum of two reactions, one that relates to an ionization energy and one that relates to an electron affinity. **(b)** Use the result from part (a), data in this chapter, and Hess's law to calculate the enthalpy of the preceding reaction. Is the reaction exothermic or endothermic? **(c)** The reaction between sodium metal and chlorine gas is highly exothermic and produces NaCl(s). Comment on this observation relative to the calculated enthalpy for the aforementioned gas-phase reaction.

CHEMICAL BONDING AS ART. The *Atomium* is a 110-m-high steel sculpture commissioned for the 1958 World's Fair in Brussels. The nine spheres represent atoms, and the connecting rods evoke the chemical bonds holding them together. One sphere sits in the center of a cube formed by the other eight, a common arrangement of the atoms in metallic elements, such as iron.

3

BASIC CONCEPTS OF CHEMICAL BONDING

WHENEVER TWO ATOMS OR IONS are strongly held together, we say there is a **chemical bond** between them. There are three general types of chemical bonds: *ionic, covalent, and metallic* (▶ **FIGURE 3.1**). We can get a glimpse of these three types of bonds by thinking about the simple act of using a stainless-steel spoon to add table salt to a glass of water. Table salt is sodium chloride, NaCl, which consists of sodium ions, Na^+, and chloride ions, Cl^-. The structure is held together by **ionic bonds**, which are due to the attractions between oppositely charged ions. The water consists mainly of H_2O molecules. The hydrogen and oxygen atoms are bonded to one another through **covalent bonds**, in which molecules are formed by the sharing of electrons between atoms. The spoon consists mainly of iron metal, in which Fe atoms are connected to one another via **metallic bonds**, which are formed by electrons that are relatively free to move through the metal. These different substances—NaCl, H_2O, and Fe metal—behave as they do because of the ways in which their constituent atoms are connected to one another.

What determines the type of bonding in any substance? How do the characteristics of these bonds give rise to different physical and chemical properties? The keys to answering the first question are found in the electronic structure of the atoms involved, discussed in Chapters 1 and 2. In this chapter and the next, we examine the relationship between the electronic structure of atoms and the ionic and covalent chemical bonds they form.

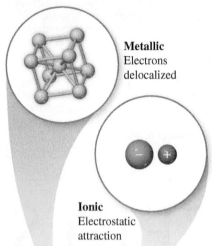

Metallic
Electrons
delocalized

Ionic
Electrostatic
attraction

Covalent
Electrons
shared

▲ **FIGURE 3.1   Ionic, covalent, and metallic bonds.** Different types of interactions between atoms lead to different types of chemical bonds.

3.1 | LEWIS SYMBOLS AND THE OCTET RULE

The electrons involved in chemical bonding are the *valence electrons,* which, for most atoms, are those in the outermost occupied shell. ∞ (Section 1.8) The American chemist G. N. Lewis (1875–1946) suggested a simple way of showing the valence electrons in an atom and tracking them during bond formation, using what are now known as either *Lewis electron-dot symbols* or simply Lewis symbols.

The **Lewis symbol** for an element consists of the element's chemical symbol plus a dot for each valence electron. Sulfur, for example, has the electron configuration $[Ne]3s^23p^4$ and therefore six valence electrons. Its Lewis symbol is

The dots are placed on the four sides of the symbol—top, bottom, left, and right—and each side can accommodate up to two electrons. All four sides are equivalent, which means that the choice of on which sides to place two electrons rather than one electron is arbitrary. In general, we spread out the dots as much as possible. In the Lewis symbol for S, for instance, we prefer the dot arrangement shown rather the arrangement having two electrons on three of the sides and none on the fourth.

The electron configurations and Lewis symbols for the main-group elements of periods 2 and 3 are shown in ▼ TABLE 3.1. Notice that the number of valence electrons in any representative element is the same as the element's group number. For example, the Lewis symbols for oxygen and sulfur, members of group 6A, both show six dots.

⚠️ **GIVE IT SOME THOUGHT**
Are all these Lewis symbols for Cl correct?

:C̈l·   :C̈l: :C̈l·

The Octet Rule

Atoms often gain, lose, or share electrons to achieve the same number of electrons as the noble gas closest to them in the periodic table. The noble gases have very stable electron arrangements, as evidenced by their high ionization energies, low affinity for additional electrons, and general lack of chemical reactivity. Because all the noble gases except He have eight valence electrons, many atoms undergoing reactions end up with eight valence electrons. This observation has led to a guideline known as the **octet rule:** *Atoms tend to gain, lose, or share electrons until they are surrounded by eight valence electrons.*

An octet of electrons consists of full *s* and *p* subshells in an atom. In a Lewis symbol, an octet is shown as four pairs of valence electrons arranged around the element symbol, as in the Lewis symbols for Ne and Ar in Table 3.1. There are exceptions to the octet rule, but it provides a useful framework for introducing many important concepts of bonding.

TABLE 3.1 · Lewis Symbols						
Group	Element	Electron Configuration	Lewis Symbol	Element	Electron Configuration	Lewis Symbol
1A	Li	$[He]2s^1$	Li·	Na	$[Ne]3s^1$	Na·
2A	Be	$[He]2s^2$	·Be·	Mg	$[Ne]3s^2$	·Mg·
3A	B	$[He]2s^22p^1$	·Ḃ·	Al	$[Ne]3s^23p^1$	·Ȧl·
4A	C	$[He]2s^22p^2$	·Ċ·	Si	$[Ne]3s^23p^2$	·Ṡi·
5A	N	$[He]2s^22p^3$	·N̈·	P	$[Ne]3s^23p^3$	·P̈·
6A	O	$[He]2s^22p^4$	:Ö:	S	$[Ne]3s^23p^4$	:S̈:
7A	F	$[He]2s^22p^5$	·F̈:	Cl	$[Ne]3s^23p^5$	·C̈l:
8A	Ne	$[He]2s^22p^6$	:N̈e:	Ar	$[Ne]3s^23p^6$	:Ȧr:

▲ **GO FIGURE**

Do you expect a similar reaction between potassium metal and elemental bromine?

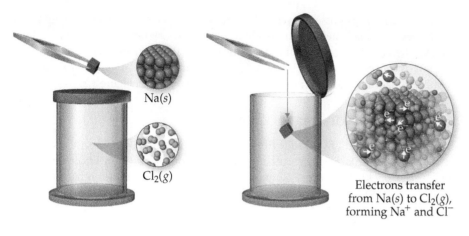

Na(s)

Cl$_2$(g)

Electrons transfer
from Na(s) to Cl$_2$(g),
forming Na$^+$ and Cl$^-$

NaCl(s) forms

Highly exothermic reaction
forming sodium chloride, an ionic
compound composed of sodium
ions, Na$^+$, and chloride ions, Cl$^-$

▲ **FIGURE 3.2**   **Reaction of sodium metal with chlorine gas to form the ionic compound sodium chloride.**

3.2 | IONIC BONDING

Ionic substances generally result from the interaction of metals on the left side of the periodic table with nonmetals on the right side (excluding the noble gases, group 8A). For example, when sodium metal, Na(s), is brought into contact with chlorine gas, Cl$_2$(g), a violent reaction ensues (▲ **FIGURE 3.2**). The product of this very exothermic reaction is sodium chloride, NaCl(s):

$$Na(s) + \tfrac{1}{2}Cl_2(g) \longrightarrow NaCl(s) \qquad \Delta H_f^\circ = -410.9 \text{ kJ} \qquad [3.1]$$

Sodium chloride is composed of Na$^+$ and Cl$^-$ ions arranged in a three-dimensional array (▶ **FIGURE 3.3**).

The formation of Na$^+$ from Na and Cl$^-$ from Cl$_2$ indicates that an electron has been lost by a sodium atom and gained by a chlorine atom—we can envision an *electron transfer* from the Na atom to the Cl atom. Two of the atomic properties discussed in Chapter 2 give us an indication of how readily electron transfer occurs: ionization energy, which indicates how easily an electron can be removed from an atom, and electron affinity, which measures how much an atom wants to gain an electron. ∞ (Sections 2.4 and 2.5) Electron transfer to form oppositely charged ions occurs when one atom readily gives up an electron (low ionization energy) and another atom readily gains an electron (high electron affinity). Thus, NaCl is a typical ionic compound because it consists of a metal of low ionization energy and a nonmetal of high electron affinity. Using Lewis electron-dot symbols (and showing a chlorine atom rather than the Cl$_2$ molecule), we can represent this reaction as

$$Na\cdot \; + \; \cdot\ddot{\underset{..}{Cl}}: \;\; \longrightarrow \;\; Na^+ \; + \; [:\ddot{\underset{..}{Cl}}:]^- \qquad [3.2]$$

The arrow indicates the transfer of an electron from the Na atom to the Cl atom. Each ion has an octet of electrons, the Na$^+$ octet being the $2s^2 2p^6$ electrons that lie below the single $3s$ valence electron of the Na atom. We have put a bracket around the chloride ion to emphasize that all eight electrons are located on it.

▲ **GO FIGURE**

If no color key were provided, is there a way for you to guess whether the green spheres represent Na$^+$ or Cl$^-$? If so, what information would you use?

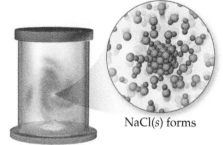

= Na$^+$

= Cl$^-$

Each Na$^+$ ion
surrounded by
six Cl$^-$ ions

Each Cl$^-$ ion
surrounded by
six Na$^+$ ions

▲ **FIGURE 3.3**   **The crystal structure of sodium chloride.**

Describe the electron transfers that occur in the formation of calcium fluoride from elemental calcium and elemental fluorine.

Ionic substances possess several characteristic properties. They are usually brittle substances with high melting points. They are usually crystalline. Furthermore, ionic crystals often can be cleaved; that is, they break apart along smooth, flat surfaces. These characteristics result from electrostatic forces that maintain the ions in a rigid, well-defined, three-dimensional arrangement such as that shown in Figure 3.3.

Energetics of Ionic Bond Formation

The formation of sodium chloride from sodium and chlorine is *very* exothermic, as indicated by the large negative enthalpy of formation value given in Equation 3.1, $\Delta H_f^\circ = -410.9$ kJ. Appendix C shows that the heat of formation of other ionic substances is also quite negative. What factors make the formation of ionic compounds so exothermic?

In Equation 3.2 we represented the formation of NaCl as the transfer of an electron from Na to Cl. Recall from Section 2.4 that the loss of electrons from an atom is always an endothermic process. Removing an electron from $Na(g)$ to form $Na^+(g)$, for instance, requires 496 kJ/mol. Recall from Section 2.5 that when a nonmetal gains an electron, the process is generally exothermic, as seen from the negative electron affinities of the elements. Adding an electron to $Cl(g)$, for example, releases 349 kJ/mol. From the magnitudes of these energies, we can see that the transfer of an electron from a Na atom to a Cl atom would not be exothermic—the overall process would be an endothermic process that requires $496 - 349 = 147$ kJ/mol. This endothermic process corresponds to the formation of sodium and chloride ions that are infinitely far apart—in other words, the positive energy change assumes that the ions do not interact with each other, which is quite different from the situation in ionic solids.

Consider the trends in ionization energies of the alkali metals and electron affinities of the halogens shown in Figures 2.9 and 2.11. For which pair is electron transfer from the alkali metal atom to the halogen atom most likely to be an exothermic process?

The principal reason ionic compounds are stable is the attraction between ions of opposite charge. This attraction draws the ions together, releasing energy and causing the ions to form a solid array, or lattice, such as that shown in Figure 3.3. A measure of how much stabilization results from arranging oppositely charged ions in an ionic solid is given by the **lattice energy**, which is *the energy required to completely separate one mole of a solid ionic compound into its gaseous ions.*

To envision this process for NaCl, imagine that the structure in Figure 3.3 expands from within, so that the distances between the ions increase until the ions are very far apart. This process requires 788 kJ/mol, which is the value of the lattice energy:

$$NaCl(s) \longrightarrow Na^+(g) + Cl^-(g) \qquad \Delta H_{lattice} = +788 \text{ kJ/mol} \qquad [3.3]$$

Notice that this process is highly endothermic. The reverse process—the coming together of $Na^+(g)$ and $Cl^-(g)$ to form $NaCl(s)$—is therefore highly exothermic ($\Delta H = -788$ kJ/mol).

▶ **TABLE 3.2** lists the lattice energies for a number of ionic compounds. The large positive values indicate that the ions are strongly attracted to one another in ionic solids. The energy released by the attraction between ions of unlike charge more than makes up for the endothermic nature of ionization energies, making the formation of ionic compounds an exothermic process. The strong attractions also cause most ionic materials to be hard and brittle with high melting points—for example, NaCl melts at 801 °C.

Compound	Lattice Energy (kJ/mol)	Compound	Lattice Energy (kJ/mol)
TABLE 3.2 • Lattice Energies for Some Ionic Compounds			
LiF	1030	$MgCl_2$	2326
LiCl	834	$SrCl_2$	2127
LiI	730		
NaF	910	MgO	3795
NaCl	788	CaO	3414
NaBr	732	SrO	3217
NaI	682		
KF	808	ScN	7547
KCl	701		
KBr	671		
CsCl	657		
CsI	600		

The magnitude of the lattice energy of an ionic solid depends on the charges of the ions, their sizes, and their arrangement in the solid. We will see in Section 10.1 that the potential energy of two interacting charged particles is given by

$$E_{el} = \frac{\kappa Q_1 Q_2}{d} \qquad [3.4]$$

In this equation Q_1 and Q_2 are the charges on the particles, d is the distance between their centers, and κ is a constant, 8.99×10^9 J-m/C^2. Equation 3.4 indicates that the attractive interaction between two oppositely charged ions increases as the magnitudes of their charges increase and as the distance between their centers decreases. Thus, *for a given arrangement of ions, the lattice energy increases as the charges on the ions increase and as their radii decrease.* The magnitude of lattice energies depends predominantly on the ionic charges because ionic radii vary over only a limited range.

SAMPLE EXERCISE 3.1 | **Magnitudes of Lattice Energies**

Without consulting Table 3.2, arrange the ionic compounds NaF, CsI, and CaO in order of increasing lattice energy.

SOLUTION

Analyze From the formulas for three ionic compounds, we must determine their relative lattice energies.

Plan We need to determine the charges and relative sizes of the ions in the compounds. We then use Equation 3.4 qualitatively to determine the relative energies, knowing that (a) the larger the ionic charges, the greater the energy and (b) the farther apart the ions are, the lower the energy.

Solve NaF consists of Na^+ and F^- ions, CsI of Cs^+ and I^- ions, and CaO of Ca^{2+} and O^{2-} ions. Because the product $Q_1 Q_2$ appears in the numerator of Equation 3.4, the lattice energy increases dramatically when the charges increase. Thus, we expect the lattice energy of CaO, which has 2+ and 2− ions, to be the greatest of the three.

The ionic charges are the same in NaF and CsI. As a result, the difference in their lattice energies depends on the difference in the distance between ions in the lattice. Because ionic size increases as we go down a group in the periodic table ∞ (Section 2.3), we know that Cs^+ is larger than Na^+ and I^- is larger than F^-. Therefore, the distance between Na^+ and F^- ions in NaF is less than the distance between the Cs^+ and I^- ions in CsI. As a result, the lattice energy of NaF should be greater than that of CsI. In order of increasing energy, therefore, we have CsI < NaF < CaO.

Check Table 3.2 confirms our predicted order is correct.

PRACTICE EXERCISE

Which substance do you expect to have the greatest lattice energy, MgF_2, CaF_2, or ZrO_2?
Answer: ZrO_2

GO FIGURE

Using this figure, can you place an upper and lower limit on the lattice energy of KF?

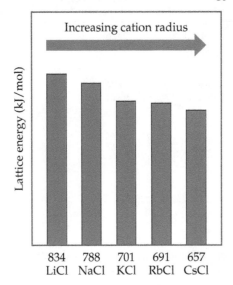

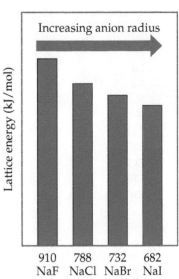

▶ **FIGURE 3.4** **Periodic trends in lattice energy as a function of cation or anion radius.**

Increasing cation radius

Lattice energy (kJ/mol)

834	788	701	691	657
LiCl	NaCl	KCl	RbCl	CsCl

Increasing anion radius

Lattice energy (kJ/mol)

910	788	732	682
NaF	NaCl	NaBr	NaI

Because lattice energy decreases as distance between ions increases, lattice energies follow trends that parallel those in ionic radius shown in Figure 2.6. In particular, because ionic radius increases as we go down a group of the periodic table, we find that, for a given type of ionic compound, lattice energy decreases as we go down a group. ▲ **FIGURE 3.4** illustrates this trend for the alkali chlorides MCl (M = Li, Na, K, Rb, Cs) and the sodium halides NaX (X = F, Cl, Br, I).

Electron Configurations of Ions of the s- and p-Block Elements

The energetics of ionic bond formation helps explain why many ions tend to have noble-gas electron configurations. For example, sodium readily loses one electron to form Na^+, which has the same electron configuration as Ne:

$$Na \qquad 1s^2 2s^2 2p^6 3s^1 = [Ne]3s^1$$
$$Na^+ \qquad 1s^2 2s^2 2p^6 \quad = [Ne]$$

Even though lattice energy increases with increasing ionic charge, we never find ionic compounds that contain Na^{2+} ions. The second electron removed would have to come from an inner shell of the sodium atom, and removing electrons from an inner shell requires a very large amount of energy. ∞ (Section 2.4) The increase in lattice energy is not enough to compensate for the energy needed to remove an inner-shell electron. Thus, sodium and the other group 1A metals are found in ionic substances only as 1+ ions.

Similarly, adding electrons to nonmetals is either exothermic or only slightly endothermic as long as the electrons are added to the valence shell. Thus, a Cl atom easily adds an electron to form Cl^-, which has the same electron configuration as Ar:

$$Cl \qquad 1s^2 2s^2 2p^6 3s^2 3p^5 = [Ne]3s^2 3p^5$$
$$Cl^- \qquad 1s^2 2s^2 2p^6 3s^2 3p^6 = [Ne]3s^2 3p^6 = [Ar]$$

To form a Cl^{2-} ion, the second electron would have to be added to the next higher shell of the Cl atom, an addition that is energetically very unfavorable. Therefore, we never observe Cl^{2-} ions in ionic compounds. We thus expect ionic compounds of the representative metals from groups 1A, 2A, and 3A to contain 1+, 2+, and 3+ cations, respectively, and usually expect ionic compounds of the representative nonmetals of groups 5A, 6A, and 7A to contain 3−, 2−, and 1− anions, respectively.

A CLOSER LOOK

CALCULATION OF LATTICE ENERGIES: THE BORN–HABER CYCLE

Lattice energies cannot be determined directly by experiment. They can, however, be calculated by envisioning the formation of an ionic compound as occurring in a series of well-defined steps. We can then use Hess's law (see Section 10.6) to combine the steps in a way that gives the lattice energy for the compound. By so doing, we construct a **Born–Haber cycle**, a thermochemical cycle named after the German scientists Max Born (1882–1970) and Fritz Haber (1868–1934), who introduced it to analyze the factors contributing to the stability of ionic compounds.

In the Born–Haber cycle for NaCl, we consider the formation of NaCl(s) from Na(s) and Cl$_2$(g) by two routes, as shown in ▶ FIGURE 3.5. The enthalpy change for the direct route (red arrow) is the heat of formation of NaCl(s):

$$Na(s) + \tfrac{1}{2}Cl_2(g) \longrightarrow NaCl(s) \quad \Delta H^\circ_f[NaCl(s)] = -411 \text{ kJ} \quad [3.5]$$

The indirect route has five steps (green arrows in Figure 3.5). First, we generate Na(g) atoms by vaporizing Na(s). Then we form Cl(g) atoms by breaking the bonds in Cl$_2$ molecules. The enthalpy changes are (Appendix C):

$$Na(s) \longrightarrow Na(g) \quad \Delta H^\circ_f[Na(g)] = 108 \text{ kJ} \quad [3.6]$$

$$\tfrac{1}{2}Cl_2(g) \longrightarrow Cl(g) \quad \Delta H^\circ_f[Cl(g)] = 122 \text{ kJ} \quad [3.7]$$

Note that both processes are endothermic.

In the next two steps we remove the electron from Na(g) to form Na$^+$(g) and then add the electron to Cl(g) to form Cl$^-$(g). The enthalpy changes for these processes equal the first ionization energy of Na, I_1(Na), and the electron affinity of Cl, denoted E(Cl), respectively: ∞ (Sections 2.4, 2.5)

$$Na(g) \longrightarrow Na^+(g) + e^- \quad \Delta H = I_1(Na) = 496 \text{ kJ} \quad [3.8]$$

$$Cl(g) + e^- \longrightarrow Cl^-(g) \quad \Delta H = E(Cl) = -349 \text{ kJ} \quad [3.9]$$

Finally, we combine the Na$^+$(g) and Cl$^-$(g) to form NaCl(s). Because forming solid NaCl is the reverse of breaking the solid into its gaseous ions, the enthalpy change for solid formation is the negative of the lattice energy, the quantity we want to determine:

$$Na^+(g) + Cl^-(g) \longrightarrow NaCl(s) \quad \Delta H = -\Delta H_{lattice} = ? \quad [3.10]$$

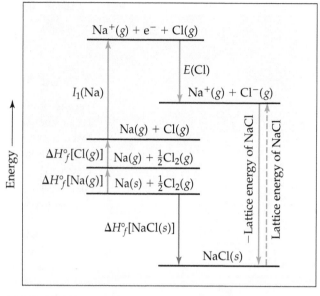

▲ **FIGURE 3.5   Born–Haber cycle for formation of NaCl.** This Hess's law representation shows the energetic relationships in the formation of the ionic solid from its elements.

The result of the five-step pathway is formation of NaCl(s) from Na(s) and $\tfrac{1}{2}$Cl$_2$(g). Thus, from Hess's law we know that the sum of the enthalpy changes for the five steps equals the enthalpy change for the direct reaction (Equation 3.5):

$$\Delta H^\circ_f[NaCl(s)] = \Delta H^\circ_f[Na(g)] + \Delta H^\circ_f[Cl(g)]$$
$$+ I_1(Na) + E(Cl) - \Delta H_{lattice}$$
$$-411 \text{ kJ} = 108 \text{ kJ} + 122 \text{ kJ} + 496 \text{ kJ} - 349 \text{ kJ} - \Delta H_{lattice}$$

Solving for $\Delta H_{lattice}$:

$$\Delta H_{lattice} = 108 \text{ kJ} + 122 \text{ kJ} + 496 \text{ kJ} - 349 \text{ kJ} + 411 \text{ kJ}$$
$$= 788 \text{ kJ}$$

Thus, the lattice energy of NaCl is 788 kJ/mol.

RELATED EXERCISES: 3.28, 3.29, 3.30, 3.83, 3.102, 3.103

SAMPLE EXERCISE 3.2   Charges on Ions

Predict the ion generally formed by (**a**) Sr, (**b**) S, (**c**) Al.

SOLUTION

Analyze We must decide how many electrons are most likely to be gained or lost by atoms of Sr, S, and Al.

Plan In each case we can use the element's position in the periodic table to predict whether the element forms a cation or an anion. We can then use its electron configuration to determine the most likely ion formed.

Solve (**a**) Strontium is a metal in group 2A and therefore forms a cation. Its electron configuration is [Kr]$5s^2$, and so we expect that the two valence electrons can be lost easily to give an Sr^{2+} ion. (**b**) Sulfur is a nonmetal in group 6A and will thus tend to be found as an anion. Its electron configuration ([Ne]$3s^23p^4$) is two electrons short of a noble-gas configuration. Thus, we expect that sulfur will form S^{2-} ions. (**c**) Aluminum is a metal in group 3A. We therefore expect it to form Al^{3+} ions.

Transition-Metal Ions

Because ionization energies increase rapidly for each successive electron removed, the lattice energies of ionic compounds are generally large enough to compensate for the loss of up to only three electrons from atoms. Thus, we find cations with charges of 1+, 2+, or 3+ in ionic compounds. Most transition metals, however, have more than three electrons beyond a noble-gas core. Silver, for example, has a $[Kr]4d^{10}5s^1$ electron configuration. Metals of group 1B (Cu, Ag, Au) often occur as 1+ ions (as in CuBr and AgCl). In forming Ag^+, the $5s$ electron is lost, leaving a completely filled $4d$ subshell. As in this example, transition metals generally do not form ions that have a noble-gas configuration. The octet rule, although useful, is clearly limited in scope.

Recall from Section 2.4 that when a positive ion forms from an atom, electrons are always lost first from the subshell having the largest value of n. Thus, *in forming ions, transition metals lose the valence-shell s electrons first, then as many d electrons as required to reach the charge of the ion.* For instance, in forming Fe^{2+} from Fe, which has the electron configuration $[Ar]3d^64s^2$, the two $4s$ electrons are lost, leading to an $[Ar]3d^6$ configuration. Removal of an additional electron gives Fe^{3+}, whose electron configuration is $[Ar]3d^5$.

⌐ **GIVE IT SOME THOUGHT**

Which element forms a 3+ ion that has the electron configuration $[Kr]4d^6$?

3.3 | COVALENT BONDING

The vast majority of chemical substances do not have the characteristics of ionic materials. Most of the substances with which we come into daily contact—such as water—tend to be gases, liquids, or solids with low melting points. Many, such as gasoline, vaporize readily. Many are pliable in their solid forms—for example, plastic bags and paraffin.

For the very large class of substances that do not behave like ionic substances, we need a different model for the bonding between atoms. G. N. Lewis reasoned that atoms might acquire a noble-gas electron configuration by sharing electrons with other atoms. A chemical bond formed by sharing a pair of electrons is a *covalent bond*.

The hydrogen molecule, H_2, provides the simplest example of a covalent bond. When two hydrogen atoms are close to each other, the two positively charged nuclei repel each other, the two negatively charged electrons repel each other, and the nuclei and electrons attract each other, as shown in ◄ **FIGURE 3.6**(a). Because the molecule is stable, we know that the attractive forces must overcome the repulsive ones. Let's take a closer look at the attractive forces that hold this molecule together.

By using quantum mechanical methods analogous to those used for atoms in Section 1.5, we can calculate the distribution of electron density in molecules. Such a calculation for H_2 shows that the attractions between the nuclei and the electrons cause electron density to concentrate between the nuclei, as shown in Figure 3.6(b). As a result, the overall electrostatic interactions are attractive. Thus, the atoms in H_2 are held together principally because the two positive nuclei are attracted to the concentration of negative charge between them. In essence, the shared pair of electrons in any covalent bond acts as a kind of "glue" to bind atoms together.

⌐ **GO FIGURE**

What would happen to the magnitudes of the attractions and repulsions represented in (a) if the nuclei were farther apart?

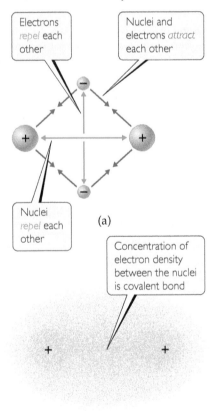

Electrons *repel* each other

Nuclei and electrons *attract* each other

Nuclei *repel* each other

(a)

Concentration of electron density between the nuclei is covalent bond

(b)

▲ **FIGURE 3.6** **The covalent bond in H_2.** (a) The attractions and repulsions among electrons and nuclei in the hydrogen molecule. (b) Electron distribution in the H_2 molecule.

◢ GIVE IT SOME THOUGHT

Ionizing an H_2 molecule to H_2^+ changes the strength of the bond. Based on the description of covalent bonding given previously, do you expect the H—H bond in H_2^+ to be weaker or stronger than the H—H bond in H_2?

Lewis Structures

The formation of covalent bonds can be represented with Lewis symbols. The formation of the H_2 molecule from two H atoms, for example, can be represented as

$$H\cdot \ + \ \cdot H \longrightarrow \ \boxed{H \!:\! H}$$

In forming the covalent bond, each hydrogen atom acquires a second electron, achieving the stable, two-electron, noble-gas electron configuration of helium.

Formation of a covalent bond between two Cl atoms to give a Cl_2 molecule can be represented in a similar way:

$$:\!\ddot{Cl}\cdot \ + \ \cdot\ddot{Cl}: \ \longrightarrow \ \boxed{:\!\ddot{Cl}\!:\!\ddot{Cl}:}$$

By sharing the bonding electron pair, each chlorine atom has eight electrons (an octet) in its valence shell, thus achieving the noble-gas electron configuration of argon.

The structures shown here for H_2 and Cl_2 are called either **Lewis structures** or *Lewis electron-dot structures*. In writing Lewis structures, we usually show each shared electron pair as a line and any unshared electron pairs as dots. Written this way, the Lewis structures for H_2 and Cl_2 are

$$H\!-\!H \qquad :\!\ddot{Cl}\!-\!\ddot{Cl}\!:$$

For nonmetals, the number of valence electrons in a neutral atom is the same as the group number. Therefore, one might predict that 7A elements, such as F, would form one covalent bond to achieve an octet; 6A elements, such as O, would form two covalent bonds; 5A elements, such as N, would form three; and 4A elements, such as C, would form four. These predictions are borne out in many compounds, as in, for example, the compounds with hydrogen of the nonmetals of the second row of the periodic table:

$$H\!-\!\ddot{\underset{\cdot\cdot}{F}}: \qquad H\!-\!\overset{\cdot\cdot}{\underset{|}{O}}: \qquad H\!-\!\overset{\cdot\cdot}{\underset{|}{N}}\!-\!H \qquad H\!-\!\overset{\overset{\textstyle H}{|}}{\underset{|}{C}}\!-\!H$$
$$\qquad\qquad\quad H \qquad\quad H \qquad\qquad H$$

SAMPLE EXERCISE 3.3 | **Lewis Structure of a Compound**

Given the Lewis symbols for nitrogen and fluorine in Table 3.1, predict the formula of the stable binary compound (a compound composed of two elements) formed when nitrogen reacts with fluorine and draw its Lewis structure.

SOLUTION

Analyze The Lewis symbols for nitrogen and fluorine reveal that nitrogen has five valence electrons and fluorine has seven.

Plan We need to find a combination of the two elements that results in an octet of electrons around each atom. Nitrogen requires three additional electrons to complete its octet, and fluorine requires one. Sharing a pair of electrons between one N atom and one F atom will result in an octet of electrons for fluorine but not for nitrogen. We therefore need to figure out a way to get two more electrons for the N atom.

Solve Nitrogen must share a pair of electrons with three fluorine atoms to complete its octet. Thus, the binary compound these two elements form must be NF_3:

$$\cdot\ddot{N}\cdot \ + \ 3\cdot\ddot{\underset{\cdot\cdot}{F}}: \ \longrightarrow \ :\!\ddot{F}\!:\!\ddot{\underset{:\ddot{F}:}{N}}\!:\!\ddot{F}: \ \longrightarrow \ :\!\ddot{F}\!-\!\overset{\cdot\cdot}{\underset{|}{N}}\!-\!\ddot{F}:$$
$$\qquad\qquad\qquad\qquad\qquad\qquad\qquad\qquad\qquad\qquad :\!\ddot{F}\!:$$

Check The Lewis structure in the center shows that each atom is surrounded by an octet of electrons. Once you are accustomed to thinking of each line in a Lewis structure as representing *two* electrons, you can just as easily use the structure on the right to check for octets.

PRACTICE EXERCISE

Compare the Lewis symbol for neon with the Lewis structure for methane, CH_4. In what important way are the electron arrangements about neon and carbon alike? In what important way are they different?

Answer: Both atoms have an octet of electrons. However, the electrons about neon are unshared electron pairs, whereas those about carbon are shared with four hydrogen atoms.

Multiple Bonds

A shared electron pair constitutes a single covalent bond, generally referred to simply as a **single bond**. In many molecules, atoms attain complete octets by sharing more than one pair of electrons. When two electron pairs are shared, two lines are drawn in the Lewis structure, representing a **double bond**. In carbon dioxide, for example, bonding occurs between carbon, with four valence electrons, and oxygen, with six:

$$:\ddot{O}: + \cdot\dot{C}\cdot + :\ddot{O}: \longrightarrow \ddot{O}::C::\ddot{O} \quad (\text{or } \ddot{O}=C=\ddot{O})$$

As the diagram shows, each oxygen atom acquires an octet by sharing two electron pairs with carbon. Carbon acquires an octet by sharing two electron pairs with each of the two oxygen atoms; each double bond involves four electrons.

A **triple bond** corresponds to the sharing of three pairs of electrons, such as in the N_2 molecule:

$$:\dot{N}\cdot + \cdot\dot{N}: \longrightarrow :N:::N: \quad (\text{or } :N\equiv N:)$$

Because each nitrogen atom has five valence electrons, three electron pairs must be shared to achieve the octet configuration.

The properties of N_2 are in complete accord with its Lewis structure. Nitrogen is a diatomic gas with exceptionally low reactivity that results from the very stable nitrogen–nitrogen bond. The nitrogen atoms are separated by only 1.10 Å. The short separation distance between the two N atoms is a result of the triple bond between the atoms. From studies of the structures of many different substances in which nitrogen atoms share one or two electron pairs, we have learned that the average distance between bonded nitrogen atoms varies with the number of shared electron pairs:

N—N	N=N	N≡N
1.47 Å	1.24 Å	1.10 Å

As a general rule, the length of the bond between two atoms decreases as the number of shared electron pairs increases.

⚓ GIVE IT SOME THOUGHT

The C—O bond length in carbon monoxide, CO, is 1.13 Å, whereas the C—O bond length in CO_2 is 1.24 Å. Without drawing a Lewis structure, do you think that CO contains a single, double, or triple bond?

3.4 | BOND POLARITY AND ELECTRONEGATIVITY

When two identical atoms bond, as in Cl_2 or H_2, the electron pairs must be shared equally. When two atoms from opposites sides of the periodic table bond, such as NaCl, there is relatively little sharing of electrons, which means that NaCl is best described as composed of Na^+ and Cl^- ions. The 3s electron of the Na atom is, in effect, transferred completely to chlorine. The bonds that are found in most substances fall somewhere between these extremes.

Bond polarity is a measure of how equally or unequally the electrons in any covalent bond are shared. A **nonpolar covalent bond** is one in which the electrons are shared equally, as in Cl_2 and N_2. In a **polar covalent bond**, one of the atoms exerts a greater attraction for the bonding electrons than the other. If the difference in relative ability to attract electrons is large enough, an ionic bond is formed.

Electronegativity

We use a quantity called electronegativity to estimate whether a given bond is nonpolar covalent, polar covalent, or ionic. **Electronegativity** is defined as the ability of an atom *in a molecule* to attract electrons to itself. The greater an atom's electronegativity, the greater its ability to attract electrons to itself. The electronegativity of an atom in a molecule is related to the atom's ionization energy and electron affinity, which are properties of isolated atoms. An atom with a very negative electron affinity and a high ionization energy both attracts electrons from other atoms and resists having its electrons attracted away; it is highly electronegative.

Electronegativity values can be based on a variety of properties, not just ionization energy and electron affinity. The American chemist Linus Pauling (1901–1994) developed the first and most widely used electronegativity scale, which is based on thermochemical data. As ▼ FIGURE 3.7 shows, there is generally an increase in electronegativity from left to right across a period—that is, from the most metallic to the most nonmetallic elements. With some exceptions (especially in the transition metals), electronegativity decreases with increasing atomic number in a group. This is what we expect because we know that ionization energies decrease with increasing atomic number in a group and electron affinities do not change very much.

You do not need to memorize electronegativity values. Instead, you should know the periodic trends so that you can predict which of two elements is more electronegative.

◢ GIVE IT SOME THOUGHT

How does the *electronegativity* of an element differ from its *electron affinity*?

◢ GO FIGURE

For the group 6A elements, what is the trend in electronegativity with increasing atomic number?

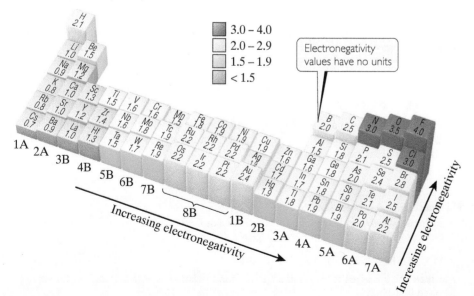

◀ **FIGURE 3.7 Electronegativity values based on Pauling's thermochemical data.**

Electronegativity and Bond Polarity

We can use the difference in electronegativity between two atoms to gauge the polarity of the bond the atoms form. Consider these three fluorine-containing compounds:

	F_2	HF	LiF
Electronegativity difference	$4.0 - 4.0 = 0$	$4.0 - 2.1 = 1.9$	$4.0 - 1.0 = 3.0$
Type of bond	Nonpolar covalent	Polar covalent	Ionic

In F_2 the electrons are shared equally between the fluorine atoms and, thus, the covalent bond is *nonpolar*. A nonpolar covalent bond results when the electronegativities of the bonded atoms are equal.

In HF the fluorine atom has a greater electronegativity than the hydrogen atom, with the result that the electrons are shared unequally—the bond is *polar*. In general, a polar covalent bond results when the atoms differ in electronegativity. In HF the more electronegative fluorine atom attracts electron density away from the less electronegative hydrogen atom, leaving a partial positive charge on the hydrogen atom and a partial negative charge on the fluorine atom. We can represent this charge distribution as

$$\overset{\delta+}{H} - \overset{\delta-}{F}$$

The $\delta+$ and $\delta-$ (read "delta plus" and "delta minus") symbolize the partial positive and negative charges, respectively.

In LiF the electronegativity difference is very large, meaning that the electron density is shifted far toward F. The resultant bond is therefore most accurately described as *ionic*.

The shift of electron density toward the more electronegative atom in a bond can be seen in the results of calculations of electron density distributions. For the three species in our example, the calculated electron density distributions are shown in ▼ FIGURE 3.8. You can see that in F_2 the distribution is symmetrical, in HF the electron density is clearly shifted toward fluorine, and in LiF the shift is even greater. These examples illustrate, therefore, that *the greater the difference in electronegativity between two atoms, the more polar their bond.*

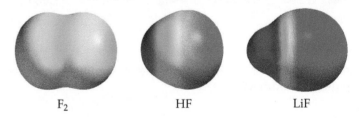

F_2 HF   LiF

▲ **FIGURE 3.8 Electron density distribution.** This computer-generated rendering shows the calculated electron-density distribution on the surface of the F_2, HF, and LiF molecules.

GIVE IT SOME THOUGHT

Based on differences in electronegativity, how would you characterize the bonding in sulfur dioxide, SO_2? Do you expect the bonds between S and O to be nonpolar, polar covalent, or ionic?

SAMPLE EXERCISE 3.4 **Bond Polarity**

In each case, which bond is more polar: **(a)** B—Cl or C—Cl, **(b)** P—F or P—Cl? Indicate in each case which atom has the partial negative charge.

SOLUTION

Analyze We are asked to determine relative bond polarities, given nothing but the atoms involved in the bonds.

Plan Because we are not asked for quantitative answers, we can use the periodic table and our knowledge of electronegativity trends to answer the question.

Solve
(a) The chlorine atom is common to both bonds. Therefore, the analysis reduces to a comparison of the electronegativities of B and C. Because boron is to the left of carbon in the periodic table, we predict that boron has the lower electronegativity. Chlorine, being on the right side of the table, has a higher electronegativity. The more polar bond will be the one between the atoms having the lowest electronegativity (boron) and the highest electronegativity (chlorine). Consequently, the B—Cl bond is more polar; the chlorine atom carries the partial negative charge because it has a higher electronegativity.

(b) In this example phosphorus is common to both bonds, and the analysis reduces to a comparison of the electronegativities of F and Cl. Because fluorine is above chlorine in the periodic table, it should be more electronegative and will form the more polar bond with P. The higher electronegativity of fluorine means that it will carry the partial negative charge.

Check
(a) Using Figure 3.7: The difference in the electronegativities of chlorine and boron is $3.0 - 2.0 = 1.0$; the difference between chlorine and carbon is $3.0 - 2.5 = 0.5$. Hence, the B—Cl bond is more polar, as we had predicted.

(b) Using Figure 3.7: The difference in the electronegativities of chlorine and phosphorus is $3.0 - 2.1 = 0.9$; the difference between fluorine and phosphorus is $4.0 - 2.1 = 1.9$. Hence, the P—F bond is more polar, as we had predicted.

PRACTICE EXERCISE
Which of the following bonds is most polar: S—Cl, S—Br, Se—Cl, or Se—Br ?
Answer: Se—Cl

Dipole Moments

The difference in electronegativity between H and F leads to a polar covalent bond in the HF molecule. As a consequence, there is a concentration of negative charge on the more electronegative F atom, leaving the less electronegative H atom at the positive end of the molecule. A molecule such as HF, in which the centers of positive and negative charge do not coincide, is a **polar molecule**. Thus, we describe both bonds and entire molecules as being polar and nonpolar.

We can indicate the polarity of the HF molecule in two ways:

$$\overset{\delta+}{\text{H}} - \overset{\delta-}{\text{F}} \quad or \quad \text{H} \overset{?:}{—} \text{F}$$

In the notation on the right, the arrow denotes the shift in electron density toward the fluorine atom. The crossed end of the arrow can be thought of as a plus sign designating the positive end of the molecule.

Polarity helps determine many properties we observe at the macroscopic level in the laboratory and in everyday life. Polar molecules align themselves with respect to one another, with the negative end of one molecule and the positive end of another attracting each other. Polar molecules are likewise attracted to ions. The negative end of a polar molecule is attracted to a positive ion, and the positive end is attracted to a negative ion. These interactions account for many properties of liquids, solids, and solutions.

How can we quantify the polarity of a molecule? Whenever two electrical charges of equal magnitude but opposite sign are separated by a distance, a **dipole** is established. The quantitative measure of the magnitude of a dipole is called its **dipole moment**, denoted μ. If two equal and opposite charges $Q+$ and $Q-$ are separated by a distance r, as in ▶ FIGURE 3.9, the magnitude of the dipole moment is the product of Q and r:

$$\mu = Qr \qquad [3.11]$$

GO FIGURE

If the charged particles are moved closer together, does μ increase, decrease, or stay the same?

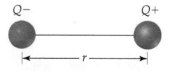

Dipole moment $\mu = Qr$

▲ **FIGURE 3.9 Dipole and dipole moment.** When charges of equal magnitude and opposite sign $Q+$ and $Q-$ are separated by a distance r, a dipole is produced.

This expression tells us that dipole moment increases as the magnitude of Q increases and as r increases. For a nonpolar molecule, such as F_2, the dipole moment is zero because there is no charge separation.

⚠️ **GIVE IT SOME THOUGHT**

Chlorine monofluoride, ClF, and iodine monofluoride, IF, are *interhalogen* compounds—compounds that contain bonds between different halogen elements. Which of these molecules has the larger dipole moment?

Dipole moments are usually reported in *debyes* (D), a unit that equals 3.34×10^{-30} coulomb-meters (C-m). For molecules, we usually measure charge in units of the electronic charge e, 1.60×10^{-19} C, and distance in angstroms. This means we need to convert units whenever we want to report a dipole moment in debyes. Suppose that two charges $1+$ and $1-$ (in units of e) are separated by 1.00 Å. The dipole moment produced is

$$\mu = Qr = (1.60 \times 10^{-19}\text{C})(1.00\ \text{Å})\left(\frac{10^{-10}\,\text{m}}{1\ \text{Å}}\right)\left(\frac{1\ \text{D}}{3.34 \times 10^{-30}\text{C-m}}\right) = 4.79\ \text{D}$$

Measurement of the dipole moments can provide us with valuable information about the charge distributions in molecules, as illustrated in Sample Exercise 3.5.

SAMPLE EXERCISE 3.5 | **Dipole Moments of Diatomic Molecules**

The bond length in the HCl molecule is 1.27 Å. **(a)** Calculate the dipole moment, in debyes, that results if the charges on the H and Cl atoms were $1+$ and $1-$, respectively. **(b)** The experimentally measured dipole moment of $HCl(g)$ is 1.08 D. What magnitude of charge, in units of e, on the H and Cl atoms leads to this dipole moment?

SOLUTION

Analyze and Plan We are asked in (a) to calculate the dipole moment of HCl that would result if there were a full charge transferred from H to Cl. We can use Equation 3.11 to obtain this result. In (b), we are given the actual dipole moment for the molecule and will use that value to calculate the actual partial charges on the H and Cl atoms.

Solve:

(a) The charge on each atom is the electronic charge, $e = 1.60 \times 10^{-19}$ C. The separation is 1.27 Å. The dipole moment is therefore

$$\mu = Qr = (1.60 \times 10^{-19}\text{C})(1.27\ \text{Å})\left(\frac{10^{-10}\,\text{m}}{1\ \text{Å}}\right)\left(\frac{1\ \text{D}}{3.34 \times 10^{-30}\text{C-m}}\right) = 6.08\ \text{D}$$

(b) We know the value of μ, 1.08 D, and the value of r, 1.27 Å. We want to calculate the value of Q:

$$Q = \frac{\mu}{r} = \frac{(1.08\ \text{D})\left(\dfrac{3.34 \times 10^{-30}\text{C-m}}{1\ \text{D}}\right)}{(1.27\ \text{Å})\left(\dfrac{10^{-10}\,\text{m}}{1\ \text{Å}}\right)} = 2.84 \times 10^{-20}\text{C}$$

We can readily convert this charge to units of e:

$$\text{Charge in } e = (2.84 \times 10^{-20}\ \text{C})\left(\frac{1\ e}{1.60 \times 10^{-19}\text{C}}\right) = 0.178e$$

Thus, the experimental dipole moment indicates that the charge separation in the HCl molecule is

$$\overset{0.178+}{\text{H}} - \overset{0.178-}{\text{Cl}}$$

Because the experimental dipole moment is less than that calculated in part (a), the charges on the atoms are much less than a full electronic charge. We could have anticipated this because the H—Cl bond is polar covalent rather than ionic.

PRACTICE EXERCISE

The dipole moment of chlorine monofluoride, $ClF(g)$, is 0.88 D. The bond length of the molecule is 1.63 Å.
(a) Which atom is expected to have the partial negative charge? **(b)** What is the charge on that atom in units of e?
Answers: **(a)** F, **(b)** 0.11−

TABLE 3.3 • Bond Lengths, Electronegativity Differences, and Dipole Moments of the Hydrogen Halides			
Compound	Bond Length (Å)	Electronegativity Difference	Dipole Moment (D)
HF	0.92	1.9	1.82
HCl	1.27	0.9	1.08
HBr	1.41	0.7	0.82
HI	1.61	0.4	0.44

▲ TABLE 3.3 presents the bond lengths and dipole moments of the hydrogen halides. Notice that as we proceed from HF to HI, the electronegativity difference decreases and the bond length increases. The first effect decreases the amount of charge separated and causes the dipole moment to decrease from HF to HI, even though the bond length is increasing. Calculations identical to those used in Sample Exercise 3.5 show that the charges on the atoms decrease from 0.41+ and 0.41− in HF to 0.057+ and 0.057− in HI. We can visualize the varying degree of electronic charge shift in these substances from computer-generated renderings based on calculations of electron distribution, as shown in ▼ FIGURE 3.10. For these molecules, the change in the electronegativity difference has a greater effect on the dipole moment than does the change in bond length.

GIVE IT SOME THOUGHT

The bond between carbon and hydrogen is one of the most important types of bonds in chemistry. The length of a H—C bond is approximately 1.1 Å. Based on this distance and differences in electronegativity, do you expect the dipole moment of an individual H—C bond to be larger or smaller than that of the H—I bond?

Before leaving this section, let's return to the LiF molecule in Figure 3.8. Under standard conditions, LiF exists as an ionic solid with an arrangement of atoms analogous to the sodium chloride structure shown in Figure 3.3. However, it is possible to generate LiF *molecules* by vaporizing the ionic solid at high temperature. The molecules have a dipole moment of 6.28 D and a bond distance of 1.53 Å. From these values we can calculate the charge on lithium and fluorine to be 0.857+ and 0.857−, respectively. This bond is extremely polar, and the presence of such large charges strongly favors the formation of an extended ionic lattice in which each lithium ion is surrounded by fluoride ions and vice versa.

GO FIGURE

How do you interpret the fact that there is no red in the HBr and HI representations?

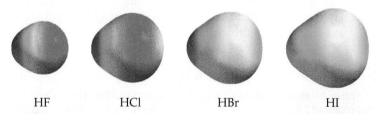

HF   HCl   HBr   HI

▲ FIGURE 3.10 **Charge separation in the hydrogen halides.** In HF, the strongly electronegative F pulls much of the electron density away from H. In HI, the I, being much less electronegative than F, does not attract the shared electrons as strongly and, consequently, there is far less polarization of the bond.

Differentiating Ionic and Covalent Bonding

To understand the interactions responsible for chemical bonding, it is advantageous to treat ionic and covalent bonding separately. That is the approach taken in this chapter, as well as in most other undergraduate-level chemistry texts. In reality, however, there is a continuum between the extremes of ionic and covalent bonding. This lack of a well-defined separation between the two types of bonding may seem unsettling or confusing at first.

The simple models of ionic and covalent bonding presented in this chapter go a long way toward understanding and predicting the structures and properties of chemical compounds. When covalent bonding is dominant, more often than not we expect compounds to exist as molecules,* having all the properties we associate with molecular substances, such as relatively low melting and boiling points and nonelectrolyte behavior when dissolved in water. When ionic bonding is dominant, we expect the compounds to be brittle, high-melting solids with extended lattice structures and exhibiting strong electrolyte behavior when dissolved in water.

There are, of course, exceptions to these general characterizations, some of which we examine later in the book. Nonetheless, the ability to quickly categorize the predominant bonding interactions in a substance as covalent or ionic imparts considerable insight into the properties of that substance. The question then becomes the best way to recognize which type of bonding dominates.

The simplest approach is to assume that the interaction between a metal and a nonmetal is ionic and that between two nonmetals is covalent. While this classification scheme is reasonably predictive, there are far too many exceptions to use it blindly. For example, tin is a metal and chlorine is a nonmetal, but $SnCl_4$ is a molecular substance that exists as a colorless liquid at room temperature. It freezes at $-33\ ^\circ C$ and boils at $114\ ^\circ C$. Clearly this substance does not have the characteristics of an ionic substance. A more sophisticated approach is to use the difference in electronegativity as the main criterion for determining whether ionic or covalent bonding will be dominant. This approach correctly predicts the bonding in $SnCl_4$ to be polar covalent based on an electronegativity difference of 1.2 and at the same time correctly predicts the bonding in NaCl to be predominantly ionic based on an electronegativity difference of 2.1.

Evaluating bonding based on electronegativity difference is a useful system, but it has one shortcoming. The electronegativity values given in Figure 3.7 do not take into account changes in bonding that accompany changes in the oxidation state of the metal. For example, Figure 3.7 gives the electronegativity difference between manganese and oxygen as $3.5 - 1.5 = 2.0$, which falls in the range where the bonding is normally considered ionic (the electronegativity difference for NaCl is $3.0 - 0.9 = 2.1$). Therefore, it is not surprising to learn that manganese(II) oxide, MnO, is a green solid that melts at $1842\ ^\circ C$ and has the same crystal structure as NaCl.

However, the bonding between manganese and oxygen is not always ionic. Manganese(VII) oxide, Mn_2O_7, is a green liquid that freezes at $5.9\ ^\circ C$, which indicates that covalent rather than ionic bonding dominates. The change in the oxidation state of manganese is responsible for the change in bonding. In general, as the oxidation state of a metal increases, so does the degree of covalent bonding. When the oxidation state of the metal is highly positive (roughly speaking, $+4$ or larger), we should expect significant covalency in the bonds it forms with nonmetals. Thus, with metals in high oxidation states we find molecular substances, such as Mn_2O_7, or polyatomic ions, such as MnO_4^- and CrO_4^{2-}, rather than ionic compounds.

GIVE IT SOME THOUGHT

You have a yellow solid that melts at 41 °C and boils at 131 °C and a green solid that melts at 2320 °C. If you are told that one of them is Cr_2O_3 and the other is OsO_4, which one do you expect to be the yellow solid?

---

*There are some exceptions to this statement, such as network solids, including diamond, silicon, and germanium, where an extended structure is formed even though the bonding is clearly covalent. These examples are discussed in Section 7.7.

3.5 | DRAWING LEWIS STRUCTURES

Lewis structures can help us understand the bonding in many compounds and are frequently used when discussing the properties of molecules. For this reason, drawing Lewis structures is an important skill that you should practice. To do so, you should use the following procedure.

1. **Sum the valence electrons from all atoms.** (Use the periodic table to help you determine the number of valence electrons in each atom.) For an anion, add one electron to the total for each negative charge. For a cation, subtract one electron from the total for each positive charge. Do not worry about keeping track of which electrons come from which atoms. Only the total number is important.

2. **Write the symbols for the atoms, show which atoms are attached to which, and connect them with a single bond (*a dash, representing* two *electrons*).** Chemical formulas are often written in the order in which the atoms are connected in the molecule or ion. The formula HCN, for example, tells you that the carbon atom is bonded to the H and to the N. In many polyatomic molecules and ions, the central atom is usually written first, as in CO_3^{2-} and SF_4. Remember that the central atom is generally less electronegative than the atoms surrounding it. In other cases, you may need more information before you can draw the Lewis structure.

3. **Complete the octets around all the atoms bonded to the central atom.** Remember, however, that a hydrogen atom has only a single pair of electrons around it.

4. **Place any leftover electrons on the central atom,** even if doing so results in more than an octet of electrons around the atom.

5. **If there are not enough electrons to give the central atom an octet, try multiple bonds.** Use one or more of the unshared pairs of electrons on the atoms bonded to the central atom to form double or triple bonds.

SAMPLE EXERCISE 3.6   **Drawing a Lewis Structure**

Draw the Lewis structure for phosphorus trichloride, PCl_3.

SOLUTION

Analyze and Plan We are asked to draw a Lewis structure from a molecular formula. Our plan is to follow the five-step procedure just described.

Solve

First, we sum the valence electrons. Phosphorus (group 5A) has five valence electrons, and each chlorine (group 7A) has seven. The total number of valence electrons is therefore

$$5 + (3 \times 7) = 26$$

Second, we arrange the atoms to show which atom is connected to which, and we draw a single bond between them. There are various ways the atoms might be arranged. In binary compounds, however, the first element in the chemical formula is generally surrounded by the remaining atoms. Thus, we begin with a skeleton structure that shows a single bond between the P atom and each Cl atom:

Cl—P—Cl
    |
    Cl

(It is not crucial that the Cl atoms be left of, right of, and below the P atom—any structure that shows each of the three Cl atoms bonded to P will work.)

Third, we complete the octets on the atoms bonded to the central atom. Placing octets around each Cl atom accounts for 24 electrons (remember, each line in our structure represents *two* electrons):

:C̈l—P—C̈l:
    |
   :C̈l:

Fourth, recalling that our total number of electrons is 26, we place the remaining two electrons on the central atom, completing the octet around it:

:C̈l—P̈—C̈l:
    |
   :C̈l:

This structure gives each atom an octet, so we stop at this point. (In checking for octets, remember to count both electrons in a single bond twice, once for each atom in the bond.)

PRACTICE EXERCISE

(a) How many valence electrons should appear in the Lewis structure for CH_2Cl_2?

(b) Draw the Lewis structure.

Answers: (a) 20, (b)

$$:\ddot{C}l—\underset{\underset{H}{|}}{\overset{\overset{H}{|}}{C}}—\ddot{C}l:$$

SAMPLE EXERCISE 3.7 Lewis Structure with a Multiple Bond

Draw the Lewis structure for HCN.

SOLUTION

Hydrogen has one valence electron, carbon (group 4A) has four, and nitrogen (group 5A) has five. The total number of valence electrons is, therefore, $1 + 4 + 5 = 10$. In principle, there are different ways in which we might choose to arrange the atoms. Because hydrogen can accommodate only one electron pair, it always has only one single bond associated with it. Therefore, C—H—N is an impossible arrangement. The remaining two possibilities are H—C—N and H—N—C. The first is the arrangement found experimentally. You might have guessed this because (a) the formula is written with the atoms in this order and (b) carbon is less electronegative than nitrogen. Thus, we begin with the skeleton structure

$$H—C—N$$

The two bonds account for four electrons. The H atom can have only two electrons associated with it, and so we will not add any more electrons to it. If we place the remaining six electrons around N to give it an octet, we do not achieve an octet on C:

$$H—C—\ddot{\ddot{N}}:$$

We therefore try a double bond between C and N, using one of the unshared pairs we placed on N. Again we end up with fewer than eight electrons on C, and so we next try a triple bond. This structure gives an octet around both C and N:

$$H—C\overset{\curvearrowleft}{\ddot{N}}: \longrightarrow H—C≡N:$$

The octet rule is satisfied for the C and N atoms, and the H atom has two electrons around it. This is a correct Lewis structure.

PRACTICE EXERCISE

Draw the Lewis structure for (a) NO^+ ion, (b) C_2H_4.

Answers: (a) $[:N≡O:]^+$, (b)

$$\underset{H}{\overset{H}{>}}C=C\underset{H}{\overset{H}{<}}$$

SAMPLE EXERCISE 3.8 Lewis Structure for a Polyatomic Ion

Draw the Lewis structure for the BrO_3^- ion.

SOLUTION

Bromine (group 7A) has seven valence electrons, and oxygen (group 6A) has six. We must add one more electron to our sum to account for the 1− charge of the ion. The total number of valence electrons is, therefore, $7 + (3 \times 6) + 1 = 26$. For oxyanions—$BrO_3^-$, SO_4^{2-}, NO_3^-, CO_3^{2-}, and so forth—the oxygen atoms surround the central nonmetal atom. After following this format and then putting in the single bonds and distributing the unshared electron pairs, we have

$$\left[:\ddot{O}—\underset{\underset{:\ddot{O}:}{|}}{Br}—\ddot{O}: \right]^-$$

Notice that the Lewis structure for an ion is written in brackets and the charge is shown outside the brackets at the upper right.

PRACTICE EXERCISE

Draw the Lewis structure for (a) ClO_2^-, (b) PO_4^{3-}.

Answers: (a) $\left[\ddot{\underset{..}{O}}-\ddot{\underset{..}{Cl}}-\ddot{\underset{..}{O}}\colon\right]^-$ (b) $\left[\begin{array}{c}\colon\ddot{O}\colon\\|\\\colon\ddot{\underset{..}{O}}-P-\ddot{\underset{..}{O}}\colon\\|\\\colon\ddot{\underset{..}{O}}\colon\end{array}\right]^{3-}$

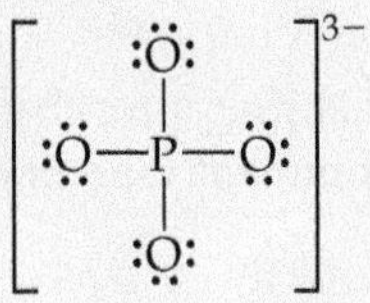

Formal Charge and Alternative Lewis Structures

When we draw a Lewis structure, we are describing how the electrons are distributed in a molecule or polyatomic ion. In some instances we can draw more than one Lewis structure and have all of them obey the octet rule. All these structures can be thought of as contributing to the *actual* arrangement of the electrons in the molecule, but not all of them will contribute to the same extent. How do we decide which of several Lewis structures is the most important? One approach is to do some "bookkeeping" of the valence electrons to determine the *formal charge* of each atom in each Lewis structure. The **formal charge** of any atom in a molecule is the charge the atom would have if all the atoms in the molecule had the same electronegativity (that is, if each bonding electron pair in the molecule were shared equally between its two atoms).

To calculate the formal charge on any atom in a Lewis structure, we assign electrons to the atom as follows:

1. *All* unshared (nonbonding) electrons are assigned to the atom on which they are found.

2. For any bond—single, double, or triple—*half* of the bonding electrons are assigned to each atom in the bond.

The formal charge of each atom is calculated *by subtracting the number of electrons assigned to the atom from the number of valence electrons in the neutral atom.*

Let's practice by calculating the formal charges in the cyanide ion, CN^-, which has the Lewis structure

$$[\colon C\equiv N\colon]^-$$

For the C atom, there are two nonbonding electrons and three electrons from the six in the triple bond ($\frac{1}{2} \times 6 = 3$) for a total of five. The number of valence electrons on a neutral C atom is four. Thus, the formal charge on C is $4 - 5 = -1$. For N, there are two nonbonding electrons and three electrons from the triple bond. Because the number of valence electrons on a neutral N atom is five, its formal charge is $5 - 5 = 0$:

$$[\overset{-1}{\colon C}\equiv \overset{0}{N}\colon]^-$$

Notice that the sum of the formal charges equals the overall charge on the ion, $1-$. The formal charges on a neutral molecule must add to zero, whereas those on an ion add to give the charge on the ion.

If we can draw several Lewis structures for a molecule, the concept of formal charge can help us decide which is the most important, which we shall call the *dominant* Lewis structure. One Lewis structure for CO_2, for instance, has two double bonds, as we saw in Section 3.2. However, we can also satisfy the octet rule by drawing a Lewis structure having one single bond and one triple bond. Calculating formal charges in these structures, we have

		$\ddot{\underset{..}{O}}=C=\ddot{\underset{..}{O}}$			$\colon\ddot{\underset{..}{O}}-C\equiv O\colon$	
Valence electrons:	6	4	6	6	4	6
−(Electrons assigned to atom):	6	4	6	7	4	5
Formal charge:	0	0	0	−1	0	+1

Note that in both cases the formal charges add up to zero, as they must because CO_2 is a neutral molecule. So, which is the more correct structure? As a general rule, when more than one Lewis structure is possible, we will use the following guidelines to choose the dominant one:

1. The dominant Lewis structure is generally the one in which the atoms bear formal charges closest to zero.
2. A Lewis structure in which any negative charges reside on the more electronegative atoms is generally more dominant than one that has negative charges on the less electronegative atoms.

Thus, the first Lewis structure of CO_2 is the dominant one because the atoms carry no formal charges and so satisfy the first guideline. The other Lewis structure shown (and the similar one that has a triple bond to the left O and a single bond to the right O) do contribute to the actual structure but to a much smaller extent.

Although the concept of formal charge helps us to arrange alternative Lewis structures in order of importance, it is important that you remember that *formal charges do not represent real charges on atoms*. These charges are just a bookkeeping convention. The actual charge distributions in molecules and ions are determined not by formal charges but by a number of other factors, including electronegativity differences between atoms.

 GIVE IT SOME THOUGHT

Suppose a Lewis structure for a neutral fluorine-containing molecule results in a formal charge on the fluorine atom of +1. What conclusion would you draw?

SAMPLE EXERCISE 3.9   **Lewis Structures and Formal Charges**

Three possible Lewis structures for the thiocyanate ion, NCS^-, are

$$[:\ddot{N}-C\equiv S:]^- \qquad [\ddot{N}=C=\ddot{S}]^- \qquad [:N\equiv C-\ddot{\ddot{S}}:]^-$$

(a) Determine the formal charges in each structure. **(b)** Based on the formal charges, which Lewis structure is the dominant one?

SOLUTION

(a) Neutral N, C, and S atoms have five, four, and six valence electrons, respectively. We can determine the formal charges in the three structures by using the rules we just discussed:

$$\underset{[:\ddot{N}-C\equiv S:]^-}{-2 \quad 0 \quad +1} \qquad \underset{[\ddot{N}=C=\ddot{S}]^-}{-1 \quad 0 \quad 0} \qquad \underset{[:N\equiv C-\ddot{\ddot{S}}:]^-}{0 \quad 0 \quad -1}$$

As they must, the formal charges in all three structures sum to 1−, the overall charge of the ion. **(b)** The dominant Lewis structure generally produces formal charges of the smallest magnitude (guideline 1). That rules out the left structure as the dominant one. Further, as discussed in Section 3.4, N is more electronegative than C or S. Therefore, we expect any negative formal charge to reside on the N atom (guideline 2). For these two reasons, the middle Lewis structure is the dominant one for NCS^-.

PRACTICE EXERCISE

The cyanate ion, NCO^-, has three possible Lewis structures. **(a)** Draw these three structures and assign formal charges in each. **(b)** Which Lewis structure is dominant?

$$\underset{\underset{(i)}{[:\ddot{N}-C\equiv O:]^-}}{-2 \quad 0 \quad +1} \qquad \underset{\underset{(ii)}{[\ddot{N}=C=\ddot{O}]^-}}{-1 \quad 0 \quad 0} \qquad \underset{\underset{(iii)}{[:N\equiv C-\ddot{\ddot{O}}:]^-}}{0 \quad 0 \quad -1}$$

Answers: **(a)**

(b) Structure (iii), which places a negative charge on oxygen, the most electronegative element in the ion, is the dominant Lewis structure.

A CLOSER LOOK

OXIDATION NUMBERS, FORMAL CHARGES, AND ACTUAL PARTIAL CHARGES

There are rules for assigning *oxidation numbers* to atoms. The concept of electronegativity is the basis of these numbers. An atom's oxidation number is the charge the atom would have if its bonds were completely ionic. That is, in determining oxidation number, all shared electrons are counted with the more electronegative atom. For example, consider the Lewis structure of HCl in ▼ FIGURE 3.11(a). To assign oxidation numbers, both electrons in the covalent bond between the atoms are assigned to the more electronegative Cl atom. This procedure gives Cl eight valence electrons, one more than in the neutral atom. Thus, its oxidation number is −1. Hydrogen has no valence electrons when they are counted this way, giving it an oxidation number of +1.

To assign formal charges in this molecule, we ignore electronegativity and assign the electrons in bonds equally to the two bonded atoms. In the case of HCl, we divide the bonding pair of electrons equally between H and Cl, as in Figure 3.11(b). In this case Cl has seven assigned electrons, the same as that of the neutral Cl atom, and H has one assigned electron. Thus, the formal charges of both Cl and H in this compound are 0.

Neither oxidation number nor formal charge gives an accurate depiction of the actual charges on atoms because oxidation numbers overstate the role of electronegativity and formal charges ignore it.

It seems reasonable that electrons in covalent bonds should be apportioned according to the relative electronegativities of the bonded atoms. From Figure 3.7 we see that Cl has an electronegativity of 3.0, while that of H is 2.1. The more electronegative Cl atom might therefore be expected to have roughly $3.0/(3.0 + 2.1) = 0.59$ of the electrical charge in the bonding pair, whereas the H atom has $2.1/(3.0 + 2.1) = 0.41$ of the charge. Because the bond consists of two electrons, the Cl atom's share is $0.59 \times 2e = 1.18e$, or $0.18e$ more than the neutral Cl atom. This gives rise to a partial negative charge of 0.18− on Cl and a partial positive charge of 0.18+ on H. (Notice again that we place the plus and minus signs *before* the magnitude in writing oxidation numbers and formal charges but *after* the magnitude in writing actual charges.)

The dipole moment of HCl gives an experimental measure of the partial charge on each atom. In Sample Exercise 3.5 we saw that the dipole moment of HCl indicates a partial charge of 0.178+ on H and 0.178− on Cl, in remarkably good agreement with our simple approximation based on electronegativities. Although our approximation method provides "ballpark" numbers for the magnitude of charge on atoms, the relationship between electronegativities and charge separation is generally more complicated. As we have already seen, computer programs employing quantum mechanical principles have been developed to obtain more accurate estimates of the partial charges on atoms, even in complex molecules. A computer-graphical representation of the charge distribution in HCl is shown in Figure 3.11(c).

RELATED EXERCISES 3.8, 3.49, 3.50, 3.51, 3.52, 3.86, 3.87, 3.90, and 3.91

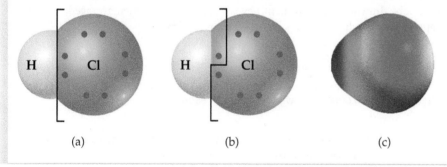

(a)   (b)   (c)

◀ FIGURE 3.11 **Oxidation number, formal charge, and electron density distribution for the HCl molecule.**

3.6 | RESONANCE STRUCTURES

We sometimes encounter molecules and ions in which the experimentally determined arrangement of atoms is not adequately described by a single dominant Lewis structure. Consider ozone, O_3, which is a bent molecule with two equal O—O bond lengths (▶ FIGURE 3.12). Because each oxygen atom contributes 6 valence electrons, the ozone molecule has 18 valence electrons. This means the Lewis structure must have one O—O single bond and one O=O double bond to attain an octet about each atom:

However, this single structure cannot by itself be dominant because it requires that one O—O bond be different from the other, contrary to the observed structure—we would expect the O=O double bond to be shorter than the O—O single bond. ∞ (Section 3.3) In drawing the Lewis structure, however, we could just as easily have put the O=O bond on the left:

▲ GO FIGURE

What feature of this structure suggests that the two outer O atoms are in some way equivalent to each other?

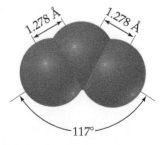

▲ FIGURE 3.12 **Molecular structure of ozone.**

GO FIGURE

Is the electron density consistent with equal weights for the two resonance structures for O_3? Explain.

Primary color   Primary color

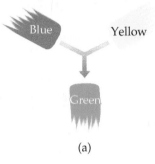

(a)

Resonance   Resonance
structure   structure

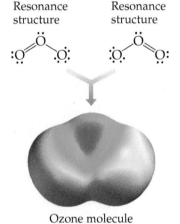

Ozone molecule

(b)

▲ FIGURE 3.13 **Resonance.** Describing a molecule as a blend of different resonance structures is similar to describing a paint color as a blend of primary colors. (a) Green paint is a blend of blue and yellow. We cannot describe green as a single primary color. (b) The ozone molecule is a blend of two resonance structures. We cannot describe the ozone molecule in terms of a single Lewis structure.

There is no reason for one of these Lewis structures to be dominant because they are equally valid representations of the molecule. The placement of the atoms in these two alternative but completely equivalent Lewis structures is the same, but the placement of the electrons is different. Lewis structures of this sort are called **resonance structures.** To describe the structure of ozone properly, we write both resonance structures and use a double-headed arrow to indicate that the real molecule is described by an average of the two:

To understand why certain molecules require more than one resonance structure, we can draw an analogy to mixing paint (◄ **FIGURE 3.13**). Blue and yellow are both primary colors of paint pigment. An equal blend of blue and yellow pigments produces green pigment. We cannot describe green paint in terms of a single primary color, yet it still has its own identity. Green paint does not oscillate between its two primary colors: It is not blue part of the time and yellow the rest of the time. Similarly, molecules such as ozone cannot be described as oscillating between the two individual Lewis structures shown previously—there are two equivalent dominant Lewis structures that contribute equally to the actual structure of the molecule.

The actual arrangement of the electrons in molecules such as O_3 must be considered as a blend of two (or more) Lewis structures. By analogy to the green paint, the molecule has its own identity separate from the individual resonance structures. For example, the ozone molecule always has two equivalent O—O bonds whose lengths are intermediate between the lengths of an oxygen–oxygen single bond and an oxygen–oxygen double bond. Another way of looking at it is to say that the rules for drawing Lewis structures do not allow us to have a single dominant structure for the ozone molecule. For example, there are no rules for drawing half-bonds. We can get around this limitation by drawing two equivalent Lewis structures that, when averaged, amount to something very much like what is observed experimentally.

GIVE IT SOME THOUGHT

The O—O bonds in ozone are often described as "one-and-a-half" bonds. Is this description consistent with the idea of resonance?

As an additional example of resonance structures, consider the nitrate ion, NO_3^-, for which three equivalent Lewis structures can be drawn:

Notice that the arrangement of atoms is the same in each structure—only the placement of electrons differs. In writing resonance structures, the same atoms must be bonded to each other in all structures, so that the only differences are in the arrangements of electrons. All three NO_3^- Lewis structures are equally dominant and taken together adequately describe the ion, in which all three N—O bond lengths are the same.

GIVE IT SOME THOUGHT

In the same sense that we describe the O—O bonds in O_3 as "one-and-a-half" bonds, how would you describe the N—O bonds in NO_3^-?

In some instances, all the possible Lewis structures for a species may not be equivalent to one another. Instead, one or more may be dominant. We will encounter examples of this as we proceed.

SAMPLE EXERCISE 3.10   **Resonance Structures**

Which is predicted to have the shorter sulfur–oxygen bonds, SO_3 or SO_3^{2-} ?

SOLUTION

The sulfur atom has six valence electrons, as does oxygen. Thus, SO_3 contains 24 valence electrons. In writing the Lewis structure, we see that three equivalent resonance structures can be drawn:

As with NO_3^-, the actual structure of SO_3 is an equal blend of all three. Thus, each S—O bond length should be about one-third of the way between the length of a single bond and the length of a double bond. That is, they should be shorter than single bonds but not as short as double bonds.

The SO_3^{2-} ion has 26 electrons, which leads to a dominant Lewis structure in which all the S—O bonds are single:

Our analysis of the Lewis structures leads us to conclude that SO_3 should have the shorter S—O bonds and SO_3^{2-} the longer ones. This conclusion is correct: The experimentally measured S—O bond lengths are 1.42 Å in SO_3 and 1.51 Å in SO_3^{2-}.

PRACTICE EXERCISE

Draw two equivalent resonance structures for the formate ion, HCO_2^-.

Answer:

Resonance in Benzene

Resonance is an important concept in describing the bonding in organic molecules, particularly *aromatic* organic molecules, a category that includes the hydrocarbon *benzene*, C_6H_6. The six C atoms are bonded in a hexagonal ring, and one H atom is bonded to each C atom. We can write two equivalent dominant Lewis structures for benzene, each of which satisfies the octet rule. These two structures are in resonance:

Note that the double bonds are in different places in the two structures. Each of these resonance structures shows three carbon–carbon single bonds and three carbon–carbon double bonds. However, experimental data show that all six C—C bonds are of equal length, 1.40 Å, intermediate between the typical bond lengths for a C—C single bond (1.54 Å) and a C=C double bond (1.34 Å). Each of the C—C bonds in benzene can be thought of as a blend of a single bond and a double bond (▶ FIGURE 3.14).

Benzene is commonly represented by omitting the hydrogen atoms and showing only the carbon–carbon framework with the vertices unlabeled. In this convention, the resonance in the molecule is represented either by two structures separated by a double-headed arrow or by a shorthand notation in which we draw a hexagon with a circle inside:

The shorthand notation reminds us that benzene is a blend of two resonance structures—it emphasizes that the C=C double bonds cannot be assigned to specific edges of the hexagon. Chemists use both representations of benzene interchangeably.

GO FIGURE

What is the significance of the dashed bonds in this ball-and-stick model?

▲ **FIGURE 3.14**   **Benzene, an "aromatic" organic compound.** The benzene molecule is a regular hexagon of carbon atoms with a hydrogen atom bonded to each one. The dashed lines represent the blending of two equivalent resonance structures, leading to C—C bonds that are intermediate between single and double bonds.

The bonding arrangement in benzene confers special stability to the molecule. As a result, millions of organic compounds contain the six-membered ring characteristic of benzene. Many of these compounds are important in biochemistry, in pharmaceuticals, and in the production of modern materials.

GIVE IT SOME THOUGHT

Each Lewis structure of benzene has three $C=C$ double bonds. Another hydrocarbon containing three $C=C$ double bonds is *hexatriene*, C_6H_8. A Lewis structure of hexatriene is

$$\begin{array}{ccccccc} H & H & H & H & H & H \\ | & | & | & | & | & | \\ C & = & C & - & C & = & C & - & C & = & C \\ | & & & & & & | \\ H & & & & & & H \end{array}$$

Do you expect hexatriene to have multiple resonance structures? If not, why is this molecule different from benzene with respect to resonance?

3.7 | EXCEPTIONS TO THE OCTET RULE

The octet rule is so simple and useful in introducing the basic concepts of bonding that you might assume it is always obeyed. In Section 3.2, however, we noted its limitation in dealing with ionic compounds of the transition metals. The rule also fails in many situations involving covalent bonding. These exceptions to the octet rule are of three main types:

1. Molecules and polyatomic ions containing an odd number of electrons
2. Molecules and polyatomic ions in which an atom has fewer than an octet of valence electrons
3. Molecules and polyatomic ions in which an atom has more than an octet of valence electrons

Odd Number of Electrons

In the vast majority of molecules and polyatomic ions, the total number of valence electrons is even, and complete pairing of electrons occurs. However, in a few molecules and polyatomic ions, such as ClO_2, NO, NO_2, and O_2^-, the number of valence electrons is odd. Complete pairing of these electrons is impossible, and an octet around each atom cannot be achieved. For example, NO contains $5 + 6 = 11$ valence electrons. The two most important Lewis structures for this molecule are

$$\ddot{N}=\ddot{O} \quad \text{and} \quad \ddot{N}=\ddot{O}$$

GIVE IT SOME THOUGHT

Which of the Lewis structures for NO is dominant based on analysis of the formal charges?

Less than an Octet of Valence Electrons

A second type of exception occurs when there are fewer than eight valence electrons around an atom in a molecule or polyatomic ion. This situation is also relatively rare (with the exception of hydrogen and helium as we have already discussed), most often encountered in compounds of boron and beryllium. As an example, let's consider boron trifluoride, BF_3. If we follow the first four steps of our procedure for drawing Lewis structures, we obtain the structure which has only six electrons around the boron atom. The formal charge is zero on both B and F, and we could complete the octet around boron by forming a double bond (step 5). In so doing, we see that there are three equivalent resonance structures (the formal charges are shown in red):

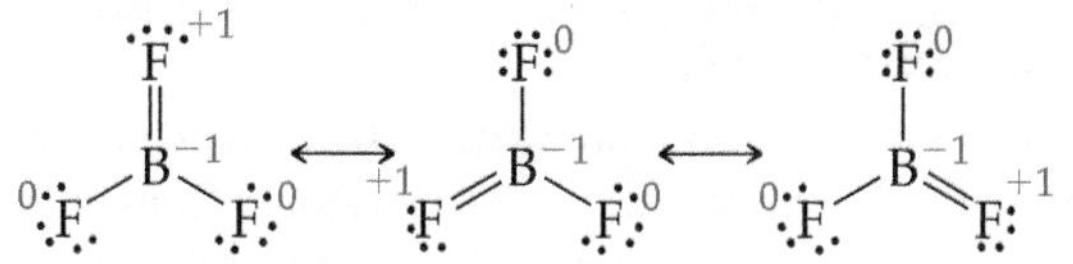

Each of these structures forces a fluorine atom to share additional electrons with the boron atom, which is inconsistent with the high electronegativity of fluorine. In fact, the formal charges tell us that this is an unfavorable situation. In each structure, the F atom involved in the $B=F$ double bond has a formal charge of $+1$, while the less electronegative B atom has a formal charge of -1. Thus, the resonance structures containing a $B=F$ double bond are less important than the one in which there are fewer than an octet of valence electrons around boron:

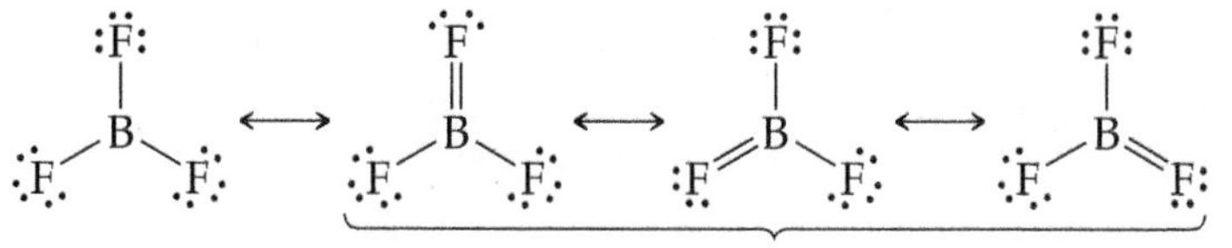

| Dominant | Less important |

We usually represent BF_3 solely by the dominant resonance structure, in which there are only six valence electrons around boron. The chemical behavior of BF_3 is consistent with this representation. In particular, BF_3 reacts energetically with molecules having an unshared pair of electrons that can be used to form a bond with boron, as, for example, in the reaction

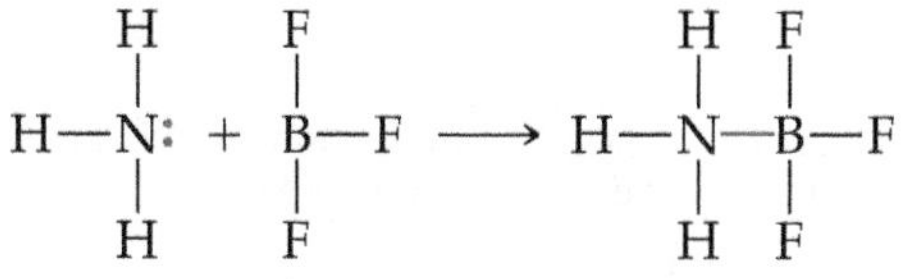

In the stable compound NH_3BF_3, boron has an octet of valence electrons.

More than an Octet of Valence Electrons

The third and largest class of exceptions consists of molecules or polyatomic ions in which there are more than eight electrons in the valence shell of an atom. When we draw the Lewis structure for PF_5, for example, we are forced to place ten electrons around the central phosphorus atom:

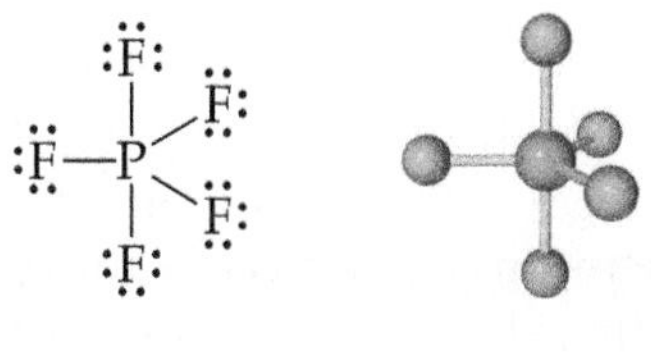

Molecules and ions with more than an octet of electrons around the central atom are often called *hypervalent*. Other examples of hypervalent species are SF_4, AsF_6^-, and ICl_4^-. The corresponding molecules with a second-period atom as the central atom, such as NCl_5 and OF_4, do *not* exist.

Hypervalent molecules are formed only for central atoms from period 3 and below in the periodic table. The principal reason for their formation is the relatively larger size of the central atom. For example, a P atom is large enough that five F (or even five Cl) atoms can be bonded to it without being too crowded. By contrast, an N atom is too small to accommodate five atoms bonded to it. Because size is a factor, hypervalent molecules occur most often when the central atom is bonded to the smallest and most electronegative atoms—F, Cl, and O.

The notion of a valence shell containing more than an octet of electrons is also consistent with the presence of unfilled nd orbitals in atoms from period 3 and below. By comparison, elements of the second period have only the $2s$ and $2p$ valence orbitals available for bonding. Detailed analyses of the bonding in molecules such as PF_5 and SF_6 suggest that the presence of unfilled $3d$ orbitals in P and S has a relatively minor impact on the formation of hypervalent molecules, and the general current belief is that the increased size of third-period atoms is the more important factor.

SAMPLE EXERCISE 3.11 | **Lewis Structure for an Ion with More than an Octet of Electrons**

Draw the Lewis structure for ICl_4^-.

SOLUTION

Iodine (group 7A) has seven valence electrons. Each chlorine atom (group 7A) also has seven. An extra electron is added to account for the 1− charge of the ion. Therefore, the total number of valence electrons is

$$7 + (4 \times 7) + 1 = 36$$

The I atom is the central atom in the ion. Putting eight electrons around each Cl atom (including a pair of electrons between I and each Cl to represent the single bond between these atoms) requires $8 \times 4 = 32$ electrons.

We are thus left with $36 - 32 = 4$ electrons to be placed on the larger iodine:

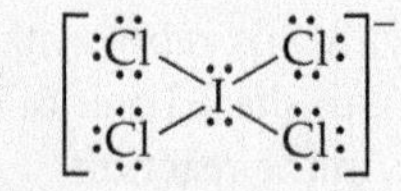

Iodine has 12 valence electrons around it, four more than needed for an octet.

PRACTICE EXERCISE

(a) Which of the following atoms is never found with more than an octet of valence electrons around it: S, C, P, Br? **(b)** Draw the Lewis structure for XeF_2.

Answers: **(a)** C, **(b)** :F̈—Ẍe—F̈:

Finally, there are Lewis structures where you might have to choose between satisfying the octet rule and obtaining the most favorable formal charges by using more than an octet of electrons. For example, consider these Lewis structures for the phosphate ion, PO_4^{3-}:

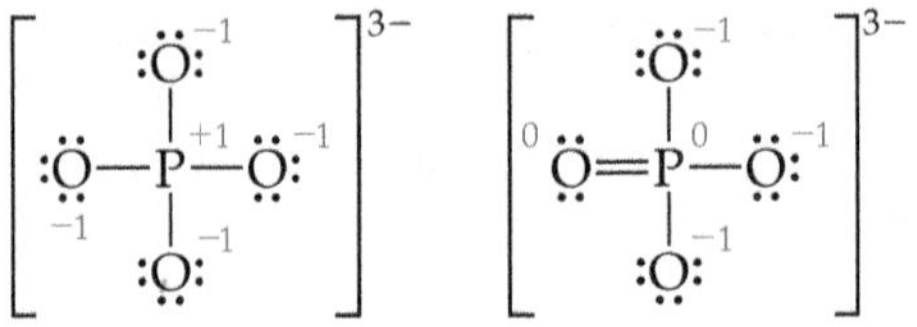

The formal charges on the atoms are shown in red. In the left structure, the P atom obeys the octet rule. In the right structure, however, the P atom has five electron pairs, leading to smaller formal charges on the atoms. (You should be able to see that there are three additional resonance structures for the Lewis structure on the right.)

Chemists are still debating which of these two structures is dominant for PO_4^{3-}. Recent theoretical calculations based on quantum mechanics suggest to some researchers that the left structure is the dominant one. Other researchers claim that the bond lengths in the ion are more consistent with the right structure being dominant. This disagreement is a convenient reminder that, in general, multiple Lewis structures can contribute to the actual electron distribution in an atom or molecule.

3.8 | STRENGTHS OF COVALENT BONDS

The stability of a molecule is related to the strengths of its covalent bonds. The strength of a covalent bond between two atoms is determined by the energy required to break the bond. It is easiest to relate bond strength to the enthalpy change in reactions in which bonds are broken. (see Section 12.4) The **bond enthalpy** is the enthalpy change, ΔH, for the breaking of a particular bond in one mole of a gaseous substance. For example, the bond enthalpy for the bond in Cl_2 is the enthalpy change when 1 mol of $Cl_2(g)$ dissociates into chlorine atoms:

$$:\ddot{\underset{..}{Cl}}-\ddot{\underset{..}{Cl}}:(g) \longrightarrow 2 :\ddot{\underset{..}{Cl}}\cdot(g)$$

We use the letter D followed by the bond in question to represent bond enthalpies. Thus, for example, $D(Cl-Cl)$ is the bond enthalpy for the Cl_2 bond, and $D(H-Br)$ is the bond enthalpy for the HBr bond.

It is relatively simple to assign bond enthalpies to the bond in a diatomic molecule because in these cases the bond enthalpy is just the energy required to break the molecule into its atoms. However, many important bonds, such as the $C-H$ bond, exist only in polyatomic molecules. For these bonds, we usually use *average* bond enthalpies. For example, the enthalpy change for the following process in which a methane molecule is decomposed into its five atoms (a process called *atomization*) can be used to define an average bond enthalpy for the $C-H$ bond, $D(C-H)$:

$$\underset{\substack{| \\ H}}{\overset{\substack{H \\ |}}{H-C-}}H(g) \longrightarrow \cdot\dot{C}\cdot(g) + 4 H\cdot(g) \qquad \Delta H = 1660 \text{ kJ}$$

Because there are four equivalent $C-H$ bonds in methane, the enthalpy of atomization is equal to the sum of the bond enthalpies of the four $C-H$ bonds. Therefore, the average $C-H$ bond enthalpy for CH_4 is $D(C-H) = (1660/4)$ kJ/mol = 415 kJ/mol.

The bond enthalpy for a given pair of atoms, say $C-H$, depends on the rest of the molecule containing the atom pair. However, the variation from one molecule to another is generally small, which supports the idea that bonding electron pairs are localized between atoms. If we consider $C-H$ bond enthalpies in many different compounds, we find that the average bond enthalpy is 413 kJ/mol, close to the 415 kJ/mol we just calculated from CH_4.

◢ GIVE IT SOME THOUGHT

How can you use the enthalpy of atomization of the hydrocarbon ethane, $C_2H_6(g)$, along with the value $D(C-H)$ = 413 kJ/mol to estimate the value for $D(C-C)$?

▶ TABLE 3.4 lists average bond enthalpies for a number of atom pairs. *The bond enthalpy is always a positive quantity*; energy is always required to break chemical bonds. Conversely, energy is *always* released when a bond forms between two gaseous atoms or molecular fragments. The greater the bond enthalpy, the stronger the bond. Further, a molecule with strong chemical bonds generally has less tendency to undergo chemical change than does one with weak bonds. For example, N_2, which has a very strong $N\equiv N$ triple bond, is very unreactive, whereas hydrazine, N_2H_4, which has an $N-N$ single bond, is highly reactive.

◢ GIVE IT SOME THOUGHT

Based on bond enthalpies, which do you expect to be more reactive, oxygen, O_2, or hydrogen peroxide, H_2O_2?

TABLE 3.4 • Average Bond Enthalpies (kJ/mol)

Single Bonds

C—H	413	N—H	391	O—H	463	F—F	155
C—C	348	N—N	163	O—O	146		
C—N	293	N—O	201	O—F	190	Cl—F	253
C—O	358	N—F	272	O—Cl	203	Cl—Cl	242
C—F	485	N—Cl	200	O—I	234		
C—Cl	328	N—Br	243			Br—F	237
C—Br	276			S—H	339	Br—Cl	218
C—I	240	H—H	436	S—F	327	Br—Br	193
C—S	259	H—F	567	S—Cl	253		
		H—Cl	431	S—Br	218	I—Cl	208
Si—H	323	H—Br	366	S—S	266	I—Br	175
Si—Si	226	H—I	299			I—I	151
Si—C	301						
Si—O	368						
Si—Cl	464						

Multiple Bonds

C=C	614	N=N	418	O_2	495
C≡C	839	N≡N	941		
C=N	615	N=O	607	S=O	523
C≡N	891			S=S	418
C=O	799				
C≡O	1072				

Bond Enthalpies and the Enthalpies of Reactions

We can use average bond enthalpies to estimate the enthalpies of reactions in which bonds are broken and new bonds are formed. This procedure allows us to estimate quickly whether a given reaction will be endothermic ($\Delta H > 0$) or exothermic ($\Delta H < 0$) even if we do not know ΔH_f° for all the species involved.

Our strategy for estimating reaction enthalpies is a straightforward application of Hess's law. (see Section 12.6) We use the fact that breaking bonds is always endothermic and forming bonds is always exothermic. We therefore imagine that the reaction occurs in two steps:

1. We supply enough energy to break those bonds in the reactants that are not present in the products. The enthalpy of the system is increased by the sum of the bond enthalpies of the bonds that are broken.

2. We form the bonds in the products that were not present in the reactants. This step releases energy and therefore lowers the enthalpy of the system by the sum of the bond enthalpies of the bonds that are formed.

The enthalpy of the reaction, ΔH_{rxn}, is estimated as the sum of the bond enthalpies of the bonds broken minus the sum of the bond enthalpies of the bonds formed:

$$\Delta H_{rxn} = \Sigma(\text{bond enthalpies of bonds broken}) - \Sigma(\text{bond enthalpies of bonds formed}) \quad [3.12]$$

Consider, for example, the gas-phase reaction between methane, CH_4, and chlorine to produce methyl chloride, CH_3Cl, and hydrogen chloride, HCl:

$$H—CH_3(g) + Cl—Cl(g) \longrightarrow Cl—CH_3(g) + H—Cl(g) \quad \Delta H_{rxn} = ? \quad [3.13]$$

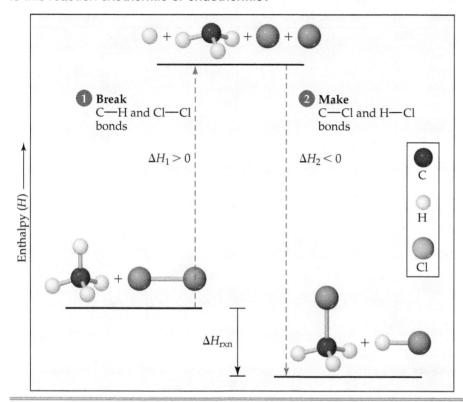

GO FIGURE:

Is this reaction exothermic or endothermic?

◀ FIGURE 3.15 **Using bond enthalpies to calculate** ΔH_{rxn}. Average bond enthalpies are used to estimate ΔH_{rxn} for the reaction in Equation 3.13.

Our two-step procedure is outlined in ▲ FIGURE 3.15. We note that the following bonds are broken and made:

Bonds broken: 1 mol C—H, 1 mol Cl—Cl

Bonds made: 1 mol C—Cl, 1 mol H—Cl

We first supply enough energy to break the C—H and Cl—Cl bonds, which raises the enthalpy of the system (indicated as $\Delta H_1 > 0$ in Figure 3.15). We then form the C—Cl and H—Cl bonds, which release energy and lower the enthalpy of the system ($\Delta H_2 < 0$). We then use Equation 3.12 and data from Table 3.4 to estimate the enthalpy of the reaction:

$$\Delta H_{rxn} = [D(C—H) + D(Cl—Cl)] - [D(Cl—Cl) + D(H—Cl)]$$
$$= (413 \text{ kJ} + 242 \text{ kJ}) - (328 \text{ kJ} + 431 \text{ kJ}) = -104 \text{ kJ}$$

The reaction is exothermic because the bonds in the products (especially the H—Cl bond) are stronger than the bonds in the reactants (especially the Cl—Cl bond).

We usually use bond enthalpies to estimate ΔH_{rxn} only if we do not have the needed ΔH_f° values readily available. For the preceding reaction, we cannot calculate ΔH_{rxn} from ΔH_f° values and Hess's law because ΔH_f° for $CH_3Cl(g)$ is not given in Appendix C. If we obtain the value of ΔH_f° for $CH_3Cl(g)$ from another source and use Equation 10.31,

$$\Delta H_{rxn}^\circ = \Sigma n \Delta H_f^\circ(\text{products}) - \Sigma m \Delta H_f^\circ(\text{reactants})$$

we find that $\Delta H_{rxn} = -99.8$ kJ for the reaction in Equation 3.13. Thus, the use of average bond enthalpies provides a reasonably accurate estimate of the actual reaction enthalpy change.

It is important to remember that bond enthalpies are derived for *gaseous* molecules and that they are often *averaged* values. Nonetheless, average bond enthalpies are useful for estimating reaction enthalpies quickly, especially for gas-phase reactions.

TABLE 3.5 • Average Bond Lengths for Some Single, Double, and Triple Bonds			
Bond	**Bond Length (Å)**	**Bond**	**Bond Length (Å)**
C—C	1.54	N—N	1.47
C=C	1.34	N=N	1.24
C≡C	1.20	N≡N	1.10
C—N	1.43	N—O	1.36
C=N	1.38	N=O	1.22
C≡N	1.16		
		O—O	1.48
C—O	1.43	O=O	1.21
C=O	1.23		
C≡O	1.13		

SAMPLE EXERCISE 3.12   Using Average Bond Enthalpies

Using data from Table 3.4, estimate ΔH for the reaction

$$2\ \text{H—}\underset{\underset{\text{H}}{|}}{\overset{\overset{\text{H}}{|}}{\text{C}}}\text{—}\underset{\underset{\text{H}}{|}}{\overset{\overset{\text{H}}{|}}{\text{C}}}\text{—H}(g)\ +\ 7\,\text{O}_2(g)\ \longrightarrow\ 4\,\text{O}{=}\text{C}{=}\text{O}(g)\ +\ 6\,\text{H—O—H}(g)$$

SOLUTION

Analyze We are asked to estimate the enthalpy change for a chemical reaction by using average bond enthalpies for the bonds broken and formed.

Plan In the reactants, we must break twelve C—H bonds and two C—C bonds in the two molecules of C_2H_6 and seven O_2 bonds in the seven O_2 molecules. In the products, we form eight C=O bonds (two in each CO_2) and twelve O—H bonds (two in each H_2O).

Solve Using Equation 3.12 and data from Table 3.4, we have

$$\Delta H = [12D(\text{C—H}) + 2D(\text{C—C}) + 7D(\text{O}_2)] - [8D(\text{C}{=}\text{O}) + 12D(\text{O—H})]$$
$$= [12(413\ \text{kJ}) + 2(348\ \text{kJ}) + 7(495\ \text{kJ})] - [8(799\ \text{kJ}) + 12(463\ \text{kJ})]$$
$$= 9117\ \text{kJ} - 11948\ \text{kJ}$$
$$= -2831\ \text{kJ}$$

Check This estimate can be compared with the value of −2856 kJ calculated from more accurate thermochemical data; the agreement is good.

PRACTICE EXERCISE

Using Table 3.4, estimate ΔH for the reaction

$$\text{H—}\underset{\underset{\text{H}}{|}}{\text{N}}\text{—}\underset{\underset{\text{H}}{|}}{\text{N}}\text{—H}(g)\ \longrightarrow\ \text{N}{\equiv}\text{N}(g)\ +\ 2\,\text{H—H}(g)$$

Answer: −86 kJ

Bond Enthalpy and Bond Length

Just as we can define an average bond enthalpy, we can also define an average bond length for a number of common bonds (▲ **TABLE 3.5**). Of particular interest is the relationship, in any atom pair, among bond enthalpy, bond length, and number of bonds between the atoms. For example, we can use data in Tables 3.4 and 3.5 to compare the bond lengths and bond enthalpies of carbon–carbon single, double, and triple bonds:

C—C	C=C	C≡C
1.54 Å	1.34 Å	1.20 Å
348 kJ/mol	614 kJ/mol	839 kJ/mol

CHEMISTRY PUT TO WORK

Explosives and Alfred Nobel

Enormous amounts of energy can be stored in chemical bonds. Perhaps the most graphic illustration of this fact is seen in certain molecular substances used as explosives. Our discussion of bond enthalpies allows us to examine more closely some of the properties of such explosive substances.

A useful explosive substance must (1) decompose very exothermically, (2) have gaseous products so that a tremendous gas pressure accompanies the decomposition, (3) decompose very rapidly, and (4) be stable enough so that it can be detonated predictably. The combination of the first three effects leads to the violent evolution of heat and gases.

To give the most exothermic reaction, an explosive should have weak chemical bonds and should decompose into molecules that have very strong bonds. Table 3.4 tells us that $N \equiv N$, $C \equiv O$, and $C = O$ bonds are among the strongest. Not surprisingly, explosives are usually designed to produce the gaseous products $N_2(g)$, $CO(g)$, and $CO_2(g)$. Water vapor is nearly always produced as well.

Many common explosives are organic molecules that contain nitro (NO_2) or nitrate (NO_3) groups attached to a carbon skeleton. The Lewis structures of two of the most familiar explosives, nitroglycerin and trinitrotoluene (TNT), are shown here (resonance structures are not shown for clarity). TNT contains the six-membered ring characteristic of benzene.

Nitroglycerin

Trinitrotoluene (TNT)

Nitroglycerin is a pale yellow, oily liquid. It is highly *shock-sensitive*: Merely shaking the liquid can cause its explosive decomposition into nitrogen, carbon dioxide, water, and oxygen gases:

$$4\ C_3H_5N_3O_9(l) \longrightarrow 6\ N_2(g) + 12\ CO_2(g) + 10\ H_2O(g) + O_2(g)$$

The large bond enthalpies of N_2 (941 kJ/mol), CO_2 (2×799 kJ/mol), and H_2O (2×463 kJ/mol) make this reaction enormously exothermic. Nitroglycerin is an exceptionally unstable explosive because it is in nearly perfect *explosive balance*: With the exception of a small amount of $O_2(g)$ produced, the only products are N_2, CO_2, and H_2O. Note also that, unlike combustion reactions, explosions are entirely self-contained. No other reagent, such as $O_2(g)$, is needed for the explosive decomposition.

Because nitroglycerin is so unstable, it is difficult to use as a controllable explosive. The Swedish inventor Alfred Nobel (▼ **FIGURE 3.16**) found that mixing nitroglycerin with an absorbent solid material such as diatomaceous earth or cellulose gives a solid explosive (*dynamite*) that is much safer than liquid nitroglycerin.

RELATED EXERCISES: 3.98 and 3.99

▲ **FIGURE 3.16 Alfred Nobel (1833–1896), Swedish inventor of dynamite.** By many accounts Nobel's discovery that nitroglycerin could be made more stable by absorbing it onto cellulose was an accident. This discovery made Nobel a wealthy man. He was also a complex and lonely man, however, who never married, was frequently ill, and suffered from chronic depression. He had invented the most powerful military explosive to date, but he strongly supported international peace movements. His will stated that his fortune be used to establish prizes awarding those who "have conferred the greatest benefit on mankind," including the promotion of peace and "fraternity between nations." The Nobel Prize is probably the most coveted award that a scientist, writer, or peace advocate can receive.

As the number of bonds between the carbon atoms increases, the bond length decreases and the bond enthalpy increases. That is, the carbon atoms are held more closely and more tightly together. In general, *as the number of bonds between two atoms increases, the bond grows shorter and stronger.* This trend is illustrated in ▶ **FIGURE 3.17** for N—N single, double, and triple bonds.

▲ GO FIGURE

The line segments in the graph both have negative slopes. Why does this make sense?

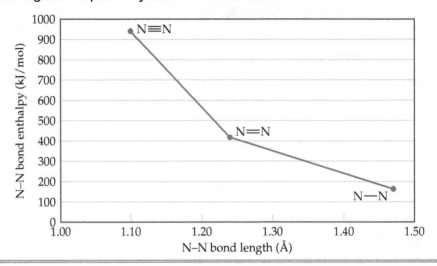

► FIGURE 3.17 **Bond strength versus bond length for N—N bonds.**

SAMPLE INTEGRATIVE EXERCISE | Putting Concepts Together

Phosgene, a substance used in poisonous gas warfare during World War I, is so named because it was first prepared by the action of sunlight on a mixture of carbon monoxide and chlorine gases. Its name comes from the Greek words *phos* (light) and *genes* (born of). Phosgene has the following elemental composition: 12.14% C, 16.17% O, and 71.69% Cl by mass. Its molar mass is 98.9 g/mol. **(a)** Determine the molecular formula of this compound. **(b)** Draw three Lewis structures for the molecule that satisfy the octet rule for each atom. (The Cl and O atoms bond to C.) **(c)** Using formal charges, determine which Lewis structure is the dominant one. **(d)** Using average bond enthalpies, estimate ΔH for the formation of gaseous phosgene from $CO(g)$ and $Cl_2(g)$.

SOLUTION

(a) The empirical formula of phosgene can be determined from its elemental composition. Assuming 100 g of the compound and calculating the number of moles of C, O, and Cl in this sample, we have

$$(12.14 \text{ g C})\left(\frac{1 \text{ mol C}}{12.01 \text{ g C}}\right) = 1.011 \text{ mol C}$$

$$(16.17 \text{ g O})\left(\frac{1 \text{ mol O}}{16.00 \text{ g O}}\right) = 1.011 \text{ mol O}$$

$$(71.69 \text{ g Cl})\left(\frac{1 \text{ mol Cl}}{35.45 \text{ g Cl}}\right) = 2.022 \text{ mol Cl}$$

The ratio of the number of moles of each element, obtained by dividing each number of moles by the smallest quantity, indicates that there is one C and one O for each two Cl in the empirical formula, $COCl_2$.

The molar mass of the empirical formula is $12.01 + 16.00 + 2(35.45) = 98.91$ g/mol, the same as the molar mass of the molecule. Thus, $COCl_2$ is the molecular formula.

(b) Carbon has four valence electrons, oxygen has six, and chlorine has seven, giving $4 + 6 + 2(7) = 24$ electrons for the Lewis structures. Drawing a Lewis structure with all single bonds does not give the central carbon atom an octet. Using multiple bonds, three structures satisfy the octet rule:

(c) Calculating the formal charges on each atom gives

$$:\overset{0}{\underset{\cdot\cdot}{O}}: \qquad :\overset{-1}{\underset{\cdot\cdot}{\overset{\cdot\cdot}{O}}}: \qquad :\overset{-1}{\underset{\cdot\cdot}{\overset{\cdot\cdot}{O}}}:$$

$$:\overset{\cdot\cdot}{\underset{\cdot\cdot}{Cl}}\overset{0}{-}\overset{0}{C}\overset{0}{-}\overset{\cdot\cdot}{\underset{\cdot\cdot}{Cl}}: \longleftrightarrow :\overset{\cdot\cdot}{\underset{\cdot\cdot}{Cl}}\overset{+1}{=}\overset{0}{C}\overset{0}{-}\overset{\cdot\cdot}{\underset{\cdot\cdot}{Cl}}: \longleftrightarrow :\overset{\cdot\cdot}{\underset{\cdot\cdot}{Cl}}\overset{0}{-}\overset{0}{C}\overset{+1}{=}\overset{\cdot\cdot}{Cl}:$$

The first structure is expected to be the dominant one because it has the lowest formal charges on each atom. Indeed, the molecule is usually represented by this single Lewis structure.

(d) Writing the chemical equation in terms of the Lewis structures of the molecules, we have

$$:C\equiv O: \quad + \quad :\overset{\cdot\cdot}{\underset{\cdot\cdot}{Cl}}-\overset{\cdot\cdot}{\underset{\cdot\cdot}{Cl}}: \quad \longrightarrow \quad :\overset{\cdot\cdot}{\underset{\cdot\cdot}{Cl}}-\overset{\overset{\displaystyle:O:}{\|}}{C}-\overset{\cdot\cdot}{\underset{\cdot\cdot}{Cl}}:$$

Thus, the reaction involves breaking a $C\equiv O$ bond and a $Cl-Cl$ bond and forming a $C=O$ bond and two $C-Cl$ bonds. Using bond enthalpies from Table 3.4, we have

$$\Delta H = D(C\equiv O) + D(Cl-Cl) - [D(C=O) + 2D(C-Cl)]$$
$$= 1072 \text{ kJ} + 242 \text{ kJ} - [799 \text{ kJ} + 2(328 \text{ kJ})] = -141 \text{ kJ}$$

Notice that the reaction is exothermic. Nevertheless, energy is needed from sunlight or another source for the reaction to begin, as is the case for the combustion of $H_2(g)$ and $O_2(g)$ to form $H_2O(g)$ (Figure 10.14).

CHAPTER SUMMARY AND KEY TERMS

INTRODUCTION AND SECTION 3.1 In this chapter we have focused on the interactions that lead to the formation of **chemical bonds**. We classify these bonds into three broad groups: **ionic bonds**, which result from the electrostatic forces that exist between ions of opposite charge; **covalent bonds**, which result from the sharing of electrons by two atoms; and **metallic bonds**, which result from a delocalized sharing of electrons in metals. The formation of bonds involves interactions of the outermost electrons of atoms, their valence electrons. The valence electrons of an atom can be represented by electron-dot symbols, called **Lewis symbols**. The tendencies of atoms to gain, lose, or share their valence electrons often follow the **octet rule**, which can be viewed as an attempt by atoms to achieve a noble-gas electron configuration.

SECTION 3.2 Ionic bonding results from the transfer of electrons from one atom to another, leading to the formation of a three-dimensional lattice of charged particles. The stabilities of ionic substances result from the strong electrostatic attractions between an ion and the surrounding ions of opposite charge. The magnitude of these interactions is measured by the **lattice energy**, which is the energy needed to separate an ionic lattice into gaseous ions. Lattice energy increases with increasing charge on the ions and with decreasing distance between the ions. The **Born–Haber cycle** is a useful thermochemical cycle in which we use Hess's law to calculate the lattice energy as the sum of several steps in the formation of an ionic compound.

SECTION 3.3 A covalent bond results from the sharing of electrons. We can represent the electron distribution in molecules by means of **Lewis structures**, which indicate how many valence electrons are involved in forming bonds and how many remain as unshared electron pairs. The octet rule helps determine how many bonds will be formed between two atoms. The sharing of one pair of electrons produces a **single bond**; the sharing of two or three pairs of electrons between two atoms produces **double** or **triple bonds**, respectively. Double and triple bonds are examples of multiple bonding between atoms. The bond length decreases as the number of bonds between the atoms increases.

SECTION 3.4 In covalent bonds, the electrons may not necessarily be shared equally between two atoms. **Bond polarity** helps describe unequal sharing of electrons in a bond. In a **nonpolar covalent bond** the electrons in the bond are shared equally by the two atoms; in a **polar covalent bond** one of the atoms exerts a greater attraction for the electrons than the other.

Electronegativity is a numerical measure of the ability of an atom to compete with other atoms for the electrons shared between them. Fluorine is the most electronegative element, meaning it has the greatest ability to attract electrons from other atoms. Electronegativity values range from 0.7 for Cs to 4.0 for F. Electronegativity generally increases from left to right in a row of the periodic table and decreases going down a column. The difference in the electronegativities of bonded atoms can be used to determine the polarity of a bond. The greater the electronegativity difference, the more polar the bond.

A **polar molecule** is one whose centers of positive and negative charge do not coincide. Thus, a polar molecule has a positive side and a negative side. This separation of charge produces a **dipole**, the magnitude of which is given by the **dipole moment**, which is measured in debyes (D). Dipole moments increase with increasing amount of charge separated and increasing distance of separation. Any diatomic molecule $X-Y$ in which X and Y have different electronegativities is a polar molecule.

Most bonding interactions lie between the extremes of covalent and ionic bonding. While it is generally true that the bonding between a metal and a nonmetal is predominantly ionic, exceptions to this guideline are not uncommon when the difference in electronegativity of the atoms is relatively small or when the oxidation state of the metal becomes large.

SECTIONS 3.5 AND 3.6 If we know which atoms are connected to one another, we can draw Lewis structures for molecules and ions by a simple procedure. Once we do so, we can determine the **formal charge** of each atom in a Lewis structure, which is the charge that the atom would have if all atoms had the same electronegativity. In general, the dominant Lewis structure will have low formal charges with any negative formal charges residing on more electronegative atoms.

Sometimes a single dominant Lewis structure is inadequate to represent a particular molecule (or ion). In such situations, we describe the molecule by using two or more **resonance structures** for the molecule. The molecule is envisioned as a blend of these multiple resonance structures. Resonance structures are important in describing the bonding in molecules such as ozone, O_3, and the organic molecule benzene, C_6H_6.

SECTION 3.7   The octet rule is not obeyed in all cases. Exceptions occur when (a) a molecule has an odd number of electrons, (b) it is not possible to complete an octet around an atom without forcing an unfavorable distribution of electrons, or (c) a large atom is surrounded by a sufficiently large number of small electronegative atoms that it has more than an octet of electrons around it. Lewis structures with more than an octet of electrons are observed for atoms in the third row and beyond in the periodic table.

SECTION 3.8   The strength of a covalent bond is measured by its **bond enthalpy**, which is the molar enthalpy change upon breaking a particular bond. Average bond enthalpies can be determined for a wide variety of covalent bonds. The strengths of covalent bonds increase with the number of electron pairs shared between two atoms. We can use bond enthalpies to estimate the enthalpy change during chemical reactions in which bonds are broken and new bonds formed. The average bond length between two atoms decreases as the number of bonds between the atoms increases, consistent with the bond being stronger as the number of bonds increases.

KEY SKILLS

- Write Lewis symbols for atoms and ions. (Section 3.1)

- Understand lattice energy and be able to arrange compounds in order of increasing lattice energy based on the charges and sizes of the ions involved. (Section 3.2)

- Use atomic electron configurations and the octet rule to write Lewis structures for molecules to determine their electron distribution. (Section 3.3)

- Use electronegativity differences to identify nonpolar covalent, polar covalent, and ionic bonds. (Section 3.4)

- Calculate charge separation in diatomic molecules based on the experimentally measured dipole moment and bond distance. (Section 3.4)

- Calculate formal charges from Lewis structures and use those formal charges to identify the dominant Lewis structure for a molecule or ion. (Section 3.5)

- Recognize molecules where resonance structures are needed to describe the bonding. (Section 3.6)

- Recognize exceptions to the octet rule and draw accurate Lewis structures even when the octet rule is not obeyed. (Section 3.7)

- Understand the relationship between bond type (single, double, and triple), bond strength (or enthalpy), and bond length. (Section 3.8)

- Use bond enthalpies to estimate enthalpy changes for reactions involving gas-phase reactants and products. (Section 3.8)

KEY EQUATIONS

- $E_{el} = \dfrac{\kappa Q_1 Q_2}{d}$ [3.4]   The potential energy of two interacting charges

- $\mu = Qr$ [3.11]   The dipole moment of two charges of equal magnitude but opposite sign, separated by a distance r

- $\Delta H_{rxn} = \Sigma(\text{bond enthalpies of bonds broken}) - \Sigma(\text{bond enthalpies of bonds formed})$ [3.12]   The enthalpy change as a function of bond enthalpies for reactions involving gas-phase molecules

EXERCISES

VISUALIZING CONCEPTS

3.1   For each of these Lewis symbols, indicate the group in the periodic table in which the element X belongs: [Section 3.1]

(a) ·Ẍ·   (b) ·X·   (c) :Ẍ·

3.2   Illustrated are four ions—A, B, X, and Y— showing their relative ionic radii. The ions shown in red carry positive charges: a

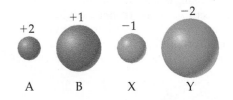

2+ charge for A and a 1+ charge for B. Ions shown in blue carry negative charges: a 1− charge for X and a 2− charge for Y. (**a**) Which combinations of these ions produce ionic compounds where there is a 1:1 ratio of cations and anions? (**b**) Among the combinations in part (a), which leads to the ionic compound having the largest lattice energy? (**c**) Which combination of ions leads to the ionic compound having the smallest lattice energy? [Section 3.2]

3.3 A portion of a two-dimensional "slab" of NaCl(*s*) is shown here (see Figure 3.3) in which the ions are numbered. (**a**) Of the following types of interactions (identified by color), which are attractive and which are repulsive: "purple-purple," "purple-green," "green-green"? Explain. (**b**) Consider the "green-green" interactions between ions 1 and 3, ions 1 and 5, and ions 3 and 5. Which one or more of these three will result in the interaction of largest magnitude? Which one or more will result in the interaction of the smallest magnitude? (**c**) Consider the "green-green" interactions between ions 1 and 5 and the "green-purple" interactions between ions 1 and 2. Which of these will have the greater magnitude? (**d**) Does your answer to part (c) help explain why NaCl is a stable ionic solid? [Section 3.2]

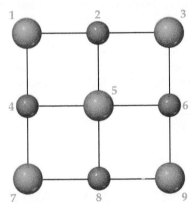

3.4 The orbital diagram that follows shows the valence electrons for a 2+ ion of an element. (**a**) What is the element? (**b**) What is the electron configuration of an atom of this element? [Section 3.2]

$4d$

3.5 In the Lewis structure shown here, A, D, E, Q, X, and Z represent elements in the first two rows of the periodic table (H—Ne). Identify all six elements so that the formal charges of all atoms are zero. [Section 3.3]

$$:\ddot{E}: \quad X$$
$$\|\quad\quad|$$
$$:\ddot{A}—D—\ddot{Q}—Z$$
$$\quad\quad\quad\ddot{}$$

3.6 Incomplete Lewis structures for the nitrous acid molecule, HNO_2, and the nitrite ion, NO_2^-, are shown below. (**a**) Complete each Lewis structure by adding electron pairs as needed. (**b**) Is the formal charge on N the same or different in these two species? (**c**) Would either HNO_2 or NO_2^- be expected to exhibit resonance? (**d**) Would you expect the N=O bond in HNO_2 to be longer, shorter, or the same length as the N—O bonds in NO_2^-? Explain. [Sections 3.5 and 3.6]

$$H—O—N=O \quad\quad O—N=O$$

3.7 The partial Lewis structure that follows is for a hydrocarbon molecule. In the full Lewis structure, each carbon atom satisfies the octet rule, and there are no unshared electron pairs in the molecule. The carbon–carbon bonds are labeled 1, 2, and 3. (**a**) Determine where the hydrogen atoms are in the molecule. (**b**) Rank the carbon–carbon bonds in order of increasing bond length. (**c**) Rank the carbon–carbon bonds in order of increasing bond enthalpy. [Sections 3.3 and 3.8]

$$C\overset{1}{=}C\overset{2}{—}C\overset{3}{\equiv}C$$

3.8 Consider the Lewis structure for the polyatomic oxyanion shown here, where X is an element from the third period (Na—Ar). By changing the overall charge, *n*, from 1− to 2− to 3− we get three different polyatomic ions. For each of these ions (**a**) identify the central atom, X; (**b**) determine the formal charge of the central atom, X; (**c**) draw a Lewis structure that makes the formal charge on the central atom equal to zero. [Sections 3.5, 3.6, and 3.7]

$$\left[\begin{array}{c} :\ddot{O}: \\ | \\ :\ddot{O}—X—\ddot{O}: \\ | \\ :\ddot{O}: \end{array} \right]^{n-}$$

LEWIS SYMBOLS (section 3.1)

3.9 (**a**) What are valence electrons? (**b**) How many valence electrons does a nitrogen atom possess? (**c**) An atom has the electron configuration $1s^2 2s^2 2p^6 3s^2 3p^2$. How many valence electrons does the atom have?

3.10 (**a**) What is the octet rule? (**b**) How many electrons must a sulfur atom gain to achieve an octet in its valence shell? (**c**) If an atom has the electron configuration $1s^2 2s^2 2p^3$, how many electrons must it gain to achieve an octet?

3.11 Write the electron configuration for silicon. Identify the valence electrons in this configuration and the nonvalence electrons. From the standpoint of chemical reactivity, what is the important difference between them?

3.12 (**a**) Write the electron configuration for the element titanium, Ti. How many valence electrons does this atom possess? (**b**) Hafnium, Hf, is also found in group 4B. Write the electron configuration for Hf. (**c**) Ti and Hf behave as though they possess the same number of valence electrons. Which of the subshells in the electron configuration of Hf behave as valence orbitals? Which behave as core orbitals?

3.13 Write the Lewis symbol for atoms of each of the following elements: (**a**) Al, (**b**) Br, (**c**) Ar, (**d**) Sr.

3.14 What is the Lewis symbol for each of the following atoms or ions: (**a**) K, (**b**) As, (**c**) Sn^{2+}, (**d**) N^{3-}?

IONIC BONDING (section 3.2)

3.15 Using Lewis symbols, diagram the reaction between magnesium and oxygen atoms to give the ionic substance MgO.

3.16 Use Lewis symbols to represent the reaction that occurs between Ca and F atoms.

3.17 Predict the chemical formula of the ionic compound formed between the following pairs of elements: (a) Al and F, (b) K and S, (c) Y and O, (d) Mg and N.

3.18 Which ionic compound is expected to form from combining the following pairs of elements: (a) barium and fluorine, (b) cesium and chlorine, (c) lithium and nitrogen, (d) aluminum and oxygen?

3.19 Write the electron configuration for each of the following ions, and determine which ones possess noble-gas configurations: (a) Sr^{2+}, (b) Ti^{2+}, (c) Se^{2-}, (d) Ni^{2+}, (e) Br^-, (f) Mn^{3+}.

3.20 Write electron configurations for the following ions, and determine which have noble-gas configurations: (a) Cd^{2+}, (b) P^{3-}, (c) Zr^{4+}, (d) Ru^{3+}, (e) As^{3-}, (f) Ag^+.

3.21 (a) Define the term *lattice energy*. (b) Which factors govern the magnitude of the lattice energy of an ionic compound?

3.22 NaCl and KF have the same crystal structure. The only difference between the two is the distance that separates cations and anions. (a) The lattice energies of NaCl and KF are given in Table 3.2. Based on the lattice energies, would you expect the Na—Cl or the K—F distance to be longer? (b) Use the ionic radii given in Figure 2.7 to estimate the Na—Cl and K—F distances. Does this estimate agree with the prediction you made based on the lattice energies?

3.23 The ionic substances KF, CaO, and ScN are isoelectronic (they have the same number of electrons). Examine the lattice energies for these substances in Table 3.2, and account for the trends you observe.

3.24 (a) Does the lattice energy of an ionic solid increase or decrease (i) as the charges of the ions increase, (ii) as the sizes of the ions increase? (b) Arrange the following substances not listed in Table 3.2 according to their expected lattice energies, listing them from lowest lattice energy to the highest: MgS, KI, GaN, LiBr.

3.25 The lattice energies of KBr and CsCl are nearly equal (Table 3.2). What can you conclude from this observation?

3.26 Explain the following trends in lattice energy: (a) NaCl > RbBr > CsBr; (b) BaO > KF; (c) SrO > $SrCl_2$.

3.27 Energy is required to remove two electrons from Ca to form Ca^{2+} and is required to add two electrons to O to form O^{2-}. Why, then, is CaO stable relative to the free elements?

3.28 List the individual steps used in constructing a Born–Haber cycle for the formation of BaI_2 from the elements. Which of the steps would you expect to be exothermic?

3.29 Use data from Appendix C, Figure 2.9, and Figure 2.11 to calculate the lattice energy of RbCl. Is this value greater than or less than the lattice energy of NaCl? Explain.

3.30 (a) Based on the lattice energies of $MgCl_2$ and $SrCl_2$ given in Table 3.2, what is the range of values that you would expect for the lattice energy of $CaCl_2$? (b) Using data from Appendix C, Figure 2.9, and Figure 2.11 and the value of the second ionization energy for Ca, 1145 kJ/mol, calculate the lattice energy of $CaCl_2$.

COVALENT BONDING, ELECTRONEGATIVITY, AND BOND POLARITY (sections 3.3 and 3.4)

3.31 (a) What is meant by the term *covalent bond*? (b) Give three examples of covalent bonding. (c) A substance XY, formed from two different elements, boils at $-33\ °C$. Is XY likely to be a covalent or an ionic substance? Explain.

3.32 Which of these elements are unlikely to form covalent bonds: S, H, K, Ar, Si? Explain your choices.

3.33 Using Lewis symbols and Lewis structures, diagram the formation of $SiCl_4$ from Si and Cl atoms.

3.34 Use Lewis symbols and Lewis structures to diagram the formation of PF_3 from P and F atoms.

3.35 (a) Construct a Lewis structure for O_2 in which each atom achieves an octet of electrons. (b) Explain why it is necessary to form a double bond in the Lewis structure. (c) The bond in O_2 is shorter than the O—O bond in compounds that contain an O—O single bond. Explain this observation.

3.36 (a) Construct a Lewis structure for hydrogen peroxide, H_2O_2, in which each atom achieves an octet of electrons. (b) Do you expect the O—O bond in H_2O_2 to be longer or shorter than the O—O bond in O_2?

3.37 (a) What is meant by the term *electronegativity*? (b) On the Pauling scale what is the range of electronegativity values for the elements? (c) Which element has the greatest electronegativity? (d) Which element has the smallest electronegativity?

3.38 (a) What is the trend in electronegativity going from left to right in a row of the periodic table? (b) How do electronegativity values generally vary going down a column in the periodic table? (c) How do periodic trends in electronegativity relate to those for ionization energy and electron affinity?

3.39 Using only the periodic table as your guide, select the most electronegative atom in each of the following sets: (a) Na, Mg, K, Ca; (b) P, S, As, Se; (c) Be, B, C, Si; (d) Zn, Ge, Ga, As.

3.40 By referring only to the periodic table, select (a) the most electronegative element in group 6A; (b) the least electronegative element in the group Al, Si, P; (c) the most electronegative element in the group Ga, P, Cl, Na; (d) the element in the group K, C, Zn, F that is most likely to form an ionic compound with Ba.

3.41 Which of the following bonds are polar: (a) B—F, (b) Cl—Cl, (c) Se—O, (d) H—I ? Which is the more electronegative atom in each polar bond?

3.42 Arrange the bonds in each of the following sets in order of increasing polarity: (a) C—F, O—F, Be—F; (b) O—Cl, S—Br, C—P; (c) C—S, B—F, N—O.

3.43 (a) From the data in Table 3.3, calculate the effective charges on the H and Br atoms of the HBr molecule in units of the electronic charge, *e*. (b) Compare your answers to part

(a) with those in Sample Exercise 3.5 for the HCl molecule. Can you explain why the values are different?

3.44 The iodine monobromide molecule, IBr, has a bond length of 2.49 Å and a dipole moment of 1.21 D. (a) Which atom of the molecule is expected to have a negative charge? Explain. (b) Calculate the effective charges on the I and Br atoms in IBr, in units of the electronic charge, e.

3.45 In the following pairs of binary compounds determine which one is a molecular substance and which one is an ionic substance. Use the appropriate naming convention (for ionic or molecular substances) to assign a name to each compound: (a) SiF_4 and LaF_3, (b) $FeCl_2$ and $ReCl_6$, (c) $PbCl_4$ and RbCl.

3.46 In the following pairs of binary compounds determine which one is a molecular substance and which one is an ionic substance. Use the appropriate naming convention (for ionic or molecular substances) to assign a name to each compound: (a) $TiCl_4$ and CaF_2, (b) ClF_3 and VF_3, (c) $SbCl_5$ and AlF_3.

LEWIS STRUCTURES; RESONANCE STRUCTURES (sections 3.5 and 3.6)

3.47 Draw Lewis structures for the following: (a) SiH_4, (b) CO, (c) SF_2, (d) H_2SO_4 (H is bonded to O), (e) ClO_2^-, (f) NH_2OH.

3.48 Write Lewis structures for the following: (a) H_2CO (both H atoms are bonded to C), (b) H_2O_2, (c) C_2F_6 (contains a C—C bond), (d) AsO_3^{3-}, (e) H_2SO_3 (H is bonded to O), (f) C_2H_2.

3.49 (a) When talking about atoms in a Lewis structure, what is meant by the term *formal charge*? (b) Does the formal charge of an atom represent the actual charge on that atom? Explain. (c) How does the formal charge of an atom in a Lewis structure differ from the oxidation number of the atom?

3.50 (a) Write a Lewis structure for the phosphorus trifluoride molecule, PF_3. Is the octet rule satisfied for all the atoms in your structure? (b) Determine the oxidation numbers of the P and F atoms. (c) Determine the formal charges of the P and F atoms. (d) Is the oxidation number for the P atom the same as its formal charge? Explain.

3.51 Write Lewis structures that obey the octet rule for each of the following, and assign oxidation numbers and formal charges to each atom: (a) OCS, (b) $SOCl_2$ (S is bonded to the two Cl atoms and to the O), (c) BrO_3^-, (d) $HClO_2$ (H is bonded to O).

3.52 For each of the following molecules or ions of sulfur and oxygen, write a single Lewis structure that obeys the octet rule, and calculate the oxidation numbers and formal charges on all the atoms: (a) SO_2, (b) SO_3, (c) SO_3^{2-}. (d) Arrange these molecules/ions in order of increasing S—O bond distance.

3.53 (a) Write one or more appropriate Lewis structures for the nitrite ion, NO_2^-. (b) With what allotrope of oxygen is it isoelectronic? (c) What would you predict for the lengths of the bonds in NO_2^- relative to N—O single bonds and double bonds?

3.54 Consider the formate ion, HCO_2^-, which is the anion formed when formic acid loses an H^+ ion. The H and the two O atoms are bonded to the central C atom. (a) Write one or more appropriate Lewis structures for this ion. (b) Are resonance structures needed to describe the structure? (c) What would you predict for the C—O bond lengths in the formate ion relative to those in CO_2?

3.55 Predict the ordering of the C—O bond lengths in CO, CO_2, and CO_3^{2-}.

3.56 Based on Lewis structures, predict the ordering of N—O bond lengths in NO^+, NO_2^-, and NO_3^-.

3.57 (a) Use the concept of resonance to explain why all six C—C bonds in benzene are equal in length. (b) Are the C—C bond lengths in benzene shorter than C—C single bonds? Are they shorter than C=C double bonds?

3.58 Mothballs are composed of naphthalene, $C_{10}H_8$, a molecule of which consists of two six-membered rings of carbon fused along an edge, as shown in this incomplete Lewis structure:

(a) Write two complete Lewis structures for naphthalene. (b) The observed C—C bond lengths in the molecule are intermediate between C—C single and C=C double bonds. Explain. (c) Represent the resonance in naphthalene in a way analogous to that used to represent it in benzene.

EXCEPTIONS TO THE OCTET RULE (section 3.7)

3.59 (a) State the octet rule. (b) Does the octet rule apply to ionic as well as to covalent compounds? Explain using examples as appropriate.

3.60 Considering the nonmetals, what is the relationship between the group number for an element (carbon, for example, belongs to group 4A; see the periodic table on the inside front cover) and the number of single covalent bonds that element needs to form to conform to the octet rule?

3.61 The chlorine oxides, in which a chlorine atom is bonded to one or more oxygen atoms, are important molecules in the chemistry of the atmosphere. Will any of the chlorine oxides obey the octet rule? Why or why not?

3.62 For elements in the third row of the periodic table and beyond, the octet rule is often not obeyed. What factors are usually cited to explain this fact?

3.63 Draw the Lewis structures for each of the following ions or molecules. Identify those that do not obey the octet rule, and explain why they do not: (a) SO_3^{2-}, (b) AlH_3, (c) N_3^-, (d) CH_2Cl_2, (e) SbF_5.

3.64 Draw the Lewis structures for each of the following molecules or ions. Which do not obey the octet rule? (a) NO, (b) BF_3, (c) ICl_2^-, (d) $OPBr_3$ (the P is the central atom), (e) XeF_4.

3.65 In the vapor phase, $BeCl_2$ exists as a discrete molecule. (a) Draw the Lewis structure of this molecule, using only single bonds. Does this Lewis structure satisfy the octet rule? **(b)** What other resonance structures are possible that satisfy the octet rule? **(c)** On the basis of the formal charges, which Lewis structure is expected to be dominant for $BeCl_2$?

3.66 **(a)** Describe the molecule xenon trioxide, XeO_3, using four possible Lewis structures, one each with zero, one, two, or three Xe—O double bonds. **(b)** Do any of these resonance structures satisfy the octet rule for every atom in the molecule? **(c)** Do any of the four Lewis structures have multiple resonance structures? If so, how many resonance structures do you find? **(d)** Which of the Lewis structures in (a) yields the most favorable formal charges for the molecule?

3.67 Consider the following statement: "For some molecules and ions, a Lewis structure that satisfies the octet rule does not lead

to the lowest formal charges, and a Lewis structure that leads to the lowest formal charges does not satisfy the octet rule." Illustrate this statement using the hydrogen sulfite ion, HSO_3^-, as an example (the H atom is bonded to one of the O atoms).

3.68 Some chemists believe that satisfaction of the octet rule should be the top criterion for choosing the dominant Lewis structure of a molecule or ion. Other chemists believe that achieving the best formal charges should be the top criterion. Consider the dihydrogen phosphate ion, $H_2PO_4^-$, in which the H atoms are bonded to O atoms. **(a)** What would be the predicted dominant Lewis structure if satisfying the octet rule is the top criterion? **(b)** What would it be if achieving the best formal charges is the top criterion? **(c)** Is there another Lewis structure you can draw that satisfies neither of these criteria?

BOND ENTHALPIES (section 3.8)

3.69 Using Table 3.4, estimate ΔH for each of the following gas-phase reactions:

(a)

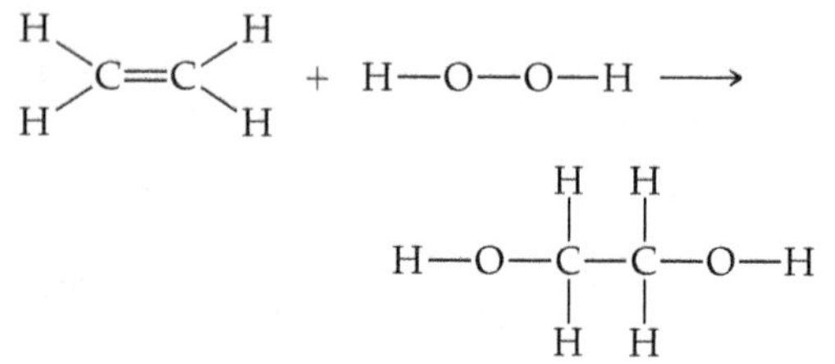

(b)

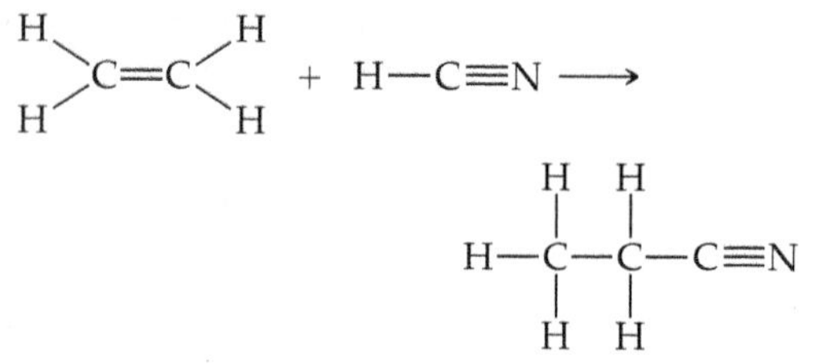

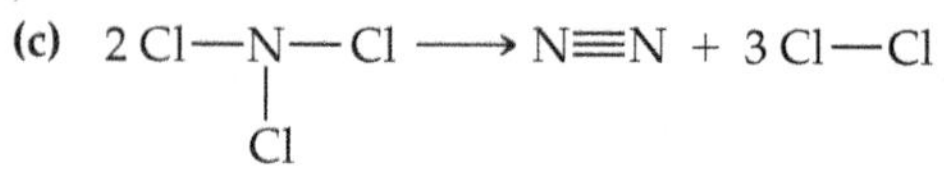

(c) $2\,Cl{-}N{-}Cl \longrightarrow N{\equiv}N + 3\,Cl{-}Cl$
         |
         Cl

3.70 Using Table 3.4, estimate ΔH for the following gas-phase reactions:

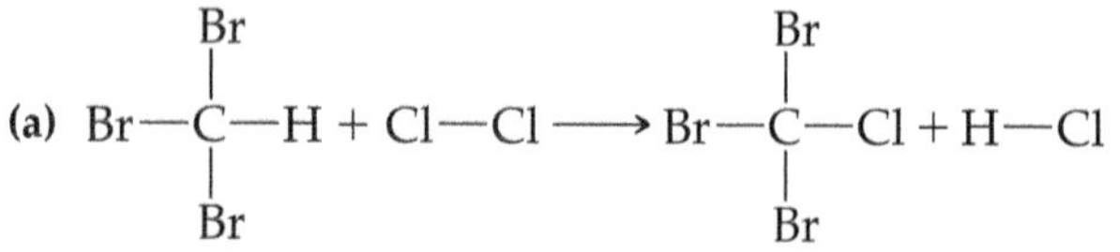

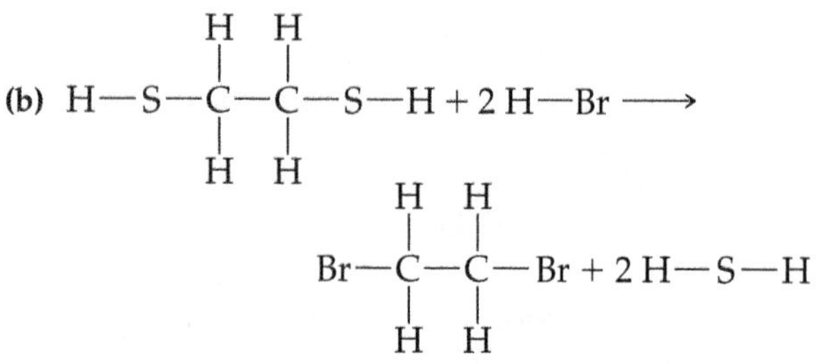

3.71 Using Table 3.4, estimate ΔH for each of the following reactions:
(a) $2\,CH_4(g) + O_2(g) \longrightarrow 2\,CH_3OH(g)$
(b) $H_2(g) + Br_2(g) \longrightarrow 2\,HBr(g)$
(c) $2\,H_2O_2(g) \longrightarrow 2\,H_2O(g) + O_2(g)$

3.72 Use Table 3.4 to estimate the enthalpy change for each of the following reactions:
(a) $H_2C{=}O(g) + HCl(g) \longrightarrow H_3C{-}O{-}Cl(g)$
(b) $H_2O_2(g) + 2\,CO(g) \longrightarrow H_2(g) + 2\,CO_2(g)$
(c) $3\,H_2C{=}CH_2(g) \longrightarrow C_6H_{12}(g)$ (the six carbon atoms form a six-membered ring with two H atoms on each C atom)

3.73 Ammonia is produced directly from nitrogen and hydrogen by using the Haber process. The chemical reaction is

$$N_2(g) + 3\,H_2(g) \longrightarrow 2\,NH_3(g)$$

(a) Use Table 3.4 to estimate the enthalpy change for the reaction. Is it exothermic or endothermic? **(b)** Compare the enthalpy change you calculate in (a) to the true enthalpy change as obtained using ΔH_f° values.

3.74 **(a)** Use bond enthalpies to estimate the enthalpy change for the reaction of hydrogen with ethylene:

$$H_2(g) + C_2H_4(g) \longrightarrow C_2H_6(g)$$

(b) Calculate the standard enthalpy change for this reaction, using heats of formation. Why does this value differ from that calculated in (a)?

3.75 Given the following bond-dissociation energies, calculate the average bond enthalpy for the Ti—Cl bond.

	ΔH(kJ/mol)
$TiCl_4(g) \longrightarrow TiCl_3(g) + Cl(g)$	335
$TiCl_3(g) \longrightarrow TiCl_2(g) + Cl(g)$	423
$TiCl_2(g) \longrightarrow TiCl(g) + Cl(g)$	444
$TiCl(g) \longrightarrow Ti(g) + Cl(g)$	519

[3.76] **(a)** Using average bond enthalpies, predict which of the following reactions will be most exothermic:
(i) $C(g) + 2\,F_2(g) \longrightarrow CF_4(g)$
(ii) $CO(g) + 3\,F_2 \longrightarrow CF_4(g) + OF_2(g)$
(iii) $CO_2(g) + 4\,F_2 \longrightarrow CF_4(g) + 2\,OF_2(g)$

(b) Explain the trend, if any, that exists between reaction exothermicity and the extent to which the carbon atom is bonded to oxygen.

ADDITIONAL EXERCISES

3.77 How many elements in the periodic table are represented by a Lewis symbol with a single dot? Are all these elements in the same group? Explain.

[3.78] From Equation 3.4 and the ionic radii given in Figure 2.7, calculate the potential energy of the following pairs of ions. Assume that the ions are separated by a distance equal to the sum of their ionic radii: (a) Na^+, Br^-; (b) Rb^+, Br^-; (c) Sr^{2+}, S^{2-}.

3.79 (a) Explain the following trend in lattice energy: BeH_2, 3205 kJ/mol; MgH_2, 2791 kJ/mol; CaH_2, 2410 kJ/mol; SrH_2, 2250 kJ/mol; BaH_2, 2121 kJ/mol. (b) The lattice energy of ZnH_2 is 2870 kJ/mol. Based on the data given in part (a), the radius of the Zn^{2+} ion is expected to be closest to that of which group 2A element?

3.80 Based on data in Table 3.2, estimate (within 30 kJ/mol) the lattice energy for (a) LiBr, (b) CsBr, (c) $CaCl_2$.

3.81 An ionic substance of formula MX has a lattice energy of 6×10^3 kJ/mol. Is the charge on the ion M likely to be 1+, 2+ or 3+? Explain your reasoning.

[3.82] From the ionic radii given in Figure 2.7, calculate the potential energy of a Ca^{2+} and O^{2-} ion pair that is just touching (the magnitude of the electronic charge is given on the back inside cover). Calculate the energy of a mole of such pairs. How does this value compare with the lattice energy of CaO (Table 3.2)? Explain the difference.

3.83 Construct a Born–Haber cycle for the formation of the hypothetical compound $NaCl_2$, where the sodium ion has a 2+ charge (the second ionization energy for sodium is given in Table 2.2). (a) How large would the lattice energy need to be for the formation of $NaCl_2$ to be exothermic? (b) If we were to estimate the lattice energy of $NaCl_2$ to be roughly equal to that of $MgCl_2$ (2326 kJ/mol from Table 3.2), what value would you obtain for the standard enthalpy of formation, ΔH_f°, of $NaCl_2$?

3.84 (a) How does a polar molecule differ from a nonpolar one? (b) Atoms X and Y have different electronegativities. Will the diatomic molecule X—Y necessarily be polar? Explain. (c) What factors affect the size of the dipole moment of a diatomic molecule?

3.85 For the following collection of nonmetallic elements, O, P, Te, I, B, (a) which two would form the most polar single bond? (b) Which two would form the longest single bond? (c) Which two would be likely to form a compound of formula XY_2? (d) Which combinations of elements would likely yield a compound of empirical formula X_2Y_3? In each case explain your answer.

3.86 The substance chlorine monoxide, ClO(g), is important in atmospheric processes that lead to depletion of the ozone layer. The ClO molecule has a dipole moment of 1.24 D and the Cl—O bond length is 1.60 Å. (a) Determine the magnitude of the charges on the Cl and O atoms in units of the electronic charge, e. (b) Based on the electronegativities of the elements, which atom would you expect to have a negative charge in the ClO molecule? (c) By using formal charges as a guide, propose the dominant Lewis structure for the molecule. Are the formal charges consistent with your answers to parts (a) and (b)? Can you reconcile any differences you find?

[3.87] Using the electronegativities of Br and Cl, estimate the partial charges on the atoms in the Br—Cl molecule. Using these partial charges and the atomic radii given in Figure 2.7, estimate the dipole moment of the molecule. The measured dipole moment is 0.57 D.

3.88 A major challenge in implementing the "hydrogen economy" is finding a safe, lightweight, and compact way of storing hydrogen for use as a fuel. The hydrides of light metals are attractive for hydrogen storage because they can store a high weight percentage of hydrogen in a small volume. For example, $NaAlH_4$ can release 5.6% of its mass as H_2 upon decomposing to NaH(s), Al(s), and $H_2(g)$. $NaAlH_4$ possesses both covalent bonds, which hold polyatomic anions together, and ionic bonds. (a) Write a balanced equation for the decomposition of $NaAlH_4$. (b) Which element in $NaAlH_4$ is the most electronegative? Which one is the least electronegative? (c) Based on electronegativity differences, what do you think is the identity of the polyatomic anion? Draw a Lewis structure for this ion.

3.89 Although I_3^- is known, F_3^- is not. Using Lewis structures, explain why F_3^- does not form.

3.90 Calculate the formal charge on the indicated atom in each of the following molecules or ions: (a) the central oxygen atom in O_3, (b) phosphorus in PF_6^-, (c) nitrogen in NO_2, (d) iodine in ICl_3, (e) chlorine in $HClO_4$ (hydrogen is bonded to O).

3.91 (a) Determine the formal charge on the chlorine atom in the hypochlorite ion, ClO^-, and the perchlorate ion, ClO_4^-, using resonance structures where the Cl atom has an octet. (b) What are the oxidation numbers of chlorine in ClO^- and in ClO_4^-? (c) Is it uncommon for the formal charge and the oxidation state to be different? Explain. (d) Perchlorate is a much stronger oxidizing agent than hypochlorite. Would you expect there to be any relationship between the oxidizing power of the oxyanion and either the oxidation state or the formal charge of chlorine?

3.92 The following three Lewis structures can be drawn for N_2O:

$$:N\equiv N-\ddot{\underset{..}{O}}: \longleftrightarrow :\ddot{N}-N\equiv O: \longleftrightarrow :\ddot{N}=N=\ddot{O}: $$

(a) Using formal charges, which of these three resonance forms is likely to be the most important? (b) The N—N bond length in N_2O is 1.12 Å, slightly longer than a typical $N\equiv N$ bond; and the N—O bond length is 1.19 Å, slightly shorter than a typical $N=O$ bond. (See Table 3.5.) Rationalize these observations in terms of the resonance structures shown previously and your conclusion for part (a).

[3.93] (a) Triazine, $C_3H_3N_3$, is like benzene except that in triazine every other C—H group is replaced by a nitrogen atom. Draw the Lewis structure(s) for the triazine molecule. (b) Estimate the carbon–nitrogen bond distances in the ring.

[3.94] Ortho-dichlorobenzene, $C_6H_4Cl_2$, is obtained when two of the adjacent hydrogen atoms in benzene are replaced with Cl atoms. A skeleton of the molecule is shown here. (a) Complete a Lewis structure for the molecule using bonds and electron pairs as needed. (b) Are there any resonance structures for the molecule? If so, sketch them. (c) Are the resonance structures in (a) and (b) equivalent to one another as they are in benzene? If not, explain what makes them different.

3.95 Consider the hypothetical molecule B—A=B. How could you use an experimentally determined structure of the molecule to decide whether resonance is important in it?

3.96 An important reaction for the conversion of natural gas to other useful hydrocarbons is the conversion of methane to ethane.

$$2\,CH_4(g) \longrightarrow C_2H_6(g) + H_2(g)$$

In practice, this reaction is carried out in the presence of oxygen, which converts the hydrogen produced to water.

$$2\,CH_4(g) + \tfrac{1}{2}O_2(g) \longrightarrow C_2H_6(g) + H_2O(g)$$

Use Table 3.4 to estimate ΔH for these two reactions. Why is the conversion of methane to ethane more favorable when oxygen is used?

3.97 Two compounds are isomers if they have the same chemical formula but a different arrangement of atoms. Use Table 3.4 to estimate ΔH for each of the following gas-phase isomerization reactions, and indicate which isomer has the lower enthalpy:

(a)

Ethanol   Dimethyl ether

(b)

Ethylene oxide   Acetaldehyde

(c)

Cyclopentene   Pentadiene

(d)

Methyl isocyanide   Acetonitrile

[3.98] With reference to the "Chemistry Put to Work" box on explosives, **(a)** use bond enthalpies to estimate the enthalpy change for the explosion of 1.00 g of nitroglycerin. **(b)** Write a balanced equation for the decomposition of TNT. Assume that, upon explosion, TNT decomposes into $N_2(g)$, $CO_2(g)$, $H_2O(g)$, and $C(s)$.

[3.99] The "plastic" explosive C-4, often used in action movies, contains the molecule *cyclotrimethylenetrinitramine*, which is often called RDX (for Royal Demolition eXplosive):

Cyclotrimethylenetrinitramine (RDX)

(a) Complete the Lewis structure for the molecule by adding unshared electron pairs where they are needed. **(b)** Does the Lewis structure you drew in part (a) have any resonance structures? If so, how many? **(c)** The molecule causes an explosion by decomposing into $CO(g)$, $N_2(g)$, and $H_2O(g)$. Write a balanced equation for the decomposition reaction. **(d)** With reference to Table 3.4, which is the weakest type of bond in the molecule? **(e)** Use average bond enthalpies to estimate the enthalpy change when 5.0 g of RDX decomposes.

3.100 The bond lengths of carbon–carbon, carbon–nitrogen, carbon–oxygen, and nitrogen–nitrogen single, double, and triple bonds are listed in Table 3.5. Plot bond enthalpy (Table 3.4) versus bond length for these bonds (as in Figure 3.17). What do you conclude about the relationship between bond length and bond enthalpy? What do you conclude about the relative strengths of C—C, C—N, C—O, and N—N bonds?

INTEGRATIVE EXERCISES

3.101 The Ti^{2+} ion is isoelectronic with the Ca atom. **(a)** Are there any differences in the electron configurations of Ti^{2+} and Ca? **(b)** With reference to Figure 1.24, comment on the changes in the ordering of the $4s$ and $3d$ subshells in Ca and Ti^{2+}. **(c)** Will Ca and Ti^{2+} have the same number of unpaired electrons? Explain.

[3.102] **(a)** Write the chemical equations that are used in calculating the lattice energy of $SrCl_2(s)$ via a Born–Haber cycle. **(b)** The second ionization energy of $Sr(g)$ is 1064 kJ/mol. Use this fact along with data in Appendix C, Figure 2.9, Figure 2.11, and Table 3.2 to calculate ΔH_f° for $SrCl_2(s)$.

[3.103] The electron affinity of oxygen is −141 kJ/mol, corresponding to the reaction

$$O(g) + e^- \longrightarrow O^-(g)$$

The lattice energy of $K_2O(s)$ is 2238 kJ/mol. Use these data along with data in Appendix C and Figure 2.9 to calculate the "second electron affinity" of oxygen, corresponding to the reaction

$$O^-(g) + e^- \longrightarrow O^{2-}(g)$$

3.104 You and a partner are asked to complete a lab entitled "Oxides of Ruthenium" that is scheduled to extend over two lab periods. The first lab, which is to be completed by your partner, is devoted to carrying out compositional analysis. In the second lab, you are to determine melting points. Upon going to lab you find two unlabeled vials, one containing a soft yellow substance and the other a black powder. You also find the following notes in your partner's notebook—*Compound 1*: 76.0% Ru and 24.0% O (by mass), *Compound 2*: 61.2% Ru and

38.8% O (by mass). **(a)** What is the empirical formula for Compound 1? **(b)** What is the empirical formula for Compound 2? **(c)** Upon determining the melting points of these two compounds, you find that the yellow compound melts at 25 °C, while the black powder does not melt up to the maximum temperature of your apparatus, 1200 °C. What is the identity of the yellow compound? What is the identity of the black compound? Be sure to use the appropriate naming convention depending on whether the compound is better described as a molecular or ionic compound.

[**3.105**] One scale for electronegativity is based on the concept that the electronegativity of any atom is proportional to the ionization energy of the atom minus its electron affinity: electronegativity $= k(\text{IE} - \text{EA})$, where k is a proportionality constant. **(a)** How does this definition explain why the electronegativity of F is greater than that of Cl even though Cl has the greater electron affinity? **(b)** Why are both ionization energy and electron affinity relevant to the notion of electronegativity? **(c)** By using data in Chapter 2, determine the value of k that would lead to an electronegativity of 4.0 for F under this definition. **(d)** Use your result from part (c) to determine the electronegativities of Cl and O using this scale. Do these values follow the trend shown in Figure 3.7?

3.106 The compound chloral hydrate, known in detective stories as knockout drops, is composed of 14.52% C, 1.83% H, 64.30% Cl, and 19.35% O by mass and has a molar mass of 165.4 g/mol. **(a)** What is the empirical formula of this substance? **(b)** What is the molecular formula of this substance? **(c)** Draw the Lewis structure of the molecule, assuming that the Cl atoms bond to a single C atom and that there are a C—C bond and two C—O bonds in the compound.

3.107 Barium azide is 62.04% Ba and 37.96% N. Each azide ion has a net charge of 1−. **(a)** Determine the chemical formula of the azide ion. **(b)** Write three resonance structures for the azide ion. **(c)** Which structure is most important? **(d)** Predict the bond lengths in the ion.

3.108 Acetylene (C_2H_2) and nitrogen (N_2) both contain a triple bond, but they differ greatly in their chemical properties. **(a)** Write the Lewis structures for the two substances. **(b)** By referring to Appendix C, look up the enthalpies of formation of acetylene and nitrogen and compare their reactivities. **(c)** Write balanced chemical equations for the complete oxidation of N_2 to form $N_2O_5(g)$ and of acetylene to form $CO_2(g)$ and $H_2O(g)$. **(d)** Calculate the enthalpy of oxidation per mole of N_2 and C_2H_2 (the enthalpy of formation of $N_2O_5(g)$ is 11.30 kJ/mol). How do these comparative values relate to your response to part (b)? Both N_2 and C_2H_2 possess triple bonds with quite high bond enthalpies (Table 3.4). What aspect of chemical bonding in these molecules or in the oxidation products seems to account for the difference in chemical reactivities?

[**3.109**] Under special conditions, sulfur reacts with anhydrous liquid ammonia to form a binary compound of sulfur and nitrogen.

The compound is found to consist of 69.6% S and 30.4% N. Measurements of its molecular mass yield a value of 184.3 g mol^{-1}. The compound occasionally detonates on being struck or when heated rapidly. The sulfur and nitrogen atoms of the molecule are joined in a ring. All the bonds in the ring are of the same length. **(a)** Calculate the empirical and molecular formulas for the substance. **(b)** Write Lewis structures for the molecule, based on the information you are given. (*Hint:* You should find a relatively small number of dominant Lewis structures.) **(c)** Predict the bond distances between the atoms in the ring. (*Note:* The S—S distance in the S_8 ring is 2.05 Å.) **(d)** The enthalpy of formation of the compound is estimated to be 480 kJ mol^{-1}. ΔH_f° of S(g) is 222.8 kJ mol^{-1}. Estimate the average bond enthalpy in the compound.

[**3.110**] A common form of elemental phosphorus is the tetrahedral P_4 molecule, where all four phosphorus atoms are equivalent:

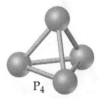

P_4

At room temperature phosphorus is a solid. **(a)** Do you think there are any unshared pairs of electrons in the P_4 molecule? **(b)** How many P—P bonds are there in the molecule? **(c)** Can you draw a Lewis structure for a linear P_4 molecule that satisfies the octet rule? **(d)** Using formal charges, what can you say about the stability of the linear molecule versus that of the tetrahedral molecule?

[**3.111**] Consider benzene (C_6H_6) in the gas phase. **(a)** Write the reaction for breaking all the bonds in $C_6H_6(g)$, and use data in Appendix C to determine the enthalpy change for this reaction. **(b)** Write a reaction that corresponds to breaking all the carbon–carbon bonds in $C_6H_6(g)$. **(c)** By combining your answers to parts (a) and (b) and using the average bond enthalpy for C—H from Table 3.4, calculate the average bond enthalpy for the carbon–carbon bonds in $C_6H_6(g)$. **(d)** Comment on your answer from part (c) as compared to the values for C—C single bonds and C=C double bonds in Table 3.4.

3.112 Average bond enthalpies are generally defined for gas-phase molecules. Many substances are liquids in their standard state. By using appropriate thermochemical data from Appendix C, calculate average bond enthalpies in the liquid state for the following bonds, and compare these values to the gas-phase values given in Table 3.4: **(a)** Br—Br, from $Br_2(l)$; **(b)** C—Cl, from $CCl_4(l)$; **(c)** O—O, from $H_2O_2(l)$ (assume that the O—H bond enthalpy is the same as in the gas phase). **(d)** What can you conclude about the process of breaking bonds in the liquid as compared to the gas phase? Explain the difference in the ΔH values between the two phases.

WHAT'S AHEAD

4.1 MOLECULAR SHAPES
We begin by discussing *molecular shapes* and examining some shapes commonly encountered in molecules.

4.2 THE VSEPR MODEL
We consider how molecular geometries can be predicted using the *valence-shell electron-pair repulsion,* or *VSEPR,* model, which is based on Lewis structures and the repulsions between regions of high electron density.

4.3 MOLECULAR SHAPE AND MOLECULAR POLARITY
Once we know the geometry of a molecule and the types of bonds it contains, we can determine whether the molecule is *polar* or *nonpolar*.

4.4 COVALENT BONDING AND ORBITAL OVERLAP
We recognize that electrons are shared between atoms in a covalent bond. In *valence-bond theory,* the bonding electrons are visualized as originating in atomic orbitals on two atoms. A covalent bond is formed when these orbitals overlap.

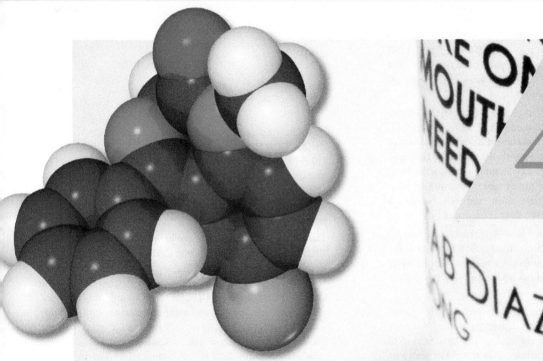

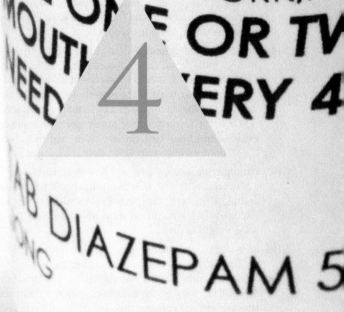

THE DRUG SHOWN HERE IS DIAZEPAM, better known as Valium. It is commonly prescribed for a wide range of disorders, including *anxiety, insomnia, seizures, muscle spasms, restless legs syndrome,* and *obsessive-compulsive disorder*. Valium was invented by Leo Sternbach at Hoffmann-LaRoche Pharmaceuticals and first licensed for use in 1960. It was the top-selling pharmaceutical in the United States from 1969 to 1982, with peak sales in 1978 of 2.3 billion tablets! It continues to be an important medication and is on the World Health Organization's Essential Drugs list.

4.5 HYBRID ORBITALS
To account for molecular shape, we consider how the orbitals of one atom mix with one another, or *hybridize*, to create *hybrid orbitals*.

4.6 MULTIPLE BONDS
Atomic orbitals that contribute to covalent bonding in a molecule can overlap in multiple ways to produce *sigma* and *pi* bonds between atoms. Single bonds generally consist of one sigma bond; multiple bonds involve one sigma and one or more pi bonds. We examine the geometric arrangements of these bonds and how they are exemplified in organic compounds.

4.7 MOLECULAR ORBITALS
We examine a more sophisticated treatment of bonding called *molecular orbital theory,* which introduces the concepts of *bonding* and *antibonding molecular orbitals*.

4.8 METALLIC BONDING
We take a closer look at metallic bonding and how it is responsible for the properties of metals, in terms of two models—the *electron-sea model* and the molecular-orbital model. We learn how overlap of atomic orbitals gives rise to *bands* in metals.

MOLECULAR GEOMETRY AND BONDING THEORIES

WE SAW IN CHAPTER 3 THAT LEWIS STRUCTURES help us understand the compositions of molecules and their covalent bonds. However, Lewis structures do not show one of the most important aspects of molecules—their overall shapes. The shape and size of molecules—sometimes referred to as molecular *architecture*—are defined by the angles and distances between the nuclei of the component atoms.

The shape and size of a molecule of a substance, together with the strength and polarity of its bonds, largely determine the properties of that substance. Some of the most dramatic examples of the important roles of molecular architecture are seen in biochemical reactions. For example, the chapter-opening photograph shows a molecular model of diazepam, better known as Valium. In the body, this relatively simple molecule enters into an extraordinary array of biochemical interactions. Valium works by binding to certain important sites in the central nervous system. Its effectiveness is highly dependent on the shape and size of the molecule as well on the charge distributions within it. Even a small modification to molecular shape or size alters the drug's effectiveness.

One of our goals in this chapter is to develop a sense of the shapes of molecules and how those shapes are governed in large measure by the kinds of bonds that exist between the atoms making up the molecules.

Our first goal is to learn the relationship between two-dimensional Lewis structures and three-dimensional molecular shapes. Armed with this knowledge, we can examine the nature of covalent bonds. The lines used to depict bonds in Lewis structures provide important clues about the orbitals that molecules use in bonding. By examining these orbitals, we can gain a greater understanding of the behavior of molecules. Mastering the material in this chapter will help you in later discussions of the physical and chemical properties of substances.

4.1 | MOLECULAR SHAPES

In Chapter 3 we used Lewis structures to account for the formulas of covalent compounds. ∞∞ (Section 3.5) Lewis structures, however, do not indicate the shapes of molecules; they simply show the number and types of bonds. For example, the Lewis structure of CCl_4 tells us only that four Cl atoms are bonded to a central C atom:

$$:\ddot{C}l:$$
$$\mspace |$$
$$:\ddot{C}l - C - \ddot{C}l:$$
$$\mspace |$$
$$:\ddot{C}l:$$

The Lewis structure is drawn with the atoms all in the same plane. As shown in ▼ **FIGURE 4.1**, however, the actual arrangement is the Cl atoms at the corners of a *tetrahedron*, a geometric object with four corners and four faces, each an equilateral triangle.

The shape of a molecule is determined by its **bond angles**, the angles made by the lines joining the nuclei of the atoms in the molecule. The bond angles of a molecule, together with the bond lengths ∞∞ (Section 3.8), define the shape and size of the molecule. In Figure 4.1, you should be able to see that there are six Cl—C—Cl bond angles in CCl_4 and that they all have the same value of 109.5°, the angle size characteristic of a tetrahedron. In addition, all four C—Cl bonds are the same length (1.78 Å). Thus, the shape and size of CCl_4 are completely described by stating that the molecule is tetrahedral with C—Cl bonds of length 1.78 Å.

We begin our discussion of molecular shapes with molecules (and ions) that, like CCl_4, have a single central atom bonded to two or more atoms of the same type. Such molecules have the general formula AB_n in which the central atom A is bonded to n

▲ **GO FIGURE**

In the space-filling model, what determines the relative sizes of the spheres?

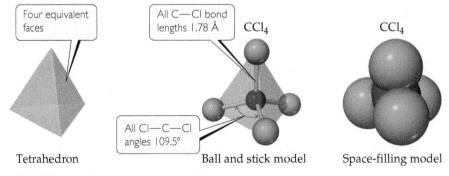

Four equivalent faces

All C—Cl bond lengths 1.78 Å CCl_4

CCl_4

All Cl—C—Cl angles 109.5°

Tetrahedron   Ball and stick model   Space-filling model

▲ **FIGURE 4.1**   **Tetrahedral shape of CCl₄.**

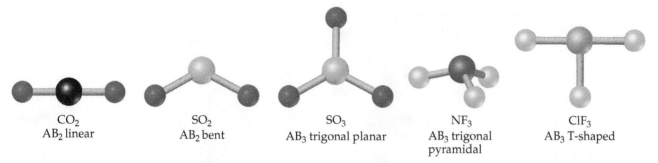

▲ FIGURE 4.2   **Shapes of AB$_2$ and AB$_3$ molecules.**

B atoms. Both CO_2 and H_2O are AB$_2$ molecules, for example, whereas SO_3 and NH_3 are AB$_3$ molecules, and so on.

The number of shapes possible for AB$_n$ molecules depends on the value of n. Those commonly found for AB$_2$ and AB$_3$ molecules are shown in ▲ **FIGURE 4.2.** An AB$_2$ molecule must be either linear (bond angle = 180°) or bent (bond angle ≠ 180°). For AB$_3$ molecules, the two most common shapes place the B atoms at the corners of an equilateral triangle. If the A atom lies in the same plane as the B atoms, the shape is *trigonal planar*. If the A atom lies above the plane of the B atoms, the shape is *trigonal pyramidal* (a pyramid with an equilateral triangle as its base). Some AB$_3$ molecules, such as ClF_3, are *T-shaped*, the relatively unusual shape shown in Figure 4.2. The atoms lie in one plane, but the angles between them vary as shown.

Compare Figures 4.1 and 4.2 to notice the difference between NF_3 and CCl_4. The CCl_4 molecule is tetrahedral because the four atoms bonded to the carbon are disposed at the four apexes of a tetrahedron around the central atom. The NF_3 molecule is pyramidal because the three atoms bonded to nitrogen lie at the base of a trigonal pyramid.

The shapes that maximize the separation of outer atoms are shown in ▼ **FIGURE 4.3.** In addition to the shapes we have already seen, this figure shows those encountered when there are five or six atoms surrounding a central atom. The trigonal bipyramid can be thought of as two face-to-face trigonal pyramids; the octahedron is like two face-to-face square pyramids.

⚠ **GO FIGURE**

Which of these molecular shapes do you expect for the SF$_6$ molecule?

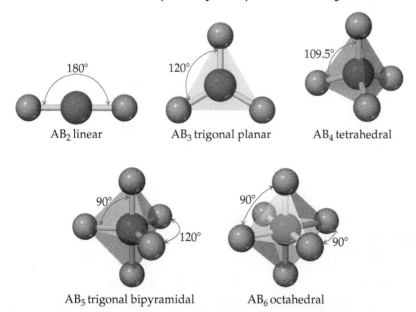

AB$_2$ linear   AB$_3$ trigonal planar   AB$_4$ tetrahedral

AB$_5$ trigonal bipyramidal   AB$_6$ octahedral

◀ FIGURE 4.3   **Shapes allowing maximum distances between atoms in AB$_n$ molecules.**

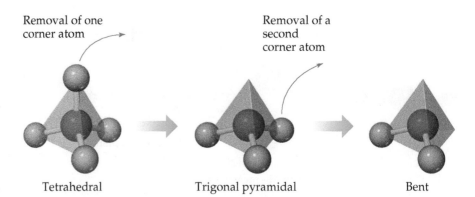

Removal of one corner atom →

Removal of a second corner atom →

Tetrahedral → Trigonal pyramidal → Bent

▶ **FIGURE 4.4** **Derivatives of the tetrahedral molecular shape.**

Some molecules have shapes other than those shown in Figure 4.3, but we can usually derive the shape of those molecules from Figure 4.3. Neither trigonal pyramidal nor bent is shown in Figure 4.3, for instance, but ▲ **FIGURE 4.4** shows how we can arrive at these shapes by removing atoms from the tetrahedral shape.

Why do so many AB$_n$ molecules have shapes related to those shown in Figure 4.3, and can we predict these shapes? When A is a representative element (one from the *s* block or *p* block of the periodic table), we can answer these questions by using the **valence-shell electron-pair repulsion (VSEPR) model**. Although the name is rather imposing, the model is quite simple. It has useful predictive capabilities, as we will see in Section 4.2.

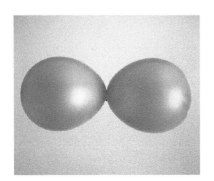

Two balloons
linear orientation

GIVE IT SOME THOUGHT

In addition to tetrahedral, another common shape for AB$_4$ molecules is *square planar.* All five atoms lie in the same plane, with the B atoms at the corners of a square and the A atom at the center of the square. Which shape in Figure 4.3 could lead to a square-planar shape upon removal of one or more atoms?

4.2 | THE VSEPR MODEL

Imagine tying two identical balloons together at their ends. As shown in ◀ **FIGURE 4.5**, the two balloons naturally orient themselves to point away from each other; that is, they try to "get out of each other's way" as much as possible. If we add a third balloon, the balloons orient themselves toward the vertices of an equilateral triangle, and if we add a fourth balloon, they adopt a tetrahedral shape. We see that an optimum geometry exists for each number of balloons.

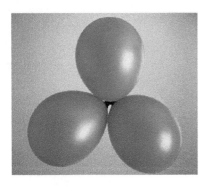

Three balloons
trigonal-planar orientation

In some ways, the electrons in molecules behave like these balloons. We have seen that a single covalent bond is formed between two atoms when a pair of electrons occupies the space between the atoms. ∞ (Section 3.3) A **bonding pair** of electrons thus defines a region in which the electrons are most likely to be found. We will refer to such a region as an **electron domain**. Likewise, a **nonbonding pair** (or **lone pair**) of electrons defines an electron domain that is located principally on one atom. For example, the Lewis structure of NH$_3$ has four electron domains around the central nitrogen atom (three bonding pairs, represented as usual by short lines, and one nonbonding pair, represented by dots):

Four balloons
tetrahedral orientation

▲ **FIGURE 4.5** **A balloon analogy for electron domains.**

$$H\!-\!\ddot{N}\!-\!H$$
$$|$$
$$H$$

Each multiple bond in a molecule also constitutes a single electron domain. Thus, the resonance structure for O$_3$ has three electron domains around the central oxygen atom (a single bond, a double bond, and a nonbonding pair of electrons):

$$:\!\ddot{O}\!-\!\ddot{O}\!=\!\ddot{O}$$

In general, *each nonbonding pair, single bond, or multiple bond produces a single electron domain around the central atom in a molecule.*

⚠ GIVE IT SOME THOUGHT

Suppose a particular AB₃ molecule has the resonance structure

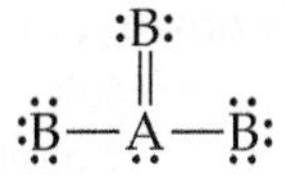

$$
\begin{array}{c}
:\!\ddot{B}: \\
\parallel \\
:\!\ddot{B}\!-\!\ddot{A}\!-\!\ddot{B}:
\end{array}
$$

Does this structure follow the octet rule? How many electron domains are there around the A atom?

The VSEPR model is based on the idea that electron domains are negatively charged and therefore repel one another. Like the balloons in Figure 4.5, electron domains try to stay out of one another's way. *The best arrangement of a given number of electron domains is the one that minimizes the repulsions among them.* In fact, the analogy between electron domains and balloons is so close that the same preferred geometries are found in both cases. Like the balloons in Figure 4.5, two electron domains orient *linearly,* three domains orient in a *trigonal-planar* fashion, and four orient *tetrahedrally.* These arrangements, together with those for five- and six-electron domains, are summarized in ▼ TABLE 4.1. If you compare the geometries in Table 4.1 with those in Figure 4.3,

TABLE 4.1 • Electron-Domain Geometries as a Function of Number of Electron Domains

Number of Electron Domains	Arrangement of Electron Domains	Electron-Domain Geometry	Predicted Bond Angles
2	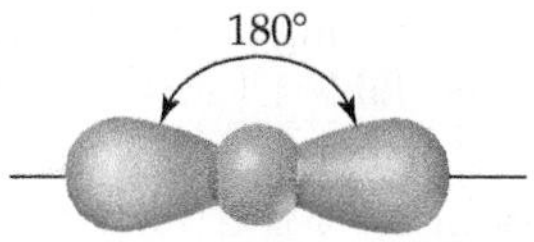 180°	Linear	180°
3	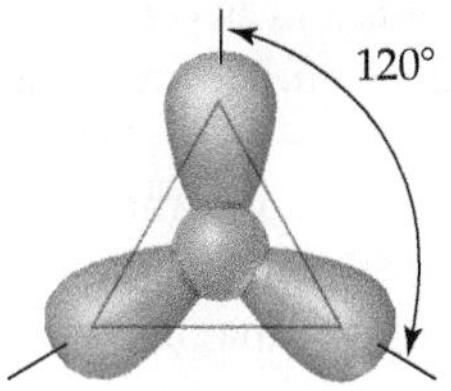 120°	Trigonal planar	120°
4	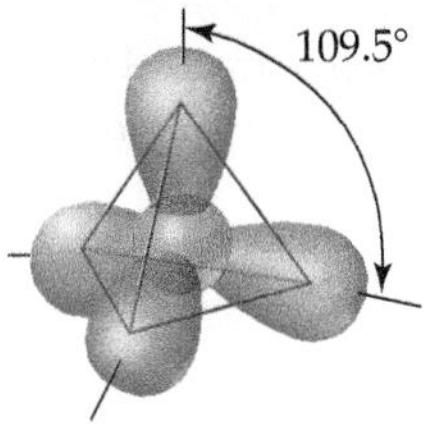 109.5°	Tetrahedral	109.5°
5	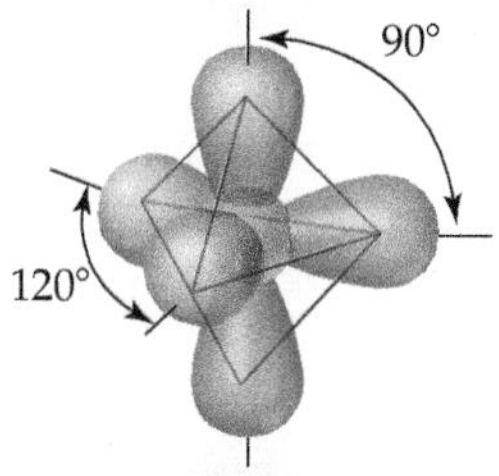 90° 120°	Trigonal bipyramidal	120° 90°
6	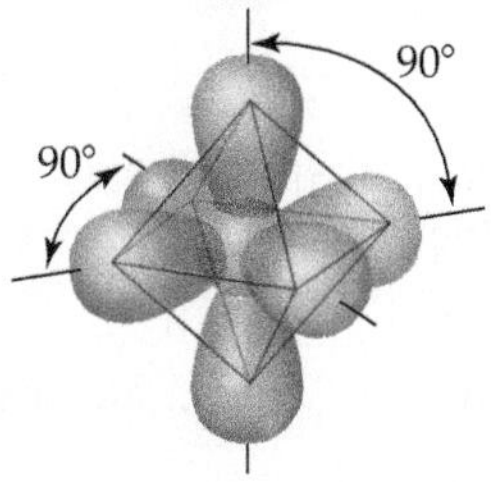 90° 90°	Octahedral	90°

you will see that they are the same. *The shapes of different AB_n molecules or ions depend on the number of electron domains surrounding the central atom.*

The arrangement of electron domains about the central atom of an AB_n molecule or ion is called its **electron-domain geometry**. In contrast, the **molecular geometry** is the arrangement of *only the atoms* in a molecule or ion—any nonbonding pairs in the molecule are *not* part of the description of the molecular geometry.

In determining the shape of any molecule, we first use the VSEPR model to predict the electron-domain geometry. From knowing how many of the domains are due to nonbonding pairs, we can then predict the molecular geometry. When all the electron domains in a molecule arise from bonds, the molecular geometry is identical to the electron-domain geometry. When, however, one or more domains involve nonbonding pairs of electrons, we must remember to ignore those domains when talking about molecular shape.

We can generalize the steps we follow in using the VSEPR model to predict the shapes of molecules or ions:

1. Draw the *Lewis structure* of the molecule or ion, and count the number of electron domains around the central atom. Each nonbonding electron pair, each single bond, each double bond, and each triple bond counts as one electron domain.

2. Determine the *electron-domain geometry* by arranging the electron domains about the central atom so that the repulsions among them are minimized, as shown in Table 4.1.

3. Use the arrangement of the bonded atoms to determine the *molecular geometry*.

▼ FIGURE 4.6 shows how these steps are applied to predict the geometry of the NH_3 molecule. The three bonds and one nonbonding pair in the Lewis structure tell us we have four electron domains. We know from Table 4.1 that the repulsions among four electron domains are minimized when the domains point toward the vertices of a tetrahedron, so the electron-domain geometry of NH_3 is tetrahedral. We know from the Lewis structure that one electron domain holds a nonbonding pair of electrons, which occupies one of the four vertices of the tetrahedron. The bonding arrangement is therefore three atoms bonded to a central atom, with the central atom not in the same plane as the three others. This is just the situation we find in the middle molecule of Figure 4.4. Hence, the molecular geometry of NH_3 is trigonal pyramidal. Notice that the tetrahedral arrangement of the four electron domains leads us to predict the trigonal-pyramidal molecular geometry.

Because the trigonal-pyramidal molecular geometry is based on a tetrahedral electron-domain geometry, the *ideal bond angles* are 109.5°. As we will soon see, bond angles deviate from ideal values when the surrounding atoms and electron domains are not identical.

◢ GIVE IT SOME THOUGHT

From the standpoint of the VSEPR model, what do nonbonding electron pairs, single bonds, and multiple bonds have in common?

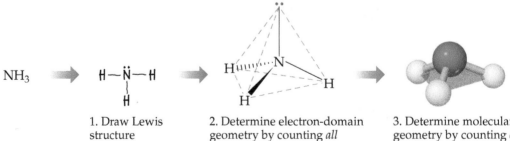

1. Draw Lewis structure

2. Determine electron-domain geometry by counting *all* electron domains, then use Table 4.1 to determine appropriate electron domain geomtry.

3. Determine molecular geometry by counting *only bonding* electron domains to see arrangement of bonded atoms (trigonal pyramidal)

▶ **FIGURE 4.6 Determining the molecular geometry of NH_3.**

As one more example, let's determine the shape of the CO_2 molecule. Its Lewis structure reveals two electron domains (each one a double bond) around the central carbon:

$$\ddot{O}{=}C{=}\ddot{O}$$

Two electron domains orient in a linear electron-domain geometry (Table 4.1). Because
neither domain is a nonbonding pair of electrons, the molecular geometry is also linear,
and the O—C—O bond angle is 180°.

▼ TABLE 4.2 summarizes the possible molecular geometries when an AB_n molecule
has four or fewer electron domains about A. These geometries are important because
they include all the shapes usually seen in molecules or ions that obey the octet rule.

**TABLE 4.2 • Electron-Domain and Molecular Geometries for Two, Three, and Four
Electron Domains around a Central Atom**

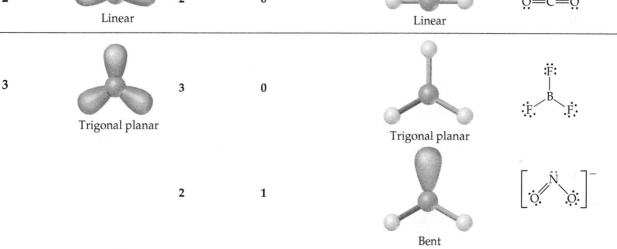

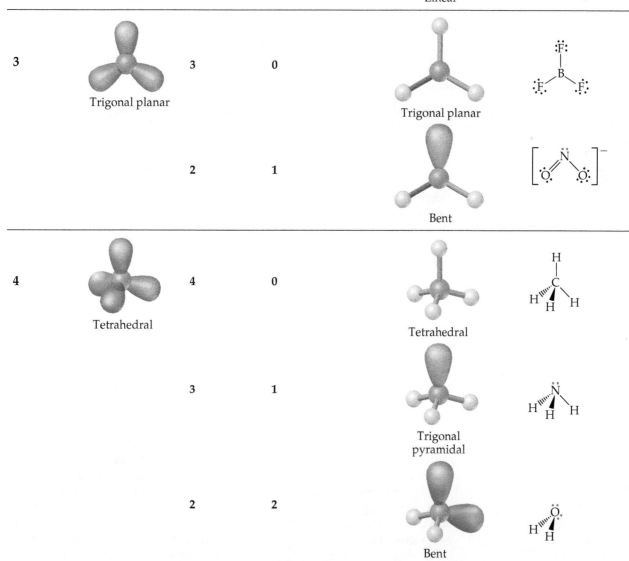

Number of Electron Domains	Electron-Domain Geometry	Bonding Domains	Nonbonding Domains	Molecular Geometry	Example
2	Linear	2	0	Linear	$\ddot{O}{=}C{=}\ddot{O}$
3	Trigonal planar	3	0	Trigonal planar	
		2	1	Bent	
4	Tetrahedral	4	0	Tetrahedral	
		3	1	Trigonal pyramidal	
		2	2	Bent	

SAMPLE EXERCISE 4.1 | **Using the VSEPR Model**

Use the VSEPR model to predict the molecular geometry of (**a**) O_3, (**b**) $SnCl_3^-$.

SOLUTION

Analyze We are given the molecular formulas of a molecule and a polyatomic ion, both conforming to the general formula AB_n and both having a central atom from the p block of the periodic table.

Plan To predict the molecular geometries, we draw their Lewis structures and count electron domains around the central atom to get the electron-domain geometry. We then obtain the molecular geometry from the arrangement of the domains that are due to bonds.

Solve

(**a**) We can draw two resonance structures for O_3:

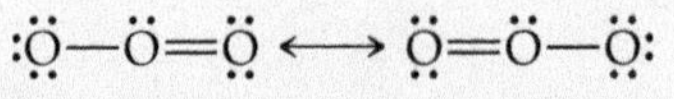

$$:\ddot{O}-\ddot{O}=\ddot{O}: \longleftrightarrow \ddot{O}=\ddot{O}-\ddot{O}:$$

Because of resonance, the bonds between the central O atom and the outer O atoms are of equal length. In both resonance structures the central O atom is bonded to the two outer O atoms and has one nonbonding pair. Thus, there are three electron domains about the central O atoms. (Remember that a double bond counts as a single electron domain.) The arrangement of three electron domains is trigonal planar (Table 4.1). Two of the domains are from bonds, and one is due to a nonbonding pair. So, the molecule has a bent shape with an ideal bond angle of 120° (Table 4.2).

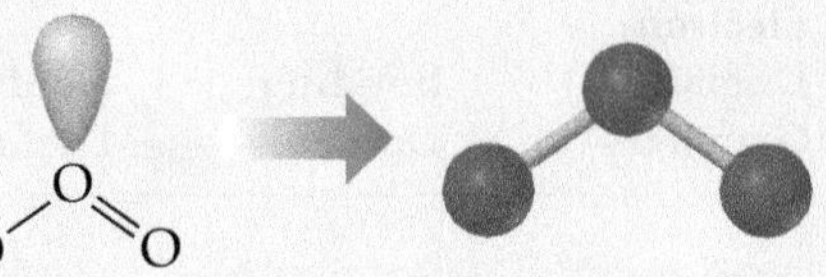

Comment As this example illustrates, when a molecule exhibits resonance, any one of the resonance structures can be used to predict the molecular geometry.

(**b**) The Lewis structure for $SnCl_3^-$ is

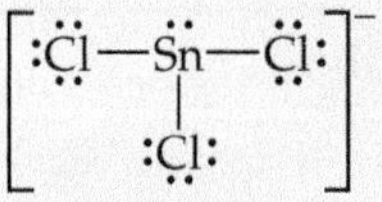

$$\left[:\ddot{Cl}-\ddot{Sn}-\ddot{Cl}:\right]^-$$
$$:\ddot{Cl}:$$

The central Sn atom is bonded to the three Cl atoms and has one nonbonding pair; thus, we have four electron domains, meaning tetrahedral electron-domain geometry (Table 4.1) with one vertex occupied by a nonbonding pair of electrons. Tetrahedral electron-domain geometry with three bonding and one nonbonding domains means the molecular geometry is trigonal pyramidal (Table 4.2).

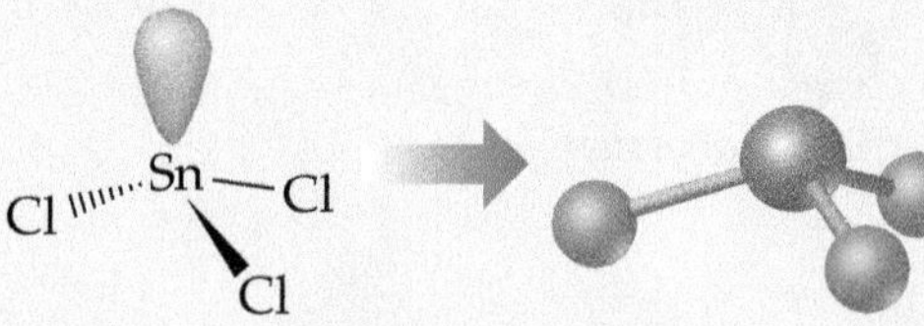

PRACTICE EXERCISE

Predict the electron-domain and molecular geometries for (**a**) $SeCl_2$, (**b**) CO_3^{2-}.

Answers: (**a**) tetrahedral, bent; (**b**) trigonal planar, trigonal planar

Effect of Nonbonding Electrons and Multiple Bonds on Bond Angles

We can refine the VSEPR model to explain slight distortions from the ideal geometries summarized in Table 4.2. For example, consider methane (CH_4), ammonia (NH_3), and water (H_2O). All three have a tetrahedral electron-domain geometry, but their bond angles differ slightly:

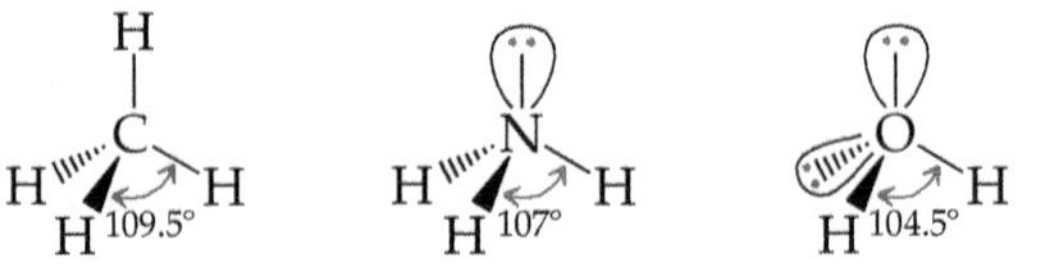

Notice that the bond angles decrease as the number of nonbonding electron pairs increases. A bonding pair of electrons is attracted by both nuclei of the bonded atoms, but a nonbonding pair is attracted primarily by only one nucleus. Because a nonbonding pair experiences less nuclear attraction, its electron domain is spread out more in space than is the electron domain for a bonding pair (▶ FIGURE 4.7). Nonbonding electron pairs therefore take up more space than bonding pairs. As a result, *electron domains for nonbonding electron pairs exert greater repulsive forces on adjacent electron domains and tend to compress bond angles.*

Because multiple bonds contain a higher electronic-charge density than single bonds, multiple bonds also represent enlarged electron domains. Consider the Lewis structure of phosgene:

$$:\ddot{\text{Cl}}$$
$$\underset{:\ddot{\text{Cl}}}{\overset{}{\text{C}}}=\ddot{\text{O}}$$

Because three electron domains surround the central atom, we might expect a trigonal-planar geometry with 120° bond angles. The double bond, however, seems to act much like a nonbonding pair of electrons, reducing the Cl—C—Cl bond angle to 111.4°:

$$\underset{\text{Cl}}{\overset{\text{Cl}}{\underset{\longleftarrow 124.3°}{\overset{\longleftarrow 124.3°}{111.4°\,\text{C}=\text{O}}}}}$$

In general, *electron domains for multiple bonds exert a greater repulsive force on adjacent electron domains than do electron domains for single bonds.*

 GIVE IT SOME THOUGHT

One resonance structure of the nitrate ion is

$$\left[\;\underset{:\ddot{\text{O}}:\qquad:\ddot{\text{O}}:}{\overset{:\text{O}:}{\overset{\|}{\text{N}}}}\;\right]^{-}$$

The bond angles in this ion are 120°. Is this observation consistent with the preceding discussion of the effect of multiple bonds on bond angles?

Molecules with Expanded Valence Shells

Atoms from period 3 and beyond may be surrounded by more than four electron pairs. ⚙ (Section 3.7) Molecules with five or six electron domains around the central atom have molecular geometries based on either a *trigonal-bipyramidal* (five domains) or *octahedral* (six domains) electron-domain geometry (▶ TABLE 4.3).

The most stable electron-domain geometry for five electron domains is the trigonal bipyramid (two trigonal pyramids sharing a base). Unlike the other arrangements we have seen, the electron domains in a trigonal bipyramid can point toward two geometrically distinct types of positions. Two domains point toward *axial positions* and three point toward *equatorial positions* (▶ FIGURE 4.8). Each axial domain makes a 90° angle with any equatorial domain. Each equatorial domain makes a 120° angle with either of the other two equatorial domains and a 90° angle with either axial domain.

Suppose a molecule has five electron domains, and there are one or more nonbonding pairs. Will the domains from the nonbonding pairs occupy axial or equatorial positions? To answer this question, we must determine which location minimizes repulsion between domains. Repulsion between two domains is much greater when they are situated 90° from each other than when they are at 120°. An equatorial domain is 90° from only two other domains (the axial domains), but an axial domain is 90° from *three* other domains (the equatorial domains). Hence, an equatorial domain experiences less repulsion than an axial domain. Because the domains from nonbonding pairs exert larger repulsions than those from bonding pairs, nonbonding domains always occupy the equatorial positions in a trigonal bipyramid.

 GIVE IT SOME THOUGHT

It might seem that a square-planar geometry of four electron domains around a central atom would be more favorable than a tetrahedron. Can you rationalize why the tetrahedron is preferred, based on angles between electron domains?

 GO FIGURE

Why is the volume occupied by the nonbonding electron pair domain larger than the volume occupied by the bonding domain?

Bonding electron pair

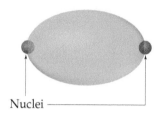

Nuclei

Nonbonding pair

Nucleus

▲ FIGURE 4.7 **Relative volumes occupied by bonding and nonbonding electron domains.**

GO FIGURE

What is the bond angle formed by an axial atom, the central atom, and any equatorial atom?

Axial position

Three equatorial positions form an equilateral triangle

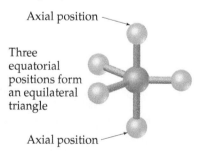

Axial position

▲ FIGURE 4.8 **In a trigonal-bipyramidal geometry, there are two types of positions for the outer atoms.**

TABLE 4.3 • Electron-Domain and Molecular Geometries for Five and Six Electron Domains around a Central Atom

Number of Electron Domains	Electron-Domain Geometry	Bonding Domains	Nonbonding Domains	Molecular Geometry	Example
5	 Trigonal bipyramidal	5	0	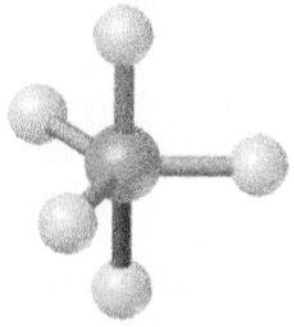 Trigonal bipyramidal	PCl_5
		4	1	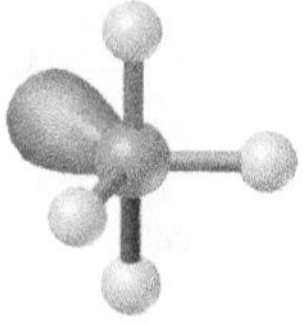 Seesaw	SF_4
		3	2	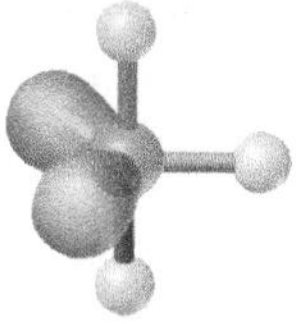 T-shaped	ClF_3
		2	3	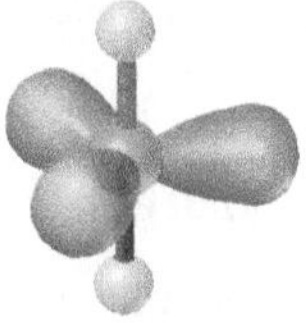 Linear	XeF_2
6	 Octahedral	6	0	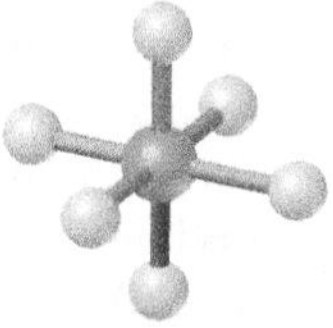 Octahedral	SF_6
		5	1	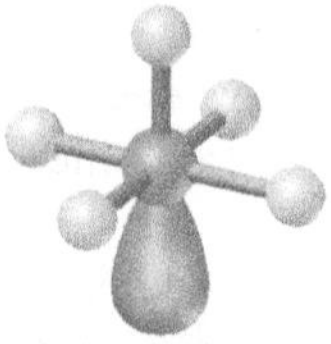 Square pyramidal	BrF_5
		4	2	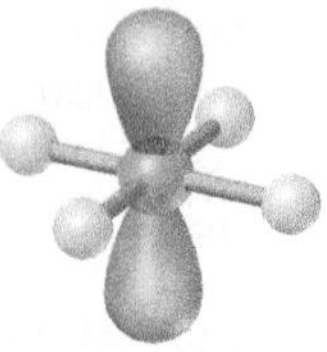 Square planar	XeF_4

The most stable electron-domain geometry for six electron domains is the *octahedron*. An octahedron is a polyhedron with six vertices and eight faces, each an equilateral triangle. An atom with six electron domains around it can be visualized as being at the center of the octahedron with the electron domains pointing toward the six vertices, as shown in Table 4.3. All the bond angles are 90°, and all six vertices are equivalent. Therefore, if an atom has five bonding electron domains and one nonbonding domain, we can put the nonbonding domain at any of the six vertices of the octahedron. The result is always a *square-pyramidal* molecular geometry. When there are two nonbonding electron domains, however, their repulsions are minimized by pointing them toward opposite sides of the octahedron, producing a *square-planar* molecular geometry, as shown in Table 4.3.

SAMPLE EXERCISE 4.2   **Molecular Geometries of Molecules with Expanded Valence Shells**

Use the VSEPR model to predict the molecular geometry of (**a**) SF_4, (**b**) IF_5.

SOLUTION

Analyze The molecules are of the AB_n type with a central *p*-block atom.

Plan We first draw Lewis structures and then use the VSEPR model to determine the electron-domain geometry and molecular geometry.

Solve
(**a**) The Lewis structure for SF_4 is

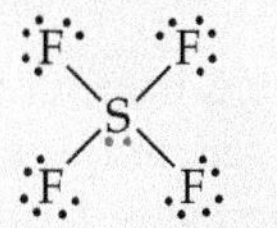

The sulfur has five electron domains around it: four from the S—F bonds and one from the nonbonding pair. Each domain points toward a vertex of a trigonal bipyramid. The domain from the nonbonding pair will point toward an equatorial position. The four bonds point toward the remaining four positions, resulting in a molecular geometry that is described as seesaw-shaped:

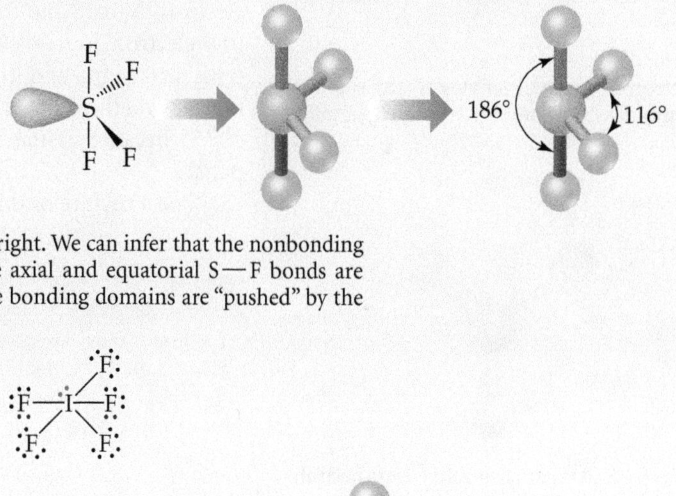

Comment The experimentally observed structure is shown on the right. We can infer that the nonbonding electron domain occupies an equatorial position, as predicted. The axial and equatorial S—F bonds are slightly bent away from the nonbonding domain, suggesting that the bonding domains are "pushed" by the nonbonding domain, which exerts a greater repulsion (Figure 4.7).

(**b**) The Lewis structure of IF_5 is

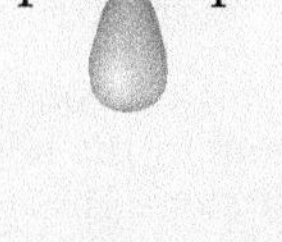

The iodine has six electron domains around it, one of which is nonbonding. The electron-domain geometry is therefore octahedral, with one position occupied by the nonbonding pair, and the molecular geometry is *square pyramidal* (Table 4.3):

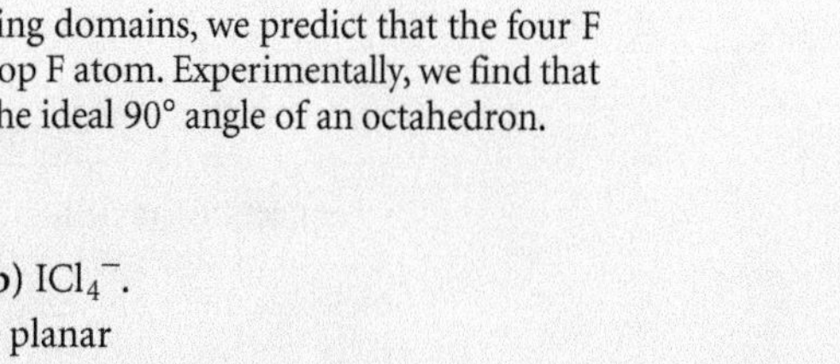

Comment Because the nonbonding domain is larger than the bonding domains, we predict that the four F atoms in the base of the pyramid will be tipped up slightly toward the top F atom. Experimentally, we find that the angle between the base atoms and top F atom is 82°, smaller than the ideal 90° angle of an octahedron.

PRACTICE EXERCISE

Predict the electron-domain and molecular geometries of (**a**) BrF_3, (**b**) ICl_4^-.
Answers: (**a**) trigonal bipyramidal, T-shaped; (**b**) octahedral, square planar

Although the electron-domain geometry around the right O is tetrahedral, the C—O—H bond is slightly less than 109.5°. Explain.

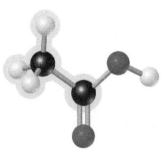

Electron-domain geometry tetrahedral, molecular geometry tetrahedral

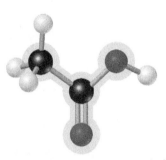

Electron-domain geometry trigonal planar, molecular geometry trigonal planar

Electron-domain geometry tetrahedral, molecular geometry bent

▲ **FIGURE 4.9** Acetic acid, CH_3COOH.

Shapes of Larger Molecules

Although the molecules and ions we have considered contain only a single central atom, the VSEPR model can be extended to more complex molecules. For the acetic acid molecule, for example,

$$H \quad :\!O:$$
$$H-C-C-\ddot{O}-H$$
$$H$$

we can use the VSEPR model to predict the geometry about each atom:

	H $H-C$ H	$:\!O:$ C	$\ddot{O}-H$
Number of electron domains	4	3	4
Electron-domain geometry	Tetrahedral	Trigonal planar	Tetrahedral
Predicted bond angles	109.5°	120°	109.5°

The left C has four electron domains (all bonding), and so the electron-domain and molecular geometries around that atom are both tetrahedral. The central C has three electron domains (counting the double bond as one domain), making both the electron-domain and the molecular geometries trigonal planar. The O on the right has four electron domains (two bonding, two nonbonding), so its electron-domain geometry is tetrahedral and its molecular geometry is bent. The bond angles about the central C atom and the O atom are expected to deviate slightly from the ideal values of 120° and 109.5° because of the spatial demands of multiple bonds and nonbonding electron pairs.

The structure of the acetic acid molecule is shown in ◀ FIGURE 4.9.

SAMPLE EXERCISE 4.3 Predicting Bond Angles

Eyedrops for dry eyes usually contain a water-soluble polymer called *poly(vinyl alcohol)*, which is based on the unstable organic molecule *vinyl alcohol*:

$$\begin{array}{cc} H & H \\ | & | \\ H-\ddot{O}-C=C-H \end{array}$$

Predict the approximate values for the H—O—C and O—C—C bond angles in vinyl alcohol.

SOLUTION

Analyze We are given a Lewis structure and asked to determine two bond angles.

Plan To predict a bond angle, we determine the number of electron domains surrounding the middle atom in the bond. The ideal angle corresponds to the electron-domain geometry around the atom. The angle will be compressed somewhat by nonbonding electrons or multiple bonds.

Solve In H—O—C, the O atom has four electron domains (two bonding, two nonbonding). The electron-domain geometry around O is therefore tetrahedral, which gives an ideal angle of 109.5°. The H—O—C angle is compressed somewhat by the nonbonding pairs, so we expect this angle to be slightly less than 109.5°.

To predict the O—C—C bond angle, we examine the middle atom in the angle. In the molecule, there are three atoms bonded to this C atom and no nonbonding pairs, and so it has three electron domains about it. The predicted electron-domain geometry is trigonal planar, resulting in an ideal bond angle of 120°. Because of the larger size of the C=C domain, the bond angle should be slightly greater than 120°.

PRACTICE EXERCISE

Predict the H—C—H and C—C—C bond angles in *propyne*:

$$H-\underset{\underset{H}{|}}{\overset{\overset{H}{|}}{C}}-C\equiv C-H$$

Answers: 109.5°, 180°

4.3 | MOLECULAR SHAPE AND MOLECULAR POLARITY

Recall that bond polarity is a measure of how equally the electrons in a bond are shared between the two atoms of the bond. As the difference in electronegativity between the two atoms increases, so does the bond polarity. ∞ (Section 3.4) We saw that the dipole moment of a diatomic molecule is a measure of the amount of charge separation in the molecule.

For a molecule consisting of more than two atoms, *the dipole moment depends on both the polarities of the individual bonds and the geometry of the molecule.* For each bond in the molecule, we consider the **bond dipole**, which is the dipole moment due only to the two atoms in that bond. Consider the linear CO_2 molecule, for example. As shown in ▶ FIGURE 4.10, each C=O bond is polar, and because the C=O bonds are identical, the bond dipoles are equal in magnitude. A plot of the molecule's electron density clearly shows that the individual bonds are polar, but what can we say about the *overall* dipole moment of the molecule?

Bond dipoles and dipole moments are vector quantities; that is, they have both a magnitude and a direction. The dipole moment of a polyatomic molecule is the vector sum of its bond dipoles. Both the magnitudes *and* the directions of the bond dipoles must be considered when summing vectors. The two bond dipoles in CO_2, although equal in magnitude, are opposite in direction. Adding them is the same as adding two numbers that are equal in magnitude but opposite in sign, such as $100 + (-100)$. The bond dipoles, like the numbers, "cancel" each other. Therefore, the dipole moment of CO_2 is zero, even though the individual bonds are polar. The geometry of the molecule dictates that the overall dipole moment be zero, making CO_2 a *nonpolar* molecule.

Now consider H_2O, a bent molecule with two polar bonds (▶ FIGURE 4.11). Again, the two bonds are identical, and the bond dipoles are equal in magnitude. Because the molecule is bent, however, the bond dipoles do not directly oppose each other and therefore do not cancel. Hence, the H_2O molecule has an overall nonzero dipole moment ($\mu = 1.85$ D) and is therefore a *polar* molecule. The oxygen atom carries a partial negative charge, and the hydrogen atoms each have a partial positive charge, as shown in the electron-density model.

GIVE IT SOME THOUGHT

The molecule O=C=S is linear and has a Lewis structure analogous to that of CO_2. Would you expect this molecule to have a dipole moment?

▶ FIGURE 4.12 shows some polar and nonpolar molecules, all with polar bonds. The molecules in which the central atom is symmetrically surrounded by identical atoms (BF_3 and CCl_4) are nonpolar. For AB_n molecules in which all the B atoms are the same, certain symmetrical shapes—linear (AB_2), trigonal planar (AB_3), tetrahedral and square planar (AB_4), trigonal bipyramidal (AB_5), and octahedral (AB_6)—must lead to nonpolar molecules even though the individual bonds might be polar.

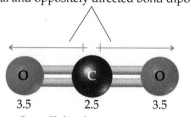

GO FIGURE

Explain how the directions of the red bond dipole arrows relate to the electron density picture.

Equal and oppositely directed bond dipoles

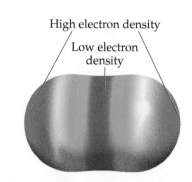

▲ FIGURE 4.10 **CO_2, a nonpolar molecule.** The numbers are electronegativity values for these two atoms.

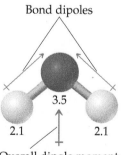

▲ FIGURE 4.11 **H_2O, a polar molecule.** The numbers are electronegativity values.

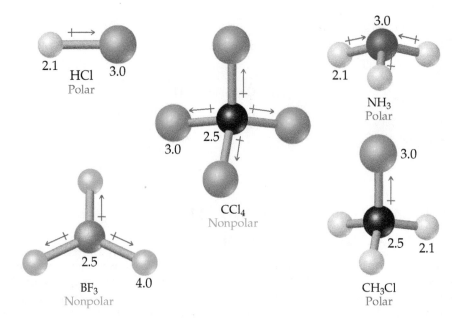

▶ **FIGURE 4.12** **Polar and nonpolar molecules containing polar bonds.** The numbers are electronegativity values.

SAMPLE EXERCISE 4.4 | **Polarity of Molecules**

Predict whether these molecules are polar or nonpolar: **(a)** BrCl, **(b)** SO_2, **(c)** SF_6.

SOLUTION

Analyze We are given three molecular formulas and asked to predict whether the molecules are polar.

Plan A molecule containing only two atoms is polar if the atoms differ in electronegativity. The polarity of a molecule containing three or more atoms depends on both the molecular geometry and the individual bond polarities. Thus, we must draw a Lewis structure for each molecule containing three or more atoms and determine its molecular geometry. We then use electronegativity values to determine the direction of the bond dipoles. Finally, we see whether the bond dipoles cancel to give a nonpolar molecule or reinforce each other to give a polar one.

Solve

(a) Chlorine is more electronegative than bromine. All diatomic molecules with polar bonds are polar molecules. Consequently, BrCl is polar, with chlorine carrying the partial negative charge:

$$Br\overset{\longrightarrow}{}Cl$$

The measured dipole moment of BrCl is $\mu = 0.57$ D.

(b) Because oxygen is more electronegative than sulfur, SO_2 has polar bonds. Three resonance forms can be written:

$$:\ddot{O}-\ddot{S}=\ddot{O}: \longleftrightarrow :\ddot{O}=\ddot{S}-\ddot{O}: \longleftrightarrow :\ddot{O}=\ddot{S}=\ddot{O}:$$

For each of these, the VSEPR model predicts a bent molecular geometry. Because the molecule is bent, the bond dipoles do not cancel, and the molecule is polar:

$$\underset{OO}{\overset{\ddot{S}}{\diagdown\diagup}}$$

Experimentally, the dipole moment of SO_2 is $\mu = 1.63$ D.

(c) Fluorine is more electronegative than sulfur, so the bond dipoles point toward fluorine. For clarity, only one S—F dipole is shown. The six S—F bonds are arranged octahedrally around the central sulfur:

$$\underset{FF}{\overset{FF}{F-S\Rightarrow F}}$$

Because the octahedral molecular geometry is symmetrical, the bond dipoles cancel, and the molecule is nonpolar, meaning that $\mu = 0$.

PRACTICE EXERCISE
Determine whether the following molecules are polar or nonpolar: (a) NF_3, (b) BCl_3.
Answers: (a) polar because polar bonds are arranged in a trigonal-pyramidal geometry, (b) nonpolar because polar bonds are arranged in a trigonal-planar geometry

4.4 | COVALENT BONDING AND ORBITAL OVERLAP

The VSEPR model provides a simple means for predicting molecular geometries but does not explain why bonds exist between atoms. In developing theories of covalent bonding, chemists have approached the problem from another direction, using quantum mechanics. How can we use atomic orbitals to explain bonding and to account for molecular geometries? The marriage of Lewis's notion of electron-pair bonds and the idea of atomic orbitals leads to a model of chemical bonding, called **valence-bond theory**, in which bonding electron pairs are concentrated in the regions between atoms and nonbonding electron pairs lie in directed regions of space. By extending this approach to include the ways in which atomic orbitals can mix with one another, we obtain an explanatory picture that corresponds to the VSEPR model.

In Lewis theory, covalent bonding occurs when atoms share electrons because the sharing concentrates electron density between the nuclei. In valence-bond theory, we visualize the buildup of electron density between two nuclei as occurring when a valence atomic orbital of one atom shares space, or *overlaps*, with a valence atomic orbital of another atom. The overlap of orbitals allows two electrons of opposite spin to share the space between the nuclei, forming a covalent bond.

The coming together of two H atoms to form H_2 is depicted in ▶ FIGURE 4.13. Each atom has a single electron in a $1s$ orbital. As the orbitals overlap, electron density is concentrated between the nuclei. Because the electrons in the overlap region are simultaneously attracted to both nuclei, they hold the atoms together, forming a covalent bond.

The idea of orbital overlap producing a covalent bond applies equally well to other molecules. In HCl, for example, chlorine has the electron configuration $[Ne]3s^2 3p^5$. All the valence orbitals of chlorine are full except one $3p$ orbital, which contains a single electron. This $3p$ electron pairs with the single $1s$ electron of H to form a covalent bond (Figure 4.13). Because the other two chlorine $3p$ orbitals are already filled with a pair of electrons, they do not participate in the bonding to hydrogen. Likewise, we can explain the covalent bond in Cl_2 in terms of the overlap of the singly occupied $3p$ orbital of one Cl atom with the singly occupied $3p$ orbital of another.

There is always an optimum distance between the two nuclei in any covalent bond. ▶ FIGURE 4.14 shows how the potential energy of a system consisting of two H atoms changes as the atoms come together to form an H_2 molecule. When the atoms are infinitely far apart, they do not "feel" each other and so the energy approaches zero. As the distance between the atoms decreases, the overlap between their $1s$ orbitals increases. Because of the resultant increase in electron density between the nuclei, the potential energy of the system decreases. That is, the strength of the bond increases, as shown by the decrease in the potential energy of the two-atom system. However, Figure 4.14 also shows that as the atoms come closer together than 0.74 Å, the energy increases sharply. This increase, which becomes significant at short internuclear distances, is due mainly to the electrostatic repulsion between the nuclei. The internuclear distance, or bond length, is the distance that corresponds to the minimum of the potential-energy curve. The potential energy at this minimum corresponds to the bond strength. Thus, the observed bond length is the distance at which the attractive forces between unlike charges (electrons and nuclei) are balanced by the repulsive forces between like charges (electron–electron and nucleus–nucleus).

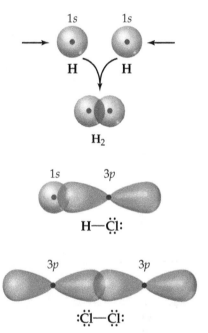

▲ **FIGURE 4.13 Covalent bonds in H_2, HCl, and Cl_2 result from overlap of atomic orbitals.**

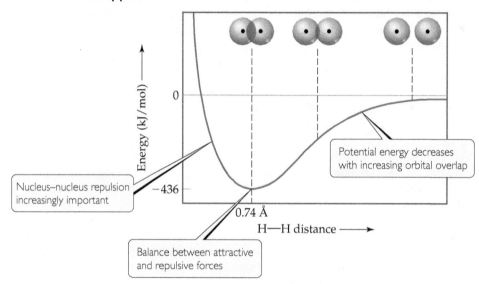

▲ GO FIGURE

On the left part of the curve the potential energy rises above zero. What causes this to happen?

▲ **FIGURE 4.14   Formation of the H$_2$ molecule as atomic orbitals overlap.**

4.5 | HYBRID ORBITALS

The VSEPR model, simple as it is, does a surprisingly good job at predicting molecular shape, despite the fact that it has no obvious relationship to the filling and shapes of atomic orbitals. For example, based on the shapes and orientations of the 2s and 2p orbitals on a carbon atom, it is not obvious why a CH$_4$ molecule should have a tetrahedral geometry. How can we reconcile the notion that covalent bonds are formed from overlap of atomic orbitals with the molecular geometries that come from the VSEPR model?

To begin with, we recall that atomic orbitals are mathematical functions that come from the quantum mechanical model for atomic structure. ∞∞ (Section 1.5) To explain molecular geometries, we can assume that the atomic orbitals on an atom (usually the central atom) mix to form new orbitals called **hybrid orbitals**. The shape of any hybrid orbital is different from the shapes of the original atomic orbitals. The process of mixing atomic orbitals is a mathematical operation called **hybridization**. The total number of atomic orbitals on an atom remains constant, so the number of hybrid orbitals on an atom equals the number of atomic orbitals that are mixed.

As we examine the common types of hybridization, notice the connection between the type of hybridization and certain of the molecular geometries predicted by the VSEPR model: linear, bent, trigonal planar, and tetrahedral.

sp Hybrid Orbitals

To illustrate the process of hybridization, consider the BeF$_2$ molecule, which has the Lewis structure

$$:\ddot{F}\!-\!Be\!-\!\ddot{F}:$$

The VSEPR model correctly predicts that BeF$_2$ is linear with two identical Be—F bonds. How can we use valence-bond theory to describe the bonding? The electron configuration of F (1$s^2$2$s^2$2p^5) indicates an unpaired electron in a 2p orbital. This electron can be paired with an unpaired Be electron to form a polar covalent bond. Which orbitals on the Be atom, however, overlap with those on the F atoms to form the Be—F bonds?

The orbital diagram for a ground-state Be atom is

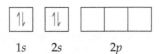

1s   2s   2p

Because it has no unpaired electrons, the Be atom in its ground state cannot bond with the fluorine atoms. The Be atom could form two bonds, however, by "promoting" one of the 2s electrons to a 2p orbital:

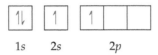

1s   2s   2p

The Be atom now has two unpaired electrons and can therefore form two polar covalent bonds with F atoms. The two bonds would not be identical, however, because a Be 2s orbital would be used to form one of the bonds and a 2p orbital would be used to form the other. Therefore, although the promotion of an electron allows two Be—F bonds to form, we still have not explained the structure of BeF₂.

We can solve this dilemma by "mixing" the 2s orbital with one 2p orbital to generate two new orbitals, as shown in ▼ FIGURE 4.15. Like p orbitals, each new orbital has two lobes. Unlike p orbitals, however, one lobe is much larger than the other. The two new orbitals are identical in shape, but their large lobes point in opposite directions. These two new orbitals, which we color-code purple in Figure 4.15, are hybrid orbitals. Because we have hybridized one s and one p orbital, we call each hybrid an *sp* hybrid orbital. *According to the valence-bond model, a linear arrangement of electron domains implies* sp *hybridization.*

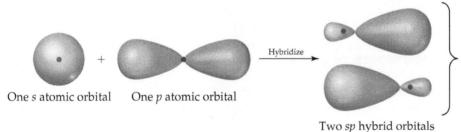

One s atomic orbital   One p atomic orbital

Hybridize →

Two sp hybrid orbitals

sp hybrid orbitals shown together (large lobes only)

▲ FIGURE 4.15   **Formation of sp hybrid orbitals.**

For the Be atom of BeF₂, we write the orbital diagram for the formation of two *sp* hybrid orbitals as

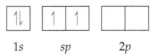

1s   sp   2p

The electrons in the *sp* hybrid orbitals can form bonds with the two fluorine atoms (▼ FIGURE 4.16). Because the *sp* hybrid orbitals are equivalent but point in opposite

GO FIGURE

Why is it reasonable to take account of only the large lobes of the Be hybrid orbitals in considering the bonding to F?

Large lobes from two Be *sp* hybrid orbitals

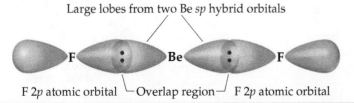

F 2p atomic orbital   Overlap region   F 2p atomic orbital

◀ FIGURE 4.16   **Formation of two equivalent Be—F bonds in BeF₂.**

directions, BeF_2 has two identical bonds and a linear geometry. The remaining two $2p$ atomic orbitals of Be remain unhybridized and are vacant. Remember also that each fluorine atom has two other valence p atomic orbitals, each containing one nonbonding electron pair. Those atomic orbitals are omitted from Figure 4.16 to keep the illustration simpler.

GIVE IT SOME THOUGHT

What is the orientation of the two unhybridized p orbitals on Be with respect to the two Be—F bonds?

sp^2 and sp^3 Hybrid Orbitals

Whenever we mix a certain number of atomic orbitals, we get the same number of hybrid orbitals. Each hybrid orbital is equivalent to the others but points in a different direction. Thus, mixing one $2s$ and one $2p$ atomic orbital yields two equivalent sp hybrid orbitals that point in opposite directions (Figure 4.15). Other combinations of atomic orbitals can be hybridized to obtain different geometries. In BF_3, for example, mixing the $2s$ and two of the $2p$ atomic orbitals yields three equivalent sp^2 (pronounced "s-p-two") hybrid orbitals (▼ FIGURE 4.17).

The three sp^2 hybrid orbitals lie in the same plane, 120° apart from one another. They are used to make three equivalent bonds with the three fluorine atoms, leading to the trigonal-planar molecular geometry of BF_3. Notice that an unfilled $2p$ atomic orbital remains unhybridized. This unhybridized orbital will be important when we discuss double bonds in Section 4.6.

GIVE IT SOME THOUGHT

In an sp^2 hybridized atom, what is the orientation of the unhybridized p atomic orbital relative to the three sp^2 hybrid orbitals?

An s atomic orbital can also mix with all three p atomic orbitals in the same subshell. For example, the carbon atom in CH_4 forms four equivalent bonds with the four

GO FIGURE.

How many atomic orbitals contribute to form the three sp^2 hybrid orbitals?

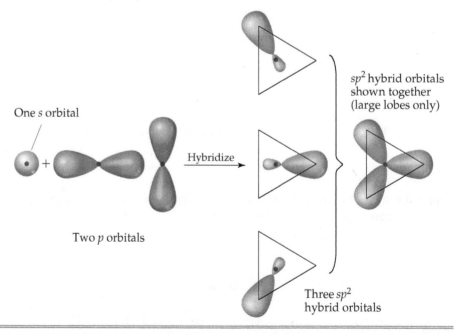

One *s* orbital

Two *p* orbitals

Hybridize

Three *sp²* hybrid orbitals

sp² hybrid orbitals shown together (large lobes only)

▶ FIGURE 4.17 **Formation of *sp²* hybrid orbitals.**

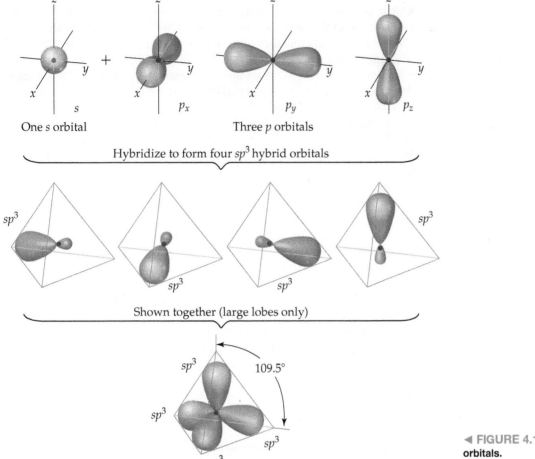

hydrogen atoms. We envision this process as resulting from the mixing of the $2s$ and all three $2p$ atomic orbitals of carbon to create four equivalent sp^3 (pronounced "s-p-three") hybrid orbitals. Each sp^3 hybrid orbital has a large lobe that points toward one vertex of a tetrahedron (▲ FIGURE 4.18). These hybrid orbitals can be used to form two-electron bonds by overlap with the atomic orbitals of another atom, such as H. Using valence-bond theory, we can describe the bonding in CH_4 as the overlap of four equivalent sp^3 hybrid orbitals on C with the $1s$ orbitals of the four H atoms to form four equivalent bonds.

The idea of hybridization is also used to describe the bonding in molecules containing nonbonding pairs of electrons. In H_2O, for example, the electron-domain geometry around the central O atom is approximately tetrahedral (► FIGURE 4.19). Thus, the four electron pairs can be envisioned as occupying sp^3 hybrid orbitals. Two of the hybrid orbitals contain nonbonding pairs of electrons, and the other two form bonds with the hydrogen atoms.

So far our discussion of hybridization has extended only to period 2 elements, specifically carbon, nitrogen, and oxygen. The elements of period 3 and beyond introduce a new consideration because in many of their compounds these elements have more than an octet of electrons in the valence shell, as we saw in Section 4.2. How do we analyze the bonding in compounds such as PCl_5, SF_6, or BrF_5? The use of only s and p orbitals on the central atom limits us to four hybrid orbitals, yet in these compounds the central atom is involved in bonding to five or six other atoms.

For such elements, the number of hybrid orbitals formed could be increased by including valence-shell d orbitals. For example, to explain the bonding in SF_6 we could include two sulfur $3d$ orbitals

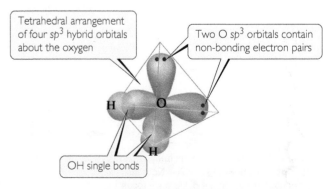

Tetrahedral arrangement of four sp^3 hybrid orbitals about the oxygen

Two O sp^3 orbitals contain non-bonding electron pairs

OH single bonds

▲ FIGURE 4.19 **Hybrid orbital description of H_2O.**

in addition to the *3s* and three *3p* orbitals. These six atomic orbitals could make six hybrid orbitals, but there is more involved in hybridization than simply finding a set of orbitals that point in the right directions; we must also consider orbital energies. The sulfur *3d* orbitals lie substantially higher in energy than the *3s* and *3p* orbitals. The amount of energy needed to form the six hybrid orbitals is greater than the amount returned by forming bonds with the six fluorine atoms. Theoretical calculations seem to show that the sulfur *3d* orbitals do not participate to a significant degree in the bonding between sulfur and the six fluorine atoms.

The valence-bond model we have developed for period 2 elements works well for compounds of period 3 elements so long as we have no more than an octet of electrons in the valence-shell orbitals. Thus, for example, it is appropriate to discuss the bonding in PF_3 or H_2Se in terms of hybrid *s* and *p* orbitals on the central atom. However, the model turns out not to be appropriate when there is more than an octet of electrons about the central atom. How then do we account for the bonding in SF_6 and other compounds of the main group elements in which the central atom has more than an octet of valence electrons? To address that question from the viewpoint of bonding theory requires a treatment beyond the scope of a general chemistry text. Fortunately, the VSEPR model, although it does not explain the bonding in such molecules, can accurately predict their geometries.

This discussion points up the important fact that models in science are not reality but rather are our attempts to describe aspects of reality that we have been able to measure, such as bond distances, bond energies, molecular geometries, and so on. A model may work well up to a certain point but not beyond it, as with the idea of hybrid orbitals. The hybrid orbital model for period 2 elements has proven very useful and is an essential part of any modern discussion of bonding and molecular geometry in organic chemistry. When it comes to substances such as SF_6, however, we encounter the limitations of the model.

Hybrid Orbital Summary

Overall, hybrid orbitals provide a convenient model for using valence-bond theory to describe covalent bonds in molecules in which the molecular geometry conforms to the electron-domain geometry predicted by the VSEPR model. The picture of hybrid orbitals has limited predictive value. When we know the electron-domain geometry, however, we can employ hybridization to describe the atomic orbitals used by the central atom in bonding.

The following steps allow us to describe the hybrid orbitals used by an atom in bonding:

1. Draw the *Lewis structure* for the molecule or ion.

2. Use the VSEPR model to determine the electron-domain geometry around the central atom.

3. Specify the *hybrid orbitals* needed to accommodate the electron pairs based on their geometric arrangement (▶ TABLE 4.4).

These steps are illustrated in ▼ FIGURE 4.20, which shows how the hybridization at N in NH_3 is determined.

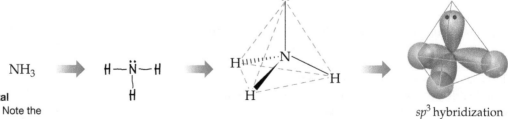

▶ FIGURE 4.20 **Hybrid orbital description of bonding in NH_3.** Note the comparison with Figure 4.6. Here we focus on the hybrid orbitals used to make bonds and hold nonbonding electron pairs.

NH_3

1. Draw Lewis structure

2. Determine electron-domain geometry about central atom from VSEPR model and Table 4.1

3. Using Table 4.4, select sp^3 hybrid orbital set

sp^3 hybridization

TABLE 4.4 • Geometric Arrangements Characteristic of Hybrid Orbital Sets

Atomic Orbital Set	Hybrid Orbital Set	Geometry	Examples
s,p	Two sp	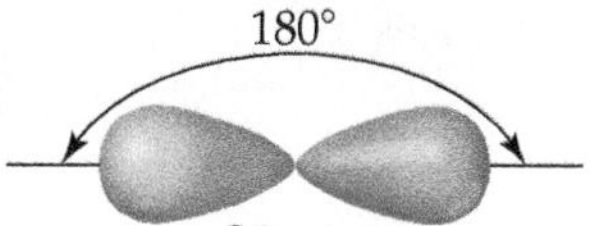 180° Linear	BeF_2, $HgCl_2$
s,p,p	Three sp^2	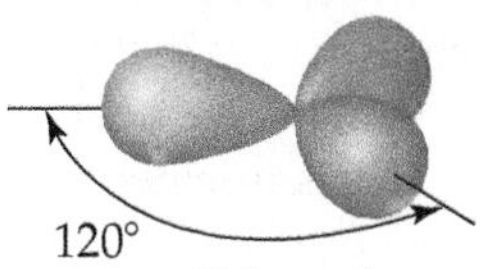 120° Trigonal planar	BF_3, SO_3
s,p,p,p	Four sp^3	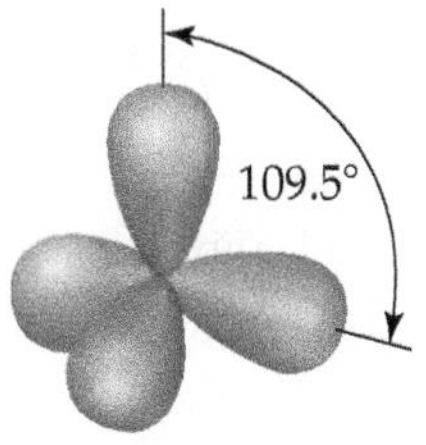 109.5° Tetrahedral	CH_4, NH_3, H_2O, NH_4^+

SAMPLE EXERCISE 4.5 **Hybridization**

Indicate the orbital hybridization around the central atom in NH_2^-.

SOLUTION

Analyze We are given the chemical formula for a polyatomic anion and asked to describe the type of hybrid orbitals surrounding the central atom.

Plan To determine the central atom hybrid orbitals, we must know the electron-domain geometry around the atom. Thus, we draw the Lewis structure to determine the number of electron domains around the central atom. The hybridization conforms to the number and geometry of electron domains around the central atom as predicted by the VSEPR model.

Solve The Lewis structure is

$$\left[\text{H}\!:\!\ddot{\text{N}}\!:\!\text{H} \right]^-$$

Because there are four electron domains around N, the electron-domain geometry is tetrahedral. The hybridization that gives a tetrahedral electron-domain geometry is sp^3 (Table 4.4). Two of the sp^3 hybrid orbitals contain nonbonding pairs of electrons, and the other two are used to make bonds with the hydrogen atoms.

PRACTICE EXERCISE

Predict the electron-domain geometry and hybridization of the central atom in SO_3^{2-}.

Answer: tetrahedral, sp^3

4.6 | MULTIPLE BONDS

In the covalent bonds we have considered thus far, the electron density is concentrated along the line connecting the nuclei (the *internuclear axis*). In other words, the line joining the two nuclei passes through the middle of the overlap region. These bonds are called **sigma (σ) bonds**. The overlap of two s orbitals in H_2, the overlap of an s and a p

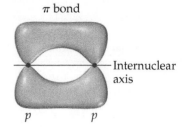

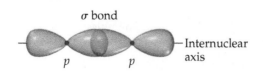

▶ **FIGURE 4.21** **Comparison of σ and π bonds.** Note that the two regions of overlap in the π bond, above and below the internuclear axis, constitute a *single* π bond.

orbital in HCl, the overlap of two *p* orbitals in Cl₂ (all shown in Figure 4.13), and the overlap of a *p* orbital and an *sp* hybrid orbital in BeF₂ (Figure 4.16) are all σ bonds.

To describe multiple bonding, we must consider a second kind of bond, this one the result of overlap between two *p* orbitals oriented perpendicularly to the internuclear axis (▲ **FIGURE 4.21**). This sideways overlap of *p* orbitals produces a **pi (π) bond**. A π bond is one in which the overlap regions lie above and below the internuclear axis. Unlike in a σ bond, in a π bond the electron density is not concentrated on the internuclear axis. Although it is not evident in Figure 4.21, the sideways orientation of *p* orbitals in a π bond makes for weaker overlap. As a result, π bonds are generally weaker than σ bonds.

In almost all cases, single bonds are σ bonds. A double bond consists of one σ bond and one π bond, and a triple bond consists of one σ bond and two π bonds:

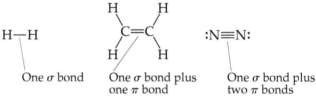

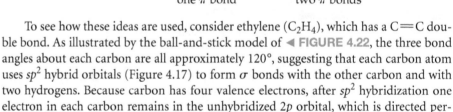

▲ **FIGURE 4.22** **Trigonal-planar molecular geometry of ethylene.** The double bond is made up of one C—C σ bond and one C—C π bond.

To see how these ideas are used, consider ethylene (C₂H₄), which has a C=C double bond. As illustrated by the ball-and-stick model of ◀ **FIGURE 4.22**, the three bond angles about each carbon are all approximately 120°, suggesting that each carbon atom uses *sp²* hybrid orbitals (Figure 4.17) to form σ bonds with the other carbon and with two hydrogens. Because carbon has four valence electrons, after *sp²* hybridization one electron in each carbon remains in the unhybridized 2*p* orbital, which is directed perpendicular to the plane that contains the three *sp²* hybrid orbitals.

Each *sp²* hybrid orbital on a carbon atom contains one electron. ▶ **FIGURE 4.23** shows how the C—H σ bonds are formed by overlap of *sp²* hybrid orbitals on C with the 1*s* orbitals on each H atom. We use eight electrons to form these four C—H bonds. The C—C σ bond is formed by the overlap of two *sp²* hybrid orbitals, one on each carbon atom, and requires two more electrons. Thus, ten of the 12 valence electrons in the C₂H₄ molecule are used to form five σ bonds.

The remaining two valence electrons reside in the unhybridized 2*p* orbitals, one electron on each carbon. These two orbitals can overlap sideways with each other, as shown in Figure 4.23. The resultant electron density is concentrated above and below the C—C bond axis, which means this is a π bond (Figure 4.21). Thus, the C=C double bond in ethylene consists of one σ bond and one π bond. You should note one point about the carbon *p* orbitals that form the π bond. It appears from Figure 4.21 that the *p* orbitals on the two carbons don't overlap sufficiently to form a π bond. The problem is that we can't show the true extent of overlap in the drawing without obscuring other aspects of the figure. Although π bonding of the *p* orbitals does occur, as pointed out earlier, π bonds are generally weaker than σ bonds.

Although we cannot experimentally observe a π bond directly (all we can observe are the positions of the atoms), the structure of ethylene provides strong support for its presence. First, the C—C bond length in ethylene (1.34 Å) is much shorter than in compounds with C—C single bonds (1.54 Å), consistent with the presence of a stronger C=C double bond. Second, all six atoms in C₂H₄ lie in the same plane. The 2*p* orbitals that make up the π bond can achieve a good overlap only when the two CH₂

GO FIGURE

Why is it important that the *sp*² hybrid orbitals of the two carbon atoms lie in the same plane?

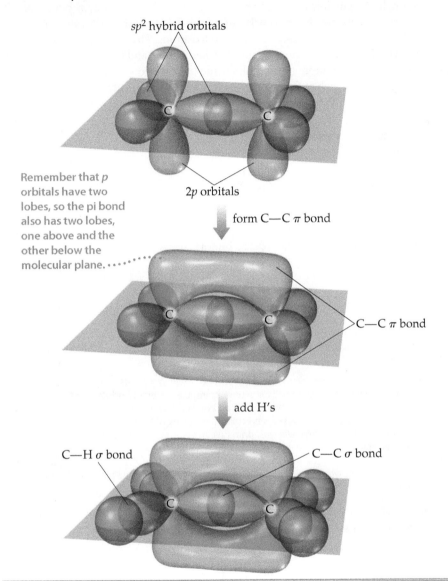

sp² hybrid orbitals

Remember that *p* orbitals have two lobes, so the pi bond also has two lobes, one above and the other below the molecular plane.

2*p* orbitals

form C—C π bond

C—C π bond

add H's

C—H σ bond

C—C σ bond

◀ FIGURE 4.23   **The orbital structure of ethylene.**

fragments lie in the same plane. If the π bond were absent, there would be no reason for the two CH_2 fragments to lie in the same plane. Because π bonds require that portions of a molecule be planar, they can introduce rigidity into molecules.

GIVE IT SOME THOUGHT

The molecule called *diazine* has the formula N_2H_2 and the Lewis structure

$$H—\ddot{N}=\ddot{N}—H$$

Do you expect diazine to be a linear molecule (all four atoms on the same line)? If not, do you expect the molecule to be planar (all four atoms in the same plane)?

Triple bonds can also be explained using hybrid orbitals. Acetylene (C_2H_2), for example, is a linear molecule containing a triple bond: $H—C{\equiv}C—H$. The linear geometry suggests that each carbon atom uses *sp* hybrid orbitals to form σ bonds with the other

◢ **GO FIGURE**

Based on the models of bonding in ethylene and acetylene, which molecule should have the higher carbon–carbon bond energy?

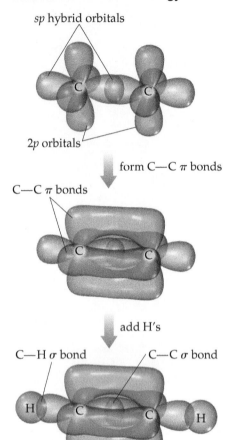

sp hybrid orbitals

2*p* orbitals

form C—C π bonds

C—C π bonds

add H's

C—H σ bond   C—C σ bond

▲ **FIGURE 4.24** **Formation of two π bonds in acetylene, C₂H₂.**

carbon and one hydrogen. Each carbon atom thus has two unhybridized 2*p* orbitals at right angles to each other and to the axis of the *sp* hybrid set (◄ **FIGURE 4.24**). These *p* orbitals overlap to form a pair of π bonds. Thus, the triple bond in acetylene consists of one σ bond and two π bonds.

Although it is possible to make π bonds from *d* orbitals, the only π bonds we will consider are those formed by the overlap of *p* orbitals. These π bonds can form only if unhybridized *p* orbitals are present on the bonded atoms. Therefore, only atoms having *sp* or *sp²* hybridization can form π bonds. Further, double and triple bonds (and hence π bonds) are more common in molecules made up of period 2 atoms, especially C, N, and O. Larger atoms, such as S, P, and Si, form π bonds less readily.

SAMPLE EXERCISE 4.6 Describing σ and π Bonds in a Molecule

Formaldehyde has the Lewis structure

$$\begin{array}{c} \text{H} \\ \diagdown \\ \text{C}=\ddot{\text{O}}: \\ \diagup \\ \text{H} \end{array}$$

Describe how the bonds in formaldehyde are formed in terms of overlaps of hybrid and unhybridized orbitals.

SOLUTION

Analyze We are asked to describe the bonding in formaldehyde in terms of hybrid orbitals.

Plan Single bonds are σ bonds, and double bonds consist of one σ bond and one π bond. The ways in which these bonds form can be deduced from the molecular geometry, which we predict using the VSEPR model.

Solve The C atom has three electron domains around it, which suggests a trigonal-planar geometry with bond angles of about 120°. This geometry implies *sp²* hybrid orbitals on C (Table 4.4). These hybrids are used to make the two C—H and one C—O σ bonds to C. There remains an unhybridized 2*p* orbital on carbon, perpendicular to the plane of the three *sp²* hybrids.

The O atom also has three electron domains around it, and so we assume it has *sp²* hybridization as well. One of these hybrid orbitals participates in the C—O σ bond, while the other two hold the two nonbonding electron pairs of the O atom. Like the C atom, therefore, the O atom has an unhybridized 2*p* orbital that is perpendicular to the plane of the molecule. These two orbitals overlap to form a C—O π bond (▼ **FIGURE 4.25**).

PRACTICE EXERCISE

(a) Predict the bond angles around each carbon atom in acetonitrile:

$$\begin{array}{c} \text{H} \\ | \\ \text{H}-\text{C}-\text{C}\equiv\text{N}: \\ | \\ \text{H} \end{array}$$

(b) Describe the hybridization at each carbon atom, and (c) determine the number of σ and π bonds in the molecule.

Answers: (a) approximately 109° around the left C and 180° around the right C; (b) *sp³*, *sp*; (c) five σ bonds and two π bonds

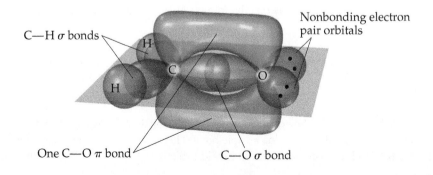

C—H σ bonds

Nonbonding electron pair orbitals

One C—O π bond

C—O σ bond

▶ **FIGURE 4.25** **Formation of σ and π bonds in formaldehyde, H₂CO.**

Resonance Structures, Delocalization, and π Bonding

In the molecules we have discussed thus far in this section, the bonding electrons are *localized*. By this we mean that the σ and π electrons are associated totally with the two atoms that form the bond. In many molecules, however, we cannot adequately describe the bonding as being entirely localized. This situation arises particularly in molecules that have two or more resonance structures involving π bonds.

One molecule that cannot be described with localized π bonds is benzene (C_6H_6), which has two resonance structures: ◻◻◻(Section 3.6)

To describe the bonding in benzene using hybrid orbitals, we first choose a hybridization scheme consistent with the geometry of the molecule. Because each carbon is surrounded by three atoms at 120° angles, the appropriate hybrid set is sp^2. Six localized C—C σ bonds and six localized C—H σ bonds are formed from the sp^2 hybrid orbitals, as shown in ▼ FIGURE 4.26(a). This leaves on each carbon a $2p$ orbital oriented perpendicular to the plane of the molecule. The situation is very much like that in ethylene except we now have six carbon $2p$ orbitals arranged in a ring [Figure 4.26(b)]. Each unhybridized $2p$ orbital is occupied by one electron, leaving six electrons to be accounted for by π bonding.

GO FIGURE

What are the two kinds of σ bonds found in benzene?

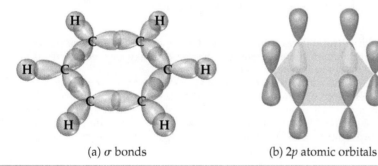

(a) σ bonds   (b) $2p$ atomic orbitals

◀ **FIGURE 4.26** σ **and** π **bond networks in benzene, C_6H_6.** (a) The σ bond framework. (b) The π bonds are formed from overlap of the unhybridized $2p$ orbitals on the six carbon atoms.

We could envision using the unhybridized $2p$ orbitals to form three localized π bonds. As shown in ▼ FIGURE 4.27, there are two equivalent ways to make these localized bonds, each corresponding to one resonance structure. However, a representation that reflects *both* resonance structures has the six π electrons "smeared out" among all six carbon atoms, as shown on the right in Figure 4.27. Notice how this combined representation corresponds to the circle-in-a-hexagon drawing we often use to represent benzene. This model leads us to predict that all the carbon–carbon bond lengths will be identical, with a bond length between that of a C—C single bond (1.54 Å) and that of a C=C double bond (1.34 Å). This prediction is consistent with the observed carbon–carbon bond length in benzene (1.40 Å).

Localized π bond   Delocalized π bond

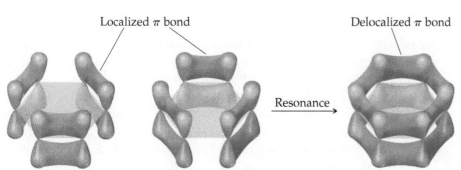

Resonance

◀ **FIGURE 4.27**   **Delocalized** π **bonds in benzene.**

Because we cannot describe the π bonds in benzene as individual bonds between neighboring atoms, we say that the π bonds are **delocalized** among the six carbon atoms. Delocalization of the electrons in its π bonds gives benzene a special stability. Delocalization of π bonds is also responsible for the color of many organic molecules. A final important point to remember about delocalized π bonds is the constraint they place on the geometry of a molecule. For optimal overlap of the unhybridized p orbitals, all the atoms involved in a delocalized π bonding network should lie in the same plane. This restriction imparts a certain rigidity to the molecule that is absent in molecules containing only σ bonds (see the "Chemistry and Life" box on vision).

If you take a course in organic chemistry, you will see many examples of how electron delocalization influences the properties of organic molecules.

SAMPLE EXERCISE 4.7 | **Delocalized Bonding**

Describe the bonding in the nitrate ion, NO_3^-. Does this ion have delocalized π bonds?

SOLUTION

Analyze Given the chemical formula for a polyatomic anion, we are asked to describe the bonding and determine whether the ion has delocalized π bonds.

Plan Our first step is to draw Lewis structures. Multiple resonance structures involving the placement of the double bonds in different locations suggest that the π component of the double bonds is delocalized.

Solve In Section 3.6 we saw that NO_3^- has three resonance structures:

$$\left[\begin{array}{c} :\!\ddot{O}: \\ \| \\ N \\ / \quad \backslash \\ :\!\ddot{O} \quad\quad \ddot{O}: \end{array} \right]^- \longleftrightarrow \left[\begin{array}{c} :\!\ddot{O}: \\ | \\ N \\ / \quad \backslash \\ :\!\ddot{O} \quad\quad \ddot{O}: \end{array} \right]^- \longleftrightarrow \left[\begin{array}{c} :\!\ddot{O}: \\ | \\ N \\ / \quad \backslash \\ :\!\ddot{O} \quad\quad \ddot{O}: \end{array} \right]^-$$

In each structure, the electron-domain geometry at nitrogen is trigonal planar, which implies sp^2 hybridization of the N atom. The sp^2 hybrid orbitals are used to construct the three N—O σ bonds present in each resonance structure.

The unhybridized $2p$ orbital on the N atom can be used to make π bonds. For any one of the three resonance structures shown, we might imagine a single localized N—O π bond formed by the overlap of the unhybridized $2p$ orbital on N and a $2p$ orbital on one of the O atoms, as shown in ◄ **FIGURE 4.28**. Because each resonance structure contributes equally to the observed structure of NO_3^-, however, we represent the π bonding as delocalized over the three N—O bonds, as shown in the figure.

PRACTICE EXERCISE

Which of these species have delocalized bonding: SO_3, SO_3^{2-}, H_2CO, O_3, NH_4^+?

Answer: SO_3 and O_3, as indicated by the presence of two or more resonance structures involving π bonding for each of these molecules

---

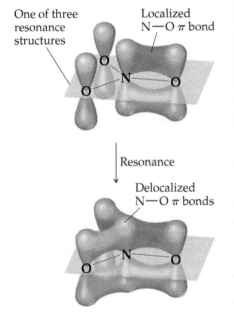

One of three resonance structures

Localized N—O π bond

Resonance

Delocalized N—O π bonds

▲ **FIGURE 4.28** **Localized and delocalized π bonds in NO_3^-.**

General Conclusions

On the basis of the examples we have seen, we can draw a few helpful conclusions for using hybrid orbitals to describe molecular structures:

1. Every pair of bonded atoms shares one or more pairs of electrons. The lines we draw in Lewis structures represent two electrons each. In every bond at least one pair of electrons is localized in the space between the atoms in a σ bond. The appropriate set of hybrid orbitals used to form the σ bonds between an atom and its neighbors is determined by the observed geometry of the molecule. The correlation between the set of hybrid orbitals and the geometry about an atom is given in Table 4.4.

2. The electrons in σ bonds are localized in the region between two bonded atoms and do not make a significant contribution to the bonding between any other two atoms.

3. When atoms share more than one pair of electrons, one pair is used to form a σ bond; the additional pairs form π bonds. The centers of charge density in a π bond lie above and below the internuclear axis.

4. Molecules with two or more resonance structures can have π bonds that extend over more than two bonded atoms. Electrons in π bonds that extend over more than two atoms are said to be "delocalized."

CHEMISTRY AND LIFE

THE CHEMISTRY OF VISION

Vision begins when light is focused by the lens of the eye onto the retina, the layer of cells lining the interior of the eyeball. The retina contains *photoreceptor* cells called rods and cones (▼ FIGURE 4.29). The rods are sensitive to dim light and are used in night vision. The cones are sensitive to colors. The tops of the rods and cones contain a molecule called *rhodopsin*, which consists of a protein, *opsin*, bonded to a reddish purple pigment called *retinal*. Structural changes around a double bond in the retinal portion of the molecule trigger a series of chemical reactions that result in vision.

We know that a double bond between two atoms is stronger than a single bond between the same atom, but our recent discussions allow us to appreciate another aspect of double bonds: the rigidity they introduce into molecules.

Imagine rotating one —CH_2 group in ethylene relative to the other —CH_2 group, as in ▶ FIGURE 4.30. This rotation destroys the overlap of *p* orbitals, breaking the π bond, a process that requires

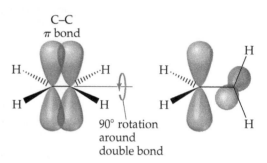

▲ FIGURE 4.30 **Rotation about the carbon–carbon double bond in ethylene breaks the π bond.**

considerable energy. Thus, the presence of a double bond restricts bond rotation in a molecule. In contrast, molecules can rotate almost freely around the bond axis in single (σ) bonds because this motion has no effect on the orbital overlap for a σ bond. This rotation allows molecules with single bonds to twist and fold almost as if their atoms were attached by hinges.

Our vision depends on the rigidity of double bonds in retinal. In its normal form, retinal is held rigid by its double bonds. Light entering the eye is absorbed by rhodopsin, and the energy is used to break the π-bond portion of the double bond shown in red in ▼ FIGURE 4.31. The molecule then rotates around this bond, changing its geometry. The retinal then separates from the opsin, triggering the reactions that produce a nerve impulse that the brain interprets as the sensation of vision. It takes as few as five closely spaced molecules reacting in this fashion to produce the sensation of vision. Thus, only five photons of light are necessary to stimulate the eye.

The retinal slowly reverts to its original form and reattaches to the opsin. The slowness of this process helps explain why intense bright light causes temporary blindness. The light causes all the retinal to separate from opsin, leaving no molecules to absorb light.

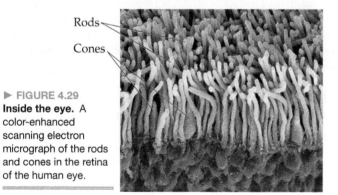

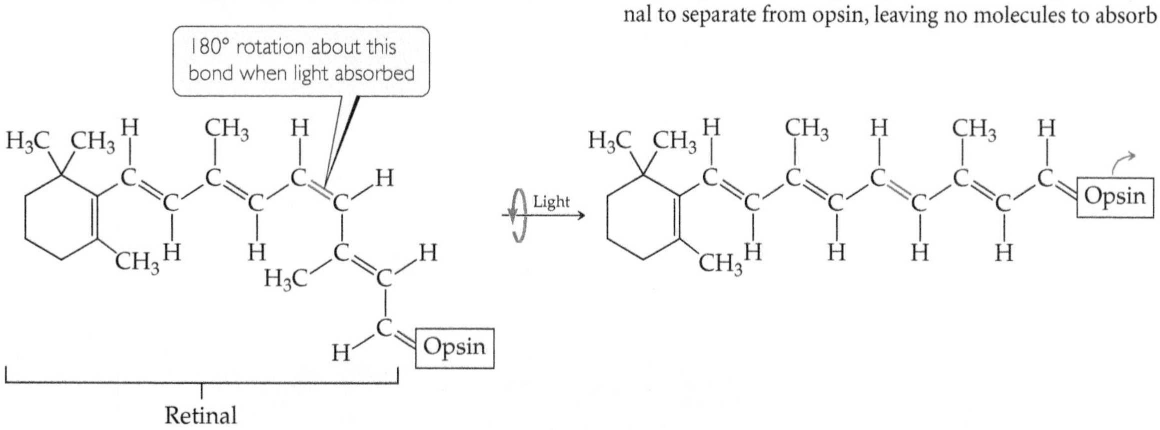

▶ FIGURE 4.29
Inside the eye. A color-enhanced scanning electron micrograph of the rods and cones in the retina of the human eye.

Rods
Cones

180° rotation about this bond when light absorbed

H_3C CH_3 H CH_3 H
C=C—C=C—C=C—H
CH_3 H   H H_3C—C=C—H
H—C=Opsin

Retinal

Light →

H_3C CH_3 H CH_3 H CH_3 H
C=C—C=C—C=C—C=C—C=Opsin
CH_3 H   H   H   H

▲ FIGURE 4.31 **The rhodopsin molecule, the chemical basis of vision.** When rhodopsin absorbs visible light, the π component of the double bond shown in red breaks, allowing rotation that produces a change in molecular geometry before the π bond re-forms.

When two atoms are bonded by a triple bond, what is the hybridization of the orbitals that make up the σ-bond component of the bond?

4.7 | MOLECULAR ORBITALS

Valence-bond theory and hybrid orbitals allow us to move in a straightforward way from Lewis structures to rationalizing the observed geometries of molecules in terms of atomic orbitals. The valence-bond model, however, does not explain all aspects of bonding. It is not successful, for example, in describing the excited states of molecules, which we must understand to explain how molecules absorb light, giving them color.

Some aspects of bonding are better explained by a more sophisticated model called **molecular orbital theory**. In Chapter 1 we saw that electrons in atoms can be described by wave functions, which we call atomic orbitals. In a similar way, molecular orbital theory describes the electrons in molecules by using specific wave functions called **molecular orbitals (MO)**.

Molecular orbitals have many of the same characteristics as atomic orbitals. For example, an MO can hold a maximum of two electrons (with opposite spins), it has a definite energy, and we can visualize its electron-density distribution by using a contour representation, as we did with atomic orbitals. Unlike atomic orbitals, however, MOs are associated with an entire molecule, not with a single atom.

The Hydrogen Molecule

We begin our study of MO theory with the hydrogen molecule, H_2. *Whenever two atomic orbitals overlap, two molecular orbitals form.* Thus, the overlap of the $1s$ orbitals of two hydrogen atoms to form H_2 produces two MOs (▼ FIGURE 4.32). One MO is formed by adding the wave functions for the two $1s$ orbitals. We refer to this as *constructive combination*. The energy of the resulting MO is lower than the energy of the two atomic orbitals from which it was made. It is called the **bonding molecular orbital**.

The other MO is formed by combining the two atomic orbitals in a way that causes the electron density to be more or less canceled in the central region where the two overlap. We refer to this as *destructive combination*. The energy of the resulting MO, referred to as the **antibonding molecular orbital**, is higher than the energy of the atomic orbitals.

As illustrated in Figure 4.32, in the bonding MO electron density is concentrated in the region between the two nuclei. This sausage-shaped MO results from summing the

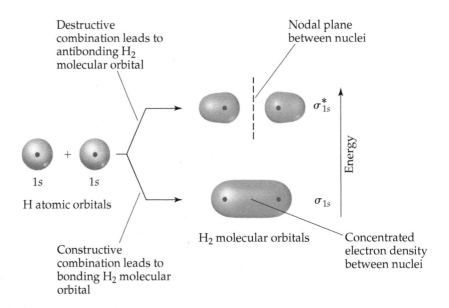

Destructive combination leads to antibonding H_2 molecular orbital

Nodal plane between nuclei

σ_{1s}^*

$1s$ $1s$

H atomic orbitals

Energy

σ_{1s}

H_2 molecular orbitals

Constructive combination leads to bonding H_2 molecular orbital

Concentrated electron density between nuclei

▶ FIGURE 4.32   **The two molecular orbitals of H_2, one a bonding MO and one an antibonding MO.**

two atomic orbitals so that the atomic orbital wave functions combine in the region between the two nuclei. Because an electron in this MO is attracted to both nuclei, the electron is more stable (it has lower energy) than it is in the $1s$ atomic orbital of an isolated hydrogen atom. Further, because this bonding MO concentrates electron density between the nuclei, it holds the atoms together in a covalent bond.

By contrast, the antibonding MO has very little electron density between the nuclei. Instead of combining in the region between the nuclei, the atomic orbital wave functions cancel each other in this region, leaving the greatest electron density on opposite sides of the two nuclei. Thus, this MO excludes electrons from the very region in which a bond must be formed. Antibonding orbitals invariably have a nodal plane in the region between the nuclei, where the electron density is zero. (The nodal plane is shown as a dashed line in Figure 4.32 and subsequent figures.) An electron in an antibonding MO is repelled from the bonding region and is therefore less stable (it has higher energy) than it is in the $1s$ atomic orbital of a hydrogen atom.

Notice from Figure 4.32 that the electron density in both the bonding MO and the antibonding MO of H_2 is centered about the internuclear axis. MOs of this type are called **sigma (σ) molecular orbitals** (by analogy to σ bonds). The bonding sigma MO of H_2 is labeled σ_{1s}; the subscript indicates that the MO is formed from two $1s$ orbitals. The antibonding sigma MO of H_2 is labeled σ_{1s}^* (read "sigma-star-one-s"); the asterisk denotes that the MO is antibonding.

The relative energies of two $1s$ atomic orbitals and the molecular orbitals formed from them are represented by an **energy-level diagram** (also called a **molecular orbital diagram**). Such diagrams show the interacting atomic orbitals on the left and right and the MOs in the middle, as shown in ▼ FIGURE 4.33. Like atomic orbitals, each MO can accommodate two electrons with their spins paired (Pauli exclusion principle). ∞ (Section 1.7)

As the MO diagram for H_2 in Figure 4.33 shows, each H atom brings one electron to the molecule, so there are two electrons in H_2. These two electrons occupy the lower-energy bonding (σ_{1s}) MO, and their spins are paired. Electrons occupying a bonding molecular orbital are called *bonding electrons*. Because the σ_{1s} MO is lower in energy than the $1s$ atomic orbitals, the H_2 molecule is more stable than the two separate H atoms.

By analogy with atomic electron configurations, the electron configurations for molecules can be written with superscripts to indicate electron occupancy. The electron configuration for H_2, then, is σ_{1s}^2.

 GO FIGURE

By referring to Figure 4.32, determine which molecular orbital in He_2 has a node between the nuclei.

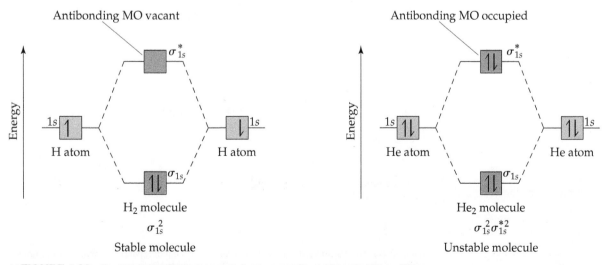

▲ **FIGURE 4.33**   **Energy-level diagrams and electron configurations for H_2 and He_2.**

Figure 4.33 also shows the energy-level diagram for the hypothetical He_2 molecule, which requires four electrons to fill its molecular orbitals. Because only two electrons can go in the σ_{1s} MO, the other two electrons must go in the σ_{1s}^* MO. The electron configuration of He_2 is thus $\sigma_{1s}^2\sigma_{1s}^{*2}$. The energy decrease realized in going from He atomic orbitals to the He bonding MO is offset by the energy increase realized in going from the atomic orbitals to the He antibonding MO.[†] Hence, He_2 is an unstable molecule. Molecular orbital theory correctly predicts that hydrogen forms diatomic molecules but helium does not.

Bond Order

In molecular orbital theory, the stability of a covalent bond is related to its **bond order**, defined as half the difference between the number of bonding electrons and the number of antibonding electrons:

$$\text{Bond order} = \tfrac{1}{2}(\text{no. of bonding electrons} - \text{no. of antibonding electrons}) \quad [4.1]$$

We take half the difference because we are used to thinking of bonds as pairs of electrons. *A bond order of 1 represents a single bond, a bond order of 2 represents a double bond, and a bond order of 3 represents a triple bond.* Because MO theory also treats molecules containing an odd number of electrons, bond orders of 1/2 , 3/2, or 5/2 are possible.

Because, as Figure 4.33 shows, H_2 has two bonding electrons and zero antibonding electrons, it has a bond order of 1. Because He_2 has two bonding electrons and two antibonding electrons, it has a bond order of 0. A bond order of 0 means that no bond exists.

 GIVE IT SOME THOUGHT

Suppose one electron in H_2 is excited from the σ_{1s} MO to the σ_{1s}^* MO. Would you expect the H atoms to remain bonded to each other, or would the molecule fall apart?

SAMPLE EXERCISE 4.8 **Bond Order**

What is the bond order of the He_2^+ ion? Would you expect this ion to be stable relative to the separated He atom and He^+ ion?

SOLUTION

Analyze We will determine the bond order for the He_2^+ ion and use it to predict whether the ion is stable.

Plan To determine the bond order, we must determine the number of electrons in the molecule and how these electrons populate the available MOs. The valence electrons of He are in the $1s$ orbital, and the $1s$ orbitals combine to give an MO diagram like that for H_2 or He_2 (Figure 4.33). If the bond order is greater than 0, we expect a bond to exist, and the ion is stable.

Solve The energy-level diagram for the He_2^+ ion is shown in ◄ **FIGURE 4.34**. This ion has three electrons. Two are placed in the bonding orbital and the third in the antibonding orbital. Thus, the bond order is

$$\text{Bond order} = \tfrac{1}{2}(2 - 1) = \tfrac{1}{2}$$

Because the bond order is greater than 0, we predict the He_2^+ ion to be stable relative to the separated He and He^+. Formation of He_2^+ in the gas phase has been demonstrated in laboratory experiments.

PRACTICE EXERCISE

Determine the bond order of the H_2^- ion.
Answer: $\tfrac{1}{2}$

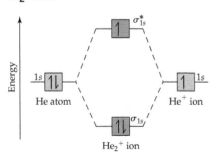

▲ GO FIGURE

Which electrons in this diagram contribute to the stability of the He_2^+ ion?

▲ **FIGURE 4.34** **Energy-level diagram for the He_2^+ ion.**

[†]Antibonding MOs are slightly more energetically unfavorable than bonding MOs are energetically favorable. Thus, whenever there is an equal number of electrons in bonding and antibonding orbitals, the energy of the molecule is slightly higher than that for the separated atoms. As a result, no bond is formed.

4.8 | METALLIC BONDING

Consider the structures of elements of the third period (Na–Ar). Argon with eight valence electrons has a complete octet; as a result it does not form any bonds. Chlorine, sulfur, and phosphorus form molecules (Cl_2, S_8, and P_4) in which the atoms make one, two, and three bonds, respectively (▶ FIGURE 4.35). Silicon forms an extended network solid in which each atom is bonded to four equidistant neighbors. Each of these elements forms $8-N$ bonds, where N is the number of valence electrons. This behavior can easily be understood through application of the octet rule.

If the $8-N$ trend continued as we move left across the periodic table, we would expect aluminum (three valence electrons) to form five bonds. Like many other metals, however, aluminum adopts a close-packed structure with 12 near neighbors. Magnesium and sodium also adopt metallic structures. What is responsible for this abrupt change in the preferred bonding mechanism? The answer is that, as noted earlier, metals do not have enough valence-shell electrons to satisfy their bonding requirements by forming localized electron-pair bonds. In response to this deficiency, the valence electrons are collectively shared. A structure in which the atoms are close-packed facilitates this delocalized sharing of electrons.

Electron-Sea Model

A simple model that accounts for some of the most important characteristics of metals is the **electron-sea model**, which pictures the metal as an array of metal cations in a "sea" of valence electrons (◀ FIGURE 4.36). The electrons are confined to the metal by electrostatic attractions to the cations, and they are uniformly distributed throughout the structure. The electrons are mobile, however, and no individual electron is confined to any particular metal ion. When a voltage is applied to a metal wire, the electrons, being negatively charged, flow through the metal toward the positively charged end of the wire.

The high thermal conductivity of metals is also accounted for by the presence of mobile electrons. The movement of electrons in response to temperature gradients permits ready transfer of kinetic energy throughout the solid.

The ability of metals to deform (their malleability and ductility) can be explained by the fact that metal atoms form bonds to many neighbors. Changes in the positions of

▲ GO FIGURE

How many nonbonding electron pairs are there per atom in chlorine, sulfur, phosphorus, and silicon?

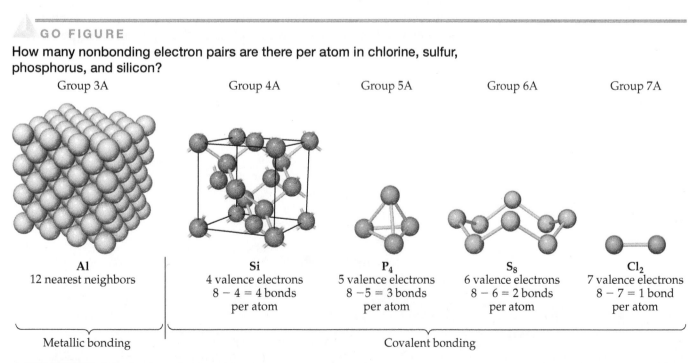

| Group 3A | Group 4A | Group 5A | Group 6A | Group 7A |

Al	**Si**	**P_4**	**S_8**	**Cl_2**
12 nearest neighbors	4 valence electrons	5 valence electrons	6 valence electrons	7 valence electrons
	$8-4=4$ bonds	$8-5=3$ bonds	$8-6=2$ bonds	$8-7=1$ bond
	per atom	per atom	per atom	per atom

Metallic bonding   Covalent bonding

▲ **FIGURE 4.35 Bonding in period 3 elements.**

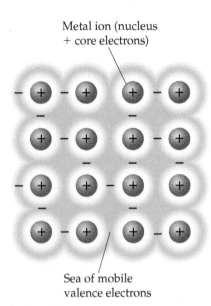

Metal ion (nucleus + core electrons)

Sea of mobile valence electrons

▲ **FIGURE 4.36 Electron-sea model of metallic bonding.** The valence electrons delocalize to form a sea of mobile electrons that surrounds and binds together an extended array of metal ions.

the atoms brought about in reshaping the metal are partly accommodated by a redistribution of electrons.

Molecular-Orbital Model

Although the electron-sea model works surprisingly well given its simplicity, it does not adequately explain many properties of metals. According to the model, for example, the strength of bonding between metal atoms should steadily increase as the number of valence electrons increases, resulting in a corresponding increase in the melting points. However, elements near the middle of the transition metal series, rather than those at the end, have the highest melting points in their respective periods (▼ FIGURE 4.37). This trend implies that the strength of metallic bonding first increases with increasing number of electrons and then decreases. Similar trends are seen in other physical properties of the metals, such as the boiling point, heat of fusion, and hardness.

To obtain a more accurate picture of the bonding in metals, we must turn to molecular-orbital theory. Let's briefly review some of the rules of the theory:

1. Atomic orbitals combine to make molecular orbitals that can extend over the entire molecule.

2. A molecular orbital can contain zero, one, or two electrons.

3. The number of molecular orbitals in a molecule equals the number of atomic orbitals that combine to form molecular orbitals.

The electronic structures of crystalline solids and small molecules have similarities as well as differences. To illustrate, consider how the molecular-orbital diagram for a chain of lithium atoms changes as we increase the length of the chain (▲ FIGURE 4.38). Each lithium atom contains a half-filled $2s$ orbital in its valence shell. The molecular-orbital diagram for Li_2 is analogous to that of an H_2 molecule: one filled bonding molecular orbital and one empty antibonding molecular orbital with a nodal plane between the atoms. ⚭ (Section 4.7) For Li_4, there are four molecular orbitals, ranging from the lowest-energy orbital, where the orbital interactions are completely bonding (0 nodal planes), to the highest-energy orbital, where all interactions are antibonding (3 nodal planes).

GO FIGURE

Which element in each period has the highest melting point? In each case, is the element you named at the beginning, middle, or end of its period?

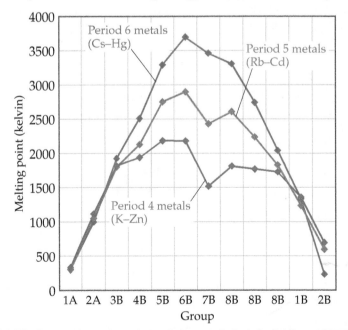

▲ **FIGURE 4.37 The melting points of metals from periods 4, 5, and 6.**

GO FIGURE

How does the energy spacing between molecular orbitals change as the number of atoms in the chain increases?

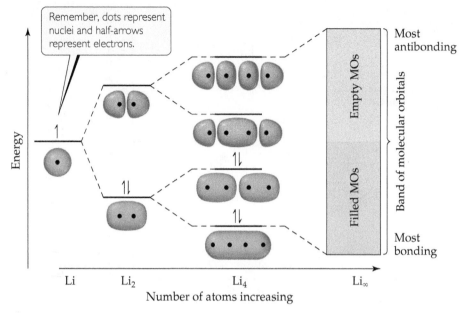

▲ FIGURE 4.38 **Discrete energy levels in individual molecules become continuous energy bands in a solid.** Occupied orbitals are shaded blue, and empty orbitals red.

As the length of the chain increases, the number of molecular orbitals increases. Regardless of chain length, the lowest-energy orbitals are always the most bonding and the highest-energy orbitals always the most antibonding. Furthermore, because each lithium atom has only one valence shell atomic orbital, the number of molecular orbitals is equal to the number of lithium atoms in the chain. Because each lithium atom has one valence electron, half of the molecular orbitals are fully occupied and the other half are empty, regardless of chain length.*

If the chain becomes very long, there are so many molecular orbitals that the energy separation between them becomes vanishingly small. As the chain length goes to infinity, the allowed energy states become a continuous **band**. For a crystal large enough to see with the eye (or even an optical microscope), the number of atoms is extremely large. Consequently, the electronic structure of the crystal is like that of the infinite chain, consisting of bands, as shown on the right-hand side of Figure 4.38.

The electronic structures of most metals are more complicated than shown in Figure 4.38 because we have to consider more than one type of atomic orbital on each atom. Because each type of orbital can give rise to its own band, the electronic structure of a solid usually consists of a series of bands. The electronic structure of a bulk solid is referred to as a **band structure**.

The band structure for a typical metal is shown schematically in ▲ **FIGURE 4.39**. The electron filling depicted corresponds to nickel metal, but the basic features of other metals are similar. The electron configuration of a nickel atom is $[Ar]3d^8 4s^2$, as shown on the left side of the figure. The energy bands that form from each of these orbitals are shown on the right side. The $4s$, $4p$, and $3d$ orbitals are treated independently, each giving rise to a band of molecular orbitals. In practice, these overlapping bands are not completely independent of each other, but for our purposes this simplification is reasonable.

The $4s$, $4p$, and $3d$ bands differ from one another in the energy range they span (represented by the heights of the rectangles on the right side of Figure 4.39) and in the number of electrons they can hold (represented by the area of the rectangles).

*This is strictly true only for chains with an even number of atoms.

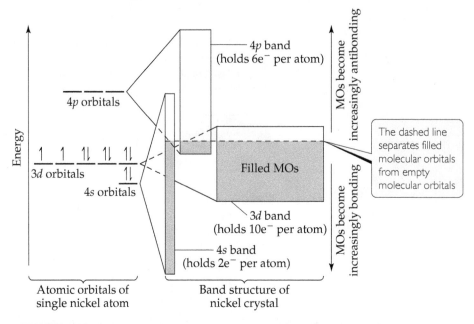

△ **GO FIGURE**

If the metal were potassium rather than nickel, which bands—*4s, 4p,* and/or *3d*—would be partially occupied?

▲ **FIGURE 4.39** **The electronic band structure of nickel.**

The 4*s*, 4*p*, and 3*d* bands can hold 2, 6, and 10 electrons per atom, respectively, two per orbital, as dictated by the Pauli exclusion principle. ⟳(Section 1.7) The energy range spanned by the 3*d* band is smaller than the range spanned by the 4*s* and 4*p* bands because the 3*d* orbitals are smaller and, therefore, overlap with orbitals on neighboring atoms less effectively. This reduces the strength of the bonding interactions, which dominate the bottom of the band, as well as the antibonding interactions, which dominate the top of the band. As a result, the 3*d* band spans a narrower range of energy than the 4*s* and 4*p* bands.

Many properties of metals can be understood from Figure 4.39. We can think of the energy band as a partially filled container for electrons. The incomplete filling of the energy band gives rise to characteristic metallic properties. The electrons in orbitals near the top of the occupied levels require very little energy input to be "promoted" to higher-energy orbitals that are unoccupied. Under the influence of any source of excitation, such as an applied electrical potential or an input of thermal energy, electrons move into previously vacant levels and are thus freed to move through the lattice, giving rise to electrical and thermal conductivity.

Without the overlap of energy bands, the periodic properties of metals could not be explained. In the absence of the *d*- and *p*-bands, we would expect the *s*-band to be half-filled for the alkali metals (group 1A) and completely filled for the alkaline-earth metals (group 2A). If that were true, metals like magnesium, calcium, and strontium would not be good electrical and thermal conductors, in disagreement with experimental observations.

While the conductivity of metals can be qualitatively understood using either the electron-sea model or the molecular-orbital model, many physical properties of transition metals, such as the melting points plotted in Figure 4.37, can be explained only with the latter model. The molecular-orbital model predicts that bonding first becomes stronger as the number of valence electrons increases and the bonding orbitals are populated. Upon moving past the middle elements of the transition metal series, the bonds grow weaker as we fill the antibonding orbitals. Strong bonds between atoms lead to metals with higher melting and boiling points, higher heats of fusion, higher hardness, and so forth.

⚓ GIVE IT SOME THOUGHT

Which element, W or Au, has the greater number of electrons in antibonding orbitals? Which one would you expect to have the higher melting point?

CHAPTER SUMMARY AND KEY TERMS

INTRODUCTION AND SECTION 4.1 The three-dimensional shapes and sizes of molecules are determined by their **bond angles** and bond lengths. Molecules with a central atom A surrounded by n atoms B, denoted AB_n, adopt a number of different geometric shapes, depending on the value of n and on the particular atoms involved. In the overwhelming majority of cases, these geometries are related to five basic shapes (linear, trigonal pyramidal, tetrahedral, trigonal bipyramidal, and octahedral).

SECTION 4.2 The **valence-shell electron-pair repulsion (VSEPR) model** rationalizes molecular geometries based on the repulsions between **electron domains**, which are regions about a central atom in which electrons are likely to be found. **Bonding pairs** of electrons, which are those involved in making bonds, and **nonbonding pairs** of electrons, also called **lone pairs**, both create electron domains around an atom. According to the VSEPR model, electron domains orient themselves to minimize electrostatic repulsions; that is, they remain as far apart as possible. Electron domains from nonbonding pairs exert slightly greater repulsions than those from bonding pairs, which leads to certain preferred positions for nonbonding pairs and to the departure of bond angles from idealized values. Electron domains from multiple bonds exert slightly greater repulsions than those from single bonds. The arrangement of electron domains around a central atom is called the **electron-domain geometry**; the arrangement of atoms is called the **molecular geometry**.

SECTION 4.3 The dipole moment of a polyatomic molecule depends on the vector sum of the dipole moments associated with the individual bonds, called the **bond dipoles**. Certain molecular shapes, such as linear AB_2 and trigonal planar AB_3, assure that the bond dipoles cancel, producing a nonpolar molecule, which is one whose dipole moment is zero. In other shapes, such as bent AB_2 and trigonal pyramidal AB_3, the bond dipoles do not cancel and the molecule will be polar (that is, it will have a nonzero dipole moment).

SECTION 4.4 **Valence-bond theory** is an extension of Lewis's notion of electron-pair bonds. In valence-bond theory, covalent bonds are formed when atomic orbitals on neighboring atoms overlap one another. The overlap region is one of low energy, or greater stability, for the two electrons because of their simultaneous attraction to two nuclei. The greater the overlap between two orbitals, the stronger will be the bond that is formed.

SECTION 4.5 To extend the ideas of valence-bond theory to polyatomic molecules, we must envision mixing s, p, and sometimes d orbitals to form **hybrid orbitals**. The process of **hybridization** leads to hybrid atomic orbitals that have a large lobe directed to overlap with orbitals on another atom to make a bond. Hybrid orbitals can also accommodate nonbonding pairs. A particular mode of hybridization can be associated with each of three common electron-domain geometries (linear $= sp$; trigonal planar $= sp^2$; tetrahedral $= sp^3$).

SECTION 4.6 Covalent bonds in which the electron density lies along the line connecting the atoms (the internuclear axis) are called **sigma (σ) bonds**. Bonds can also be formed from the sideways overlap of p orbitals. Such a bond is called a **pi (π) bond**. A double bond, such as that in C_2H_4, consists of one σ bond and one π bond; a triple bond, such as that in C_2H_2, consists of one σ and two π bonds. The formation of a π bond requires that molecules adopt a specific orientation; the two CH_2 groups in C_2H_4, for example, must lie in the same plane. As a result, the presence of π bonds introduces rigidity into molecules. In molecules that have multiple bonds and more than one resonance structure, such as C_6H_6, the π bonds are **delocalized**; that is, the π bonds are spread among several atoms.

SECTION 4.7 **Molecular orbital theory** is another model used to describe the bonding in molecules. In this model the electrons exist in allowed energy states called **molecular orbitals (MOs)**. An MO can extend over all the atoms of a molecule. Like an atomic orbital, a molecular orbital has a definite energy and can hold two electrons of opposite spin. We can think of molecular orbitals as built up by combining atomic orbitals on different atomic centers. In the simplest case, the combination of two atomic orbitals leads to the formation of two MOs, one at lower energy and one at higher energy relative to the energy of the atomic orbitals. The lower-energy MO concentrates charge density in the region between the nuclei and is called a **bonding molecular orbital**. The higher-energy MO excludes electrons from the region between the nuclei and is called an **antibonding molecular orbital**. Occupation of bonding MOs favors bond formation, whereas occupation of antibonding MOs is unfavorable. The bonding and antibonding MOs formed by the combination of s orbitals are **sigma (σ) molecular orbitals**; they lie on the internuclear axis.

The combination of atomic orbitals and the relative energies of the molecular orbitals are shown by an **energy-level** (or **molecular orbital**) **diagram**. When the appropriate number of electrons are put into the MOs, we can calculate the **bond order** of a bond, which is half the difference between the number of electrons in bonding MOs and the number of electrons in antibonding MOs. A bond order of 1 corresponds to a single bond, and so forth. Bond orders can be fractional numbers.

SECTION 4.8 The properties of metals can be accounted for in a qualitative way by the **electron-sea model**, in which the electrons are visualized as being free to move throughout the metal. In the molecular-orbital model the valence atomic orbitals of the metal atoms interact to form energy **bands** that are incompletely filled by valence electrons. Consequently, the electronic structure of a bulk solid is referred to as a **band structure**. The orbitals that constitute the energy band are delocalized over the atoms of the metal, and their energies are closely spaced. In a metal the valence shell s, p, and d orbitals form bands and these bands overlap resulting in one or more partially filled bands. Because the energy differences between orbitals *within a band* are extremely small, promoting electrons to higher-energy orbitals requires very little energy. This gives rise to high electrical and thermal conductivity, as well as other characteristic metallic properties.

KEY SKILLS

- Be able to describe the three-dimensional shapes of molecules using the VSEPR model. (Section 4.2)
- Determine whether a molecule is polar or nonpolar based on its geometry and the individual bond dipole moments. (Section 4.3)
- Be able to explain the role of orbital overlap in the formation of covalent bonds. (Section 4.4)
- Be able to specify the hybridization state of atoms in molecules based on observed molecular structures. (Section 4.5)
- Be able to sketch how orbitals overlap to form sigma (σ) and pi (π) bonds. (Section 4.6)
- Be able to explain the existence of delocalized π bonds in molecules such as benzene. (Section 4.6)
- Be able to explain the concept of bonding and antibonding orbitals. (Section 4.7)
- Use the molecular-orbital model to qualitatively predict the trends in melting point, boiling point, and hardness of metals. [Section 4.8]

KEY EQUATION

- Bond order $= \frac{1}{2}$ (no. of bonding electrons $-$ no. of antibonding electrons)   [4.1]

EXERCISES

VISUALIZING CONCEPTS

4.1 A certain AB_4 molecule has a "seesaw" shape:

From which of the fundamental geometries shown in Figure 4.3 could you remove one or more atoms to create a molecule having this seesaw shape? [Section 4.1]

4.2 **(a)** If these three balloons are all the same size, what angle is formed between the red one and the green one? **(b)** If additional air is added to the blue balloon so that it gets larger, what happens to the angle between the red and green balloons? **(c)** What aspect of the VSEPR model is illustrated by part (b)? [Section 4.2]

4.3 For each molecule (a)-(f), indicate how many different electron-domain geometries are consistent with the molecular geometry shown. [Section 4.2]

(a)

(b)

(c)

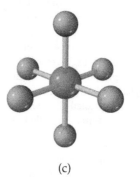

(d)

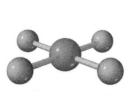

(e)

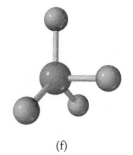

(f)

4.4 The molecule shown here is *difluoromethane* (CH_2F_2), which is used as a refrigerant called R-32. **(a)** Based on the structure, how many electron domains surround the C atom in this molecule? **(b)** Would the molecule have a nonzero dipole moment? **(c)** If the molecule is polar, in what direction will the overall dipole moment vector point in the molecule? [Sections 4.2 and 4.3]

4.5 The following plot shows the potential energy of two Cl atoms as a function of the distance between them. (a) To what does an energy of zero correspond in this diagram? (b) According to the valence-bond model, why does the energy decrease as the Cl atoms move from a large separation to a smaller one? (c) What is the significance of the Cl—Cl distance at the minimum point in the plot? (d) Why does the energy rise at Cl—Cl distances less than that at the minimum point in the plot? (e) How can you estimate the bond strength of the Cl—Cl bond from the plot? [Section 4.4]

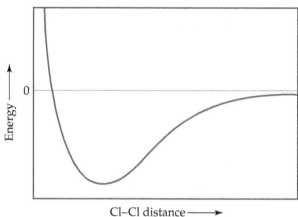

4.6 In the series SiF_4, PF_3, and SF_2, estimate the F—X—F bond angle in each case and explain your rationale. [Section 4.2]

4.7 The orbital diagram that follows presents the final step in the formation of hybrid orbitals by a silicon atom. What type of hybrid orbital is produced in this hybridization? [Section 4.5]

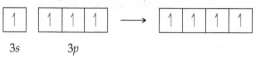

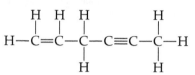

4.8 In the hydrocarbon

$$H-\overset{\underset{|}{H}}{C}=\overset{\underset{|}{H}}{C}-\overset{\underset{|}{H}}{\underset{|}{\overset{H}{C}}}-C\equiv C-\overset{\underset{|}{H}}{\underset{|}{\overset{H}{C}}}-H$$

(a) What is the hybridization at each carbon atom in the molecule? (b) How many σ bonds are there in the molecule? (c) How many π bonds? (d) Identify all the 120° bond angles in the molecule. [Section 4.6]

MOLECULAR SHAPES; THE VSEPR MODEL (sections 4.1 and 4.2)

4.9 An AB_2 molecule is described as linear, and the A—B bond length is known. (a) Does this information completely describe the geometry of the molecule? (b) Can you tell how many nonbonding pairs of electrons are around the A atom from this information?

4.10 (a) Methane (CH_4) and the perchlorate ion (ClO_4^-) are both described as tetrahedral. What does this indicate about their bond angles? (b) The NH_3 molecule is trigonal pyramidal, while BF_3 is trigonal planar. Which of these molecules is flat?

4.11 How does a trigonal pyramid differ from a tetrahedron so far as molecular geometry is concerned?

4.12 Describe the bond angles to be found in each of the following molecular structures: (a) planar trigonal, (b) tetrahedral, (c) octahedral, (d) linear.

4.13 (a) What is meant by the term *electron domain*? (b) Explain in what way electron domains behave like the balloons in Figure 4.5. Why do they do so?

4.14 What property of the electron causes electron domains to have an effect on molecular shapes?

4.15 (a) How does one determine the number of electron domains in a molecule or ion? (b) What is the difference between a *bonding electron domain* and a *nonbonding electron domain*?

4.16 Would you expect the nonbonding electron-pair domain in NH_3 to be greater or less in size than for the corresponding one in PH_3? Explain.

4.17 In which of these molecules or ions does the presence of nonbonding electron pairs produce an effect on molecular shape, assuming they are all in the gaseous state? (a) SiH_4, (b) PF_3, (c) HBr, (d) HCN, (e) SO_2.

4.18 In which of the following molecules can you confidently predict the bond angles about the central atom, and for which would you be a bit uncertain? Explain in each case. (a) H_2S, (b) BCl_3, (c) CH_3I, (d) CBr_4, (e) $TeBr_4$.

4.19 How many nonbonding electron pairs are there in each of the following molecules: (a) $(CH_3)_2S$, (b) HCN, (c) H_2C_2, (d) CH_3F?

4.20 Describe the characteristic electron-domain geometry of each of the following numbers of electron domains about a central atom: (a) 3, (b) 4, (c) 5, (d) 6.

4.21 What is the difference between the electron-domain geometry and the molecular geometry of a molecule? Use the water molecule as an example in your discussion. Why do we need to make this distinction?

4.22 An AB_3 molecule is described as having a trigonal-bipyramidal electron-domain geometry. How many nonbonding domains are on atom A? Explain.

4.23 Give the electron-domain and molecular geometries of a molecule that has the following electron domains on its central atom: (a) four bonding domains and no nonbonding domains, (b) three bonding domains and two nonbonding domains, (c) five bonding domains and one nonbonding domain, (d) four bonding domains and two nonbonding domains.

4.24 What are the electron-domain and molecular geometries of a molecule that has the following electron domains on its central atom? (a) three bonding domains and no nonbonding domains, (b) three bonding domains and one nonbonding domain, (c) two bonding domains and two nonbonding domains.

4.25 Give the electron-domain and molecular geometries for the following molecules and ions: (a) HCN, (b) SO_3^{2-}, (c) SF_4, (d) PF_6^-, (e) NH_3Cl^+, (f) N_3^-.

4.26 Draw the Lewis structure for each of the following molecules or ions, and predict their electron-domain and molecular geometries: **(a)** AsF_3, **(b)** CH_3^+, **(c)** BrF_3, **(d)** ClO_3^-, **(e)** XeF_2, **(f)** BrO_2^-.

4.27 The figure that follows shows ball-and-stick drawings of three possible shapes of an AF_3 molecule. **(a)** For each shape, give the electron-domain geometry on which the molecular geometry is based. **(b)** For each shape, how many nonbonding electron domains are there on atom A? **(c)** Which of the following elements will lead to an AF_3 molecule with the shape in (ii): Li, B, N, Al, P, Cl? **(d)** Name an element A that is expected to lead to the AF_3 structure shown in (iii). Explain your reasoning.

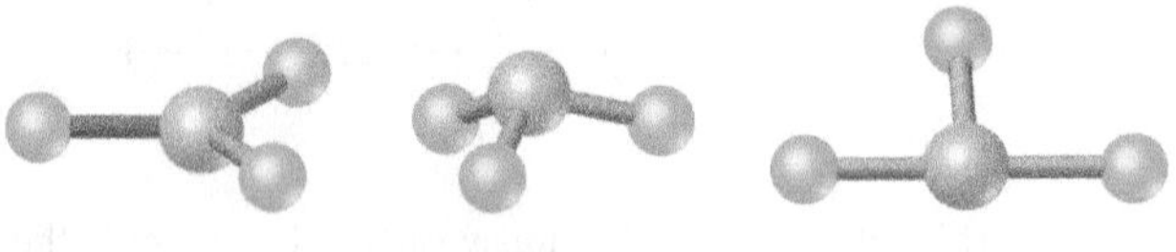

(i)   (ii)   (iii)

4.28 The figure that follows contains ball-and-stick drawings of three possible shapes of an AF_4 molecule. **(a)** For each shape, give the electron-domain geometry on which the molecular geometry is based. **(b)** For each shape, how many nonbonding electron domains are there on atom A? **(c)** Which of the following elements will lead to an AF_4 molecule with the shape in (iii): Be, C, S, Se, Si, Xe? **(d)** Name an element A that is expected to lead to the AF_4 structure shown in (i).

(i)   (ii)   (iii)

4.29 Give the approximate values for the indicated bond angles in the following molecules:

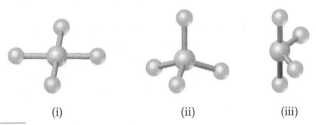

(a) 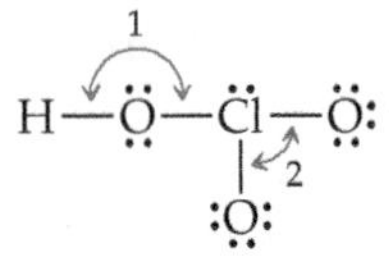 H—O̤—Cl—O̤:
             |
            :O̤:

(b) 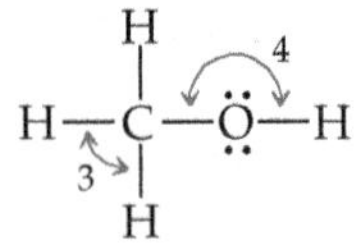 H—C—O̤—H
         |
         H

(c) H—C≡C—H

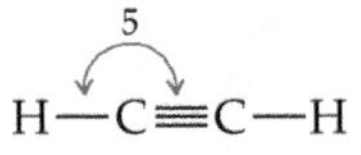

(d) 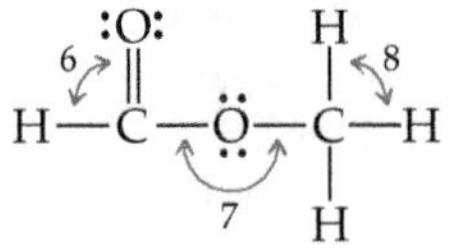 H—C—O̤—C—H
          :O: H
           || |
                               H

4.30 Give approximate values for the indicated bond angles in the following molecules:

(a) 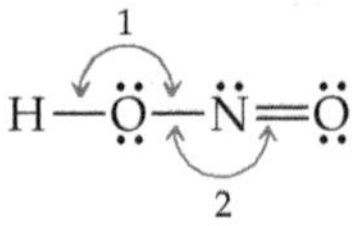 H—O̤—N̈=O̤

(b) 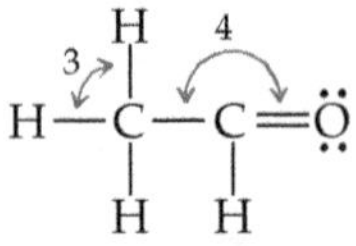 H—C—C=O̤
         | |
         H   H
         H

(c) H—N—O̤—H
         |
         H
         H

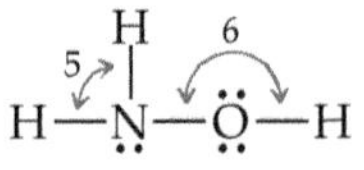

(d) 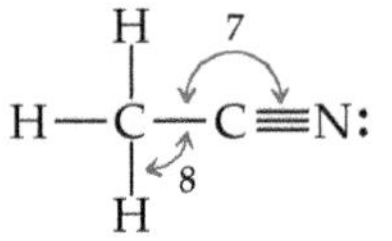 H—C—C≡N:
         |
         H

4.31 In which of the following AF_n molecules or ions is there more than one F—A—F bond angle: SiF_4, PF_5, SF_4, AsF_3?

4.32 The three species NH_2^-, NH_3, and NH_4^+ have H—N—H bond angles of 105°, 107°, and 109°, respectively. Explain this variation in bond angles.

4.33 **(a)** Explain why BrF_4^- is square planar, whereas BF_4^- is tetrahedral. **(b)** How would you expect the H—X—H bond angle to vary in the series H_2O, H_2S, H_2Se? Explain. (*Hint:* The size of an electron pair domain depends in part on the electronegativity of the central atom.)

4.34 **(a)** Explain why the following ions have different bond angles: ClO_2^- and NO_2^-. Predict the bond angle in each case. **(b)** Explain why the XeF_2 molecule is linear.

SHAPES AND POLARITY OF POLYATOMIC MOLECULES (section 4.3)

4.35 What is the distinction between a bond dipole and a molecular dipole moment?

4.36 Consider a molecule with formula AX_3. Supposing the A—X bond is polar, how would you expect the dipole moment of the AX_3 molecule to change as the X—A—X bond angle increases from 100° to 120°?

4.37 **(a)** Does SCl_2 have a dipole moment? If so, in which direction does the net dipole point? **(b)** Does $BeCl_2$ have a dipole moment? If so, in which direction does the net dipole point?

4.38 **(a)** The PH_3 molecule is polar. Does this offer experimental proof that the molecule cannot be planar? Explain. **(b)** It turns out that ozone, O_3, has a small dipole moment. How is this possible, given that all the atoms are the same?

4.39 **(a)** Consider the AF_3 molecules in Exercise 4.29. Which of these will have a nonzero dipole moment? Explain. **(b)** Which of the AF_4 molecules in Exercise 4.30 will have a zero dipole moment?

4.40 **(a)** What conditions must be met if a molecule with polar bonds is nonpolar? **(b)** What geometries will signify nonpolar molecules for AB_2, AB_3, and AB_4 geometries?

4.41 Predict whether each of the following molecules is polar or nonpolar: **(a)** IF, **(b)** CS_2, **(c)** SO_3, **(d)** PCl_3, **(e)** SF_6, **(f)** IF_5.

4.42 Predict whether each of the following molecules is polar or nonpolar: **(a)** CCl_4, **(b)** NH_3, **(c)** SF_4, **(d)** XeF_4, **(e)** CH_3Br, **(f)** GaH_3.

4.43 Dichloroethylene ($C_2H_2Cl_2$) has three forms (isomers), each of which is a different substance. **(a)** Draw Lewis structures of the three isomers, all of which have a carbon–carbon double bond. **(b)** Which of these isomers has a zero dipole moment? **(c)** How many isomeric forms can chloroethylene, C_2H_3Cl, have? Would they be expected to have dipole moments?

4.44 Dichlorobenzene, $C_6H_4Cl_2$, exists in three forms (isomers) called *ortho*, *meta*, and *para*:

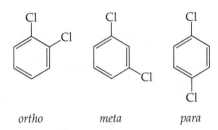

| *ortho* | *meta* | *para* |

Which of these has a nonzero dipole moment? Explain.

ORBITAL OVERLAP; HYBRID ORBITALS (sections 4.4 and 4.5)

4.45 **(a)** What is meant by the term *orbital overlap*? **(b)** Describe what a chemical bond is in terms of electron density between two atoms.

4.46 Draw sketches illustrating the overlap between the following orbitals on two atoms: **(a)** the $2s$ orbital on each atom, **(b)** the $2p_z$ orbital on each atom (assume both atoms are on the z-axis), **(c)** the $2s$ orbital on one atom and the $2p_z$ orbital on the other atom.

4.47 Consider the bonding in an MgH_2 molecule. **(a)** Draw a Lewis structure for the molecule, and predict its molecular geometry. **(b)** What hybridization scheme is used in MgH_2? **(c)** Sketch one of the two-electron bonds between an Mg hybrid orbital and an H $1s$ atomic orbital.

4.48 How would you expect the extent of overlap of the bonding atomic orbitals to vary in the series IF, ICl, IBr, and I_2? Explain your answer.

4.49 Fill in the blank spaces in the following chart. If the molecule column is blank, find an example that fulfills the conditions of the rest of the row.

Molecule	Electron-Domain Geometry	Hybridization of Central Atom	Dipole Moment? Yes or No
CO_2			
		sp^3	Yes
		sp^3	No
	Trigonal planar		No
SF_4			
	Octahedral		No
		sp^2	Yes
	Trigonal bipyramidal		No
XeF_2			

4.50 Why are there no sp^4 or sp^5 hybrid orbitals?

4.51 **(a)** Starting with the orbital diagram of a boron atom, describe the steps needed to construct hybrid orbitals appropriate to describe the bonding in BF_3. **(b)** What is the name given to the hybrid orbitals constructed in (a)? **(c)** Sketch the large lobes of the hybrid orbitals constructed in part (a). **(d)** Are any valence atomic orbitals of B left unhybridized? If so, how are they oriented relative to the hybrid orbitals?

4.52 **(a)** Starting with the orbital diagram of a sulfur atom, describe the steps needed to construct hybrid orbitals appropriate to describe the bonding in SF_2. **(b)** What is the name given to the hybrid orbitals constructed in (a)? **(c)** Sketch the large lobes of these hybrid orbitals. **(d)** Would the hybridization scheme in part (a) be appropriate for SF_4? Explain.

4.53 Indicate the hybridization of the central atom in **(a)** BCl_3, **(b)** $AlCl_4^-$, **(c)** CS_2, **(d)** GeH_4.

4.54 What is the hybridization of the central atom in **(a)** $SiCl_4$, **(b)** HCN, **(c)** SO_3, **(d)** $TeCl_2$.

4.55 Shown here are three pairs of hybrid orbitals, with each set at a characteristic angle. For each pair, determine the type of hybridization, if any, that could lead to hybrid orbitals at the specified angle.

  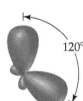

4.56 **(a)** Which geometry and central atom hybridization would you expect in the series BH_4^-, CH_4, NH_4^+? **(b)** What would you expect for the magnitude and direction of the bond dipoles in this series? **(c)** Write the formulas for the analogous species of the elements of period 3; would you expect them to have the same hybridization at the central atom?

MULTIPLE BONDS (section 4.6)

4.57 **(a)** Draw a picture showing how two p orbitals on two different atoms can be combined to make a sigma bond. **(b)** Sketch a π bond that is constructed from p orbitals. **(c)** Which is generally stronger, a σ bond or a π bond? Explain. **(d)** Can two s orbitals combine to form a π bond? Explain.

4.58 **(a)** If the valence atomic orbitals of an atom are sp hybridized, how many unhybridized p orbitals remain in the valence shell? How many π bonds can the atom form? **(b)** Imagine that you could hold two atoms that are bonded together, twist them, and not change the bond length.

Would it be easier to twist (rotate) around a single σ bond or around a double (σ plus π) bond, or would they be the same? Explain.

4.59 (a) Draw Lewis structures for ethane (C_2H_6), ethylene (C_2H_4), and acetylene (C_2H_2). (b) What is the hybridization of the carbon atoms in each molecule? (c) Predict which molecules, if any, are planar. (d) How many σ and π bonds are there in each molecule? (e) Suppose that silicon could form molecules that are precisely the analogs of ethane, ethylene, and acetylene. How would you describe the bonding about Si in terms of hybrid orbitals? Silicon does not readily form some of the analogous compounds containing π bonds. Why might this be the case?

4.60 The nitrogen atoms in N_2 participate in multiple bonding, whereas those in hydrazine, N_2H_4, do not. (a) Draw Lewis structures for both molecules. (b) What is the hybridization of the nitrogen atoms in each molecule? (c) Which molecule has the stronger N—N bond?

4.61 Propylene, C_3H_6, is a gas that is used to form the important polymer called polypropylene. Its Lewis structure is

$$H-C=C-C-H$$

(a) What is the total number of valence electrons in the propylene molecule? (b) How many valence electrons are used to make σ bonds in the molecule? (c) How many valence electrons are used to make π bonds in the molecule? (d) How many valence electrons remain in nonbonding pairs in the molecule? (e) What is the hybridization at each carbon atom in the molecule?

4.62 Ethyl acetate, $C_4H_8O_2$, is a fragrant substance used both as a solvent and as an aroma enhancer. Its Lewis structure is

(a) What is the hybridization at each of the carbon atoms of the molecule? (b) What is the total number of valence electrons in ethyl acetate? (c) How many of the valence electrons are used to make σ bonds in the molecule? (d) How many valence electrons are used to make π bonds? (e) How many valence electrons remain in nonbonding pairs in the molecule?

4.63 Consider the Lewis structure for glycine, the simplest amino acid:

(a) What are the approximate bond angles about each of the two carbon atoms, and what are the hybridizations of the orbitals on each of them? (b) What are the hybridizations of the orbitals on the two oxygens and the nitrogen atom, and what are the approximate bond angles at the nitrogen? (c) What is the total number of σ bonds in the entire molecule, and what is the total number of π bonds?

4.64 Acetylsalicylic acid, better known as aspirin, has the Lewis structure

(a) What are the approximate values of the bond angles labeled 1, 2, and 3? (b) What hybrid orbitals are used about the central atom of each of these angles? (c) How many σ bonds are in the molecule?

4.65 (a) What is the difference between a localized π bond and a delocalized one? (b) How can you determine whether a molecule or ion will exhibit delocalized π bonding? (c) Is the π bond in NO_2^- localized or delocalized?

4.66 (a) Write a single Lewis structure for SO_3, and determine the hybridization at the S atom. (b) Are there other equivalent Lewis structures for the molecule? (c) Would you expect SO_3 to exhibit delocalized π bonding? Explain.

4.67 Predict the molecular geometry of each of the following molecules:

(a) $H-C\equiv C-C\equiv C-C\equiv N$

(b)

(c) $H-N=N-H$

4.68 What hybridization do you expect for the atom indicated in red in each of the following species?
(a) $CH_3CO_2^-$; (b) PH_4^+; (c) AlF_3; (d) $H_2C=CH-CH_2^+$

MOLECULAR ORBITALS AND SECOND-ROW DIATOMIC MOLECULES (section 4.7)

4.69 (a) What is the difference between hybrid orbitals and molecular orbitals? (b) How many electrons can be placed into each MO of a molecule? (c) Can antibonding molecular orbitals have electrons in them?

4.70 (a) If you combine two atomic orbitals on two different atoms to make a new orbital, is this a hybrid orbital or a molecular orbital? (b) If you combine two atomic orbitals on *one* atom to

make a new orbital, is this a hybrid orbital or a molecular orbital? (c) Does the Pauli exclusion principle (Section 1.7) apply to MOs? Explain.

4.71 Consider the H_2^+ ion. (a) Sketch the molecular orbitals of the ion and draw its energy-level diagram. (b) How many electrons are there in the H_2^+ ion? (c) Draw the electron configuration of the ion in terms of its MOs. (d) What is the bond order in H_2^+? **(e)** Suppose that the ion is excited by light so that an electron moves from a lower-energy to a higher-energy MO. Would you expect the excited-state H_2^+ ion to be stable or to fall apart? Explain.

4.72 **(a)** Sketch the molecular orbitals of the H_2^- ion and draw its energy-level diagram. **(b)** Write the electron configuration of the ion in terms of its MOs. **(c)** Calculate the bond order in H_2^-. **(d)** Suppose that the ion is excited by light, so that an electron moves from a lower-energy to a higher-energy

molecular orbital. Would you expect the excited-state H_2^- ion to be stable? Explain.

4.73 Draw a picture that shows all three $2p$ orbitals on one atom and all three $2p$ orbitals on another atom. **(a)** Imagine the atoms coming close together to bond. How many σ bonds can the two sets of $2p$ orbitals make with each other? **(b)** How many π bonds can the two sets of $2p$ orbitals make with each other? **(c)** How many antibonding orbitals, and of what type, can be made from the two sets of $2p$ orbitals?

METALLIC BONDING (section 4.8)

4.74 Explain how the electron-sea model accounts for the high electrical and thermal conductivity of metals.

4.75 **(a)** Compare the electronic structures of atomic chromium and atomic selenium. In what respects are they similar, and in what respects do they differ? **(b)** Chromium is a metal, and selenium is a nonmetal. What factors are important in determining this difference in properties?

4.76 The molecular-orbital diagrams for two- and four-atom linear chains of lithium atoms are shown in Figure 4.38. Construct a molecular-orbital diagram for a chain containing six lithium atoms and use it to answer the following questions. **(a)** How many molecular orbitals are there in the diagram? **(b)** How many nodes are in the lowest-energy molecular orbital? **(c)** How many nodes are in the highest-energy molecular orbital? **(d)** How many nodes are in the

highest-energy occupied molecular orbital (HOMO)? **(e)** How many nodes are in the lowest-energy unoccupied molecular orbital (LUMO)?

4.77 Repeat Exercise 4.76 for a linear chain of eight lithium atoms.

4.78 Which would you expect to be the more ductile element, **(a)** Ag or Mo, **(b)** Zn or Si? In each case explain your reasoning.

4.79 How do you account for the observation that the alkali metals, like sodium and potassium, are soft enough to be cut with a knife?

4.80 Explain this trend in melting points: Y 1522 °C, Zr 1852 °C, Nb 2468 °C, Mo 2617 °C.

4.81 For each of the following groups which metal would you expect to have the highest melting point; **(a)** gold (Au), rhenium (Re), or cesium (Cs); **(b)** rubidium (Rb), molybdenum (Mo), or indium (In); **(c)** ruthenium (Ru), strontium (Sr), or cadmium (Cd)?

ADDITIONAL EXERCISES

4.82 **(a)** What is the physical basis for the VSEPR model? **(b)** When applying the VSEPR model, we count a double or triple bond as a single electron domain. Why is this justified?

4.83 What is the fundamental basis on which we assign electrons to electron domains in pairs and with their spins paired?

4.84 The molecules SiF_4, SF_4, and XeF_4 have molecular formulas of the type AF_4, but the molecules have different molecular geometries. Predict the shape of each molecule, and explain why the shapes differ.

4.85 Consider the molecule PF_4Cl. **(a)** Draw a Lewis structure for the molecule, and predict its electron-domain geometry. **(b)** Which would you expect to take up more space, a $P-F$ bond or a $P-Cl$ bond? Explain. **(c)** Predict the molecular geometry of PF_4Cl. How did your answer for part (b) influence your answer here in part (c)? **(d)** Would you expect the molecule to distort from its ideal electron-domain geometry? If so, how would it distort?

[4.86] The vertices of a tetrahedron correspond to four alternating corners of a cube. By using analytical geometry, demonstrate that the angle made by connecting two of the vertices to a point at the center of the cube is 109.5°, the characteristic angle for tetrahedral molecules.

4.87 From their Lewis structures, determine the number of σ and π bonds in each of the following molecules or ions: **(a)** CO_2;

(b) cyanogen, $(CN)_2$; **(c)** formaldehyde, H_2CO; **(d)** formic acid, HCOOH, which has one H and two O atoms attached to C.

4.88 The lactic acid molecule, $CH_3CH(OH)COOH$, gives sour milk its unpleasant, sour taste. **(a)** Draw the Lewis structure for the molecule, assuming that carbon always forms four bonds in its stable compounds. **(b)** How many π and how many σ bonds are in the molecule? **(c)** Which CO bond is shortest in the molecule? **(d)** What is the hybridization of atomic orbitals around the carbon atom associated with that short bond? **(e)** What are the approximate bond angles around each carbon atom in the molecule?

4.89 The PF_3 molecule has a dipole moment of 1.03 D, but BF_3 has a dipole moment of zero. How can you explain the difference?

4.90 An AB_5 molecule adopts the geometry shown here. **(a)** What is the name of this geometry? **(b)** Do you think there are any nonbonding electron pairs on atom A? Why or why not? **(c)** Suppose the atoms B are halogen atoms. Can you determine uniquely to which group in the periodic table atom A belongs?

4.91 There are two compounds of the formula Pt(NH₃)₂Cl₂:

$$Cl-\underset{\underset{NH_3}{|}}{\overset{\overset{NH_3}{|}}{Pt}}-Cl \qquad Cl-\underset{\underset{NH_3}{|}}{\overset{\overset{Cl}{|}}{Pt}}-NH_3$$

The compound on the right, *cisplatin,* is used in cancer therapy. The compound on the left, *transplatin,* is ineffective for cancer therapy. Both compounds have a square-planar geometry. (**a**) Which compound has a nonzero dipole moment? (**b**) The reason cisplatin is a good anticancer drug is that it binds tightly to DNA. Cancer cells are rapidly dividing, producing a lot of DNA. Consequently, cisplatin kills cancer cells at a faster rate than normal cells. However, since normal cells also are making DNA, cisplatin also attacks healthy cells, which leads to unpleasant side effects. The way both molecules bind to DNA involves the Cl⁻ ions leaving the Pt ion, to be replaced by two nitrogens in DNA. Draw a picture in which a long vertical line represents a piece of DNA. Draw the Pt(NH₃)₂ fragments of cisplatin and transplatin with the proper shape. Also draw them attaching to your DNA line. Can you explain from your drawing why the shape of the cisplatin causes it to bind to DNA more effectively than transplatin?

[**4.92**] The O—H bond lengths in the water molecule (H_2O) are 0.96 Å, and the H—O—H angle is 104.5°. The dipole moment of the water molecule is 1.85 D. (**a**) In what directions do the bond dipoles of the O—H bonds point? In what direction does the dipole moment vector of the water molecule point? (**b**) Calculate the magnitude of the bond dipole of the O—H bonds. (*Note:* You will need to use vector addition to do this.) (**c**) Compare your answer from part (b) to the dipole moments of the hydrogen halides (Table 3.3). Is your answer in accord with the relative electronegativity of oxygen?

[**4.93**] The reaction of three molecules of fluorine gas with a Xe atom produces the substance xenon hexafluoride, XeF_6:

$$Xe(g) + 3 F_2(g) \longrightarrow XeF_6(s)$$

(**a**) Draw a Lewis structure for XeF_6. (**b**) If you try to use the VSEPR model to predict the molecular geometry of XeF_6, you run into a problem. What is it? (**c**) What could you do to resolve the difficulty in part (b)? (**d**) The molecule IF_7 has a pentagonal-bipyramidal structure (five equatorial fluorine atoms at the vertices of a regular pentagon and two axial fluorine atoms). Based on the structure of IF_7, suggest a structure for XeF_6.

[**4.94**] The Lewis structure for allene is

$$\underset{\underset{H}{\diagup}}{\overset{\overset{H}{\diagdown}}{C}}=C=\underset{\underset{H}{\diagdown}}{\overset{\overset{H}{\diagup}}{C}}$$

Make a sketch of the structure of this molecule that is analogous to Figure 4.25. In addition, answer the following three questions: (**a**) Is the molecule planar? (**b**) Does it have a nonzero dipole moment? (**c**) Would the bonding in allene be described as delocalized? Explain.

[**4.95**] The azide ion, N_3^-, is linear with two N—N bonds of equal length, 1.16 Å. (**a**) Draw a Lewis structure for the azide ion. (**b**) With reference to Table 3.5, is the observed N—N bond length consistent with your Lewis structure? (**c**) What hybridization scheme would you expect at each of the nitrogen atoms in N_3^-? (**d**) Show which hybridized and unhybridized orbitals are involved in the formation of σ and π bonds in N_3^-. (**e**) It is often observed that σ bonds that involve an sp hybrid orbital are shorter than those that involve only sp^2 or sp^3 hybrid orbitals. Can you propose a reason for this? Is this observation applicable to the observed bond lengths in N_3^-?

[**4.96**] In ozone, O_3, the two oxygen atoms on the ends of the molecule are equivalent to one another. (**a**) What is the best choice of hybridization scheme for the atoms of ozone? (**b**) For one of the resonance forms of ozone, which of the orbitals are used to make bonds and which are used to hold nonbonding pairs of electrons? (**c**) Which of the orbitals can be used to delocalize the π electrons? (**d**) How many electrons are delocalized in the π system of ozone?

4.97 Butadiene, C_4H_6, is a planar molecule that has the following carbon–carbon bond lengths:

$$H_2C\underset{1.34\,\text{Å}}{=\!=\!=}CH\underset{1.48\,\text{Å}}{-\!\!-\!\!-}CH\underset{1.34\,\text{Å}}{=\!=\!=}CH_2$$

(**a**) Predict the bond angles around each of the carbon atoms and sketch the molecule.

(**b**) Compare the bond lengths to the average bond lengths listed in Table 3.5. Can you explain any differences?

INTEGRATIVE EXERCISES

4.98 A compound composed of 2.1% H, 29.8% N, and 68.1% O has a molar mass of approximately 50 g/mol. (**a**) What is the molecular formula of the compound? (**b**) What is its Lewis structure if H is bonded to O? (**c**) What is the geometry of the molecule? (**d**) What is the hybridization of the orbitals around the N atom? (**e**) How many σ and how many π bonds are there in the molecule?

4.99 Sulfur tetrafluoride (SF_4) reacts slowly with O_2 to form sulfur tetrafluoride monoxide (OSF_4) according to the following unbalanced reaction:

$$SF_4(g) + O_2(g) \longrightarrow OSF_4(g)$$

The O atom and the four F atoms in OSF_4 are bonded to a central S atom. (**a**) Balance the equation. (**b**) Write a Lewis structure of OSF_4 in which the formal charges of all atoms are zero. (**c**) Use average bond enthalpies (Table 3.4) to estimate the enthalpy of the reaction. Is it endothermic or exothermic? (**d**) Determine the electron-domain geometry of OSF_4, and write two possible molecular geometries for the molecule based on this electron-domain geometry. (**e**) Which of the molecular geometries in part (d) is more likely to be observed for the molecule? Explain.

4.100 (**a**) Compare the bond enthalpies (Table 3.4) of the carbon–carbon single, double, and triple bonds to deduce an average π-bond contribution to the enthalpy. What fraction of a single bond does this quantity represent? (**b**) Make a similar comparison of nitrogen–nitrogen bonds. What do you observe? (**c**) Write Lewis structures of N_2H_4, N_2H_2, and N_2, and determine the hybridization around nitrogen in each case. (**d**) Propose a reason for the large difference in your observations of parts (a) and (b).

WHAT'S AHEAD

BECAUSE THE LEAVES OF THE LOTUS PLANT are highly water repellent, any water on a leaf beads up to minimize contact with the leaf surface.

INTERMOLECULAR FORCES

THE LOTUS PLANT GROWS in aquatic environments. In order to thrive in such an environment the surface of a lotus leaf is highly water repellent. Scientists call surfaces with this property "superhydrophobic." The superhydrophobic character of the lotus leaf not only allows it to float on water but also causes any water that falls on the leaf to bead up and roll off. The water drops collect dirt as they roll off, keeping the leaf clean, even in the muddy ponds and lakes where lotus plants tend to grow. Because of its self-cleaning properties, the lotus plant is considered a symbol of purity in many Eastern cultures.

What forces cause the lotus leaf to repel water so efficiently? Although this plant's self-cleaning nature has been known for millennia, the effect was not fully understood until the 1970s when scanning electron microscopy images revealed a rough, one might say mountainous, leaf surface (▶ FIGURE 5.1). The rough surface helps minimize contact between water and leaf.

Another important factor contributing to the plant's self-cleaning nature is the contrast between the molecular composition of the leaf and that of the water. The leaf is coated by hydrocarbon molecules that are held together by forces that are different

▲ FIGURE 5.1 **A microscopic view of a water droplet on the surface of a lotus leaf.**

from those that hold the water molecules together. As a result the water molecules preferentially surround themselves with other water molecules, thereby minimizing their contact with the surface.

The lotus effect has inspired scientists to design superhydrophobic surfaces for applications such as self-cleaning windows and water-repellent clothing. To understand the lotus effect and other phenomena involving liquids and solids, we must understand **intermolecular forces**, the forces that exist *between* molecules. Only by understanding the nature and strength of these forces can we understand how the composition and structure of a substance are related to its physical properties in the liquid or solid state.

5.1 | A MOLECULAR COMPARISON OF GASES, LIQUIDS, AND SOLIDS

As we will learn in Chapter 8, the molecules in a gas are widely separated and in a state of constant, chaotic motion. One of the key tenets of kinetic-molecular theory is the assumption that we can neglect the interactions between molecules. ∞∞ (Section 8.7) The properties of liquids and solids are quite different from gases largely because the intermolecular forces in liquids and solids are much stronger. A comparison of the properties of gases, liquids, and solids is given in ▼ TABLE 5.1.

In liquids the intermolecular attractive forces are strong enough to hold particles close together. Thus, liquids are much denser and far less compressible than gases. Unlike gases, liquids have a definite volume, independent of the size and shape of their container. The attractive forces in liquids are not strong enough, however, to keep the particles from moving past one another. Thus, any liquid can be poured, and assumes the shape of the container it occupies.

In solids the intermolecular attractive forces are strong enough to hold particles close together and to lock them virtually in place. Solids, like liquids, are not very compressible because the particles have little free space between them. Because the particles in a solid or liquid are fairly close together compared with those of a gas, we often refer to solids and liquids as *condensed phases*. We will study solids in Chapter 7. For now it is sufficient to know that the particles of a solid are not free to undergo long-range movement, which makes solids rigid.*

TABLE 5.1 • Some Characteristic Properties of the States of Matter	
Gas	Assumes both volume and shape of its container
	Expands to fill its container
	Is compressible
	Flows readily
	Diffusion within a gas occurs rapidly
Liquid	Assumes shape of portion of container it occupies
	Does not expand to fill its container
	Is virtually incompressible
	Flows readily
	Diffusion within a liquid occurs slowly
Solid	Retains own shape and volume
	Does not expand to fill its container
	Is virtually incompressible
	Does not flow
	Diffusion within a solid occurs extremely slowly

*The atoms in a solid are able to vibrate in place. As the temperature of a solid increases, the vibrational motion increases.

GO FIGURE

For a given substance, do you expect the density of the substance in its liquid state to be closer to the density in the gaseous state or in the solid state?

Strength of intermolecular attractions increasing

Gas   **Liquid**   **Crystalline solid**

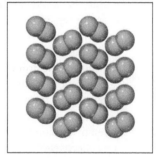

Chlorine, Cl_2
Particles far apart;
possess complete
freedom of motion

Bromine, Br_2
Particles are closely packed but
randomly oriented; retain freedom
of motion; rapidly change neighbors

Iodine, I_2
Particles are closely packed in
an ordered array; positions
are essentially fixed

▲ **FIGURE 5.2   Gases, liquids, and solids.** Chlorine, bromine, and iodine are all made up of diatomic molecules as a result of covalent bonding. However, due to differences in the strength of the intermolecular forces, they exist in three different states at room temperature and standard pressure: Cl_2 gaseous, Br_2 liquid, I_2 solid.

▲ FIGURE 5.2 compares the three states of matter. *The state of a substance depends largely on the balance between the kinetic energies of the particles (atoms, molecules or ions) and the interparticle energies of attraction.* The kinetic energies, which depend on temperature, tend to keep the particles apart and moving. The interparticle attractions tend to draw the particles together. Substances that are gases at room temperature have much weaker interparticle attractions than those that are liquids; substances that are liquids have weaker interparticle attractions than those that are solids. The different states of matter adopted by the halogens at room temperature—iodine is solid, bromine is a liquid, and chlorine is a gas—is a direct consequence of a decrease in the strength of the intermolecular forces as we move from I_2 to Br_2 to Cl_2.

We can change a substance from one state to another by heating or cooling, which changes the average kinetic energy of the particles. NaCl, for example, a solid at room temperature, melts at 1074 K and boils at 1686 K under 1 atm pressure, and Cl_2, a gas at room temperature, liquefies at 239 K and solidifies at 172 K under 1 atm pressure. As the temperature of a gas decreases, the average kinetic energy of its particles decreases, allowing the attractions between the particles to first draw the particles close together, forming a liquid, and then to virtually lock them in place, forming a solid. Increasing the pressure on a gas can also drive transformations from gas to liquid to solid because the increased pressure brings the molecules closer together, thus making intermolecular forces more effective. For example, propane (C_3H_8) is a gas at room temperature and 1 atm pressure, whereas liquefied propane (LP) is a liquid at room temperature because it is stored under much higher pressure.

5.2 | INTERMOLECULAR FORCES

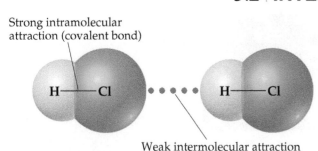

Strong intramolecular attraction (covalent bond)

H—Cl • • • • • H—Cl

Weak intermolecular attraction

▲ FIGURE 5.3 **Intermolecular and intramolecular forces.**

The strengths of intermolecular forces in different substances vary over a wide range but are generally much weaker than intramolecular forces—ionic, metallic or covalent bonds (◄ FIGURE 5.3). Less energy, therefore, is required to vaporize a liquid or melt a solid than to break covalent bonds. For example, only 16 kJ/mol is required to overcome the intermolecular attractions in liquid HCl in order to vaporize it. In contrast, the energy required to break the covalent bond in HCl is 431 kJ/mol. Thus, when a molecular substance such as HCl changes from solid to liquid to gas, the molecules remain intact.

Many properties of liquids, including *boiling points,* reflect the strength of the intermolecular forces. A liquid boils when bubbles of its vapor form within the liquid. The molecules of the liquid must overcome their attractive forces in order to separate and form a vapor. The stronger the attractive forces, the higher the temperature at which the liquid boils. Similarly, the *melting points* of solids increase as the strengths of the intermolecular forces increase. As shown in ▼ TABLE 5.2, the melting and boiling points of substances in which the particles are held together by chemical bonds tend to be much higher than those of substances in which the particles are held together by intermolecular forces.

Three types of intermolecular attractions exist between electrically neutral molecules: dispersion forces, dipole–dipole attractions, and hydrogen bonding. The first two are collectively called *van der Waals forces* after Johannes van der Waals, who developed the equation for predicting the deviation of gases from ideal behavior. Another kind of attractive force, the ion–dipole force, is important in solutions.

All intermolecular interactions are electrostatic, involving attractions between positive and negative species, much like ionic bonds. ∞ (Section 3.2) Why then are intermolecular forces so much weaker than ionic bonds? Recall from Equation 3.4 that electrostatic interactions get stronger as the magnitude of the charges increases and weaker as the distance between charges increases. The charges responsible for intermolecular forces are generally much smaller than the charges in ionic compounds. For example, from its dipole moment it is possible to estimate charges of +0.178 and −0.178 for the hydrogen and chlorine ends of the HCl molecule (see Sample Exercise 3.5). Furthermore, the distances between molecules are often larger than the distances between atoms held together by chemical bonds.

TABLE 5.2 • Melting and Boiling Points of Representative Substances			
Force Holding Particles Together	Substance	Melting Point (K)	Boiling Point (K)
Chemical bonds			
Covalent bonds	Diamond (C)	3800	4300
Metallic bonds	Beryllium (Be)	1560	2742
Ionic bonds	Lithium fluoride (LiF)	1118	1949
Intermolecular forces			
Dispersion force	Nitrogen (N_2)	63	77
Dipole–dipole force	Hydrogen chloride (HCl)	158	188
Hydrogen bonding force	Hydrogen fluoride (HF)	190	293

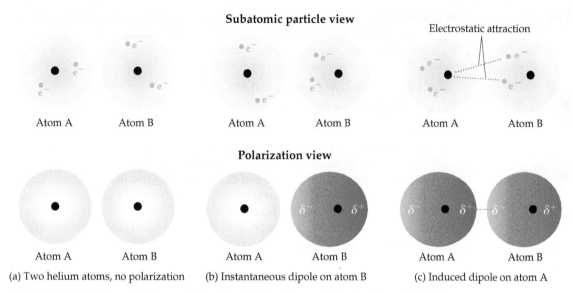

(a) Two helium atoms, no polarization   (b) Instantaneous dipole on atom B   (c) Induced dipole on atom A

▲ **FIGURE 5.4   Dispersion forces.** "Snapshots" of the charge distribution for a pair of helium atoms at three instants.

Dispersion Forces

You might think there would be no electrostatic interactions between electrically neutral, nonpolar atoms and/or molecules. Yet some kind of attractive interactions must exist because nonpolar gases like helium, argon, and nitrogen can be liquefied. Fritz London, a German-American physicist, first proposed the origin of this attraction in 1930. London recognized that the motion of electrons in an atom or molecule can create an *instantaneous,* or momentary, dipole moment.

In a collection of helium atoms, for example, the *average* distribution of the electrons about each nucleus is spherically symmetrical, as shown in ▲ **FIGURE 5.4**(a). The atoms are nonpolar and so possess no permanent dipole moment. The *instantaneous* distribution of the electrons, however, can be different from the average distribution. If we could freeze the motion of the electrons at any given instant, both electrons could be on one side of the nucleus. At just that instant, the atom has an instantaneous dipole moment as shown in Figure 5.4(b). The motions of electrons in one atom influence the motions of electrons in its neighbors. The instantaneous dipole on one atom can induce an instantaneous dipole on an adjacent atom, causing the atoms to be attracted to each other as shown in Figure 5.4(c). This attractive interaction is called the **dispersion force** (or the *London dispersion force* in some texts). It is significant only when molecules are very close together.

The strength of the dispersion force depends on the ease with which the charge distribution in a molecule can be distorted to induce an instantaneous dipole. The ease with which the charge distribution is distorted is called the molecule's **polarizability**. We can think of the polarizability of a molecule as a measure of the "squashiness" of its electron cloud: The greater the polarizability, the more easily the electron cloud can be distorted to give an instantaneous dipole. Therefore, more polarizable molecules have larger dispersion forces.

In general, polarizability increases as the number of electrons in an atom or molecule increases. The strength of dispersion forces therefore tends to increase with increasing atomic or molecular size. Because molecular size and mass generally parallel each other, *dispersion forces tend to increase in strength with increasing molecular weight.* We can see this in the boiling points of the halogens and noble gases (▶ **FIGURE 5.5**), where dispersion forces are the only intermolecular forces at work.

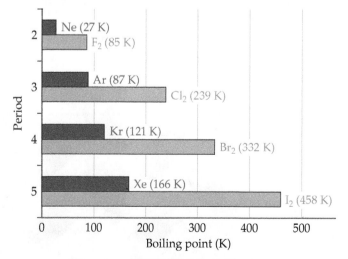

▲ **FIGURE 5.5   Boiling points of the halogens and noble gases.** This plot shows how the boiling points increase as the molecular weight increases due to stronger dispersion forces.

Linear molecule, larger surface area enhances intermolecular contact and increases dispersion force····.

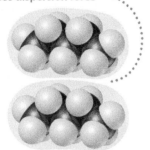

n-Pentane (C_5H_{12})
bp = 309.4 K

Spherical molecule, smaller surface area diminishes intermolecular contact and decreases dispersion force····.

Neopentane (C_5H_{12})
bp = 282.7 K

▲ FIGURE 5.6 **Molecular shape affects intermolecular attraction.** Molecules of *n*-pentane make more contact with each other than do neopentane molecules. Thus, *n*-pentane has stronger intermolecular attractive forces and a higher boiling point.

In both families the molecular weight increases on moving down the periodic table. The higher molecular weights translate into stronger dispersion forces, which in turn lead to higher boiling points.

▲ GIVE IT SOME THOUGHT

List the substances CCl_4, CBr_4, and CH_4 in order of increasing boiling point.

Molecular shape also influences the magnitudes of dispersion forces. For example, *n*-pentane* and neopentane (◄ FIGURE 5.6) have the same molecular formula (C_5H_{12}), yet the boiling point of *n*-pentane is about 27 K higher than that of neopentane. The difference can be traced to the different shapes of the two molecules. Intermolecular attraction is greater for *n*-pentane because the molecules can come in contact over the entire length of the long, somewhat cylindrical molecules. Less contact is possible between the more compact and nearly spherical neopentane molecules.

Dipole–Dipole Forces

The presence of a permanent dipole moment in polar molecules gives rise to **dipole–dipole forces**. These forces originate from electrostatic attractions between the partially positive end of one molecule and partially negative end of a neighboring molecule. Repulsions can also occur when the positive (or negative) ends of two molecules are in close proximity. Dipole–dipole forces are effective only when molecules are very close together.

To see the effect of dipole–dipole forces, we compare the boiling points of two compounds of similar molecular weight: acetonitrile (CH_3CN, MW 41 amu, bp 355 K) and propane ($CH_3CH_2CH_3$, MW 44 amu, bp 231 K). Acetonitrile is a polar molecule, with a dipole moment of 3.9 D, so dipole–dipole forces are present. However, propane is essentially nonpolar, which means that dipole–dipole forces are absent. Because acetonitrile and propane have similar molecular weights, dispersion forces are similar for these two molecules. Therefore, the higher boiling point of acetonitrile can be attributed to dipole–dipole forces.

To better understand these forces, consider how CH_3CN molecules pack together in the solid and liquid states. In the solid [▼ FIGURE 5.7(a)], the molecules are arranged with the negatively charged nitrogen end of each molecule close to the positively charged —CH_3 ends of its neighbors. In the liquid [Figure 5.7(b)], the molecules are free to move with respect to one another, and their arrangement becomes more disordered. This means that, at any given instant, both attractive and repulsive dipole–dipole interactions are present.

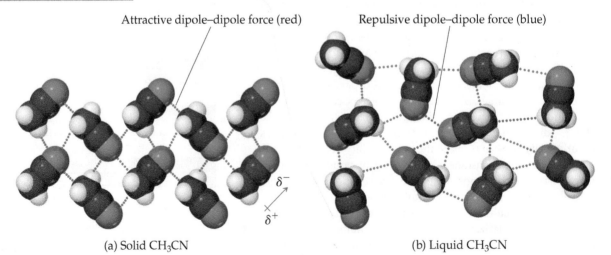

Attractive dipole–dipole force (red)   Repulsive dipole–dipole force (blue)

δ^-
δ^+

(a) Solid CH_3CN (b) Liquid CH_3CN

▲ FIGURE 5.7 **Dipole–dipole interactions.** The dipole–dipole interactions in (a) crystalline CH_3CN and (b) liquid CH_3CN.

*The *n* in *n*-pentane is an abbreviation for the word *normal*. A normal hydrocarbon is one in which the carbon atoms are arranged in a straight chain.

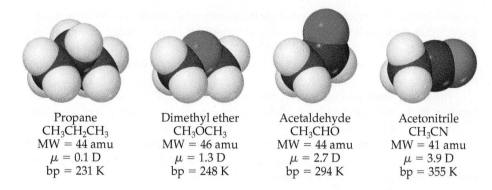

Propane	Dimethyl ether	Acetaldehyde	Acetonitrile
$CH_3CH_2CH_3$	CH_3OCH_3	CH_3CHO	CH_3CN
MW = 44 amu	MW = 46 amu	MW = 44 amu	MW = 41 amu
μ = 0.1 D	μ = 1.3 D	μ = 2.7 D	μ = 3.9 D
bp = 231 K	bp = 248 K	bp = 294 K	bp = 355 K

Increasing polarity
Increasing strength of dipole–dipole forces

◀ FIGURE 5.8 Molecular weights, dipole moments, and boiling points of several simple organic substances.

However, not only are there more attractive interactions than repulsive ones, but also molecules that are attracting each other spend more time near each other than do molecules that are repelling each other. The overall effect is a net attraction strong enough to keep the molecules in liquid CH_3CN from moving apart to form a gas.

For molecules of approximately equal mass and size, the strength of intermolecular attractions increases with increasing polarity, a trend we see in ▲ FIGURE 5.8. Notice how the boiling point increases as the dipole moment increases.

Hydrogen Bonding

▼ FIGURE 5.9 shows the boiling points of the binary compounds that form between hydrogen and the elements in groups 4A through 7A. The boiling points of the compounds containing group 4A elements (CH_4 through SnH_4, all nonpolar) increase systematically moving down the group. This is the expected trend because polarizability and, hence, dispersion forces generally increase as molecular weight increases. The three heavier members of groups 5A, 6A, and 7A follow the same trend, but NH_3, H_2O, and HF have boiling points that

GO FIGURE

Why is the boiling point of SnH_4 higher than that of CH_4?

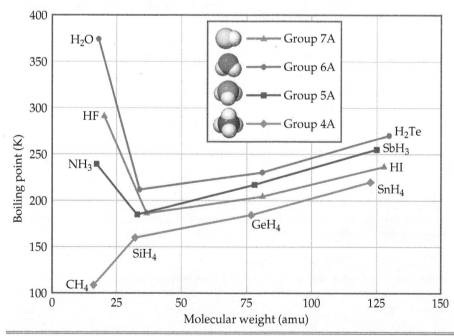

◀ FIGURE 5.9 Boiling points of the covalent hydrides of the elements in groups 4A–7A as a function of molecular weight.

◢ **GO FIGURE**

To form a hydrogen bond what must the non-hydrogen atom (N, O, or F) involved in the bond possess?

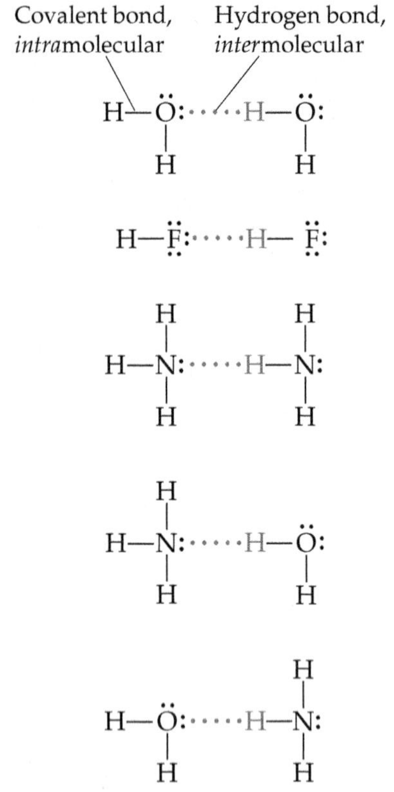

Covalent bond, *intra*molecular   Hydrogen bond, *inter*molecular

H—Ö:····H—Ö:
    | |
    H   H

H—F̈:····H—F̈:

    H   H
    | |
H—N:····H—N:
    | |
    H   H

    H
    |
H—N:····H—Ö:
    | |
    H   H

                   H
                   |
H—Ö:····H—N:
    | |
    H   H

▲ **FIGURE 5.10   Hydrogen bonding.**

are much higher than expected. In fact, these three compounds also have many other characteristics that distinguish them from other substances of similar molecular weight and polarity. For example, water has a high melting point, a high specific heat, and a high heat of vaporization. Each of these properties indicates that the intermolecular forces are abnormally strong.

The strong intermolecular attractions in HF, H_2O, and NH_3 result from hydrogen bonding. **Hydrogen bonding** *is a special type of intermolecular attraction between the hydrogen atom in a polar bond (particularly H—F, H—O, and H—N) and nonbonding electron pair on a nearby small electronegative ion or atom usually F, O, or N (in another molecule).* For example, a hydrogen bond exists between the H atom in an HF molecule and the F atom of an adjacent HF molecule, as shown in ◀ FIGURE 5.10 along with several additional examples.

Hydrogen bonds can be considered a type of dipole–dipole attraction. Because N, O, and F are so electronegative, a bond between hydrogen and any of these elements is quite polar, with hydrogen at the positive end (remember the + on the right-hand side of the dipole symbol represents the positive end of the dipole):

$$\overset{\longleftarrow\;+}{\text{N—H}} \qquad \overset{\longleftarrow\;+}{\text{O—H}} \qquad \overset{\longleftarrow\;+}{\text{F—H}}$$

The hydrogen atom has no inner electrons. Thus, the positive side of the dipole has the concentrated charge of the nearly bare hydrogen nucleus. This positive charge is attracted to the negative charge of an electronegative atom in a nearby molecule. Because the electron-poor hydrogen is so small, it can approach an electronegative atom very closely and, thus, interact strongly with it.

| **SAMPLE EXERCISE 5.1** | **Identifying Substances That Can Form Hydrogen Bonds** |

In which of these substances is hydrogen bonding likely to play an important role in determining physical properties: methane (CH_4), hydrazine (H_2NNH_2), methyl fluoride (CH_3F), hydrogen sulfide (H_2S)?

SOLUTION

Analyze We are given the chemical formulas of four compounds and asked to predict whether they can participate in hydrogen bonding. All the compounds contain H, but hydrogen bonding usually occurs only when the hydrogen is covalently bonded to N, O, or F.

Plan We analyze each formula to see if it contains N, O, or F directly bonded to H. There also needs to be a nonbonding pair of electrons on an electronegative atom (usually N, O, or F) in a nearby molecule, which can be revealed by drawing the Lewis structure for the molecule.

Solve The foregoing criteria eliminate CH_4 and H_2S, which do not contain H bonded to N, O, or F. They also eliminate CH_3F, whose Lewis structure shows a central C atom surrounded by three H atoms and an F atom. (Carbon always forms four bonds, whereas hydrogen and fluorine form one each.) Because the molecule contains a C—F bond and not a H—F bond, it does not form hydrogen bonds. In H_2NNH_2, however, we find N—H bonds, and the Lewis structure shows a nonbonding pair of electrons on each N atom, telling us hydrogen bonds can exist between the molecules:

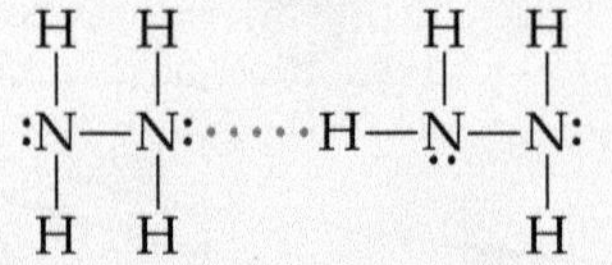

       H   H   H   H
       | | | |
   :N—N:·····H—N—N:
       | | | |
       H   H   H

Check Although we can generally identify substances that participate in hydrogen bonding based on their containing N, O, or F covalently bonded to H, drawing the Lewis structure for the interaction provides a way to check the prediction.

PRACTICE EXERCISE

In which of these substances is significant hydrogen bonding possible: methylene chloride (CH_2Cl_2), phosphine (PH_3), hydrogen peroxide (HOOH), acetone (CH_3COCH_3)?
Answer: HOOH

The energies of hydrogen bonds vary from about 5 kJ/mol to 25 kJ/mol, although there are isolated examples of hydrogen bond energies close to 100 kJ/mol. Thus, hydrogen bonds are typically much weaker than covalent bonds, which have bond enthalpies of 150–1100 kJ/mol (see Table 3.4). Nevertheless, because hydrogen bonds are generally stronger than dipole–dipole or dispersion forces, they play important roles in many chemical systems, including those of biological significance. For example, hydrogen bonds help stabilize the structures of proteins and are also responsible for the way that DNA is able to carry genetic information.

One remarkable consequence of hydrogen bonding is seen in the densities of ice and liquid water. In most substances the molecules in the solid are more densely packed than in the liquid, making the solid phase denser than the liquid phase. By contrast, the density of ice at 0 °C (0.917 g/mL) is less than that of liquid water at 0 °C (1.00 g/mL), so ice floats on liquid water.

The lower density of ice can be understood in terms of hydrogen bonding. In ice, the H_2O molecules assume the ordered, open arrangement shown in ▼ FIGURE 5.11. This arrangement optimizes hydrogen bonding between molecules, with each H_2O molecule forming hydrogen bonds to four neighboring H_2O molecules. These hydrogen bonds, however, create the cavities seen in the middle image of Figure 5.11. When ice melts,

---

GO FIGURE

What is the approximate H—O····H bond angle in ice, where H—O is the covalent bond and O····H is the hydrogen bond?

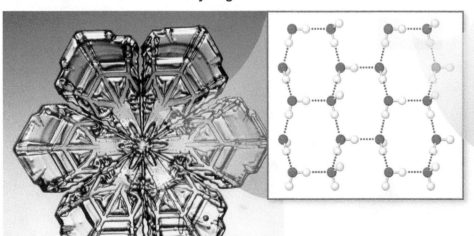

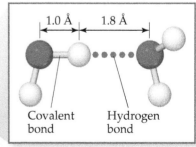

◄ **FIGURE 5.11** **Hydrogen bonding in ice.** The empty channels in the structure of ice make water less dense as a solid than as a liquid.

▲ **FIGURE 5.12** **Expansion of water upon freezing.**

the motions of the molecules cause the structure to collapse. The hydrogen bonding in the liquid is more random than in the solid but is strong enough to hold the molecules close together. Consequently, liquid water has a denser structure than ice, meaning that a given mass of water occupies a smaller volume than the same mass of ice.

The expansion of water upon freezing (◄ FIGURE 5.12) is responsible for many phenomena we take for granted. It causes icebergs to float and water pipes to burst in cold weather. The lower density of ice compared to liquid water also profoundly affects life on Earth. Because ice floats, it covers the top of the water when a lake freezes, thereby insulating the water. If ice were denser than water, ice forming at the top of a lake would sink to the bottom, and the lake could freeze solid. Most aquatic life could not survive under these conditions.

Ion–Dipole Forces

An **ion–dipole force** exists between an ion and a polar molecule (▼ FIGURE 5.13). Cations are attracted to the negative end of a dipole, and anions are attracted to the positive end. The magnitude of the attraction increases as either the ionic charge or the magnitude of the dipole moment increases. Ion–dipole forces are especially important for solutions of ionic substances in polar liquids, such as a solution of NaCl in water.

GIVE IT SOME THOUGHT

In which mixture do you expect to find ion–dipole forces: CH_3OH in water or $Ca(NO_3)_2$ in water?

Comparing Intermolecular Forces

We can identify the intermolecular forces operative in a substance by considering its composition and structure. *Dispersion forces are found in all substances.* The strength of these attractive forces increases with increasing molecular weight and depends on molecular shapes. With polar molecules dipole–dipole forces are also operative, but these forces often make a smaller contribution to the total intermolecular attraction than dispersion forces. For example, in liquid HCl dispersion forces are estimated to account for more than 80% of the total attraction between molecules, while dipole–dipole attractions account for the rest. Hydrogen bonds, when present, make an important contribution to the total intermolecular interaction. In general, the energies associated with dispersion and dipole–dipole forces are 2–10 kJ/mol, while the energies of hydrogen bonds are 5–25 kJ/mol. Ion–dipole attractions have energies of approximately 15 kJ/mol. All these interactions are considerably weaker than covalent and ionic bonds, which have energies that are hundreds of kilojoules per mole.

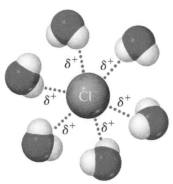

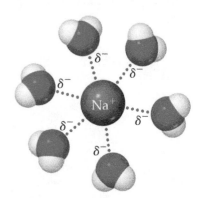

▶ **FIGURE 5.13** **Ion–dipole forces.**

Positive ends of polar molecules are oriented toward negatively charged anion

Negative ends of polar molecules are oriented toward positively charged cation

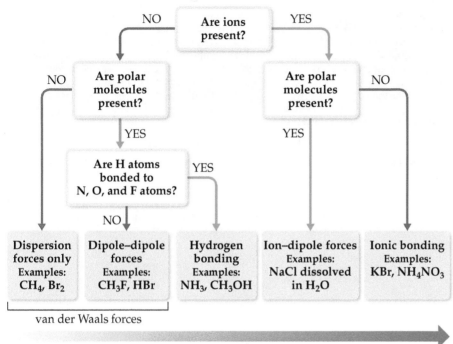

◄ FIGURE 5.14 **Flowchart for determining intermolecular forces.** Multiple types of intermolecular forces can be at work in a given substance or mixture. In particular, dispersion forces occur in all substances.

When comparing the relative strengths of intermolecular attractions, consider these generalizations:

1. When the molecules of two substances have comparable molecular weights and shapes, dispersion forces are approximately equal in the two substances. Differences in the magnitudes of the intermolecular forces are due to differences in the strengths of dipole–dipole attractions. The intermolecular forces get stronger as molecule polarity increases, with those molecules capable of hydrogen bonding having the strongest interactions.

2. When the molecules of two substances differ widely in molecular weights, dispersion forces tend to determine which substance has the stronger intermolecular attractions. Intermolecular attractive forces are generally higher in the substance with higher molecular weight.

▲ FIGURE 5.14 presents a systematic way of identifying the intermolecular forces in a particular system.

It is important to realize that the effects of all these attractions are additive. For example, acetic acid, CH_3COOH, and 1-propanol, $CH_3CH_2CH_2OH$, have the same molecular weight, 60 amu, and both are capable of forming hydrogen bonds. However, a pair of acetic acid molecules can form two hydrogen bonds, whereas a pair of 1-propanol molecules can form only one (▶ FIGURE 5.15). Hence, the boiling point of acetic acid is higher. These effects can be important, especially for very large polar molecules such as proteins, which have multiple dipoles over their surfaces. These molecules can be held together in solution to a surprisingly high degree due to the presence of multiple dipole–dipole attractions.

SAMPLE EXERCISE 5.2 | **Predicting Types and Relative Strengths of Intermolecular Attractions**

List the substances $BaCl_2$, H_2, CO, HF, and Ne in order of increasing boiling point.

SOLUTION

Analyze We need to assess the intermolecular forces in these substances and use that information to determine the relative boiling points.

Plan The boiling point depends in part on the attractive forces in each substance. We need to order these according to the relative strengths of the different kinds of intermolecular attractions.

Each molecule can form two hydrogen bonds with a neighbor

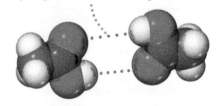

Acetic acid, CH_3COOH
MW = 60 amu
bp = 391 K

Each molecule can form one hydrogen bond with a neighbor

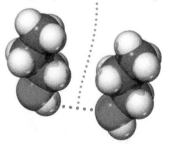

1-Propanol, $CH_3CH_2CH_2OH$
MW = 60 amu
bp = 370 K

▲ FIGURE 5.15 **Hydrogen bonding in acetic acid and 1-propanol.** The greater the number of hydrogen bonds possible, the more tightly the molecules are held together and, therefore, the higher the boiling point.

Solve The attractive forces are stronger for ionic substances than for molecular ones, so $BaCl_2$ should have the highest boiling point. The intermolecular forces of the remaining substances depend on molecular weight, polarity, and hydrogen bonding. The molecular weights are H_2 (2), CO (28), HF (20), and Ne (20). The boiling point of H_2 should be the lowest because it is nonpolar and has the lowest molecular weight. The molecular weights of CO, HF, and Ne are similar. Because HF can hydrogen bond, however, it should have the highest boiling point of the three. Next is CO, which is slightly polar and has the highest molecular weight. Finally, Ne, which is nonpolar, should have the lowest boiling point of these three. The predicted order of boiling points is, therefore,

$$H_2 < Ne < CO < HF < BaCl_2$$

Check The boiling points reported in the literature are H_2 (20 K), Ne (27 K), CO (83 K), HF (293 K), and $BaCl_2$ (1813 K)—in agreement with our predictions.

PRACTICE EXERCISE

(a) Identify the intermolecular attractions present in the following substances, and (b) select the substance with the highest boiling point: CH_3CH_3, CH_3OH, and CH_3CH_2OH.

Answers: (a) CH_3CH_3 has only dispersion forces, whereas the other two substances have both dispersion forces and hydrogen bonds, (b) CH_3CH_2OH

CHEMISTRY PUT TO WORK

Ionic Liquids

The strong electrostatic attractions between cations and anions are responsible for the fact that most ionic compounds are solids at room temperature, with high melting and boiling points. However, the melting point of an ionic compound can be low if the ionic charges are not too high and the cation–anion distance is sufficiently large. For example, the melting point of NH_4NO_3, where both cation and anion are larger polyatomic ions, is 170 °C. If the ammonium cation is replaced by the even larger ethylammonium cation, $CH_3CH_2NH_3^+$, the melting point drops to 12 °C, making ethylammonium nitrate a liquid at room temperature! Ethylammonium nitrate is an example of an *ionic liquid*: a salt that is a liquid at room temperature.

Not only is $CH_3CH_2NH_3^+$ larger than NH_4^+ but also it is less symmetric. In general, the larger and more irregularly shaped the ions in an ionic substance, the better the chances of forming an ionic liquid. Although many cations form ionic liquids, one of the most popular is the 1-butyl-3-methylimidazolium cation (bmim⁺, ▼ FIGURE 5.16 and ▶ TABLE 5.3), which has two arms of different lengths coming off a five-atom central ring. This feature gives bmim⁺ an irregular shape, which makes it difficult for the molecules to pack together in a solid.

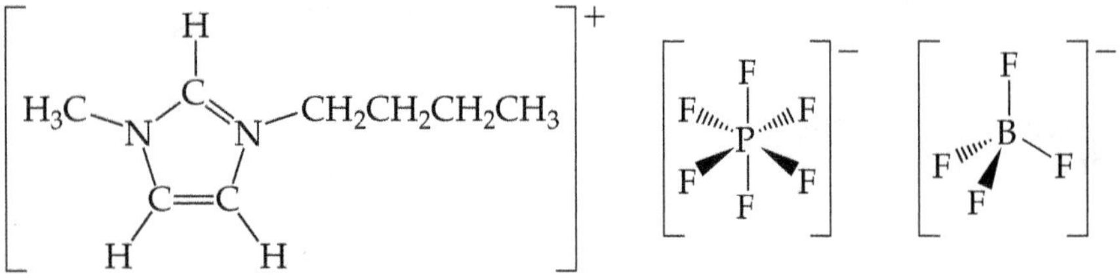

TABLE 5.3 • Melting Point and Decomposition Temperature of Four 1-Butyl-3-methylimidazolium (bmim⁺) Salts

Cation	Anion	Melting Point (°C)	Decomposition Temperature (°C)
bmim⁺	Cl⁻	41	254
bmim⁺	I⁻	−72	265
bmim⁺	PF_6^-	10	349
bmim⁺	BF_4^-	−81	403

Common anions found in ionic liquids include the PF_6^-, BF_4^-, and halide ions.

Ionic liquids have properties that are attractive for some applications. Unlike most molecular liquids, they tend to have a very low vapor pressure. Because they are nonvolatile (that is, they don't evaporate), they tend to be nonflammable and remain in the liquid state at temperatures up to 673 K. Most molecular substances are liquids only at much lower temperatures, for example, 373 K or less in many cases (see Table 5.2). Because they are good solvents for a wide range of inorganic, organic, and polymeric substances, ionic liquids can be used for a variety of reactions and separations. These properties make them attractive replacements for volatile organic solvents in many industrial processes. Relative to traditional organic solvents, ionic liquids offer the promise of reduced volumes, safer handling, and easier reuse. For these reasons and others, there is considerable excitement about the promise of ionic liquids for reducing the environmental impact of industrial chemical processes.

▲ FIGURE 5.16   **Representative ions found in ionic liquids.**

1-Butyl-3-methylimidazolium (bmim⁺) cation

PF_6^- anion

BF_4^- anion

RELATED EXERCISES: 5.25, 5.26, 5.43

5.3 | LIQUID CRYSTALS

In 1888 Frederick Reinitzer, an Austrian botanist, discovered that the organic compound cholesteryl benzoate has an interesting and unusual property, shown in ▼ FIGURE 5.17. Solid cholesteryl benzoate melts at 145 °C, forming a viscous milky liquid; then at 179 °C the milky liquid becomes clear and remains that way at temperatures above 179 °C. When cooled, the clear liquid turns viscous and milky at 179 °C, and the milky liquid solidifies at 145 °C. Reinitzer's work represents the first systematic report of what we call a **liquid crystal**, the term we use today for the viscous, milky state.

Instead of passing directly from the solid phase to the liquid phase when heated, some substances, such as cholesteryl benzoate, pass through an intermediate liquid crystalline phase that has some of the structure of solids and some of the freedom of motion of liquids. Because of the partial ordering, liquid crystals may be viscous and possess properties intermediate between those of solids and those of liquids. The region in which they exhibit these properties is marked by sharp transition temperatures, as in Reinitzer's sample.

Today liquid crystals are used as pressure and temperature sensors and as the display element in such devices as digital watches and laptop computers. They can be used for these applications because the weak intermolecular forces that hold the molecules together in the liquid crystalline phase are easily affected by changes in temperature, pressure, and electric fields.

Types of Liquid Crystals

Substances that form liquid crystals are often composed of rod-shaped molecules that are somewhat rigid in the middle. In the liquid phase, these molecules are oriented randomly. In the liquid crystalline phase, by contrast, the molecules are arranged in specific patterns as illustrated in ▶ FIGURE 5.18. Depending on the nature of the ordering, liquid crystals are classified as nematic, smectic A, smectic C, or cholesteric.

In a **nematic liquid crystal**, the molecules are aligned so that their long axes tend to point in the same direction but the ends are not aligned with one another. In **smectic A** and **smectic C liquid crystals**, the molecules maintain the long-axis alignment seen in nematic crystals, but in addition they pack into layers.

145 °C < T < 179 °C
Liquid crystalline phase

T > 179 °C
Liquid phase

◀ FIGURE 5.17 **Cholesteryl benzoate in its liquid and liquid crystalline states.**

Liquid phase

Molecules arranged randomly

Nematic liquid crystalline phase

Long axes of molecules aligned, but ends are not aligned

Smectic A liquid crystalline phase

Molecules aligned in layers, long axes of molecules perpendicular to layer planes

Smectic C liquid crystalline phase

Molecules aligned in layers, long axes of molecules inclined with respect to layer planes

▶ **FIGURE 5.18 Molecular order in nematic and smectic liquid crystals.** In the liquid phase of any substance, the molecules are arranged randomly, whereas in the liquid crystalline phases the molecules are arranged in a partially ordered way.

Two molecules that exhibit liquid crystalline phases are shown in ▼ **FIGURE 5.19**. The lengths of these molecules are much greater than their widths. The double bonds, including those in the benzene rings, add rigidity to the molecules, and the rings, because they are flat, help the molecules stack with one another. The polar CH_3O and COOH groups give rise to dipole–dipole interactions and promote alignment of the molecules. Thus, the molecules order themselves quite naturally along their long axes. They can, however, rotate around their axes and slide parallel to one another. In smectic liquid crystals, the intermolecular forces (dispersion forces, dipole–dipole attractions, and hydrogen bonding) limit the ability of the molecules to slide past one another.

In a **cholesteric liquid crystal**, the molecules are arranged in layers, with their long axes parallel to the other molecules within the same layer.* Upon moving from one layer to the next, the orientation of the molecules rotates, resulting in the spiral pattern shown in ▶ **FIGURE 5.20**. These liquid crystals are so named because many derivatives of cholesterol adopt this structure.

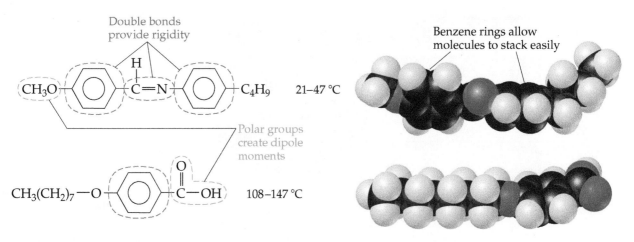

▲ **FIGURE 5.19 Molecular structure and liquid crystal temperature range for two typical liquid crystalline materials.**

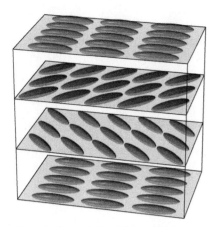 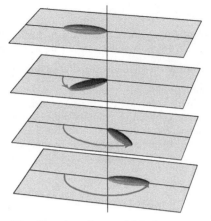

In a cholesteric liquid crystal the molecules pack into layers; the long axis of each molecule is oriented parallel to its neighbors within the same layer

The direction along which the molecules point rotates from one layer to the next, resulting in a spiraling pattern resembling the threads of a screw

▲ FIGURE 5.20 **Molecular order in a cholesteric liquid crystal.**

The molecular arrangement in cholesteric liquid crystals produces unusual coloring patterns with visible light. Changes in temperature and pressure change the order and, hence, the color. Cholesteric liquid crystals are used to monitor temperature changes in situations where conventional methods are not feasible. For example, they can detect hot spots in microelectronic circuits, which may signal the presence of flaws. They can also be fashioned into thermometers for measuring the skin temperature of infants. Because cholesteric liquid crystal displays can be built that draw very little power, they are also being investigated for use in electronic paper (▶ FIGURE 5.21).

SAMPLE EXERCISE 5.3 **Properties of Liquid Crystals**

Which of these substances is most likely to exhibit liquid crystalline behavior?

$$CH_3-CH_2-\overset{\overset{\displaystyle CH_3}{|}}{\underset{\underset{\displaystyle CH_3}{|}}{C}}-CH_2-CH_3$$

(i)

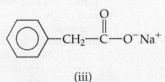

$$CH_3CH_2-\underset{}{\bigcirc}-N{=}N-\underset{}{\bigcirc}-\overset{\overset{\displaystyle O}{\|}}{C}-OCH_3$$

(ii)

$$\bigcirc-CH_2-\overset{\overset{\displaystyle O}{\|}}{C}-O^-\ Na^+$$

(iii)

▲ FIGURE 5.21 **Electronic paper (e-paper) based on cholesteric liquid crystal technology.**

*Cholesteric liquid crystals are sometimes called chiral nematic phases because the molecules within each plane adopt an arrangement similar to a nematic liquid crystal.

SOLUTION

Analyze We have three molecules with different structures, and we are asked to determine which one is most likely to be a liquid crystalline substance.

Plan We need to identify all structural features that might induce liquid crystalline behavior.

Solve Molecule (i) is not likely to be liquid crystalline because the absence of double and/or triple bonds make this molecule flexible rather than rigid. Molecule (iii) is ionic and the generally high melting points of ionic materials make it unlikely that this substance is liquid crystalline. Molecule (ii) possesses the characteristic long axis and the kinds of structural features often seen in liquid crystals: The molecule has a rodlike shape, the double bonds and benzene rings provide rigidity, and the polar $COOCH_3$ group creates a dipole moment.

PRACTICE EXERCISE

Suggest a reason why decane

$$CH_3CH_2CH_2CH_2CH_2CH_2CH_2CH_2CH_2CH_3$$

does not exhibit liquid crystalline behavior.

Answer: Because rotation can occur about carbon–carbon single bonds, molecules whose backbone consists predominantly of C—C single bonds are too flexible; the molecules tend to coil in random ways and, thus, are not rodlike.

CHEMISTRY PUT TO WORK

Liquid Crystal Displays

Liquid crystals displays (LCDs) are widely used in electronic devices such as watches, calculators, and computer screens. These applications are possible because an applied electrical field changes the orientation of liquid crystal molecules and thus affects the optical properties of the device.

LCDs come in a variety of designs, but the structure illustrated in ▼ FIGURE 5.22 is typical. A thin layer (5–20 μm) of liquid crystalline material is placed between electrically conducting, transparent glass electrodes. Ordinary light passes through a vertical polarizer that permits light in only the vertical plane to pass. Using a special process during fabrication, the liquid crystal molecules are oriented so that the molecules at the front electrode are oriented vertically and those at the back electrode horizontally. The orientation of the molecules in between the two electrodes varies systematically from vertical to horizontal, as shown in Figure 5.22(a). The plane of polarization of the light is turned by 90° as it passes through the liquid crystal layer and is thus in the correct orientation to pass through the

horizontal polarizer. In a watch display, a mirror reflects the light back, and the light retraces its path, allowing the device to look bright. When a voltage is applied to the plates, the liquid crystalline molecules align with the voltage, as shown in Figure 5.22(b). The light rays thus are not properly oriented to pass through the horizontal polarizer, and the device appears dark. Displays of this kind are called "twisted nematic." As the name implies, materials that order as nematic liquid crystals are used for this application.

Liquid crystal displays for computer and televisions employ a light source in place of the reflector, but the principle is the same. The screen is divided into a large number of tiny cells, with the voltages at points on the screen surface controlled by transistors made from thin films of amorphous silicon. Red-green-blue color filters are employed to provide full color. The entire display is refreshed at a frequency of about 60 Hz, so the display can change rapidly with respect to the response time of the human eye. Displays of this kind are remarkable technical achievements based on a combination of basic scientific discovery and creative engineering.

RELATED EXERCISES: 5.30, 5.44

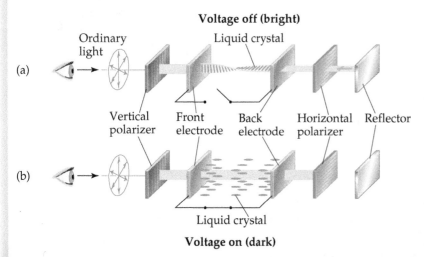

Voltage off (bright)

(a) Ordinary light — Liquid crystal — Vertical polarizer — Front electrode — Back electrode — Horizontal polarizer — Reflector

(b) Liquid crystal

Voltage on (dark)

◀ FIGURE 5.22 **Schematic illustration of the operation of a twisted nematic liquid crystal display (LCD).** (a) When the voltage is off, the molecules in the liquid crystal are aligned so that they rotate the polarization of the light by 90°. This alignment allows light to pass through both the vertical and horizontal polarizers before being reflected and retracing its path to give a bright display. (b) When a voltage is applied to the electrodes, the liquid crystal molecules align parallel to the light path. In this state the light retains the vertical polarization and cannot pass through the horizontal polarizer. The area covered by the front electrode therefore appears dark.

SAMPLE INTEGRATIVE EXERCISE   Putting Concepts Together

The substance CS_2 has a melting point of $-110.8\ ^\circ$C and a boiling point of $46.3\ ^\circ$C. Its density at $20\ ^\circ$C is $1.26\ \text{g/cm}^3$. It is highly flammable. (**a**) What is the name of this compound? (**b**) List the intermolecular forces that CS_2 molecules exert on one other. (**c**) Write a balanced equation for the combustion of this compound in air. (You will have to decide on the most likely oxidation products.) (**d**) The critical temperature and pressure for CS_2 are 552 K and 78 atm, respectively. Compare these values with those for CO_2 (Table 11.2) and discuss the possible origins of the differences. (**e**) Would you expect the density of CS_2 at $40\ ^\circ$C to be greater or less than at $20\ ^\circ$C ? What accounts for the difference?

SOLUTION

(**a**) The compound is named carbon disulfide, in analogy with the naming of other binary molecular compounds such as carbon dioxide.

(**b**) Only dispersion forces affect CS_2; it does not have a dipole moment, based upon its molecular shape, and obviously cannot undergo hydrogen bonding.

(**c**) The most likely products of the combustion will be CO_2 and SO_2. Under some conditions SO_3 might be formed, but this would be the less likely outcome. Thus, we have the following equation for combustion:

$$CS_2(l) + 3\ O_2(g) \longrightarrow CO_2(g) + 2\ SO_2(g)$$

(**d**) The critical temperature and pressure of CS_2 (552 K and 78 atm) are both higher than those given for CO_2 (304 K and 73 atm). The difference in critical temperatures is especially notable. The higher values for CS_2 arise from the greater dispersion attractions between the CS_2 molecules compared with CO_2. These greater attractions are due to the larger size of the sulfur compared to oxygen and, therefore, its greater polarizability.

(**e**) The density would be lower at the higher temperature. Density decreases with increasing temperature because the molecules possess higher kinetic energies. Their more energetic movements result in larger average distances between molecules, which translate into lower densities.

CHAPTER SUMMARY AND KEY TERMS

INTRODUCTION AND SECTION 5.1   Substances that are gases or liquids at room temperature are usually composed of molecules. In gases the intermolecular attractive forces are negligible compared to the kinetic energies of the molecules; thus, the molecules are widely separated and undergo constant, chaotic motion. In liquids the **intermolecular forces** are strong enough to keep the molecules in close proximity; nevertheless, the molecules are free to move with respect to one another. In solids the intermolecular attractive forces are strong enough to restrain molecular motion and to force the particles to occupy specific locations in a three-dimensional arrangement.

SECTION 5.2   Three types of intermolecular forces exist between neutral molecules: **dispersion forces**, **dipole–dipole forces**, and **hydrogen bonding**. Dispersion forces operate between all molecules (and atoms, for atomic substances such as He, Ne, Ar, and so forth). As molecular weight increases, the **polarizability** of a molecule increases, which results in stronger dispersion forces. Molecular shape is also an important factor. Dipole–dipole forces increase in strength as the polarity of the molecule increases. Hydrogen bonding occurs in compounds containing O—H, N—H, and F—H bonds. Hydrogen bonds are generally stronger than dipole–dipole or dispersion forces. **Ion–dipole forces** are important in solutions in which ionic compounds are dissolved in polar solvents.

SECTION 5.3   A **liquid crystal** is a substance that exhibits one or more ordered phases at a temperature above the melting point of the solid. In a **nematic liquid crystal** the molecules are aligned along a common direction, but the ends of the molecules are not lined up. In a smectic liquid crystal the ends of the molecules are lined up so that the molecules form layers. In **smectic A liquid crystals** the long axes of the molecules line up perpendicular to the layers. In **smectic C liquid crystals** the long axes of molecules are inclined with respect to the layers. A **cholesteric liquid crystal** is composed of molecules that align parallel to each other within a layer, as they do in nematic liquid crystalline phases, but the direction along which the long axes of the molecules align rotates from one layer to the next to form a helical structure. Substances that form liquid crystals are generally composed of molecules with fairly rigid, elongated shapes, as well as polar groups to help align molecules through dipole-dipole interactions.

KEY SKILLS

- Identify the intermolecular attractive interactions (dispersion, dipole–dipole, hydrogen bonding, ion–dipole) that exist between molecules or ions based on their composition and molecular structure and be able to compare the relative strengths of these intermolecular forces. (Section 5.2)

- Explain the concept of polarizability and how it relates to dispersion forces. (Section 5.2)

- Understand how the molecular arrangements characteristic of nematic, smectic, and cholesteric liquid crystals differ from ordinary liquids and from each other. Be able to recognize the features of molecules that favor formation of liquid crystalline phases. (Section 5.3)

EXERCISES

VISUALIZING CONCEPTS

5.1 Does the diagram

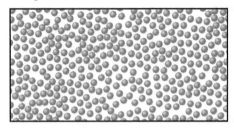

best describe a crystalline solid, a liquid, or a gas? Explain. [Section 5.1]

5.2 (a) Which kind of intermolecular attractive force is shown in each case here?

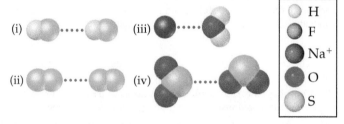

(b) Predict which of the four interactions is the weakest. [Section 5.2]

MOLECULAR COMPARISONS OF GASES, LIQUIDS, AND SOLIDS (SECTION 5.1)

5.3 List the three states of matter in order of (a) increasing molecular disorder and (b) increasing intermolecular attractions. (c) Which state of matter is most easily compressed?

5.4 (a) How does the average kinetic energy of molecules compare with the average energy of attraction between molecules in solids, liquids, and gases? (b) Why does increasing the temperature cause a solid substance to change in succession from a solid to a liquid to a gas? (c) What happens to a gas if you put it under extremely high pressure?

5.5 Arrange substances CCl_4, Si, and Ar in order of increasing boiling point.

5.6 Arrange substances Ga, Ne, and Br_2 in order of increasing boiling point.

5.7 At standard temperature and pressure the molar volume of Cl_2 and NH_3 gases are 22.06 L and 22.40 L, respectively. (a) Given the different molecular weights, dipole moments, and molecular shapes, why are their molar volumes nearly the same? (b) On cooling to 160 K, both substances form crystalline solids. Do you expect the molar volumes to decrease or increase on cooling to 160 K? (c) The densities of crystalline Cl_2 and NH_3 at 160 K are 2.02 g/cm^3 and 0.84 g/cm^3, respectively. Calculate their molar volumes. (d) Are the molar volumes in the solid state as similar as they are in the gaseous state? Explain. (e) Would you expect the molar volumes in the liquid state to be closer to those in the solid or gaseous state?

5.8 Benzoic acid, C_6H_5COOH, melts at 122 °C. The density in the liquid state at 130 °C is 1.08 g/cm^3. The density of solid benzoic acid at 15 °C is 1.266 g/cm^3. (a) In which of these two states is the average distance between molecules greater? (b) Explain the difference in densities at the two temperatures in terms of the relative kinetic energies of the molecules.

INTERMOLECULAR FORCES (section 5.2)

5.9 Which type of intermolecular attractive force operates between (a) all molecules, (b) polar molecules, (c) the hydrogen atom of a polar bond and a nearby small electronegative atom?

5.10 Based on what you have learned about intermolecular forces, would you say that matter is fundamentally attracted or repulsed by other matter?

5.11 Describe the intermolecular forces that must be overcome to convert these substances from a liquid to a gas: (a) SO_2, (b) CH_3COOH, (c) H_2S.

5.12 Which type of intermolecular force accounts for each of these differences: (a) CH_3OH boils at 65 °C; CH_3SH boils at 6 °C. (b) Xe is liquid at atmospheric pressure and 120 K, whereas Ar is a gas under the same conditions. (c) Kr, atomic weight 84, boils at 120.9 K, whereas Cl_2, molecular weight about 71, boils at 238 K. (d) Acetone boils at 56 °C, whereas 2-methylpropane boils at −12 °C.

$$CH_3-\overset{\overset{\displaystyle O}{\|}}{C}-CH_3 \qquad CH_3-\overset{\overset{\displaystyle CH_3}{|}}{CH}-CH_3$$

Acetone   2-Methylpropane

5.13 (a) What is meant by the term *polarizability*? (b) Which of the following atoms would you expect to be most polarizable: N, P, As, Sb? Explain. (c) Put the following molecules in order of increasing polarizability: $GeCl_4$, CH_4, $SiCl_4$, SiH_4, and $GeBr_4$. (d) Predict the order of boiling points of the substances in part (c).

5.14 True or false:

(a) For molecules with similar molecular weights, the dispersion forces become stronger as the molecules become more polarizable.

(b) For the noble gases the dispersion forces decrease while the boiling points increase as you go down the column in the periodic table.

(c) In terms of the total attractive forces for a given substance dipole–dipole interactions, when present, are always larger than dispersion forces.

(d) All other factors being the same, dispersion forces between linear molecules are greater than dispersion forces between molecules whose shapes are nearly spherical.

5.15 Which member in each pair has the larger dispersion forces: (a) H_2O or H_2S, (b) CO_2 or CO, (c) SiH_4 or GeH_4?

5.16 Which member in each pair has the stronger intermolecular dispersion forces: (a) Br_2 or O_2, (b) $CH_3CH_2CH_2CH_2SH$ or $CH_3CH_2CH_2CH_2CH_2SH$, (c) $CH_3CH_2CH_2Cl$ or $(CH_3)_2CHCl$?

5.17 Butane and 2-methylpropane, whose space-filling models are shown at the top of the next column, are both nonpolar and have the same molecular formula, C_4H_{10}, yet butane has the higher boiling point (-0.5 °C compared to -11.7 °C). Explain.

 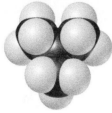

(a) Butane   (b) 2-Methylpropane

5.18 Propyl alcohol ($CH_3CH_2CH_2OH$) and isopropyl alcohol [$(CH_3)_2CHOH$], whose space-filling models are shown, have boiling points of 97.2 °C and 82.5 °C, respectively. Explain why the boiling point of propyl alcohol is higher, even though both have the molecular formula C_3H_8O.

(a) Propyl alcohol   (b) Isopropyl alcohol

5.19 (a) What atoms must a molecule contain to participate in hydrogen bonding with other molecules of the same kind? (b) Which of the following molecules can form hydrogen bonds with other molecules of the same kind: CH_3F, CH_3NH_2, CH_3OH, CH_3Br?

5.20 Rationalize the difference in boiling points in each pair: (a) HF (20 °C) and HCl (-85 °C), (b) $CHCl_3$ (61 °C) and $CHBr_3$ (150 °C), (c) Br_2 (59 °C) and ICl (97 °C).

5.21 Ethylene glycol ($HOCH_2CH_2OH$), the major substance in antifreeze, has a normal boiling point of 198 °C. By comparison, ethyl alcohol (CH_3CH_2OH) boils at 78 °C at atmospheric pressure. Ethylene glycol dimethyl ether ($CH_3OCH_2CH_2OCH_3$) has a normal boiling point of 83 °C, and ethyl methyl ether ($CH_3CH_2OCH_3$) has a normal boiling point of 11 °C. (a) Explain why replacement of a hydrogen on the oxygen by a CH_3 group generally results in a lower boiling point. (b) What are the major factors responsible for the difference in boiling points of the two ethers?

5.22 Identify the type or types of intermolecular forces present in each substance and then select the substance in each pair that has the higher boiling point: (a) propane C_3H_8 or *n*-butane C_4H_{10}, (b) diethyl ether $CH_3CH_2OCH_2CH_3$ or 1-butanol $CH_3CH_2CH_2CH_2OH$, (c) sulfur dioxide SO_2 or sulfur trioxide SO_3, (d) phosgene Cl_2CO or formaldehyde H_2CO.

5.23 Look up and compare the normal boiling points and normal melting points of H_2O and H_2S. (a) Based on these physical properties, which substance has stronger intermolecular forces? What kind of intermolecular forces exist for each molecule? (b) Predict whether solid H_2S is more or less dense than liquid H_2S. How does this compare to H_2O? Explain. (c) Water has an unusually high specific heat. Is this related to its intermolecular forces? Explain.

5.24 The following quote about ammonia (NH_3) is from a textbook of inorganic chemistry: "It is estimated that 26% of the hydrogen bonding in NH_3 breaks down on melting, 7% on warming from the melting to the boiling point, and the final 67% on transfer to the gas phase at the boiling point." From the standpoint of the kinetic energy of the molecules, explain (a) why there is a decrease of hydrogen-bonding energy on melting and (b) why most of the loss in hydrogen bonding occurs in the transition from the liquid to the vapor state.

5.25 A number of salts containing the tetrahedral polyatomic anion, BF_4^-, are ionic liquids, whereas salts containing the somewhat larger tetrahedral ion SO_4^{2-} do not form ionic liquids. Explain this observation.

5.26 The generic structural formula for a 1-alkyl-3-methylimidazolium cation is

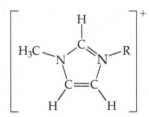

where R is a $-CH_2(CH_2)_nCH_3$ alkyl group. The melting points of the salts that form between the 1-alkyl-3-methylimidazolium cation and the PF_6^- anion are as follows:
R = CH_2CH_3 (m.p. = 60 °C), R = $CH_2CH_2CH_3$ (m.p. = 40 °C), R = $CH_2CH_2CH_2CH_3$ (m.p. = 10 °C) and
R = $CH_2CH_2CH_2CH_2CH_2CH_3$ (m.p. = -61 °C). Why does the melting point decrease as the length of alkyl group increases?

LIQUID CRYSTALS (section 5.3)

5.27 In terms of the arrangement and freedom of motion of the molecules, how are the nematic liquid crystalline phase and an ordinary liquid phase similar? How are they different?

5.28 What observations made by Reinitzer on cholesteryl benzoate suggested that this substance possesses a liquid crystalline phase?

5.29 The molecules shown in Figure 5.19 possess polar groups (that is, groupings of atoms that give rise to sizable dipole moments within the molecules). How might the presence of polar groups enhance the tendency toward liquid crystal formation?

5.30 One of the more effective liquid crystalline substances employed in LCDs is the molecule

$$CH_3(CH_2)_2CH=CH-CH\begin{smallmatrix}CH_2-CH_2\\ \\ CH_2-CH_2\end{smallmatrix}CH-CH\begin{smallmatrix}CH_2-CH_2\\ \\ CH_2-CH_2\end{smallmatrix}CH-C\equiv N$$

(a) How many double bonds are there in this molecule? (b) Describe the features of the molecule that make it prone to show liquid crystalline behavior.

5.31 For a given substance, the liquid crystalline phase tends to be more viscous than the liquid phase. Why?

5.32 Describe how a cholesteric liquid crystal phase differs from a nematic phase.

5.33 It often happens that a substance possessing a smectic liquid crystalline phase just above the melting point passes into a nematic liquid crystalline phase at a higher temperature. Account for this type of behavior.

5.34 The smectic liquid crystalline phase can be said to be more highly ordered than the nematic phase. In what sense is this true?

ADDITIONAL EXERCISES

5.35 As the intermolecular attractive forces between molecules increase in magnitude, do you expect each of the following to increase or decrease in magnitude? (a) vapor pressure, (b) heat of vaporization, (c) boiling point, (d) freezing point, (e) viscosity, (f) surface tension, (g) critical temperature.

5.36 Suppose you have two colorless molecular liquids, one boiling at −84 °C, the other at 34 °C, and both at atmospheric pressure. Which of the following statements is correct? For each statement that is not correct, modify the statement so that it is correct. (a) The higher-boiling liquid has greater total intermolecular forces than the lower-boiling liquid. (b) The lower-boiling liquid must consist of nonpolar molecules. (c) The lower-boiling liquid has a lower molecular weight than the higher-boiling liquid. (d) The two liquids have identical vapor pressures at their normal boiling points. (e) At −84 °C both liquids have vapor pressures of 760 mm Hg.

5.37 Two isomers of the planar compound 1,2-dichloroethylene are shown here.

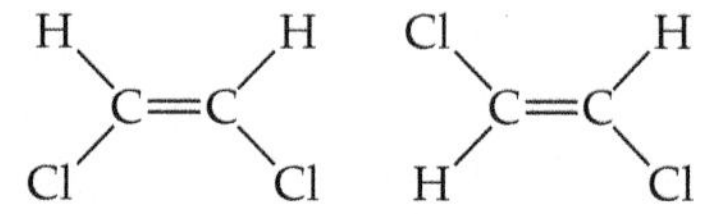

cis isomer   trans isomer

(a) Which of the two isomers will have the stronger dipole–dipole forces? (b) One isomer has a boiling point of 60.3 °C and the other 47.5 °C. Which isomer has which boiling point?

5.38 In dichloromethane, CH_2Cl_2 ($\mu = 1.60$ D), the dispersion force contribution to the intermolecular attractive forces is about five times larger than the dipole–dipole contribution. Compared to CH_2Cl_2, would you expect the relative importance of the dipole–dipole contribution to increase or decrease (a) in dibromomethane ($\mu = 1.43$ D), (b) in difluoromethane ($\mu = 1.93$ D)? Explain.

5.39 When an atom or group of atoms is substituted for an H atom in benzene (C_6H_6), the boiling point changes. Explain the order of the following boiling points: C_6H_6 (80 °C), C_6H_5Cl (132 °C), C_6H_5Br (156 °C), C_6H_5OH (182 °C).

5.40 The DNA double helix (Figure 24.30) at the atomic level looks like a twisted ladder, where the "rungs" of the ladder consist of molecules that are hydrogen-bonded together. Sugar and phosphate groups make up the sides of the ladder. Shown are the structures of the adenine-thymine (AT) "base pair" and the guanine-cytosine (GC) base pair:

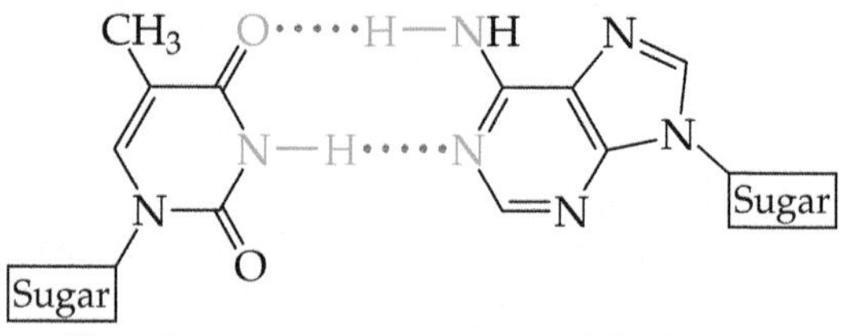

Thymine   Adenine

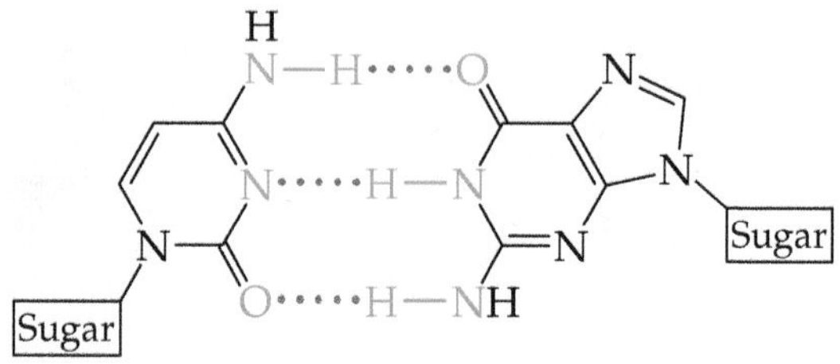

Cytosine   Guanine

You can see that AT base pairs are held together by two hydrogen bonds, and the GC base pairs are held together by three hydrogen bonds. Which base pair is more stable to heating? Why?

5.41 Ethylene glycol ($HOCH_2CH_2OH$) is the major component of antifreeze. It is a slightly viscous liquid, not very volatile at room temperature, with a boiling point of 198 °C. Pentane (C_5H_{12}), which has about the same molecular weight, is a nonviscous liquid that is highly volatile at room temperature and whose boiling point is 36.1 °C. Explain the differences in the physical properties of the two substances.

5.42 Use the normal boiling points

propane, C_3H_8, −42.1 °C
butane, C_4H_{10}, −0.5 °C
pentane, C_5H_{12}, 36.1 °C
hexane, C_6H_{14}, 68.7 °C
heptane, C_7H_{16}, 98.4 °C

to estimate the normal boiling point of octane, C_8H_{18}. Explain the trend in the boiling points.

5.43 One of the attractive features of ionic liquids is their low vapor pressure, which in turn tends to make them nonflammable. Why do you think ionic liquids have lower vapor pressures than most room-temperature molecular liquids?

5.44 A watch with a liquid crystal display (LCD) does not function properly when it is exposed to low temperatures during a trip to Antarctica. Explain why the LCD might not function well at low temperature.

INTEGRATIVE EXERCISE

5.45 Acetone, $(CH_3)_2CO$, is widely used as an industrial solvent. **(a)** Draw the Lewis structure for the acetone molecule and predict the geometry around each carbon atom. **(b)** Is the acetone molecule polar or nonpolar? **(c)** What kinds of intermolecular attractive forces exist between acetone molecules? **(d)** 1-Propanol, $CH_3CH_2CH_2OH$, has a molecular weight that is very similar to that of acetone, yet acetone boils at 56.5 °C and 1-propanol boils at 97.2 °C. Explain the difference.

WHAT'S AHEAD

6.1 GENERAL CHARACTERISTICS OF ORGANIC MOLECULES
We begin with a review of the structures and reactivities of organic compounds.

6.2 INTRODUCTION TO HYDROCARBONS
We consider *hydrocarbons*, compounds containing only C and H, including the hydrocarbons called *alkanes*, which contain only

single bonds. We also look at *isomers*, compounds with identical compositions but different molecular structures.

6.3 ALKENES, ALKYNES, AND AROMATIC HYDROCARBONS
We next explore hydrocarbons with one or more C=C bonds, called *alkenes*, and those with one or more C≡C bonds, called *alkynes*. *Aromatic* hydrocarbons have at least one planar ring with delocalized π electrons.

TO COMMUNICATE WITH OTHER members of their species, insects release chemicals called pheromones into their environment.

6.4 ORGANIC FUNCTIONAL GROUPS
We recognize that a central organizing principle of organic chemistry is the *functional group*, a group of atoms at which most of the compound's chemical reactions occur.

6.5 CHIRALITY IN ORGANIC CHEMISTRY
We learn that compounds with nonsuperimposable mirror images are *chiral* and that chirality plays important roles in organic and biological chemistry.

THE CHEMISTRY OF LIFE: ORGANIC AND BIOLOGICAL CHEMISTRY

INSECTS COMMUNICATE BY RELEASING substances called pheromones, which they detect with their antennae. There are sex, alarm, defense, and trail pheromones. For example, isoamyl acetate [3-methylbutyl acetate, $(CH_3)_2CHCH_2COOCH_3$] is an alarm pheromone for bees, attracting other bees and provoking them to sting. Mammals, including humans, may also respond to pheromones, although the identity and function of pheromones in humans are not conclusive. Nevertheless, google "pheromone" and you will find hundreds of sources trying to sell you a pheromone, claiming that it will make you irresistible to the opposite sex.

Although biological systems are almost unimaginably complex, they are nevertheless constructed of molecules of quite modest size, as, for instance, the isoamyl acetate pheromone just described. To understand biology, therefore, we need to understand the chemical behaviors of molecules. This chapter is about the molecules, composed mainly of carbon, hydrogen, oxygen, and nitrogen, that form the basis of organic and biological chemistry.

More than 16 million carbon-containing compounds are known. Chemists make thousands of new compounds every year, about 90% of which contain carbon. The study of compounds whose molecules contain carbon constitutes the branch of chemistry known as **organic chemistry**. This term arose from the eighteenth-century belief that organic compounds could be formed only by living (that is, organic) systems. This idea was disproved in 1828 by the German chemist Friedrich Wöhler when he synthesized urea (H_2NCONH_2), an organic substance found in the urine of mammals, by heating ammonium cyanate (NH_4OCN), an inorganic ("nonliving") substance.

The study of the chemistry of living species is called *biological chemistry*, *chemical biology*, or **biochemistry**. In this chapter, we present some of the elementary aspects of both organic chemistry and biochemistry.

6.1 | GENERAL CHARACTERISTICS OF ORGANIC MOLECULES

What is it about carbon that leads to the tremendous diversity in its compounds and allows it to play such crucial roles in biology and society? Let's consider some general features of organic molecules and, as we do, review principles we learned in earlier chapters.

The Structures of Organic Molecules

Because carbon has four valence electrons ($[He]2s^2 2p^2$), it forms four bonds in virtually all its compounds. When all four bonds are single bonds, the electron pairs are disposed in a tetrahedral arrangement. ∞(Section 4.2) In the hybridization model, the carbon 2s and 2p orbitals are then sp^3 hybridized. ∞(Section 4.5) When there is one double bond, the arrangement is trigonal planar (sp^2 hybridization). With a triple bond, it is linear (sp hybridization). Examples are shown in ▼ FIGURE 6.1.

Almost every organic molecule contains C—H bonds. Because the valence shell of H can hold only two electrons, hydrogen forms only one covalent bond. As a result,

---

◢ GO FIGURE
What is the geometry around the bottom carbon atom in acetonitrile?

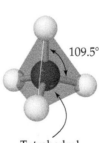
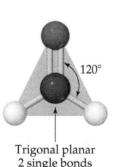
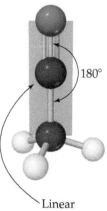

► FIGURE 6.1 **Carbon geometries.** The three common geometries around carbon are tetrahedral as in methane (CH_4), trigonal planar as in formaldehyde (CH_2O), and linear as in acetonitrile (CH_3CN). Notice that in all cases each carbon atom forms four bonds.

Tetrahedral
4 single bonds
sp^3 hybridization

Trigonal planar
2 single bonds
1 double bond
sp^2 hybridization

Linear
1 single bond
1 triple bond
sp hybridization

109.5°

120°

180°

hydrogen atoms are always located on the *surface* of organic molecules whereas the C—C bonds form the *backbone*, or *skeleton*, of the molecule, as in the propane molecule:

$$H-\overset{\overset{\displaystyle H}{|}}{\underset{\underset{\displaystyle H}{|}}{C}}-\overset{\overset{\displaystyle H}{|}}{\underset{\underset{\displaystyle H}{|}}{C}}-\overset{\overset{\displaystyle H}{|}}{\underset{\underset{\displaystyle H}{|}}{C}}-H$$

The Stabilities of Organic Substances

Carbon forms strong bonds with a variety of elements, especially H, O, N, and the halogens. ∞ (Section 3.8) Carbon also has an exceptional ability to bond to itself, forming a variety of molecules made up of chains or rings of carbon atoms. Most reactions with low or moderate activation energy (Section 14.5) begin when a region of high electron density on one molecule encounters a region of low electron density on another molecule. The regions of high electron density may be due to the presence of a multiple bond or to the more electronegative atom in a polar bond. Because of their strength and lack of polarity, both C—C single bonds and C—H bonds are relatively unreactive. To better understand the implications of these facts, consider ethanol:

$$H-\overset{\overset{\displaystyle H}{|}}{\underset{\underset{\displaystyle H}{|}}{C}}-\overset{\overset{\displaystyle H}{|}}{\underset{\underset{\displaystyle H}{|}}{C}}-O-H$$

The differences in the electronegativity values of C (2.5) and O (3.5) and of O and H (2.1) indicate that the C—O and O—H bonds are quite polar. Thus, many reactions of ethanol involve these bonds while the hydrocarbon portion of the molecule remains intact. A group of atoms such as the C—O—H group, which determines how an organic molecule reacts (in other words, how the molecule *functions*), is called a **functional group**. The functional group is the center of reactivity in an organic molecule.

GIVE IT SOME THOUGHT

Which bond is most likely to be the location of a chemical reaction: C═N, C—C, or C—H?

Solubility and Acid–Base Properties of Organic Substances

In most organic substances, the most prevalent bonds are carbon–carbon and carbon–hydrogen, which have low polarity. For this reason, the overall polarity of organic molecules is often low, which makes them generally soluble in nonpolar solvents and not very soluble in water. Organic molecules that are soluble in polar solvents are those that have polar groups on the molecule surface, such as glucose and ascorbic acid (► FIGURE 6.2). Organic molecules that have a long, nonpolar part bonded to a polar, ionic part, such as the stearate ion shown in Figure 6.2, function as *surfactants* and are used in soaps and detergents. The nonpolar part of the molecule extends into a nonpolar medium such as grease or oil, and the polar part extends into a polar medium such as water.

Many organic substances contain acidic or basic groups. The most important acidic organic substances are the carboxylic acids, which bear the functional group —COOH. The most important basic organic substances are amines, which bear the —NH₂, —NHR, or —NR₂ groups, where R is an organic group made up of carbon and hydrogen atoms.

As you read this chapter, you will find many concept links (∞) to related materials in earlier chapters. *We strongly encourage you to follow these links and review the earlier material.* Doing so will enhance your understanding and appreciation of organic chemistry and biochemistry.

GO FIGURE

How would replacing OH groups on ascorbic acid with CH₃ groups affect the substance's solubility in (a) polar solvents and (b) nonpolar solvents?

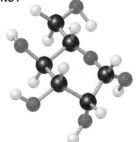

Glucose ($C_6H_{12}O_6$)

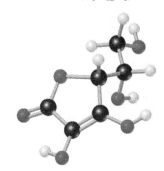

Ascorbic acid ($HC_6H_7O_6$)

Stearate ($C_{17}H_{35}COO^-$)

▲ FIGURE 6.2 **Organic molecules soluble in polar solvents.**

6.2 | INTRODUCTION TO HYDROCARBONS

Because carbon compounds are so numerous, it is convenient to organize them into families that have structural similarities. The simplest class of organic compounds is the *hydrocarbons*, compounds composed of only carbon and hydrogen. The key structural feature of hydrocarbons (and of most other organic substances) is the presence of stable carbon–carbon bonds. Carbon is the only element capable of forming stable, extended chains of atoms bonded through single, double, or triple bonds.

Hydrocarbons can be divided into four types, depending on the kinds of carbon–carbon bonds in their molecules. ▼ TABLE 6.1 shows an example of each type.

Alkanes contain only single bonds. **Alkenes**, also known as *olefins*, contain at least one $C{=}C$ double bond, and **alkynes** contain at least one $C{\equiv}C$ triple bond. In **aromatic hydrocarbons** the carbon atoms are connected in a planar ring structure, joined by both σ and delocalized π bonds between carbon atoms. Benzene (C_6H_6) is the best-known example of an aromatic hydrocarbon.

Each type of hydrocarbon exhibits different chemical behaviors, as we will see shortly. The physical properties of all four types, however, are similar in many ways. Because hydrocarbon molecules are relatively nonpolar, they are almost completely insoluble in water but dissolve readily in nonpolar solvents. Their melting points and boiling points are determined by dispersion forces. ∞ (Section 5.2) As a result, hydrocarbons of very low molecular weight, such as C_2H_6 (bp $= -89\ °C$), are gases at room temperature; those of moderate molecular weight, such as C_6H_{14} (bp $= 69\ °C$), are liquids; and those of high molecular weight, such as $C_{22}H_{46}$ (mp $= 44\ °C$), are solids.

▶ TABLE 6.2 lists the ten simplest alkanes. Many of these substances are familiar because they are used so widely. Methane is a major component of natural gas and is used for home heating and in gas stoves and water heaters. Propane is the major component of bottled gas used for home heating and cooking in areas where natural gas is not available. Butane is used in disposable lighters and in fuel canisters for gas camping stoves and lanterns. Alkanes with from 5 to 12 carbon atoms per molecule are used to make gasoline. Notice that each succeeding compound in Table 6.2 has an additional CH_2 unit.

TABLE 6.1 • The Four Hydrocarbon Types

Type		Example		
Alkane	Ethane	CH_3CH_3		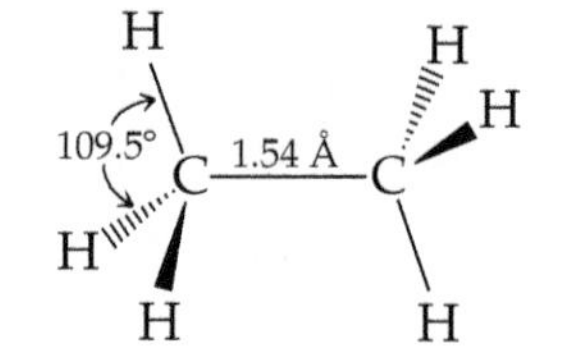
Alkene	Ethylene	$CH_2{=}CH_2$	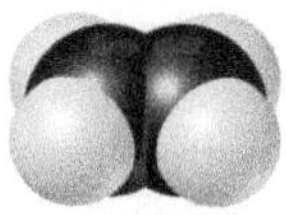	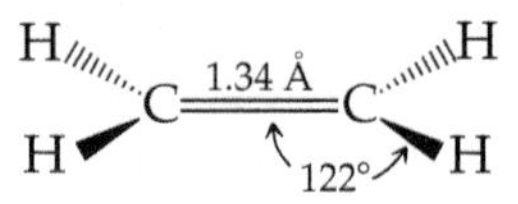
Alkyne	Acetylene	$CH{\equiv}CH$	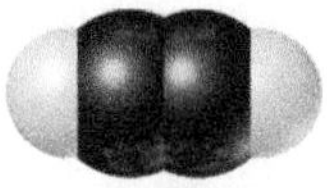	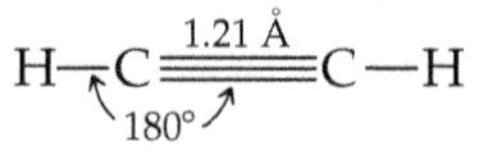
Aromatic	Benzene	C_6H_6	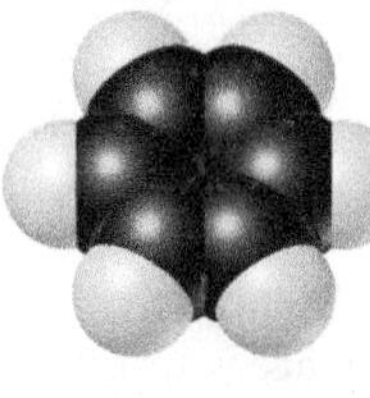	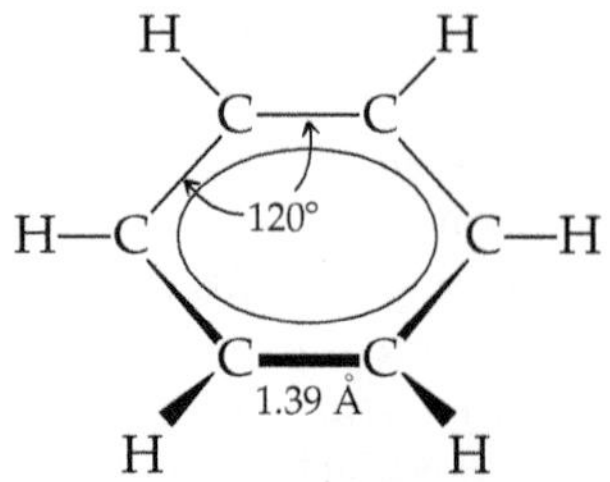

TABLE 6.2 • First Ten Members of the Straight-Chain Alkane Series

Molecular Formula	Condensed Structural Formula	Name	Boiling Point (°C)
CH_4	CH_4	Methane	−161
C_2H_6	CH_3CH_3	Ethane	−89
C_3H_8	$CH_3CH_2CH_3$	Propane	−44
C_4H_{10}	$CH_3CH_2CH_2CH_3$	Butane	−0.5
C_5H_{12}	$CH_3CH_2CH_2CH_2CH_3$	Pentane	36
C_6H_{14}	$CH_3CH_2CH_2CH_2CH_2CH_3$	Hexane	68
C_7H_{16}	$CH_3CH_2CH_2CH_2CH_2CH_2CH_3$	Heptane	98
C_8H_{18}	$CH_3CH_2CH_2CH_2CH_2CH_2CH_2CH_3$	Octane	125
C_9H_{20}	$CH_3CH_2CH_2CH_2CH_2CH_2CH_2CH_2CH_3$	Nonane	151
$C_{10}H_{22}$	$CH_3CH_2CH_2CH_2CH_2CH_2CH_2CH_2CH_2CH_3$	Decane	174

The formulas for the alkanes given in Table 6.2 are written in a notation called *condensed structural formulas*. This notation reveals the way in which atoms are bonded to one another but does not require drawing in all the bonds. For example, the structural formula and the condensed structural formulas for butane (C_4H_{10}) are

$$H_3C-CH_2-CH_2-CH_3$$

or

$$CH_3CH_2CH_2CH_3$$

⚠ GIVE IT SOME THOUGHT

How many C—H and C—C bonds are formed by the middle carbon atom of propane?

Structures of Alkanes

According to the VSEPR model, the molecular geometry about each carbon atom in an alkane is tetrahedral. ∞ (Section 4.2) The bonding may be described as involving sp^3-hybridized orbitals on the carbon, as pictured in ▶ FIGURE 6.3 for methane. ∞ (Section 4.5)

Rotation about a carbon–carbon single bond is relatively easy and occurs rapidly at room temperature. To visualize such rotation, imagine grasping either methyl group of the propane molecule in ▶ FIGURE 6.4 and rotating the group relative to the rest of the molecule. Because motion of this sort occurs rapidly in alkanes, a long-chain alkane molecule is constantly undergoing motions that cause it to change its shape, something like a length of chain that is being shaken.

Structural Isomers

The alkanes in Table 6.2 are called *straight-chain hydrocarbons* because all the carbon atoms are joined in a continuous chain. Alkanes consisting of four or more carbon atoms can also form *branched chains*, and when they do, they are called *branched-chain hydrocarbons*. (The branches in organic molecules are often called *side chains*.) ▶ TABLE 6.3, for example, shows all the straight-chain and branched-chain alkanes containing four and five carbon atoms.

Compounds that have the same molecular formula but different bonding arrangements (and hence different structures) are called **structural isomers**. Thus, C_4H_{10} has two structural isomers and C_5H_{12} has three. The structural isomers of a given alkane differ slightly from one another in physical properties, as the melting and boiling points in Table 6.3 indicate.

The number of possible structural isomers increases rapidly with the number of carbon atoms in the alkane. There are 18 isomers with the molecular formula C_8H_{18}, for example, and 75 with the molecular formula $C_{10}H_{22}$.

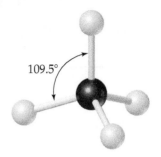

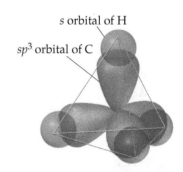
s orbital of H

sp^3 orbital of C

▲ FIGURE 6.3   **Bonds about carbon in methane.** This tetrahedral molecular geometry is found around all carbons in alkanes.

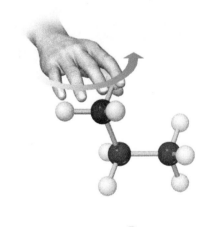

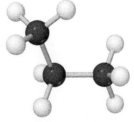

▲ FIGURE 6.4   **Rotation about a C—C bond occurs easily and rapidly in all alkanes.**

TABLE 6.3 • Isomers of C_4H_{10} and C_5H_{12}

Systematic Name (Common Name)	Structural Formula	Condensed Structural Formula	Space-filling Model	Melting Point (°C)	Boiling Point (°C)
Butane (*n*-butane)	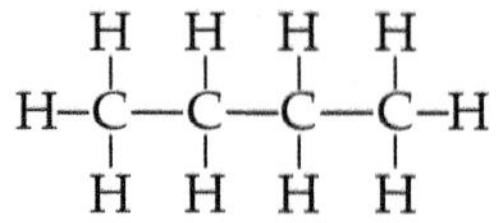 H H H H H–C–C–C–C–H H H H H	$CH_3CH_2CH_2CH_3$	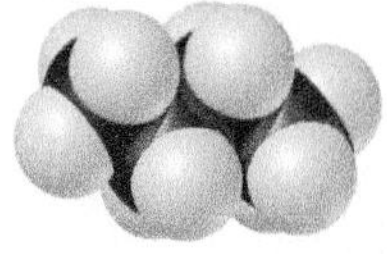	−138 °C	−0.5 °C
2-Methylpropane (isobutane)	H H H H–C–C–C–H H | H H–C–H H	$CH_3-CH-CH_3$ $\quad\quad\;\; \|$ $\quad\quad CH_3$		−159 °C	−12 °C
Pentane (*n*-pentane)	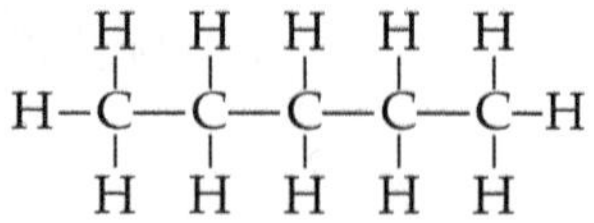 H H H H H H–C–C–C–C–C–H H H H H H	$CH_3CH_2CH_2CH_2CH_3$		−130 °C	+36 °C
2-Methylbutane (isopentane)	H H–C–H H | H H H–C–C–C–C–H H H H H	CH_3 $\|$ $CH_3-CH-CH_2-CH_3$		−160 °C	+28 °C
2,2-Dimethylpropane (neopentane)	H H–C–H H | H H–C–C–C–H H | H H–C–H H	CH_3 $\|$ CH_3-C-CH_3 $\|$ CH_3		−16 °C	+9 °C

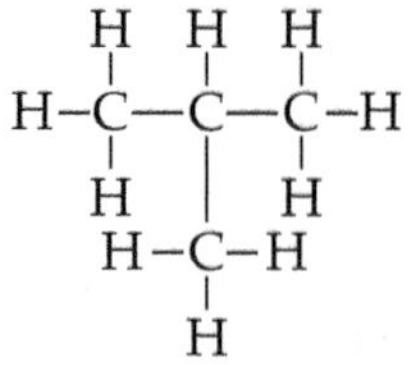

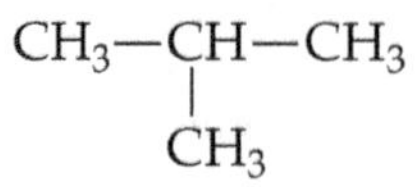

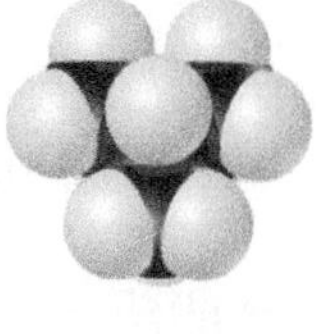

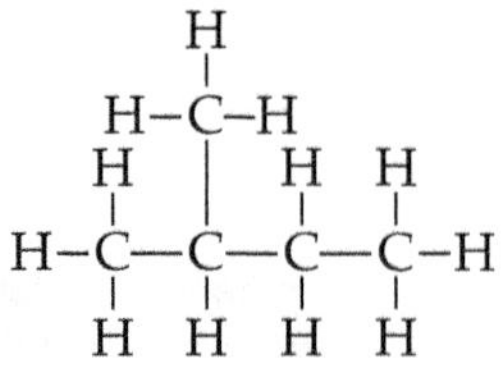

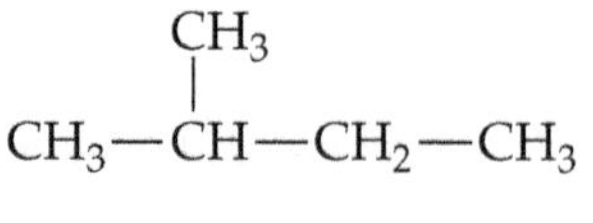

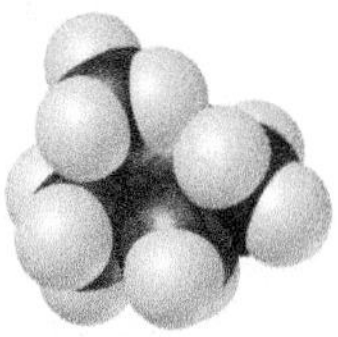

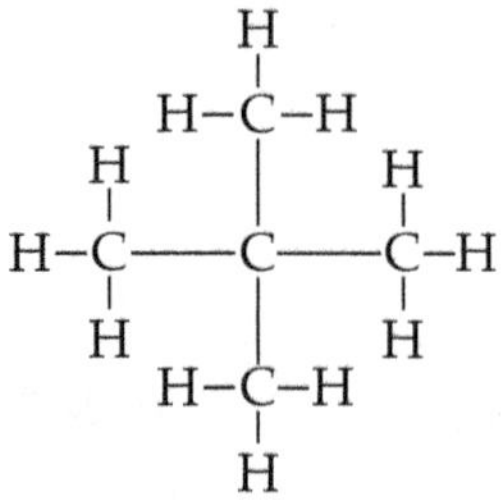

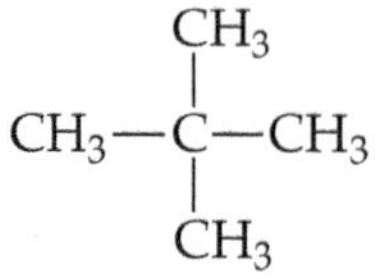

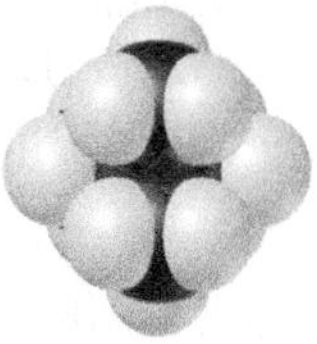

◢ GIVE IT SOME THOUGHT

What evidence can you cite to support the fact that although isomers have the same molecular formula they are in fact different compounds?

Nomenclature of Alkanes

In the first column of Table 6.3, the names in parentheses are called the *common names*. The common name of the isomer with no branches begins with the letter *n* (indicating the "normal" structure). When one CH_3 group branches off the major chain, the common name of the isomer begins with *iso-*, and when two CH_3 groups branch off, the common name begins with *neo-*. As the number of isomers grows, however, it becomes impossible to find a suitable prefix to denote each isomer by a common name. The need for a systematic means of naming organic compounds was recognized as early as 1892, when an organization called the International Union of Chemistry met in Geneva to formulate rules for naming organic substances. Since that time the task of updating the rules for naming compounds has fallen to the International Union of Pure and Applied Chemistry (IUPAC). Chemists everywhere, regardless of their nationality, subscribe to a common system for naming compounds.

The IUPAC names for the isomers of butane and pentane are the ones given first in Table 6.3. These systematic names, as well as those of other organic compounds, have three parts to them:

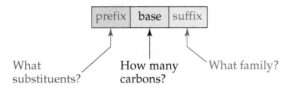

The following steps summarize the procedures used to name alkanes, which all have names ending with *-ane*. We use a similar approach to write the names of other organic compounds.

1. **Find the longest continuous chain of carbon atoms, and use the name of this chain (given in Table 6.2) as the base name.** Be careful in this step because the longest chain may not be written in a straight line, as in the following structure:

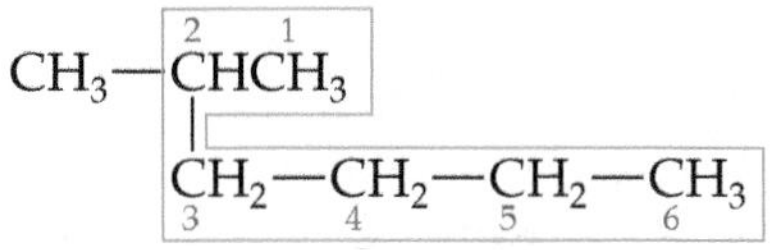

$$CH_3 - \overset{2}{C}H\overset{1}{C}H_3$$
$$\underset{3}{C}H_2 - \underset{4}{C}H_2 - \underset{5}{C}H_2 - \underset{6}{C}H_3$$

2-Methyl*hexane*

Because the longest continuous chain contains six C atoms, this isomer is named as a substituted hexane. Groups attached to the main chain are called *substituents* because they are substituted in place of an H atom on the main chain. In this molecule the CH_3 group not enclosed by the blue outline is the only substituent in the molecule.

2. **Number the carbon atoms in the longest chain, beginning with the end nearest a substituent.** In our example, we number the C atoms beginning at the upper right because that places the CH_3 substituent on C2 of the chain. (If we had numbered from the lower right, the CH_3 would be on C5.) The chain is numbered from the end that gives the lower number to the substituent position.

3. **Name each substituent.** A substituent formed by removing an H atom from an alkane is called an **alkyl group**. Alkyl groups are named by replacing the *-ane* ending of the alkane name with *-yl*. The methyl group (CH_3), for example, is derived from methane (CH_4) and the ethyl group (C_2H_5) is derived from ethane (C_2H_6). ▶ TABLE 6.4 lists six common alkyl groups.

4. **Begin the name with the number or numbers of the carbon or carbons to which each substituent is bonded.** For our compound, the name 2-methylhexane indicates the presence of a methyl group on C2 of a hexane (six-carbon) chain.

5. **When two or more substituents are present, list them in alphabetical order.** The presence of two or more of the same substituent is indicated by the prefixes *di-* (two), *tri-* (three), *tetra-* (four), *penta-* (five), and so forth. The prefixes are ignored in determining the alphabetical order of the substituents:

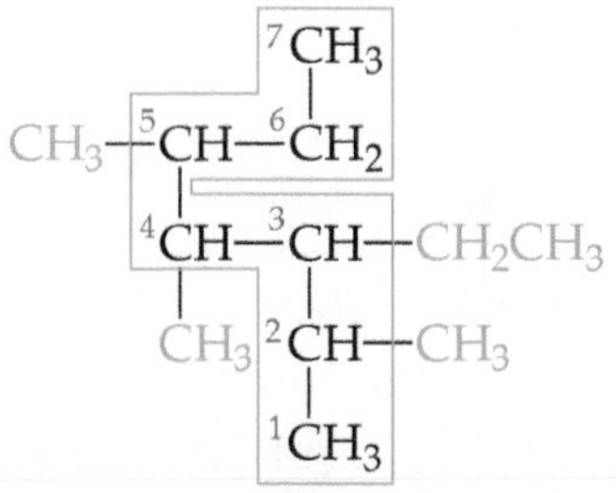

$$^7CH_3$$
$$CH_3 - \overset{5}{C}H - \overset{6}{C}H_2$$
$$^4CH - \overset{3}{C}H - CH_2CH_3$$
$$CH_3\ ^2CH - CH_3$$
$$^1CH_3$$

3-Ethyl-2,4,5-trimethylheptane

TABLE 6.4 • Condensed Structural Formulas and Common Names for Several Alkyl Groups

Group	Name
CH_3-	Methyl
CH_3CH_2-	Ethyl
$CH_3CH_2CH_2-$	Propyl
$CH_3CH_2CH_2CH_2-$	Butyl
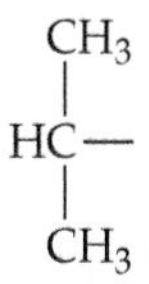 $\begin{matrix} CH_3 \\ \mid \\ HC- \\ \mid \\ CH_3 \end{matrix}$	Isopropyl
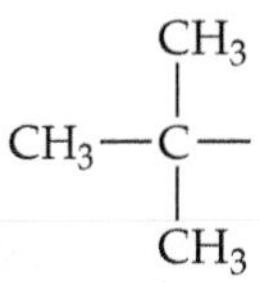 $\begin{matrix} CH_3 \\ \mid \\ CH_3-C- \\ \mid \\ CH_3 \end{matrix}$	*tert*-Butyl

SAMPLE EXERCISE 6.1 Naming Alkanes

Give the systematic name for the following alkane:

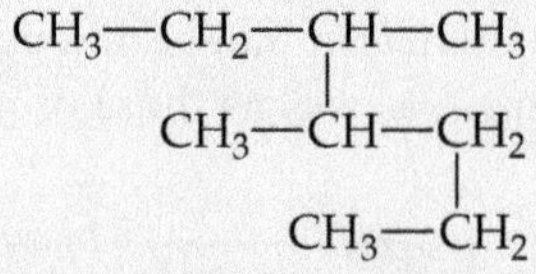

$$CH_3—CH_2—CH—CH_3$$
$$CH_3—CH—CH_2$$
$$CH_3—CH_2$$

SOLUTION

Analyze We are given the condensed structural formula of an alkane and asked to give its name.

Plan Because the hydrocarbon is an alkane, its name ends in -*ane*. The name of the parent hydrocarbon is based on the longest continuous chain of carbon atoms. Branches are alkyl groups, named after the number of C atoms in the branch and located by counting C atoms along the longest continuous chain.

Solve The longest continuous chain of C atoms extends from the upper left CH_3 group to the lower left CH_3 group and is seven C atoms long:

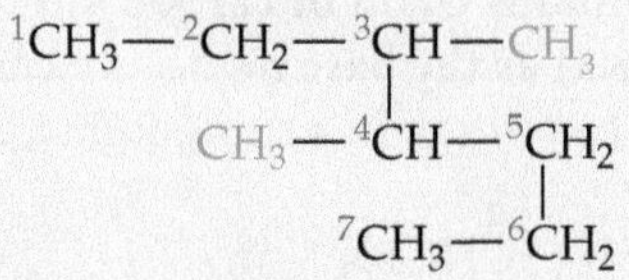

$$^1CH_3—^2CH_2—^3CH—CH_3$$
$$CH_3—^4CH—^5CH_2$$
$$^7CH_3—^6CH_2$$

The parent compound is thus heptane. There are two methyl groups branching off the main chain. Hence, this compound is a dimethylheptane. To specify the location of the two methyl groups, we must number the C atoms from the end that gives the lower two numbers to the carbons bearing side chains. This means that we should start numbering at the upper left carbon. There is a methyl group on C3 and one on C4. The compound is thus 3,4-dimethylheptane.

PRACTICE EXERCISE

Name the following alkane:

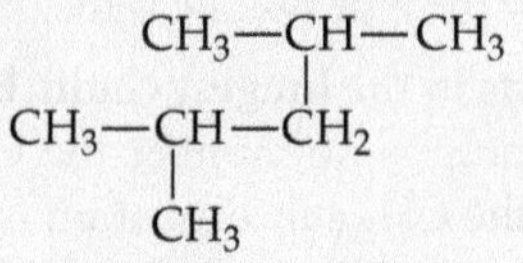

$$CH_3—CH—CH_3$$
$$CH_3—CH—CH_2$$
$$CH_3$$

Answer: 2,4-dimethylpentane

SAMPLE EXERCISE 6.2 Writing Condensed Structural Formulas

Write the condensed structural formula for 3-ethyl-2-methylpentane.

SOLUTION

Analyze We are given the systematic name for a hydrocarbon and asked to write its condensed structural formula.

Plan Because the name ends in -*ane*, the compound is an alkane, meaning that all the carbon–carbon bonds are single bonds. The parent hydrocarbon is pentane, indicating five C atoms (Table 6.2). There are two alkyl groups specified, an ethyl group (two carbon atoms, C_2H_5) and a methyl group (one carbon atom, CH_3). Counting from left to right along the five-carbon chain, the name tells us that the ethyl group is attached to C3 and the methyl group is attached to C2.

Solve We begin by writing five C atoms attached by single bonds. These represent the backbone of the parent pentane chain:

$$C—C—C—C—C$$

We next place a methyl group on the second C and an ethyl group on the third C of the chain. We then add hydrogens to all the other C atoms to make four bonds to each carbon:

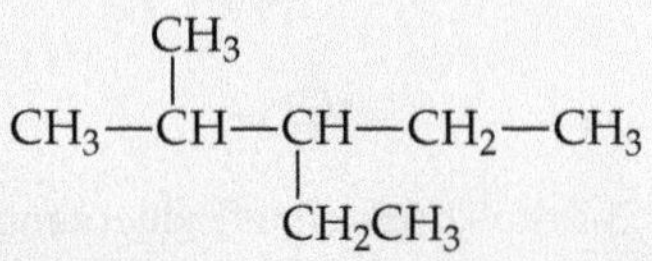

$$CH_3$$
$$CH_3—CH—CH—CH_2—CH_3$$
$$CH_2CH_3$$

The formula can be written more concisely as

$$CH_3CH(CH_3)CH(C_2H_5)CH_2CH_3$$

where the branching alkyl groups are indicated in parentheses.

PRACTICE EXERCISE

Write the condensed structural formula for 2,3-dimethylhexane.

$$\overset{\displaystyle CH_3}{\underset{|}{}} \quad \overset{\displaystyle CH_3}{\underset{|}{}}$$

Answer: $CH_3CH—CHCH_2CH_2CH_3$ or $CH_3CH(CH_3)CH(CH_3)CH_2CH_2CH_3$

Cycloalkanes

Alkanes that form rings, or cycles, are called **cycloalkanes**. As ▼ FIGURE 6.5 illustrates, cycloalkane structures are sometimes drawn as *line structures*, which are polygons in which each corner represents a CH_2 group. This method of representation is similar to that used for benzene rings. ⚬⚬⚬ (Section 3.6) (Remember from our benzene discussion that in aromatic structures each vertex represents a CH group, not a CH_2 group.)

Carbon rings containing fewer than five carbon atoms are strained because the C—C—C bond angles must be less than the 109.5° tetrahedral angle. The amount of strain increases as the rings get smaller. In cyclopropane, which has the shape of an equilateral triangle, the angle is only 60°; this molecule is therefore much more reactive than propane, its straight-chain analog.

Reactions of Alkanes

Because they contain only C—C and C—H bonds, most alkanes are relatively unreactive. At room temperature, for example, they do not react with acids, bases, or strong oxidizing agents. Their low chemical reactivity, as noted in Section 6.1, is due primarily to the strength and lack of polarity of C—C and C—H bonds.

Alkanes are not completely inert, however. One of their most commercially important reactions is *combustion* in air, which is the basis of their use as fuels. For example, the complete combustion of ethane proceeds as follows:

$$2\,C_2H_6(g) + 7\,O_2(g) \longrightarrow 4\,CO_2(g) + 6\,H_2O(l) \qquad \Delta H° = -2855 \text{ kJ}$$

GO FIGURE

The general formula for straight-chain alkanes is C_nH_{2n+2}. What is the general formula for cycloalkanes?

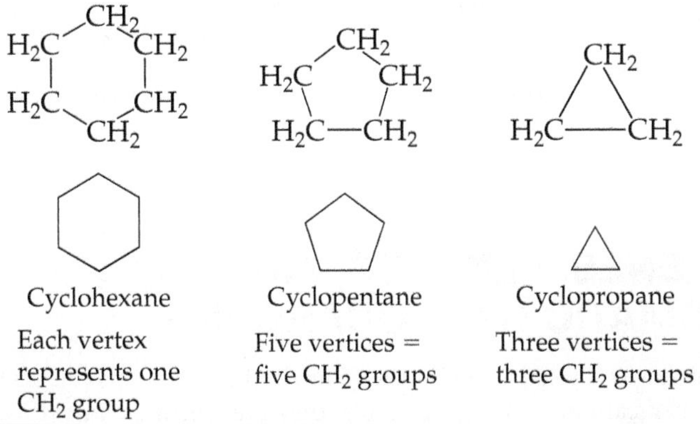

Cyclohexane

Each vertex represents one CH_2 group

Cyclopentane

Five vertices = five CH_2 groups

Cyclopropane

Three vertices = three CH_2 groups

▲ FIGURE 6.5   **Condensed structural formulas and line structures for three cycloalkanes.**

CHEMISTRY PUT TO WORK

Gasoline

Petroleum, or crude oil, is a mixture of hydrocarbons plus smaller quantities of other organic compounds containing nitrogen, oxygen, or sulfur. The tremendous demand for petroleum to meet the world's energy needs has led to the tapping of oil wells in such forbidding places as the North Sea and northern Alaska.

The usual first step in the *refining*, or processing, of petroleum is to separate it into fractions on the basis of boiling point (▼ TABLE 6.5). Because gasoline is the most commercially important of these fractions, various processes are used to maximize its yield.

Gasoline is a mixture of volatile alkanes and aromatic hydrocarbons. In a traditional automobile engine, a mixture of air and gasoline vapor is compressed by a piston and then ignited by a spark plug. The burning of the gasoline should create a strong, smooth expansion of gas, forcing the piston outward and imparting force along the driveshaft of the engine. If the gas burns too rapidly, the piston receives a single hard slam rather than a strong, smooth push. The result is a "knocking" or "pinging" sound and a reduction in the efficiency with which energy produced by the combustion is converted to work.

The *octane number* of a gasoline is a measure of its resistance to knocking. Gasolines with high octane numbers burn more smoothly and are thus more effective fuels (▶ FIGURE 6.6). Branched alkanes and aromatic hydrocarbons have higher octane numbers than straight-chain alkanes. The octane number of gasoline is obtained by comparing its knocking characteristics with those of isooctane (2,2,4-trimethylpentane) and heptane. Isooctane is assigned an octane number of 100, and heptane is assigned 0. Gasoline with the same knocking characteristics as a mixture of 91% isooctane and 9% heptane, for instance, is rated as 91 octane.

▲ **FIGURE 6.6 Octane rating.** The octane rating of gasoline measures its resistance to knocking when burned in an engine. The octane rating of the gasoline in the foreground is 89.

The gasoline obtained by fractionating petroleum (called *straight-run* gasoline) contains mainly straight-chain hydrocarbons and has an octane number around 50. To increase its octane rating, it is subjected to a process called *reforming*, which converts the straight-chain alkanes into branched-chain ones.

Cracking is used to produce aromatic hydrocarbons and to convert some of the less-volatile fractions of petroleum into compounds suitable for use as automobile fuel. In cracking, the hydrocarbons are mixed with a catalyst and heated to 400 °C to 500 °C. The catalysts used are either clay minerals or synthetic Al_2O_3–SiO_2 mixtures. In addition to forming molecules more suitable for gasoline, cracking results in the formation of such low-molecular-weight hydrocarbons as ethylene and propene. These substances are used in a variety of reactions to form plastics and other chemicals.

Adding compounds called either *antiknock agents* or octane enhancers increases the octane rating of gasoline. Until the mid-1970s the principal antiknock agent was tetraethyl lead, $(C_2H_5)_4Pb$. It is no longer used, however, because of the environmental hazards of lead and because it poisons catalytic converters. ⚭ (Section 14.7 "Chemistry Put to Work: Catalytic Converters") Aromatic compounds such as toluene ($C_6H_5CH_3$) and oxygenated hydrocarbons such as ethanol (CH_3CH_2OH) are now generally used as antiknock agents.

RELATED EXERCISES: 6.18, 6.19

TABLE 6.5 • Hydrocarbon Fractions from Petroleum

Fraction	Size Range of Molecules	Boiling-Point Range (°C)	Uses
Gas	C_1 to C_5	−160 to 30	Gaseous fuel, production of H_2
Straight-run gasoline	C_5 to C_{12}	30 to 200	Motor fuel
Kerosene, fuel oil	C_{12} to C_{18}	180 to 400	Diesel fuel, furnace fuel, cracking
Lubricants	C_{16} and up	350 and up	Lubricants
Paraffins	C_{20} and up	Low-melting solids	Candles, matches
Asphalt	C_{36} and up	Gummy residues	Surfacing roads

6.3 | ALKENES, ALKYNES, AND AROMATIC HYDROCARBONS

Because alkanes have only single bonds, they contain the largest possible number of hydrogen atoms per carbon atom. As a result, they are called *saturated hydrocarbons*. Alkenes, alkynes, and aromatic hydrocarbons contain multiple bonds (double, triple, or delocalized π bonds). As a result, they contain less hydrogen than an alkane with the

GO FIGURE

How many isomers are there for propene, C_3H_6?

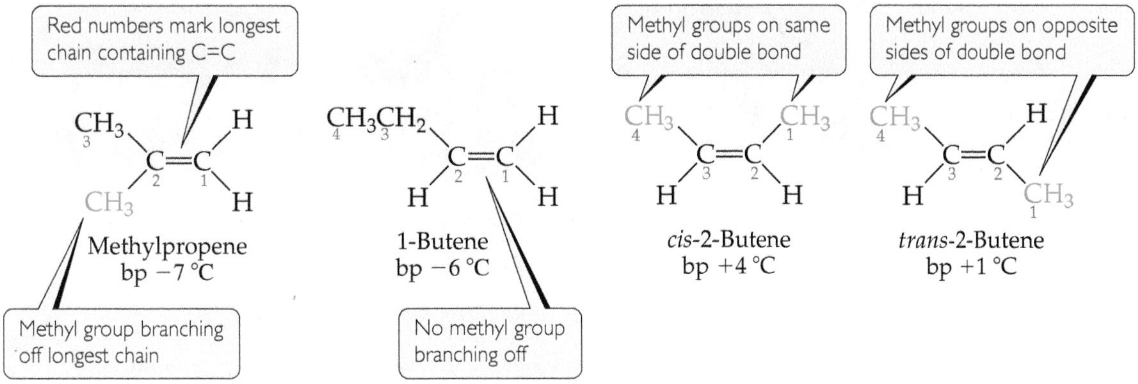

▲ FIGURE 6.7 **The alkene C_4H_8 has four structural isomers.**

same number of carbon atoms. Collectively, they are called *unsaturated hydrocarbons*. On the whole, unsaturated molecules are more reactive than saturated ones.

Alkenes

Alkenes are unsaturated hydrocarbons that contain at least one C=C bond. The simplest alkene is CH_2=CH_2, called ethene (IUPAC) or ethylene, which plays important roles as a plant hormone in seed germination and fruit ripening. The next member of the series is CH_3—CH=CH_2, called propene or propylene. Alkenes with four or more carbon atoms have several isomers. For example, the alkene C_4H_8 has the four structural isomers shown in ▲ FIGURE 6.7. Notice both their structures and their names.

The names of alkenes are based on the longest continuous chain of carbon atoms that contains the double bond. The chain is named by changing the ending of the name of the corresponding alkane from -*ane* to -*ene*. The compound on the left in Figure 6.7, for example, has a double bond as part of a three-carbon chain; thus, the parent alkene is propene.

The location of the double bond along an alkene chain is indicated by a prefix number that designates the double-bond carbon atom that is nearest an end of the chain. The chain is always numbered from the end that brings us to the double bond sooner and hence gives the smallest-numbered prefix. In propene the only possible location for the double bond is between the first and second carbons; thus, a prefix indicating its location is unnecessary. For butene (Figure 6.7) there are two possible positions for the double bond, either after the first carbon (1-butene) or after the second carbon (2-butene).

GIVE IT SOME THOUGHT

How many distinct locations are there for a double bond in a five-carbon linear chain?

If a substance contains two or more double bonds, the location of each is indicated by a numerical prefix, and the ending of the name is altered to identify the number of double bonds: diene (two), triene (three), and so forth. For example, CH_2=CH—CH_2—CH=CH_2 is 1,4-pentadiene.

The two isomers on the right in Figure 6.7 differ in the relative locations of their methyl groups. These two compounds are **geometric isomers**, compounds that have the same molecular formula and the same groups bonded to one another but differ in the spatial arrangement of these groups. In the cis isomer the two methyl groups are on the same side of the double bond, whereas in the trans isomer they are on opposite sides. Geometric isomers possess distinct physical properties and can differ significantly from each other in their chemical behavior.

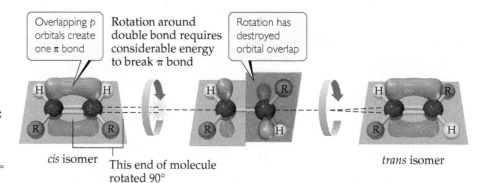

▶ **FIGURE 6.8** **Geometric isomers exist because rotation about a carbon–carbon double bond requires too much energy to occur at ordinary temperatures.**

Geometric isomerism in alkenes arises because, unlike the $C-C$ bond, the $C=C$ bond resists twisting. Recall from Section 4.6 that the double bond between two carbon atoms consists of a σ and a π bond. ▲ **FIGURE 6.8** shows a cis alkene. The carbon–carbon bond axis and the bonds to the hydrogen atoms and to the alkyl groups (designated R) are all in a plane, and the p orbitals that form the π bond are perpendicular to that plane. As Figure 6.8 shows, rotation around the carbon–carbon double bond requires the π bond to be broken, a process that requires considerable energy (about 250 kJ/mol). Because rotation doesn't occur easily around the carbon–carbon bond, the cis and trans isomers of an alkene cannot readily interconvert and, therefore, exist as distinct compounds.

SAMPLE EXERCISE 6.3 | **Drawing Isomers**

Draw all the structural and geometric isomers of pentene, C_5H_{10}, that have an unbranched hydrocarbon chain.

SOLUTION

Analyze We are asked to draw all the isomers (both structural and geometric) for an alkene with a five-carbon chain.

Plan Because the compound is named pentene and not pentadiene or pentatriene, we know that the five-carbon chain contains only one carbon–carbon double bond. Thus, we begin by placing the double bond in various locations along the chain, remembering that the chain can be numbered from either end. After finding the different unique locations for the double bond, we consider whether the molecule can have cis and trans isomers.

Solve There can be a double bond after either the first carbon (1-pentene) or second carbon (2-pentene). These are the only two possibilities because the chain can be numbered from either end. Thus, what we might erroneously call 3-pentene is actually 2-pentene, as seen by numbering the carbon chain from the other end:

$$\overset{1}{C}=\overset{2}{C}-\overset{3}{C}-\overset{4}{C}-\overset{5}{C}$$

$$\overset{1}{C}-\overset{2}{C}=\overset{3}{C}-\overset{4}{C}-\overset{5}{C}$$

$$\overset{1}{C}-\overset{2}{C}-\overset{3}{C}=\overset{4}{C}-\overset{5}{C} \quad \text{renumbered as} \quad \overset{5}{C}-\overset{4}{C}-\overset{3}{C}=\overset{2}{C}-\overset{1}{C}$$

$$\overset{1}{C}-\overset{2}{C}-\overset{3}{C}-\overset{4}{C}=\overset{5}{C} \quad \text{renumbered as} \quad \overset{5}{C}-\overset{4}{C}-\overset{3}{C}-\overset{2}{C}=\overset{1}{C}$$

Because the first C atom in 1-pentene is bonded to two H atoms, there are no cis-trans isomers. There are cis and trans isomers for 2-pentene, however. Thus, the three isomers for pentene are

$$CH_2=CH-CH_2-CH_2-CH_3$$
1-Pentene

cis-2-Pentene

trans-2-Pentene

(You should convince yourself that *cis*-3-pentene is identical to *cis*-2-pentene and *trans*-3-pentene is identical to *trans*-2-pentene. However, *cis*-2-pentene and *trans*-2-pentene are the correct names because they have smaller numbered prefixes.)

PRACTICE EXERCISE

How many straight-chain isomers are there of hexene, C_6H_{12}?

Answer: five (1-hexene, *cis*-2-hexene, *trans*-2-hexene, *cis*-3-hexene, *trans*-3-hexene)

Alkynes

Alkynes are unsaturated hydrocarbons containing one or more $C\equiv C$ bonds. The simplest alkyne is acetylene (C_2H_2), a highly reactive molecule. When acetylene is burned in a stream of oxygen in an oxyacetylene torch, the flame reaches about 3200 K. Because alkynes in general are highly reactive, they are not as widely distributed in nature as alkenes; alkynes, however, are important intermediates in many industrial processes.

Alkynes are named by identifying the longest continuous chain containing the triple bond and modifying the ending of the name of the corresponding alkane from *-ane* to *-yne*, as shown in Sample Exercise 6.4.

SAMPLE EXERCISE 6.4   **Naming Unsaturated Hydrocarbons**

Name the following compounds:

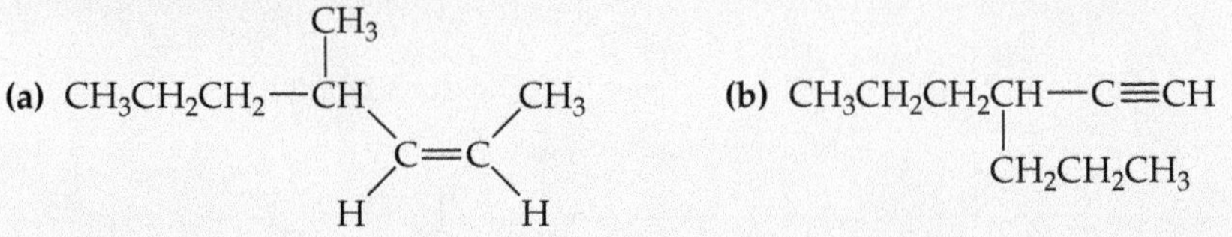

(a)
$$CH_3CH_2CH_2-\underset{\underset{C=C}{|}}{CH}$$

(b) $CH_3CH_2CH_2CH-C\equiv CH$
      with $CH_2CH_2CH_3$ branch below the CH

SOLUTION

Analyze We are given the condensed structural formulas for an alkene and an alkyne and asked to name the compounds.

Plan In each case the name is based on the number of carbon atoms in the longest continuous carbon chain that contains the multiple bond. In the alkene, care must be taken to indicate whether cis-trans isomerism is possible and, if so, which isomer is given.

Solve

(a) The longest continuous chain of carbons that contains the double bond is seven carbons long, so the parent hydrocarbon is heptene. Because the double bond begins at carbon 2 (numbering from the end closer to the double bond), we have 2-heptene. With a methyl group at carbon atom 4, we have 4-methyl-2-heptene. The geometrical configuration at the double bond is cis (that is, the alkyl groups are bonded to the double bond on the same side). Thus, the full name is 4-methyl-*cis*-2-heptene.

(b) The longest continuous chain containing the triple bond has six carbons, so this compound is a derivative of hexyne. The triple bond comes after the first carbon (numbering from the right), making it 1-hexyne. The branch from the hexyne chain contains three carbon atoms, making it a propyl group. Because this substituent is located on C3 of the hexyne chain, the molecule is 3-propyl-1-hexyne.

PRACTICE EXERCISE

Draw the condensed structural formula for 4-methyl-2-pentyne.

Answer: $CH_3-C\equiv C-\underset{\underset{CH_3}{|}}{CH}-CH_3$

Addition Reactions of Alkenes and Alkynes

The presence of carbon–carbon double or triple bonds in hydrocarbons markedly increases their chemical reactivity. The most characteristic reactions of alkenes and alkynes are **addition reactions**, in which a reactant is added to the two atoms that form the multiple bond. A simple example is the addition of a halogen to ethylene:

$$H_2C=CH_2 + Br_2 \longrightarrow \underset{\underset{Br \quad Br}{|\quad\ |}}{H_2C-CH_2} \qquad [6.1]$$

The pair of electrons that forms the π bond in ethylene is uncoupled and is used to form two σ bonds to the two bromine atoms. The σ bond between the carbon atoms is retained.

Addition of H_2 to an alkene converts it to an alkane:

$$CH_3CH{=}CHCH_3 + H_2 \xrightarrow{\text{Ni, 500 °C}} CH_3CH_2CH_2CH_3 \qquad [6.2]$$

The reaction between an alkene and H_2, referred to as *hydrogenation*, does not occur readily at ordinary temperatures and pressures. One reason for the lack of reactivity of H_2 toward alkenes is the stability of the H_2 bond. To promote the reaction, a catalyst is used to assist in rupturing the H—H bond. The most widely used catalysts are finely divided metals on which H_2 is adsorbed. ∞ (Section 14.7)

Hydrogen halides and water can also add to the double bond of alkenes, as in these reactions of ethylene:

$$CH_2{=}CH_2 + HBr \longrightarrow CH_3CH_2Br \qquad [6.3]$$

$$CH_2{=}CH_2 + H_2O \xrightarrow{\text{H}_2\text{SO}_4} CH_3CH_2OH \qquad [6.4]$$

The addition of water is catalyzed by a strong acid, such as H_2SO_4.

The addition reactions of alkynes resemble those of alkenes, as shown in these examples:

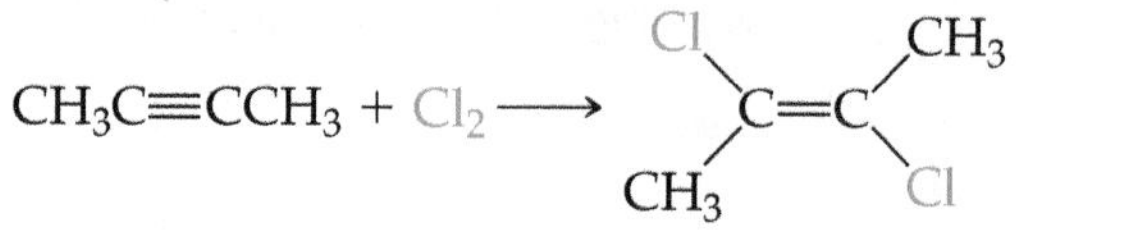

$$CH_3C{\equiv}CCH_3 + Cl_2 \longrightarrow \qquad [6.5]$$

2-Butyne   *trans*-2,3-Dichloro-2-butene

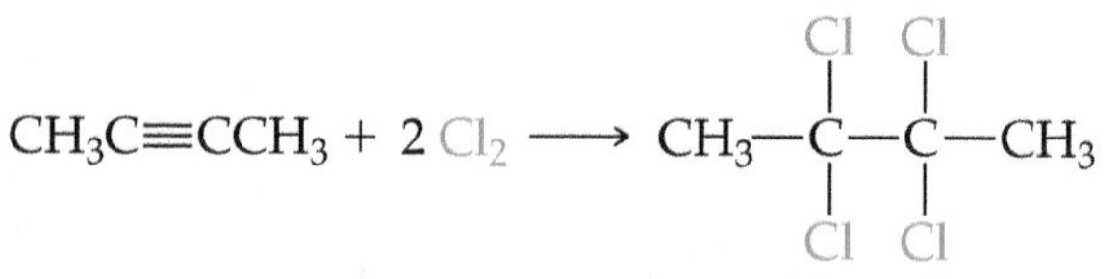

$$CH_3C{\equiv}CCH_3 + 2\,Cl_2 \longrightarrow CH_3{-}\underset{\underset{Cl}{|}}{\overset{\overset{Cl}{|}}{C}}{-}\underset{\underset{Cl}{|}}{\overset{\overset{Cl}{|}}{C}}{-}CH_3 \qquad [6.6]$$

2-Butyne   2,2,3,3-Tetrachlorobutane

SAMPLE EXERCISE 6.5 | **Identifying the Product of a Hydrogenation Reaction**

Write the condensed structural formula for the product of the hydrogenation of 3-methyl-1-pentene.

SOLUTION

Analyze We are asked to predict the compound formed when a particular alkene undergoes hydrogenation (reaction with H_2) and to write the condensed structural formula of the product.

Plan To determine the condensed structural formula of the product, we must first write the condensed structural formula or Lewis structure of the reactant. In the hydrogenation of the alkene, H_2 adds to the double bond, producing an alkane.

Solve The name of the starting compound tells us that we have a chain of five C atoms with a double bond at one end (position 1) and a methyl group on C3:

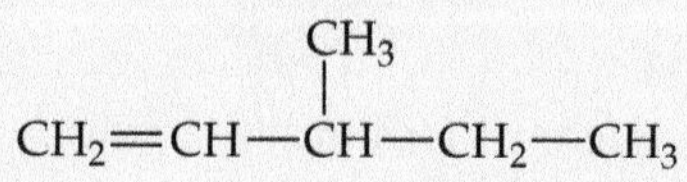

$$CH_2{=}CH{-}\underset{\underset{CH_3}{|}}{CH}{-}CH_2{-}CH_3$$

Hydrogenation—the addition of two H atoms to the carbons of the double bond—leads to the following alkane:

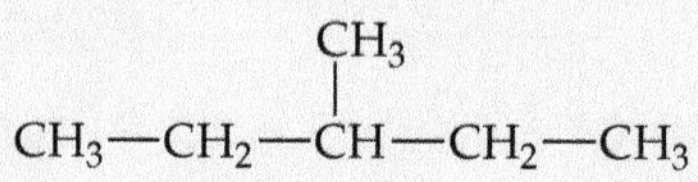

$$CH_3{-}CH_2{-}\underset{\underset{CH_3}{|}}{CH}{-}CH_2{-}CH_3$$

Comment The longest chain in this alkane has five carbon atoms; the product is therefore 3-methylpentane.

PRACTICE EXERCISE

Addition of HCl to an alkene forms 2-chloropropane. What is the alkene?
Answer: propene

A CLOSER LOOK

MECHANISM OF ADDITION REACTIONS

As the understanding of chemistry has grown, chemists have advanced from simply cataloging reactions known to occur to explaining *how* they occur. An explanation of how a reaction occurs is called a *mechanism.* ∞∞(Section 14.6)

The addition reaction between HBr and an alkene, for instance, is thought to proceed in two steps. In the first step, which is rate determining ∞∞(Section 14.6), the HBr attacks the electron-rich double bond, transferring a proton to one of the double-bond carbons. In the reaction of 2-butene with HBr, for example, the first step is

$$CH_3CH=CHCH_3 + HBr \longrightarrow \left[CH_3\overset{\delta+}{CH}{=\!=}CHCH_3 \atop {\overset{|}{H} \atop Br\,^{\delta-}} \right]$$

$$\longrightarrow CH_3\overset{+}{CH}{-}CH_2CH_3 + Br^- \qquad [6.7]$$

The electron pair that formed the π bond is used to form the new C—H bond.

The second, faster step is addition of Br⁻ to the positively charged carbon. The bromide ion donates a pair of electrons to the carbon, forming the C—Br bond:

$$CH_3\overset{+}{CH}{-}CH_2CH_3 + Br^- \longrightarrow \left[CH_3\overset{\delta+}{CH}{-}CH_2CH_3 \atop {\overset{|}{Br}\,^{\delta-}} \right]$$

$$\longrightarrow CH_3\underset{\overset{|}{Br}}{CH}CH_2CH_3 \qquad [6.8]$$

Because the rate-determining step involves both the alkene and the acid, the rate law for the reaction is second order, first order in the alkene and first order in HBr:

$$Rate = -\frac{\Delta[CH_3CH=CHCH_3]}{\Delta t} = k[CH_3CH=CHCH_3][HBr]$$

$$[6.9]$$

The energy profile for the reaction is shown in ▼ FIGURE 6.9. The first energy maximum represents the transition state in the first step, and the second maximum represents the transition state in the second step. The energy minimum represents the energies of the intermediate species, $CH_3\overset{+}{CH}{-}CH_2CH_3$ and Br^-.

To show electron movement in reactions like these, chemists often use curved arrows pointing in the direction of electron flow. For the addition of HBr to 2-butene, for example, the shifts in electron positions are shown as

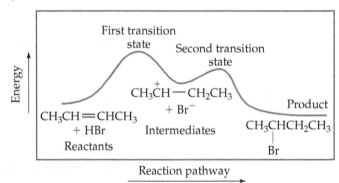

GO FIGURE

What features of an energy profile allow you to distinguish between an intermediate and a transition state?

▲ FIGURE 6.9 **Energy profile for addition of HBr to 2-butene.** The two maxima tell you that this is a two-step mechanism.

Aromatic Hydrocarbons

The simplest aromatic hydrocarbon, benzene (C_6H_6), is shown in ▼ FIGURE 6.10 along with some other aromatic hydrocarbons. Benzene is the most important aromatic hydrocarbon, and most of our discussion focuses on it.

◀ FIGURE 6.10 **Line formulas and common names of several aromatic compounds.** The aromatic rings are represented by hexagons with a circle inscribed inside to denote delocalized π bonds. Each corner represents a carbon atom. Each carbon is bound to three other atoms—either three carbons or two carbons and a hydrogen—so that each carbon has the requisite four bonds.

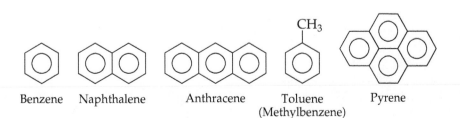

Benzene   Naphthalene   Anthracene   Toluene (Methylbenzene)   Pyrene

Stabilization of π Electrons by Delocalization

The planar structure of benzene, with its 120° bond angles, suggests a high degree of un-saturation. You might therefore expect benzene to resemble the alkenes and to be highly reactive. Benzene and the other aromatic hydrocarbons, however, are much more stable than alkenes because the π electrons are delocalized in the π orbitals. ∞ (Section 4.6)

We can estimate the stabilization of the π electrons in benzene by comparing the energy required to form cyclohexane by adding hydrogen to benzene, to cyclohexene (one double bond) and to 1,4-cyclohexadiene (two double bonds):

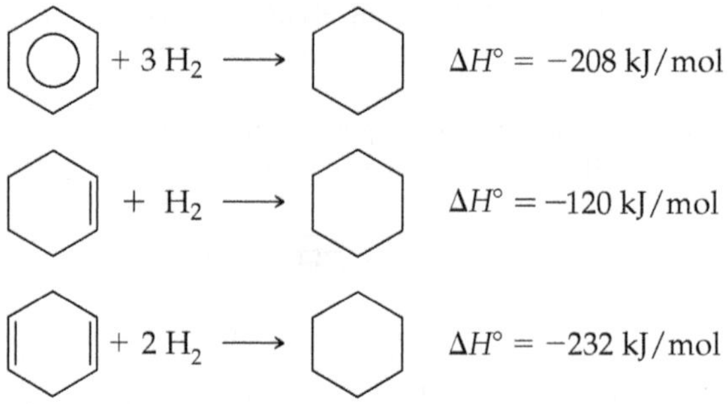

$\Delta H° = -208$ kJ/mol

$\Delta H° = -120$ kJ/mol

$\Delta H° = -232$ kJ/mol

From the second and third reactions, it appears that the energy required to hydrogenate each double bond is roughly 118 kJ/mol for each bond. Benzene contains the equivalent of three double bonds. We might expect, therefore, the energy required to hydrogenate ben-zene to be about 3 times -118, or -354 kJ/mol, if benzene behaved as though it were "cyclohexatriene," that is, if it behaved as though it had three isolated double bonds in a ring. Instead, the energy released is 146 kJ less than this, indicating that benzene is more stable than would be expected for three double bonds. The difference of 146 kJ/mol between the "expected" heat (that is, enthalpy) of hydrogenation, -354 kJ/mol, and the observed heat of hydrogenation, -208 kJ/mol, is due to stabilization of the π electrons through delocalization in the π orbitals that extend around the ring.

Substitution Reactions

Although aromatic hydrocarbons are unsaturated, *they do not readily undergo addition reactions.* The delocalized π bonding causes aromatic compounds to behave quite dif-ferently from alkenes and alkynes. Benzene, for example, does not add Cl_2 or Br_2 to its double bonds under ordinary conditions. In contrast, aromatic hydrocarbons undergo **substitution reactions** relatively easily. In a substitution reaction one hydrogen atom of a molecule is removed and replaced (substituted) by another atom or group of atoms. When benzene is warmed in a mixture of nitric and sulfuric acids, for example, one of the benzene hydrogens is replaced by the nitro group, NO_2:

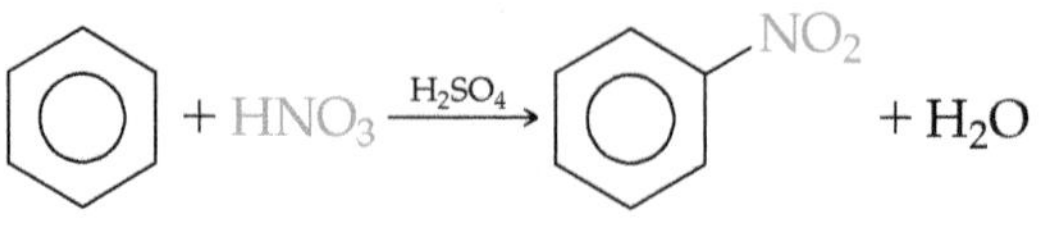

Benzene   Nitrobenzene

$+ HNO_3 \xrightarrow{H_2SO_4}$ ... $+ H_2O$ [6.10]

More vigorous treatment results in substitution of a second nitro group into the molecule:

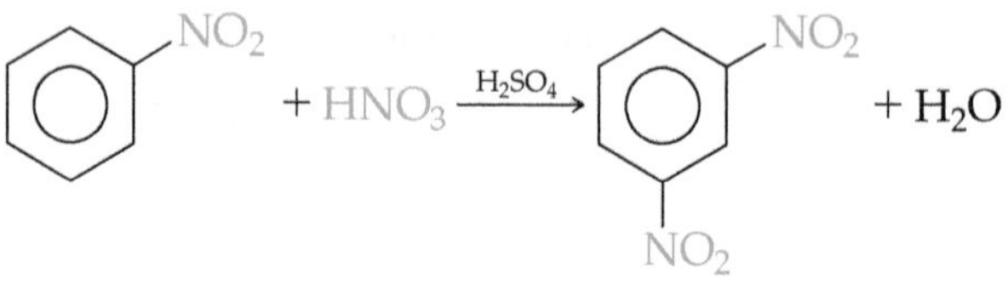

$+ HNO_3 \xrightarrow{H_2SO_4}$ ... $+ H_2O$ [6.11]

There are three isomers of benzene that contain two nitro groups—*ortho*-, *meta*-, and *para*-dinitrobenzene:

ortho-Dinitrobenzene   *meta*-Dinitrobenzene   *para*-Dinitrobenzene
mp 118 °C   mp 90 °C   mp 174 °C

In the reaction of Equation 6.11, the principal product is the *meta* isomer.

Bromination of benzene, carried out with $FeBr_3$ as a catalyst, is another substitution reaction:

$$\text{Benzene} + Br_2 \xrightarrow{FeBr_3} \text{Bromobenzene} + HBr \qquad [6.12]$$

In a similar reaction, called the *Friedel-Crafts reaction*, alkyl groups can be substituted onto an aromatic ring by reacting an alkyl halide with an aromatic compound in the presence of $AlCl_3$ as a catalyst:

$$\text{Benzene} + CH_3CH_2Cl \xrightarrow{AlCl_3} \text{Ethylbenzene} + HCl \qquad [6.13]$$

 GIVE IT SOME THOUGHT

When the aromatic hydrocarbon naphthalene, shown in Figure 6.10, reacts with nitric and sulfuric acids, two compounds containing one nitro group are formed. Draw the structures of these two compounds.

6.4 | ORGANIC FUNCTIONAL GROUPS

The $C{=}C$ double bonds of alkenes and $C{\equiv}C$ triple bonds of alkynes are just two of many functional groups in organic molecules. As noted earlier, these functional groups each undergo characteristic reactions, and the same is true of all other functional groups. Each kind of functional group often undergoes the same kinds of reactions in every molecule, regardless of the size and complexity of the molecule. Thus, the chemistry of an organic molecule is largely determined by the functional groups it contains.

▶ TABLE 6.6 lists the most common functional groups. Notice that, except for $C{=}C$ and $C{\equiv}C$, they all contain either O, N, or a halogen atom, X.

We can think of organic molecules as being composed of functional groups bonded to one or more alkyl groups. The alkyl groups, which are made of $C{-}C$ and $C{-}H$ single bonds, are the less reactive portions of the molecules. In describing general features of organic compounds, chemists often use the designation R to represent any alkyl group: methyl, ethyl, propyl, and so on. Alkanes, for example, which contain no functional group, are represented as $R{-}H$. Alcohols, which contain the group $-OH$, are represented as $R{-}OH$. If two or more different alkyl groups are present in a molecule, we designate them R, R′, R″, and so forth.

TABLE 6.6 • Common Functional Groups

Functional Group	Compound Type	Suffix or Prefix	Example Structural Formula	Ball-and-stick Model	Systematic Name (common name)
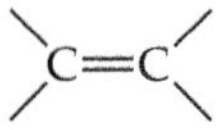 $\diagup$C=C$\diagdown$	Alkene	-ene	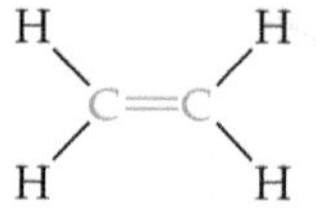 H, H / C=C / H, H	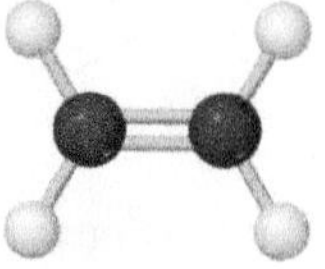	Ethene (Ethylene)
—C≡C—	Alkyne	-yne	H—C≡C—H		Ethyne (Acetylene)
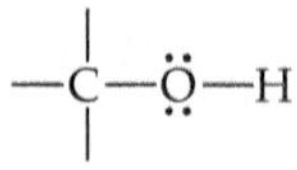 —C—Ö—H	Alcohol	-ol	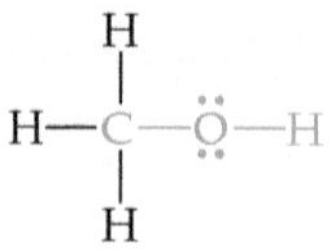 H—C—Ö—H	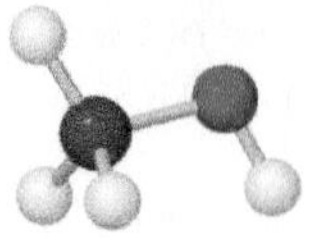	Methanol (Methyl alcohol)
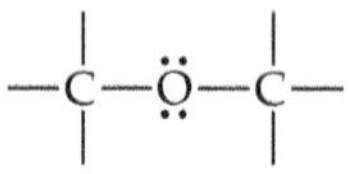 —C—Ö—C—	Ether	ether	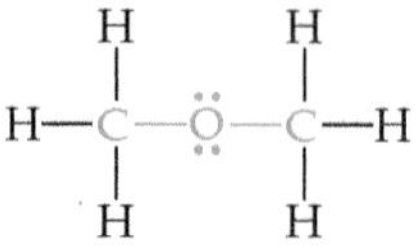 H—C—Ö—C—H	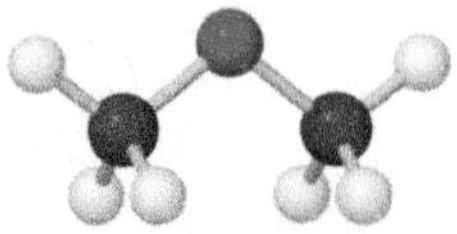	Dimethyl ether
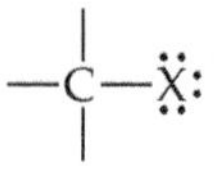 —C—Ẍ: (X = halogen)	Haloalkane	halo-	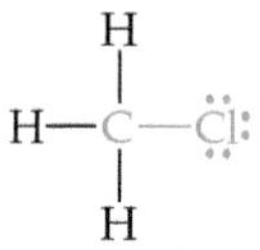 H—C—Cl:	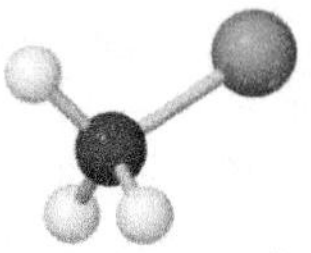	Chloromethane (Methyl chloride)
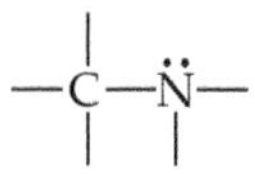 —C—N̈—	Amine	-amine	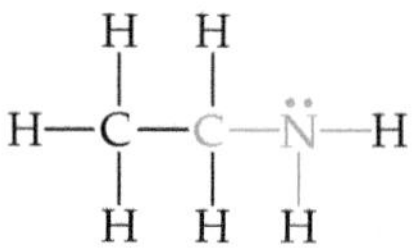 H—C—C—N—H	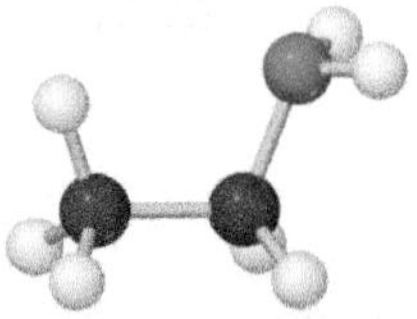	Ethylamine
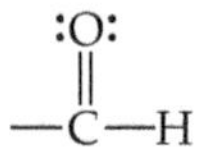 :O: ‖ —C—H	Aldehyde	-al	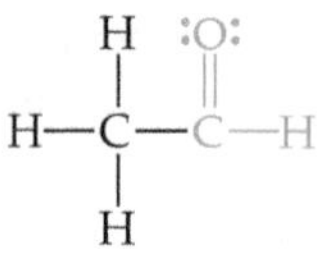 H—C—C—H	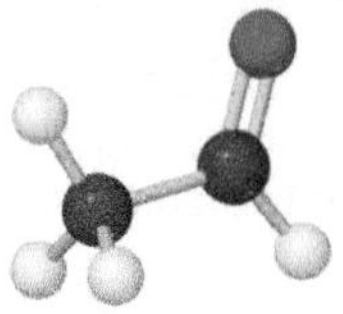	Ethanal (Acetaldehyde)
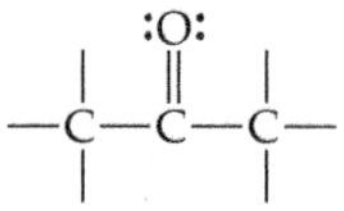 :O: ‖ —C—C—C—	Ketone	-one	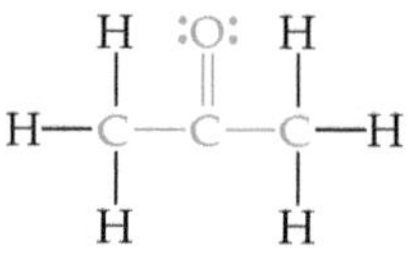 H—C—C—C—H	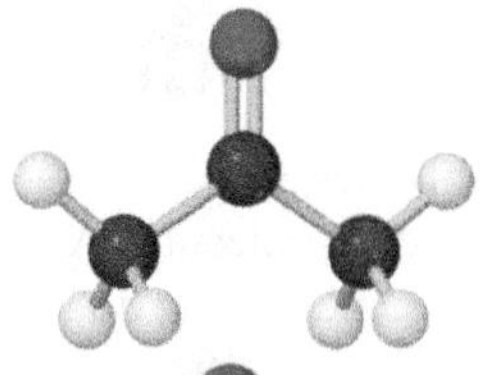	Propanone (Acetone)
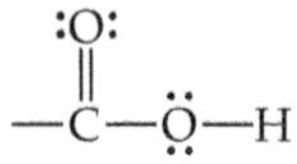 :O: ‖ —C—Ö—H	Carboxylic acid	-oic acid	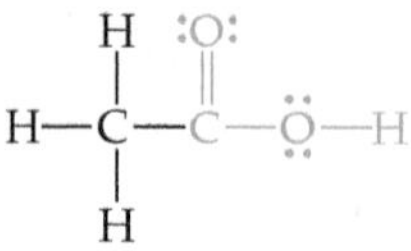 H—C—C—Ö—H	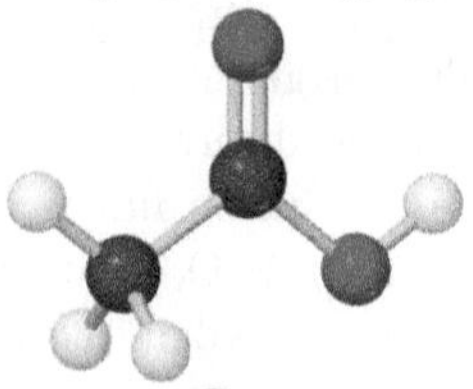	Ethanoic acid (Acetic acid)
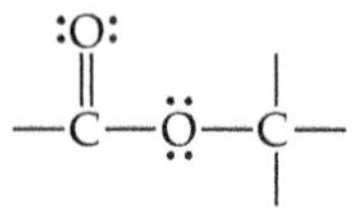 :O: ‖ —C—Ö—C—	Ester	-oate	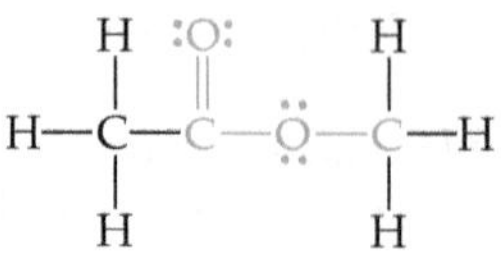 H—C—C—Ö—C—H	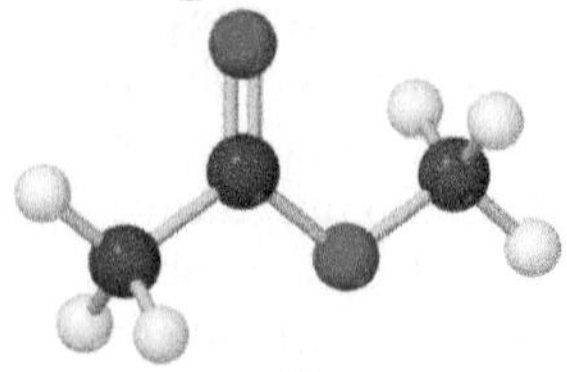	Methyl ethanoate (Methyl acetate)
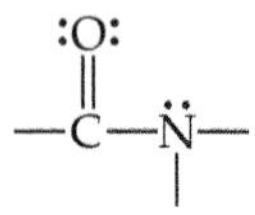 :O: ‖ —C—N̈—	Amide	-amide	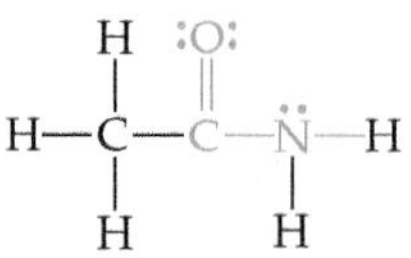 H—C—C—N—H	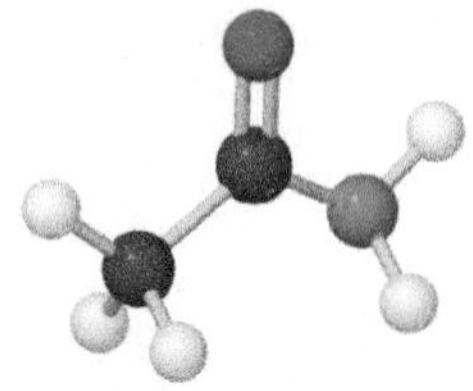	Ethanamide (Acetamide)

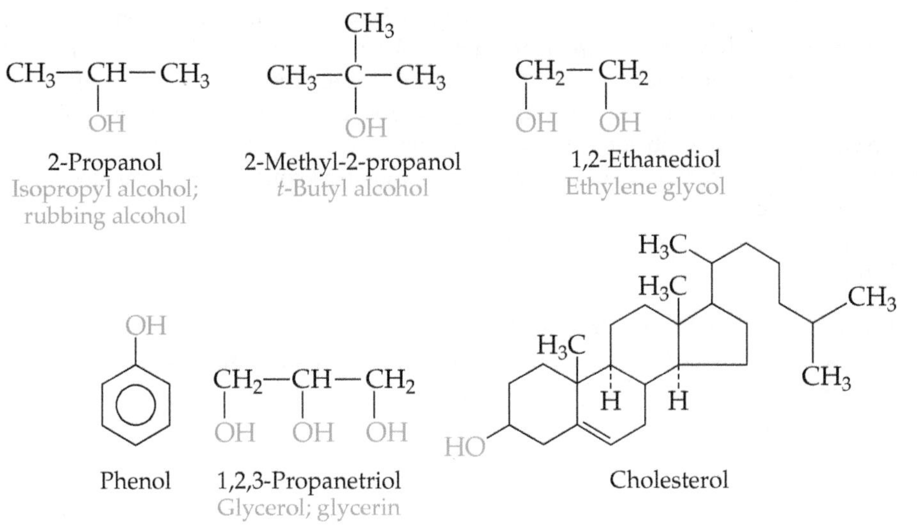

$$CH_3-\underset{\underset{OH}{|}}{CH}-CH_3 \qquad CH_3-\underset{\underset{OH}{|}}{\overset{\overset{CH_3}{|}}{C}}-CH_3 \qquad \underset{\underset{OH}{|}}{CH_2}-\underset{\underset{OH}{|}}{CH_2}$$

2-Propanol   **2-Methyl-2-propanol**   **1,2-Ethanediol**
Isopropyl alcohol;   *t*-Butyl alcohol   Ethylene glycol
rubbing alcohol

Phenol $$\underset{\underset{OH}{|}}{CH_2}-\underset{\underset{OH}{|}}{CH}-\underset{\underset{OH}{|}}{CH_2}$$ **Cholesterol**

Phenol   **1,2,3-Propanetriol**
          Glycerol; glycerin

◀ **FIGURE 6.11   Condensed structural formulas of six important alcohols.** Common names are given in blue.

Alcohols

Alcohols are hydrocarbon derivatives in which one or more hydrogens of a parent hydrocarbon have been replaced by the functional group —OH, called either the *hydroxyl group* or the *alcohol group*. Note in ▲ **FIGURE 6.11** that the name for an alcohol ends in *-ol*. The simple alcohols are named by changing the last letter in the name of the corresponding alkane to *-ol*—for example, ethan*e* becomes ethan*ol*. Where necessary, the location of the OH group is designated by a numeric prefix that indicates the number of the carbon atom bearing the OH group.

The O—H bond is polar, so alcohols are much more soluble in polar solvents than are hydrocarbons. The —OH functional group can also participate in hydrogen bonding. As a result, the boiling points of alcohols are much higher than those of their parent alkanes.

▶ **FIGURE 6.12** shows several commercial products that consist entirely or in large part of an organic alcohol.

The simplest alcohol, methanol (methyl alcohol), has many industrial uses and is produced on a large scale by heating carbon monoxide and hydrogen under pressure in the presence of a metal oxide catalyst:

$$CO(g) + 2\,H_2(g) \xrightarrow[400\,°C]{200-300\ atm} CH_3OH(g) \qquad [6.14]$$

Because methanol has a very high octane rating as an automobile fuel, it is used as a gasoline additive and as a fuel in its own right.

Ethanol (ethyl alcohol, C_2H_5OH) is a product of the fermentation of carbohydrates such as sugars and starches. In the absence of air, yeast cells convert these carbohydrates into ethanol and CO_2:

$$C_6H_{12}O_6(aq) \xrightarrow{\text{yeast}} 2\,C_2H_5OH(aq) + 2\,CO_2(g) \qquad [6.15]$$

In the process, the yeast cells derive energy necessary for growth. This reaction is carried out under carefully controlled conditions to produce beer, wine, and other beverages in which ethanol is the active ingredient.

The simplest polyhydroxyl alcohol (an alcohol containing more than one OH group) is 1,2-ethanediol (ethylene glycol, $HOCH_2CH_2OH$), the major ingredient in automobile antifreeze. Another common polyhydroxyl alcohol is 1,2,3-propanetriol [glycerol, $HOCH_2CH(OH)CH_2OH$], a viscous liquid that dissolves readily in water and is used in cosmetics as a skin softener and in foods and candies to keep them moist.

Phenol is the simplest compound with an OH group attached to an aromatic ring. One of the most striking effects of the aromatic group is the greatly increased acidity of the OH group. Phenol is about 1 million times more acidic in water than a nonaromatic alcohol. Even so, it is not a very strong acid ($K_a = 1.3 \times 10^{-10}$). Phenol is used industrially to make plastics and dyes, and as a topical anesthetic in throat sprays.

▲ **FIGURE 6.12   Everyday alcohols.** Many of the products we use every day— from rubbing alcohol to hair spray and antifreeze—are composed either entirely or mainly of alcohols.

Cholesterol, shown in Figure 6.11, is a biochemically important alcohol. The OH group forms only a small component of this molecule, so cholesterol is only slightly soluble in water (0.26 g per 100 mL of H_2O). Cholesterol is a normal component of our bodies; when present in excessive amounts, however, it may precipitate from solution. It precipitates in the gallbladder to form crystalline lumps called *gallstones*. It may also precipitate against the walls of veins and arteries and thus contribute to high blood pressure and other cardiovascular problems.

Ethers

Compounds in which two hydrocarbon groups are bonded to one oxygen are called **ethers**. Ethers can be formed from two molecules of alcohol by splitting out a molecule of water. The reaction is catalyzed by sulfuric acid, which takes up water to remove it from the system:

$$CH_3CH_2-OH + H-OCH_2CH_3 \xrightarrow{H_2SO_4} CH_3CH_2-O-CH_2CH_3 + H_2O$$

[6.16]

A reaction in which water is split out from two substances is called a *condensation reaction.* ∞ (Section 7.8)

Both diethyl ether and the cyclic ether tetrahydrofuran are common solvents for organic reactions:

$$CH_3CH_2-O-CH_2CH_3$$

Diethyl ether   Tetrahydrofuran (THF)

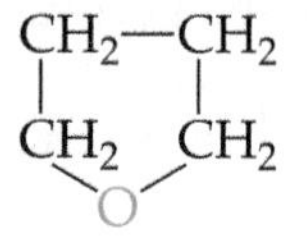

Aldehydes and Ketones

Several of the functional groups listed in Table 6.6 contain the **carbonyl group**, $C=O$. This group, together with the atoms attached to its carbon, defines several important functional groups that we consider in this section.

In **aldehydes** the carbonyl group has at least one hydrogen atom attached:

Methanal
Formaldehyde

Ethanal
Acetaldehyde

In **ketones** the carbonyl group occurs at the interior of a carbon chain and is therefore flanked by carbon atoms:

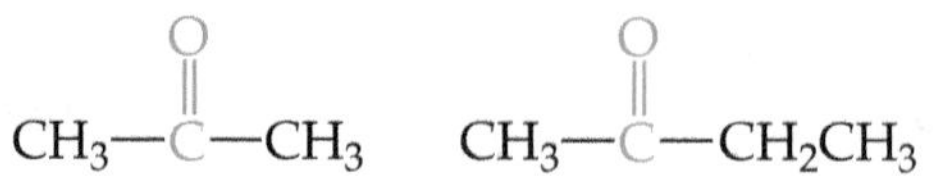

Propanone
Acetone

2-Butanone
Methyl ethyl ketone

Notice that the systematic names of aldehydes contain *-al* and that ketone names contain *-one*.

Aldehydes and ketones can be prepared by controlled oxidation of alcohols. Complete oxidation results in formation of CO_2 and H_2O, as in the burning of methanol:

$$CH_3OH(g) + \tfrac{3}{2}O_2(g) \longrightarrow CO_2(g) + 2\,H_2O(g)$$

Controlled partial oxidation to form other organic substances, such as aldehydes and ketones, is carried out by using various oxidizing agents, such as air, hydrogen peroxide (H_2O_2), ozone (O_3), and potassium dichromate ($K_2Cr_2O_7$).

GIVE IT SOME THOUGHT

Write the condensed structural formula for the ketone that would result from partial oxidation of the alcohol

$$CH_2-CHOH$$
$$CH_2 \qquad CH_2$$
$$CH_2$$

Many compounds found in nature contain an aldehyde or ketone functional group. Vanilla and cinnamon flavorings are naturally occurring aldehydes. Two isomers of the ketone carvone impart the characteristic flavors of spearmint leaves and caraway seeds.

Ketones are less reactive than aldehydes and are used extensively as solvents. Acetone, the most widely used ketone, is completely miscible with water, yet it dissolves a wide range of organic substances.

Carboxylic Acids and Esters

Carboxylic acids contain the *carboxyl* functional group, often written COOH. These weak acids are widely distributed in nature and are common in consumer products [▶ FIGURE 6.13(a)]. They are also important in the manufacture of polymers used to make fibers, films, and paints. ▼ FIGURE 6.14 shows the formulas of several carboxylic acids.

The common names of many carboxylic acids are based on their historical origins. Formic acid, for example, was first prepared by extraction from ants; its name is derived from the Latin word *formica*, "ant."

Carboxylic acids can be produced by oxidation of alcohols in which the OH group is attached to a CH_2 group. Under appropriate conditions, the aldehyde may be isolated as the first product of oxidation, as in the sequence

$$CH_3CH_2OH + (O) \longrightarrow CH_3\overset{O}{\overset{\|}{C}}H + H_2O \qquad [6.17]$$
Ethanol $\qquad\qquad$ Acetaldehyde

$$CH_3\overset{O}{\overset{\|}{C}}H + (O) \longrightarrow CH_3\overset{O}{\overset{\|}{C}}OH \qquad [6.18]$$
Acetaldehyde $\qquad$ Acetic acid

where (O) represents any oxidant that can provide oxygen atoms. The air oxidation of ethanol to acetic acid is responsible for causing wines to turn sour, producing vinegar.

(a)

(b)

▲ FIGURE 6.13 **Everyday carboxylic acids and esters.** (a) Vinegar contains acetic acid; vitamin C is ascorbic acid; citrus fruits and tomatoes contain citric acid; and aspirin is acetylsalicylic acid (which is both an acid and an ester). (b) Many sunburn lotions contain the ester benzocaine; some nail polish removers contain ethyl acetate; vegetable oils are also esters.

GO FIGURE

Which of these substances have both a carboxylic acid functional group and an alcohol functional group?

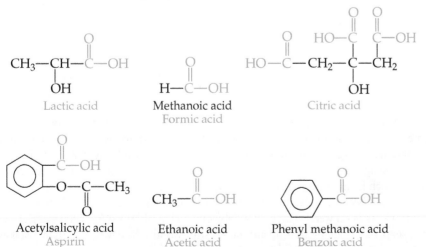

Acetylsalicylic acid
Aspirin

Ethanoic acid
Acetic acid

Phenyl methanoic acid
Benzoic acid

◀ FIGURE 6.14 **Structural formulas of common carboxylic acids.** The monocarboxylic acids are generally referred to by their common names, given in blue type.

Acetic acid can also be produced by the reaction of methanol with carbon monoxide in the presence of a rhodium catalyst:

$$CH_3OH + CO \xrightarrow{\text{catalyst}} CH_3-\overset{\overset{\displaystyle O}{\|}}{C}-OH \qquad [6.19]$$

This reaction involves, in effect, the insertion of a carbon monoxide molecule between the CH_3 and OH groups. A reaction of this kind is called *carbonylation*.

Carboxylic acids can undergo condensation reactions with alcohols to form esters:

$$CH_3-\overset{\overset{\displaystyle O}{\|}}{C}-OH + HO-CH_2CH_3 \longrightarrow CH_3-\overset{\overset{\displaystyle O}{\|}}{C}-O-CH_2CH_3 + H_2O \qquad [6.20]$$

Acetic acid   Ethanol   Ethyl acetate

Esters are compounds in which the H atom of a carboxylic acid is replaced by a carbon-containing group:

$$-\overset{\overset{\displaystyle O}{\|}}{C}-O-\overset{\displaystyle |}{\underset{\displaystyle |}{C}}-$$

Figure 6.13(b) shows some commercial products containing esters. The name of any ester consists of the name of the group contributed by the alcohol followed by the name of the group contributed by the carboxylic acid, with the -*ic* replaced by -*ate*. For example, the ester formed from ethyl alcohol, CH_3CH_2OH, and butyric acid, $CH_3(CH_2)_2COOH$, is

$$CH_3CH_2CH_2\overset{\overset{\displaystyle O}{\|}}{C}-OCH_2CH_3$$

Ethyl   butyrate

Notice that the chemical formula generally has the group originating from the acid written first, which is opposite of the way the ester is named.

Esters generally have very pleasant odors and are largely responsible for the pleasant aromas of fruit. Pentyl acetate ($CH_3COOCH_2CH_2CH_2CH_2CH_3$), for example, is responsible for the odor of bananas.

An ester treated with an acid or a base in aqueous solution is *hydrolyzed*; that is, the molecule is split into an alcohol and a carboxylic acid or its anion:

$$CH_3CH_2-\overset{\overset{\displaystyle O}{\|}}{C}-O-CH_3 + Na^+ + OH^- \longrightarrow$$

Methyl propionate

$$CH_3CH_2-\overset{\overset{\displaystyle O}{\|}}{C}-O^- + Na^+ + CH_3OH \qquad [6.21]$$

Sodium propionate   Methanol

The **hydrolysis** of an ester in the presence of a base is called **saponification**, a term that comes from the Latin word for soap, *sapon*. Naturally occurring esters include fats and oils, and in making soap an animal fat or a vegetable oil is boiled with a strong base. The resultant soap consists of a mixture of salts of long-chain carboxylic acids (called fatty acids), which form during the saponification reaction.

Soap has been manufactured and used for thousands of years. Directions for making soap from cassia oil were written on a Babylonian clay tablet around 2200 B.C. For a long time, soap was made by heating animal fat with wood ashes, which contain potassium carbonate (also known as potash) and made the solution basic. The modern commercial process for making soap usually uses sodium hydroxide as the base. Using potassium hydroxide produces soft or liquid soaps.

SAMPLE EXERCISE 6.6 | **Naming Esters and Predicting Hydrolysis Products**

In a basic aqueous solution, esters react with hydroxide ion to form the salt of the carboxylic acid and the alcohol from which the ester is constituted. Name each of the following esters, and indicate the products of their reaction with aqueous base.

(a) 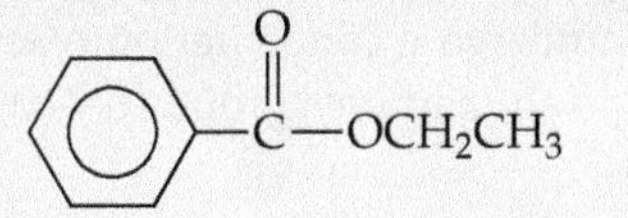 [structure] **(b)** 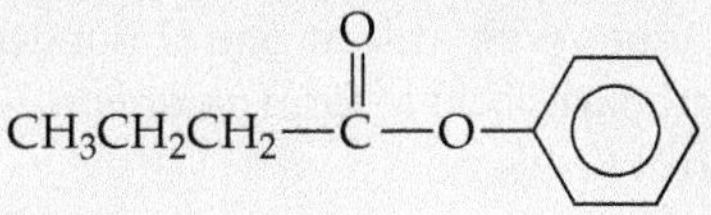 $CH_3CH_2CH_2$—C—O—[phenyl]

SOLUTION

Analyze We are given two esters and asked to name them and to predict the products formed when they undergo hydrolysis (split into an alcohol and carboxylate ion) in basic solution.

Plan Esters are formed by the condensation reaction between an alcohol and a carboxylic acid. To name an ester, we must analyze its structure and determine the identities of the alcohol and acid from which it is formed. We can identify the alcohol by adding an OH to the alkyl group attached to the O atom of the carboxyl (COO) group. We can identify the acid by adding an H to the O atom of the carboxyl group. We have learned that the first part of an ester name indicates the alcohol portion and the second indicates the acid portion. The name conforms to how the ester undergoes hydrolysis in base, reacting with base to form an alcohol and a carboxylate anion.

Solve
(a) This ester is derived from ethanol (CH_3CH_2OH) and benzoic acid (C_6H_5COOH). Its name is therefore ethyl benzoate. The net ionic equation for reaction of ethyl benzoate with hydroxide ion is

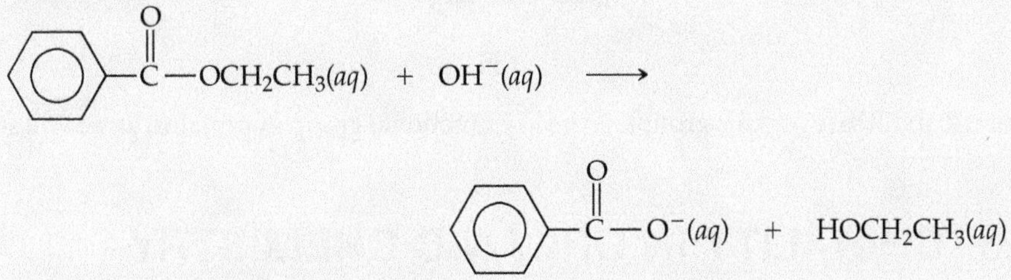

The products are benzoate ion and ethanol.
(b) This ester is derived from phenol (C_6H_5OH) and butanoic acid (commonly called butyric acid) ($CH_3CH_2CH_2COOH$). The residue from the phenol is called the phenyl group. The ester is therefore named phenyl butyrate. The net ionic equation for the reaction of phenyl butyrate with hydroxide ion is

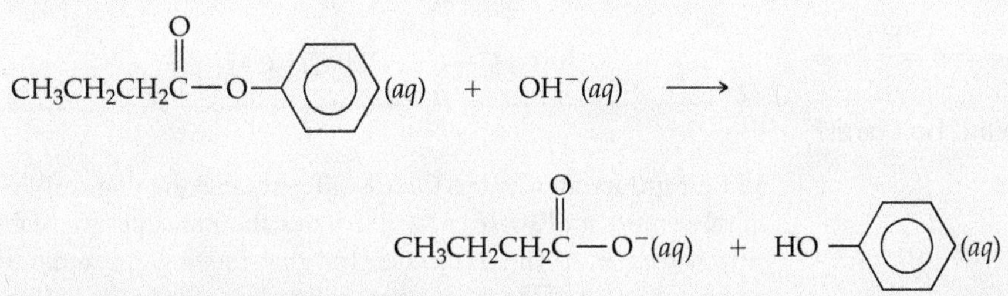

The products are butyrate ion and phenol.

PRACTICE EXERCISE

Write the condensed structural formula for the ester formed from propyl alcohol and propionic acid.

Answer: CH_3CH_2C—O—$CH_2CH_2CH_3$ (with O double bond)

Amines and Amides

Amines are compounds in which one or more of the hydrogens of ammonia (NH_3) are replaced by an alkyl group:

$$CH_3CH_2NH_2 \qquad (CH_3)_3N \qquad \text{⬡}-NH_2$$

Ethylamine Trimethylamine Phenylamine
Aniline

As we have seen earlier, they are the most common organic bases.

An amine with at least one H bonded to N can undergo a condensation reaction with a carboxylic acid to form an **amide**, which contains the carbonyl group ($C{=}O$) attached to N (Table 6.6):

$$\underset{CH_3\overset{\displaystyle\overset{O}{\|}}{C}-OH}{} + H-N(CH_3)_2 \longrightarrow CH_3\overset{\displaystyle\overset{O}{\|}}{C}-N(CH_3)_2 + H_2O \qquad [6.22]$$

We may consider the amide functional group to be derived from a carboxylic acid with an NRR′ group replacing the OH of the acid, as in these examples:

$$CH_3\overset{\displaystyle\overset{O}{\|}}{C}-NH_2 \qquad \text{⬡}-\overset{\displaystyle\overset{O}{\|}}{C}-NH_2$$

Ethanamide Phenylmethanamide
Acetamide Benzamide

The amide linkage

$$R-\overset{\displaystyle\overset{O}{\|}}{\underset{\underset{H}{|}}{C}}-N-R'$$

where R and R′ are organic groups, is the key functional group in proteins, as we will see in Section 6.7.

6.5 | CHIRALITY IN ORGANIC CHEMISTRY

A molecule possessing a nonsuperimposable mirror image is termed **chiral** (Greek *cheir*, "hand"). *Compounds containing carbon atoms with four different attached groups are inherently chiral.* A carbon atom with four different attached groups is called a *chiral center*. For example, consider 2-bromopentane:

$$CH_3-\overset{\displaystyle\overset{Br}{|}}{\underset{\underset{H}{|}}{C}}-CH_2CH_2CH_3$$

All four groups attached to C2 are different, making that carbon a chiral center. ◄ **FIGURE 6.15** illustrates the nonsuperimposable mirror images of this molecule. Imagine moving the molecule shown to the left of the mirror over to the right of the mirror. If you then turn it in every possible way, you will conclude that it cannot be superimposed on the molecule shown to the right of the mirror. Nonsuperimposable mirror images are called either *optical isomers* or *enantiomers*. Organic chemists use the labels *R* and *S* to distinguish the two forms. We need not go into the rules for deciding on the labels.

The two members of an enantiomer pair have identical physical properties and identical chemical properties when they react with nonchiral reagents. Only in a chiral environment do they

GO FIGURE

If you replace Br with CH_3, will the compound be chiral?

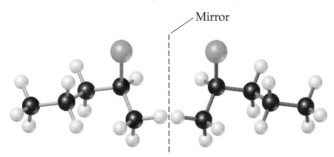

Mirror

▲ **FIGURE 6.15 The two enantiomeric forms of 2-bromopentane.** The mirror-image isomers are not superimposable on each other.

behave differently from each other. One interesting property of chiral substances is that their solutions may rotate the plane of polarized light.

Chirality is common in organic substances. It is not often observed, however, because when a chiral substance is synthesized in a typical reaction, the two enantiomers are formed in precisely the same quantity. The resulting mixture is called a *racemic mixture*, and it does not rotate the plane of polarized light because the two forms rotate the light to equal extents in opposite directions.

Many drugs are chiral substances. When a drug is administered as a racemic mixture, often only one enantiomer has beneficial results. The other is either inert, or nearly so, or may even have a harmful effect. For example, the drug *(R)*-albuterol (▼ FIGURE 6.16) is a bronchodilator used to relieve the symptoms of asthma. The enantiomer *(S)*-albuterol is not only ineffective as a bronchodilator but also actually counters the effects of *(R)*-albuterol. As another example, the nonsteroidal analgesic ibuprofen is a chiral molecule usually sold as the racemic mixture. However, a preparation consisting of just the more active enantiomer, *(S)*-ibuprofen (▼ FIGURE 6.17), relieves pain and reduces inflammation more rapidly than the racemic mixture. For this reason, the chiral version of the drug may in time come to replace the racemic one.

 GIVE IT SOME THOUGHT

What are the requirements on the four groups attached to a carbon atom in order that it be a chiral center?

(R)-Albuterol

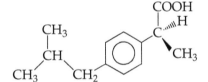

▲ **FIGURE 6.16** **(R)-Albuterol.** This compound, which acts as a bronchodilator in patients with asthma, is one member of an enantiomer pair. The other member, *(S)*-albuterol, does not have the same physiological effect.

▲ **FIGURE 6.17** **(S)-Ibuprofen.** For relieving pain and reducing inflammation, the ability of this enantiomer far outweighs that of the *(R)* isomer.

CHAPTER SUMMARY AND KEY TERMS

INTRODUCTION AND SECTION 6.1 This chapter introduces **organic chemistry**, which is the study of carbon compounds (typically compounds containing carbon–carbon bonds), and **biochemistry**, which is the study of the chemistry of living organisms. We have encountered many aspects of organic chemistry in earlier chapters. Carbon forms four bonds in its stable compounds. The C—C single bonds and the C—H bonds tend to have low reactivity. Those bonds that have a high electron density (such as multiple bonds or bonds with an atom of high electronegativity) tend to be the sites of reactivity in an organic compound. These sites of reactivity are called **functional groups**.

SECTION 6.2 The simplest types of organic compounds are hydrocarbons, those composed of only carbon and hydrogen. There are four

major kinds of hydrocarbons: alkanes, alkenes, alkynes, and aromatic hydrocarbons. **Alkanes** are composed of only C—H and C—C single bonds. **Alkenes** contain one or more carbon–carbon double bonds. **Alkynes** contain one or more carbon–carbon triple bonds. **Aromatic hydrocarbons** contain cyclic arrangements of carbon atoms bonded through both σ and delocalized π bonds. Alkanes are saturated hydrocarbons; the others are unsaturated.

Alkanes may form straight-chain, branched-chain, and cyclic arrangements. Isomers are substances that possess the same molecular formula but differ in the arrangements of atoms. In **structural isomers** the bonding arrangements of the atoms differ. Different isomers are given different systematic names. The naming of hydrocarbons is based on the longest continuous chain of carbon atoms in the structure.

The locations of **alkyl groups**, which branch off the chain, are specified by numbering along the carbon chain.

Alkanes with ring structures are called **cycloalkanes**. Alkanes are relatively unreactive. They do, however, undergo combustion in air, and their chief use is as sources of heat energy produced by combustion.

SECTION 6.3   The names of alkenes and alkynes are based on the longest continuous chain of carbon atoms that contains the multiple bond, and the location of the multiple bond is specified by a numerical prefix. Alkenes exhibit not only structural isomerism but geometric (*cis-trans*) isomerism as well. In **geometric isomers** the bonds are the same, but the molecules have different geometries. Geometric isomerism is possible in alkenes because rotation about the C=C double bond is restricted.

Alkenes and alkynes readily undergo **addition reactions** to the carbon–carbon multiple bonds. Additions of acids, such as HBr, proceed via a rate-determining step in which a proton is transferred to one of the alkene or alkyne carbon atoms. Addition reactions are difficult to carry out with aromatic hydrocarbons, but **substitution reactions** are easily accomplished in the presence of catalysts.

SECTION 6.4   The chemistry of organic compounds is dominated by the nature of their functional groups. The functional groups we have considered are

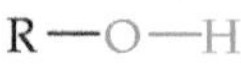

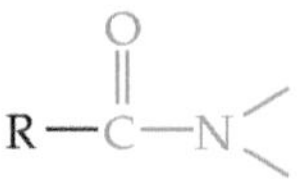

R, R', and R" represent hydrocarbon groups—for example, methyl (CH_3) or phenyl (C_6H_5).

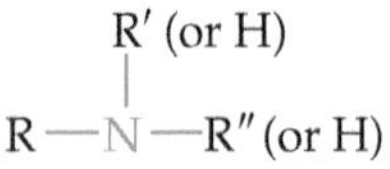

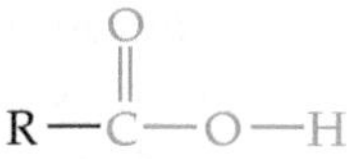

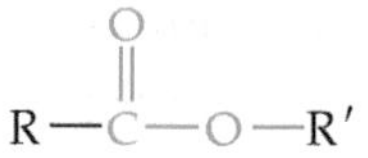

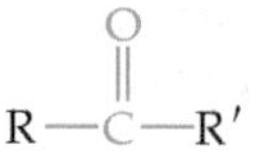

Alcohols are hydrocarbon derivatives containing one or more OH groups. **Ethers** are formed by a condensation reaction of two molecules of alcohol. Several functional groups contain the **carbonyl** (C=O) **group**, including **aldehydes**, **ketones**, **carboxylic acids**, **esters**, and **amides**. Aldehydes and ketones can be produced by oxidation of certain alcohols. Further oxidation of the aldehydes produces carboxylic acids. Carboxylic acids can form esters by a condensation reaction with alcohols, or they can form amides by a condensation reaction with amines. Esters undergo **hydrolysis** (**saponification**) in the presence of strong bases.

SECTION 6.5   Molecules that possess nonsuperimposable mirror images are termed **chiral**. The two nonsuperimposable forms of a chiral molecule are called *enantiomers*. In carbon compounds a chiral center is created when all four groups bonded to a central carbon atom are different, as in 2-bromobutane. Many of the molecules occurring in living systems, such as the amino acids, are chiral and exist in nature in only one enantiomeric form. Many drugs of importance in human medicine are chiral, and the enantiomers may produce very different biochemical effects. For this reason, synthesis of only the effective isomers of chiral drugs has become a high priority.

KEY SKILLS

- Distinguish among alkanes, alkenes, alkynes, and aromatic hydrocarbons. (Section 6.2)
- Draw hydrocarbon structures based on their names and name hydrocarbons based on their structures. (Sections 6.2 and 6.3)
- Distinguish between addition reactions and substitution reactions. (Section 6.3)
- Know the structures of the functional groups: alkene, alkyne, alcohol, carbonyl, ether, aldehyde, ketone, carboxylic acid, amine, amide. (Section 6.4)
- Understand what makes a compound chiral and be able to recognize a chiral substance. (Section 6.5)

EXERCISES

VISUALIZING CONCEPTS

6.1 All the structures shown here have the molecular formula C_8H_{18}. Which structures are the same molecule? (*Hint:* One way to answer this question is to determine the chemical name for each structure.) [Section 6.2]

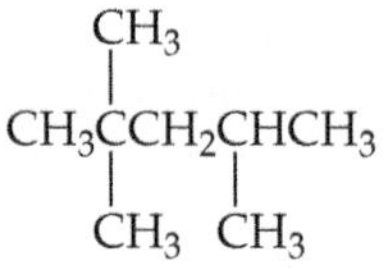

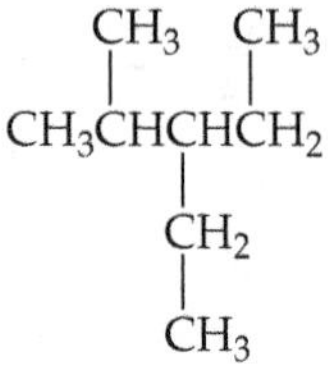

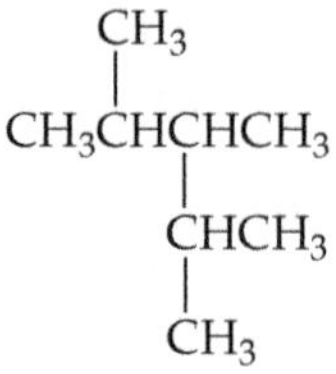

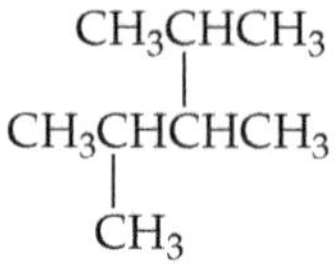

6.2 Which of these molecules is unsaturated? [Section 6.3]

$CH_3CH_2CH_2CH_3$

(a)

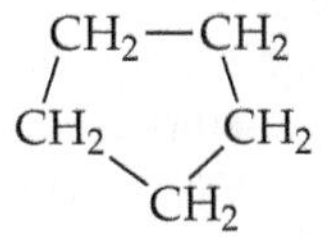

(b)

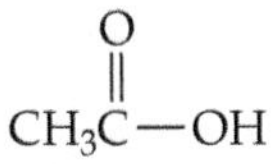

(c)

$CH_3CH{=}CHCH_3$

(d)

6.3 Which of these molecules most readily undergoes an addition reaction? [Section 6.3]

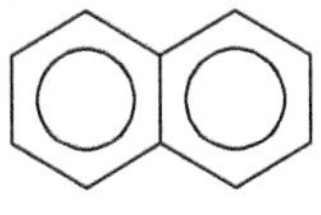

(a)

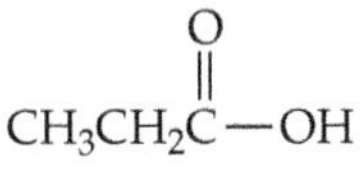

(b)

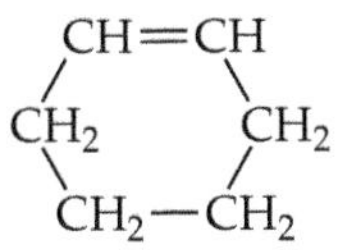

(c)

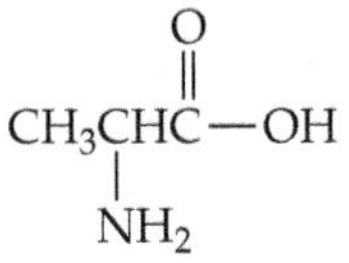

(d)

6.4 Which of these compounds would you expect to have the highest boiling point? Explain. [Section 6.4]

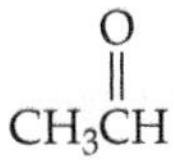

(a)

CH_3CH_2OH

(b)

$CH_3C{\equiv}CH$

(c)

(d)

6.5 Which of these compounds can be a member of an isomer pair? In each case where isomerism is possible, identify the type or types of isomerism. [Sections 6.2, 6.4]

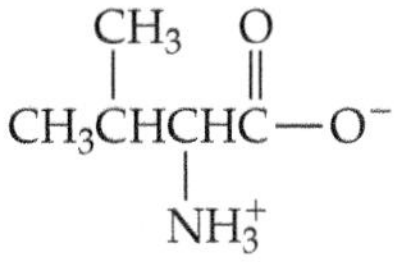

(a)

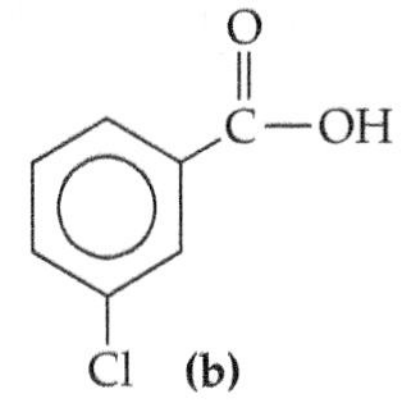

(b)

$CH_3CH_2CH{=}CHCH_3$

(c)

$CH_3CH_2CH_3$

(d)

INTRODUCTION TO ORGANIC COMPOUNDS; HYDROCARBONS (sections 6.1 and 6.2)

6.6 What are the characteristic hybrid orbitals employed by **(a)** carbon in an alkane, **(b)** carbon in a double bond in an alkene, **(c)** carbon in the benzene ring, **(d)** carbon in a triple bond in an alkyne?

6.7 What are the approximate bond angles **(a)** about carbon in an alkane, **(b)** about a doubly bonded carbon atom in an alkene, **(c)** about a triply bonded carbon atom in an alkyne?

6.8 Predict the ideal values for the bond angles about each carbon atom in the following molecule. Indicate the hybridization of orbitals for each carbon.

$$CH_3CCCH_2COOH$$

6.9 Identify the carbon atom(s) in the structure shown that has (have) each of the following hybridizations: **(a)** sp^3, **(b)** sp, **(c)** sp^2.

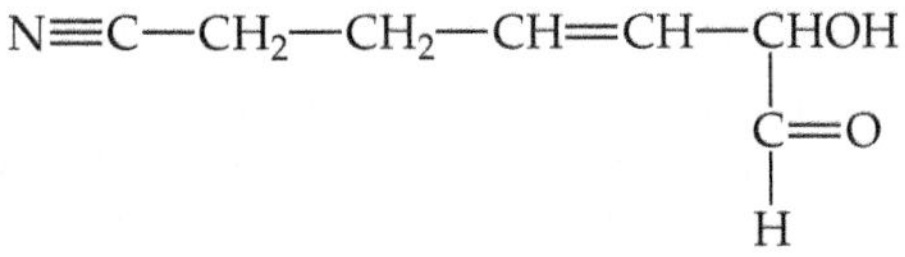

6.10 Are carbon monoxide or ammonia considered organic molecules? Why or why not?

6.11 Organic compounds containing C—O and C—Cl bonds are more reactive than simple alkane hydrocarbons. Considering the comparative values of C—H, C—C, C—O, and C—Cl bond enthalpies (Table 3.4), why is this so?

6.12 **(a)** What is the difference between a straight-chain and branched-chain alkane? **(b)** What is the difference between an alkane and an alkyl group?

6.13 What structural features help us identify a compound as **(a)** an alkane, **(b)** a cycloalkane, **(c)** an alkene, **(d)** an alkyne, **(e)** a saturated hydrocarbon, **(f)** an aromatic hydrocarbon?

6.14 Give the the name or condensed structural formula, as appropriate:

(a) 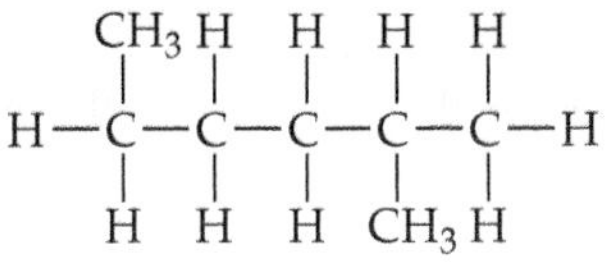

(b) 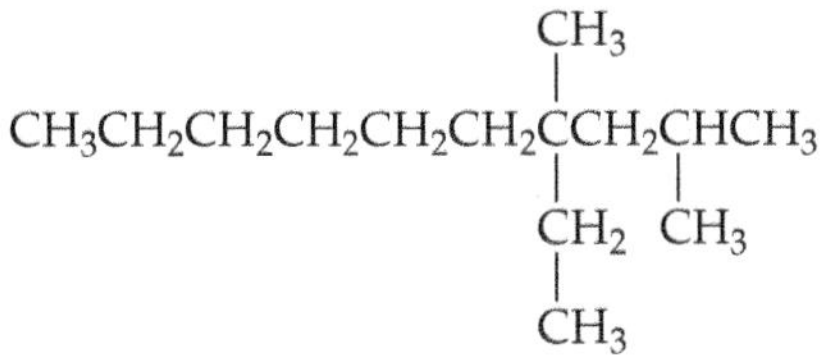

(c) 2-methylheptane
(d) 4-ethyl-2,3-dimethyloctane
(e) 1,2-dimethylcyclohexane

6.15 Give the name or condensed structural formula, as appropriate:

(a) 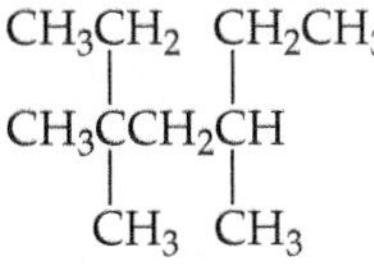

(b) 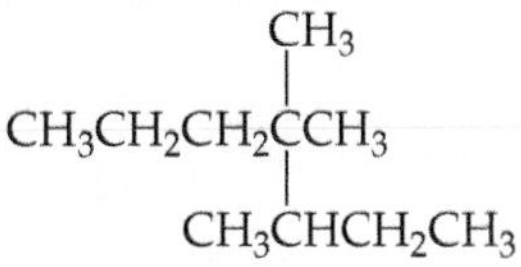

(c) 2,5,6-trimethylnonane

(d) 3-propyl-4,5-methyldecane

(e) 1-ethyl-3-methylcyclohexane

6.16 Give the name or condensed structural formula, as appropriate:

(a) 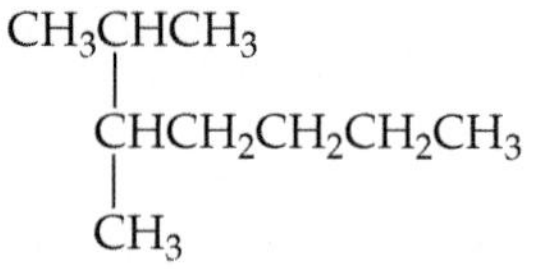 CH₃CHCH₃
       |
       CHCH₂CH₂CH₂CH₃
       |
       CH₃

(b) 2,2-dimethylpentane

(c) 4-ethyl-1,1-dimethylcyclohexane

(d) (CH₃)₂CHCH₂CH₂C(CH₃)₃

(e) CH₃CH₂CH(C₂H₅)CH₂CH₂CH₂CH₃

6.17 Give the name or condensed structural formula, as appropriate:

(a) 3-phenylpentane

(b) 2,3-dimethylhexane

(c) 2-ethyl-2-methylhepane

(d) CH₃CH₂CH(CH₃)CH₂CH(CH₃)₂

(e) 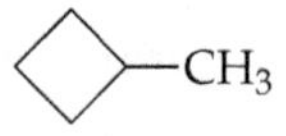 ◇—CH₃

6.18 What is the octane number of a mixture that is 35% heptane and 65% isooctane?

6.19 Describe two ways in which the octane number of a gasoline consisting of alkanes can be increased.

ALKENES, ALKYNES, AND AROMATIC HYDROCARBONS (section 6.3)

6.20 (a) Why are alkanes said to be saturated? (b) Is C₄H₆ a saturated hydrocarbon? Why or why not?

6.21 (a) Is the compound CH₃CH=CH₂ saturated or unsaturated? Explain. (b) What is wrong with the formula CH₃CH₂CH=CH₃?

6.22 Give the molecular formula of a hydrocarbon containing five carbon atoms that is (a) an alkane, (b) a cycloalkane, (c) an alkene, (d) an alkyne. Which are saturated and which are unsaturated hydrocarbons?

6.23 Give the molecular formula of a cyclic alkane, a cyclic alkene, a linear alkyne, and an aromatic hydrocarbon that in each case contains six carbon atoms. Which are saturated and which are unsaturated hydrocarbons?

6.24 Enediynes are a class of compounds that include some antibiotic drugs. Draw the structure of an "enediyne" fragment that contains six carbons in a row. (*Hint: di* means "two.")

6.25 Give the general formula for any cyclic alkene, that is, a cyclic hydrocarbon with one double bond.

6.26 Write the condensed structural formulas for as many alkenes and alkynes as you can think of that have the molecular formula C₆H₁₀.

6.27 Draw all the possible noncyclic structural isomers of C₅H₁₀. Name each compound.

6.28 Name or write the condensed structural formula for the following compounds:

(a) *trans* -2-pentene

(b) 2,5-dimethyl-4-octene

(c)

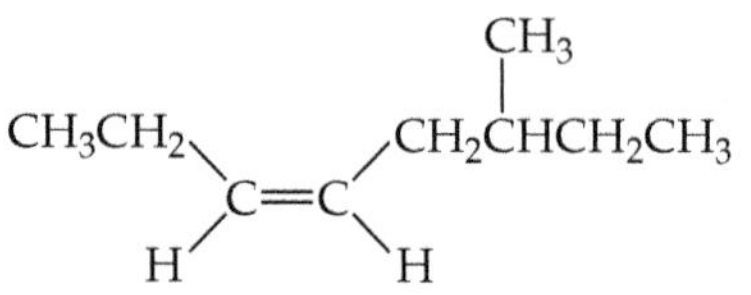

(d) 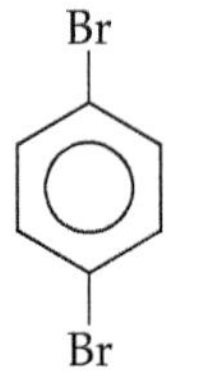 Br

        Br

(e) 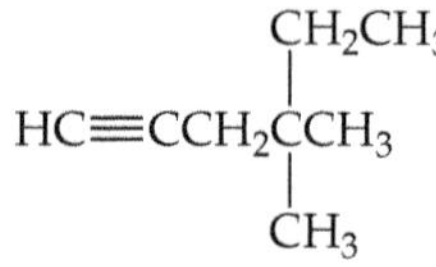
       CH₂CH₃
       |
HC≡CCH₂CCH₃
       |
       CH₃

6.29 Name or write the condensed structural formula for the following compounds:

(a) 4-methyl-2-pentene

(b) *cis*-2,5-dimethyl-3-hexene

(c) ortho-dimethylbenzene

(d) HC≡CCH₂CH₃

(e) *trans*-CH₃CH=CHCH₂CH₂CH₂CH₃

6.30 Why is geometric isomerism possible for alkenes but not for alkanes and alkynes?

6.31 Draw all structural and geometric isomers of butene and name them.

6.32 Indicate whether each of the following molecules is capable of geometrical (cis-trans) isomerism. For those that are, draw the structures: (a) 1,1-dichloro-1-butene, (b) 2,4-dichloro-2-butene, (c) 1,4-dichlorobenzene, (d) 4,5-dimethyl-2-pentyne.

6.33 Draw the three distinct geometric isomers of 2,4-hexadiene.

6.34 (a) What is the difference between a substitution reaction and an addition reaction? Which one is commonly observed with alkenes and which one with aromatic hydrocarbons? (b) Using condensed structural formulas, write the balanced equation for the addition reaction of 2-pentene with Br₂ and name the resulting compound. (c) Write a balanced chemical equation for the substitution reaction of Cl₂ with benzene to make *para*-dichlorobenzene in the presence of FeCl₃ as a catalyst.

6.35 Using condensed structural formulas, write a balanced chemical equation for each of the following reactions: (a) hydrogenation of cyclohexene; (b) addition of H₂O to *trans*-2-pentene using H₂SO₄ as a catalyst (two products); (c) reaction of 2-chloropropane with benzene in the presence of AlCl₃.

6.36 (a) When cyclopropane is treated with HI, 1-iodopropane is formed. A similar type of reaction does not occur with cyclopentane or cyclohexane. How do you account for the reactivity of cyclopropane? (b) Suggest a method of preparing ethylbenzene, starting with benzene and ethylene as the only organic reagents.

6.37 **(a)** One test for the presence of an alkene is to add a small amount of bromine, a red-brown liquid, and look for the disappearance of the red-brown color. This test does not work for detecting the presence of an aromatic hydrocarbon. Explain. **(b)** Write a series of reactions leading to *para*-bromoethylbenzene, beginning with benzene and using other reagents as needed. What isomeric side products might also be formed?

6.38 The rate law for addition of Br_2 to an alkene is first order in Br_2 and first order in the alkene. Does this fact prove that the mechanism of addition of Br_2 to an alkene proceeds in the same manner as for addition of HBr? Explain.

6.39 Describe the intermediate that is thought to form in the addition of a hydrogen halide to an alkene, using cyclohexene as the alkene in your description.

6.40 The molar heat of combustion of gaseous cyclopropane is -2089 kJ/mol; that for gaseous cyclopentane is -3317 kJ/mol. Calculate the heat of combustion per CH_2 group in the two cases, and account for the difference.

6.41 The heat of combustion of decahydronaphthalene ($C_{10}H_{18}$) is -6286 kJ/mol. The heat of combustion of naphthalene ($C_{10}H_8$) is -5157 kJ/mol. [In both cases $CO_2(g)$ and $H_2O(l)$ are the products.] Using these data and data in Appendix C, calculate the heat of hydrogenation of naphthalene. Does this value provide any evidence for aromatic character in naphthalene?

FUNCTIONAL GROUPS AND CHIRALITY (sections 6.4 and 6.5)

6.42 Identify the functional groups in each of the following compounds:

(a) H_3C-CH_2-OH

(c) $H_3C-\overset{\displaystyle H}{N}-CH_2CH=CH_2$

(b)

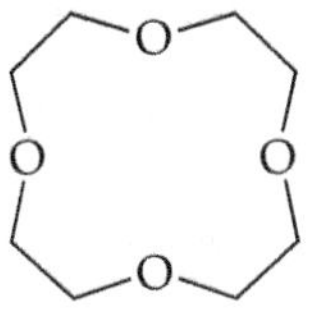

(d)

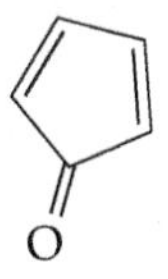

(e) $CH_3CH_2CH_2CH_2CHO$

(f) $CH_3C\equiv CCH_2COOH$

6.43 Identify the functional groups in each of the following compounds:

(a)

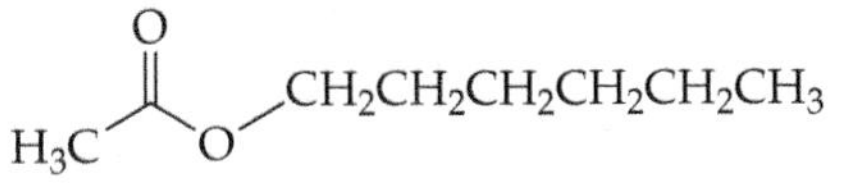

(b)

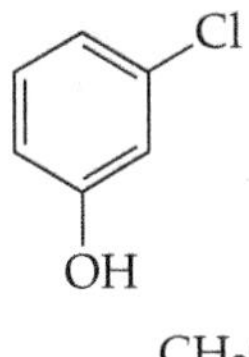

(c)

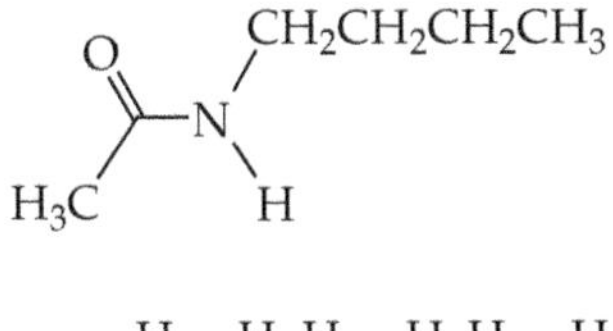

(d)

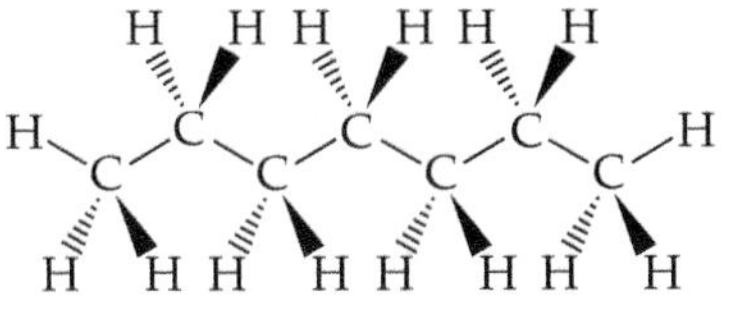

(e)

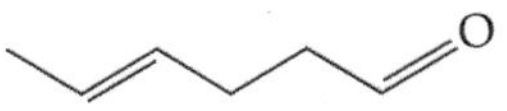

(f)

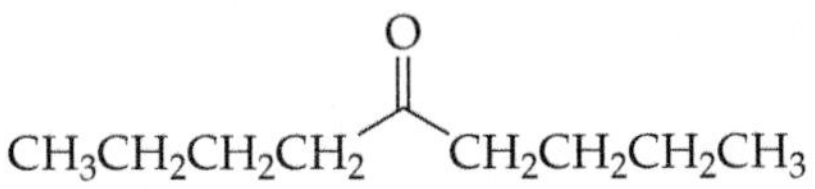

6.44 Give the structural formula for **(a)** an aldehyde that is an isomer of acetone, **(b)** an ether that is an isomer of 1-propanol.

6.45 **(a)** Give the empirical formula and structural formula for a cyclic ether containing four carbon atoms in the ring. **(b)** Write the structural formula for a straight-chain compound that is a structural isomer of your answer to part (a).

6.46 The IUPAC name for a carboxylic acid is based on the name of the hydrocarbon with the same number of carbon atoms. The ending *-oic* is appended, as in ethanoic acid, which is the IUPAC name for acetic acid. Draw the structure of the following acids: **(a)** methanoic acid, **(b)** pentanoic acid, **(c)** 2-chloro-3-methyldecanoic acid.

6.47 Aldehydes and ketones can be named in a systematic way by counting the number of carbon atoms (including the carbonyl carbon) that they contain. The name of the aldehyde or ketone is based on the hydrocarbon with the same number of carbon atoms. The ending *-al* for aldehyde or *-one* for ketone is added as appropriate. Draw the structural formulas for the following aldehydes or ketones: **(a)** propanal, **(b)** 2-pentanone, **(c)** 3-methyl-2-butanone, **(d)** 2-methylbutanal.

6.48 Draw the condensed structure of the compounds formed by condensation reactions between **(a)** benzoic acid and ethanol, **(b)** ethanoic acid and methylamine, **(c)** acetic acid and phenol. Name the compound in each case.

6.49 Draw the condensed structures of the compounds formed from **(a)** butanoic acid and methanol, **(b)** benzoic acid and 2-propanol, **(c)** propanoic acid and dimethylamine. Name the compound in each case.

6.50 Write a balanced chemical equation using condensed structural formulas for the saponification (base hydrolysis) of **(a)** methyl propionate, **(b)** phenyl acetate.

6.51 Write a balanced chemical equation using condensed structural formulas for **(a)** the formation of butyl propionate from the appropriate acid and alcohol, **(b)** the saponification (base hydrolysis) of methyl benzoate.

6.52 Would you expect pure acetic acid to be a strongly hydrogen-bonded substance? How do the melting and boiling points of the substance (16.7 °C and 118 °C) support your answer?

6.53 Acetic anhydride is formed from acetic acid in a condensation reaction that involves the removal of a molecule of water from between two acetic acid molecules. Write the chemical equation for this process, and show the structure of acetic anhydride.

6.54 Write the condensed structural formula for each of the following compounds: (**a**) 2-pentanol, (**b**) 1,2-propanediol, (**c**) ethyl acetate, (**d**) diphenyl ketone, (**e**) methyl ethyl ether.

6.55 Write the condensed structural formula for each of the following compounds: (**a**) 2-ethyl-1-hexanol, (**b**) methyl phenyl ketone, (**c**) *para*-bromobenzoic acid, (**d**) ethyl butyl ether, (**e**) *N, N*-dimethylbenzamide.

6.56 Draw the structure for 2-bromo-2-chloro-3-methylpentane, and indicate any chiral carbons in the molecule.

6.57 Does 3-chloro-3-methylhexane have optical isomers? Why or why not?

ADDITIONAL EXERCISES

6.58 Draw the condensed structural formulas for two different molecules with the formula C_3H_4O.

6.59 How many structural isomers are there for a five-member straight carbon chain with one double bond? For a six-member straight carbon chain with two double bonds?

6.60 Draw the condensed structural formulas for the cis and trans isomers of 2-pentene. Can cyclopentene exhibit cis-trans isomerism? Explain.

6.61 If a molecule is an "ene-one," what functional groups must it have?

6.62 Write the structural formulas for as many alcohols as you can think of that have empirical formula C_3H_6O.

6.63 Identify each of the functional groups in these molecules:

(a)

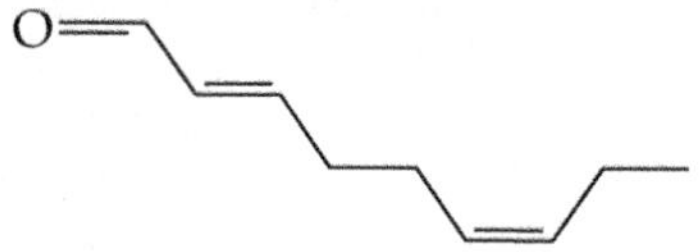

(Responsible for the odor of cucumbers)

(b)

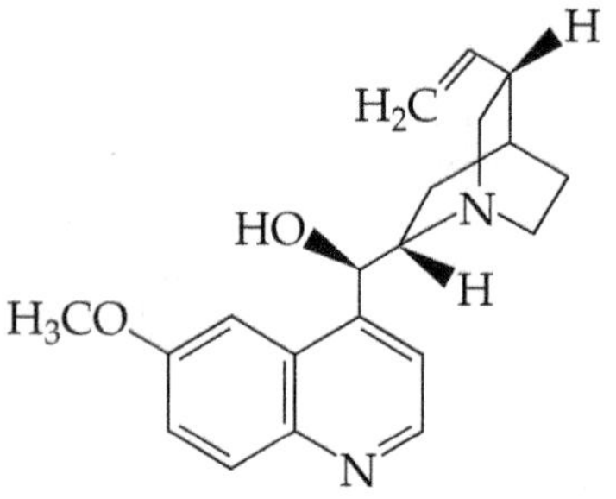

(Quinine — an antimalarial drug)

(c)

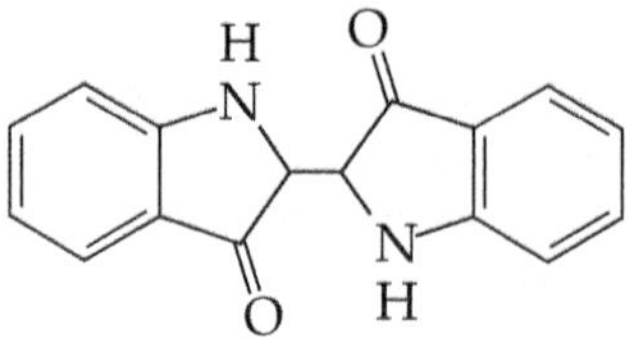

(Indigo — a blue dye)

(d)

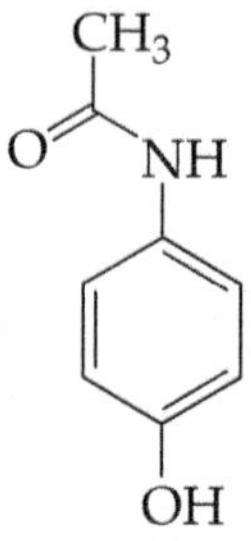

(Acetaminophen — aka Tylenol)

6.64 Write a condensed structural formula for each of the following: (**a**) an acid with the formula $C_4H_8O_2$, (**b**) a cyclic ketone with the formula C_5H_8O, (**c**) a dihydroxy compound with the formula $C_3H_8O_2$, (**d**) a cyclic ester with the formula $C_5H_8O_2$.

6.65 Although carboxylic acids and alcohols both contain an —OH group, one is acidic in water and the other is not. Explain the difference.

[6.66] Indole smells terrible in high concentrations but has a pleasant floral-like odor when highly diluted. Its structure is

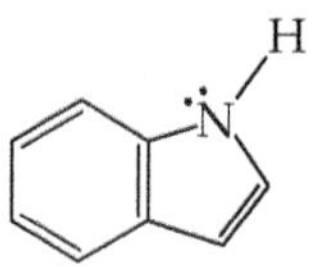

The molecule is planar, and the nitrogen is a very weak base, with $K_b = 2 \times 10^{-12}$. Explain how this information indicates that the indole molecule is aromatic.

6.67 Locate the chiral carbon atoms, if any, in each molecule:

(**a**) $HOCH_2CH_2\overset{\displaystyle O}{\overset{\|}{C}}CH_2OH$

(**b**) $HOCH_2\overset{\displaystyle OH}{\overset{|}{C}H}\overset{\displaystyle O}{\overset{\|}{C}}CH_2OH$

(**c**) $HO\overset{\displaystyle O}{\overset{\|}{C}}CH\overset{\displaystyle CH_3}{\overset{|}{C}H}C_2H_5$
$\quad\quad\quad\underset{\displaystyle NH_2}{|}$

INTEGRATIVE EXERCISES

6.68 Explain why the boiling point of ethanol (78 °C) is much higher than that of its isomer, dimethyl ether (−25 °C), and why the boiling point of CH_2F_2 (−52 °C) is far above that of CH_4 (−128 °C).

[6.69] An unknown organic compound is found on elemental analysis to contain 68.1% carbon, 13.7% hydrogen, and 18.2% oxygen by mass. It is slightly soluble in water. Upon careful oxidation it is converted into a compound that behaves chemically like a ketone and contains 69.7% carbon, 11.7% hydrogen, and 18.6% oxygen by mass. Indicate two or more reasonable structures for the unknown.

6.70 An organic compound is analyzed and found to contain 66.7% carbon, 11.2% hydrogen, and 22.1% oxygen by mass. The compound boils at 79.6 °C. At 100 °C and 0.970 atm, the vapor has a density of 2.28 g/L. The compound has a carbonyl group and cannot be oxidized to a carboxylic acid. Suggest a structure for the compound.

[6.71] An unknown substance is found to contain only carbon and hydrogen. It is a liquid that boils at 49 °C at 1 atm pressure. Upon analysis it is found to contain 85.7% carbon and 14.3% hydrogen by mass. At 100 °C and 735 torr, the vapor of this unknown has a density of 2.21 g/L. When it is dissolved in hexane solution and bromine water is added, no reaction occurs. What is the identity of the unknown compound?

7.1 CLASSIFICATIONS OF SOLIDS
We see that solids can be classified according to the types of bonding interactions that hold the atoms together. This classification helps us make general predictions about the properties of solids.

7.2 MOLECULAR SOLIDS
We take a brief look at the solids that form when molecules are held together by weak intermolecular forces.

7.3 COVALENT-NETWORK SOLIDS
We learn about solids in which the atoms are held together by extended networks of covalent bonds. We learn how the electronic structure and properties of semiconductors differ from those of metals.

7.4 POLYMERIC SOLIDS
We investigate *polymers*—long chainlike molecules in which the motif of a small molecule is repeated many times over. We see how both molecular shape and interactions between polymer chains affect the physical properties of polymers.

THE HARD DRIVE OF A COMPUTER is made from an extremely smooth glass disc coated with a thin layer of a magnetic alloy of cobalt. To store and retrieve information, the read/write head must glide over the disc at a height of ~1 μm (less than 1/200 the width of a human hair) while the disk moves at speeds in excess of 7000 rpm. Devices such as this would not be possible without advanced solid-state materials.

7.5 NANOMATERIALS
We learn how the physical and chemical properties of materials change when their crystals become very small. These effects begin to occur when materials have sizes on the order of 1–100 nm. We explore lower-dimensional forms of carbon—fullerenes, carbon nanotubes, and graphene.

SOLIDS AND MODERN MATERIALS

MODERN DEVICES LIKE COMPUTERS and cell phones are built from solids with very specific physical properties. For example, the integrated circuit that is at the heart of many electronic devices is built from semiconductors like silicon, metals like copper, and insulators like hafnium oxide. Hard drives, which store information in computers and other devices, consist of a thin layer of a magnetic alloy deposited on glass substrate.

Scientists and engineers turn almost exclusively to solids for materials used in many other technologies: alloys for magnets and airplane turbines, semiconductors for solar cells and light-emitting diodes, polymers for packaging and biomedical applications. Chemists have contributed to the discovery and development of new materials either by inventing new substances or by developing the means for processing natural materials to form substances that have specific electrical, magnetic, optical, or mechanical properties. In this chapter, we explore the structures and properties of solids. As we do so, we will examine some of the solid materials used in modern technology.

7.1 | CLASSIFICATIONS OF SOLIDS

Solids can be as hard as diamond or as soft as wax. Some readily conduct electricity, whereas others do not. The shapes of some solids can easily be manipulated, while others are brittle and resistant to any change in shape. The physical properties as well as the structures of solids are dictated by the types of bonds that hold the atoms in place. We can classify solids according to those forces (▼ FIGURE 7.1).

Metallic solids are held together by a delocalized "sea" of collectively shared valence electrons. This form of bonding allows metals to conduct electricity. It is also responsible for the fact that most metals are relatively strong without being brittle. **Ionic solids** are held together by the mutual attraction between cations and anions. Differences between ionic and metallic bonding make the electrical and mechanical properties of ionic solids very different from those of metals. **Covalent-network solids** are held together by an extended network of covalent bonds. This type of bonding can result in materials that are extremely hard, like diamond, and it is also responsible for the unique properties of semiconductors. **Molecular solids** are held together by the intermolecular forces we studied in Chapter 5: dispersion forces, dipole–dipole interactions, and hydrogen bonds. Because these forces are relatively weak, molecular solids tend to be soft and have low melting points.

We will also consider two classes of solids that do not fall neatly into the preceding categories: polymers and nanomaterials. **Polymers** contain long chains of atoms, where the atoms within a given chain are connected by covalent bonds and adjacent chains held to one another largely by weaker intermolecular forces. Polymers are normally stronger and have higher melting points than molecular solids, and they are more flexible than metallic, ionic, or covalent-network solids. **Nanomaterials** are solids in which the dimensions of individual crystals have been reduced to the order of 1–100 nm. As we will see, the properties of conventional materials change when their crystals become this small.

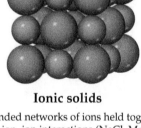

Metallic solids

Extended networks of atoms held together by metallic bonding (Cu, Fe)

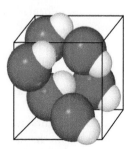

Ionic solids

Extended networks of ions held together by ion–ion interactions (NaCl, MgO)

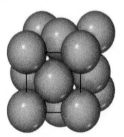

Covalent-network solids

Extended networks of atoms held together by covalent bonds (C, Si)

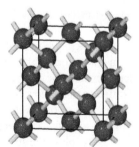

Molecular solids

Discrete molecules held together by intermolecular forces (HBr, H_2O)

▲ FIGURE 7.1 **Classifications of solids according to predominant bonding type.**

7.2 | MOLECULAR SOLIDS

Molecular solids consist of atoms or molecules held together by dipole–dipole forces, dispersion forces, and/or hydrogen bonds. Because these intermolecular forces are weak, molecular solids are soft and have relatively low melting points (usually below 200 °C). Most substances that are gases or liquids at room temperature form molecular solids at low temperature. Examples include Ar, H_2O, and CO_2.

The properties of molecular solids depend in large part on the strengths of the forces between molecules. Consider, for example, the properties of sucrose (table sugar, $C_{12}H_{22}O_{11}$). Each sucrose molecule has eight –OH groups, which allows for the formation of multiple hydrogen bonds. Consequently, sucrose exists as a crystalline solid at room temperature, and its melting point, 184 °C, is relatively high for a molecular solid.

Molecular shape is also important because it dictates how efficiently molecules pack together in three dimensions. Benzene (C_6H_6), for example, is a highly symmetrical planar molecule. ∞(Section 3.6) It has a higher melting point than toluene, a compound in which one of the hydrogen atoms of benzene has been replaced by a CH_3 group (▶ FIGURE 7.2). The lower symmetry of toluene molecules prevents them from packing as efficiently as benzene molecules. As a result, the intermolecular forces that depend on close contact are not as effective and the melting point is lower. In contrast, the boiling point of toluene is higher than that of benzene, indicating that the intermolecular attractive forces are larger in liquid toluene than in liquid benzene. The melting and boiling points of phenol, another substituted benzene shown in Figure 7.2, are higher than those of benzene because the OH group of phenol can form hydrogen bonds.

▲ **GO FIGURE**

In which substance, benzene or toluene, are the intermolecular forces stronger? In which substance do the molecules pack

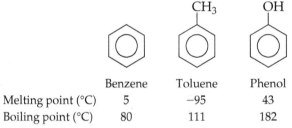

	Benzene	Toluene	Phenol
Melting point (°C)	5	−95	43
Boiling point (°C)	80	111	182

▲ **FIGURE 7.2 Melting and boiling points for benzene, toluene, and phenol.**

7.3 | COVALENT-NETWORK SOLIDS

Covalent-network solids consist of atoms held together in large networks by covalent bonds. Because covalent bonds are much stronger than intermolecular forces, these solids are much harder and have higher melting points than molecular solids. Diamond and graphite, two allotropes of carbon, are two of the most familiar covalent-network solids. Other examples are silicon, germanium, quartz (SiO_2), silicon carbide (SiC), and boron nitride (BN).

In diamond, each carbon atom is bonded tetrahedrally to four other carbon atoms (▼ FIGURE 7.3). The structure of diamond can be derived from the zinc blende structure if carbon atoms replace both the zinc and sulfide ions. The carbon atoms are sp^3-hybridized and held together by strong carbon–carbon single covalent bonds. The strength and directionality of these bonds make diamond the hardest known material. For this reason, industrial-grade diamonds are employed in saw blades used for the

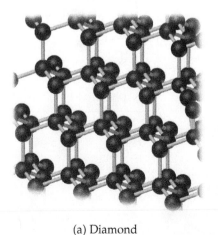

(a) Diamond   (b) Graphite

◀ **FIGURE 7.3 The structures of (a) diamond and (b) graphite.** The blue color in (b) is added to emphasize the planarity of the carbon layers.

most demanding cutting jobs. The stiff, interconnected bond network is also responsible for the fact that diamond is one of the best-known thermal conductors. Not surprisingly, diamond has a high melting point, 3550 °C.

In graphite (Figure 7.3b), the carbon atoms form covalently bonded layers that are held together by intermolecular forces. Graphite has a hexagonal unit cell containing two layers offset so that the carbon atoms in a given layer sit over the middle of the hexagons of the layer below. Each carbon is covalently bonded to three other carbons in the same layer to form interconnected hexagonal rings. The distance between adjacent carbon atoms in the plane, 1.42 Å, is very close to the C—C distance in benzene, 1.395 Å. In fact, the bonding resembles that of benzene, with delocalized π bonds extending over the layers. ∞∞(Section 4.6) Electrons move freely through the delocalized orbitals, making graphite a good electrical conductor along the layers. (In fact, graphite is used as a conducting electrode in batteries.) These sp^2-hybridized sheets of carbon atoms are separated by 3.35 Å from one another, and the sheets are held together only by dispersion forces. Thus, the layers readily slide past one another when rubbed, giving graphite a greasy feel. This tendency is enhanced when impurity atoms are trapped between the layers, as is typically the case in commercial forms of the material.

Graphite is used as a lubricant and as the "lead" in pencils. The enormous differences in physical properties of graphite and diamond—both of which are pure carbon—arise from differences in their three-dimensional structure and bonding.

Semiconductors

Silicon and germanium lie immediately below carbon in the periodic table. Like carbon, each of these elements has four valence electrons, just the right number to satisfy the octet rule by forming single covalent bonds with four neighbors. Hence, silicon and germanium, as well as the gray form of tin, crystallize with the same infinite network of covalent bonds as diamond.

When atomic s and p orbitals overlap, they form bonding molecular orbitals and antibonding molecular orbitals. Each pair of s orbitals overlaps to give one bonding and one antibonding molecular orbital, whereas the p orbitals overlap to give three bonding and three antibonding molecular orbitals. The extended network of bonds leads to the formation of the same type of bands we saw in discussing the electronic structures of metals in Section 4.8. The band that forms from bonding molecular orbitals is called the **valence band**, and the band that forms from antibonding orbitals is called the **conduction band** (▼ FIGURE 7.4). In a semiconductor, the valence band is filled with electrons and the conduction band is empty. These two bands are separated by an energy band gap, E_g.

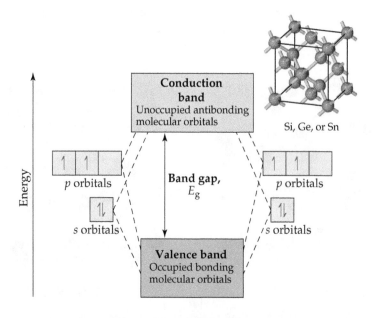

▶ FIGURE 7.4 **The electronic band structure of semiconductors that have the diamond crystal structure.**

Semiconductors can be divided into two classes, **elemental semiconductors**, which contain only one type of atom, and **compound semiconductors**, which contain two or more elements. The elemental semiconductors all come from group 4A. As we move down the periodic table, bond distances increase, which decreases orbital overlap. This decrease in overlap reduces the difference between the bonding molecular orbitals of the valence band and the antibonding molecular orbitals of the conduction band. As a result, the **band gap** decreases on going from diamond (5.5 eV) to silicon (1.11 eV) to germanium (0.67 eV) to gray tin (0.08 eV). Moving one element down to lead, the band gap collapses altogether. As a result, lead has the structure and properties of a metal.

Note that in discussing semiconductors, the electron volt, eV, is the preferred energy unit: $1 \text{ eV} = 1.602 \times 10^{-19}$ J. *

Compound semiconductors maintain the same *average* valence electron count as elemental semiconductors—four per atom. For example, when gallium (group 3A) and arsenic (group 5A) combine to form gallium arsenide, GaAs, each Ga atom contributes three electrons and each As atom contributes five, which averages out to four per atom—the same number as in silicon or germanium. Hence, GaAs is a semiconductor. Other examples are InP, where indium contributes three valence electrons and phosphorus contributes five, and CdTe, where cadmium provides two valence electrons and tellurium contributes six. In both cases, the average is again four valence electrons per atom. GaAs, InP, and CdTe all crystallize with a zinc blende structure.

There is a tendency for the band gap of a compound semiconductor to increase as the difference in group numbers increases. For example, the band gap in a Ge semiconductor (made up of only group 4A atoms) is 0.67 eV, but the gap in a GaAs semiconductor (made up of 3A atoms and 5A atoms) is 1.43 eV. If we increase the difference in group number to four, as in ZnSe (groups 2B and 6A), the band gap increases to 2.70 eV. Increasing the horizontal separation of the elements even more leads to a band gap of 3.05 eV in CuBr. This progression is a result of the transition from pure covalent bonding in elemental semiconductors to polar covalent bonding in compound semiconductors. As the difference in electronegativity of the elements increases, the bonding becomes more polar and the band gap increases.

Electrical engineers manipulate both the orbital overlap and the bond polarity to control the band gaps of compound semiconductors for use in a wide range of electrical and optical devices. The band gaps of several elemental and compound semiconductors are given in ▼ TABLE 7.1.

TABLE 7.1 • Band Gaps of Select Elemental and Compound Semiconductors

Material	Structure Type	Band Gap Energy, eV[†]
Si	Diamond	1.11
AlP	Zinc blende	2.43
Ge	Diamond	0.67
GaAs	Zinc blende	1.43
ZnSe	Zinc blende	2.58
CuBr	Zinc blende	3.05
Sn[‡]	Diamond	0.08
InSb	Zinc blende	0.18
CdTe	Zinc blende	1.50

	13 **Al**	14 **Si**	15 **P**
30 **Zn**	31 **Ga**	32 **Ge**	33 **As**	34 **Se**
48 **Cd**	49 **In**	50 **Sn**	51 **Sb**	52 **Te**

[†] Band gap energies are room temperature values, $1 \text{ eV} = 1.602 \times 10^{-19}$ J.
[‡] These data are for gray tin, the semiconducting allotrope of tin. The other allotrope, white tin, is a metal.

*In some cases it is useful to use the *molar equivalent* of an electron volt, that is, the kinetic energy that would be gained by 1 mol of electrons passing through a potential difference of 1 V. This number is obtained by multiplying 1 eV by Avogadro's number and is equal to 96.48534 kJ/mol.

SAMPLE EXERCISE 7.1	Qualitative Comparison of Semiconductor Band Gaps

Will GaP have a larger or smaller band gap than ZnS? Will it have a larger or smaller band gap than GaN?

SOLUTION

Analyze The size of the band gap depends on the vertical and horizontal positions of the elements in the periodic table. The band gap will increase when either of the following conditions is met: (1) The elements are located higher up in the periodic table, where enhanced orbital overlap leads to a larger splitting between bonding and antibonding orbitals, or (2) the horizontal separation between the elements increases, which leads to an increase in the electronegativity difference and bond polarity.

Plan We must look at the periodic table and compare the relative positions of the elements in each case.

Solve Gallium is in the fourth period and group 3A. Phosphorus is in the third period and group 5A. Zinc and sulfur are in the same periods as gallium and phosphorus, respectively. However, zinc, in group 2B, is one element to the left of gallium; sulfur in group 6A is one element to the right of phosphorus. Thus, we would expect the electronegativity difference to be larger for ZnS, which should result in ZnS having a larger band gap than GaP.

For both GaP and GaN the more electropositive element is gallium. So we need only compare the positions of the more electronegative elements, P and N. Nitrogen is located above phosphorus in group 5A. Therefore, based on increased orbital overlap, we would expect GaN to have a larger band gap than GaP.

Check External references show that the band gap of GaP is 2.26 eV, ZnS is 3.6 eV, and GaN is 3.4 eV.

PRACTICE EXERCISE

Will ZnSe have a larger or smaller band gap than ZnS?

Answer: Because zinc is common to both compounds and selenium is below sulfur in the periodic table, the band gap of ZnSe will be smaller than ZnS.

Semiconductor Doping

The electrical conductivity of a semiconductor is influenced by the presence of small numbers of impurity atoms. The process of adding controlled amounts of impurity atoms to a material is known as **doping**. Consider what happens when a few phosphorus atoms (known as dopants) replace silicon atoms in a silicon crystal. In pure Si all of the valence-band molecular orbitals are filled and all of the conduction-band molecular orbitals are empty, as ▼ FIGURE 7.5(a) shows. Because phosphorus has five valence electrons but

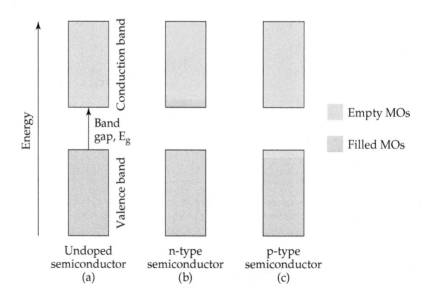

▶ FIGURE 7.5 **The addition of small amounts of impurities (doping) to a semiconductor changes the electronic properties of the material.**

silicon has only four, the "extra" electrons that come with the dopant phosphorus atoms are forced to occupy the conduction band [Figure 7.5(b)]. The doped material is called an *n-type* semiconductor, *n* signifying that the number of *n*egatively charged electrons in the conduction band has increased. These extra electrons can move very easily in the conduction band. Thus, just a few parts per million (ppm) of phosphorus in silicon can increase silicon's intrinsic conductivity by a factor of a million!

The dramatic change in conductivity in response to the addition of a trace amount of a dopant means that extreme care must be taken to control the impurities in semiconductors. It also provides an opportunity for controlling the electrical conductivity through precise control of the type and concentration of dopants.

It is also possible to dope semiconductors with atoms that have fewer valence electrons than the host material. Consider what happens when a few aluminum atoms replace silicon atoms in a silicon crystal. Aluminum has only three valence electrons compared to silicon's four. Thus, there are electron vacancies, known as **holes**, in the valence band when silicon is doped with aluminum [Figure 7.5(c)]. Since the negatively charged electron is not there, the hole can be thought of as having a positive charge. Any adjacent electron that jumps into the hole leaves behind a new hole. Thus, the positive hole moves about in the lattice like a particle.* A material like this is called a *p-type* semiconductor, *p* signifying that the number of *p*ositive holes in the material has increased.

As with n-type conductivity, p-type dopant levels of only parts per million can lead to a millionfold increase in conductivity—but in this case, the holes in the valence band are doing the conduction [Figure 7.5(c)].

The junction of an n-type semiconductor with a p-type semiconductor forms the basis for diodes, transistors, solar cells, and other devices.

SAMPLE EXERCISE 7.2 | **Identifying Types of Semiconductors**

Which of the following elements, if doped into silicon, would yield an n-type semiconductor: Ga, As, or C?

SOLUTION

Analyze An n-type semiconductor means that the dopant atoms must have more valence electrons than the host material. Silicon is the host material in this case.

Plan We must look at the periodic table and determine the number of valence electrons associated with Si, Ga, As, and C. The elements with more valence electrons than silicon are the ones that will produce an n-type material upon doping.

Solve Si is in column 4A, and so has four valence electrons. Ga is in column 3A, and so has three valence electrons. As is in column 5A, and so has five valence electrons; C is in column 4A, and so has four valence electrons. Therefore, As, if doped into silicon, would yield an n-type semiconductor.

PRACTICE EXERCISE

Suggest an element that could be used to dope silicon to yield a p-type material.

Answer: Because Si is in group 4A, we need to pick an element in group 3A. Boron and aluminum are both good choices—both are in group 3A. In the semiconductor industry boron and aluminum are commonly used dopants for silicon.

7.4 | POLYMERIC SOLIDS

In nature we find many substances of very high molecular weight, running into millions of amu, that make up much of the structure of living organisms and tissues. Some examples are starch and cellulose, which abound in plants, as well as proteins, which are found in both plants and animals. In 1827 Jons Jakob Berzelius coined the word **polymer** (from the Greek *polys*, "many," and *meros*, "parts") to denote molecular substances of high molecular weight formed by the *polymerization* (joining together) of **monomers**, molecules with low molecular weight.

---

*This movement is analogous to watching people changing seats in a classroom; you can watch the people (electrons) move about the seats (atoms), or you can watch the empty seats (holes) "move."

Solid-State Lighting

Artificial lighting is so widespread we take it for granted. Major savings in energy would be realized if incandescent lights can be replaced by light-emitting diodes (LEDs). Because LEDs are made from semiconductors, this is an appropriate place to take a closer look at the operation of an LED.

The heart of an LED is a p–n diode, which is formed by bringing an n-type semiconductor in contact with a p-type semiconductor. In the junction where they meet there are very few electrons or holes to carry the charge and the conductivity decreases. When an appropriate voltage is applied, it drives electrons from the conduction band of the n-doped side into the junction, where they meet holes that are pushed in from the valence band of the p-doped side. The electrons fall into the empty holes, and their energy is converted into light whose photons have energy equal to the band gap (▼ FIGURE 7.6). In this way electrical energy is converted into optical energy.

Because the wavelength of light that is emitted depends on the band gap of the semiconductor, the color of light produced by the LED can be controlled by appropriate choice of semiconductor. Most red LEDs are made of a mixture of GaP and GaAs. The band gap of GaP is 2.26 eV (3.62×10^{-19} J), which corresponds to a green photon with a wavelength of 549 nm, while GaAs has a band gap of 1.43 eV (2.29×10^{-19} J), which corresponds to an infrared photon with a wavelength of 867 nm. ∞ (Section 1.1 and 1.2) By forming solid solutions of these two compounds, with stoichiometries of $GaP_{1-x}As_x$, the band gap can be adjusted to any intermediate value. Thus, $GaP_{1-x}As_x$ is the solid solution of choice for red, orange, and yellow LEDs. Green LEDs are made from mixtures of GaP and AlP ($E_g = 2.43$ eV, $\lambda = 510$ nm).

Red LEDs have been in the market for decades, but to make white light an efficient blue LED was needed. The first prototype bright blue LED was demonstrated in Japan in 1993. In 2006, only 13 years later, over $4 billion worth of blue LEDs were sold worldwide. The blue LEDs are based on combinations of GaN ($E_g = 3.4$ eV, $\lambda = 365$ nm) and InN ($E_g = 2.4$ eV, $\lambda = 517$ nm). With the availability of blue LEDs there are various strategies for making white LEDs. In some cases, light is combined from blue, green, and red LEDs. More commonly a blue LED is coated with a phosphor, a material that converts some of the blue light into yellow light. In either case the combined colors appear white to the eye. Some examples of different color LEDs are shown in ▼ FIGURE 7.7.

RELATED EXERCISES: 7.22, 7.23, 7.24, 7.25

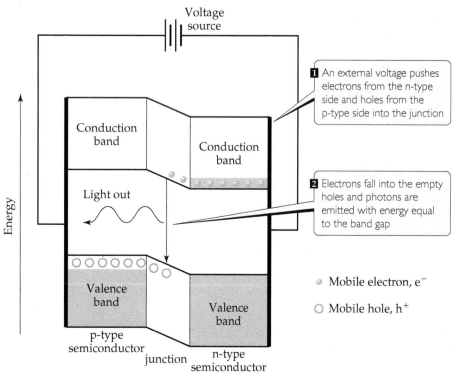

Voltage source

Conduction band

Conduction band

Light out

Valence band

Valence band

Energy

p-type semiconductor

junction

n-type semiconductor

1 An external voltage pushes electrons from the n-type side and holes from the p-type side into the junction

2 Electrons fall into the empty holes and photons are emitted with energy equal to the band gap

○ Mobile electron, e^-

○ Mobile hole, h^+

▲ **FIGURE 7.6** **Light-emitting diodes.** The heart of a light-emitting diode is a p–n junction in which an applied voltage drives electrons and holes to combine and give off light.

▲ **FIGURE 7.7** **Different colors of light-emitting diodes.**

Historically natural polymers, such as wool, leather, silk, and natural rubber, were processed into usable materials. During the past 70 years or so, chemists have learned to form synthetic polymers by polymerizing monomers through controlled chemical reactions. A great many of these synthetic polymers have a backbone of carbon–carbon bonds because carbon atoms have an exceptional ability to form strong stable bonds with one another.

Plastics are materials that can be formed into various shapes, usually by the application of heat and pressure. **Thermoplastic** materials can be reshaped. For example, plastic milk containers are made from the polymer *polyethylene*. These containers can be melted down and the polymer recycled for some other use. In contrast, a **thermosetting plastic** is shaped through irreversible chemical processes and, therefore, cannot be reshaped readily. An **elastomer** is a material that exhibits rubbery or elastic behavior. When subjected to stretching or bending, an elastomer regains its original shape upon removal of the distorting force, if it has not been distorted beyond some elastic limit. Rubber is the most familiar example of an elastomer.

Some polymers, such as nylon and polyesters, both of which are thermosetting plastics, can be formed into fibers that, like hair, are very long relative to their cross-sectional area. These fibers can be woven into fabrics and cords and fashioned into clothing, tire cord, and other useful objects.

Making Polymers

The simplest example of a polymerization reaction is the formation of polyethylene from ethylene molecules (▼ FIGURE 7.8). In this reaction, the double bond in each ethylene molecule "opens up," and two of the electrons originally in this bond are used to form new C—C single bonds with two other ethylene molecules. This type of polymerization, in which monomers are coupled through their multiple bonds, is called **addition polymerization.**

We can write the equation for the polymerization reaction as follows:

$$n\ CH_2{=}CH_2 \longrightarrow \left[\begin{array}{cc} H & H \\ | & | \\ C & C \\ | & | \\ H & H \end{array}\right]_n$$

Here n represents the large number—ranging from hundreds to many thousands—of monomer molecules (ethylene in this case) that react to form one polymer molecule. Within the polymer, a repeat unit (the unit shown in brackets in equation above) appears over and over along the entire chain. The ends of the chain are capped by carbon–hydrogen bonds or by some other bond, so that the end carbons have four bonds.

Polyethylene is an important material; its annual production exceeds 170 billion pounds each year. Although its composition is simple, the polymer is not easy to make. The right manufacturing conditions were identified only after many years of research. Today many forms of polyethylene, varying widely in physical properties, are known.

Polymers of other chemical compositions provide still greater variety in physical and chemical properties. ▶ TABLE 7.2 lists several other common polymers obtained by addition polymerization.

Ethylene

Polyethylene

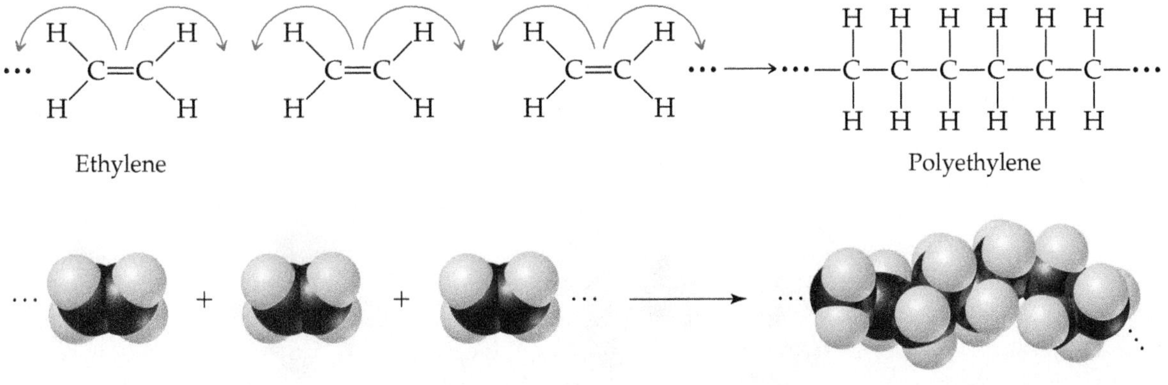

▲ FIGURE 7.8   **The polymerization of ethylene monomers to make the polymer polyethylene.**

TABLE 7.2 • Polymers of Commercial Importance

Polymer	Structure	Uses
Addition Polymers		
Polyethylene	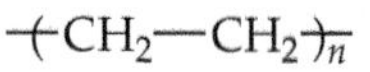 $-(CH_2-CH_2)_n-$	Films, packaging, bottles
Polypropylene	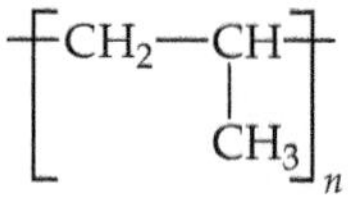 $\begin{bmatrix} CH_2-CH \\ \quad\quad\; CH_3 \end{bmatrix}_n$	Kitchenware, fibers, appliances
Polystyrene	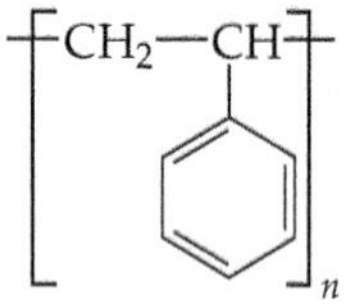 $\begin{bmatrix} CH_2-CH \\ \quad\quad C_6H_5 \end{bmatrix}_n$	Packaging, disposable food containers, insulation
Polyvinyl chloride (PVC)	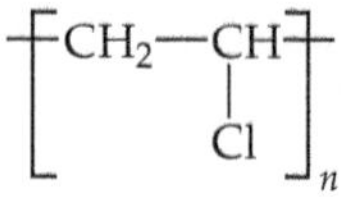 $\begin{bmatrix} CH_2-CH \\ \quad\quad\; Cl \end{bmatrix}_n$	Pipe fittings, clear film for meat packaging
Condensation Polymers		
Polyurethane	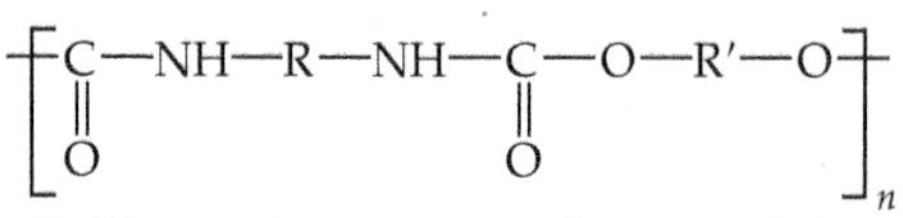 $\begin{bmatrix} C-NH-R-NH-C-O-R'-O \\ \| \quad\quad\quad\quad\quad\quad\;\; \| \\ O \quad\quad\quad\quad\quad\quad\;\; O \end{bmatrix}_n$ $R, R' = -CH_2-CH_2-$ (for example)	"Foam" furniture stuffing, spray-on insulation, automotive parts, footwear, water-protective coatings
Polyethylene terephthalate (a polyester)	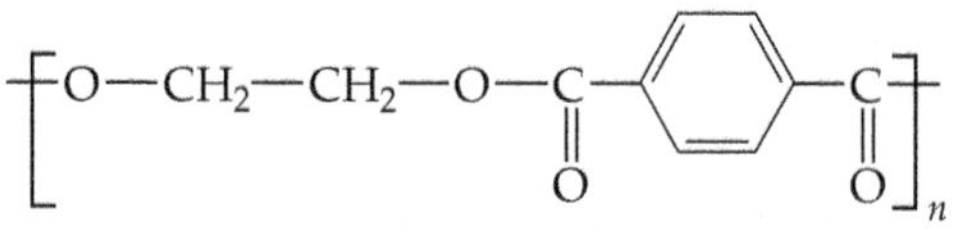 $\begin{bmatrix} O-CH_2-CH_2-O-C-\!\!\bigcirc\!\!-C \\ \quad\quad\quad\quad\quad\quad\; \| \quad\quad\quad \| \\ \quad\quad\quad\quad\quad\quad O \quad\quad\quad O \end{bmatrix}_n$	Tire cord, magnetic tape, apparel, soft-drink bottles
Nylon 6,6	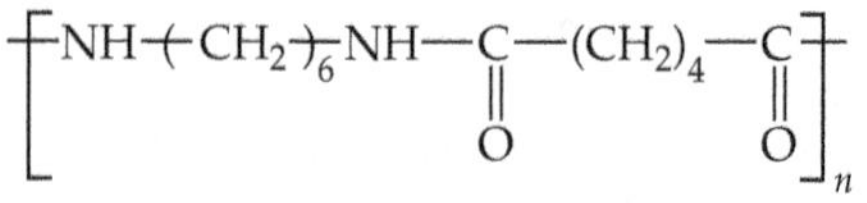 $\begin{bmatrix} NH-(CH_2)_6-NH-C-(CH_2)_4-C \\ \quad\quad\quad\quad\quad\quad\quad\; \| \quad\quad\quad\quad\quad \| \\ \quad\quad\quad\quad\quad\quad\quad O \quad\quad\quad\quad\quad O \end{bmatrix}_n$	Home furnishings, apparel, carpet, fishing line, toothbrush bristles
Polycarbonate	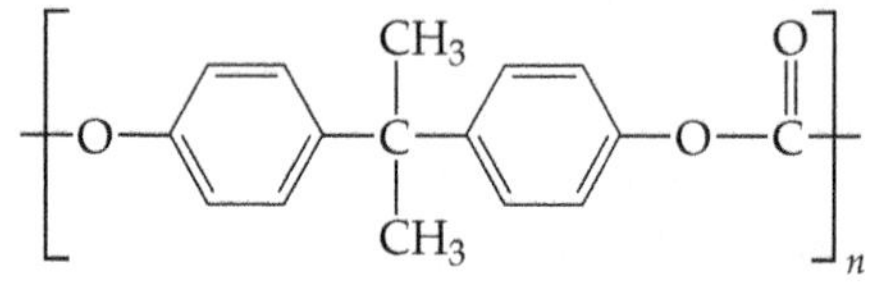 $\begin{bmatrix} \quad\quad\quad\quad CH_3 \quad\quad\quad\quad\; O \\ O-\!\!\bigcirc\!\!-C-\!\!\bigcirc\!\!-O-C \\ \quad\quad\quad\quad CH_3 \end{bmatrix}_n$	Shatterproof eyeglass lenses, CDs, DVDs, bulletproof windows, greenhouses

A second general reaction used to synthesize commercially important polymers is **condensation polymerization**. In a condensation reaction two molecules are joined to form a larger molecule by elimination of a small molecule, such as H_2O. For example, an amine (a compound containing $-NH_2$) reacts with a carboxylic acid (a compound containing $-COOH$) to form a bond between N and C plus an H_2O molecule (▼ FIGURE 7.9).

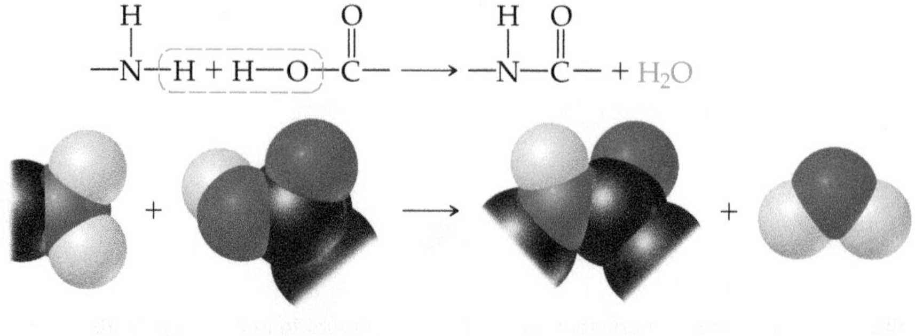

▲ FIGURE 7.9 **A condensation polymerization.**

CHEMISTRY PUT TO WORK

Recycling Plastics

If you look at the bottom of a plastic container, you are likely to see a recycle symbol containing a number, as shown in ▶ FIGURE 7.10. The number and the letter abbreviation below it indicate the kind of polymer from which the container is made, as summarized in ▼ TABLE 7.3. (The chemical structures of these polymers are shown in Table 7.2.) These symbols make it possible to sort containers by composition. In general, the lower the number, the greater the ease with which the material can be recycled.

TABLE 7.3 • Categories Used for Recycling Polymeric Materials in the United States

Number	Abbreviation	Polymer
1	PET or PETE	Polyethylene terephthalate
2	HDPE	High-density polyethylene
3	V or PVC	Polyvinyl chloride (PVC)
4	LDPE	Low-density polyethylene
5	PP	Polypropylene
6	PS	Polystyrene

▲ **FIGURE 7.10 Recycling symbols.** Most plastic containers manufactured today carry a recycling symbol indicating the type of polymer used to make the container and the polymer's suitability for recycling.

$$n \; H{-}N{\overset{H}{|}}{\left(CH_2\right)_6}N{\overset{H}{|}}{-}H \; + \; n \; HO\overset{O}{\overset{\|}{C}}{\left(CH_2\right)_4}\overset{O}{\overset{\|}{C}}OH \; \longrightarrow \; {\left[N(CH_2)_6\overset{H}{\overset{|}{N}}{-}\overset{O}{\overset{\|}{C}}(CH_2)_4\overset{O}{\overset{\|}{C}}\right]}_n \; + \; 2n \; H_2O$$

Diamine   Adipic acid   Nylon 6,6

◀ **FIGURE 7.11**
The formation of the copolymer nylon 6,6.

Polymers formed from two different monomers are called **copolymers**. In the formation of many nylons, a *diamine*, a compound with an —NH_2 group at each end, is reacted with a *diacid*, a compound with a —COOH group at each end. For example, the copolymer nylon 6,6 is formed when a diamine that has six carbon atoms and an amino group on each end is reacted with adipic acid, which also has six carbon atoms (▲ FIGURE 7.11). A condensation reaction occurs on each end of the diamine and the acid. The components of H_2O are split out, and N—C bonds are formed between molecules.

Table 7.2 lists nylon 6,6 and some other common polymers obtained by condensation polymerization. Notice that these polymers have backbones containing N or O atoms as well as C atoms.

 GIVE IT SOME THOUGHT

Is this molecule a better starting material for an addition polymer or a condensation polymer?

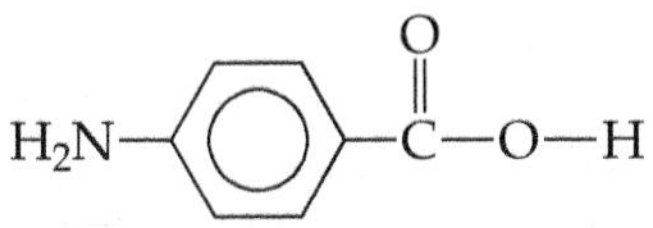

$$H_2N{-}\hexagon{-}\overset{O}{\overset{\|}{C}}{-}O{-}H$$

Structure and Physical Properties of Polymers

The simple structural formulas given for polyethylene and other polymers are deceptive. Because four bonds surround each carbon atom in polyethylene, the atoms are arranged in a tetrahedral fashion, so that the chain is not straight as we have depicted it. Furthermore, the atoms are relatively free to rotate around the C—C single bonds. Rather than

▲ **FIGURE 7.12** **A segment of a polyethylene chain.** This segment consists of 28 carbon atoms. In commercial polyethylenes, the chain lengths range from about 10^3 to 10^5 CH_2 units.

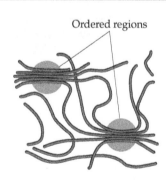

▲ **FIGURE 7.13** **Interactions between polymer chains.** In the circled regions, the forces that operate between adjacent segments of the chains lead to ordering analogous to the ordering in crystals, though less regular.

▲ **FIGURE 7.14** **Cross-linking of polymer chains.** The cross-linking groups (red) constrain the relative motions of the polymer chains, making the material harder and less flexible than when the cross-links are not present.

being straight and rigid, therefore, the chains are flexible, folding readily (◄ **FIGURE 7.12**). The flexibility in the molecular chains causes any material made of this polymer to be very flexible.

Both synthetic and natural polymers commonly consist of a collection of *macromolecules* (large molecules) of different molecular weights. Depending on the conditions of formation, the molecular weights may be distributed over a wide range or may be closely clustered around an average value. In part because of this distribution in molecular weights, polymers are largely amorphous (noncrystalline) materials. Rather than exhibiting a well-defined crystalline phase with a sharp melting point, polymers soften over a range of temperatures. They may, however, possess short-range order in some regions of the solid, with chains lined up in regular arrays as shown in ◄ **FIGURE 7.13**. The extent of such ordering is indicated by the degree of **crystallinity** of the polymer. Mechanical stretching or pulling to align the chains as the molten polymer is drawn through small holes can frequently enhance the crystallinity of a polymer. Intermolecular forces between the polymer chains hold the chains together in the ordered crystalline regions, making the polymer denser, harder, less soluble, and more resistant to heat. ▼ **TABLE 7.4** shows how the properties of polyethylene change as the degree of crystallinity increases.

The linear structure of polyethylene is conducive to intermolecular interactions that lead to crystallinity. However, the degree of crystallinity in polyethylene strongly depends on the average molecular weight. Polymerization results in a mixture of macromolecules with varying values of *n* and, hence, varying molecular weights. Low-density polyethylene (LDPE), used in forming films and sheets, has an average molecular weight in the range of 10^4 amu and has substantial chain branching. That is, there are side chains off the main chain of the polymer. These side chains inhibit the formation of crystalline regions, reducing the density of the material. High-density polyethylene (HDPE), used to form bottles, drums, and pipes, has an average molecular weight in the range of 10^6 amu. This form has fewer side chains and thus a higher degree of crystallinity.

🔺 **GIVE IT SOME THOUGHT**

In copolymers made of ethylene and vinyl acetate monomers, melting point and degree of crystallinity decrease as the percentage of vinyl acetate increases. Suggest an explanation.

Ethylene

Vinyl acetate

Polymers can be made stiffer by introducing chemical bonds between chains. Forming bonds between chains is called **cross-linking** (► **FIGURE 7.14**). The greater the number of cross-links, the more rigid the polymer. Whereas thermoplastic materials consist of independent polymer chains, thermosetting ones become cross-linked when heated; the cross-links allow them to hold their shapes.

TABLE 7.4 • **Properties of Polyethylene as a Function of Crystallinity**

	Crystallinity				
	55%	**62%**	**70%**	**77%**	**85%**
Melting point (°C)	109	116	125	130	133
Density (g/cm³)	0.92	0.93	0.94	0.95	0.96
Stiffness*	25	47	75	120	165
Yield stress*	1700	2500	3300	4200	5100

*These test results show that the mechanical strength of the polymer increases with increased crystallinity. The physical units for the stiffness test are psi × 10^{-3} (psi = pounds per square inch); those for the yield stress test are psi. Discussion of the exact meaning and significance of these tests is beyond the scope of this text.

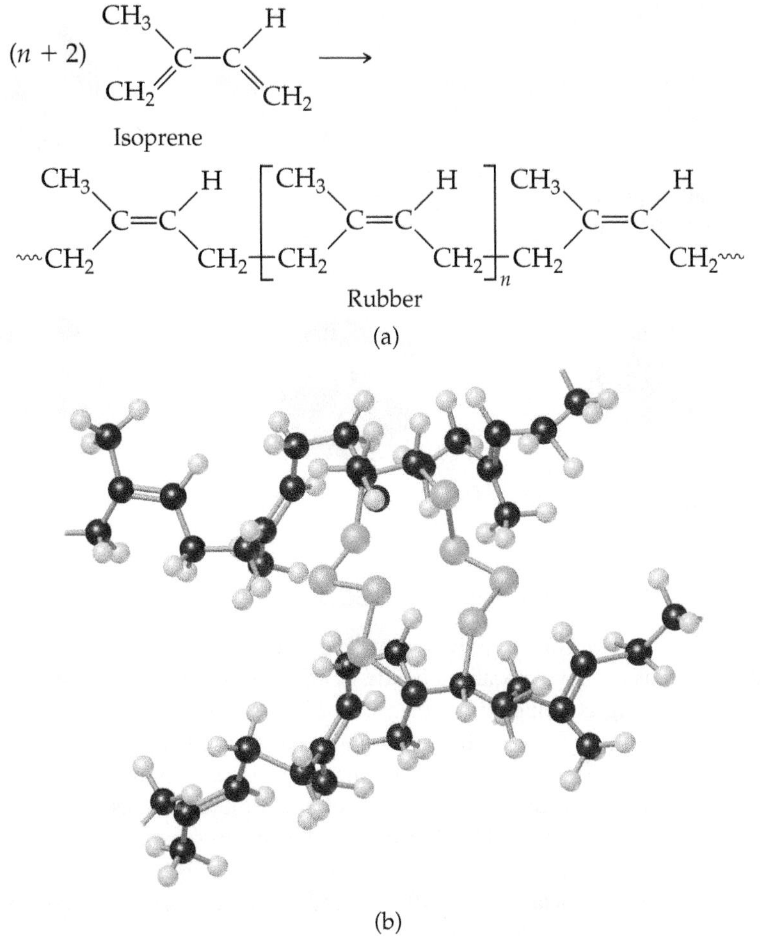

◄ **FIGURE 7.15 Vulcanization of natural rubber.** (a) Formation of polymeric natural rubber from the monomer isoprene. (b) Adding sulfur to rubber creates sulfur-atom links between chains. These links form as the carbon-carbon double bonds in the natural rubber polymer open up.

An important example of cross-linking is the **vulcanization** of natural rubber, a process discovered by Charles Goodyear in 1839. Natural rubber is formed from a liquid resin derived from the inner bark of the *Hevea brasiliensis* tree. Chemically, it is a polymer of isoprene, C_5H_8 (▲ **FIGURE 7.15**). Because rotation about the carbon–carbon double bond does not readily occur, the orientation of the groups bound to the carbons is rigid. In natural rubber, the chain extensions are on the same side of the double bond, as shown in Figure 7.15(a).

Natural rubber is not a useful polymer because it is too soft and too chemically reactive. Goodyear accidentally discovered that adding sulfur and then heating the mixture makes the rubber harder and reduces its susceptibility to oxidation or other chemical attack. The sulfur changes rubber into a thermosetting polymer by cross-linking the polymer chains through reactions at some of the double bonds, as shown schematically in Figure 7.15(b). Cross-linking of about 5% of the double bonds creates a flexible, resilient rubber. When the rubber is stretched, the cross-links help prevent the chains from slipping, so that the rubber retains its elasticity. Because heating was an important step in his process, Goodyear named it after Vulcan, the Roman god of fire.

7.5 | NANOMATERIALS

The prefix *nano* means 10^{-9}. When people speak of "nanotechnology," they usually mean making devices that are on the 1–100-nm scale. It turns out that the properties of semiconductors and metals change in this size range. **Nanomaterials**—materials that have dimensions on the 1–100-nm scale—are under intense investigation in research laboratories around the world, and chemistry plays a central role in this investigation.

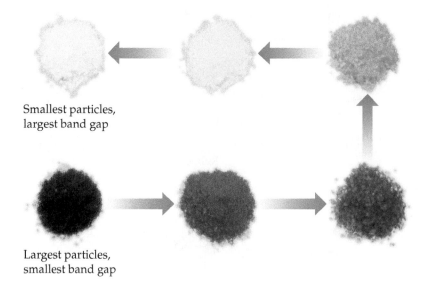

► **FIGURE 7.16 Cd₃P₂ powders with different particle sizes.** The arrows indicate decreasing particle size and a corresponding increase in the band gap energy.

Smallest particles, largest band gap

Largest particles, smallest band gap

Semiconductors on the Nanoscale

In small molecules, electrons occupy discrete molecular orbitals whereas in macroscale solids the electrons occupy delocalized bands. At what point does a molecule get so large that it starts behaving as though it has delocalized bands rather than localized molecular orbitals? For semiconductors, both theory and experiment tell us that the answer is roughly at 1 to 10 nm (about 10–100 atoms across). The exact number depends on the specific semiconductor material. The equations of quantum mechanics that were used for electrons in atoms can be applied to electrons (and holes) in semiconductors to estimate the size where materials undergo a crossover from molecular orbitals to bands. Because these effects become important at 1 to 10 nm, semiconductor particles with diameters in this size range are called *quantum dots*.

One of the most spectacular effects of reducing the size of a semiconductor crystal is that the band gap changes substantially with size in the 1–10-nm range. As the particle gets smaller, the band gap gets larger, an effect observable by the naked eye, as shown in ▲ **FIGURE 7.16**. On the macro level, the semiconductor cadmium phosphide looks black because its band gap is small ($E_g = 0.5$ eV), and it absorbs all wavelengths of visible light. As the crystals are made smaller, the material progressively changes color until it looks white! It looks white because now no visible light is absorbed. The band gap is so large that only high-energy ultraviolet light can excite electrons into the conduction band ($E_g > 3.0$ eV).

Making quantum dots is most easily accomplished using chemical reactions in solution. For example, to make CdS, you can mix $Cd(NO_3)_2$ and Na_2S in water. If you do not do anything else, you will precipitate large crystals of CdS. However, if you first add a negatively charged polymer to the water (such as polyphosphate, $-(OPO_2)_n-$), the Cd^{2+} associates with the polymer, like tiny "meatballs" in the polymer "spaghetti." When sulfide is added, CdS particles grow, but the polymer keeps them from forming large crystals. A great deal of fine-tuning of reaction conditions is necessary to produce nanocrystals that are of uniform size and shape.

As we learned in Section 7.3 some semiconductor devices can emit light when a voltage is applied. Another way to make semiconductors emit light is to illuminate them with light whose photons have energies larger than the energy of the band gap of the semiconductor. This process is called *photoluminescence*. A valence-band electron absorbs a photon and is promoted to the conduction band. If the excited electron then falls back down into the hole it left in the valence band, it emits a photon having energy equal to the band gap energy. In the case of quantum dots, the band gap is tunable with the crystal size, and thus all the colors of the rainbow can be obtained from just one material, as shown for CdSe in ◄ **FIGURE 7.17**.

GO FIGURE

As the size of the quantum dots decreases, does the wavelength of the emitted light increase or decrease?

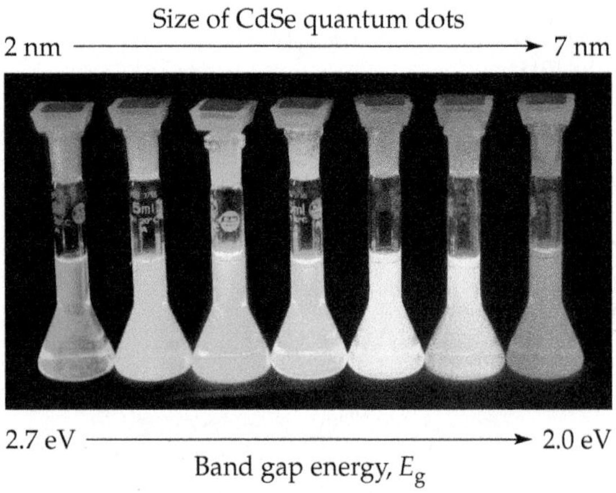

Size of CdSe quantum dots
2 nm ⟶ 7 nm

2.7 eV ⟶ 2.0 eV
Band gap energy, E_g

▲ **FIGURE 7.17 Photoluminescence.** When illuminated with ultraviolet light, these solutions, each containing nanoparticles of the semiconductor CdSe, emit light that corresponds to their respective band gap energies. The light emitted depends on the size of the CdSe nanoparticles.

⚓ **GIVE IT SOME THOUGHT**

Large crystals of ZnS can show photoluminescence, emitting ultraviolet photons with energies equal to the band gap energy and a wavelength of 340 nm. Is it possible to shift the luminescence so that the emitted photons are in the visible region of the spectrum by making appropriately sized nanocrystals?

Quantum dots are being explored for applications ranging from electronics to lasers to medical imaging because they are very bright, very stable, and small enough to be taken up by living cells even after being coated with a biocompatible surface layer.

Semiconductors do not have to be shrunk to the nanoscale in all three dimensions in order to show new properties. They can be laid down in relatively large two-dimensional areas on a substrate but be only a few nanometers thick to make *quantum wells*. *Quantum wires*, in which the semiconductor wire diameter is only a few nanometers but its length is very long, have also been made by various chemical routes. In both quantum wells and quantum wires, measurements along the nanoscale dimension(s) show quantum behavior, but in the long dimension, the properties seem to be just like those of the bulk material.

Metals on the Nanoscale

Metals also have unusual properties on the 1–100-nm-length scale. Fundamentally, this is because the mean free path ∞ (Section 8.8) of an electron in a metal at room temperature is typically about 1–100 nm. So when the particle size of a metal is 100 nm or less, one might expect unusual effects.

Although it was not fully understood, people have known for hundreds of years that metals are different when they are very finely divided. Dating back to the middle ages, the makers of stained-glass windows knew that gold dispersed in molten glass made the glass a beautiful deep red (▶ FIGURE 7.18). Much later, in 1857, Michael Faraday reported that dispersions of small gold particles could be made stable and were deeply colored—some of the original colloidal solutions that he made are still in the Royal Institution of Great Britain's Faraday Museum in London (▼ FIGURE 7.19).

Other physical and chemical properties of metallic nanoparticles are also different from the properties of the bulk materials. Gold particles less than 20 nm in diameter melt at a far lower temperature than bulk gold, for instance, and when the particles are between 2 and 3 nm in diameter, gold is no longer a "noble," unreactive metal; in this size range it becomes chemically reactive.

At nanoscale dimensions, silver has properties analogous to those of gold in its beautiful colors, although it is more reactive than gold. Currently, there is great interest in research laboratories around the world in taking advantage of the unusual optical properties of metal nanoparticles for applications in biomedical imaging and chemical detection.

Fullerenes, Carbon Nanotubes, and Graphene

We have seen that elemental carbon is quite versatile. In its sp^3-hybridized solid-state form, it is diamond; in its sp^2-hybridized solid-state form, it is graphite. Over the past three decades, scientists have discovered that sp^2-hybridized carbon can also form discrete molecules, one-dimensional tubes, and two-dimensional sheets. Each of these forms of carbon shows very interesting properties.

Until the mid-1980s, pure solid carbon was thought to exist in only two forms: the covalent-network solids diamond and graphite. In 1985, however, a group of researchers led by Richard Smalley and Robert Curl of Rice University in Houston and Harry Kroto of the University of Sussex, England, vaporized a sample of graphite with an intense pulse of laser light and used a stream of helium gas to carry the vaporized carbon into a mass spectrometer. The mass spectrum showed peaks corresponding to clusters of carbon atoms, with a particularly strong peak corresponding to molecules composed of 60 carbon atoms, C_{60}.

▲ **FIGURE 7.18 Stained glass window from the Chartres Cathedral in France.** Gold nanoparticles are responsible for the red color in this window, which dates from the 12th century.

▲ **FIGURE 7.19 The solutions of colloidal gold nanoparticles made by Michael Faraday in the 1850s.** These are on display in the Faraday Museum, London.

▲ GO FIGURE

How many bonds does each carbon atom in C_{60} make? Based on this observation would you expect the bonding in C_{60} to be more like that in diamond or that in graphite?

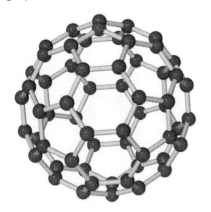

▲ **FIGURE 7.20 Buckminsterfullerene, C_{60}.** The molecule has a highly symmetric structure in which the 60 carbon atoms sit at the vertices of a truncated icosahedron. The bottom view shows only the bonds between carbon atoms.

Because C_{60} clusters were so preferentially formed, the group proposed a radically different form of carbon, namely, nearly spherical C_{60} *molecules*. They proposed that the carbon atoms of C_{60} form a "ball" with 32 faces, 12 of them pentagons and 20 hexagons (▶ FIGURE 7.20), exactly like a soccer ball. The shape of this molecule is reminiscent of the geodesic dome invented by the U.S. engineer and philosopher R. Buckminster Fuller, so C_{60} was whimsically named "buckminsterfullerene," or "buckyball" for short. Since the discovery of C_{60}, other related molecules of carbon atoms have been discovered. These molecules are now known as fullerenes.

Appreciable amounts of buckyball can be prepared by electrically evaporating graphite in an atmosphere of helium gas. About 14% of the resulting soot consists of C_{60} and a related molecule, C_{70}, which has a more elongated structure. The carbon-rich gases from which C_{60} and C_{70} condense also contain other fullerenes, mostly containing more carbon atoms, such as C_{76} and C_{84}. The smallest possible fullerene, C_{20}, was first detected in 2000. This small, ball-shaped molecule is much more reactive than the larger fullerenes. Because fullerenes are composed of individual molecules, they dissolve in various organic solvents, whereas diamond and graphite do not. This solubility permits fullerenes to be separated from the other components of soot and even from one another. It also allows the study of their reactions in solution.

Soon after the discovery of C_{60}, chemists discovered carbon nanotubes (▼ FIGURE 7.21). You can think of these as sheets of graphite rolled up and capped at one or both ends by half of a C_{60} molecule. Carbon nanotubes are made in a manner similar to that used to make C_{60}. They can be made in either *multiwall* or *single-walled* forms. Multiwall carbon nanotubes consist of tubes within tubes, nested together, whereas single-walled carbon nanotubes consist of single tubes. Single-walled carbon nanotubes can be 1000 nm long or even longer but are only about 1 nm in diameter. Depending on the diameter of the graphite sheet and how it is rolled up, carbon nanotubes can behave as either semiconductors or metals.

The fact that carbon nanotubes can be made either semiconducting or metallic without any doping is unique among solid-state materials, and a great deal of work is going on to make carbon-based electronic devices. Carbon nanotubes are also being explored for their mechanical properties. The carbon–carbon bonded framework of the nanotubes means that the imperfections that might appear in a metal nanowire of similar dimensions are nearly absent. Experiments on individual carbon nanotubes suggest that they are stronger than steel, if steel were the dimensions of a carbon nanotube. Carbon nanotubes have been spun into fibers with polymers, adding great strength and toughness to the composite material.

The two-dimensional form of carbon, graphene, is the most recent low-dimensional form of carbon to be experimentally isolated and studied. Although its properties had been the subject of theoretical predictions for over 60 years, it was not until 2004 that

▶ **FIGURE 7.21 Atomic models of carbon nanotubes.** Left: "Armchair" nanotube, which shows metallic behavior. Right: "Zigzag" nanotube, which can be either semiconducting or metallic, depending on tube diameter.

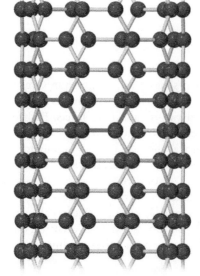

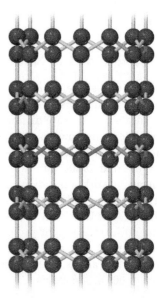

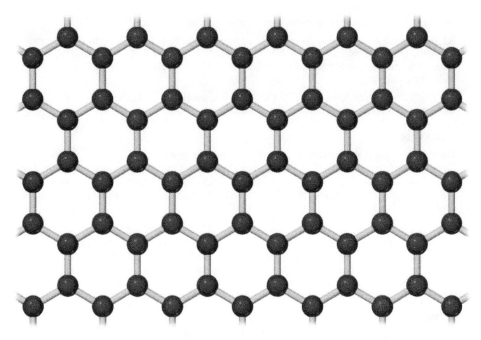

◀ **FIGURE 7.22   A portion of a two-dimensional graphene sheet.**

researchers at the University of Manchester in England isolated and identified individual sheets of carbon atoms with the honeycomb structure shown in ▲ **FIGURE 7.22**. Amazingly, the technique they used to isolate single-layer graphene was to successively peel away thin layers of graphite using an adhesive tape. Individual layers of graphene were then transferred to a silicon wafer having a precisely defined overcoat of SiO_2. When a single layer of graphene is left on the wafer, an interference-like contrast pattern results that can be seen with an optical microscope. If not for this simple yet effective way to scan for individual graphene crystals, they would probably still remain undiscovered. Subsequently, it has been shown that graphene can be deposited on clean surfaces of other types of crystals. The scientists who led the effort at the University of Manchester, Andre Geim and Konstantin Novoselov, were awarded the 2010 Nobel prize in physics for their work.

The properties of graphene are remarkable. It is very strong and has a record thermal conductivity, topping carbon nanotubes in both categories. Graphene is a semimetal, which means its electronic structure is like that of a semiconductor in which the energy gap is exactly zero. The combination of graphene's two-dimensional character and the fact that it is a semimetal allows the electrons to travel very long distances, up to 0.3 μm, without scattering from another electron, atom, or impurity. Graphene can sustain electrical current densities six orders of magnitude higher than those sustainable in copper. Scientists are currently exploring ways to incorporate graphene in various technologies.

SAMPLE INTEGRATIVE EXERCISE   Putting Concepts Together

A conducting polymer is a polymer that can conduct electricity. Some polymers can be made semiconducting; others can be nearly metallic. Polyacetylene is an example of a polymer that is a semiconductor. It can also be doped to increase its conductivity.

Polyacetylene is made from acetylene in a reaction that looks simple but is actually tricky to do:

$$H-C\equiv C-H \qquad \left[\!\!\begin{array}{c} CH=CH \end{array}\!\!\right]_n$$

Acetylene   Polyacetylene

(a) What is the hybridization of the carbon atoms, and the geometry around those atoms, in acetylene and in polyacetylene?

(b) Write a balanced equation to make polyacetylene from acetylene.

(c) Acetylene is a gas at room temperature and pressure (298 K, 1.00 atm). How many grams of polyacetylene can you make from a 5.00-L vessel of acetylene gas at room temperature and room pressure? Assume acetylene behaves ideally, and that the polymerization reaction occurs with 100% yield.

(d) Using the average bond enthalpies in Table 3.4, predict whether the formation of polyacetylene from acetylene is endothermic or exothermic.

SOLUTION

Analyze For part (a), we need to recall what we have learned about sp, sp^2, and sp^3 hybridization and geometry. ∞ (Section 4.5) For part (b), we need to write a balanced equation. For part (c), we need to use the ideal-gas equation. ∞ (Section 8.4) For part (d), we need to recall the definitions of endothermic and exothermic and how bond enthalpies can be used to predict overall reaction enthalpies. ∞ (Section 3.8)

Plan For part (a), we should draw out the chemical structures of the reactant and product. For part (b), we need to make sure the equation is properly balanced. For part (c), we need to convert from liters of gas to moles of gas, using the ideal-gas equation ($PV = nRT$); then we need to convert from moles of acetylene gas to moles of polyacetylene using the answer from part (b); then we can convert to grams of polyacetylene. For part (d), we need to recall that $\Delta H_{rxn} = \Sigma$(bond enthalpies of bonds broken) $- \Sigma$(bond enthalpies of bonds formed).

Solve

(a) Carbon always forms four bonds. Thus, each C atom must have a single bond to H and a triple bond to the other C atom in acetylene. As a result, each C atom has two electron domains and must be sp hybridized. This sp hybridization also means that the H—C—C angles in acetylene are 180° and the molecule is linear.

We can write out the partial structure of polyacetylene as follows:

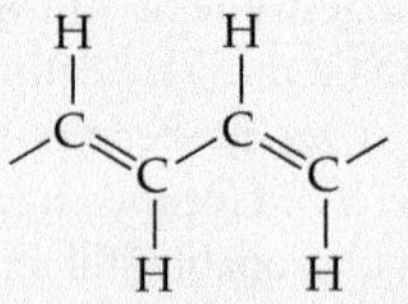

Each carbon is identical but now has three bonding electron domains that surround it. Therefore, the hybridization of each carbon atom is sp^2, and each carbon has local trigonal planar geometry with 120° angles.

(b) We can write:

$$n\, C_2H_2(g) \longrightarrow -[CH{=}CH]_n-$$

Note that all atoms originally present in acetylene end up in the polyacetylene product.

(c) We can use the ideal-gas equation as follows:

$$PV = nRT$$
$$(1.00\ \text{atm})(5.00\ \text{L}) = n(0.08206\ \text{L-atm/K-mol})(298\ \text{K})$$
$$n = 0.204\ \text{mol}$$

Acetylene has a molar mass of 26.0 g/mol; therefore, the mass of 0.204 mol is

$$(0.204\ \text{mol})(26.0\ \text{g/mol}) = 5.32\ \text{g acetylene}$$

Note that from the answer to part (b), all the atoms in acetylene go into polyacetylene. Due to conservation of mass, then, the mass of polyacetylene produced must also be 5.32 g, if we assume 100% yield.

(d) Let's consider the case for $n = 1$. We note that the reactant side of the equation in part (b) has one C≡C triple bond and two C—H single bonds. The product side of the equation in part (b) has one C=C double bond, one C—C single bond (to link to the adjacent monomer), and two C—H single bonds. Therefore, we are breaking one C≡C triple bond and are forming one C=C double bond and one C—C single bond. Accordingly, the enthalpy change for polyacetylene formation is:

$$\Delta H_{rxn} = (\text{C}{\equiv}\text{C triple bond enthalpy}) - (\text{C}{=}\text{C double bond enthalpy})$$
$$- (\text{C}{-}\text{C single bond enthalpy})$$
$$\Delta H_{rxn} = (839\ \text{kJ/mol}) - (614\ \text{kJ/mol}) - (348\ \text{kJ/mol})$$
$$= -123\ \text{kJ/mol}$$

Because ΔH is a negative number, the reaction releases heat and is exothermic.

CHAPTER SUMMARY AND KEY TERMS

INTRODUCTION AND SECTION 7.1 The structures and properties of solids can be classified according to the forces that hold the atoms together. **Metallic solids** are held together by a delocalized sea of collectively shared valence electrons. **Ionic solids** are held together by the mutual attraction between cations and anions. **Covalent-network solids** are held together by an extended network of covalent bonds. **Molecular solids** are held together by weak intermolecular forces. **Polymers** contain very long chains of atoms held together by covalent bonds. These chains are usually held to one another by weaker intermolecular forces. **Nanomaterials** are solids where the dimensions of individual crystals have been reduced to the order of 1–100 nm.

SECTION 7.2 **Molecular solids** consist of atoms or molecules held together by intermolecular forces. Because these forces are relatively weak, molecular solids tend to be soft and possess low melting points. The melting point depends on the strength of the intermolecular forces, as well as the efficiency with which the molecules can pack together.

SECTION 7.3 **Covalent-network solids** consist of atoms held together in large networks by covalent bonds. These solids are much harder and have higher melting points than molecular solids. Important examples include diamond, where the carbons are tetrahedrally coordinated to each other, and graphite where the carbon atoms form hexagonal layers through sp^2 bonds.

Elemental semiconductors, like Si and Ge, as well as **compound semiconductors**, like GaAs, InP, and CdTe, are important examples of covalent-network solids. In a semiconductor the filled bonding molecular orbitals make up the **valence band**, while the empty antibonding molecular orbitals make up the **conduction band**. The valence and conduction bands are separated by an energy that is referred to as the **band gap**. The size of the band gap increases as the bond distance decreases, and as the difference in electronegativity between the two elements increases.

Doping semiconductors changes their ability to conduct electricity by orders of magnitude. An n-type semiconductor is one that is doped so that there are excess electrons in the conduction band; a p-type semiconductor is one that is doped so that there are missing electrons, which are called **holes**, in the valence band.

SECTION 7.4 **Polymers** are molecules of high molecular weight formed by joining together large numbers of small molecules called monomers. **Plastics** are materials that can be formed into various shapes, usually by the application of heat and pressure. **Thermoplastic** polymers can be reshaped, typically through heating, in contrast to **thermosetting plastics**, which are formed into objects through an irreversible chemical process and cannot readily be reshaped. An **elastomer** is a material that exhibits elastic behavior; that is, it returns to its original shape following stretching or bending.

In an **addition polymerization** reaction, the molecules form new linkages by opening existing π bonds. Polyethylene forms, for example, when the carbon–carbon double bonds of ethylene open up. In a **condensation polymerization** reaction, the monomers are joined by splitting out a small molecule from between them. The various kinds of nylon are formed, for example, by removing a water molecule from between an amine and a carboxylic acid. A polymer formed from two different monomers is called a **copolymer**.

Polymers are largely amorphous, but some materials possess a degree of **crystallinity**. For a given chemical composition, the crystallinity depends on the molecular weight and the degree of branching along the main polymer chain. Polymer properties are also strongly affected by **cross-linking**, in which short chains of atoms connect the long polymer chains. Rubber is cross-linked by short chains of sulfur atoms in a process called **vulcanization**.

SECTION 7.5 When one or more dimensions of a material become sufficiently small, generally smaller than 100 nm, the properties of the material change. Materials with dimensions on this length scale are called **nanomaterials**. Quantum dots are semiconductor particles with diameters of 1–10 nm. In this size range the material's band gap energy becomes size-dependent. Metal nanoparticles have different chemical and physical properties in the 1–100-nm size range. Gold, for example, is more reactive and no longer has a golden color. Nanoscience has produced a number of previously unknown forms of sp^2-hybridized carbon. Fullerenes, like C_{60}, are large molecules containing only carbon atoms. Carbon nanotubes are sheets of graphite rolled up. They can behave as either semiconductors or metals depending on how the sheet was rolled. Graphene, which is an isolated layer from graphite, is a two-dimensional form of carbon. Applications of these nanomaterials are being developed now for imaging, electronics, and medicine.

KEY SKILLS

- Classify solids based on their bonding/intermolecular forces and understand how difference in bonding relates to physical properties. [Section 7.1]

- Be able to use the periodic table to qualitatively compare the band gap energies of semiconductors. [Section 7.3]

- Understand how n-type and p-type doping can be used to control the conductivity of semiconductors. [Section 7.3]

- Understand how polymers are formed from monomers and recognize the features of a molecule that allow it to react to form a polymer. Understand the differences between addition polymerization and condensation polymerization. [Section 7.4]

- Understand how the interactions between polymer chains impact the physical properties of polymers. [Section 7.4]

- Understand how the properties of bulk semiconductors and metals change as the size of the crystals decreases into the nanometer-length scale. [Section 7.5]

- Be familiar with the structures and unique properties of fullerenes, carbon nanotubes, and graphene. [Section 7.5]

EXERCISES

VISUALIZING CONCEPTS

7.1 The electronic structure of a doped semiconductor is shown here. (a) Which band, A or B, is the valence band? (b) Which band is the conduction band? (c) Which band consists of bonding molecular orbitals? (d) Is this an example of an n-type or p-type doped semiconductor? (e) If the semiconductor is germanium, which of the following elements could be the dopant: Ga, Si, or P? [Section 7.3]

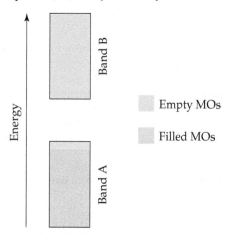

Empty MOs

Filled MOs

7.2 Shown here are cartoons of two different polymers. Based on these cartoons, which polymer would you expect to be denser? Which one would have the higher melting point? [Section 7.4]

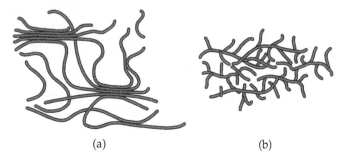

(a)   (b)

7.3 The accompanying image shows photoluminescence from four different samples of CdTe nanocrystals, each embedded in a polymer matrix. The photoluminescence occurs because the samples are being irradiated by a UV light source. The nanocrystals in each vial have different average sizes. The sizes are 4.0, 3.5, 3.2, and 2.8 nm. (a) Which vial contains the 4.0-nm nanocrystals? (b) Which vial contains the 2.8-nm nanocrystals? (c) Crystals of CdTe that have sizes that are larger than approximately 100 nm have a band gap of 1.5 eV. What would be the wavelength and frequency of light emitted from these crystals? What type of light is this? [Sections 7.3 and 7.5]

CLASSIFICATIONS OF SOLIDS (section 7.1)

7.4 Covalent bonding occurs in both molecular and covalent-network solids. Why do these two kinds of solids differ so greatly in their hardness and melting points?

7.5 Silicon is the fundamental component of integrated circuits. Si has the same structure as diamond. Is Si a molecular, metallic, ionic, or covalent-network solid?

7.6 What kinds of attractive forces exist between particles in (a) molecular crystals, (b) covalent-network crystals, (c) ionic crystals, (d) metallic crystals?

7.7 Which type (or types) of crystalline solid is characterized by each of the following: (a) high mobility of electrons throughout the solid; (b) softness, relatively low melting point; (c) high melting point and poor electrical conductivity; (d) network of covalent bonds?

7.8 Indicate the type of crystal (molecular, metallic, ionic, or covalent-network) each of the following would form upon

solidification: (a) $CaCO_3$, (b) Pt, (c) ZrO_2 (melting point, 2677 °C), (d) table sugar ($C_{12}H_{22}O_{11}$), (e) benzene (C_6H_6), (f) I_2.

7.9 Indicate the type of crystal (molecular, metallic, ionic, or covalent-network) each of the following would form upon solidification: (a) InAs, (b) MgO, (c) HgS, (d) In, (e) HBr.

7.10 A white substance melts with some decomposition at 730 °C. As a solid, it does not conduct electricity, but it dissolves in water to form a conducting solution. Which type of solid (molecular, metallic, covalent-network, or ionic) might the substance be?

7.11 You are given a white substance that sublimes at 3000 °C; the solid is a nonconductor of electricity and is insoluble in water. Which type of solid (molecular, metallic, covalent-network, or ionic) might this substance be?

MOLECULAR SOLIDS (section 7.2)

7.12 Classify each of the following statements as true or false:

(a) Although both molecular solids and covalent-network solids have covalent bonds, the melting points of molecular solids are much lower because their covalent bonds are much weaker.

(b) Other factors being equal, highly symmetric molecules tend to form solids with higher melting points than asymmetrically shaped molecules.

7.13 Classify each of the following statements as true or false:

(a) For molecular solids the melting point generally increases as the strengths of the covalent bonds increase.

(b) For molecular solids the melting point generally increases as the strengths of the intermolecular forces increase.

COVALENT-NETWORK SOLIDS (section 7.3)

7.14 Both covalent-network solids and ionic solids can have melting points well in excess of room temperature, and both can be poor conductors of electricity in their pure form. However, in other ways their properties are quite different.
(a) Which type of solid is more likely to dissolve in water?
(b) Which type of solid can become an electrical conductor via chemical substitution?

7.15 Which of the following properties are typical characteristics of a covalent-network solid, a metallic solid, or both: (a) ductility, (b) hardness, (c) high melting point?

7.16 For each of the following pairs of semiconductors, which one will have the larger band gap: (a) CdS or CdTe, (b) GaN or InP, (c) GaAs or InAs?

7.17 For each of the following pairs of semiconductors, which one will have the larger band gap: (a) InP or InAs, (b) Ge or AlP, (c) AgI or CdTe?

7.18 If you want to dope GaAs to make an n-type semiconductor with an element to replace Ga, which element(s) would you pick?

7.19 If you want to dope GaAs to make a p-type semiconductor with an element to replace As, which element(s) would you pick?

7.20 Silicon has a band gap of 1.1 eV at room temperature. (a) What wavelength of light would a photon of this energy correspond to? (b) Draw a vertical line at this wavelength in the figure shown, which shows the light output of the sun as a function of wavelength. Does silicon absorb all, none, or a portion of the visible light that comes from the sun?

7.21 Cadmium telluride is an important material for solar cells. (a) What is the band gap of CdTe? (b) What wavelength of light would a photon of this energy correspond to? (c) Draw a vertical line at this wavelength in the figure shown with Exercise 7.69, which shows the light output of the sun as a function of wavelength. (d) With respect to silicon, does CdTe absorb a larger or smaller portion of the solar spectrum?

7.22 The semiconductor GaP has a band gap of 2.2 eV. Green LEDs are made from pure GaP. What wavelength of light would be emitted from an LED made from GaP?

7.23 The first LEDs were made from GaAs, which has a band gap of 1.43 eV. What wavelength of light would be emitted from an LED made from GaAs? What region of the electromagnetic spectrum does this light correspond to: UV, visible, or IR?

7.24 GaAs and GaP (E_g = 2.26 eV) make solid solutions that have the same crystal structure as the parent materials, with As and P randomly distributed throughout the crystal. GaP_xAs_{1-x} exists for any value of x. If we assume that the band gap varies linearly with composition between $x = 0$ and $x = 1$, estimate the band gap for $GaP_{0.5}As_{0.5}$. What wavelength of light does this correspond to?

7.25 Red light-emitting diodes are made from GaAs and GaP solid solutions, GaP_xAs_{1-x} (see Exercise 7.24). The original red LEDs emitted light with a wavelength of 660 nm. If we assume that the band gap varies linearly with composition between $x = 0$ and $x = 1$, estimate the composition (the value of x) that is used in these LEDs.

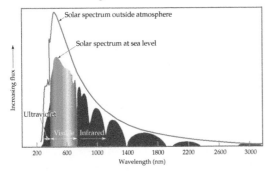

POLYMERIC SOLIDS (section 7.4)

7.26 What is a monomer? Give three examples of monomers taken from the examples given in this chapter.

7.27 The molecular formula of *n*-decane is $CH_3(CH_2)_8CH_3$. Decane is not considered a polymer, whereas polyethylene is. What is the distinction?

7.28 An ester is a compound formed by a condensation reaction between a carboxylic acid and an alcohol. Read the discussion of esters in Section 6.4 and then give an example of a reaction forming an ester. How might this kind of reaction be extended to form a polymer (a polyester)?

7.29 Write a chemical equation for formation of a polymer via a condensation reaction from the monomers succinic acid ($HOOCCH_2CH_2COOH$) and ethylenediamine ($H_2NCH_2CH_2NH_2$).

7.30 Draw the structure of the monomer(s) employed to form each of the following polymers shown in Table 7.2: (a) polyvinyl chloride, (b) nylon 6,6, (c) polyethylene terephthalate.

7.31 Write the chemical equation that represents the formation of (a) polychloroprene from chloroprene (polychloroprene is used in highway-pavement seals, expansion joints, conveyor belts, and wire and cable jackets);

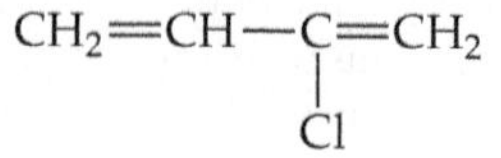

$$CH_2\!=\!CH\!-\!\underset{\underset{Cl}{|}}{C}\!=\!CH_2$$

Chloroprene

(b) polyacrylonitrile from acrylonitrile (polyacrylonitrile is used in home furnishings, craft yarns, clothing, and many other items).

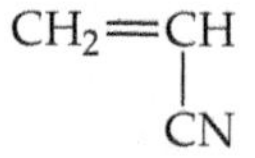

$$CH_2\!=\!\underset{\underset{CN}{|}}{CH}$$

Acrylonitrile

7.32 The nylon Nomex®, a condensation polymer, has the following structure:

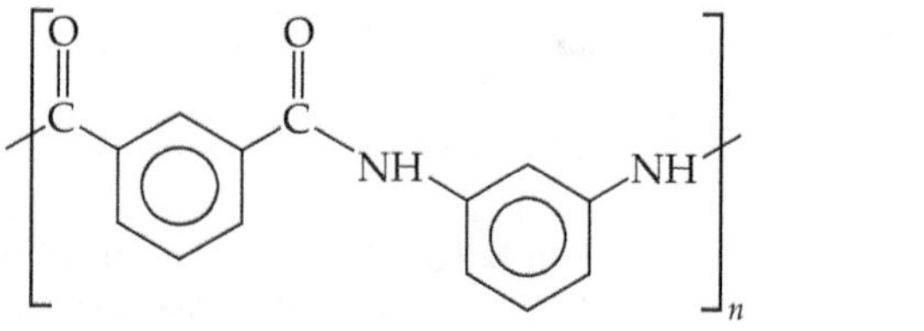

Draw the structures of the two monomers that yield Nomex®.

7.33 Proteins are polymers formed by condensation reactions of amino acids, which have the general structure

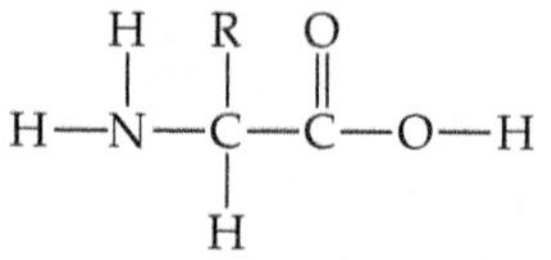

In this structure, R represents $-H$, $-CH_3$, or another group of atoms. Draw the general structure for a polyamino acid polymer formed by condensation polymerization of the molecule shown here.

7.34 What molecular features make a polymer flexible? Explain how cross-linking affects the chemical and physical properties of the polymer.

7.35 What molecular structural features cause high-density polyethylene to be denser than low-density polyethylene?

7.36 Are high molecular weights and a high degree of crystallinity always desirable properties of a polymer? Explain.

7.37 Briefly describe each of the following: (a) elastomer, (b) thermoplastic, (c) thermosetting plastic.

NANOMATERIALS (section 7.5)

7.38 Explain why "bands" may not be the most accurate description of bonding in a solid when the solid has nanoscale dimensions.

7.39 CdS has a band gap of 2.4 eV. If large crystals of CdS are illuminated with ultraviolet light, they emit light equal to the band gap energy. (a) What color is the emitted light? (b) Would appropriately sized CdS quantum dots be able to emit blue light? (c) What about red light?

7.40 True or false:
(a) The band gap of a semiconductor decreases as the particle size decreases in the 1–10-nm range.
(b) The light that is emitted from a semiconductor, upon external stimulation, becomes longer in wavelength as the particle size of the semiconductor decreases.

7.41 True or false:
If you want a semiconductor that emits blue light, you could either use a material that has a band gap corresponding to the energy of a blue photon or you could use a material that has a smaller band gap but make an appropriately sized nanoparticle of the same material.

7.42 Gold adopts a face-centered cubic structure with a unit cell edge of 4.08 Å. How many gold atoms are there in a sphere that is 20 nm in diameter? Recall that the volume of a sphere is $\frac{4}{3}\pi r^3$.

7.43 Cadmium telluride, CdTe, takes the zinc blende structure (Figure 7.26) with a unit cell edge length of 6.49 Å. There are four cadmium atoms and four tellurium atoms per unit cell. How many of each type of atom are there in a cubic crystal with an edge length of 5.00 nm?

ADDITIONAL EXERCISES

7.44 Teflon® is a polymer formed by the polymerization of $F_2C\!=\!CF_2$. Draw the structure of a section of this polymer. What type of polymerization reaction is required to form it?

7.45 Hydrogen bonding between polyamide chains plays an important role in determining the properties of a nylon such as nylon 6,6 (Table 7.2). Draw the structural formulas for two adjacent chains of nylon 6,6 and show where hydrogen-bonding interactions could occur between them.

INTEGRATIVE EXERCISE

[7.46] Although polyethylene can twist and turn in random ways, the most stable form is a linear one with the carbon backbone oriented as shown in the following figure:

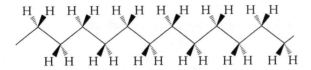

The solid wedges in the figure indicate bonds from carbon that come out of the plane of the page; the dashed wedges indicate bonds that lie behind the plane of the page.

(a) What is the hybridization of orbitals at each carbon atom? What angles do you expect between the bonds?

(b) Now imagine that the polymer is polypropylene rather than polyethylene. Draw structures for polypropylene in which (i) the CH$_3$ groups all lie on the same side of the plane of the paper (this form is called isotactic polypropylene); (ii) the CH$_3$ groups lie on alternating sides of the plane (syndiotactic polypropylene); or (iii) the CH$_3$ groups are randomly distributed on either side (atactic polypropylene). Which of these forms would you expect to have the highest crystallinity and melting point, and which the lowest? Explain in terms of intermolecular interactions and molecular shapes.

(c) Polypropylene fibers have been employed in athletic wear. The product is said to be superior to cotton or polyester clothing in wicking moisture away from the body through the fabric to the outside. Explain the difference between polypropylene and polyester or cotton (which has many —OH groups along the molecular chain) in terms of intermolecular interactions with water.

WHAT'S AHEAD

EARTH'S ATMOSPHERE, which is mostly made of nitrogen and oxygen gases, extends about 350 miles up from Earth's surface. Over 95% of the mass of the atmosphere, however, is in the 30 miles closest to the surface. Most of what we perceive as "weather" occurs in the first 10 miles above the surface.

GASES

IN THE PAST SEVERAL CHAPTERS we learned about the electronic structure of atoms and about how atoms combine to form molecules and ionic substances. In everyday life, however, we do not have any direct experience with atoms. Instead, we encounter matter as gases, liquids, or solids made up of enormous numbers of atoms or molecules. Large collections of gas atoms and gas molecules in the atmosphere, for example, are responsible for weather—the gentle breezes and the gales, the humidity and the rain. Hurricanes, such as the one shown in the chapter-opening photo, are large storms (up to 500 miles in diameter) that form over the ocean and are characterized by a low-pressure center (the "eye"), heavy rains, and violent winds, with wind speeds up to 200 miles per hour. Hurricane formation is still not completely understood, but in general the atoms and molecules of the atmosphere are driven by a combination of low pressures, warm temperatures at the sea surface that rapidly cool with height, and high humidity to produce the storms.

We now know that the properties of gases (as well as those of liquids and solids) are readily understood in terms of the behavior of their component atoms, ions, and molecules; in this chapter we examine the physical properties of gases and explain these properties in terms of the behavior of gas molecules.

8.1 | CHARACTERISTICS OF GASES

In many ways gases are the most easily understood form of matter. Even though different gaseous substances may have very different *chemical* properties, they behave quite similarly as far as their *physical* properties are concerned. For example, we live in an atmosphere composed of the mixture of gases we refer to as air, a mixture of primarily N_2 (78%) and O_2 (21%), with small amounts of several other gases, including Ar (0.9%). Although N_2 and O_2 have very different chemical properties—O_2 supports human life but N_2 does not, to name just one difference—these two components of air behave physically as one gaseous material because their physical properties are essentially identical. Of the few elements that exist as gases at ordinary temperatures and pressures, He, Ne, Ar, Kr, and Xe are monatomic and H_2, N_2, O_2, F_2, and Cl_2 are diatomic. Many molecular compounds are gases, and ▼ TABLE 8.1 lists a few of them. Notice that all of these gases are composed entirely of nonmetallic elements. Furthermore, all have simple molecular formulas and, therefore, low molar masses.

Substances that are liquids or solids under ordinary conditions can also exist in the gaseous state, where they are often referred to as **vapors**. The substance H_2O, for example, can exist as liquid water, solid ice, or water vapor.

Gases differ significantly from solids and liquids in several respects. For example, a gas expands spontaneously to fill its container. Consequently, the volume of a gas equals the volume of its container. Gases also are highly compressible: When pressure is applied to a gas, its volume readily decreases. Solids and liquids, on the other hand, do not expand to fill their containers and are not readily compressible.

Two or more gases form a homogeneous mixture regardless of the identities or relative proportions of the gases; the atmosphere serves as an excellent example. Two or more liquids or two or more solids may or may not form homogeneous mixtures, depending on their chemical nature. For example, when water and gasoline are mixed, the two liquids remain as separate layers. In contrast, the water vapor and gasoline vapors above the liquids form a homogeneous gas mixture.

The characteristic properties of gases—expanding to fill a container, being highly compressible, forming homogeneous mixtures—arise because the molecules are relatively far apart. In any given volume of air, for example, the molecules take up only about 0.1% of the total volume with the rest being empty space. Thus, each molecule behaves largely as though the others were not present. As a result, different gases behave similarly even though they are made up of different molecules.

 GIVE IT SOME THOUGHT

Do the compounds in Table 8.1 have small (less than 100 g/mol) or large molecular weights?

TABLE 8.1 • Some Common Compounds That Are Gases at Room Temperature		
Formula	**Name**	**Characteristics**
HCN	Hydrogen cyanide	Very toxic, slight odor of bitter almonds
H_2S	Hydrogen sulfide	Very toxic, odor of rotten eggs
CO	Carbon monoxide	Toxic, colorless, odorless
CO_2	Carbon dioxide	Colorless, odorless
CH_4	Methane	Colorless, odorless, flammable
C_2H_4	Ethene (Ethylene)	Colorless, ripens fruit
C_3H_8	Propane	Colorless, odorless, bottled gas
N_2O	Nitrous oxide	Colorless, sweet odor, laughing gas
NO_2	Nitrogen dioxide	Toxic, red-brown, irritating odor
NH_3	Ammonia	Colorless, pungent odor
SO_2	Sulfur dioxide	Colorless, irritating odor

8.2 | PRESSURE

In everyday terms, **pressure** conveys the idea of force, a push that tends to move something in a given direction. Pressure, P, is defined in science as the force, F, that acts on a given area, A.

$$P = \frac{F}{A} \qquad [8.1]$$

Gases exert a pressure on any surface with which they are in contact. The gas in an inflated balloon, for example, exerts a pressure on the inside surface of the balloon.

Atmospheric Pressure and the Barometer

People, coconuts, and nitrogen molecules all experience an attractive gravitational force that pulls them toward the center of Earth. When a coconut comes loose from a tree, for example, this force causes the coconut to be accelerated toward Earth, its speed increasing as its potential energy is converted into kinetic energy. ∞(Section 10.1) The gas atoms and molecules of the atmosphere also experience a gravitational acceleration. Because these particles have such tiny masses, however, their thermal energies of motion (their kinetic energies) override the gravitational forces, so the particles that make up the atmosphere don't pile up at Earth's surface. Nevertheless, the gravitational force does operate, and it causes the atmosphere as a whole to press down on Earth's surface, creating atmospheric pressure, defined as the force exerted by the atmosphere on a given surface area.

You can demonstrate the existence of atmospheric pressure with an empty plastic water bottle. If you suck on the mouth of the empty bottle, chances are you can cause the bottle to partially cave in. When you break the partial vacuum you have created, the bottle pops out to its original shape. The bottle caves in because, once you've sucked out some of the air molecules, air molecules in the atmosphere exert a force on the outside of the bottle that is greater than the force exerted by the lesser number of air molecules inside the bottle. We calculate the magnitude of this atmospheric pressure as follows: The force, F, exerted by any object is the product of its mass, m, and its acceleration, a: $F = ma$. The acceleration given by Earth's gravitational force to any object located near Earth's surface is 9.8 m/s^2. Now imagine a column of air 1 m^2 in cross section extending through the entire atmosphere (▶ FIGURE 8.1). That column has a mass of roughly 10,000 kg. The downward gravitational force exerted on this column is

$$F = (10{,}000 \text{ kg})(9.8 \text{ m/s}^2) = 1 \times 10^5 \text{ kg-m/s}^2 = 1 \times 10^5 \text{ N}$$

where N is the abbreviation for *newton*, the SI unit for force: $1 \text{ N} = 1 \text{ kg-m/s}^2$. The pressure exerted by the column is this force divided by the cross-sectional area, A, over which the force is applied. Because our air column has a cross-sectional area of 1 m^2, we have for the magnitude of atmospheric pressure at sea level

$$P = \frac{F}{A} = \frac{1 \times 10^5 \text{ N}}{1 \text{ m}^2} = 1 \times 10^5 \text{ N/m}^2 = 1 \times 10^5 \text{ Pa} = 1 \times 10^2 \text{ kPa}$$

The SI unit of pressure is the **pascal** (Pa), named for Blaise Pascal (1623–1662), a French scientist who studied pressure: $1 \text{ Pa} = 1 \text{ N/m}^2$. A related pressure unit is the **bar**: $1 \text{ bar} = 10^5 \text{ Pa} = 10^5 \text{ N/m}^2$. Thus, the atmospheric pressure at sea level we just calculated, 100 kPa, can be reported as 1 bar. (The actual atmospheric pressure at any location depends on weather conditions and altitude.) Another pressure unit is pounds per square inch (psi, lbs/in.^{2}). At sea level, atmospheric pressure is 14.7 psi.

▲ GIVE IT SOME THOUGHT

Assume the top of your head has a surface area of 10 in. × 10 in. How many pounds of air are you carrying on your head if you are at sea level?

In the seventeenth century many scientists and philosophers believed that the atmosphere had no weight. Evangelista Torricelli (1608–1647), a student of Galileo's,

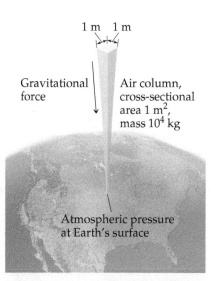

1 m   1 m

Gravitational force

Air column, cross-sectional area 1 m^2, mass 10^4 kg

Atmospheric pressure at Earth's surface

▲ FIGURE 8.1   **Calculating atmospheric pressure.**

▲ GO FIGURE

What happens to _h,_ the height of the mercury column, if the atmospheric pressure increases?

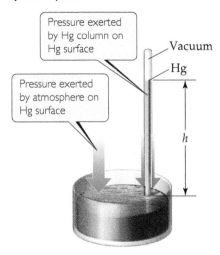

Pressure exerted by Hg column on Hg surface

Vacuum

Hg

Pressure exerted by atmosphere on Hg surface

_h_

▲ **FIGURE 8.2   A mercury barometer.**

proved this untrue. He invented the _barometer_ (◀ FIGURE 8.2), which is made from a glass tube more than 760 mm long that is closed at one end, completely filled with mercury, and inverted into a dish of mercury. (Care must be taken so that no air gets into the tube.) When the tube is inverted into the dish, some of the mercury flows out of the tube, but a column of mercury remains in the tube. Torricelli argued that the mercury surface in the dish experiences the full force of Earth's atmosphere, which pushes the mercury up the tube until the pressure exerted by the mercury column downward, due to gravity, equals the atmospheric pressure at the base of the tube. Therefore the height, _h,_ of the mercury column is a measure of atmospheric pressure and changes as atmospheric pressure changes.

Although Torricelli's explanation met with fierce opposition, it also had supporters. Blaise Pascal, for example, had one of Torricelli's barometers carried to the top of a mountain and compared its reading there with the reading on a duplicate barometer at the base of the mountain. As the barometer was carried up, the height of the mercury column diminished, as expected, because the amount of atmosphere pressing down on the mercury in the dish decreased as the instrument was carried higher. These and other experiments eventually prevailed, and the idea that the atmosphere has weight became accepted.

Standard atmospheric pressure, which corresponds to the typical pressure at sea level, is the pressure sufficient to support a column of mercury 760 mm high. In SI units this pressure is 1.01325×10^5 Pa. Standard atmospheric pressure defines some common non–SI units used to express gas pressure, such as the **atmosphere** (atm) and the _millimeter of mercury_ (mm Hg). The latter unit is also called the **torr**, after Torricelli: 1 torr = 1 mm Hg. Thus, we have

$$1 \text{ atm} = 760. \text{ mm Hg} = 760. \text{ torr} = 1.01325 \times 10^5 \text{ Pa} = 101.325 \text{ kPa} = 1.01325 \text{ bar}$$

We will usually express gas pressure in atmospheres, pascals, kilopascals, or torr, so you should be comfortable converting pressures from one unit to another.

SAMPLE EXERCISE 8.1   **Converting Pressure Units**

(a) Convert 0.357 atm to torr. **(b)** Convert 6.6×10^{-2} torr to atmospheres. **(c)** Convert 147.2 kPa to torr.

SOLUTION

Analyze In each case we are given the pressure in one unit and asked to convert it to another unit. Our task, therefore, is to choose the appropriate conversion factors.

Plan We can use dimensional analysis to perform the desired conversions.

Solve

(a) To convert atmospheres to torr, we use the relationship 760 torr = 1 atm:

$$(0.357 \text{ atm})\left(\frac{760 \text{ torr}}{1 \text{ atm}}\right) = 271 \text{ torr}$$

Note that the units cancel in the required manner.

(b) We use the same relationship as in part (a). To get the appropriate units to cancel, we must use the conversion factor as follows:

$$(6.6 \times 10^{-2} \text{ torr})\left(\frac{1 \text{ atm}}{760 \text{ torr}}\right) = 8.7 \times 10^{-5} \text{ atm}$$

(c) The relationship 760 torr = 101.325 kPa allows us to write an appropriate conversion factor for this problem:

$$(147.2 \text{ kPa})\left(\frac{760 \text{ torr}}{101.325 \text{ kPa}}\right) = 1104 \text{ torr}$$

Check In each case, compare the magnitude of the answer with the starting value. The torr is a much smaller unit than the atmosphere (since there are 760 torr in 1 atm), so we expect the _numerical_ answer to be larger than the starting quantity in (a) and smaller in (b). In (c) notice that there are nearly 8 torr per kPa, so the numerical answer in torr should be about eight times larger than its value in kPa, consistent with our calculation.

PRACTICE EXERCISE

(a) In countries that use the metric system, atmospheric pressure in weather reports is given in kilopascals. Convert a pressure of 745 torr to kilopascals. **(b)** The pressure at the center of Hurricane Katrina was 902 mbar (millibars). There are 1000 mbar in 1 bar; convert this pressure to atmospheres.

Answers: **(a)** 99.3 kPa, **(b)** 0.890 atm

We use various devices to measure the pressures of enclosed gases. Tire gauges, for example, measure the pressure of air in automobile and bicycle tires. In laboratories we sometimes use a *manometer*, which operates on a principle similar to that of a barometer, as shown in Sample Exercise 8.2.

SAMPLE EXERCISE 8.2 **Using a Manometer to Measure Gas Pressure**

On a certain day a laboratory barometer indicates that the atmospheric pressure is 764.7 torr. A sample of gas is placed in a flask attached to an open-end mercury manometer (▶ **FIGURE 8.3**), and a meter stick is used to measure the height of the mercury in the two arms of the U tube. The height of the mercury in the open-end arm is 136.4 mm, and the height in the arm in contact with the gas in the flask is 103.8 mm. What is the pressure of the gas in the flask (**a**) in atmospheres, (**b**) in kilopascals?

SOLUTION

Analyze We are given the atmospheric pressure (764.7 torr) and the mercury heights in the two arms of the manometer and asked to determine the gas pressure in the flask. Recall that millimeters of mercury is a pressure unit. We know that the gas pressure from the flask must be greater than atmospheric pressure because the mercury level in the arm on the flask side (103.8 mm) is lower than the level in the arm open to the atmosphere (136.4 mm). Therefore, the gas from the flask is pushing mercury from the arm in contact with the flask into the arm open to the atmosphere.

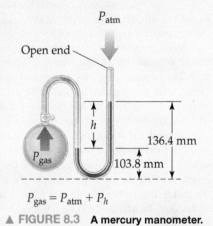

$$P_{gas} = P_{atm} + P_h$$

▲ **FIGURE 8.3** **A mercury manometer.**

Plan We will use the difference in height between the two arms (h in Figure 8.3) to obtain the amount by which the pressure of the gas exceeds atmospheric pressure. Because an open-end mercury manometer is used, the height difference directly measures the pressure difference in mm Hg or torr between the gas and the atmosphere.

Solve

(**a**) The pressure of the gas equals the atmospheric pressure plus h:

$$P_{gas} = P_{atm} + h$$
$$= 764.7 \text{ torr} + (136.4 \text{ torr} - 103.8 \text{ torr})$$
$$= 797.3 \text{ torr}$$

We convert the pressure of the gas to atmospheres:

$$P_{gas} = (797.3 \text{ torr})\left(\frac{1 \text{ atm}}{760 \text{ torr}}\right) = 1.049 \text{ atm}$$

(**b**) To calculate the pressure in kPa, we employ the conversion factor between atmospheres and kPa:

$$1.049 \text{ atm}\left(\frac{101.3 \text{ kPa}}{1 \text{ atm}}\right) = 106.3 \text{ kPa}$$

Check The calculated pressure is a bit more than 1 atm, which is about 101 kPa. This makes sense because we anticipated that the pressure in the flask would be greater than the atmospheric pressure (764.7 torr = 1.01 atm) acting on the manometer.

PRACTICE EXERCISE
Convert a pressure of 0.975 atm into Pa and kPa.
Answers: 9.88×10^4 Pa and 98.8 kPa

8.3 | THE GAS LAWS

Four variables are needed to define the physical condition, or *state*, of a gas: temperature, pressure, volume, and amount of gas, usually expressed as number of moles. The equations that express the relationships among these four variables are known as the *gas laws*. Because volume is easily measured, the first gas laws to be studied expressed the effect of one of the variables on volume, with the remaining two variables held constant.

CHEMISTRY AND LIFE

BLOOD PRESSURE

When your blood pressure is measured, two values are reported, such as 120/80 (120 over 80). The first measurement is *systolic pressure,* the maximum pressure when the heart is pumping. The second is *diastolic pressure,* the pressure when the heart is in the resting part of its pumping cycle. The units associated with these pressure measurements are torr.

Blood pressure is measured using a pressure gauge attached to a closed, air-filled cuff applied like a tourniquet to the arm (▶ FIGURE 8.4). The pressure gauge may be a mercury manometer or related device. A small pump is used to increase the pressure in the cuff until it is above the systolic pressure and therefore prevents blood from flowing. The pressure inside the cuff is slowly reduced until blood just begins to pulse through the artery, and the person measuring the pressure hears, through a stethoscope, a characteristic sound. At this point the pressure in the cuff equals the pressure that the blood exerts inside the artery. Reading the gauge gives the systolic pressure. The pressure in the cuff is then reduced further until the blood flows freely, indicated by another characteristic sound. The pressure at this point is the diastolic pressure.

Hypertension is abnormally high blood pressure. The usual criterion is a blood pressure greater than 140/90, although recent studies suggest that health risks increase for systolic readings above 120. Hypertension significantly increases the workload on the heart and places a stress on the walls of the blood vessels throughout the body. These effects increase the risk of aneurysms, heart attacks, and strokes.

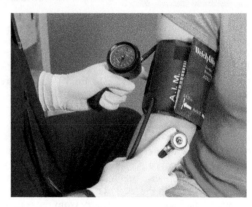

▲ FIGURE 8.4 **Measuring blood pressure.**

The Pressure–Volume Relationship: Boyle's Law

An inflated weather balloon released at Earth's surface expands as it rises (◀ FIGURE 8.5) because the pressure of the atmosphere decreases with increasing elevation. Thus, for our first pressure–volume relationship we can use our experience with balloons to say that gas volume increases as the pressure exerted on the gas decreases.

British chemist Robert Boyle (1627–1691) first investigated the relationship between the pressure of a gas and its volume, using a J-shaped tube like that shown in ▼ FIGURE 8.6. In the tube on the left, a quantity of gas is trapped above a column of mercury. Boyle then changed the pressure on the gas by adding mercury to the tube. He found that the volume of the gas decreased as the pressure increased. For example, doubling the pressure caused the gas volume to decrease to half its original value.

GO FIGURE

Does atmospheric pressure increase or decrease as altitude increases? (Neglect changes in temperature.)

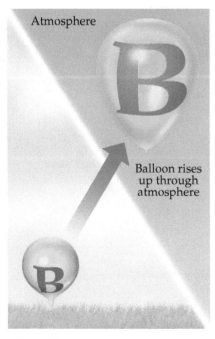

▲ FIGURE 8.5 **As a balloon rises in the atmosphere, its volume increases.**

GO FIGURE

What is the total pressure on the gas after the 760 mm Hg has been added?

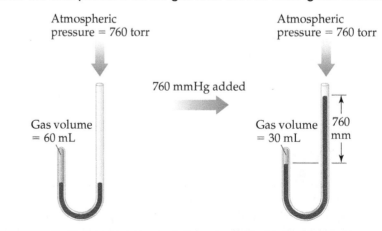

▲ FIGURE 8.6 **Boyle's experiment relating pressure and volume for a gas.**

GO FIGURE

What would a plot of *P* versus 1/*V* look like for a fixed quantity of gas at a fixed temperature?

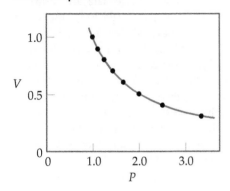
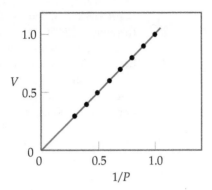

▲ **FIGURE 8.7   Boyle's Law.** For a fixed quantity of gas at constant temperature, the volume of the gas is inversely proportional to its pressure.

Boyle's law, which summarizes these observations, states that *the volume of a fixed quantity of gas maintained at constant temperature is inversely proportional to the pressure.* When two measurements are inversely proportional, one gets smaller as the other gets larger. Boyle's law can be expressed mathematically as

$$V = \text{constant} \times \frac{1}{P} \quad \text{or} \quad PV = \text{constant} \qquad [8.2]$$

The value of the constant depends on temperature and on the amount of gas in the sample.

The graph of *V* versus *P* in ▲ **FIGURE 8.7** shows the curve obtained for a given quantity of gas at a fixed temperature. A linear relationship is obtained when *V* is plotted versus 1/*P* as shown on the right in Figure 8.7.

Boyle's law occupies a special place in the history of science because Boyle was the first to carry out experiments in which one variable was systematically changed to determine the effect on another variable. The data from the experiments were then employed to establish an empirical relationship—a "law."

We apply Boyle's law every time we breathe. The rib cage, which can expand and contract, and the diaphragm, a muscle beneath the lungs, govern the volume of the lungs. Inhalation occurs when the rib cage expands and the diaphragm moves downward. Both actions increase the volume of the lungs, thus decreasing the gas pressure inside the lungs. Atmospheric pressure then forces air into the lungs until the pressure in the lungs equals atmospheric pressure. Exhalation reverses the process—the rib cage contracts and the diaphragm moves up, decreasing the volume of the lungs. Air is forced out of the lungs by the resulting increase in pressure.

GIVE IT SOME THOUGHT

What happens to the pressure of a gas if you double its volume while its temperature is held constant?

The Temperature–Volume Relationship: Charles's Law

As ▶ **FIGURE 8.8** illustrates, the volume of an inflated balloon increases when the temperature of the gas inside the balloon increases and decreases when the temperature of the gas decreases.

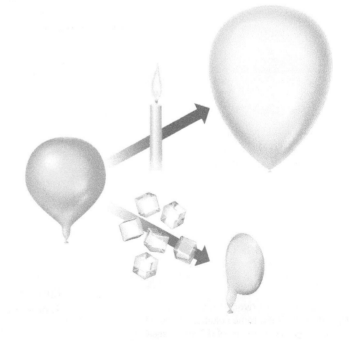

▲ **FIGURE 8.8   The effect of temperature on volume.**

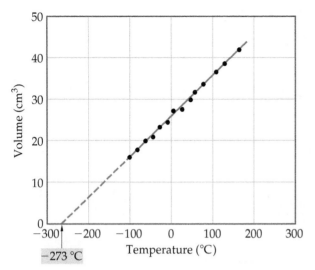

▲ **FIGURE 8.9** **Charles's Law.** For a fixed quantity of gas at constant pressure, the volume of the gas is proportional to its temperature.

The relationship between gas volume and temperature—volume increases as temperature increases and decreases as temperature decreases—was discovered in 1787 by French scientist Jacques Charles (1746–1823). Some typical volume–temperature data are shown in **FIGURE 8.9**. Notice that the extrapolated (dashed) line passes through −273 °C. Note also that the gas is predicted to have zero volume at this temperature. This condition is never realized, however, because all gases liquefy or solidify before reaching this temperature.

In 1848 William Thomson (1824–1907), a British physicist whose title was Lord Kelvin, proposed an absolute-temperature scale, now known as the Kelvin scale. On this scale 0 K, called *absolute zero*, equals −273.15 °C. In terms of the Kelvin scale, **Charles's law** states: *The volume of a fixed amount of gas maintained at constant pressure is directly proportional to its absolute temperature.* Thus, doubling the absolute temperature causes the gas volume to double. Mathematically, Charles's law takes the form

$$V = \text{constant} \times T \quad \text{or} \quad \frac{V}{T} = \text{constant} \qquad [8.3]$$

with the value of the constant depending on the pressure and on the amount of gas.

 GIVE IT SOME THOUGHT

Does the volume of a fixed quantity of gas decrease to half its original value when the temperature is lowered from 100 °C to 50 °C ?

The Quantity–Volume Relationship: Avogadro's Law

The relationship between the quantity of a gas and its volume follows from the work of Joseph Louis Gay-Lussac (1778–1823) and Amedeo Avogadro (1776–1856).

Gay-Lussac was one of those extraordinary figures in the history of science who could truly be called an adventurer. In 1804 he ascended to 23,000 ft in a hot-air balloon—an exploit that held the altitude record for several decades. To better control the balloon, Gay-Lussac studied the properties of gases. In 1808 he observed the *law of combining volumes*: At a given pressure and temperature, the volumes of gases that react with one another are in the ratios of small whole numbers. For example, two volumes of hydrogen gas react with one volume of oxygen gas to form two volumes of water vapor.

Three years later Amedeo Avogadro interpreted Gay-Lussac's observation by proposing what is now known as **Avogadro's hypothesis**: *Equal volumes of gases at the same temperature and pressure contain equal numbers of molecules.* For example, 22.4 L of any gas at 0 °C and 1 atm contain 6.02×10^{23} gas molecules (that is, 1 mol), as depicted in ▼ **FIGURE 8.10**.

GO FIGURE

How many moles of gas are in each vessel?

▶ **FIGURE 8.10** **Avogadro's hypothesis.** At the same volume, pressure, and temperature, samples of different gases have the same number of molecules but different masses.

	He	N_2	CH_4
Volume	22.4 L	22.4 L	22.4 L
Pressure	1 atm	1 atm	1 atm
Temperature	0 °C	0 °C	0 °C
Mass of gas	4.00 g	28.0 g	16.0 g
Number of gas molecules	6.02×10^{23}	6.02×10^{23}	6.02×10^{23}

Avogadro's law follows from Avogadro's hypothesis: *The volume of a gas main-tained at constant temperature and pressure is directly proportional to the number of moles of the gas.* That is,

$$V = \text{constant} \times n \qquad [8.4]$$

where *n* is number of moles. Thus, for instance, doubling the number of moles of gas causes the volume to double if *T* and *P* remain constant.

SAMPLE EXERCISE 8.3 | **Evaluating the Effects of Changes in *P, V, n*, and *T* on a Gas**

Suppose we have a gas confined to a cylinder with a movable piston. ∞ (Sections 10.2, 10.3) Consider the following changes (assuming no leaks): **(a)** Heat the gas from 298 K to 360 K at constant pressure. **(b)** Reduce the volume from 1 L to 0.5 L at constant temperature. **(c)** Inject additional gas, keeping temperature and volume constant. Indicate how each change affects the average distance between molecules, the pressure of the gas, and the number of moles of gas in the cylinder.

SOLUTION

Analyze We need to think how each change affects (1) the distance between molecules, (2) the pressure of the gas, and (3) the number of moles of gas in the cylinder.

Plan We will use the gas laws and the general properties of gases to analyze each situation.

Solve

(a) Heating the gas while maintaining constant pressure will cause the piston to move and the volume to increase (Charles's law). Thus, the distance between molecules will increase. At constant pressure, obviously, the pressure will not change. The total number of moles of gas remains the same.

(b) Compressing the gas into a smaller volume does not change the total number of gas molecules; thus, the total number of moles remains the same. The average distance between molecules, however, must decrease because of the smaller volume. The reduction in volume causes the pressure to increase (Boyle's law).

(c) Injecting more gas into the cylinder while keeping the volume and temperature constant results in more molecules and, thus, an increase in the number of moles of gas in the cylinder. The average distance between molecules must decrease because their number per unit volume increases. Avogadro's law tells us that the volume of the cylinder should have increased when we added more gas, but here the volume is fixed. Boyle's law comes to our aid: If the volume is low, then pressure is high. Therefore, we expect that the pressure will increase in the cylinder if we inject more gas, keeping volume and temperature constant.

PRACTICE EXERCISE

Recall that density is mass per volume. What happens to the density of a gas as **(a)** the gas is heated in a constant-volume container; **(b)** the gas is compressed at constant temperature; **(c)** additional gas is added to a constant-volume container?

Answers: **(a)** no change, **(b)** increases, **(c)** increases

---

8.4 | THE IDEAL-GAS EQUATION

All three laws we just examined were obtained by holding two of the four variables *P, V, T,* and *n* constant and seeing how the remaining two variables affect each other. We can express each law as a proportionality relationship. Using the symbol ∝ for "is proportional to," we have

$$\textit{Boyle's law:} \qquad V \propto \frac{1}{P} \quad (\text{constant } n, T)$$

$$\textit{Charles's law:} \qquad V \propto T \quad (\text{constant } n, P)$$

$$\textit{Avogadro's law:} \qquad V \propto n \quad (\text{constant } P, T)$$

We can combine these relationships into a general gas law:

$$V \propto \frac{nT}{P}$$

and if we call the proportionality constant *R*, we obtain an equality:

$$V = R\left(\frac{nT}{P}\right)$$

which we can rearrange to

$$PV = nRT \qquad\qquad [8.5]$$

which is the **ideal-gas equation** (also called the **ideal-gas law**). An **ideal gas** is a hypothetical gas whose pressure, volume, and temperature relationships are described completely by the ideal-gas equation.

In deriving the ideal-gas equation, we assume (a) that the molecules of an ideal gas do not interact with one another and (b) that the combined volume of the molecules is much smaller than the volume the gas occupies; for this reason, we consider the molecules as taking up no space in the container. In many cases, the small error introduced by these assumptions is acceptable. If more accurate calculations are needed, we can correct for the assumptions if we know something about the attraction molecules have for one another and if we know the diameter of the molecules.

The term *R* in the ideal-gas equation is the **gas constant**. The value and units of *R* depend on the units of *P, V, n,* and *T*. The value for *T* in the ideal-gas equation must *always* be the absolute temperature (in kelvins instead of degrees Celsius). The quantity of gas, *n*, is normally expressed in moles. The units chosen for pressure and volume are most often atmospheres and liters, respectively. However, other units can be used. In most countries other than the United States, the pascal is most commonly used for pressure. ◀ TABLE 8.2 shows the numerical value for *R* in various units. In working with the ideal-gas equation, you must choose the form of *R* in which the units agree with the units of *P, V, n,* and *T* given in the problem. In this chapter we will most often use *R* = 0.08206 L-atm/mol-K because pressure is most often given in atmospheres.

Suppose we have 1.000 mol of an ideal gas at 1.000 atm and 0.00 °C (273.15 K). According to the ideal-gas equation, the volume of the gas is

$$V = \frac{nRT}{P} = \frac{(1.000\ \text{mol})(0.08206\ \text{L-atm/mol-K})(273.15\ \text{K})}{1.000\ \text{atm}} = 22.41\ \text{L}$$

The conditions 0 °C and 1 atm are referred to as **standard temperature and pressure (STP)**. The volume occupied by 1 mol of ideal gas at STP, 22.41 L, is known as the *molar volume* of an ideal gas at STP.

TABLE 8.2 • Numerical Values of the Gas Constant *R* in Various Units

Units	Numerical Value
L-atm/mol-K	0.08206
J/mol-K*	8.314
cal/mol-K	1.987
m³-Pa/mol-K*	8.314
L-torr/mol-K	62.36

*SI unit

◢ GIVE IT SOME THOUGHT

How many molecules are in 22.41 L of an ideal gas at STP?

The ideal-gas equation accounts adequately for the properties of most gases under a variety of circumstances. The equation is not exactly correct, however, for any real gas. Thus, the measured volume for given values of *P, n,* and *T* might differ from the volume calculated from *PV* = *nRT* (▼ FIGURE 8.11). Although real gases do not always behave

◢ GO FIGURE

Suggest an explanation for the "ideal" nature of helium compared to the other gases.

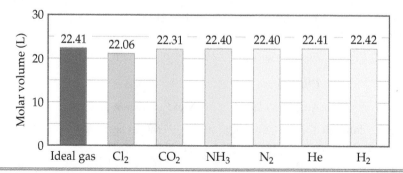

▶ FIGURE 8.11 **Comparison of molar volumes at STP.**

ideally, their behavior differs so little from ideal behavior that we can ignore any deviations for all but the most accurate work.

SAMPLE EXERCISE 8.4 | Using the Ideal-Gas Equation

Calcium carbonate, $CaCO_3(s)$, the principal compound in limestone, decomposes upon heating to $CaO(s)$ and $CO_2(g)$. A sample of $CaCO_3$ is decomposed, and the carbon dioxide is collected in a 250-mL flask. After decomposition is complete, the gas has a pressure of 1.3 atm at a temperature of 31 °C. How many moles of CO_2 gas were generated?

SOLUTION

Analyze We are given the volume (250 mL), pressure (1.3 atm), and temperature (31 °C) of a sample of CO_2 gas and asked to calculate the number of moles of CO_2 in the sample.

Plan Because we are given V, P, and T, we can solve the ideal-gas equation for the unknown quantity, n.

Solve In analyzing and solving gas law problems, it is helpful to tabulate the information given in the problems and then to convert the values to units that are consistent with those for R (0.08206 L-atm/mol-K). In this case the given values are

$V = 250$ mL $= 0.250$ L
$P = 1.3$ atm
$T = 31$ °C $= (31 + 273)$ K $= 304$ K

Remember: *Absolute temperature must always be used when the ideal-gas equation is solved.*

We now rearrange the ideal-gas equation (Equation 8.5) to solve for n

$$n = \frac{PV}{RT}$$

$$n = \frac{(1.3 \text{ atm})(0.250 \text{ L})}{(0.08206 \text{ L-atm/mol-K})(304 \text{ K})} = 0.013 \text{ mol } CO_2$$

Check Appropriate units cancel, thus ensuring that we have properly rearranged the ideal-gas equation and have converted to the correct units.

PRACTICE EXERCISE

Tennis balls are usually filled with either air or N_2 gas to a pressure above atmospheric pressure to increase their bounce. If a tennis ball has a volume of 144 cm^3 and contains 0.33 g of N_2 gas, what is the pressure inside the ball at 24 °C ?

Answer: 2.0 atm

STRATEGIES IN CHEMISTRY

CALCULATIONS INVOLVING MANY VARIABLES

In this chapter we encounter a variety of problems based on the ideal-gas equation, which contains four variables—P, V, n, and T—and one constant, R. Depending on the type of problem, we might need to solve for any of the four variables.

To extract the necessary information from problems involving more than one variable, we suggest the following steps:

1. **Tabulate information.** Read the problems carefully to determine which variable is the unknown and which variables have numeric values given. Every time you encounter a numerical value, jot it down. In many cases constructing a table of the given information will be useful.

2. **Convert to consistent units.** Make certain that quantities are converted to the proper units. In using the ideal-gas equation, for example, we usually use the value of R that has units of L-atm/mol-K. If you are given a pressure in torr, you will need to convert it to atmospheres before using this value of R in your calculations.

3. **If a single equation relates the variables, solve the equation for the unknown.** For the ideal-gas equation, these algebraic rearrangements will all be used at one time or another:

$$P = \frac{nRT}{V}, \quad V = \frac{nRT}{P}, \quad n = \frac{PV}{RT}, \quad T = \frac{PV}{nR}$$

4. **Use dimensional analysis.** Carry the units through your calculation. Using dimensional analysis enables you to check that you have solved an equation correctly. If the units in the equation cancel to give the units of the desired variable, you have probably used the equation correctly.

Sometimes you will not be given explicit values for several variables, making it look like a problem cannot be solved. In these cases, however, you will be given information that can be used to determine the needed variables. For example, suppose you are using the ideal-gas equation to calculate a pressure in a problem that gives a value for T but not for n or V. However, the problem states that "the sample contains 0.15 mol of gas per liter." We can turn this statement into the expression

$$\frac{n}{V} = 0.15 \text{ mol/L}$$

Solving the ideal-gas equation for pressure yields

$$P = \frac{nRT}{V} = \left(\frac{n}{V}\right)RT$$

Thus, we can solve the equation even though we are not given values for n and V.

As we have continuously stressed, the most important thing you can do to become proficient at solving chemistry problems is to do the practice exercises and end-of-chapter exercises. By using systematic procedures, such as those described here, you should be able to minimize difficulties in solving problems involving many variables.

Relating the Ideal-Gas Equation and the Gas Laws

The gas laws we discussed in Section 8.3 are special cases of the ideal-gas equation. For example, when n and T are held constant, the product nRT contains three constants and so must itself be a constant:

$$PV = nRT = \text{constant} \quad \text{or} \quad PV = \text{constant} \qquad [8.6]$$

Thus, we have Boyle's law. We see that if n and T are constant, the values of P and V can change, but the product PV must remain constant.

We can use Boyle's law to determine how the volume of a gas changes when its pressure changes. For example, if a cylinder fitted with a movable piston holds 50.0 L of O_2 gas at 18.5 atm and 21 °C, what volume will the gas occupy if the temperature is maintained at 21 °C while the pressure is reduced to 1.00 atm? Because the product PV is a constant when a gas is held at constant n and T, we know that

$$P_1V_1 = P_2V_2 \qquad [8.7]$$

where P_1 and V_1 are initial values and P_2 and V_2 are final values. Dividing both sides of this equation by P_2 gives the final volume, V_2:

$$V_2 = V_1 \times \frac{P_1}{P_2} = (50.0 \text{ L})\left(\frac{18.5 \text{ atm}}{1.00 \text{ atm}}\right) = 925 \text{ L}$$

The answer is reasonable because a gas expands as its pressure decreases.

In a similar way, we can start with the ideal-gas equation and derive relationships between any other two variables, V and T (Charles's law), n and V (Avogadro's law), or P and T.

SAMPLE EXERCISE 8.5 | **Calculating the Effect of Temperature Changes on Pressure**

The gas pressure in an aerosol can is 1.5 atm at 25 °C. Assuming that the gas obeys the ideal-gas equation, what is the pressure when the can is heated to 450 °C?

SOLUTION

Analyze We are given the initial pressure (1.5 atm) and temperature (25 °C) of the gas and asked for the pressure at a higher temperature (450 °C).

Plan The volume and number of moles of gas do not change, so we must use a relationship connecting pressure and temperature. Converting temperature to the Kelvin scale and tabulating the given information, we have

	P	T
INITIAL	1.5 atm	298 K
FINAL	P_2	723 K

Solve To determine how P and T are related, we start with the ideal-gas equation and isolate the quantities that do not change (n, V, and R) on one side and the variables (P and T) on the other side.

$$\frac{P}{T} = \frac{nR}{V} = \text{constant}$$

Because the quotient P/T is a constant, we can write

$$\frac{P_1}{T_1} = \frac{P_2}{T_2}$$

(where the subscripts 1 and 2 represent the initial and final states, respectively). Rearranging to solve for P_2 and substituting the given data give

$$P_2 = (1.5 \text{ atm})\left(\frac{723 \text{ K}}{298 \text{ K}}\right) = 3.6 \text{ atm}$$

Check This answer is intuitively reasonable—increasing the temperature of a gas increases its pressure.

Comment It is evident from this example why aerosol cans carry a warning not to incinerate.

PRACTICE EXERCISE

The pressure in a natural-gas tank is maintained at 2.20 atm. On a day when the temperature is −15 °C, the volume of gas in the tank is 3.25×10^3 m^3. What is the volume of the same quantity of gas on a day when the temperature is 31 °C?
Answer: 3.83×10^3 m^3

We are often faced with the situation in which P, V, and T all change for a fixed number of moles of gas. Because n is constant in this situation, the ideal-gas equation gives

$$\frac{PV}{T} = nR = \text{constant}$$

If we represent the initial and final conditions by subscripts 1 and 2, respectively, we can write

$$\frac{P_1 V_1}{T_1} = \frac{P_2 V_2}{T_2} \qquad\qquad [8.8]$$

This equation is often called the *combined gas law*.

SAMPLE EXERCISE 8.6	Calculating the Effect of Changing P and T on Gas Volume

An inflated balloon has a volume of 6.0 L at sea level (1.0 atm) and is allowed to ascend until the pressure is 0.45 atm. During ascent, the temperature of the gas falls from 22 °C to −21 °C. Calculate the volume of the balloon at its final altitude.

SOLUTION

Analyze We need to determine a new volume for a gas sample when both pressure and temperature change.

Plan Let's again proceed by converting temperatures to kelvins and tabulating our information.

	P	**V**	**T**
INITIAL	1.0 atm	6.0 L	295 K
FINAL	0.45 atm	V_2	252 K

Because n is constant, we can use Equation 8.8.

Solve Rearranging Equation 8.8 to solve for V_2 gives

$$V_2 = V_1 \times \frac{P_1}{P_2} \times \frac{T_2}{T_1} = (6.0\ \text{L})\left(\frac{1.0\ \text{atm}}{0.45\ \text{atm}}\right)\left(\frac{252\ \text{K}}{295\ \text{K}}\right) = 11\ \text{L}$$

Check The result appears reasonable. Notice that the calculation involves multiplying the initial volume by a ratio of pressures and a ratio of temperatures. Intuitively, we expect decreasing pressure to cause the volume to increase. Similarly, decreasing temperature should cause the volume to decrease. Because the pressure difference is more dramatic than the temperature difference, we expect the effect of the pressure change to predominate in determining the final volume, as it does.

PRACTICE EXERCISE

A 0.50-mol sample of oxygen gas is confined at 0 °C and 1.0 atm in a cylinder with a movable piston. The piston compresses the gas so that the final volume is half the initial volume and the final pressure is 2.2 atm. What is the final temperature of the gas in degrees Celsius?

Answer: 27 °C

8.5 | FURTHER APPLICATIONS OF THE IDEAL-GAS EQUATION

In this section, we use the ideal-gas equation first to define the relationship between the density of a gas and its molar mass, and then to calculate the volumes of gases formed or consumed in chemical reactions.

Gas Densities and Molar Mass

Recall that density has units of mass per unit volume ($d = m/V$). We can arrange the ideal-gas equation to obtain the similar units of moles per unit volume:

$$\frac{n}{V} = \frac{P}{RT}$$

If we multiply both sides of this equation by the molar mass, $\mathcal{M}$, which is the number of grams in 1 mol of a substance, we obtain

$$\frac{n\mathcal{M}}{V} = \frac{P\mathcal{M}}{RT} \qquad [8.9]$$

The term on the left equals the density in grams per liter:

$$\frac{\text{moles}}{\text{liter}} \times \frac{\text{grams}}{\text{mole}} = \frac{\text{grams}}{\text{liter}}$$

Thus, the density of the gas is also given by the expression on the right in Equation 8.9:

$$d = \frac{n\mathcal{M}}{V} = \frac{P\mathcal{M}}{RT} \qquad [8.10]$$

▲ FIGURE 8.12 **Carbon dioxide gas flows downhill because it is denser than air.** The CO_2 "fog" is not the gas made visible but rather is made up of drops of water that have condensed from water vapor in the air.

This equation tells us that the density of a gas depends on its pressure, molar mass, and temperature. The higher the molar mass and pressure, the denser the gas. The higher the temperature, the less dense the gas. Although gases form homogeneous mixtures, a less dense gas will lie above a denser gas in the absence of mixing. For example, CO_2 has a higher molar mass than N_2 or O_2 and is therefore denser than air. For this reason, CO_2 released from a CO_2 fire extinguisher blankets a fire, preventing O_2 from reaching the combustible material. "Dry ice," which is solid CO_2, converts directly to CO_2 gas at room temperature, and the resulting "fog" (which is actually condensed water droplets cooled by the CO_2) flows downhill in air (◄ FIGURE 8.12).

When we have equal molar masses of two gases at the same pressure but different temperatures, the hotter gas is less dense than the cooler one, so the hotter gas rises. The difference between the densities of hot and cold air is responsible for the lift of hot-air balloons. It is also responsible for many phenomena in weather, such as the formation of large thunderhead clouds during thunderstorms.

⊿ **GIVE IT SOME THOUGHT**

Is water vapor more or less dense than N_2 under the same conditions of temperature and pressure?

SAMPLE EXERCISE 8.7   **Calculating Gas Density**

What is the density of carbon tetrachloride vapor at 714 torr and 125 °C ?

SOLUTION

Analyze We are asked to calculate the density of a gas given its name, its pressure, and its temperature. From the name we can write the chemical formula of the substance and determine its molar mass.

Plan We can use Equation 8.10 to calculate the density. Before we can do that, however, we must convert the given quantities to the appropriate units, degrees Celsius to kelvins and pressure to atmospheres. We must also calculate the molar mass of CCl_4.

Solve The absolute temperature is $125 + 273 = 398$ K. The pressure is (714 torr) $(1 \text{ atm}/760 \text{ torr}) = 0.939$ atm. The molar mass of CCl_4 is $12.01 + (4)(35.45) = 153.8$ g/mol. Therefore,

$$d = \frac{(0.939 \text{ atm})(153.8 \text{ g/mol})}{(0.08206 \text{ L-atm/mol-K})(398 \text{ K})} = 4.42 \text{ g/L}$$

Check If we divide molar mass (g/mol) by density (g/L), we end up with L/mol. The numerical value is roughly $154/4.4 = 35$. That is in the right ballpark for the molar volume of a gas heated to 125 °C at near atmospheric pressure, so our answer is reasonable.

PRACTICE EXERCISE

The mean molar mass of the atmosphere at the surface of Titan, Saturn's largest moon, is 28.6 g/mol. The surface temperature is 95 K, and the pressure is 1.6 atm. Assuming ideal behavior, calculate the density of Titan's atmosphere.

Answer: 5.9 g/L

Equation 8.10 can be rearranged to solve for the molar mass of a gas:

$$\mathcal{M} = \frac{dRT}{P} \qquad [8.11]$$

Thus, we can use the experimentally measured density of a gas to determine the molar mass of the gas molecules, as shown in Sample Exercise 8.8.

SAMPLE EXERCISE 8.8 Calculating the Molar Mass of a Gas

A large evacuated flask initially has a mass of 134.567 g. When the flask is filled with a gas of unknown molar mass to a pressure of 735 torr at 31 °C, its mass is 137.456 g. When the flask is evacuated again and then filled with water at 31 °C, its mass is 1067.9 g. (The density of water at this temperature is 0.997 g/mL.) Assuming the ideal-gas equation applies, calculate the molar mass of the gas.

SOLUTION

Analyze We are given the temperature (31 °C) and pressure (735 torr) for a gas, together with information to determine its volume and mass, and we are asked to calculate its molar mass.

Plan We need to use the mass information given to calculate the volume of the container and the mass of the gas in it. From this we calculate the gas density and then apply Equation 8.11 to calculate the molar mass of the gas.

Solve The gas mass is the difference between the mass of the flask filled with gas and the mass of the evacuated flask:

$$137.456 \text{ g} - 134.567 \text{ g} = 2.889 \text{ g}$$

The gas volume equals the volume of water the flask can hold, calculated from the mass and density of the water. The mass of the water is the difference between the masses of the full and evacuated flask:

$$1067.9 \text{ g} - 134.567 \text{ g} = 933.3 \text{ g}$$

Rearranging the equation for density ($d = m/V$), we have

$$V = \frac{m}{d} = \frac{(933.3 \text{ g})}{(0.997 \text{ g/mL})} = 936 \text{ mL} = 0.936 \text{ L}$$

Knowing the mass of the gas (2.889 g) and its volume (0.936 L), we can calculate the density of the gas:

$$2.889 \text{ g}/0.936 \text{ L} = 3.09 \text{ g/L}$$

After converting pressure to atmospheres and temperature to kelvins, we can use Equation 8.11 to calculate the molar mass:

$$\mathcal{M} = \frac{dRT}{P}$$

$$= \frac{(3.09 \text{ g/L})(0.08206 \text{ L-atm/mol-K})(304 \text{ K})}{(0.09671) \text{ atm}}$$

$$= 79.7 \text{ g/mol}$$

Check The units work out appropriately, and the value of molar mass obtained is reasonable for a substance that is gaseous near room temperature.

PRACTICE EXERCISE

Calculate the average molar mass of dry air if it has a density of 1.17 g/L at 21 °C and 740.0 torr.

Answer: 29.0 g/mol

Volumes of Gases in Chemical Reactions

We are often concerned with knowing the identity and/or quantity of a gas involved in a chemical reaction. Thus, it is useful to be able to calculate the volumes of gases consumed or produced in reactions. Such calculations are based on the mole concept and balanced chemical equations. The coefficients in a balanced chemical equation tell us the relative amounts (in moles) of reactants and products in a reaction. The ideal-gas equation relates the number of moles of a gas to *P*, *V*, and *T*.

CHEMISTRY PUT TO WORK

Gas Pipelines

Throughout the developed world, mostly invisible underground pipelines move massive quantities of liquids and gases over hundreds of miles. Essentially all substances that are gases at STP are transported commercially by pipeline, but the largest volume transported by far is natural gas (▼ **FIGURE 8.13**). This methane-rich gas from oil and gas wells is processed to remove particulates, water, and various gaseous impurities such as hydrogen sulfide and carbon dioxide. The gas is then compressed to pressures ranging from 3.5 MPa (35 atm) to 10 MPa (100 atm), depending on the age and diameter of the pipe. Large compressor stations along the pipeline, spaced at 50- to 100-mile intervals, maintain pressure.

Natural gas is a major source of energy for the United States. To meet this demand, methane must be transported from source wells throughout the United States and Canada to all parts of the nation. The total length of pipeline for natural-gas transport in the United States is about 6×10^5 km and growing. The United States is divided into seven regions. The total deliverability of natural gas to the seven regions exceeds 2.7×10^{12} L (measured at STP), almost 100 billion cubic feet per day! The total pipeline volume is not large enough for the enormous quantities of natural gas placed into and taken out of the system on a continuing basis. For this reason, underground storage facilities, such as salt caverns and other natural formations, are employed to hold large quantities of gas.

RELATED EXERCISE: 8.126

◀ FIGURE 8.13 **Natural gas pipeline network in the United States.** The thickest arrow represents flow of 15,000 million cubic feet of gas per day; the thinnest arrow represents flow of 1000 million cubic feet per day.

SAMPLE EXERCISE 8.9 | Relating a Gas Volume to the Amount of Another Substance in a Reaction

Automobile air bags are inflated by nitrogen gas generated by the rapid decomposition of sodium azide, NaN_3:

$$2\ NaN_3(s) \longrightarrow 2\ Na(s) + 3\ N_2(g)$$

If an air bag has a volume of 36 L and is to be filled with nitrogen gas at 1.15 atm and 26.0 °C, how many grams of NaN_3 must be decomposed?

SOLUTION

Analyze This is a multistep problem. We are given the volume, pressure, and temperature of the N_2 gas and the chemical equation for the reaction by which the N_2 is generated. We must use this information to calculate the number of grams of NaN_3 needed to obtain the necessary N_2.

Plan We need to use the gas data (P, V, and T) and the ideal-gas equation to calculate the number of moles of N_2 gas that should be formed for the air bag to operate correctly. We can then use the balanced equation to determine the number of moles of NaN_3 needed. Finally, we can convert moles of NaN_3 to grams.

$$\boxed{\text{Gas data}} \longrightarrow \boxed{\text{mol } N_2} \longrightarrow \boxed{\text{mol } NaN_3} \longrightarrow \boxed{\text{g } NaN_3}$$

Solve The number of moles of N_2 is determined using the ideal-gas equation:

$$n = \frac{PV}{RT} = \frac{(1.15 \text{ atm})(36 \text{ L})}{(0.08206 \text{ L-atm/mol-K})(299 \text{ K})} = 1.69 \text{ mol } N_2$$

We use the coefficients in the balanced equation to calculate the number of moles of NaN_3:

$$(1.69 \text{ mol } N_2)\left(\frac{2 \text{ mol } NaN_3}{3 \text{ mol } N_2}\right) = 1.12 \text{ mol } NaN_3$$

Finally, using the molar mass of NaN_3, we convert moles of NaN_3 to grams:

$$(1.12 \text{ mol } NaN_3)\left(\frac{65.0 \text{ g } NaN_3}{1 \text{ mol } NaN_3}\right) = 73 \text{ g } NaN_3$$

Check The units cancel properly at each step in the calculation, leaving us with the correct units in the answer, g NaN_3.

PRACTICE EXERCISE

In the first step in the industrial process for making nitric acid, ammonia reacts with oxygen in the presence of a suitable catalyst to form nitric oxide and water vapor:

$$4 \text{ NH}_3(g) + 5 \text{ O}_2(g) \longrightarrow 4 \text{ NO}(g) + 6 \text{ H}_2\text{O}(g)$$

How many liters of $NH_3(g)$ at 850 °C and 5.00 atm are required to react with 1.00 mol of $O_2(g)$ in this reaction?

Answer: 14.8 L

8.6 | GAS MIXTURES AND PARTIAL PRESSURES

Thus far we have considered mainly pure gases—those that consist of only one substance in the gaseous state. How do we deal with mixtures of two or more different gases? While studying the properties of air, John Dalton made an important observation: *The total pressure of a mixture of gases equals the sum of the pressures that each would exert if it were present alone.* The pressure exerted by a particular component of a mixture of gases is called the **partial pressure** of that component. Dalton's observation is known as **Dalton's law of partial pressures.**

GIVE IT SOME THOUGHT

How is the pressure exerted by N_2 gas affected when some O_2 is introduced into a container if the temperature and volume remain constant?

If we let P_t be the total pressure of a mixture of gases and P_1, P_2, P_3, and so forth be the partial pressures of the individual gases, we can write Dalton's law of partial pressures as

$$P_t = P_1 + P_2 + P_3 + \cdots \qquad [8.12]$$

This equation implies that each gas behaves independently of the others, as we can see by the following analysis. Let n_1, n_2, n_3, and so forth be the number of moles of each of the gases in the mixture and n_t be the total number of moles of gas. If each gas obeys the ideal-gas equation, we can write

$$P_1 = n_1\left(\frac{RT}{V}\right); \quad P_2 = n_2\left(\frac{RT}{V}\right); \quad P_3 = n_3\left(\frac{RT}{V}\right); \quad \text{and so forth}$$

All the gases are at the same temperature and occupy the same volume. Therefore, by substituting into Equation 8.12, we obtain

$$P_t = (n_1 + n_2 + n_3 + \cdots)\left(\frac{RT}{V}\right) = n_t\left(\frac{RT}{V}\right) \qquad [8.13]$$

That is, at constant temperature and constant volume the total pressure of a gas sample is determined by the total number of moles of gas present, whether that total represents just one gas or a mixture of gases.

SAMPLE EXERCISE 8.10   Applying Dalton's Law of Partial Pressures

A mixture of 6.00 g $O_2(g)$ and 9.00 g $CH_4(g)$ is placed in a 15.0-L vessel at 0 °C. What is the partial pressure of each gas, and what is the total pressure in the vessel?

SOLUTION

Analyze We need to calculate the pressure for two gases in the same volume and at the same temperature.

Plan Because each gas behaves independently, we can use the ideal-gas equation to calculate the pressure each would exert if the other were not present. The total pressure is the sum of these two partial pressures.

Solve We first convert the mass of each gas to moles:

$$n_{O_2} = (6.00 \text{ g } O_2)\left(\frac{1 \text{ mol } O_2}{32.0 \text{ g } O_2}\right) = 0.188 \text{ mol } O_2$$

$$n_{CH_4} = (9.00 \text{ g } CH_4)\left(\frac{1 \text{ mol } CH_4}{16.0 \text{ g } CH_4}\right) = 0.563 \text{ mol } CH_4$$

We use the ideal-gas equation to calculate the partial pressure of each gas:

$$P_{O_2} = \frac{n_{O_2}RT}{V} = \frac{(0.188 \text{ mol})(0.08206 \text{ L-atm/mol-K})(273\text{K})}{15.0\text{L}} = 0.281 \text{ atm}$$

$$P_{CH_4} = \frac{n_{CH_2}RT}{V} = \frac{(0.563 \text{ mol})(0.08206 \text{ L-atm/mol-K})(273 \text{ K})}{15.0 \text{ L}} = 0.841 \text{ atm}$$

According to Dalton's law of partial pressures (Equation 8.12), the total pressure in the vessel is the sum of the partial pressures: $P_t = P_{O_2} + P_{CH_4} = 0.281 \text{ atm} + 0.841 \text{ atm} = 1.122 \text{ atm}$

Check A pressure of roughly 1 atm seems right for a mixture of about 0.2 mol O_2 and a bit more than 0.5 mol CH_4, together in a 15-L volume, because 1 mol of an ideal gas at 1 atm pressure and 0 °C occupies about 22 L.

PRACTICE EXERCISE

What is the total pressure exerted by a mixture of 2.00 g of $H_2(g)$ and 8.00 g of $N_2(g)$ at 273 K in a 10.0-L vessel?

Answer: 2.86 atm

Partial Pressures and Mole Fractions

●Nitrogen ●Oxygen ◐Other gases

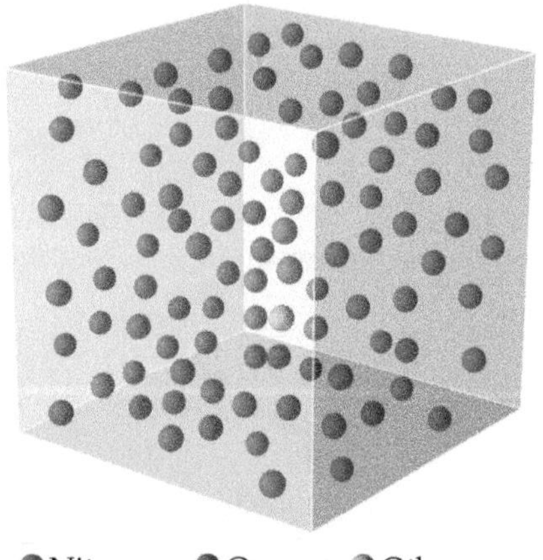

▲ **FIGURE 8.14 Air is approximately 78% nitrogen, 21% oxygen, plus a mixture of many other gases.**

Because each gas in a mixture behaves independently, we can relate the amount of a given gas in a mixture to its partial pressure. For an ideal gas, we can write

$$\frac{P_1}{P_t} = \frac{n_1 RT/V}{n_t RT/V} = \frac{n_1}{n_t} \qquad [8.14]$$

The ratio n_1/n_t is called the *mole fraction of gas 1*, which we denote X_1. The **mole fraction**, *X,* is a dimensionless number that expresses the ratio of the number of moles of one component in a mixture to the total number of moles in the mixture. Thus, for gas 1 we have

$$X_1 = \frac{\text{moles of compound 1}}{\text{total moles}} = \frac{n_1}{n_t} \qquad [8.15]$$

We can combine Equations 8.14 and 8.15 to give

$$P_1 = \left(\frac{n_1}{n_t}\right)P_t = X_1 P_t \qquad [8.16]$$

The mole fraction of N_2 in air is 0.78—that is, 78% of the molecules in air are N_2 (◄ **FIGURE 8.14**). This means that if the barometric pressure is 760 torr, the partial pressure of N_2 is

$$P_{N_2} = (0.78)(760 \text{ torr}) = 590 \text{ torr}$$

This result makes intuitive sense: Because N_2 makes up 78% of the mixture, it contributes 78% of the total pressure.

SAMPLE EXERCISE 8.11   Relating Mole Fractions and Partial Pressures

A study of the effects of certain gases on plant growth requires a synthetic atmosphere composed of 1.5 mol percent CO_2, 18.0 mol percent O_2, and 80.5 mol percent Ar. **(a)** Calculate the partial pressure of O_2 in the mixture if the total pressure of the atmosphere is to be 745 torr. **(b)** If this atmosphere is to be held in a 121-L space at 295 K, how many moles of O_2 are needed?

SOLUTION

Analyze For (a) we need to calculate the partial pressure of O_2 given its mole percent and the total pressure of the mixture. For (b) we need to calculate the number of moles of O_2 in the mixture given its volume (121 L), temperature (745 torr), and partial pressure from part (a).

Plan We calculate the partial pressures using Equation 8.16, and then use P_{O_2}, V, and T in the ideal-gas equation to calculate the number of moles of O_2.

Solve

(a) The mole percent is the mole fraction times 100. Therefore, the mole fraction of O_2 is 0.180. Equation 8.16 gives

$$P_{O_2} = (0.180)(745 \text{ torr}) = 134 \text{ torr}$$

(b) Tabulating the given variables and converting to appropriate units, we have

$$P_{O_2} = (134 \text{ torr})\left(\frac{1 \text{ atm}}{760 \text{ torr}}\right) = 0.176 \text{ atm}$$
$$V = 121 \text{ L}$$
$$n_{O_2} = ?$$
$$R = 0.08206 \frac{\text{L-atm}}{\text{mol-K}}$$
$$T = 295 \text{ K}$$

Solving the ideal-gas equation for n_{O_2}, we have

$$n_{O_2} = P_{O_2}\left(\frac{V}{RT}\right)$$
$$= (0.176 \text{ atm})\frac{121 \text{ L}}{(0.08206 \text{ L-atm/mol-K})(295 \text{ K})} = 0.879 \text{ mol}$$

Check The units check out, and the answer seems to be the right order of magnitude.

PRACTICE EXERCISE

From data gathered by *Voyager 1*, scientists have estimated the composition of the atmosphere of Titan, Saturn's largest moon. The pressure on the surface of Titan is 1220 torr. The atmosphere consists of 82 mol percent N_2, 12 mol percent Ar, and 6.0 mol percent CH_4. Calculate the partial pressure of each gas.

Answer: 1.0×10^3 torr N_2, 1.5×10^2 torr Ar, and 73 torr CH_4

Collecting Gases over Water

An experiment often run in general chemistry laboratories involves determining the number of moles of gas generated in a reaction. Sometimes the gas is collected over water. For example, solid potassium chlorate, $KClO_3$, can be decomposed by heating it in the arrangement shown in ▼ FIGURE 8.15. The balanced equation for the reaction is

$$2 \text{ KClO}_3(s) \longrightarrow 2 \text{ KCl}(s) + 3 \text{ O}_2(g) \qquad [8.17]$$

The oxygen gas is collected in a bottle that is initially filled with water and inverted in a water pan.

Once the reaction is complete, the volume of gas collected is measured by raising or lowering the bottle as necessary until the water levels inside and outside the bottle are the same. When this condition is met, the pressure inside the bottle is equal to atmospheric

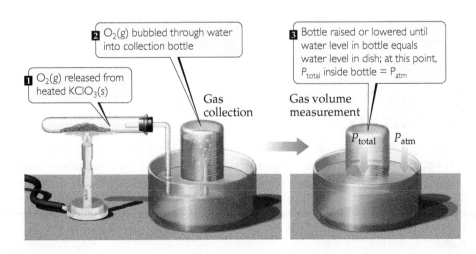

2 $O_2(g)$ bubbled through water into collection bottle

3 Bottle raised or lowered until water level in bottle equals water level in dish; at this point, P_{total} inside bottle = P_{atm}

1 $O_2(g)$ released from heated $KClO_3(s)$

Gas collection

Gas volume measurement

P_{total} P_{atm}

◀ FIGURE 8.15 Collecting a water-insoluble gas over water.

pressure. The total pressure inside is the sum of the pressure of gas collected and the pressure of water vapor in equilibrium with liquid water:

$$P_{total} = P_{gas} + P_{H_2O} \qquad [8.18]$$

Values for P_{H_2O} at various temperatures are listed in Appendix B.

SAMPLE EXERCISE 8.12 | **Calculating the Amount of Gas Collected over Water**

When a sample of $KClO_3$ is partially decomposed in the setup shown in Figure 8.15, the volume of gas collected is 0.250 L at 26 °C and 765 torr total pressure. **(a)** How many moles of O_2 are collected? **(b)** How many grams of $KClO_3$ were decomposed?

SOLUTION

(a) Analyze We need to calculate the number of moles of O_2 gas in a container that also contains water vapor.

Plan We are given values for V and T. To use the ideal-gas equation to calculate the unknown, n_{O_2}, we must know the partial pressure of O_2 in the system. We can calculate this partial pressure from the total pressure (765 torr) and the vapor pressure of water.

Solve The partial pressure of the O_2 gas is the difference between the total pressure and the pressure of the water vapor at 26 °C, 25 torr (Appendix B):

$$P_{O_2} = 765 \text{ torr} - 25 \text{ torr} = 740 \text{ torr}$$

We use the ideal-gas equation to calculate the number of moles of O_2:

$$n_{O_2} = \frac{P_{O_2}V}{RT} = \frac{(740 \text{ torr})(1 \text{ atm}/760 \text{ torr})(0.250 \text{ L})}{(0.08206 \text{ L-atm/mol-K})(299 \text{ K})} = 9.92 \times 10^{-3} \text{ mol } O_2$$

(b) Analyze We need to calculate the number of moles of reactant $KClO_3$ decomposed.

Plan We can use the number of moles of O_2 formed and the balanced chemical equation to determine the number of moles of $KClO_3$ decomposed, which we can then convert to grams of $KClO_3$.

Solve From Equation 8.17, we have 2 mol $KCl_3 \simeq 3$ mol O_2. The molar mass of $KClO_3$ is 122.6 g/mol. Thus, we can convert the number of moles of O_2 from part (a) to moles of $KClO_3$ and then to grams of $KClO_3$:

$$(9.92 \times 10^{-3} \text{ mol } O_2)\left(\frac{2 \text{ mol } KClO_3}{3 \text{ mol } O_2}\right)\left(\frac{122.6 \text{ g } KClO_3}{1 \text{ mol } KClO_3}\right) = 0.811 \text{ g } KClO_3$$

Check The units cancel appropriately in the calculations. The numbers of moles of O_2 and $KClO_3$ seem reasonable, given the small volume of gas collected.

PRACTICE EXERCISE

Ammonium nitrite, NH_4NO_2, decomposes on heating to form N_2 gas:

$$NH_4NO_2(s) \longrightarrow N_2(g) + 2 H_2O(l)$$

When a sample of NH_4NO_2 is decomposed in the apparatus of Figure 8.15, 511 mL of N_2 gas is collected over water at 26 °C and 745 torr total pressure. How many grams of NH_4NO_2 were decomposed?

Answer: 1.26 g

8.7 | THE KINETIC-MOLECULAR THEORY OF GASES

The ideal-gas equation describes *how* gases behave but not *why* they behave as they do. Why does a gas expand when heated at constant pressure? Or why does its pressure increase when the gas is compressed at constant temperature? To understand the physical properties of gases, we need a model that helps us picture what happens to gas particles when conditions such as pressure or temperature change. Such a model, known as the **kinetic-molecular theory of gases**, was developed over a period of about 100 years, culminating in 1857 when Rudolf Clausius (1822–1888) published a complete and satisfactory form of the theory.

The kinetic-molecular theory (the theory of moving molecules) is summarized by the following statements:

1. Gases consist of large numbers of molecules that are in continuous, random motion. (The word *molecule* is used here to designate the smallest particle of any gas even though some gases, such as the noble gases, consist of individual atoms. All we learn about gas behavior from the kinetic-molecular theory applies equally to atomic gases.)

2. The combined volume of all the molecules of the gas is negligible relative to the total volume in which the gas is contained.

3. Attractive and repulsive forces between gas molecules are negligible.

4. Energy can be transferred between molecules during collisions but, as long as temperature remains constant, the *average* kinetic energy of the molecules does not change with time.

5. The average kinetic energy of the molecules is proportional to the absolute temperature. At any given temperature the molecules of all gases have the same average kinetic energy.

The kinetic-molecular theory explains both pressure and temperature at the molecular level. The pressure of a gas is caused by collisions of the molecules with the walls of the container (▶ FIGURE 8.16). The magnitude of the pressure is determined by how often and how forcefully the molecules strike the walls.

The absolute temperature of a gas is a measure of the *average* kinetic energy of its molecules. If two gases are at the same temperature, their molecules have the same average kinetic energy (statement 5 of the kinetic-molecular theory). If the absolute temperature of a gas is doubled, the average kinetic energy of its molecules doubles. Thus, molecular motion increases with increasing temperature.

Pressure inside container comes from collisions of gas molecules with container walls

▲ FIGURE 8.16   **The molecular origin of gas pressure.**

Distributions of Molecular Speed

Although collectively the molecules in a sample of gas have an *average* kinetic energy and hence an average speed, the individual molecules are moving at different speeds. Each molecule collides frequently with other molecules. Momentum is conserved in each collision, but one of the colliding molecules might be deflected off at high speed while the other is nearly stopped. The result is that, at any instant, the molecules in the sample have a wide range of speeds. In ▼ FIGURE 8.17(a), which shows the distribution of molecular speeds for nitrogen gas at 0 °C and 100 °C, we see that a larger fraction of the 100 °C molecules moves at the higher speeds. This means that the 100 °C sample has the higher average kinetic energy.

GO FIGURE

Estimate the fraction of molecules at 100 °C with speeds less than 300 m/s.

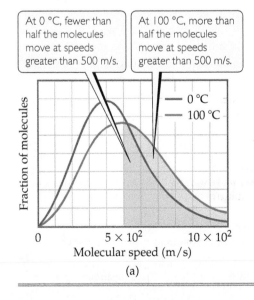

At 0 °C, fewer than half the molecules move at speeds greater than 500 m/s.

At 100 °C, more than half the molecules move at speeds greater than 500 m/s.

— 0 °C
— 100 °C

Fraction of molecules

0   5 × 10²   10 × 10²
Molecular speed (m/s)
(a)

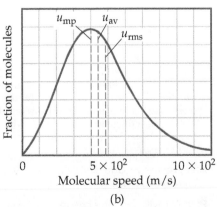

Fraction of molecules

u_{mp} u_{av}
u_{rms}

0   5 × 10²   10 × 10²
Molecular speed (m/s)
(b)

◀ FIGURE 8.17   **Distribution of molecular speeds for nitrogen gas.** (a) The effect of temperature on molecular speed. The relative area under the curve for a range of speeds gives the relative fraction of molecules that have those speed. (b) Position of most probable (u_{mp}), average (u_{av}), and root-mean-square (u_{rms}) speeds of gas molecules. The data shown here are for nitrogen gas at 0 °C.

In any graph of the distribution of molecular speeds in a gas sample, the peak of the curve represents the most probable speed, u_{mp}, which is the speed of the largest number of molecules [Figure 8.17(b)]. The most probable speeds in Figure 8.17(a), for instance, are 4×10^2 m/s for the 0 °C sample and 5×10^2 m/s for the 100 °C sample. Figure 8.17(b) also shows the **root-mean-square (rms) speed**, u_{rms}, of the molecules. This is the speed of a molecule possessing a kinetic energy identical to the average kinetic energy of the sample. The rms speed is not quite the same as the average (mean) speed, u_{av}. The difference between the two is small, however. In Figure 8.17(b), for example, the root-mean-square speed is almost 5×10^2 m/s and the average speed is about 4.5×10^2 m/s.

If you calculate the rms speeds as we will in Section 8.8, you will find that the rms speed is almost 6×10^2 m/s for the 100 °C sample but slightly less than 5×10^2 m/s for the 0 °C sample. Notice that the distribution curve broadens as we go to a higher temperature, which tells us that the range of molecular speeds increases with temperature.

The rms speed is important because the average kinetic energy of the gas molecules in a sample is equal to $\frac{1}{2} m(u_{rms})^2$. (Section 10.1) Because mass does not change with temperature, the increase in the average kinetic energy $\frac{1}{2} m(u_{rms})^2$ as the temperature increases implies that the rms speed of the molecules (as well as their average speed) increases as temperature increases.

GIVE IT SOME THOUGHT

Consider three gases all at 298 K: HCl, H_2, and O_2. List the gases in order of increasing average speed.

Application of Kinetic-Molecular Theory to the Gas Laws

The empirical observations of gas properties as expressed by the various gas laws are readily understood in terms of the kinetic-molecular theory. The following examples illustrate this point:

1. **An increase in volume at constant temperature causes pressure to decrease.** A constant temperature means that the average kinetic energy of the gas molecules remains unchanged. This means that the rms speed of the molecules remains unchanged. When the volume is increased, the molecules must move a longer distance between collisions. Consequently, there are fewer collisions per unit time with the container walls, which means the pressure decreases. Thus, kinetic-molecular theory explains Boyle's law.

2. **A temperature increase at constant volume causes pressure to increase.** An increase in temperature means an increase in the average kinetic energy of the molecules and in u_{rms}. Because there is no change in volume, the temperature increase causes more collisions with the walls per unit time because the molecules are all moving faster. Furthermore, the momentum in each collision increases (the molecules strike the walls more forcefully). A greater number of more forceful collisions means the pressure increases, and the theory explains this increase.

SAMPLE EXERCISE 8.13   Applying the Kinetic-Molecular Theory

A sample of O_2 gas initially at STP is compressed to a smaller volume at constant temperature. What effect does this change have on (a) the average kinetic energy of the molecules, (b) their average speed, (c) the number of collisions they make with the container walls per unit time, (d) the number of collisions they make with a unit area of container wall per unit time?

SOLUTION

Analyze We need to apply the concepts of the kinetic-molecular theory of gases to a gas compressed at constant temperature.

Plan We will determine how each of the quantities in (a)–(d) is affected by the change in volume at constant temperature.

A CLOSER LOOK

THE IDEAL-GAS EQUATION

The ideal-gas equation can be derived from the five statements given in the text for the kinetic-molecular theory. Rather than perform the derivation, however, let's consider in qualitative terms how the ideal-gas equation might follow from these statements. The total force of the molecular collisions on the walls and hence the pressure (force per unit area, Section 8.2) produced by these collisions depend both on how strongly the molecules strike the walls (impulse imparted per collision) and on the rate at which the collisions occur:

$$P \propto \text{impulse imparted per collision} \times \text{collision rate}$$

For a molecule traveling at the rms speed, the impulse imparted by a collision with a wall depends on the momentum of the molecule; that is, it depends on the product of the molecule's mass and speed: mu_{rms}. The collision rate is proportional to the number of molecules per unit volume, n/V, and to their speed, which is u_{rms} because we are talking about only molecules traveling at this speed. If there are more molecules in a container, there will be more frequent collisions with the walls. As the molecular speed increases or the container volume decreases, the time required for molecules to travel from one wall to another is reduced, and the molecules collide more frequently with the walls. Thus, we have

$$P \propto mu_{rms} \times \frac{n}{V} \times u_{rms} \propto \frac{nm(u_{rms})^2}{V} \qquad [8.19]$$

Because the average kinetic energy, $\frac{1}{2}m(u_{rms})^2$, is proportional to temperature, we have $m(u_{rms})^2 \propto T$. Making this substitution in Equation 8.19 gives

$$P \propto \frac{nm(u_{rms})^2}{V} \propto \frac{nT}{V} \qquad [8.20]$$

If we put in a proportionality constant, calling it R, the gas constant, you can see that we obtain the ideal-gas equation:

$$P = \frac{nRT}{V} \qquad [8.21]$$

Swiss mathematician Daniel Bernoulli (1700–1782) conceived of a model for gases that was, for all practical purposes, the same as the model described by the kinetic-molecular theory of gases. From this model, Bernoulli derived Boyle's law and the ideal-gas equation. His was one of the first examples in science of developing a mathematical model from a set of assumptions, or hypothetical statements. However, Bernoulli's work on this subject was completely ignored, only to be rediscovered a hundred years later by Clausius and others. It was ignored because it conflicted with popular beliefs and was in conflict with Isaac Newton's incorrect model for gases. Those idols of the times had to fall before the way was clear for the kinetic-molecular theory. As this story illustrates, science is not a straight road running from here to the "truth." The road is built by humans, so it zigs and zags.

RELATED EXERCISES: 8.77, 8.78, 8.79, and 8.80

Solve (a) Because the average kinetic energy of the O_2 molecules is determined only by temperature, this energy is unchanged by the compression. (b) Because the average kinetic energy of the molecules does not change, their average speed remains constant. (c) The number of collisions with the walls per unit time increases because the molecules are moving in a smaller volume but with the same average speed as before. Under these conditions they must encounter a wall more frequently. (d) The number of collisions with a unit area of wall per unit time increases because the total number of collisions with the walls per unit time increases and the area of the walls decreases.

Check In a conceptual exercise of this kind, there is no numerical answer to check. All we can check in such cases is our reasoning in the course of solving the problem.

PRACTICE EXERCISE

How is the rms speed of N_2 molecules in a gas sample changed by (a) an increase in temperature, (b) an increase in volume, (c) mixing with a sample of Ar at the same temperature?

Answers: (a) increases, (b) no effect, (c) no effect

8.8 | MOLECULAR EFFUSION AND DIFFUSION

According to the kinetic-molecular theory of gases, the average kinetic energy of *any* collection of gas molecules, $\frac{1}{2}m(u_{rms})^2$, has a specific value at a given temperature. Thus, for two gases at the same temperature a gas composed of low-mass particles, such as He, has the same average kinetic energy as one composed of more massive particles, such as Xe. The mass of the particles in the He sample is smaller than that in the Xe sample. Consequently, the He particles must have a higher rms speed than the Xe particles. The equation that expresses this fact quantitatively is

$$u_{rms} = \sqrt{\frac{3RT}{\mathcal{M}}} \qquad [8.22]$$

where $\mathcal{M}$ is the molar mass of the particles, which can be derived from the kinetic-molecular theory. Because $\mathcal{M}$ appears in the denominator, the less massive the gas particles, the higher their rms speed.

How does root-mean-square speed vary with molar mass?

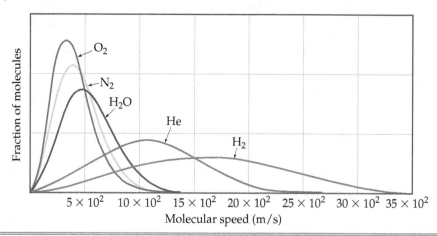

▶ FIGURE 8.18 **The effect of molar mass on molecular speed at 25 °C.**

▲ FIGURE 8.18 shows the distribution of molecular speeds for several gases at 25 °C. Notice how the distributions are shifted toward higher speeds for gases of lower molar masses.

SAMPLE EXERCISE 8.14 | **Calculating a Root-Mean-Square Speed**

Calculate the rms speed of the molecules in a sample of N_2 gas at 25 °C.

SOLUTION

Analyze We are given the identity of a gas and the temperature, the two quantities we need to calculate the rms speed.

Plan We calculate the rms speed using Equation 8.22.

Solve We must convert each quantity in our equation to SI units. We will also use R in units of J/mol-K (Table 8.2) to make the units cancel correctly.

$$T = 25 + 273 = 298 \text{ K}$$

$$\mathcal{M} = 28.0 \text{ g/mol} = 28.0 \times 10^{-3} \text{ kg/mol}$$

$$R = 8.314 \text{ J/mol-K} = 8.314 \text{ kg-m}^2/\text{s}^2\text{-mol-K} \quad (\text{Since } 1 \text{ J} = 1 \text{ kg-m}^2/\text{s}^2)$$

$$u_{rms} = \sqrt{\frac{3(8.314 \text{ kg-m}^2/\text{s}^2\text{-mol-K})(298 \text{ K})}{28.0 \times 10^{-3} \text{ kg/mol}}} = 5.15 \times 10^2 \text{ m/s}$$

Comment This corresponds to a speed of 1150 mi/hr. Because the average molecular weight of air molecules is slightly greater than that of N_2, the rms speed of air molecules is a little lower than that for N_2.

PRACTICE EXERCISE

What is the rms speed of an atom in a sample of He gas at 25 °C?

Answer: 1.36×10^3 m/s

Gas molecules in top half effuse through pinhole only when they happen to hit pinhole

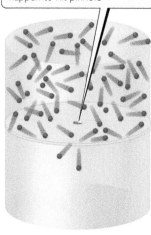

▲ FIGURE 8.19 **Effusion.**

The most probable speed of a gas molecule can also be derived:

$$u_{mp} = \sqrt{\frac{2RT}{\mathcal{M}}} \qquad [8.23]$$

◢ **GIVE IT SOME THOUGHT**

What is the ratio of u_{rms} to u_{mp} for a certain gas at a given temperature?

The dependence of molecular speed on mass has two interesting consequences. The first is **effusion**, which is the escape of gas molecules through a tiny hole (◀ FIGURE 8.19). The second is **diffusion**, which is the spread of one substance throughout a space or throughout a second substance. For example, the molecules of a perfume diffuse throughout a room.

Graham's Law of Effusion

In 1846 Thomas Graham (1805–1869) discovered that the effusion rate of a gas is inversely proportional to the square root of its molar mass. Assume we have two gases at the same temperature and pressure in two containers with identical pinholes. If the rates of effusion of the two gases are r_1 and r_2 and their molar masses are $\mathcal{M}_1$ and $\mathcal{M}_2$, **Graham's law** states that

$$\frac{r_1}{r_2} = \sqrt{\frac{\mathcal{M}_2}{\mathcal{M}_1}} \qquad [8.24]$$

a relationship that indicates that the lighter gas has the higher effusion rate.

The only way for a molecule to escape from its container is for it to "hit" the hole in the partitioning wall of Figure 8.19. The faster the molecules are moving, the greater is the likelihood that a molecule will hit the hole and effuse. This implies that the rate of effusion is directly proportional to the rms speed of the molecules. Because R and T are constant, we have, from Equation 8.22

$$\frac{r_1}{r_2} = \frac{u_{\text{rms1}}}{u_{\text{rms2}}} = \sqrt{\frac{3RT/\mathcal{M}_1}{3RT/\mathcal{M}_2}} = \sqrt{\frac{\mathcal{M}_2}{\mathcal{M}_1}} \qquad [8.25]$$

As expected from Graham's law, helium escapes from containers through tiny pinhole leaks more rapidly than other gases of higher molecular weight (▼ **FIGURE 8.20**).

GO FIGURE

Because pressure and temperature are constant in this figure but volume changes, which other quantity in the ideal-gas equation must also change?

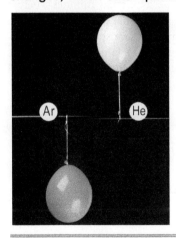

Both gases effuse through pores in balloon, but lighter helium gas effuses faster than heavier argon gas

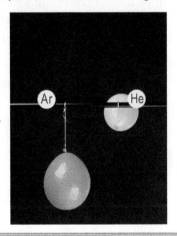

◄ FIGURE 8.20 **An illustration of Graham's law of effusion.**

SAMPLE EXERCISE 8.15 | **Applying Graham's Law**

An unknown gas composed of homonuclear diatomic molecules effuses at a rate that is 0.355 times the rate at which O_2 gas effuses at the same temperature. Calculate the molar mass of the unknown and identify it.

SOLUTION

Analyze We are given the rate of effusion of an unknown gas relative to that of O_2 and asked to find the molar mass and identity of the unknown. Thus, we need to connect relative rates of effusion to relative molar masses.

Plan We use Equation 8.24, to determine the molar mass of the unknown gas. If we let r_x and $\mathcal{M}_x$ represent the rate of effusion and molar mass of the gas, we can write

$$\frac{r_x}{r_{O_2}} = \sqrt{\frac{\mathcal{M}_{O_2}}{\mathcal{M}_x}}$$

Solve From the information given,

$$r_x = 0.355 \times r_{O_2}$$

Thus,

$$\frac{r_x}{r_{O_2}} = 0.355 = \sqrt{\frac{32.0\ \text{g/mol}}{\mathcal{M}_x}}$$

$$\frac{32.0\ \text{g/mol}}{\mathcal{M}_x} = (0.355)^2 = 0.126$$

$$\mathcal{M}_x = \frac{32.0\ \text{g/mol}}{0.126} = 254\ \text{g/mol}$$

Because we are told that the unknown gas is composed of homonuclear diatomic molecules, it must be an element. The molar mass must represent twice the atomic weight of the atoms in the unknown gas. We conclude that the unknown gas is I_2.

PRACTICE EXERCISE

Calculate the ratio of the effusion rates of N_2 gas and O_2 gas.

Answer: $r_{N_2}/r_{O_2} = 1.07$

Diffusion and Mean Free Path

Although diffusion, like effusion, is faster for lower-mass molecules than for higher-mass ones, molecular collisions make diffusion more complicated than effusion.

Graham's law, Equation 8.24, approximates the ratio of the diffusion rates of two gases under identical conditions. We can see from the horizontal axis in Figure 8.18 that the speeds of molecules are quite high. For example, the rms speed of molecules of N_2 gas at room temperature is 515 m/s. In spite of this high speed, if someone opens a vial of perfume at one end of a room, some time elapses—perhaps a few minutes—before the scent is detected at the other end of the room. This tells us that the diffusion rate of gases throughout a volume of space is much slower than molecular speeds.* This difference is due to molecular collisions, which occur frequently for a gas at atmospheric pressure—about 10^{10} times per second for each molecule. Collisions occur because real gas molecules have finite volumes.

CHEMISTRY PUT TO WORK

Gas Separations

The fact that lighter molecules move at higher average speeds than more massive ones has many interesting applications. For example, developing the atomic bomb during World War II required scientists to separate the relatively low-abundance uranium isotope ^{235}U (0.7%) from the much more abundant ^{238}U (99.3%). This separation was accomplished by converting the uranium into a volatile compound, UF_6, that was then allowed to pass through a porous barrier. (Because of the pore diameters, this process is not simple effusion. Nevertheless, the way in which rate of passing through the pores depends on molar mass is essentially the same as in effusion.) The slight difference in molar mass between $^{235}UF_6$ and $^{238}UF_6$ caused the molecules to move at slightly different rates:

$$\frac{r_{235}}{r_{238}} = \sqrt{\frac{352.04}{349.03}} = 1.0043$$

Thus, the gas initially appearing on the opposite side of the barrier was very slightly enriched in ^{235}U. The process was repeated thousands of times, leading to a nearly complete separation of the two isotopes.

Separation of uranium isotopes by effusion has been largely replaced by a technique that uses centrifuges. In this procedure, cylindrical rotors containing UF_6 vapor spin at high speed inside an evacuated casing. Molecules of $^{238}UF_6$ move closer to the spinning walls, whereas molecules of $^{235}UF_6$ remain in the middle of the cylinders. A stream of gas moves the $^{235}UF_6$ from the center of one centrifuge into another. Plants that use centrifuges consume less energy than those that use effusion and can be constructed in a more compact, modular fashion. Such plants are frequently in the news today as countries such as Iran and North Korea enrich uranium in the ^{235}U isotope for both nuclear power and nuclear weaponry.

RELATED EXERCISES: 8.89 and 8.90

---

*The rate at which the perfume moves across the room also depends on how well stirred the air is from temperature gradients and the movement of people. Nevertheless, even with the aid of these factors, it still takes much longer for the molecules to traverse the room than one would expect from their rms speed.

Because of molecular collisions, the direction of motion of a gas molecule is constantly changing. Therefore, the diffusion of a molecule from one point to another consists of many short, straight-line segments as collisions buffet it around in random directions (▶ FIGURE 8.21).

The average distance traveled by a molecule between collisions, called the molecule's **mean free path**, varies with pressure as the following analogy illustrates. Imagine walking through a shopping mall. When the mall is crowded (high pressure), the average distance you can walk before bumping into someone is short (short mean free path). When the mall is empty (low pressure), you can walk a long way (long mean free path) before bumping into someone. The mean free path for air molecules at sea level is about 60 nm. At about 100 km in altitude, where the air density is much lower, the mean free path is about 10 cm, over 1 million times longer than at Earth's surface.

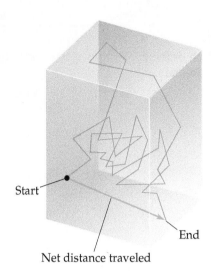

Start

Net distance traveled

End

▲ FIGURE 8.21 **Diffusion of a gas molecule.** For clarity, no other gas molecules in the container are shown.

⚠ GIVE IT SOME THOUGHT

Will these changes increase, decrease, or have no effect on the mean free path of the molecules in a gas sample?
a. increasing pressure.
b. increasing temperature.

8.9 | REAL GASES: DEVIATIONS FROM IDEAL BEHAVIOR

The extent to which a real gas departs from ideal behavior can be seen by rearranging the ideal-gas equation to solve for n:

$$\frac{PV}{RT} = n \qquad\qquad [8.26]$$

This form of the equation tells us that for 1 mol of ideal gas, the quantity PV/RT equals 1 at all pressures. In ▼ FIGURE 8.22 PV/RT is plotted as a function of P for 1 mol of several real gases. At high pressures (generally above 10 atm) the deviation from ideal behavior ($PV/RT = 1$) is large and different for each gas. *Real gases, in other words, do not behave ideally at high pressure.* At lower pressures (usually below 10 atm), however, the deviation from ideal behavior is small, and we can use the ideal-gas equation without generating serious error.

⚠ GO FIGURE

Does molar mass correlate with nonideal-gas behavior below 200 atm?

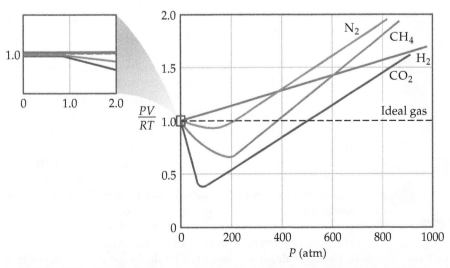

▲ FIGURE 8.22 **The effect of pressure on the behavior of several real gases.** Data for 1 mol of gas in all cases. Data for N_2, CH_4, and H_2 are at 300 K; for CO_2 data are at 313 K because under high pressure CO_2 liquefies at 300 K.

True or false: Nitrogen gas behaves more like an ideal gas as the temperature increases.

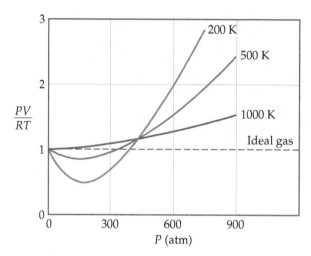

▶ **FIGURE 8.23** **The effect of temperature and pressure on the behavior of nitrogen gas.**

Deviation from ideal behavior also depends on temperature. As temperature increases, the behavior of a real gas more nearly approaches that of the ideal gas (▲ FIGURE 8.23). In general, *the deviation from ideal behavior increases as temperature decreases,* becoming significant near the temperature at which the gas liquefies.

⚠ **GIVE IT SOME THOUGHT**

Under which conditions do you expect helium gas to deviate most from ideal behavior?
a. 100 K and 1 atm,
b. 100 K and 5 atm, or
c. 300 K and 2 atm.

The basic assumptions of the kinetic-molecular theory of gases give us insight into why real gases deviate from ideal behavior. The molecules of an ideal gas are assumed to occupy no space and have no attraction for one another. *Real molecules, however, do have finite volumes and do attract one another.* As ◀ FIGURE 8.24 shows, the unoccupied space in which real molecules can move is less than the container volume. At low pressures the combined volume of the gas molecules is negligible relative to the container volume. Thus, the unoccupied volume available to the molecules is essentially the container volume. At high pressures, the combined volume of the gas molecules is *not* negligible relative to the container volume. Now the unoccupied volume available to the molecules is less than the container volume. At high pressures, therefore, gas volumes tend to be slightly greater than those predicted by the ideal-gas equation.

Another reason for nonideal behavior at high pressures is that the attractive forces between molecules come into play at the short intermolecular distances found when molecules are crowded together at high pressures. Because of these attractive forces, the impact of a given molecule with the container wall is lessened. If we could stop the motion in a gas, as illustrated in ▶ FIGURE 8.25, we would see that a molecule about to collide with the wall experiences the attractive forces of nearby molecules. These attractions lessen the force with which the molecule hits the wall. As a result, the gas pressure is less than that of an ideal gas. This effect decreases PV/RT to below its ideal value, as seen at the lower pressures in Figures 8.22 and 8.23. When the pressure is sufficiently high, however, the volume effects dominate and PV/RT increases to above the ideal value.

Low pressure   High pressure

▲ **FIGURE 8.24** **Gases behave more ideally at low pressure than at high pressure.** The combined volume of the molecules can be neglected at low pressure but not at high pressure.

How would you expect the pressure of a gas to change if suddenly the intermolecular forces were repulsive rather than attractive?

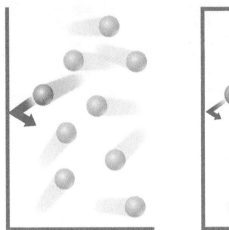
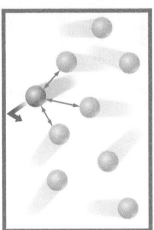

Ideal gas   Real gas

▲ FIGURE 8.25   **In any real gas, attractive intermolecular forces reduce pressure to values lower than in an ideal gas.**

Temperature determines how effective attractive forces between gas molecules are in causing deviations from ideal behavior at lower pressures. Figure 8.23 shows that, at pressures below about 400 atm, cooling increases the extent to which a gas deviates from ideal behavior. As the gas cools, the average kinetic energy of the molecules decreases. This drop in kinetic energy means the molecules do not have the energy needed to overcome intermolecular attraction, and the molecules will be more likely to stick to each other than bounce off each other.

As the temperature of a gas increases—as, say, from 200 K to 1000 K in Figure 8.23—the negative deviation of PV/RT from the ideal value of 1 disappears. As noted earlier, the deviations seen at high temperatures stem mainly from the effect of the finite volumes of the molecules.

◢ GIVE IT SOME THOUGHT

List two reasons why gases deviate from ideal behavior.

The van der Waals Equation

Engineers and scientists who work with gases at high pressures often cannot use the ideal-gas equation because departures from ideal behavior are too large. One useful equation developed to predict the behavior of real gases was proposed by the Dutch scientist Johannes van der Waals (1837–1923).

Van der Waals recognized that the ideal-gas equation could be corrected to account for the effects of intermolecular attractive forces and for molecular volumes. He introduced two constants for these corrections: a, a measure of how strongly the gas molecules attract one another, and b, a measure of the finite volume occupied by the molecules. His description of gas behavior is known as the **van der Waals equation**:

$$\left(P + \frac{n^2 a}{V^2}\right)(V - nb) = nRT \qquad\qquad [8.27]$$

The term $n^2 a/V^2$ accounts for the attractive forces. The equation adjusts the pressure upward by adding $n^2 a/V^2$ because attractive forces between molecules tend to reduce the pressure (Figure 8.25). The added term has the form $n^2 a/V^2$ because the attractive force between pairs of molecules increases as the square of the number of molecules per unit volume, $(n/V)^2$.

TABLE 8.3 • Van der Waals Constants for Gas Molecules

Substance	$a(L^2\text{-atm/mol}^2)$	b (L/mol)
He	0.0341	0.02370
Ne	0.211	0.0171
Ar	1.34	0.0322
Kr	2.32	0.0398
Xe	4.19	0.0510
H_2	0.244	0.0266
N_2	1.39	0.0391
O_2	1.36	0.0318
Cl_2	6.49	0.0562
H_2O	5.46	0.0305
CH_4	2.25	0.0428
CO_2	3.59	0.0427
CCl_4	20.4	0.1383

The term nb accounts for the small but finite volume occupied by the gas molecules (Figure 8.24). The van der Waals equation subtracts nb to adjust the volume downward to give the volume that would be available to the molecules in the ideal case. The constants a and b, called *van der Waals constants,* are experimentally determined, positive quantities that differ from one gas to another. Notice in ▲ TABLE 8.3 that a and b generally increase with increasing molecular mass. Larger, more massive molecules have larger volumes and tend to have greater intermolecular attractive forces.

SAMPLE EXERCISE 8.16 | **Using the van der Waals Equation**

If 1.000 mol of an ideal gas were confined to 22.41 L at 0.0 °C, it would exert a pressure of 1.000 atm. Use the van der Waals equation and Table 8.3 to estimate the pressure exerted by 1.000 mol of $Cl_2(g)$ in 22.41 L at 0.0 °C.

SOLUTION

Analyze We need to determine a pressure. Because we will use the van der Waals equation, we must identify the appropriate values for the constants that appear there.

Plan Solving Equation 8.27 for P, we have

$$P = \frac{nRT}{V - nb} - \frac{n^2a}{V^2}$$

Solve Substituting $n = 1.000$ mol, $R = 0.08206$ L-atm/mol-K, $T = 273.2$ K, $V = 22.41$ L, $a = 6.49$ L²-atm/mol², and $b = 0.0562$ L/mol:

$$P = \frac{(1.000 \text{ mol})(0.08206 \text{ L-atm/mol-K})(273.2 \text{ K})}{22.41 \text{ L} - (1.000 \text{ mol})(0.0562 \text{ L/mol})} - \frac{(1.000 \text{ mol})^2(6.49 \text{ L}^2\text{-atm/mol}^2)}{(22.14 \text{ L})^2}$$

$$= 1.003 \text{ atm} - 0.013 \text{ atm} = 0.990 \text{ atm}$$

Check We expect a pressure not far from 1.000 atm, which would be the value for an ideal gas, so our answer seems very reasonable.

Comment Notice that the term 1.003 atm is the pressure corrected for molecular volume. This value is higher than the ideal value, 1.000 atm, because the volume in which the molecules are free to move is smaller than the container volume, 22.41 L. Thus, the molecules collide more frequently with the container walls. The term 0.013 atm corrects for intermolecular forces. The intermolecular attractions between molecules reduce the pressure to 0.990 atm. We conclude, therefore, that the intermolecular attractions are the main cause of the slight deviation of $Cl_2(g)$ from ideal behavior under the stated experimental conditions.

PRACTICE EXERCISE

A sample of 1.000 mol of $CO_2(g)$ is confined to a 3.000-L container at 0.000 °C. Calculate the pressure of the gas using (**a**) the ideal-gas equation and (**b**) the van der Waals equation.

Answers: (**a**) 7.47 atm, (**b**) 7.18 atm

SAMPLE INTEGRATIVE EXERCISE Putting Concepts Together

Cyanogen, a highly toxic gas, is 46.2% C and 53.8% N by mass. At 25 °C and 751 torr, 1.05 g of cyanogen occupies 0.500 L. **(a)** What is the molecular formula of cyanogen? Predict **(b)** its molecular structure and **(c)** its polarity.

SOLUTION

Analyze We need to determine the molecular formula of a gas from elemental analysis data and data on its properties. Then we need to predict the structure of the molecule and from that, its polarity.

(a) Plan We can use the percentage composition of the compound to calculate its empirical formula. Then we can determine the molecular formula by comparing the mass of the empirical formula with the molar mass.

Solve To determine the empirical formula, we assume we have a 100-g sample and calculate the number of moles of each element in the sample:

$$\text{Moles C} = (46.2 \text{ g C})\left(\frac{1 \text{ mol C}}{12.01 \text{ g C}}\right) = 3.85 \text{ mol C}$$

$$\text{Moles N} = (53.8 \text{ g N})\left(\frac{1 \text{ mol N}}{14.01 \text{ g N}}\right) = 3.84 \text{ mol N}$$

Because the ratio of the moles of the two elements is essentially 1:1, the empirical formula is CN. To determine the molar mass, we use Equation 8.11.

$$\mathcal{M} = \frac{dRT}{P} = \frac{(1.05 \text{ g}/0.500 \text{ L})(0.08206 \text{ L-atm/mol-K})(298 \text{ K})}{(751/760)\text{atm}} = 52.0 \text{ g/mol}$$

The molar mass associated with the empirical formula CN is $12.0 + 14.0 = 26.0$ g/mol. Dividing the molar mass by that of its empirical formula gives $(52.0 \text{ g/mol})/(26.0 \text{ g/mol}) = 2.00$. Thus, the molecule has twice as many atoms of each element as the empirical formula, giving the molecular formula C_2N_2.

(b) Plan To determine the molecular structure, we must determine the Lewis structure. ∞ (Section 3.5) We can then use the VSEPR model to predict the structure. ∞ (Section 4.2)

Solve The molecule has $2(4) + 2(5) = 18$ valence-shell electrons. By trial and error, we seek a Lewis structure with 18 valence electrons in which each atom has an octet and the formal charges are as low as possible. The structure

$$:N\equiv C - C \equiv N:$$

meets these criteria. (This structure has zero formal charge on each atom.)

The Lewis structure shows that each atom has two electron domains. (Each nitrogen has a nonbonding pair of electrons and a triple bond, whereas each carbon has a triple bond and a single bond.) Thus, the electron-domain geometry around each atom is linear, causing the overall molecule to be linear.

(c) Plan To determine the polarity of the molecule, we must examine the polarity of the individual bonds and the overall geometry of the molecule.

Solve Because the molecule is linear, we expect the two dipoles created by the polarity in the carbon–nitrogen bond to cancel each other, leaving the molecule with no dipole moment.

CHAPTER SUMMARY AND KEY TERMS

SECTION 8.1 Substances that are gases at room temperature tend to be molecular substances with low molar masses. Air, a mixture composed mainly of N_2 and O_2, is the most common gas we encounter. Some liquids and solids can also exist in the gaseous state, where they are known as **vapors**. Gases are compressible; they mix in all proportions because their component molecules are far apart from each other.

SECTION 8.2 To describe the state or condition of a gas, we must specify four variables: pressure (P), volume (V), temperature (T), and quantity (n). Volume is usually measured in liters, temperature in kelvins, and quantity of gas in moles. **Pressure** is the force per unit area. It is expressed in SI units as **pascals**, Pa ($1 \text{ Pa} = 1 \text{ N/m}^2$). A related unit, the **bar**, equals 10^5 Pa. In chemistry, **standard atmospheric pressure** is used to define the **atmosphere** (atm) and the **torr** (also called the millimeter of mercury). One atmosphere of pressure equals 101.325 kPa, or 760 torr. A barometer is often used to measure the atmospheric pressure. A manometer can be used to measure the pressure of enclosed gases.

SECTIONS 8.3 AND 8.4 Studies have revealed several simple gas laws: For a constant quantity of gas at constant temperature, the volume of the gas is inversely proportional to the pressure (**Boyle's law**).

For a fixed quantity of gas at constant pressure, the volume is directly proportional to its absolute temperature (**Charles's law**). Equal volumes of gases at the same temperature and pressure contain equal numbers of molecules (**Avogadro's hypothesis**). For a gas at constant temperature and pressure, the volume of the gas is directly proportional to the number of moles of gas (**Avogadro's law**). Each of these gas laws is a special case of the ideal-gas equation.

The **ideal-gas equation**, $PV = nRT$, is the equation of state for an **ideal gas**. The term R in this equation is the **gas constant**. We can use the ideal-gas equation to calculate variations in one variable when one or more of the others are changed. Most gases at pressures less than 10 atm and temperatures near 273 K and above obey the ideal-gas equation reasonably well. The conditions of 273 K (0 °C) and 1 atm are known as the **standard temperature and pressure (STP)**. In all applications of the ideal-gas equation we must remember to convert temperatures to the absolute-temperature scale (the Kelvin scale).

SECTIONS 8.5 AND 8.6 Using the ideal-gas equation, we can relate the density of a gas to its molar mass: $\mathcal{M} = dRT/P$. We can also use the ideal-gas equation to solve problems involving gases as reactants or products in chemical reactions.

In gas mixtures the total pressure is the sum of the **partial pressures** that each gas would exert if it were present alone under the same conditions (**Dalton's law of partial pressures**). The partial pressure of a component of a mixture is equal to its mole fraction times the total pressure: $P_1 = X_1 P_t$. The **mole fraction** is the ratio of the moles of one component of a mixture to the total moles of all components. In calculating the quantity of a gas collected over water, correction must be made for the partial pressure of water vapor in the gas mixture.

SECTION 8.7 The **kinetic-molecular theory of gases** accounts for the properties of an ideal gas in terms of a set of statements about the nature of gases. Briefly, these statements are as follows: Molecules are in continuous chaotic motion. The volume of gas molecules is negligible compared to the volume of their container. The gas molecules neither attract nor repel each other. The average kinetic energy of the gas molecules is proportional to the absolute temperature and does not change if the temperature remains constant.

The individual molecules of a gas do not all have the same kinetic energy at a given instant. Their speeds are distributed over a wide range; the distribution varies with the molar mass of the gas and with temperature. The **root-mean-square (rms) speed**, u_{rms}, varies in proportion to the square root of the absolute temperature and inversely with the square root of the molar mass: $u_{rms} = \sqrt{3RT/\mathcal{M}}$. The most probable speed of a gas molecule is given by $u_{mp} = \sqrt{2RT/\mathcal{M}}$.

SECTION 8.8 It follows from kinetic-molecular theory that the rate at which a gas undergoes **effusion** (escapes through a tiny hole) is inversely proportional to the square root of its molar mass (**Graham's law**). The **diffusion** of one gas through the space occupied by a second gas is another phenomenon related to the speeds at which molecules move. Because molecules undergo frequent collisions with one another, the **mean free path**—the mean distance traveled between collisions—is short. Collisions between molecules limit the rate at which a gas molecule can diffuse.

SECTION 8.9 Departures from ideal behavior increase in magnitude as pressure increases and as temperature decreases. The extent of nonideality of a real gas can be seen by examining the quantity $PV = RT$ for one mole of the gas as a function of pressure; for an ideal gas, this quantity is exactly 1 at all pressures. Real gases depart from ideal behavior because the molecules possess finite volume and because the molecules experience attractive forces for one another. The **van der Waals equation** is an equation of state for gases that modifies the ideal-gas equation to account for intrinsic molecular volume and intermolecular forces.

KEY SKILLS

- Convert between pressure units with an emphasis on torr and atmospheres. (Section 8.2)

- Calculate P, V, n, or T using the ideal-gas equation. (Section 8.4)

- Understand how the gas laws relate to the ideal-gas equation and apply the gas laws in calculations. (Sections 8.3 and 8.4)

- Calculate the density or molecular weight of a gas. (Section 8.5)

- Calculate the volume of gas consumed or formed in a chemical reaction. (Section 8.5)

- Calculate the total pressure of a gas mixture given its partial pressures or given information for calculating partial pressures. (Section 8.6)

- Describe the kinetic-molecular theory of gases and how it explains the pressure and temperature of a gas, the gas laws, and the rates of effusion and diffusion. (Sections 8.7 and 8.8)

- Explain why intermolecular attractions and molecular volumes cause real gases to deviate from ideal behavior at high pressure or low temperature. (Section 8.9)

KEY EQUATIONS

- $PV = nRT$ [8.5]   Ideal-gas equation

- $\dfrac{P_1 V_1}{T_1} = \dfrac{P_2 V_2}{T_2}$ [8.8]   The combined gas law, showing how P, V, and T are related for a constant n

- $d = \dfrac{P\mathcal{M}}{RT}$ [8.10]   Calculating the density or molar mass of a gas

- $P_t = P_1 + P_2 + P_3 + \ldots$ [8.12]   Relating the total pressure of a gas mixture to the partial pressures of its components (Dalton's law of partial pressures)

- $P_1 = \left(\dfrac{n_1}{n_t}\right) P_t = X_1 P_t$ [8.16]   Relating partial pressure to mole fraction

- $u_{rms} = \sqrt{\dfrac{3RT}{\mathcal{M}}}$ [8.22]   Definition of the root-mean-square (rms) speed of gas molecules

- $\dfrac{r_1}{r_2} = \sqrt{\dfrac{\mathcal{M}_2}{\mathcal{M}_1}}$ [8.24]   Relating the relative rates of effusion of two gases to their molar masses

EXERCISES

VISUALIZING CONCEPTS

8.1 Mars has an average atmospheric pressure of 0.007 atm. Would it be easier or harder to drink from a straw on Mars than on Earth? Explain. [Section 8.2]

8.2 You have a sample of gas in a container with a movable piston, such as the one in the drawing. **(a)** Redraw the container to show what it might look like if the temperature of the gas is increased from 300 K to 500 K while the pressure is kept constant. **(b)** Redraw the container to show what it might look like if the external pressure on the piston is increased from 1.0 atm to 2.0 atm while the temperature is kept constant. **(c)** Redraw the container to show what it might look like if the temperature of the gas decreases from 300 K to 200 K while the pressure is kept constant (assume the gas does not liquefy). [Section 8.3]

8.3 Consider the sample of gas depicted here. What would the drawing look like if the volume and temperature remained constant while you removed enough of the gas to decrease the pressure by a factor of 2? [Section 8.3]

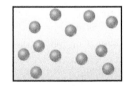

8.4 Imagine that the reaction $2\,CO(g) + O_2(g) \longrightarrow 2\,CO_2(g)$ occurs in a container that has a piston that moves to maintain a constant pressure when the reaction occurs at constant temperature. **(a)** What happens to the volume of the container as a result of the reaction? Explain. **(b)** If the piston is not allowed to move, what happens to the pressure as a result of the reaction? [Sections 8.3 and 8.5]

8.5 Suppose you have a fixed amount of an ideal gas at a constant volume. If the pressure of the gas is doubled while the volume is held constant, what happens to its temperature? [Section 8.4]

8.6 The apparatus shown here has two gas-filled containers and one empty container, all attached to a hollow horizontal tube.

When the valves are opened and the gases are allowed to mix at constant temperature, what is the distribution of atoms in each container? Assume that the containers are of equal volume and ignore the volume of the connecting tube. Which gas has the greater partial pressure after the valves are opened? [Section 8.6]

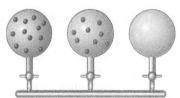

8.7 The accompanying drawing represents a mixture of three different gases. **(a)** Rank the three components in order of increasing partial pressure. **(b)** If the total pressure of the mixture is 1.40 atm, calculate the partial pressure of each gas. [Section 8.6]

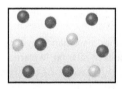

8.8 On a single plot, qualitatively sketch the distribution of molecular speeds for **(a)** Kr(g) at −50 °C, **(b)** Kr(g) at 0 °C, **(c)** Ar(g) at 0 °C. [Section 8.7]

8.9 Consider the following graph. **(a)** If curves A and B refer to two different gases, He and O_2, at the same temperature, which is which? Explain. **(b)** If A and B refer to the same gas at two different temperatures, which represents the higher temperature? **(c)** Redraw the graph and put in vertical lines that indicate the approximate positions of the most probable speeds and root-mean-square speeds for each curve. [Section 8.7]

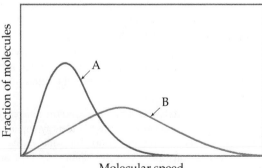

Molecular speed

8.10 Consider the following samples of gases:

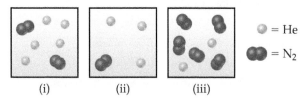

(i)   (ii)   (iii)

If the three samples are all at the same temperature, rank them with respect to (**a**) total pressure, (**b**) partial pressure of helium, (**c**) density, (**d**) average kinetic energy of particles. [Section 8.6 and 8.7]

8.11 A thin glass tube 1 m long is filled with Ar gas at 1 atm, and the ends are stoppered with cotton plugs:

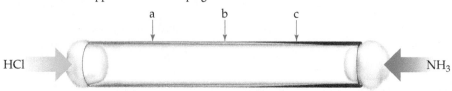

HCl gas is introduced at one end of the tube, and simultaneously NH_3 gas is introduced at the other end. When the two gases diffuse through the cotton plugs down the tube and meet, a white ring appears due to the formation of $NH_4Cl(s)$. At which location—a, b, or c—do you expect the ring to form? Explain your choice. [Section 8.8]

8.12 Which substances in Table 8.3 would you expect to deviate most from ideal-gas behavior at low temperature and high pressure? Which would deviate least? Explain. [Section 8.9]

GAS CHARACTERISTICS; PRESSURE (sections 8.1 and 8.2)

8.13 How does a gas compare with a liquid for each of the following properties: (**a**) density, (**b**) compressibility, (**c**) ability to mix with other substances of the same phase to form homogeneous mixtures, (**d**) ability to conform to the shape of its container?

8.14 (**a**) A liquid and a gas are moved to larger containers. How does their behavior differ once they are in the larger containers? Explain the difference in molecular terms. (**b**) Although liquid water and carbon tetrachloride, $CCl_4(l)$, do not mix, their vapors form a homogeneous mixture. Explain. (**c**) Gas densities are generally reported in grams per liter, whereas liquid densities are reported in grams per milliliter. Explain the molecular basis for this difference.

8.15 Suppose that a woman weighing 130 lb and wearing high-heeled shoes momentarily places all her weight on the heel of one foot. If the area of the heel is 0.50 in.^{2}, calculate the pressure exerted on the underlying surface in (**a**) kilopascals, (**b**) atmospheres, and (**c**) pounds per square inch.

8.16 A set of bookshelves rests on a hard floor surface on four legs, each having a cross-sectional dimension of 3.0 × 4.1 cm in contact with the floor. The total mass of the shelves plus the books stacked on them is 262 kg. Calculate the pressure in pascals exerted by the shelf footings on the surface.

8.17 (**a**) How high in meters must a column of water be to exert a pressure equal to that of a 760-mm column of mercury? The density of water is 1.0 g/mL, whereas that of mercury is 13.6 g/mL. (**b**) What is the pressure, in atmospheres, on the body of a diver if he is 39 ft below the surface of the water when atmospheric pressure at the surface is 0.97 atm?

8.18 The compound 1-iodododecane is a nonvolatile liquid with a density of 1.20 g/mL. The density of mercury is 13.6 g/mL. What do you predict for the height of a barometer column based on 1-iodododecane, when the atmospheric pressure is 749 torr?

8.19 Each of the following statements concerns a mercury barometer such as that shown in Figure 8.2. Identify any incorrect statements and correct them. (**a**) The tube must be 1 cm^2 in cross-sectional area. (**b**) At equilibrium the force of gravity per unit area acting on the mercury column equals the force of gravity per unit area acting on the atmosphere. (**c**) The column

of mercury is held up by the vacuum at the top of the column. (**d**) If you took the mercury barometer with you on a trip from the beach to high mountains, the height of the mercury column would increase with elevation.

8.20 Suppose you make a mercury barometer using a glass tube about 50 cm in length, closed at one end. What would you expect to see if the tube is filled with mercury and inverted in a mercury dish, as in Figure 8.2? Explain.

8.21 The typical atmospheric pressure on top of Mt. Everest (29,028 ft) is about 265 torr. Convert this pressure to (**a**) atm, (**b**) mm Hg, (**c**) pascals, (**d**) bars, (**e**) psi.

8.22 Perform the following conversions: (**a**) 0.912 atm to torr, (**b**) 0.685 bar to kilopascals, (**c**) 655 mm Hg to atmospheres, (**d**) 1.323×10^5 Pa to atmospheres, (**e**) 2.50 atm to psi.

8.23 In the United States, barometric pressures are generally reported in inches of mercury (in. Hg). On a beautiful summer day in Chicago the barometric pressure is 30.45 in. Hg. (**a**) Convert this pressure to torr. (**b**) Convert this pressure to atm. (**c**) A meteorologist explains the nice weather by referring to a "high-pressure area." In light of your answer to parts (a) and (b), explain why this term makes sense.

8.24 Hurricane Wilma of 2005 is the most intense hurricane on record in the Atlantic basin, with a low-pressure reading of 882 mbar (millibars). Convert this reading into (**a**) atmospheres, (**b**) torr, and (**c**) inches of Hg.

8.25 If the atmospheric pressure is 0.995 atm, what is the pressure of the enclosed gas in each of the three cases depicted in the drawing? Assume that the gray liquid is mercury.

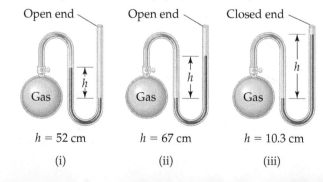

Open end   Open end   Closed end

Gas   Gas   Gas

h = 52 cm h = 67 cm h = 10.3 cm

(i)   (ii)   (iii)

8.26 An open-end manometer containing mercury is connected to a container of gas, as depicted in Sample Exercise 8.2. What is the pressure of the enclosed gas in torr in each of the following situations? (a) The mercury in the arm attached to the gas is 15.4 mm higher than in the one open to the atmosphere; atmospheric pressure is 0.985 atm. (b) The mercury in the arm attached to the gas is 12.3 mm lower than in the one open to the atmosphere; atmospheric pressure is 0.99 atm.

THE GAS LAWS (section 8.3)

8.27 You have a gas confined to a cylinder with a movable piston. What would happen to the gas pressure inside the cylinder if you do the following? (a) Decrease the volume to one-fourth the original volume while holding the temperature constant. (b) Reduce the temperature (in kelvins) to half its original value while holding the volume constant. (c) Reduce the amount of gas to one-fourth while keeping the volume and temperature constant.

8.28 A fixed quantity of gas at 21 °C exhibits a pressure of 752 torr and occupies a volume of 5.12 L. (a) Calculate the volume the gas will occupy if the pressure is increased to 1.88 atm while the temperature is held constant. (b) Calculate the volume the gas will occupy if the temperature is increased to 175 °C while the pressure is held constant.

8.29 (a) How is the law of combining volumes explained by Avogadro's hypothesis? (b) Consider a 1.0-L flask containing neon gas and a 1.5-L flask containing xenon gas. Both gases are at the same pressure and temperature. According to Avogadro's law, what can be said about the ratio of the number of atoms in the two flasks? (c) Will 1 mol of an ideal gas always occupy the same volume at a given temperature and pressure? Explain.

8.30 Nitrogen and hydrogen gases react to form ammonia gas as follows:

$$N_2(g) + 3 H_2(g) \longrightarrow 2 NH_3(g)$$

At a certain temperature and pressure, 1.2 L of N_2 reacts with 3.6 L of H_2. If all the N_2 and H_2 are consumed, what volume of NH_3, at the same temperature and pressure, will be produced?

THE IDEAL-GAS EQUATION (section 8.4)

8.31 (a) What is an ideal gas? (b) Show how Boyle's law, Charles's law, and Avogadro's law can be combined to give the ideal-gas equation. (c) Write the ideal-gas equation, and give the units used for each term when $R = 0.08206$ L-atm/mol-K. (d) If you measure pressure in bars instead of atmospheres, calculate the corresponding value of R in L-bar/mol-K.

8.32 (a) What conditions are represented by the abbreviation STP? (b) What is the molar volume of an ideal gas at STP? (c) Room temperature is often assumed to be 25 °C. Calculate the molar volume of an ideal gas at 25 °C and 1 atm pressure.

8.33 Suppose you are given two 1-L flasks and told that one contains a gas of molar mass 30, the other a gas of molar mass 60, both at the same temperature. The pressure in flask A is X atm, and the mass of gas in the flask is 1.2 g. The pressure in flask B is 0.5X atm, and the mass of gas in that flask is 1.2 g. Which flask contains the gas of molar mass 30, and which contains the gas of molar mass 60?

8.34 Suppose you are given two flasks at the same temperature, one of volume 2 L and the other of volume 3 L. The 2-L flask contains 4.8 g of gas, and the gas pressure is X atm. The 3-L flask contains 0.36 g of gas, and the gas pressure is 0.1X. Do the two gases have the same molar mass? If not, which contains the gas of higher molar mass?

8.35 Complete the following table for an ideal gas:

P	V	n	T
2.00 atm	1.00 L	0.500 mol	? K
0.300 atm	0.250 L	? mol	27 °C
650 torr	? L	0.333 mol	350 K
? atm	585 mL	0.250 mol	295 K

8.36 Calculate each of the following quantities for an ideal gas: (a) the volume of the gas, in liters, if 1.50 mol has a pressure of 1.25 atm at a temperature of −6 °C; (b) the absolute temperature of the gas at which 3.33×10^{-3} mol occupies 478 mL at 750 torr; (c) the pressure, in atmospheres, if 0.00245 mol occupies 413 mL at 138 °C; (d) the quantity of gas, in moles, if 126.5 L at 54 °C has a pressure of 11.25 kPa.

8.37 The Goodyear blimps, which frequently fly over sporting events, hold approximately 175,000 ft^3 of helium. If the gas is at 23 °C and 1.0 atm, what mass of helium is in a blimp?

8.38 A neon sign is made of glass tubing whose inside diameter is 2.5 cm and whose length is 5.5 m. If the sign contains neon at a pressure of 1.78 torr at 35 °C, how many grams of neon are in the sign? (The volume of a cylinder is $\pi r^2 h$.)

8.39 (a) Calculate the number of molecules in a deep breath of air whose volume is 2.25 L at body temperature, 37 °C, and a pressure of 735 torr. (b) The adult blue whale has a lung capacity of 5.0×10^3 L. Calculate the mass of air (assume an average molar mass 28.98 g/mol) contained in an adult blue whale's lungs at 0.0 °C and 1.00 atm, assuming the air behaves ideally.

8.40 (a) If the pressure exerted by ozone, O_3, in the stratosphere is 3.0×10^{-3} atm and the temperature is 250 K, how many ozone molecules are in a liter? (b) Carbon dioxide makes up approximately 0.04% of Earth's atmosphere. If you collect a 2.0-L sample from the atmosphere at sea level (1.00 atm) on a warm day (27 °C), how many CO_2 molecules are in your sample?

8.41 A scuba diver's tank contains 0.29 kg of O_2 compressed into a volume of 2.3 L. (a) Calculate the gas pressure inside the tank at 9 °C. (b) What volume would this oxygen occupy at 26 °C and 0.95 atm?

8.42 An aerosol spray can with a volume of 250 mL contains 2.30 g of propane gas (C_3H_8) as a propellant. (a) If the can is at 23 °C, what is the pressure in the can? (b) What volume would the propane occupy at STP? (c) The can's label says that exposure to temperatures above 130 °F may cause the can to burst. What is the pressure in the can at this temperature?

8.43 Chlorine is widely used to purify municipal water supplies and to treat swimming pool waters. Suppose that the volume of a particular sample of Cl_2 gas is 8.70 L at 895 torr and 24 °C. **(a)** How many grams of Cl_2 are in the sample? **(b)** What volume will the Cl_2 occupy at STP? **(c)** At what temperature will the volume be 15.00 L if the pressure is 8.76×10^2 torr? **(d)** At what pressure will the volume equal 5.00 L if the temperature is 58 °C ?

8.44 Many gases are shipped in high-pressure containers. Consider a steel tank whose volume is 55.0 gallons that contains O_2 gas at a pressure of 16,500 kPa at 23 °C. **(a)** What mass of O_2 does the tank contain? **(b)** What volume would the gas occupy at STP? **(c)** At what temperature would the pressure in the tank equal 150.0 atm? **(d)** What would be the pressure of the gas, in kPa, if it were transferred to a container at 24 °C whose volume is 55.0 L?

8.45 In an experiment reported in the scientific literature, male cockroaches were made to run at different speeds on a miniature treadmill while their oxygen consumption was measured. In one hour the average cockroach running at 0.08 km/hr consumed 0.8 mL of O_2 at 1 atm pressure and 24 °C per gram of insect mass. **(a)** How many moles of O_2 would be consumed in 1 hr by a 5.2-g cockroach moving at this speed? **(b)** This same cockroach is caught by a child and placed in a 1-qt fruit jar with a tight lid. Assuming the same level of continuous activity as in the research, will the cockroach consume more than 20% of the available O_2 in a 48-hr period? (Air is 21 mol percent O_2.)

8.46 The physical fitness of athletes is measured by "V_{O_2} max," which is the maximum volume of oxygen consumed by an individual during incremental exercise (for example, on a treadmill). An average male has a V_{O_2} max of 45 mL O_2/kg body mass/min, but a world-class male athlete can have a V_{O_2} max reading of 88.0 mL O_2/kg body mass/min. **(a)** Calculate the volume of oxygen, in mL, consumed in 1 hr by an average man who weighs 185 lbs and has a V_{O_2} max reading of 47.5

mL O_2/kg body mass/min. **(b)** If this man lost 20 lb, exercised, and increased his V_{O_2} max to 65.0 mL O_2/kg body mass/min, how many mL of oxygen would he consume in 1 hr?

8.47 Mercury is a liquid at room temperature and pressure, but its vapor is present in the atmosphere from natural sources, such as volcanoes, and from human ("anthropogenic") activities such as coal burning and gold mining. Elemental Hg becomes extremely toxic when oxidized to Hg(I) or Hg(II) compounds. **(a)** The Environmental Protection Agency has estimated that 119 tons of mercury are currently emitted to Earth's atmosphere annually due to human activities; this has decreased significantly from the mid-1970s before pollution controls were in place. What volume would the 119 tons of mercury occupy if it were a pure vapor at 1.00 atm and 298 K? **(b)** Geological records suggest that before the Industrial Revolution began in 1750, the baseline level of atmospheric Hg was 35 ppb (parts per billion, by volume, or 35 L Hg for every 10^9 L of air); current estimates are 245 ppb. For an estimated atmospheric volume of 51×10^{12} m^3, calculate the number of moles Hg estimated to be in the atmosphere today.

8.48 After the large eruption of Mount St. Helens in 1980, gas samples from the volcano were taken by sampling the downwind gas plume. The unfiltered gas samples were passed over a gold-coated wire coil to absorb mercury (Hg) present in the gas. The mercury was recovered from the coil by heating it and then analyzed. In one particular set of experiments scientists found a mercury vapor level of 1800 ng of Hg per cubic meter in the plume at a gas temperature of 10 °C. Calculate **(a)** the partial pressure of Hg vapor in the plume, **(b)** the number of Hg atoms per cubic meter in the gas, **(c)** the total mass of Hg emitted per day by the volcano if the daily plume volume was 1600 km^3.

FURTHER APPLICATIONS OF THE IDEAL-GAS EQUATION (section 8.5)

8.49 Which gas is most dense at 1.00 atm and 298 K: CO_2, N_2O, or Cl_2? Explain.

8.50 Rank the following gases from least dense to most dense at 1.00 atm and 298 K: SO_2, HBr, CO_2. Explain.

8.51 Which of the following statements best explains why a closed balloon filled with helium gas rises in air?
(a) Helium is a monatomic gas, whereas nearly all the molecules that make up air, such as nitrogen and oxygen, are diatomic.
(b) The average speed of helium atoms is higher than the average speed of air molecules, and the higher speed of collisions with the balloon walls propels the balloon upward.
(c) Because the helium atoms are of lower mass than the average air molecule, the helium gas is less dense than air. The mass of the balloon is thus less than the mass of the air displaced by its volume.
(d) Because helium has a lower molar mass than the average air molecule, the helium atoms are in faster motion. This means that the temperature of the helium is higher than the air temperature. Hot gases tend to rise.

8.52 Which of the following statements best explains why nitrogen gas at STP is less dense than Xe gas at STP?
(a) Because Xe is a noble gas, there is less tendency for the Xe atoms to repel one another, so they pack more densely in the gas state.

(b) Xe atoms have a higher mass than N_2 molecules. Because both gases at STP have the same number of molecules per unit volume, the Xe gas must be denser.
(c) The Xe atoms are larger than N_2 molecules and thus take up a larger fraction of the space occupied by the gas.
(d) Because the Xe atoms are much more massive than the N_2 molecules, they move more slowly and thus exert less upward force on the gas container and make the gas appear denser.

8.53 **(a)** Calculate the density of NO_2 gas at 0.970 atm and 35 °C. **(b)** Calculate the molar mass of a gas if 2.50 g occupies 0.875 L at 685 torr and 35 °C.

8.54 **(a)** Calculate the density of sulfur hexafluoride gas at 707 torr and 21 °C. **(b)** Calculate the molar mass of a vapor that has a density of 7.135 g/L at 12 °C and 743 torr.

8.55 In the Dumas-bulb technique for determining the molar mass of an unknown liquid, you vaporize the sample of a liquid that boils below 100 °C in a boiling-water bath and determine the mass of vapor required to fill the bulb (see drawing, next page). From the following data, calculate the molar mass of the unknown liquid: mass of unknown vapor, 1.012 g; volume of bulb, 354 cm^3; pressure, 742 torr; temperature, 99 °C.

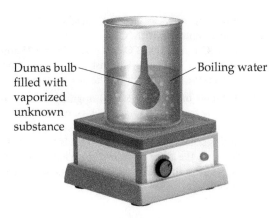

Dumas bulb filled with vaporized unknown substance

Boiling water

8.56 The molar mass of a volatile substance was determined by the Dumas-bulb method described in Exercise 8.55. The unknown vapor had a mass of 0.846 g; the volume of the bulb was 354 cm^3, pressure 752 torr, and temperature 100 °C. Calculate the molar mass of the unknown vapor.

8.57 Magnesium can be used as a "getter" in evacuated enclosures to react with the last traces of oxygen. (The magnesium is usually heated by passing an electric current through a wire or ribbon of the metal.) If an enclosure of 0.452 L has a partial pressure of O_2 of 3.5×10^{-6} torr at 27 °C, what mass of magnesium will react according to the following equation?

$$2\,Mg(s) + O_2(g) \longrightarrow 2\,MgO(s)$$

8.58 Calcium hydride, CaH_2, reacts with water to form hydrogen gas:

$$CaH_2(s) + 2\,H_2O(l) \longrightarrow Ca(OH)_2(aq) + 2\,H_2(g)$$

This reaction is sometimes used to inflate life rafts, weather balloons, and the like, when a simple, compact means of generating H_2 is desired. How many grams of CaH_2 are needed to generate 145 L of H_2 gas if the pressure of H_2 is 825 torr at 21 °C ?

PARTIAL PRESSURES (section 8.6)

8.63 Consider the apparatus shown in the following drawing. **(a)** When the valve between the two containers is opened and the gases allowed to mix, how does the volume occupied by the N_2 gas change? What is the partial pressure of N_2 after mixing? **(b)** How does the volume of the O_2 gas change when the gases mix? What is the partial pressure of O_2 in the mixture? **(c)** What is the total pressure in the container after the gases mix?

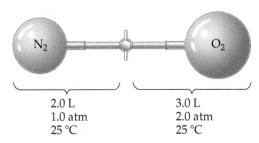

N_2 O_2

2.0 L   3.0 L
1.0 atm   2.0 atm
25 °C   25 °C

8.64 Consider a mixture of two gases, A and B, confined in a closed vessel. A quantity of a third gas, C, is added to the same vessel at the same temperature. How does the addition of gas C affect the following: **(a)** the partial pressure of gas A, **(b)** the total pressure in the vessel, **(c)** the mole fraction of gas B?

8.65 A mixture containing 0.765 mol He(g), 0.330 mol Ne(g), and 0.110 mol Ar(g) is confined in a 10.00-L vessel at 25 °C. **(a)** Calculate the partial pressure of each of the gases in the mixture. **(b)** Calculate the total pressure of the mixture.

8.59 The metabolic oxidation of glucose, $C_6H_{12}O_6$, in our bodies produces CO_2, which is expelled from our lungs as a gas:

$$C_6H_{12}O_6(aq) + 6\,O_2(g) \longrightarrow 6\,CO_2(g) + 6\,H_2O(l)$$

(a) Calculate the volume of dry CO_2 produced at body temperature (37 °C) and 0.970 atm when 24.5 g of glucose is consumed in this reaction. **(b)** Calculate the volume of oxygen you would need, at 1.00 atm and 298 K, to completely oxidize 50.0 g of glucose.

8.60 Both Jacques Charles and Joseph Louis Guy-Lussac were avid balloonists. In his original flight in 1783, Jacques Charles used a balloon that contained approximately 31,150 L of H_2. He generated the H_2 using the reaction between iron and hydrochloric acid:

$$Fe(s) + 2\,HCl(aq) \longrightarrow FeCl_2(aq) + H_2(g)$$

How many kilograms of iron were needed to produce this volume of H_2 if the temperature was 22 °C ?

8.61 Hydrogen gas is produced when zinc reacts with sulfuric acid:

$$Zn(s) + H_2SO_4(aq) \longrightarrow ZnSO_4(aq) + H_2(g)$$

If 159 mL of wet H_2 is collected over water at 24 °C and a barometric pressure of 738 torr, how many grams of Zn have been consumed? (The vapor pressure of water is tabulated in Appendix B.)

8.62 Acetylene gas, $C_2H_2(g)$, can be prepared by the reaction of calcium carbide with water:

$$CaC_2(s) + 2\,H_2O(l) \longrightarrow Ca(OH)_2(s) + C_2H_2(g)$$

Calculate the volume of C_2H_2 that is collected over water at 23 °C by reaction of 1.524 g of CaC_2 if the total pressure of the gas is 753 torr. (The vapor pressure of water is tabulated in Appendix B.)

8.66 A deep-sea diver uses a gas cylinder with a volume of 10.0 L and a content of 51.2 g of O_2 and 32.6 g of He. Calculate the partial pressure of each gas and the total pressure if the temperature of the gas is 19 °C.

8.67 The atmospheric concentration of CO_2 gas is presently 390 ppm (parts per million, by volume; that is, 390 L of every 10^6 L of the atmosphere are CO_2). What is the mole fraction of CO_2 in the atmosphere?

8.68 A plasma-screen TV contains thousands of tiny cells filled with a mixture of Xe, Ne, and He gases that emits light of specific wavelengths when a voltage is applied. A particular plasma cell, 0.900 mm × 0.300 mm × 10.0 mm, contains 4% Xe in a 1:1 Ne:He mixture at a total pressure of 500 torr. Calculate the number of Xe, Ne, and He atoms in the cell and state the assumptions you need to make in your calculation.

8.69 A piece of dry ice (solid carbon dioxide) with a mass of 5.50 g is placed in a 10.0-L vessel that already contains air at 705 torr and 24 °C. After the carbon dioxide has totally vaporized, what is the partial pressure of carbon dioxide and the total pressure in the container at 24 °C?

8.70 A sample of 5.00 mL of diethylether ($C_2H_5OC_2H_5$, density = 0.7134 g/mL) is introduced into a 6.00-L vessel that already contains a mixture of N_2 and O_2, whose partial pressures are $P_{N_2} = 0.751$ atm and $P_{O_2} = 0.208$ atm. The temperature is held at 35.0 °C, and the diethylether totally evaporates. **(a)** Calculate the partial pressure of the diethylether. **(b)** Calculate the total pressure in the container.

8.71 A mixture of gases contains 0.75 mol N_2, 0.30 mol O_2, and 0.15 mol CO_2. If the total pressure of the mixture is 2.15 atm, what is the partial pressure of each component?

8.72 A mixture of gases contains 10.25 g of N_2, 1.83 g of H_2, and 7.95 g of NH_3. If the total pressure of the mixture is 1.85 atm, what is the partial pressure of each component?

8.73 At an underwater depth of 250 ft, the pressure is 8.38 atm. What should the mole percent of oxygen be in the diving gas for the partial pressure of oxygen in the mixture to be 0.21 atm, the same as in air at 1 atm?

8.74 (a) What are the mole fractions of each component in a mixture of 15.08 g of O_2, 8.17 g of N_2, and 2.64 g of H_2? (b) What is the partial pressure in atm of each component of this mixture if it is held in a 15.50-L vessel at 15 °C?

8.75 A quantity of N_2 gas originally held at 5.25 atm pressure in a 1.00-L container at 26 °C is transferred to a 12.5-L container at 20 °C. A quantity of O_2 gas originally at 5.25 atm and 26 °C in a 5.00-L container is transferred to this same container. What is the total pressure in the new container?

8.76 A sample of 3.00 g of $SO_2(g)$ originally in a 5.00-L vessel at 21 °C is transferred to a 10.0-L vessel at 26 °C. A sample of 2.35 g $N_2(g)$ originally in a 2.50-L vessel at 20 °C is transferred to this same 10.0-L vessel. (a) What is the partial pressure of $SO_2(g)$ in the larger container? (b) What is the partial pressure of $N_2(g)$ in this vessel? (c) What is the total pressure in the vessel?

KINETIC-MOLECULAR THEORY OF GASES; EFFUSION AND DIFFUSION (sections 8.7 and 8.8)

8.77 What change or changes in the state of a gas bring about each of the following effects? (a) The number of impacts per unit time on a given container wall increases. (b) The average energy of impact of molecules with the wall of the container decreases. (c) The average distance between gas molecules increases. (d) The average speed of molecules in the gas mixture is increased.

8.78 Indicate which of the following statements regarding the kinetic-molecular theory of gases are correct. For those that are false, formulate a correct version of the statement. (a) The average kinetic energy of a collection of gas molecules at a given temperature is proportional to $m^{1/2}$. (b) The gas molecules are assumed to exert no forces on each other. (c) All the molecules of a gas at a given temperature have the same kinetic energy. (d) The volume of the gas molecules is negligible in comparison to the total volume in which the gas is contained. (e) All gas molecules move with the same speed if they are at the same temperature.

8.79 What property or properties of gases can you point to that support the assumption that most of the volume in a gas is empty space?

8.80 Newton had an incorrect theory of gases in which he assumed that all gas molecules repel one another and the walls of their container. Thus, the molecules of a gas are statically and uniformly distributed, trying to get as far apart as possible from one another and the vessel walls. This repulsion gives rise to pressure. Explain why Charles's law argues for the kinetic-molecular theory and against Newton's model.

8.81 Explain the difference between average speed and root-mean-square speed. Which is larger for a given gas sample at a fixed temperature?

[8.82] You have an evacuated container of fixed volume and known mass and introduce a known mass of a gas sample. Measuring the pressure at constant temperature over time, you are surprised to see it slowly dropping. You measure the mass of the gas-filled container and find that the mass is what it should be—gas plus container—and the mass does not change over time, so you do not have a leak. Suggest an explanation for your observations.

8.83 The temperature of a 5.00-L container of N_2 gas is increased from 20 °C to 250 °C. If the volume is held constant, predict qualitatively how this change affects the following: (a) the average kinetic energy of the molecules; (b) the root-mean-square speed of the molecules; (c) the strength of the impact of an average molecule with the container walls; (d) the total number of collisions of molecules with walls per second.

8.84 Suppose you have two 1-L flasks, one containing N_2 at STP, the other containing CH_4 at STP. How do these systems compare with respect to (a) number of molecules, (b) density, (c) average kinetic energy of the molecules, (d) rate of effusion through a pinhole leak?

8.85 (a) Place the following gases in order of increasing average molecular speed at 25 °C: Ne, HBr, SO_2, NF_3, CO. (b) Calculate the rms speed of NF_3 molecules at 25 °C. (c) Calculate the most probable speed of an ozone molecule in the stratosphere, where the temperature is 270 K.

8.86 (a) Place the following gases in order of increasing average molecular speed at 300 K: CO, SF_6, H_2S, Cl_2, HBr. (b) Calculate and compare the rms speeds of CO and Cl_2 molecules at 300 K. (c) Calculate and compare the most probable speeds of CO and Cl_2 molecules at 300 K.

8.87 Explain the difference between effusion and diffusion.

[8.88] At constant pressure, the mean free path (λ) of a gas molecule is directly proportional to temperature. At constant temperature, λ is inversely proportional to pressure. If you compare two different gas molecules at the same temperature and pressure, λ is inversely proportional to the square of the diameter of the gas molecules. Put these facts together to create a formula for the mean free path of a gas molecule with a proportionality constant (call it R_{mfp}, like the ideal-gas constant) and define units for R_{mfp}.

8.89 Hydrogen has two naturally occurring isotopes, ^1H and ^2H. Chlorine also has two naturally occurring isotopes, ^{35}Cl and ^{37}Cl. Thus, hydrogen chloride gas consists of four distinct types of molecules: $^1H^{35}Cl$, $^1H^{37}Cl$, $^2H^{35}Cl$, and $^2H^{37}Cl$. Place these four molecules in order of increasing rate of effusion.

8.90 As discussed in the "Chemistry Put to Work" box in Section 8.8, enriched uranium can be produced by gaseous diffusion of UF_6. Suppose a process were developed to allow diffusion of gaseous uranium atoms, U(g). Calculate the ratio of diffusion rates for ^{235}U and ^{238}U, and compare it to the ratio for UF_6 given in the essay.

8.91 Arsenic(III) sulfide sublimes readily, even below its melting point of 320 °C. The molecules of the vapor phase are found to effuse through a tiny hole at 0.28 times the rate of effusion of Ar atoms under the same conditions of temperature and pressure. What is the molecular formula of arsenic(III) sulfide in the gas phase?

8.92 A gas of unknown molecular mass was allowed to effuse through a small opening under constant-pressure conditions. It required 105 s for 1.0 L of the gas to effuse. Under identical experimental conditions it required 31 s for 1.0 L of O_2 gas to effuse. Calculate the molar mass of the unknown gas. (Remember that the faster the rate of effusion, the shorter the time required for effusion of 1.0 L; that is, rate and time are inversely proportional.)

NONIDEAL-GAS BEHAVIOR (section 8.9)

8.93 (a) List two experimental conditions under which gases deviate from ideal behavior. (b) List two reasons why the gases deviate from ideal behavior. (c) Explain how the function PV/RT can be used to show how gases behave nonideally.

8.94 The planet Jupiter has a surface temperature of 140 K and a mass 318 times that of Earth. Mercury (the planet) has a surface temperature between 600 K and 700 K and a mass 0.05 times that of Earth. On which planet is the atmosphere more likely to obey the ideal-gas law? Explain.

8.95 Based on their respective van der Waals constants (Table 8.3), is Ar or CO_2 expected to behave more nearly like an ideal gas at high pressures? Explain.

8.96 Briefly explain the significance of the constants a and b in the van der Waals equation.

8.97 In Sample Exercise 8.16, we found that one mole of Cl_2 confined to 22.41 L at 0 °C deviated slightly from ideal behavior. Calculate the pressure exerted by 1.00 mol Cl_2 confined to a smaller volume, 5.00 L, at 25 °C. (a) First use the ideal-gas equation and (b) then use the van der Waals equation for your calculation. (Values for the van der Waals constants are given in Table 8.3.) (c) Why is the difference between the result for an ideal gas and that calculated using the van der Waals equation greater when the gas is confined to 5.00 L compared to 22.4 L?

8.98 Calculate the pressure that CCl_4 will exert at 40 °C if 1.00 mol occupies 33.3 L, assuming that (a) CCl_4 obeys the ideal-gas equation; (b) CCl_4 obeys the van der Waals equation. (Values for the van der Waals constants are given in Table 8.3.) (c) Which would you expect to deviate more from ideal behavior under these conditions, Cl_2 or CCl_4? Explain.

[**8.99**] Table 8.3 shows that the van der Waals b parameter has units of L/mol. This implies that we can calculate the size of atoms or molecules from b. Using the value of b for Xe, calculate the radius of a Xe atom and compare it to the value found in Figure 7.6, 1.30 Å. Recall that the volume of a sphere is $(4/3)\pi r^3$.

[**8.100**] Table 8.3 shows that the van der Waals b parameter has units of L/mol. This means that we can calculate the sizes of atoms or molecules from the b parameter. Refer back to the discussion in Section 7.3. Is the van der Waals radius we calculate from the b parameter of Table 8.3 more closely associated with the bonding or nonbonding atomic radius discussed there? Explain.

ADDITIONAL EXERCISES

8.101 A gas bubble with a volume of 1.0 mm^3 originates at the bottom of a lake where the pressure is 3.0 atm. Calculate its volume when the bubble reaches the surface of the lake where the pressure is 730 torr, assuming that the temperature doesn't change.

8.102 A 15.0-L tank is filled with helium gas at a pressure of 1.00×10^2 atm. How many balloons (each 2.00 L) can be inflated to a pressure of 1.00 atm, assuming that the temperature remains constant and that the tank cannot be emptied below 1.00 atm?

8.103 To minimize the rate of evaporation of the tungsten filament, 1.4×10^{-5} mol of argon is placed in a 600-cm^3 lightbulb. What is the pressure of argon in the lightbulb at 23 °C?

8.104 Carbon dioxide, which is recognized as the major contributor to global warming as a "greenhouse gas," is formed when fossil fuels are combusted, as in electrical power plants fueled by coal, oil, or natural gas. One potential way to reduce the amount of CO_2 added to the atmosphere is to store it as a compressed gas in underground formations. Consider a 1000-megawatt coal-fired power plant that produces about 6×10^6 tons of CO_2 per year. (a) Assuming ideal-gas behavior, 1.00 atm, and 27 °C, calculate the volume of CO_2 produced by this power plant. (b) If the CO_2 is stored underground as a liquid at 10 °C and 120 atm and a density of 1.2 g/cm^3, what volume does it possess? (c) If it is stored underground as a gas at 36 °C and 90 atm, what volume does it occupy?

8.105 Propane, C_3H_8, liquefies under modest pressure, allowing a large amount to be stored in a container. (a) Calculate the number of moles of propane gas in a 110-L container at 3.00 atm and 27 °C. (b) Calculate the number of moles of liquid propane that can be stored in the same volume if the density of the liquid is 0.590 g/mL. (c) Calculate the ratio of the number of moles of liquid to moles of gas. Discuss this ratio in light of the kinetic-molecular theory of gases.

[**8.106**] Nickel carbonyl, $Ni(CO)_4$, is one of the most toxic substances known. The present maximum allowable concentration in laboratory air during an 8-hr workday is 1 ppb (parts per billion) by volume, which means that there is one mole of $Ni(CO)_4$ for every 10^9 moles of gas. Assume 24 °C and 1.00 atm pressure. What mass of $Ni(CO)_4$ is allowable in a laboratory room that is 12 ft × 20 ft × 9 ft?

8.107 When a large evacuated flask is filled with argon gas, its mass increases by 3.224 g. When the same flask is again evacuated and then filled with a gas of unknown molar mass, the mass increase is 8.102 g. (a) Based on the molar mass of argon, estimate the molar mass of the unknown gas. (b) What assumptions did you make in arriving at your answer?

8.108 Consider the arrangement of bulbs shown in the drawing. Each of the bulbs contains a gas at the pressure shown. What is the pressure of the system when all the stopcocks are opened, assuming that the temperature remains constant? (We can neglect the volume of the capillary tubing connecting the bulbs.)

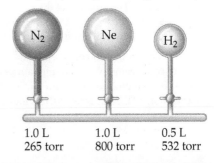

N_2	Ne	H_2
1.0 L	1.0 L	0.5 L
265 torr	800 torr	532 torr

8.109 Assume that a single cylinder of an automobile engine has a volume of $524 \, cm^3$. **(a)** If the cylinder is full of air at 74 °C and 0.980 atm, how many moles of O_2 are present? (The mole fraction of O_2 in dry air is 0.2095.) **(b)** How many grams of C_8H_{18} could be combusted by this quantity of O_2, assuming complete combustion with formation of CO_2 and H_2O?

8.110 Assume that an exhaled breath of air consists of 74.8% N_2, 15.3% O_2, 3.7% CO_2, and 6.2% water vapor. **(a)** If the total pressure of the gases is 0.985 atm, calculate the partial pressure of each component of the mixture. **(b)** If the volume of the exhaled gas is 455 mL and its temperature is 37 °C, calculate the number of moles of CO_2 exhaled. **(c)** How many grams of glucose ($C_6H_{12}O_6$) would need to be metabolized to produce this quantity of CO_2? (The chemical reaction is the same as that for combustion of $C_6H_{12}O_6$. See Problem 8.59.)

8.111 A 1.42-g sample of helium and an unknown mass of O_2 are mixed in a flask at room temperature. The partial pressure of the helium is 42.5 torr, and that of the oxygen is 158 torr. What is the mass of the oxygen?

8.112 A gaseous mixture of O_2 and Kr has a density of 1.104 g/L at 355 torr and 400 K. What is the mole percent O_2 in the mixture?

8.113 The density of a gas of unknown molar mass was measured as a function of pressure at 0 °C, as in the table that follows. **(a)** Determine a precise molar mass for the gas. [*Hint:* Graph d/P versus P.] **(b)** Why is d/P not a constant as a function of pressure?

Pressure (atm)	1.00	0.666	0.500	0.333	0.250
Density (g/L)	2.3074	1.5263	1.1401	0.7571	0.5660

8.114 A glass vessel fitted with a stopcock valve has a mass of 337.428 g when evacuated. When filled with Ar, it has a mass of 339.854 g. When evacuated and refilled with a mixture of Ne and Ar, under the same conditions of temperature and pressure, it has a mass of 339.076 g. What is the mole percent of Ne in the gas mixture?

8.115 You have a sample of gas at −33 °C. You wish to increase the rms speed by a factor of 2. To what temperature should the gas be heated?

8.116 Consider the following gases, all at STP: Ne, SF_6, N_2, CH_4. **(a)** Which gas is most likely to depart from the assumption of the kinetic-molecular theory that says there are no attractive or repulsive forces between molecules? **(b)** Which one is closest to an ideal gas in its behavior? **(c)** Which one has the highest root-mean-square molecular speed at a given temperature? **(d)** Which one has the highest total molecular volume relative to the space occupied by the gas? **(e)** Which has the highest average kinetic-molecular energy? **(f)** Which one would effuse more rapidly than N_2? **(g)** Which one would have the largest van der Waals b parameter?

8.117 Does the effect of intermolecular attraction on the properties of a gas become more significant or less significant if **(a)** the gas is compressed to a smaller volume at constant temperature; **(b)** the temperature of the gas is increased at constant volume?

8.118 Which of the noble gases other than radon would you expect to depart most readily from ideal behavior?

8.119 It turns out that the van der Waals constant b equals four times the total volume actually occupied by the molecules of a mole of gas. Using this figure, calculate the fraction of the volume in a container actually occupied by Ar atoms **(a)** at STP, **(b)** at 200 atm pressure and 0 °C. (Assume for simplicity that the ideal-gas equation still holds.)

[8.120] Large amounts of nitrogen gas are used in the manufacture of ammonia, principally for use in fertilizers. Suppose 120.00 kg of $N_2(g)$ is stored in a 1100.0-L metal cylinder at 280 °C. **(a)** Calculate the pressure of the gas, assuming ideal-gas behavior. **(b)** By using data in Table 8.3, calculate the pressure of the gas according to the van der Waals equation. **(c)** Under the conditions of this problem, which correction dominates, the one for finite volume of gas molecules or the one for attractive interactions?

INTEGRATIVE EXERCISES

8.121 Cyclopropane, a gas used with oxygen as a general anesthetic, is composed of 85.7% C and 14.3% H by mass. **(a)** If 1.56 g of cyclopropane has a volume of 1.00 L at 0.984 atm and 50.0 °C, what is the molecular formula of cyclopropane? **(b)** Judging from its molecular formula, would you expect cyclopropane to deviate more or less than Ar from ideal-gas behavior at moderately high pressures and room temperature? Explain. **(c)** Would cyclopropane effuse through a pinhole faster or more slowly than methane, CH_4?

[8.122] Consider the combustion reaction between 25.0 mL of liquid methanol (density = 0.850 g/mL) and 12.5 L of oxygen gas measured at STP. The products of the reaction are $CO_2(g)$ and $H_2O(g)$. Calculate the volume of liquid H_2O formed if the reaction goes to completion and you condense the water vapor.

8.123 An herbicide is found to contain only C, H, N, and Cl. The complete combustion of a 100.0-mg sample of the herbicide in excess oxygen produces 83.16 mL of CO_2 and 73.30 mL of H_2O vapor at STP. A separate analysis shows that the sample also contains 16.44 mg of Cl. **(a)** Determine the percent composition of the substance. **(b)** Calculate its empirical formula. **(c)** What other information would you need to know about this compound to calculate its true molecular formula?

8.124 A 4.00-g sample of a mixture of CaO and BaO is placed in a 1.00-L vessel containing CO_2 gas at a pressure of 730 torr and a temperature of 25 °C. The CO_2 reacts with the CaO and BaO, forming $CaCO_3$ and $BaCO_3$. When the reaction is complete, the pressure of the remaining CO_2 is 150 torr. **(a)** Calculate the number of moles of CO_2 that have reacted. **(b)** Calculate the mass percentage of CaO in the mixture.

[8.125] Ammonia and hydrogen chloride react to form solid ammonium chloride:

$$NH_3(g) + HCl(g) \longrightarrow NH_4Cl(s)$$

Two 2.00-L flasks at 25 °C are connected by a valve, as shown in the drawing on the next page. One flask contains 5.00 g $NH_3(g)$, and the other contains 5.00 g $HCl(g)$. When the valve is opened, the gases react until one is completely consumed. (a) Which gas will remain in the system after the reaction is complete? (b) What will be the final pressure of the system after the reaction is complete? (Neglect the volume of the ammonium chloride formed.) (c) What mass of ammonium chloride will be formed?

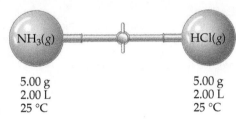

5.00 g   5.00 g
2.00 L   2.00 L
25 °C   25 °C

8.126 The "Chemistry Put to Work" box on pipelines in Section 8.5 mentions that the total deliverability of natural gas (methane, CH_4) to the various regions of the United States is on the order of 2.7×10^{12} L per day, measured at STP. Calculate the total enthalpy change for combustion of this quantity of methane. (*Note*: Less than this amount of methane is actually combusted daily. Some of the delivered gas is passed through to other regions.)

8.127 Chlorine dioxide gas (ClO_2) is used as a commercial bleaching agent. It bleaches materials by oxidizing them. In the course of these reactions, the ClO_2 is itself reduced. (a) What is the Lewis structure for ClO_2? (b) Why do you think that ClO_2 is reduced so readily? (c) When a ClO_2 molecule gains an electron, the chlorite ion, ClO_2^-, forms. Draw the Lewis structure for ClO_2^-. (d) Predict the O—Cl—O bond angle in the ClO_2^- ion. (e) One method of preparing ClO_2 is by the reaction of chlorine and sodium chlorite:

$$Cl_2(g) + 2\, NaClO_2(s) \longrightarrow 2\, ClO_2(g) + 2\, NaCl(s)$$

If you allow 15.0 g of $NaClO_2$ to react with 2.00 L of chlorine gas at a pressure of 1.50 atm at 21 °C, how many grams of ClO_2 can be prepared?

8.128 Natural gas is very abundant in many Middle Eastern oil fields. However, the costs of shipping the gas to markets in other parts of the world are high because it is necessary to liquefy the gas, which is mainly methane and has a boiling point at atmospheric pressure of -164 °C. One possible strategy is to oxidize the methane to methanol, CH_3OH, which has a boiling point of 65 °C and can therefore be shipped more readily. Suppose that 10.7×10^9 ft^3 of methane at atmospheric pressure and 25 °C is oxidized to methanol. (a) What volume of methanol is formed if the density of CH_3OH is 0.791 g/mL ? (b) Write balanced chemical equations for the oxidations of methane and methanol to $CO_2(g)$ and $H_2O(l)$. Calculate the total enthalpy change for complete combustion of the 10.7×10^9 ft^3 of methane just described and for complete combustion of the equivalent amount of methanol, as calculated in part (a). (c) Methane, when liquefied, has a density of 0.466 g/mL; the density of methanol at 25 °C is 0.791 g/mL. Compare the enthalpy change upon combustion of a unit volume of liquid methane and liquid methanol. From the standpoint of energy production, which substance has the higher enthalpy of combustion per unit volume?

[8.129] Gaseous iodine pentafluoride, IF_5, can be prepared by the reaction of solid iodine and gaseous fluorine:

$$I_2(s) + 5\, F_2(g) \longrightarrow 2\, IF_5(g)$$

A 5.00-L flask containing 10.0 g I_2 is charged with 10.0 g F_2, and the reaction proceeds until one of the reagents is completely consumed. After the reaction is complete, the temperature in the flask is 125 °C. (a) What is the partial pressure of IF_5 in the flask? (b) What is the mole fraction of IF_5 in the flask (c) Draw the Lewis structure of IF_5. (d) What is the total mass of reactants and products in the flask?

[8.130] A 6.53-g sample of a mixture of magnesium carbonate and calcium carbonate is treated with excess hydrochloric acid. The resulting reaction produces 1.72 L of carbon dioxide gas at 28 °C and 743 torr pressure. (a) Write balanced chemical equations for the reactions that occur between hydrochloric acid and each component of the mixture. (b) Calculate the total number of moles of carbon dioxide that forms from these reactions. (c) Assuming that the reactions are complete, calculate the percentage by mass of magnesium carbonate in the mixture.

WHAT'S AHEAD

9.1 EARTH'S ATMOSPHERE

We begin with a look at the temperature profile, pressure profile, and chemical composition of Earth's atmosphere. We then examine *photoionization* and *photodissociation*, reactions that result from atmospheric absorption of solar radiation.

9.2 HUMAN ACTIVITIES AND EARTH'S ATMOSPHERE

We next examine the effect human activities have on the atmosphere. We discuss how atmospheric ozone is depleted by reactions involving human-made gases and how acid rain and smog are the result of atmospheric reactions involving compounds produced by human activity.

9.3 EARTH'S WATER

We examine the global water cycle, which describes how water moves from the ground to surface water to the atmosphere and back into the ground. We compare the chemical compositions of *seawater*, *freshwater*, and *groundwater*.

THE BIG ISLAND of Hawaii.

9.4 HUMAN ACTIVITIES AND EARTH'S WATER
We consider how Earth's water is connected to the global climate
and examine one measure of water quality: dissolved oxygen

concentration. Water for drinking and for irrigation must be free of
salts and pollutants.

CHEMISTRY OF THE ENVIRONMENT

THE RICHNESS OF LIFE ON Earth, represented in the chapter-opening photograph, is, as far as we know, unique. Earth's atmosphere, the energy received from the Sun, and the abundance of water on our planet are all features currently believed to be necessary for life.

As technology has advanced and the world human population has increased, humans have put new and greater stresses on the environment. Paradoxically, the very technology that can cause pollution also provides the tools to help understand and manage the environment in a beneficial way. Chemistry is often at the heart of environmental issues. The economic growth of both developed and developing nations depends critically on chemical processes that range from treatment of water supplies to industrial processes. Some of these processes produce products or by-products that are harmful to the environment.

We are now in a position to apply the principles we have learned in preceding chapters to an understanding of how our environment operates and how human activities affect it. To understand and protect the environment in which we live, we must understand how human-made and natural chemical compounds interact on land and in the sea and sky. Our daily decisions as consumers mirror those of leading experts and governmental leaders: In making each decision, we must weigh the costs versus the benefits of our actions. Unfortunately, the environmental impacts of our decisions are often subtle and not immediately evident.

9.1 | EARTH'S ATMOSPHERE

Because most of us have never been very far from Earth's surface, we often take for granted the many ways in which the atmosphere determines the environment in which we live. In this section we examine some of the important characteristics of our planet's atmosphere.

The temperature of the atmosphere varies with altitude (◄ FIGURE 9.1), and the atmosphere is divided into four regions based on this temperature profile. Just above the surface, in the **troposphere**, the temperature normally decreases with increasing altitude, reaching a minimum of about 215 K at about 10 km. Nearly all of us live our entire lives in the troposphere. Howling winds and soft breezes, rain, and sunny skies—all that we normally think of as "weather"—occur in this region. Commercial jet aircraft typically fly about 10 km (33,000 ft) above Earth, an altitude that defines the upper limit of the troposphere, which we call the *tropopause.*

Above the tropopause, air temperature increases with altitude, reaching a maximum of about 275 K at about 50 km. The region from 10 km to 50 km is the **stratosphere**, and above it are the *mesosphere* and *thermosphere*. Notice in Figure 9.1 that the temperature extremes that form the boundaries between adjacent regions are denoted by the suffix *-pause*. The boundaries are important because gases mix across them relatively slowly. For example, pollutant gases generated in the troposphere pass through the tropopause and find their way into the stratosphere only very slowly.

Atmospheric pressure decreases with increasing elevation (Figure 9.1), declining much more rapidly at lower elevations than at higher ones because of the atmosphere's compressibility. Thus, the pressure decreases from an average value of 760 torr (101 kPa) at sea level to 2.3×10^{-3} torr $(3.1 \times 10^{-4}$ kPa) at 100 km, to only 1.0×10^{-6} torr $(1.3 \times 10^{-7}$ kPa) at 200 km.

The troposphere and stratosphere together account for 99.9% of the mass of the atmosphere, 75% of which is the mass in the troposphere. Consequently, most of the chemistry that follows focuses on these two regions.

GO FIGURE

At what altitude is the atmospheric temperature lowest?

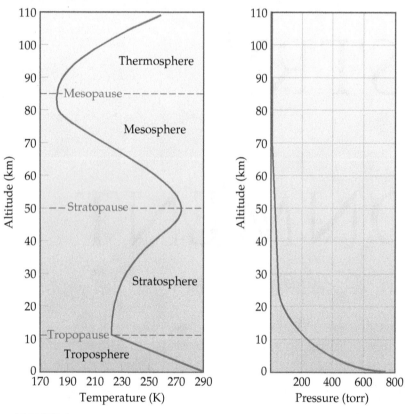

▲ **FIGURE 9.1** **Temperature and pressure in the atmosphere vary as a function of altitude above sea level.**

Composition of the Atmosphere

Earth's atmosphere is constantly bombarded by radiation and energetic particles from the Sun. This barrage of energy has profound chemical and physical effects, especially in the upper regions of the atmosphere, above about 80 km (▶ FIGURE 9.2). In addition, because of Earth's gravitational field, heavier atoms and molecules tend to sink in the atmosphere, leaving lighter atoms and molecules at the top of the atmosphere. (This is why, as just noted, 75 percent of the atmosphere's mass is in the troposphere.) Because of all these factors, the composition of the atmosphere is not uniform.

▶ TABLE 9.1 shows the composition of dry air near sea level. Note that although traces of many substances are present, N_2 and O_2 make up about 99% of sea-level air. The noble gases and CO_2 make up most of the remainder.

TABLE 9.1 • The Major Components of Dry Air Near Sea Level

Component*	Content (mole fraction)	Molar Mass (g/mol)
Nitrogen	0.78084	28.013
Oxygen	0.20948	31.998
Argon	0.00934	39.948
Carbon dioxide	0.000382	44.0099
Neon	0.00001818	20.183
Helium	0.00000524	4.003
Methane	0.000002	16.043
Krypton	0.00000114	83.80
Hydrogen	0.0000005	2.0159
Nitrous oxide	0.0000005	44.0128
Xenon	0.000000087	131.30

*Ozone, sulfur dioxide, nitrogen dioxide, ammonia, and carbon monoxide are present as trace gases in variable amounts.

High-energy solar particles create excited N and O atoms; visible light results as electrons in these atoms fall from upper-level states to lower-level states

▲ FIGURE 9.2 **The aurora borealis (northern lights).**

When applied to substances in aqueous solution, the concentration unit *parts per million* refers to grams of substance per million grams of solution. When dealing with gases, however, 1 ppm means one part by *volume* in 1 million volumes of the whole. Because volume is proportional to number of moles of gas via the ideal-gas equation ($PV = nRT$), volume fraction and mole fraction are the same. Thus, 1 ppm of a trace constituent of the atmosphere amounts to 1 mol of that constituent in 1 million moles of air; that is, the concentration in parts per million is equal to the mole fraction times 10^6. For example, Table 9.1 lists the mole fraction of CO_2 in the atmosphere as 0.000382, which means its concentration in parts per million is $0.000382 \times 10^6 = 382$ ppm.

Other minor constituents of the troposphere, in addition to CO_2, are listed in ▼ TABLE 9.2.

Before we consider the chemical processes that occur in the atmosphere, let's review some of the properties of the two major components, N_2 and O_2. Recall that the N_2 molecule possesses a triple bond between the nitrogen atoms. ∞ (Section 3.3) This very strong bond (bond energy 941 kJ/mol) is largely responsible for the very low reactivity of N_2. The bond energy in O_2 is only 495 kJ/mol, making O_2 much more reactive than N_2. For example, oxygen reacts with many substances to form oxides. The oxides of nonmetals, such as SO_2, usually form acidic solutions when dissolved in water. The oxides of active metals, such as CaO, form basic solutions when dissolved in water.

TABLE 9.2 • Sources and Typical Concentrations of Some Minor Atmospheric Constituents

Constituent	Sources	Typical Concentration
Carbon dioxide, CO_2	Decomposition of organic matter, release from oceans, fossil-fuel combustion	382 ppm throughout troposphere
Carbon monoxide, CO	Decomposition of organic matter, industrial processes, fossil-fuel combustion	0.05 ppm in unpolluted air; 1–50 ppm in urban areas
Methane, CH_4	Decomposition of organic matter, natural-gas seepage, livestock emissions	1.77 ppm throughout troposphere
Nitric oxide, NO	Atmospheric electrical discharges, internal combustion engines, combustion of organic matter	0.01 ppm in unpolluted air; 0.2 ppm in smog
Ozone, O_3	Atmospheric electrical discharges, diffusion from the stratosphere, photochemical smog	0 to 0.01 ppm in unpolluted air; 0.5 ppm in photochemical smog
Sulfur dioxide, SO_2	Volcanic gases, forest fires, bacterial action, fossil-fuel combustion, industrial processes	0 to 0.01 ppm in unpolluted air; 0.1–2 ppm in polluted urban areas

---

SAMPLE EXERCISE 9.1 | **Calculating the Concentration of Water in Air**

What is the concentration, in parts per million, of water vapor in a sample of air if the partial pressure of the water is 0.80 torr and the total pressure of the air is 735 torr?

SOLUTION

Analyze We are given the partial pressure of water vapor and the total pressure of an air sample and asked to determine the water vapor concentration.

Plan Recall that the partial pressure of a component in a mixture of gases is given by the product of its mole fraction and the total pressure of the mixture ⟶ (Section 8.6):

$$P_{H_2O} = X_{H_2O}P_t$$

Solve Solving for the mole fraction of water vapor in the mixture, X_{H_2O}, gives

$$X_{H_2O} = \frac{P_{H_2O}}{P_t} = \frac{0.80 \text{ torr}}{735 \text{ torr}} = 0.0011$$

The concentration in ppm is the mole fraction times 10^6:

$$0.0011 \times 10^6 = 1100 \text{ ppm}$$

PRACTICE EXERCISE

The concentration of CO in a sample of air is 4.3 ppm. What is the partial pressure of the CO if the total air pressure is 695 torr?

Answer: 3.0×10^{-3} torr

Photochemical Reactions in the Atmosphere

Although the atmosphere beyond the stratosphere contains only a small fraction of the atmospheric mass, it forms the outer defense against the hail of radiation and high-energy particles that continuously bombard Earth. As the bombarding radiation passes through the upper atmosphere, it causes two kinds of chemical changes: *photodissociation* and *photoionization*. These processes protect us from high-energy radiation by absorbing most of the radiation before it reaches the troposphere. If it were not for these photochemical processes, plant and animal life as we know it could not exist on Earth.

The Sun emits radiant energy over a wide range of wavelengths (▼ FIGURE 9.3). To understand the connection between the wavelength of radiation and its effect on

---

GO FIGURE

Why doesn't the solar spectrum at sea level perfectly match the solar spectrum outside the atmosphere?

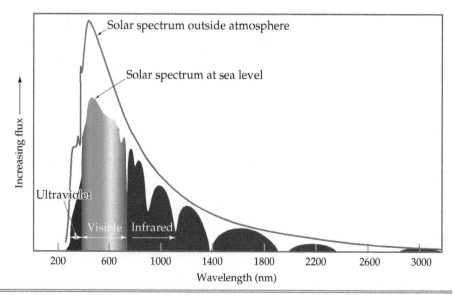

▶ **FIGURE 9.3** **The solar spectrum above Earth's atmosphere compared to that at sea level.** The more structured curve at sea level is due to gases in the atmosphere absorbing specific wavelengths of light. "Flux," the unit on the vertical axis, is light energy per area per unit of time.

atoms and molecules, recall that electromagnetic radiation can be pictured as a stream of photons. ∞ (Section 1.2) The energy of each photon is given by $E = h\nu$, where h is Planck's constant and ν is the radiation frequency. For a chemical change to occur when radiation strikes atoms or molecules, two conditions must be met. First, the incoming photons must have sufficient energy to break a chemical bond or remove an electron from the atom or molecule. Second, the atoms or molecules being bombarded must absorb these photons. When these requirements are met, the energy of the photons is used to do the work associated with some chemical change.

The rupture of a chemical bond resulting from absorption of a photon by a molecule is called **photodissociation**. No ions are formed when the bond between two atoms is cleaved by photodissociation. Instead, half the bonding electrons stay with one atom and half stay with the other atom. The result is two electrically neutral particles.

One of the most important processes occurring above an altitude of about 120 km is photodissociation of the oxygen molecule:

$$\overset{..}{\underset{..}{O}}=\overset{..}{\underset{.}{O}}: + h\nu \longrightarrow :\overset{..}{\underset{..}{O}} + \overset{..}{\underset{..}{O}}: \qquad [9.1]$$

The minimum energy required to cause this change is determined by the bond energy (or *dissociation energy*) of O_2, 495 kJ/mol.

SAMPLE EXERCISE 9.2 | **Calculating the Wavelength Required to Break a Bond**

What is the maximum wavelength of light, in nanometers, that has enough energy per photon to dissociate the O_2 molecule?

SOLUTION

Analyze We are asked to determine the wavelength of a photon that has just enough energy to break the $O=O$ double bond in O_2.

Plan We first need to calculate the energy required to break the $O=O$ double bond in one molecule and then find the wavelength of a photon of this energy.

Solve The dissociation energy of O_2 is 495 kJ/mol. Using this value and Avogadro's number, we can calculate the amount of energy needed to break the bond in a single O_2 molecule:

$$\left(495 \times 10^3 \, \frac{J}{mol}\right)\left(\frac{1 \, mol}{6.022 \times 10^{23} \, molecules}\right) = 8.22 \times 10^{-19} \, \frac{J}{molecule}$$

We next use the Planck relationship, $E = h\nu$, ∞ (Equation 1.2) to calculate the frequency ν of a photon that has this amount of energy:

$$\nu = \frac{E}{h} = \frac{8.22 \times 10^{-19} \, J}{6.626 \times 10^{-34} \, J\text{-s}} = 1.24 \times 10^{15} \, s^{-1}$$

Finally, we use the relationship between frequency and wavelength ∞ (Section 1.1) to calculate the wavelength of the light:

$$\lambda = \frac{c}{\nu} = \left(\frac{3.00 \times 10^8 \, m/s}{1.24 \times 10^{15}/s}\right)\left(\frac{10^9 \, nm}{1 \, m}\right) = 242 \, nm$$

Thus, light of wavelength 242 nm, which is in the ultraviolet region of the electromagnetic spectrum, has sufficient energy per photon to photodissociate an O_2 molecule. Because photon energy increases as wavelength *decreases*, any photon of wavelength *shorter* than 242 nm will have sufficient energy to dissociate O_2.

PRACTICE EXERCISE
The bond energy in N_2 is 941 kJ/mol. What is the longest wavelength a photon can have and still have sufficient energy to dissociate N_2?
Answer: 127 nm

Fortunately for us, O_2 absorbs much of the high-energy, short-wavelength radiation from the solar spectrum before that radiation reaches the lower atmosphere. As it does, atomic oxygen, O, is formed. The dissociation of O_2 is very extensive at higher elevations. At 400 km, for example, only 1% of the oxygen is in the form of O_2; 99% is atomic oxygen. At 130 km, O_2 and atomic oxygen are just about equally abundant.

Below 130 km, O_2 is more abundant than atomic oxygen because most of the solar energy has been absorbed in the upper atmosphere.

The dissociation energy of N_2 is very high, 941 kJ/mol. Analogous to Practice Exercise 9.2, only photons having a wavelength shorter than 127 nm possess sufficient energy to dissociate N_2. Furthermore, N_2 does not readily absorb photons, even when they possess sufficient energy. As a result, very little atomic nitrogen is formed in the upper atmosphere by photodissociation of N_2.

Other photochemical processes besides photodissociation occur in the upper atmosphere, although their discovery has taken many twists and turns. In 1901 Guglielmo Marconi received a radio signal in St. John's, Newfoundland, that had been transmitted from Land's End, England, 2900 km away. Because people at the time thought radio waves traveled in straight lines, they assumed that the curvature of Earth's surface would make radio communication over large distances impossible. Marconi's successful experiment suggested that Earth's atmosphere in some way substantially affects radio-wave propagation. His discovery led to intensive study of the upper atmosphere. In about 1924, the existence of electrons in the upper atmosphere was established by experimental studies.

The electrons in the upper atmosphere result mainly from **photoionization**, which occurs when a molecule in the upper atmosphere absorbs solar radiation and the absorbed energy causes an electron to be ejected from the molecule. The molecule then becomes a positively charged ion. For photoionization to occur, therefore, a molecule must absorb a photon, and the photon must have enough energy to remove an electron. (Section 2.4)

Four important photoionization processes occurring in the atmosphere above about 90 km are shown in ▼ TABLE 9.3. Photons of any wavelength shorter than the maximum lengths given in the table have enough energy to cause photoionization. A look back at Figure 9.3, however, shows you that virtually all of these high-energy photons are filtered out of the radiation reaching Earth because they are absorbed by the upper atmosphere.

▲ GIVE IT SOME THOUGHT

Explain the difference between photoionization and photodissociation.

Ozone in the Stratosphere

Although N_2, O_2, and atomic oxygen absorb photons having wavelengths shorter than 240 nm, ozone, O_3, is the key absorber of photons having wavelengths ranging from 240 to 310 nm, in the ultraviolet region of the electromagnetic spectrum. Ozone in the upper atmosphere protects us from these harmful high-energy photons, which would otherwise penetrate to Earth's surface. Let's consider how ozone forms in the upper atmosphere and how it absorbs photons.

By the time radiation from the Sun reaches an altitude of 90 km above Earth's surface, most of the short-wavelength radiation capable of photoionization has been absorbed. At this altitude, however, radiation capable of dissociating the O_2 molecule is sufficiently intense for photodissociation of O_2 (Equation 9.1) to remain important down to an altitude of 30 km. In the region between 30 and 90 km, however, the concentration of

TABLE 9.3 • Photoionization Reactions for Four Components of the Atmosphere

Process	Ionization Energy (kJ/mol)	λ_{max} (nm)
$N_2 + h\nu \longrightarrow N_2^+ + e^-$	1495	80.1
$O_2 + h\nu \longrightarrow O_2^+ + e^-$	1205	99.3
$O + h\nu \longrightarrow O^+ + e^-$	1313	91.2
$NO + h\nu \longrightarrow NO^+ + e^-$	890	134.5

O_2 is much greater than the concentration of atomic oxygen. From this finding, we conclude that the oxygen atoms formed by photodissociation of O_2 in this region frequently collide with O_2 molecules and form ozone:

$$:\ddot{O} + O_2 \longrightarrow O_3^* \qquad [9.2]$$

The asterisk on O_3 denotes that the molecule contains an excess of energy. This reaction releases 105 kJ/mol. This energy must be transferred away from the O_3^* molecule quickly or else the molecule will fly apart into O_2 and atomic O —a decomposition that is the reverse of the reaction by which O_3^* is formed.

An energy-rich O_3^* molecule can release its excess energy by colliding with another atom or molecule and transferring some of the excess energy to it. Let's use M to represent the atom or molecule with which O_3^* collides. (Usually M is N_2 or O_2 because these are the most abundant molecules in the atmosphere.) The formation of O_3^* and the transfer of excess energy to M are summarized by the equations

$$O(g) + O_2(g) \rightleftharpoons O_3^*(g) \qquad [9.3]$$

$$\underline{O_3^*(g) + M(g) \longrightarrow O_3(g) + M^*(g)} \qquad [9.4]$$

$$O(g) + O_2(g) + M(g) \longrightarrow O_3(g) + M^*(g) \qquad [9.5]$$

The rate at which the reactions of Equations 9.3 and 9.4 proceed depends on two factors that vary in opposite directions with increasing altitude. First, the Equation 9.3 reaction depends on the presence of O atoms. At low altitudes, most of the radiation energetic enough to dissociate O_2 into O atoms has been absorbed; thus, O atoms are more plentiful at higher altitudes. Second, Equations 9.3 and 9.4 both depend on molecular collisions. ∞∞ (Section 14.5) The concentration of molecules is greater at low altitudes, and so the rates of both reactions are greater at lower altitudes. Because these two reactions vary with altitude in opposite directions, the highest rate of O_3 formation occurs in a band at an altitude of about 50 km, near the stratopause (Figure 9.1). Overall, roughly 90% of Earth's ozone is found in the stratosphere.

 GIVE IT SOME THOUGHT

Why don't O_2 and N_2 molecules filter out ultraviolet light with wavelengths between 240 and 310 nm?

The photodissociation of ozone reverses the reaction that forms it. We thus have a cycle of ozone formation and decomposition, summarized as follows:

$$O_2(g) + h\nu \longrightarrow O(g) + O(g)$$

$$O(g) + O_2(g) + M(g) \longrightarrow O_3(g) + M^*(g) \quad \text{(heat released)}$$

$$O_3(g) + h\nu \longrightarrow O_2(g) + O(g)$$

$$O(g) + O(g) + M(g) \longrightarrow O_2(g) + M^*(g) \quad \text{(heat released)}$$

The first and third processes are photochemical; they use a solar photon to initiate a chemical reaction. The second and fourth are exothermic chemical reactions. The net result of the four reactions is a cycle in which solar radiant energy is converted into thermal energy. The ozone cycle in the stratosphere is responsible for the rise in temperature that reaches its maximum at the stratopause (Figure 9.1).

The reactions of the ozone cycle account for some, but not all, of the facts about the ozone layer. Many chemical reactions occur that involve substances other than oxygen. We must also consider the effects of turbulence and winds that mix up the stratosphere. A complicated picture results. The overall result of ozone formation and removal reactions, coupled with atmospheric turbulence and other factors, is to produce the upper-atmosphere ozone profile shown in ▶ FIGURE 9.4, with a maximum ozone concentration occurring at an altitude of about 25 km. This band of relatively high ozone concentration is referred to as the "ozone layer" or the "ozone shield."

GO FIGURE

Estimate the ozone concentration in moles per liter for the peak value in this graph.

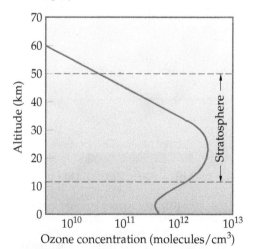

▲ FIGURE 9.4   **Variation in ozone concentration in the atmosphere as a function of altitude.**

Photons with wavelengths shorter than about 300 nm are energetic enough to break many kinds of single chemical bonds. Thus, the "ozone shield" is essential for our continued well-being. The ozone molecules that form this essential shield against high-energy radiation represent only a tiny fraction of the oxygen atoms present in the stratosphere, however, because these molecules are continually destroyed even as they are formed.

▲ FIGURE 9.5 **Mount Pinatubo erupts, June 1991.**

9.2 | HUMAN ACTIVITIES AND EARTH'S ATMOSPHERE

Both natural and *anthropogenic* (human-caused) events can modify Earth's atmosphere. One impressive natural event was the eruption of Mount Pinatubo in June 1991 (◀ FIGURE 9.5). The volcano ejected approximately 10 km³ of material into the stratosphere, causing a 10% drop in the amount of sunlight reaching Earth's surface during the next 2 years. That drop in sunlight led to a temporary 0.5 °C drop in Earth's surface temperature. The volcanic particles that made it to the stratosphere remained there for approximately 3 years, *raising* the temperature of the stratosphere by several degrees due to light absorption. Measurements of the stratospheric ozone concentration showed significantly increased ozone decomposition in this 3-year period.

Eruption of the Icelandic volcano Eyjafjallajökull in 2010, though not as large as the Pinatubo eruption, has similarly affected the atmosphere over large regions of the Northern Hemisphere.

The Ozone Layer and Its Depletion

The ozone layer protects Earth's surface from damaging ultraviolet (UV) radiation. Therefore, if the concentration of ozone in the stratosphere decreases substantially, more UV radiation will reach Earth's surface, causing unwanted photochemical reactions, including reactions correlated with skin cancer. Satellite monitoring of ozone, which began in 1978, has revealed a depletion of ozone in the stratosphere that is particularly severe over Antarctica, a phenomenon known as the *ozone hole* (◀ FIGURE 9.6). The first scientific paper on this phenomenon appeared in 1985, and the National Aeronautics and Space Administration (NASA) maintains an "Ozone Hole Watch" website with daily updates and data from 1999 to the present.

In 1995 the Nobel Prize in Chemistry was awarded to F. Sherwood Rowland, Mario Molina, and Paul Crutzen for their studies of ozone depletion. In 1970 Crutzen showed that naturally occurring nitrogen oxides catalytically destroy ozone. Rowland and Molina recognized in 1974 that chlorine from **chlorofluorocarbons** (CFCs) may deplete the ozone layer. These substances, principally $CFCl_3$ and CF_2Cl_2, do not occur in nature and have been widely used as propellants in spray cans, as refrigerant and air-conditioner gases, and as foaming agents for plastics. They are virtually unreactive in the lower atmosphere. Furthermore, they are relatively insoluble in water and are therefore not removed from the atmosphere by rainfall or by dissolution in the oceans. Unfortunately, the lack of reactivity that makes them commercially useful also allows them to survive in the atmosphere and to diffuse into the stratosphere. It is estimated that several million tons of chlorofluorocarbons are now present in the atmosphere.

As CFCs diffuse into the stratosphere, they are exposed to high-energy radiation, which can cause photodissociation. Because C—Cl bonds are considerably weaker than C—F bonds, free chlorine atoms are formed readily in the presence of light with wavelengths in the range from 190 to 225 nm, as shown in this typical reaction:

$$CF_2Cl_2(g) + h\nu \longrightarrow CF_2Cl(g) + Cl(g) \qquad [9.6]$$

Calculations suggest that chlorine atom formation occurs at the greatest rate at an altitude of about 30 km, the altitude at which ozone is at its highest concentration.

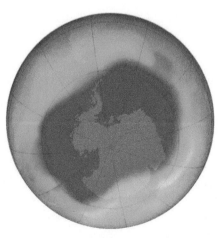

Total ozone (Dobson units)

110   220   330   440   550

▲ FIGURE 9.6 **Ozone present in the Southern Hemisphere, Sept. 24, 2006.** This data was taken from an orbiting satellite. This day had the lowest stratospheric ozone concentration yet recorded. One "Dobson unit" corresponds to 2.69×10^{16} ozone molecules in a 1 cm² column of atmosphere.

Atomic chlorine reacts rapidly with ozone to form chlorine monoxide and molecular oxygen:

$$Cl(g) + O_3(g) \longrightarrow ClO(g) + O_2(g) \qquad [9.7]$$

This reaction follows a second-order rate law with a very large rate constant:

$$\text{Rate} = k[Cl][O_3] \qquad k = 7.2 \times 10^9 \, M^{-1} s^{-1} \text{ at 298 K} \qquad [9.8]$$

Under certain conditions, the ClO generated in Equation 9.7 can react to regenerate free Cl atoms. One way that this can happen is by photodissociation of ClO:

$$ClO(g) + h\nu \longrightarrow Cl(g) + O(g) \qquad [9.9]$$

The Cl atoms generated in Equations 9.6 and 9.9 can react with more O_3, according to Equation 9.7. The result is a sequence of reactions that accomplishes the Cl-catalyzed decomposition of O_3 to O_2:

$$2\,Cl(g) + 2\,O_3(g) \longrightarrow 2\,ClO(g) + 2\,O_2(g)$$

$$2\,ClO(g) + h\nu \longrightarrow 2\,Cl(g) + 2\,O(g)$$

$$\underline{O(g) + O(g) \longrightarrow O_2(g)}$$

$$2\,Cl(g) + 2\,O_3(g) + 2\,ClO(g) + 2\,O(g) \longrightarrow 2\,Cl(g) + 2\,ClO(g) + 3\,O_2(g) + 2\,O(g)$$

The equation can be simplified by eliminating like species from each side to give

$$2\,O_3(g) \xrightarrow{\ Cl\ } 3\,O_2(g) \qquad [9.10]$$

Because the rate of Equation 9.7 increases linearly with [Cl], the rate at which ozone is destroyed increases as the quantity of Cl atoms increases. Thus, the greater the amount of CFCs that diffuse into the stratosphere, the faster the destruction of the ozone layer. Even though troposphere-to-stratosphere diffusion rates are slow, a thinning of the ozone layer over the South Pole has been observed, particularly during September and October (Figure 9.6).

 GIVE IT SOME THOUGHT

Since the rate of ozone destruction depends on [Cl], can Cl be considered a catalyst for the reaction of Equation 9.10?

Because of the environmental problems associated with CFCs, steps have been taken to limit their manufacture and use. A major step was the signing in 1987 of the Montreal Protocol on Substances That Deplete the Ozone Layer, in which participating nations agreed to reduce CFC production. More stringent limits were set in 1992, when representatives of approximately 100 nations agreed to ban the production and use of CFCs by 1996, with some exceptions for "essential uses." Since then, the production of CFCs has indeed dropped precipitously, and the size of the ozone hole has leveled off. Nevertheless, because CFCs are unreactive and because they diffuse so slowly into the stratosphere, scientists estimate that ozone depletion will continue for many years to come. What substances have replaced CFCs? At this time, the main alternatives are hydrofluorocarbons, compounds in which C—H bonds replace the C—Cl bonds of CFCs. One such compound in current use is CH_2FCF_3, known as HFC-134a.

There are no naturally occurring CFCs, but some natural sources contribute chlorine and bromine to the atmosphere, and, just like halogens from CFC, these naturally occurring Cl and Br atoms can participate in ozone-depleting reactions. The principal natural sources are methyl bromide and methyl chloride, which are emitted from the oceans. It is estimated that these molecules contribute less than a third of the total Cl and Br in the atmosphere; the remaining two-thirds is a result of human activities.

Volcanoes are a source of HCl, but generally the HCl they release reacts with water in the troposphere and does not make it to the upper atmosphere.

Sulfur Compounds and Acid Rain

TABLE 9.4 • Median Concentrations of Atmospheric Pollutants in a Typical Urban Atmosphere

Pollutant	Concentration (ppm)
Carbon monoxide	10
Hydrocarbons	3
Sulfur dioxide	0.08
Nitrogen oxides	0.05
Total oxidants (ozone and others)	0.02

Sulfur-containing compounds are present to some extent in the natural, unpolluted atmosphere. They originate in the bacterial decay of organic matter, in volcanic gases, and from other sources listed in Table 9.2. The amount of these compounds released into the atmosphere worldwide from natural sources is about 24×10^{12} g per year, less than the amount from human activities, about 79×10^{12} g per year (principally related to combustion of fuels).

Sulfur compounds, chiefly sulfur dioxide, SO_2, are among the most unpleasant and harmful of the common pollutant gases. ◀ TABLE 9.4 shows the concentrations of several pollutant gases in a *typical* urban environment (where by *typical* we mean one that is not particularly affected by smog). According to these data, the level of sulfur dioxide is 0.08 ppm or higher about half the time. This concentration is considerably lower than that of other pollutants, notably carbon monoxide. Nevertheless, SO_2 is regarded as the most serious health hazard among the pollutants shown, especially for people with respiratory difficulties.

Combustion of coal accounts for about 65% of the SO_2 released annually in the United States, and combustion of oil accounts for another 20%. The majority of this amount is from coal-burning electrical power plants, which generate about 50% of our electricity. The extent to which SO_2 emissions are a problem when coal is burned depends on the amount of sulfur in the coal. Because of concern about SO_2 pollution, low-sulfur coal is in greater demand and is thus more expensive. Much of the coal from east of the Mississippi is relatively high in sulfur content, up to 6% by mass. Much of the coal from the western states has a lower sulfur content, but also a lower heat content per unit mass, so the difference in sulfur content per unit of heat produced is not as large as is often assumed.

China, which gets 70 percent of its energy from coal, is the world's largest generator of SO_2, producing about 22 million tons annually. As a result, that nation has a major problem with SO_2 pollution and has set targets to reduce emissions with some success. In 2010, the U.S. Environmental Protection Agency set new standards to reduce SO_2 emissions, the first change in nearly 40 years. The old standard of 140 parts per billion, measured over 24 hours, will be replaced by a standard of 75 parts per billion, measured over 1 hour.

Sulfur dioxide is harmful to both human health and property; furthermore, atmospheric SO_2 can be oxidized to SO_3 by several pathways (such as reaction with O_2 or O_3). When SO_3 dissolves in water, it produces sulfuric acid:

$$SO_3(g) + H_2O(l) \longrightarrow H_2SO_4(aq)$$

Many of the environmental effects ascribed to SO_2 are actually due to H_2SO_4.

The presence of SO_2 in the atmosphere and the sulfuric acid it produces result in the phenomenon of **acid rain**. (Nitrogen oxides, which form nitric acid, are also major contributors to acid rain.) Uncontaminated rainwater generally has a pH value of about 5.6. The primary source of this natural acidity is CO_2, which reacts with water to form carbonic acid, H_2CO_3. Acid rain typically has a pH value of about 4. This acidity has affected many lakes in northern Europe, the northern United States, and Canada, reducing fish populations and affecting other parts of the ecological network in the lakes and surrounding forests.

The pH of most natural waters containing living organisms is between 6.5 and 8.5, but as ▶ FIGURE 9.7 shows, freshwater pH values are far below 6.5 in many parts of the continental United States. At pH levels below 4.0, all vertebrates, most invertebrates, and many microorganisms are destroyed. The lakes most susceptible to damage are those with low concentrations of basic ions, such as HCO_3^-, that would act as a buffer to minimize changes in pH. Some of these lakes are recovering as sulfur emissions from fossil fuel combustion decrease, in part because of the Clean Air Act, which has resulted in a reduction of more than 40% in SO_2 emissions from power plants since 1980.

Because acids react with metals and with carbonates, acid rain is corrosive both to metals and to stone building materials. Marble and limestone, for example, whose major constituent is $CaCO_3$, are readily attacked by acid rain (▶ FIGURE 9.8). Billions of dollars each year are lost because of corrosion due to SO_2 pollution.

One way to reduce the quantity of SO_2 released into the environment is to remove sulfur from coal and oil before these fuels are burned. Although difficult and expensive,

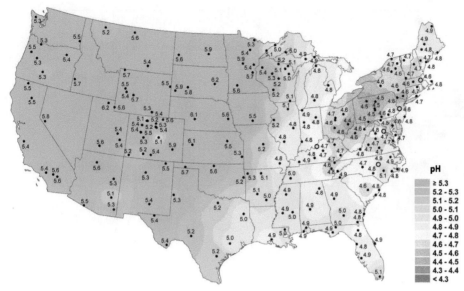

▲ **FIGURE 9.7** **Water pH values from freshwater sites across the United States, 2008.** The numbered dots indicate the locations of monitoring stations.

(a)   (b)

▲ **FIGURE 9.8** **Damage from acid rain.** The right photograph, recently taken, shows how the statue has lost detail in its carvings.

several methods have been developed. Powdered limestone ($CaCO_3$), for example, can be injected into the furnace of a power plant, where it decomposes into lime (CaO) and carbon dioxide:

$$CaCO_3(s) \longrightarrow CaO(s) + CO_2(g)$$

The CaO then reacts with SO_2 to form calcium sulfite:

$$CaO(s) + SO_2(g) \longrightarrow CaSO_3(s)$$

The solid particles of $CaSO_3$, as well as much of the unreacted SO_2, can be removed from the furnace gas by passing it through an aqueous suspension of CaO (▶ **FIGURE 9.9**). Not all the SO_2 is removed, however, and given the enormous quantities of coal and oil burned worldwide, pollution by SO_2 will probably remain a problem for some time.

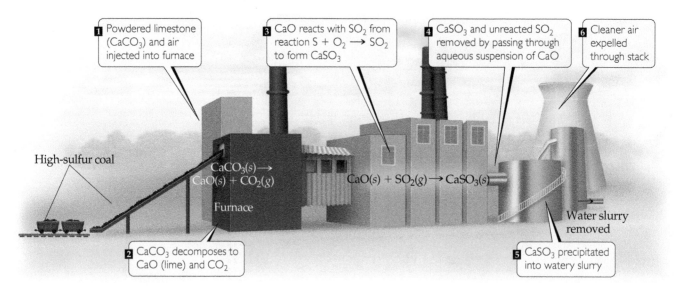

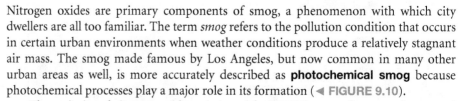

▲ **FIGURE 9.9 One method for removing SO$_2$ from combusted fuel.**

▲ **FIGURE 9.10 Photochemical smog is produced largely by the action of sunlight on vehicle exhaust gases.**

⏶ GIVE IT SOME THOUGHT

What chemical behavior associated with sulfur oxides gives rise to acid rain?

Nitrogen Oxides and Photochemical Smog

Nitrogen oxides are primary components of smog, a phenomenon with which city dwellers are all too familiar. The term *smog* refers to the pollution condition that occurs in certain urban environments when weather conditions produce a relatively stagnant air mass. The smog made famous by Los Angeles, but now common in many other urban areas as well, is more accurately described as **photochemical smog** because photochemical processes play a major role in its formation (◀ FIGURE 9.10).

The majority of nitrogen oxide emissions (about 50%) comes from cars, buses, and other forms of transportation. Nitric oxide, NO, forms in small quantities in the cylinders of internal combustion engines in the reaction

$$N_2(g) + O_2(g) \rightleftharpoons 2\,NO(g) \quad \Delta H = 180.8\,kJ \qquad [9.11]$$

As noted in the "Chemistry Put to Work" box in Section 12.7, the equilibrium constant for this reaction increases from about 10^{-15} at 300 K to about 0.05 at 2400 K (approximate temperature in the cylinder of an engine during combustion). Thus, the reaction is more favorable at higher temperatures. In fact, some NO is formed in any high-temperature combustion. As a result, electrical power plants are also major contributors to nitrogen oxide pollution.

Before the installation of pollution-control devices on automobiles, typical emission levels of NO$_x$ were 4 grams per mile. (The x is either 1 or 2 because both NO and NO$_2$ are formed, although NO predominates.) Starting in 2004, the auto emission standards for NO$_x$ called for a phased-in reduction to 0.07 g/mi by 2009, which was achieved.

In air, nitric oxide is rapidly oxidized to nitrogen dioxide:

$$2\,NO(g) + O_2(g) \rightleftharpoons 2\,NO_2(g) \quad \Delta H = -113.1\,kJ \qquad [9.12]$$

The equilibrium constant for this reaction decreases from about 10^{12} at 300 K to about 10^{-5} at 2400 K.

The photodissociation of NO$_2$ initiates the reactions associated with photochemical smog. Dissociation of NO$_2$ requires 304 kJ/mol, which corresponds to a photon wavelength of 393 nm. In sunlight, therefore, NO$_2$ dissociates to NO and O:

$$NO_2(g) + h\nu \longrightarrow NO(g) + O(g) \qquad [9.13]$$

The atomic oxygen formed undergoes several reactions, one of which gives ozone, as described earlier:

$$O(g) + O_2 + M(g) \longrightarrow O_3(g) + M^*(g) \qquad [9.14]$$

Although it is an essential UV screen in the upper atmosphere, ozone is an undesirable pollutant in the troposphere. It is extremely reactive and toxic, and breathing air that contains appreciable amounts of ozone can be especially dangerous for asthma sufferers, exercisers, and the elderly. We therefore have two ozone problems: excessive amounts in many urban environments, where it is harmful, and depletion in the stratosphere, where its presence is vital.

In addition to nitrogen oxides and carbon monoxide, an automobile engine also emits unburned *hydrocarbons* as pollutants. These organic compounds are the principal components of gasoline and of many compounds we use as fuel (propane, C_3H_8, and butane, C_4H_{10}; for example), but are major ingredients of smog. A typical engine without effective emission controls emits about 10 to 15 g of hydrocarbons per mile. Current standards require that hydrocarbon emissions be less than 0.075 g per mile. Hydrocarbons are also emitted naturally from living organisms (see "A Closer Look" box later in this section).

Reduction or elimination of smog requires that the ingredients essential to its formation be removed from automobile exhaust. Catalytic converters reduce the levels of NO_x and hydrocarbons, two of the major ingredients of smog. (See the "Chemistry Put to Work: Catalytic Converters" in Section 14.7.)

 GIVE IT SOME THOUGHT

What photochemical reaction involving nitrogen oxides initiates the formation of photochemical smog?

Greenhouse Gases: Water Vapor, Carbon Dioxide, and Climate

In addition to screening out harmful short-wavelength radiation, the atmosphere is essential in maintaining a reasonably uniform and moderate temperature on Earth's surface. Earth is in overall thermal balance with its surroundings. This means that the planet radiates energy into space at a rate equal to the rate at which it absorbs energy from the Sun. ▼ FIGURE 9.11 shows the distribution of radiation to and from Earth's

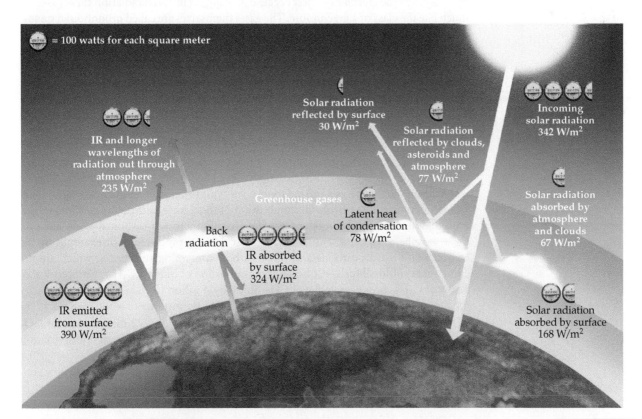

▲ FIGURE 9.11 **Earth's thermal balance.** The amount of radiation reaching the surface of the planet is approximately equal to the amount radiated back into space.

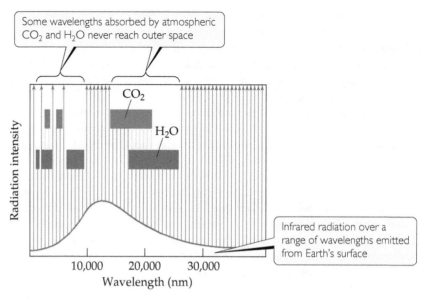

▲ FIGURE 9.12   Portions of the infrared radiation emitted by Earth's surface that are absorbed by atmospheric CO₂ and H₂O.

surface, and ▲ FIGURE 9.12 shows which portion of the infrared radiation leaving the surface is absorbed by atmospheric water vapor and carbon dioxide. In absorbing this radiation, these two atmospheric gases help maintain a livable uniform temperature at the surface by holding in, as it were, the infrared radiation, which we feel as heat.

The influence of H_2O, CO_2, and certain other atmospheric gases on Earth's temperature is called the *greenhouse effect* because in trapping infrared radiation these gases act much like the glass of a greenhouse. The gases themselves are called **greenhouse gases**.

Water vapor makes the largest contribution to the greenhouse effect. The partial pressure of water vapor in the atmosphere varies greatly from place to place and time to time but is generally highest near Earth's surface and drops off with increasing elevation. Because water vapor absorbs infrared radiation so strongly, it plays the major role in maintaining the atmospheric temperature at night, when the surface is emitting radiation into space and not receiving energy from the Sun. In very dry desert climates, where the water-vapor concentration is low, it may be extremely hot during the day but very cold at night. In the absence of a layer of water vapor to absorb and then radiate part of the infrared radiation back to Earth, the surface loses this radiation into space and cools off very rapidly.

Carbon dioxide plays a secondary but very important role in maintaining the surface temperature. The worldwide combustion of fossil fuels, principally coal and oil, on a prodigious scale in the modern era has sharply increased carbon dioxide levels in the atmosphere. To get a sense of the amount of CO_2 produced—for example, by the combustion of hydrocarbons and other carbon-containing substances, which are the components of fossil fuels—consider the combustion of butane, C_4H_{10}. Combustion of 1.00 g of C_4H_{10} produces 3.03 g of CO_2. Similarly, a gallon (3.78 L) of gasoline (density 0.7 g/mL, approximate composition C_8H_{18}) produces about 8 kg of CO_2. Combustion of fossil fuels releases about 2.2×10^{16} g (22 billion tons) of CO_2 into the atmosphere annually, with the largest quantity coming from transportation vehicles.

Much CO_2 is absorbed into oceans or used by plants. Nevertheless, we are now generating CO_2 much faster than it is being absorbed or used. Analysis of air trapped in ice cores taken from Antarctica and Greenland makes it possible to determine the

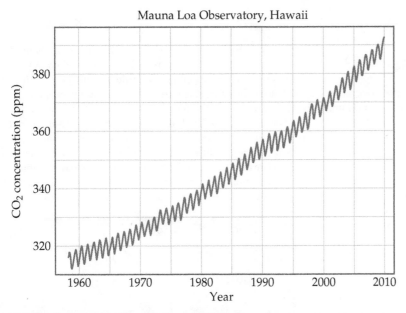

▲ FIGURE 9.13 Rising CO₂ levels. The sawtooth shape of the graph is due to regular seasonal variations in CO_2 concentration for each year.

atmospheric levels of CO_2 during the past 160,000 years. These measurements reveal that the level of CO_2 remained fairly constant from the last Ice Age, some 10,000 years ago, until roughly the beginning of the Industrial Revolution, about 300 years ago. Since that time, the concentration of CO_2 has increased by about 30% to a current high of about 386 ppm (▲ **FIGURE 9.13**).

A consensus is emerging among scientists that this increase in atmospheric CO_2 is perturbing Earth's climate and may be responsible for the observed increase in the average global air temperature of 0.3 °C to 0.6 °C over the past century. Scientists often use the term *climate change* instead of *global warming* to refer to this effect because as the Earth's temperature increases, it affects winds and ocean currents in ways that can cool some areas and warm others.

On the basis of present and expected future rates of fossil-fuel use, the atmospheric CO_2 level is expected to double from its present level sometime between 2050 and 2100. Computer models predict that this increase will result in an average global temperature increase of 1 °C to 3 °C. Because so many factors go into determining climate, we cannot predict with certainty what changes will occur because of this warming. Clearly, however, humanity has acquired the potential, by changing the concentrations of CO_2 and other heat-trapping gases in the atmosphere, to substantially alter the climate of the planet.

The climate change threat posed by atmospheric CO_2 has sparked considerable research into ways of capturing the gas at its largest combustion sources and storing it under ground or under the seafloor. There is also much interest in developing new ways to use CO_2 as a chemical feedstock. However, the approximately 115 million tons of CO_2 used annually by the global chemical industry is but a small fraction of the approximately 24 billion tons of annual CO_2 emissions. The use of CO_2 as a raw material will probably never be great enough to reduce its atmospheric concentration.

 GIVE IT SOME THOUGHT

Explain why nighttime temperatures remain higher in locations where there is higher humidity.

A CLOSER LOOK

OTHER GREENHOUSE GASES

Although CO_2 receives most of the attention, other gases contribute to the greenhouse effect, including methane, CH_4, hydrofluorocarbons (HFCs), and chlorofluorocarbons (CFCs).

HFCs have replaced CFCs in a host of applications, including refrigerants and air-conditioner gases. Although they do not contribute to the depletion of the ozone layer, HFCs are nevertheless strong greenhouse gases. Their total concentration in the atmosphere is still small (40 parts per trillion), but this amount is increasing about 10% per year. Thus, these substances are becoming increasingly important contributors to the greenhouse effect.

Methane already makes a significant contribution to the greenhouse effect. Each methane molecule has about 25 times the greenhouse effect of a CO_2 molecule. Studies of atmospheric gas trapped long ago in the Greenland and Antarctic ice sheets show that the atmospheric methane concentration has increased from preindustrial values of 0.3 to 0.7 ppm to the present value of about 1.8 ppm. The major sources of methane are associated with agriculture and fossil-fuel use.

Methane is formed in biological processes that occur in low-oxygen environments. Anaerobic bacteria, which flourish in swamps and landfills, near the roots of rice plants, and in the digestive systems of cows and other ruminant animals, produce methane (▶ FIGURE 9.14). It also leaks into the atmosphere during natural-gas extraction and transport. It is estimated that about two-thirds of present-day methane emissions, which are increasing by about 1% per year, are related to human activities.

Methane has a half-life in the atmosphere of about 10 years, whereas CO_2 is much longer-lived. This might seem a good thing, but there are indirect effects to consider. Methane is oxidized in the stratosphere, producing water vapor, a powerful greenhouse gas that is otherwise virtually absent from the stratosphere. In the troposphere, methane is attacked by reactive species such as OH radicals or nitrogen oxides, eventually producing other greenhouse gases, such as O_3. It has been estimated that the climate-changing effects of CH_4 are more than half those of CO_2. Given this large contribution, important reductions of the greenhouse effect could be achieved by reducing methane emissions or capturing the emissions for use as a fuel.

▲ FIGURE 9.14 **Methane production.** Ruminant animals, such as cows and sheep, produce methane in their digestive systems.

9.3 | EARTH'S WATER

Water covers 72% of Earth's surface and is essential to life. Our bodies are about 65% water by mass. Because of extensive hydrogen bonding, water has unusually high melting and boiling points and a high heat capacity. ⊙⊙ (Section 5.2) Water's highly polar character is responsible for its exceptional ability to dissolve a wide range of ionic and polar-covalent substances. Many reactions occur in water, including reactions in which H_2O itself is a reactant. Recall, for example, that H_2O can participate in acid–base reactions as either a proton donor or a proton acceptor. All these properties play a role in our environment.

The Global Water Cycle

All the water on Earth is connected in a global water cycle (▶ FIGURE 9.15). Most of the processes depicted here rely on the phase changes of water. For instance, warmed by the Sun, liquid water in the oceans evaporates into the atmosphere as water vapor and condenses into liquid water droplets that we see as clouds. Water droplets in the clouds can crystallize to ice, which can precipitate as hail or snow. Once on the ground, the hail or snow melts to liquid water, which soaks into the ground. If conditions are right, it is also possible for ice on the ground to sublime to water vapor in the atmosphere.

 GIVE IT SOME THOUGHT

Consider the phase diagram for water shown in Figure 11.12. In what pressure range and in what temperature range must H_2O exist in order for $H_2O(s)$ to sublime to $H_2O(g)$?

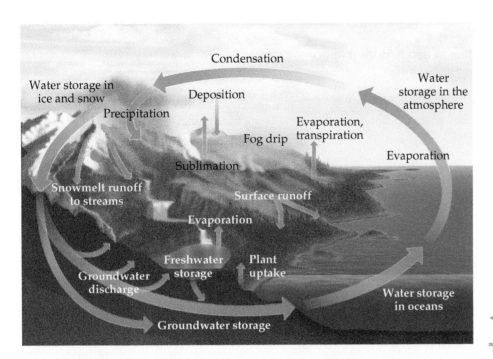

◀ **FIGURE 9.15** **The global water cycle.**

Salt Water: Earth's Oceans and Seas

The vast layer of salty water that covers so much of the planet is in actuality one large connected body and is generally constant in composition. For this reason, oceanographers speak of a *world ocean* rather than of the separate oceans we learn about in geography books.

The world ocean is huge, having a volume of 1.35×10^9 km^3 and containing 97.2% of all the water on Earth. Of the remaining 2.8%, 2.1% is in the form of ice caps and glaciers. All the freshwater—in lakes, in rivers, and in the ground—amounts to only 0.6%. Most of the remaining 0.1% is in brackish (salty) water, such as that in the Great Salt Lake in Utah.

Seawater is often referred to as saline water. The **salinity** of seawater is the mass in grams of dry salts present in 1 kg of seawater. In the world ocean, salinity averages about 35. To put it another way, seawater contains about 3.5% dissolved salts by mass. The list of elements present in seawater is very long. Most, however, are present only in very low concentrations. ▼ TABLE 9.5 lists the 11 ionic species most abundant in seawater.

TABLE 9.5 • Ionic Constituents of Seawater Present in Concentrations Greater Than 0.001 g/kg (1 ppm)		
Ionic Constituent	**Salinity**	**Concentration (M)**
Chloride, Cl^-	19.35	0.55
Sodium, Na^+	10.76	0.47
Sulfate, SO_4^{2-}	2.71	0.028
Magnesium, Mg^{2+}	1.29	0.054
Calcium, Ca^{2+}	0.412	0.010
Potassium, K^+	0.40	0.010
Carbon dioxide*	0.106	2.3×10^{-3}
Bromide, Br^-	0.067	8.3×10^{-4}
Boric acid, H_3BO_3	0.027	4.3×10^{-4}
Strontium, Sr^{2+}	0.0079	9.1×10^{-5}
Fluoride, F^-	0.0013	7.0×10^{-5}

*CO_2 is present in seawater as HCO_3^- and CO_3^{2-}.

⚠ GO FIGURE

Look at the trend in density as a function of depth; does it mirror the trend in salinity or in temperature?

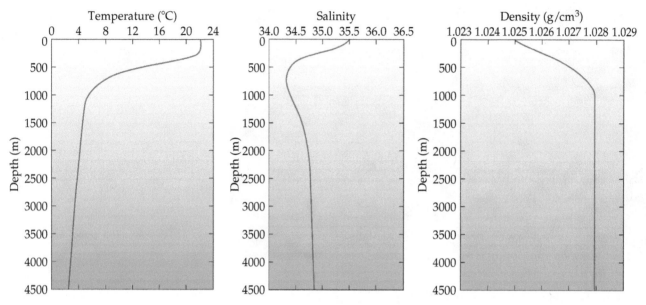

▲ FIGURE 9.16   **Average temperature, salinity, and density of seawater as a function of depth.** (From Windows to the Universe, University Corporation for Atmospheric Research. Copyright © 2004 University Corporation for Atmospheric Research. All rights reserved.)

Seawater temperature, salinity, and density vary as a function of depth (▲ FIGURE 9.16). Sunlight penetrates well only 200 m into the water; the region between 200 m and 1000 m deep is the "twilight zone," where visible light is faint. Below 1000 m, the ocean is pitch-black and cold, about 4 °C. The transport of heat, salt, and other chemicals throughout the ocean is influenced by these changes in the physical properties of seawater, and in turn the changes in the way heat and substances are transported affects ocean currents and the global climate.

The sea is so vast that if the concentration of a substance in seawater is 1 part per billion (1×10^{-6} g per kilogram of water), there is 1×10^{12} kg of the substance in the world ocean. Nevertheless, because of high extracting costs, only three substances are obtained from seawater in commercially important amounts: sodium chloride, bromine (from bromide salts), and magnesium (from its salts).

Absorption of CO_2 by the ocean plays a large role in global climate. Because carbon dioxide and water form carbonic acid, the H_2CO_3 concentration in the ocean increases as the water absorbs atmospheric CO_2. Most of the carbon in the ocean, however, is in the form of HCO_3^- and CO_3^{2-} ions, which form a buffer system that maintains the ocean's pH between 8.0 and 8.3. The pH of the ocean is predicted to decrease as the concentration of CO_2 in the atmosphere increases.

Freshwater and Groundwater

Freshwater is the term used to denote natural waters that have low concentrations (less than 500 ppm) of dissolved salts and solids. Freshwater includes the waters of lakes, rivers, ponds, and streams. The United States is fortunate in its abundance of freshwater—1.7×10^{15} L (660 trillion gallons) is the estimated reserve, which is renewed by rainfall. An estimated 9×10^{11} L of freshwater is used every day in the United States. Most of this is used for agriculture (41%) and hydroelectric power (39%), with small amounts for industry (6%), household needs (6%), and drinking water (1%). An adult drinks about 2 L of water per day. In the United States, our daily use of

▲ GO FIGURE

What factors influence how long it takes for water to migrate from a deep

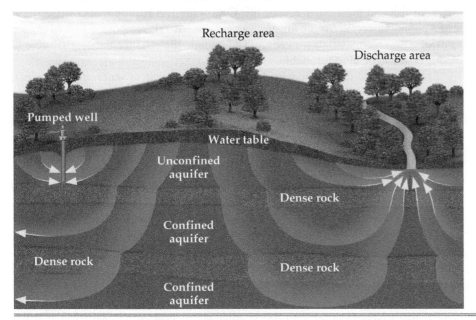

◄ **FIGURE 9.17 Groundwater is water located in aquifers below the soil.** An unconfined aquifer, that has no dense rock between it and the water table, can hold water for days or years. Confined aquifers can hold water for centuries or millenia, depending on their depth. Aquifers are discharged through wells or rivers, and are recharged from water flowing through the soil (e.g., from rain).

water per person far exceeds this subsistence level, amounting to an average of about 300 L/day for personal consumption and hygiene. We use about 8 L/person for cooking and drinking, about 120 L/person for cleaning (bathing, laundering, and housecleaning), 80 L/person for flushing toilets, and 80 L/person for watering lawns.

The total amount of freshwater on Earth is not a very large fraction of the total water present. Indeed, freshwater is one of our most precious resources. It forms by evaporation from the oceans and the land. The water vapor that accumulates in the atmosphere is transported by global atmospheric circulation, eventually returning to Earth as rain, snow, and other forms of precipitation (Figure 9.15).

As water runs off the land on its way to the oceans, it dissolves a variety of cations (mainly Na^+, K^+, Mg^{2+}, Ca^{2+}, and Fe^{2+}), anions (mainly Cl^-, SO_4^{2-}, and HCO_3^-), and gases (principally O_2, N_2, and CO_2). As we use water, it becomes laden with additional dissolved material, including the wastes of human society. As our population and output of environmental pollutants increase, we find that we must spend ever-increasing amounts of money and resources to guarantee a supply of freshwater.

Approximately 20% of the world's freshwater is under the soil, in the form of *groundwater*. Groundwater resides in *aquifers*, which are layers of porous rock that hold water. The water in aquifers can be very pure and accessible for human consumption if near the surface (▲ **FIGURE 9.17**). Dense rock that does not allow water to readily penetrate can hold groundwater for years or even millennia.

The nature of the rock that contains the groundwater has a large influence on the water's chemical composition. If minerals in the rock are water soluble to some extent, ions can leach out of the rock and remain dissolved in the groundwater. Arsenic in the form of $HAsO_4^{2-}$, $H_2AsO_4^-$, and H_3AsO_3 are found in groundwater across the world, most infamously in Bangladesh, at concentrations poisonous to humans.

9.4 | HUMAN ACTIVITIES AND EARTH'S WATER

All life on Earth depends on the availability of suitable water. Some organisms can thrive under temperature, pH, and ionic conditions where other organisms would die. Many human activities rely on waste disposal via Earth's waters, even today, and this practice can be detrimental to aquatic organisms.

▲ **FIGURE 9.18** **Eutrophication.** This rapid accumulation of dead and decaying plant matter in a body of water uses up the water's oxygen supply, making the water unsuitable for aquatic animals.

Dissolved Oxygen and Water Quality

The amount of O_2 dissolved in water is an important indicator of water quality. Water fully saturated with air at 1 atm and 20 °C contains about 9 ppm of O_2. Oxygen is necessary for fish and most other aquatic life. Cold-water fish require water containing at least 5 ppm of dissolved oxygen for survival. Aerobic bacteria consume dissolved oxygen to oxidize organic materials for energy. The organic material the bacteria are able to oxidize is said to be **biodegradable**.

Excessive quantities of biodegradable organic materials in water are detrimental because they remove the oxygen necessary to sustain normal animal life. Typical sources of these biodegradable materials, which are called *oxygen-demanding wastes*, include sewage, industrial wastes from food-processing plants and paper mills, and liquid waste from meatpacking plants.

In the presence of oxygen, the carbon, hydrogen, nitrogen, sulfur, and phosphorus in biodegradable material end up mainly as CO_2, HCO_3^-, H_2O, NO_3^-, SO_4^{2-}, and phosphates. The formation of these oxidation products sometimes reduces the amount of dissolved oxygen to the point where aerobic bacteria can no longer survive. Anaerobic bacteria then take over the decomposition process, forming CH_4, NH_3, H_2S, PH_3, and other products, several of which contribute to the offensive odors of some polluted waters.

Plant nutrients, particularly nitrogen and phosphorus, contribute to water pollution by stimulating excessive growth of aquatic plants. The most visible results of excessive plant growth are floating algae and murky water. What is more significant, however, is that as plant growth becomes excessive, the amount of dead and decaying plant matter increases rapidly, a process called *eutrophication* (◄ FIGURE 9.18). The processes by which plants decay consumes O_2, and without sufficient oxygen, the water cannot sustain animal life.

The most significant sources of nitrogen and phosphorus compounds in water are domestic sewage (phosphate-containing detergents and nitrogen-containing body wastes), runoff from agricultural land (fertilizers contain both nitrogen and phosphorus), and runoff from livestock areas (animal wastes contain nitrogen).

> ◢ **GIVE IT SOME THOUGHT**
>
> If a test on a sample of polluted water shows a considerable decrease in dissolved oxygen over a five-day period, what can we conclude about the nature of the pollutants present?

Water Purification: Desalination

Because of its high salt content, seawater is unfit for human consumption and for most of the uses to which we put water. In the United States the salt content of municipal water supplies is restricted by health codes to no more than about 0.05% by mass. This amount is much lower than the 3.5% dissolved salts present in seawater and the 0.5% or so present in brackish water found underground in some regions. The removal of salts from seawater or brackish water to make the water usable is called **desalination**.

Water can be separated from dissolved salts by *distillation* because water is a volatile substance and the salts are nonvolatile. The principle of distillation is simple enough, but carrying out the process on a large scale presents many problems. As water is distilled from seawater, for example, the salts become more and more concentrated and eventually precipitate out. Distillation is also an energy-intensive process.

Seawater can also be desalinated using **reverse osmosis**. Recall that osmosis is the net movement of solvent molecules, but not solute molecules, through a semipermeable membrane. In osmosis, the solvent passes from the more dilute solution into the more concentrated one. However, if sufficient external pressure is applied, osmosis can be stopped and, at still higher pressures, reversed. When reverse osmosis occurs, solvent passes from the more concentrated into the more dilute solution. In a modern reverse-osmosis facility, hollow fibers are used as the semipermeable membrane (◄ FIGURE 9.19). Water is introduced under pressure into the fibers, and desalinated water is recovered.

> **GO FIGURE**
>
> What feature of this process is responsible for its being called *reverse* osmosis?

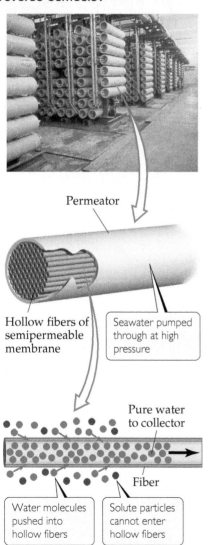

Permeator

Hollow fibers of semipermeable membrane

Seawater pumped through at high pressure

Pure water to collector

Fiber

Water molecules pushed into hollow fibers

Solute particles cannot enter hollow fibers

▲ **FIGURE 9.19** **Reverse osmosis.**

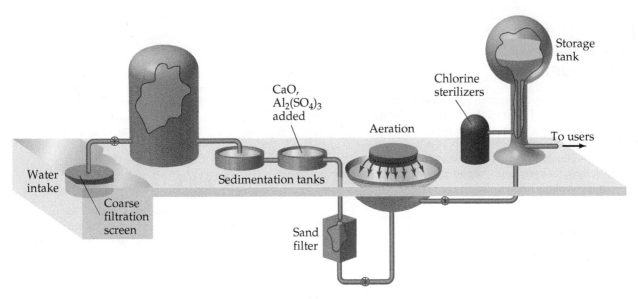

▲ **FIGURE 9.20** **Common steps in treating water for a public water system.**

The world's largest desalination plant, in Jubail, Saudi Arabia, provides 50% of that country's drinking water by using reverse osmosis to desalinate seawater from the Persian Gulf. Such plants are becoming increasingly common in the United States. The largest, near Tampa Bay, Florida, has been operating since 2007 and produces 35 million gallons of drinking water a day by reverse osmosis. Small-scale, manually operated reverse-osmosis desalinators are used in camping, traveling, and at sea.

Water Purification: Municipal Treatment

The water needed for domestic, agricultural, and industrial use is taken either from lakes, rivers, and underground sources or from reservoirs. Much of the water that finds its way into municipal water systems is "used" water, meaning it has already passed through one or more sewage systems or industrial plants. Consequently, this water must be treated before it is distributed to our faucets.

Municipal water treatment usually involves five steps (▲ **FIGURE 9.20**). After coarse filtration through a screen, the water is allowed to stand in large sedimentation tanks where sand and other minute particles settle out. To aid in removing very small particles, the water may first be made slightly basic with CaO. Then $Al_2(SO_4)_3$ is added and reacts with OH^- ions to form a spongy, gelatinous precipitate of $Al(OH)_3$ ($K_{sp} = 1.3 \times 10^{-33}$). This precipitate settles slowly, carrying suspended particles down with it, thereby removing nearly all finely divided matter and most bacteria. The water is then filtered through a sand bed. Following filtration, the water may be sprayed into the air (aeration) to hasten oxidation of dissolved organic substances.

The final step normally involves treating the water with a chemical agent to ensure the destruction of bacteria. Ozone is more effective, but chlorine is less expensive. Liquefied Cl_2 is dispensed from tanks through a metering device directly into the water supply. The amount used depends on the presence of other substances with which the chlorine might react and on the concentrations of bacteria and viruses to be removed. The sterilizing action of chlorine is probably due not to Cl_2 itself but to hypochlorous acid, which forms when chlorine reacts with water:

$$Cl_2(aq) + H_2O(l) \longrightarrow HClO(aq) + H^+(aq) + Cl^-(aq) \qquad [9.15]$$

As many as a billion people worldwide lack access to clean water. According to the United Nations, 95% of the world's cities still dump raw sewage into their water supplies. Thus, it should come as no surprise that 80% of all the health maladies in developing countries can be traced to waterborne diseases associated with unsanitary water.

One promising development is a device called the LifeStraw (▶ **FIGURE 9.21**). When a person sucks water through the straw, the water first encounters a textile filter

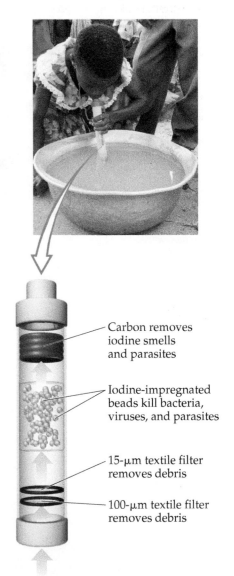

Carbon removes iodine smells and parasites

Iodine-impregnated beads kill bacteria, viruses, and parasites

15-μm textile filter removes debris

100-μm textile filter removes debris

▲ **FIGURE 9.21** **A LifeStraw purifies water as it is drunk.**

A CLOSER LOOK

WATER SOFTENING

Water containing a relatively high concentration of Ca^{2+}, Mg^{2+}, and other divalent cations is called *hard water*. Although the presence of these ions is generally not a health threat, they can make water unsuitable for some household and industrial uses. For example, these ions react with soap to form an insoluble soap scum, the stuff of bathtub rings.

In addition, mineral deposits may form when water containing these ions is heated. When water containing calcium ions and bicarbonate ions is heated, some carbon dioxide is driven off. As a result, the solution becomes less acidic and insoluble calcium carbonate forms:

$$Ca^{2+}(aq) + 2\,HCO_3^-(aq) \longrightarrow CaCO_3(s) + CO_2(g) + H_2O(l)$$

The solid $CaCO_3$ coats the surface of hot-water systems and teakettles, reducing heating efficiency (▼ FIGURE 9.22). These deposits, called *scale*, can be especially serious in boilers where water is heated under pressure in pipes running through a furnace.

▲ FIGURE 9.22 **Scale formation.** The interior of this water pipe has been coated with $CaCO_3$ and other insoluble salts deposited from hard water.

Removal of the ions that cause hard water is called *water softening*. In the *lime-soda process* used for large-scale municipal water-softening operations, the water is treated with calcium hydroxide (prepared from lime) and, sodium carbonate (sometimes called soda ash) to precipitate Ca^{2+} as $CaCO_3$ and Mg^{2+} as $Mg(OH)_2$:

$$Ca^{2+}(aq) + CO_3^{2-}(aq) \longrightarrow CaCO_3(s)$$

$$Mg^{2+}(aq) + 2\,OH^-(aq) \longrightarrow Mg(OH)_2(s)$$

In *ion exchange*, a typical household method for softening water, hard water is passed through an ion-exchange resin made up of plastic beads with covalently bound anion groups such as $-COO^-$ or $-SO_3^-$. These negatively charged groups have Na^+ ions to balance their charges. The Ca^{2+} and other cations in the hard water are attracted to the anionic groups and displace the lower-charged Na^+ into the water. Thus, one type of ion is exchanged for another. To maintain charge balance, $2\,Na^+$ enter the water for each Ca^{2+} removed. If we represent the resin with its anionic site as $R-COO^-$, we can write the equation for the process as

$$2\,Na(R-COO)(s) + Ca^{2+}(aq) \rightleftharpoons$$
$$Ca(R-COO)_2(s) + 2\,Na^+(aq)$$

Water softened in this way contains an increased concentration of Na^+. Although Na^+ does not form precipitates or cause other problems associated with hard-water cations, individuals concerned about their sodium intake, such as those who have high blood pressure (hypertension), should avoid drinking water softened in this way.

When all the available Na^+ ions have been displaced from the ion-exchange resin, the resin is regenerated by flushing it with a concentrated solution of NaCl. The high concentration of Na^+ forces the equilibrium in the preceding equation to shift to the left, causing the Na^+ to displace the hard-water cations, which are flushed down the drain.

with a mesh opening of 100 μm followed by a second textile filter with a mesh opening of 15 μm. These filters remove debris and even clusters of bacteria. The water next encounters a chamber of iodine-impregnated beads, where bacteria, viruses, and parasites are killed. Finally, the water passes through granulated active carbon, which removes the smell of iodine as well as the parasites that have not been taken by the filters or killed by the iodine.

Water disinfection is one of the greatest public health innovations in human history. It has dramatically decreased the incidences of waterborne bacterial diseases such as cholera and typhus. However, this great benefit comes at a price.

In 1974 scientists in Europe and the United States discovered that chlorination of water produces a group of by-products previously undetected. These by-products are called *trihalomethanes* (THMs) because all have a single carbon atom and three halogen atoms: $CHCl_3$, $CHCl_2Br$, $CHClBr_2$, and $CHBr_3$. These and many other chlorine- and bromine-containing organic substances are produced by the reaction of dissolved chlorine with the organic materials present in nearly all natural waters, as well as with substances that are by-products of human activity. Recall that chlorine dissolves in water to form the oxidizing agent HClO:

$$Cl_2(g) + H_2O(l) \longrightarrow HClO(aq) + H^+(aq) + Cl^-(aq) \qquad [9.16]$$

The HClO in turn reacts with organic substances to form THMs. Bromine enters the reaction sequence through the reaction of HClO with dissolved bromide ion:

$$HOCl(aq) + Br^-(aq) \longrightarrow HBrO(aq) + Cl^-(aq) \qquad [9.17]$$

Then both HBrO(aq) and HClO(aq) can halogenate organic substances to form the THMs.

Some THMs and other halogenated organic substances are suspected carcinogens; others interfere with the body's endocrine system. As a result, the World Health Organization and the U.S. Environmental Protection Agency have placed concentration limits of 80 μg/L (80 ppb) on the total quantity of THMs in drinking water. The goal is to reduce the levels of THMs and other disinfection by-products in the drinking water supply while preserving the antibacterial effectiveness of the water treatment. In some cases, lowering the concentration of chlorine may provide adequate disinfection while reducing the concentrations of THMs formed. Alternative oxidizing agents, such as ozone or chlorine dioxide, produce less of the halogenated substances but have their own disadvantages. For example, each is capable of oxidizing dissolved bromide, as shown here for ozone:

$$O_3(aq) + Br^-(aq) + H_2O(l) \longrightarrow HBrO(aq) + O_2(aq) + OH^-(aq) \qquad [9.18]$$

$$HBrO(aq) + 2\,O_3(aq) \longrightarrow BrO_3^-(aq) + 2\,O_2(aq) + H^+(aq) \qquad [9.19]$$

Bromate ion, BrO_3^-, has been shown to cause cancer in animal tests. Bromate's cancer-causing potential has led Los Angeles, for example, to add 3 million black plastic balls to one of its drinking water reservoirs to prevent bromate from forming via photochemical processes (▶ FIGURE 9.23).

At present, there seem to be no completely satisfactory alternatives to chlorination or ozonation, and we are faced with a consideration of benefit versus risk. In this case, the risks of cancer from THMs and related substances in municipal water are very low relative to the risks of cholera, typhus, and gastrointestinal disorders from untreated water. When the water supply is cleaner to begin with, less disinfectant is needed and thus the risk of THMs is lowered. Once THMs form, their concentrations in the water supply can be reduced by aeration because the THMs are more volatile than water. Alternatively, they can be removed by adsorption onto activated charcoal or other adsorbents.

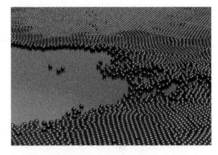

▲ FIGURE 9.23 **Preventing photochemical bromate reactions.** The black plastic balls added to this Los Angeles drinking water reservoir keep sunlight from entering the water and initiating reactions that form harmful bromate ions.

Osmosis

Certain materials, including many membranes in biological systems and synthetic substances such as cellophane, are *semipermeable*. When in contact with a solution, these materials allow only small molecules—water molecules, for instance—to pass through their network of tiny pores.

Consider a situation in which only solvent molecules are able to pass through a semipermeable membrane placed between two solutions of different concentrations. The rate at which the solvent passes from the less concentrated solution (lower solute concentration but higher solvent concentration) to the more concentrated solution (higher solute concentration but lower solvent concentration) is greater than the rate in the opposite direction. Thus, there is a net movement of solvent molecules from the solution with a lower solute concentration into the one with a higher solute concentration. In this process, called **osmosis**, *the net movement of solvent is always toward the solution with the higher solute concentration*, as if the solutions were driven to attain equal concentrations.

▶ FIGURE 9.24 shows the osmosis that occurs between an aqueous solution and pure water. The U-tube contains water on the left and an aqueous solution on the right.

There is a net movement of water through the membrane from left to right, As a result, the liquid levels in the two arms become unequal. Eventually, the pressure difference resulting from the unequal liquid heights becomes so large that the net flow of water ceases. The pressure required to stop osmosis from a pure solvent to a solution is the **osmotic pressure** of the solution. If an external pressure equal to the osmotic pressure is applied to the solution, the liquid levels in the two arms can be equalized, as shown in the right panel of Figure 9.24.

The osmotic pressure obeys a law similar in form to the ideal-gas law, $\Pi V = nRT$, where Π is the osmotic pressure, V is the volume of the solution, n is the number of moles of solute, R is the ideal-gas constant, and T is the Kelvin temperature. From this equation, we can write

$$\Pi = \left(\frac{n}{V}\right)RT = MRT \qquad [9.20]$$

where M is the molarity of the solution. Because the osmotic pressure for any solution depends on the solution concentration, osmotic pressure is a colligative property.

If two solutions of identical osmotic pressure are separated by a semipermeable membrane, no osmosis will occur. The two solutions are *isotonic* with respect to each other. If one solution is of lower osmotic pressure, it is *hypotonic* with respect to the more concentrated solution. The more concentrated solution is *hypertonic* with respect to the dilute solution.

GIVE IT SOME THOUGHT

Of two KBr solutions, one 0.50 *m* and the other 0.20 *m*, which is hypotonic with respect to the other?

Osmosis plays an important role in living systems. The membranes of red blood cells, for example, are semipermeable. Placing a red blood cell in a solution that is *hyper*tonic relative to the intracellular solution (the solution inside the cells) causes water to move out of the cell (▶ FIGURE 9.25). This causes the cell to shrivel, a process

GO FIGURE

If the pure water in the left arm of the U-tube is replaced by a solution more

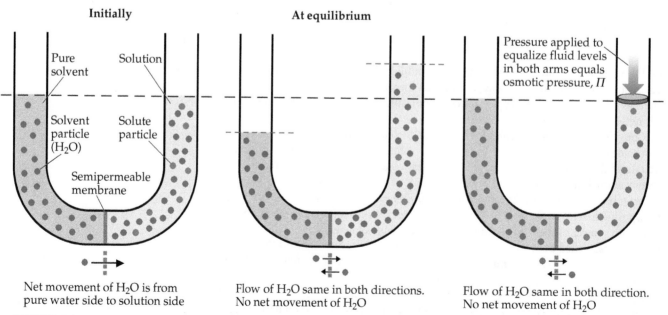

▲ FIGURE 9.24 **Osmosis.**

GO FIGURE

If the fluid surrounding a patient's red blood cells is depleted in electrolytes, is crenation or hemolysis more likely to occur?

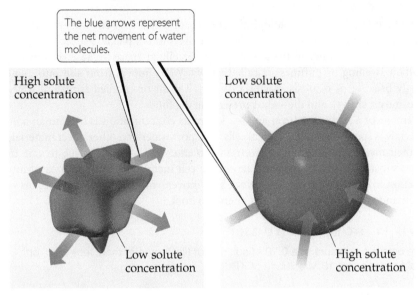

The blue arrows represent the net movement of water molecules.

High solute concentration

Low solute concentration

Low solute concentration

High solute concentration

Crenation of red blood cell placed in hypertonic environment

Hemolysis of red blood cell placed in hypotonic environment

◀ **FIGURE 9.25** **Osmosis through red blood cell wall.**

called *crenation*. Placing the cell in a solution that is *hypo*tonic relative to the intracellular fluid causes water to move into the cell. This may cause the cell to rupture, a process called *hemolysis*. People who need body fluids or nutrients replaced but cannot be fed orally are given solutions by intravenous (IV) infusion, which feeds nutrients directly into the veins. To prevent crenation or hemolysis of red blood cells, the IV solutions must be isotonic with the intracellular fluids of the blood cells.

SAMPLE EXERCISE 9.3 **Calculation Involving Osmotic Pressure**

The average osmotic pressure of blood is 7.7 atm at 25 °C. What molarity of glucose ($C_6H_{12}O_6$) will be isotonic with blood?

SOLUTION

Analyze We are asked to calculate the concentration of glucose in water that would be isotonic with blood, given that the osmotic pressure of blood at 25 °C is 7.7 atm.

Plan Because we are given the osmotic pressure and temperature, we can solve for the concentration.

Solve

$$\Pi = MRT$$
$$M = \frac{\Pi}{RT} = \frac{7.7 \text{ atm}}{\left(0.0821 \dfrac{\text{L-atm}}{\text{mol-K}}\right)(298 \text{ K})} = 0.31 \, M$$

Comment In clinical situations the concentrations of solutions are generally expressed as mass percentages. The mass percentage of a 0.31 M solution of glucose is 5.3%. The concentration of NaCl that is isotonic with blood is 0.16 M, because NaCl ionizes to form two particles, Na^+ and Cl^- (a 0.155 M solution of NaCl is 0.310 M in particles). A 0.16 M solution of NaCl is 0.9 mass % in NaCl. This kind of solution is known as a physiological saline solution.

There are many interesting biological examples of osmosis. A cucumber placed in concentrated brine loses water via osmosis and shrivels into a pickle. People who eat a lot of salty food retain water in tissue cells and intercellular space because of osmosis. The resultant swelling or puffiness is called *edema*. Water moves from soil into plant roots partly because of osmosis. Bacteria on salted meat or candied fruit lose water through osmosis, shrivel, and die—thus preserving the food.

Movement of a substance from an area where its concentration is high to an area where it is low is spontaneous. Biological cells transport water and other select materials through their membranes, permitting nutrients to enter and waste materials to exit. In some cases substances must be moved across the cell membrane from an area of low concentration to one of high concentration. This movement—called *active transport*—is not spontaneous, so cells must expend energy to do it.

 GIVE IT SOME THOUGHT

Is the osmotic pressure of a 0.10 M solution of NaCl greater than, less than, or equal to that of a 0.10 M solution of KBr?

CHAPTER SUMMARY AND KEY TERMS

SECTION 9.1 In this section we examined the physical and chemical properties of Earth's atmosphere. The complex temperature variations in the atmosphere give rise to four regions, each with characteristic properties. The lowest of these regions, the **troposphere**, extends from Earth's surface up to an altitude of about 12 km. Above the troposphere, in order of increasing altitude, are the **stratosphere**, mesosphere, and thermosphere. In the upper reaches of the atmosphere, only the simplest chemical species can survive the bombardment of highly energetic particles and radiation from the Sun. The average molecular weight of the atmosphere at high elevations is lower than that at Earth's surface because the lightest atoms and molecules diffuse upward and also because of **photodissociation**, which is the breaking of bonds in molecules because of the absorption of light. Absorption of radiation may also lead to the formation of ions via **photoionization**.

SECTION 9.2 Ozone is produced in the upper atmosphere from the reaction of atomic oxygen with O_2. Ozone is itself decomposed by absorption of a photon or by reaction with an active species such as Cl. **Chlorofluorocarbons** can undergo photodissociation in the stratosphere, introducing atomic chlorine, which is capable of catalytically destroying ozone. A marked reduction in the ozone level in the upper atmosphere would have serious adverse consequences because the ozone layer filters out certain wavelengths of ultraviolet light that are not removed by any other atmospheric component. In the troposphere the chemistry of trace atmospheric components is of major importance. Many of these minor components are pollutants. Sulfur dioxide is one of the more noxious and prevalent examples. It is oxidized in air to form sulfur trioxide, which, upon dissolving in water, forms sulfuric acid. The oxides of sulfur are major contributors to **acid rain**. One method of preventing the escape of SO_2 from industrial operations is to react it with CaO to form calcium sulfite ($CaSO_3$).

Photochemical smog is a complex mixture in which both nitrogen oxides and ozone play important roles. Smog components are generated mainly in automobile engines, and smog control consists largely of controlling auto emissions.

Carbon dioxide and water vapor are the major components of the atmosphere that strongly absorb infrared radiation. CO_2 and H_2O are therefore critical in maintaining Earth's surface temperature. The concentrations of CO_2 and other so-called **greenhouse gases** in the atmosphere are thus important in determining worldwide climate. Because of the extensive combustion of fossil fuels (coal, oil, and natural gas), the concentration of carbon dioxide in the atmosphere is steadily increasing.

SECTION 9.3 Earth's water is largely in the oceans and seas; only a small fraction is freshwater. Seawater contains about 3.5% by mass of dissolved salts and is described as having a **salinity** (grams of dry salts per 1 kg seawater) of 35. Seawater's density and salinity vary with depth. Because most of the world's water is in the oceans, humans may eventually need to recover freshwater from seawater. The global water cycle involves continuous phase changes of water.

SECTION 9.4 Freshwater contains many dissolved substances including dissolved oxygen, which is necessary for fish and other aquatic life. Substances that are decomposed by bacteria are said to be **biodegradable**. Because the oxidation of biodegradable substances by aerobic bacteria consumes dissolved oxygen, these substances are called oxygen-demanding wastes. The presence of an excess amount of oxygen-demanding wastes in water can sufficiently deplete the dissolved oxygen to kill fish and produce offensive odors. Plant nutrients can contribute to the problem by stimulating the growth of plants that become oxygen-demanding wastes when they die.

Desalination is the removal of dissolved salts from seawater or brackish water to make it fit for human consumption. Desalination may be accomplished by distillation or by **reverse osmosis**.

The water available from freshwater sources may require treatment before it can be used domestically. The several steps generally used in municipal water treatment include coarse filtration, sedimentation, sand filtration, aeration, sterilization, and sometimes water softening. Water softening is required when the water contains significant concentrations of ions such as Mg^{2+} and Ca^{2+}, which react with soap to form soap scum. Water containing such ions is called hard water. The lime-soda process, which involves adding CaO and Na₂CO₃ to hard water, is sometimes used for large-scale municipal water softening. Individual homes usually rely on ion exchange, a process by which hard-water ions are exchanged for Na⁺ ions.

KEY SKILLS

- Describe the regions of Earth's atmosphere in terms of how temperature varies with altitude. (Section 9.1)
- Describe the composition of the atmosphere in terms of the major components in dry air at sea level. (Section 9.1)
- Calculate concentrations of gases in parts per million (ppm). (Section 9.1)
- Describe the processes of photodissociation and photoionization and their role in the upper atmosphere. (Section 9.1)
- Use bond energies and ionization energies to calculate the minimum frequency or maximum wavelength needed to cause photodissociation or photoionization. (Section 9.1)
- Explain the role of ozone in the upper atmosphere. (Section 9.1)
- Explain how chlorofluorocarbons (CFCs) are involved in depleting the ozone layer. (Section 9.2)
- Describe the origins and behavior of sulfur oxides and nitrogen oxides as air pollutants, including the generation of acid rain and photochemical smog. (Section 9.2)
- Describe how water and carbon dioxide in the atmosphere affect atmospheric temperature via the greenhouse effect. (Section 9.2)
- Describe the global water cycle. (Section 9.3)
- Explain what is meant by the salinity of water and describe the process of reverse osmosis as a means of desalination. (Section 9.4)
- List the major cations, anions, and gases present in natural waters and describe the relationship between dissolved oxygen and water quality. (Section 9.4)
- List the main steps involved in treating water for domestic uses. (Section 9.4)

EXERCISES

VISUALIZING CONCEPTS

9.1 At 273 K and 1 atm pressure, one mole of an ideal gas occupies 22.4 L. ∞ (Section 8.4) **(a)** Looking back at Figure 9.1, do you predict that 1 mole of an ideal gas in the middle of the stratosphere would occupy a greater or smaller volume than 22.4 L? **(b)** Looking at Figure 9.1, we see that the temperature is lower at 85 km altitude than at 50 km. Does this mean that one mole of an ideal gas would occupy less volume at 85 km than at 50 km? Explain. **(c)** In which parts of the atmosphere would you expect gases to behave most ideally (ignoring any photochemical reactions)? [Section 9.1]

9.2 Molecules in the upper atmosphere tend to contain double and triple bonds rather than single bonds. Suggest an explanation. [Section 9.1]

9.3 The figure shows the three lowest regions of Earth's atmosphere. **(a)** Name each and indicate the approximate elevations at which the boundaries occur. **(b)** In which region is ozone a pollutant? In which region does it filter UV solar radiation? **(c)** In which region is infrared radiation from Earth's surface most strongly reflected back? **(d)** An aurora borealis is due to excitation of atoms and molecules in the atmosphere 55–95 km above Earth's surface. Which regions in the figure are involved in an aurora borealis? **(e)** Compare the changes in relative concentrations of water vapor and carbon dioxide with increasing elevation in these three regions.

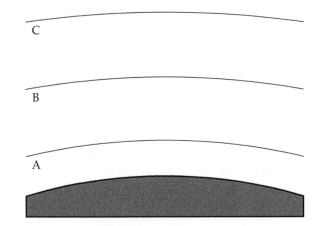

9.4 You are working with an artist who has been commissioned to make a sculpture for a big city in the eastern United States. The artist is wondering what material to use to make her sculpture because she has heard that acid rain in the eastern United States might destroy it over time. You take samples of granite, marble, bronze, and other materials, and place them outdoors for a long time in the big city. You periodically examine the appearance and measure the mass of the samples. **(a)** What observations would lead you to conclude that one or more of the materials are well-suited for the sculpture? (b) What chemical process (or processes) is (are) the most likely responsible for any observed changes in the materials? [Section 9.2]

9.5 Where does the energy come from to evaporate the estimated 425,000 km^3 of water that annually leaves the oceans? [Section 9.3]

9.6 Distinguish among salt water, freshwater, and groundwater. [Section 9.3]

9.7 How does carbon dioxide interact with the world ocean? [Section 9.3]

9.8 The following picture represents an ion-exchange column, in which water containing "hard" ions, such as Ca^{2+}, is added to the top of the column, and water containing "soft" ions, such as Na$^+$, comes out the bottom. Explain what is happening in the column. [Section 9.4]

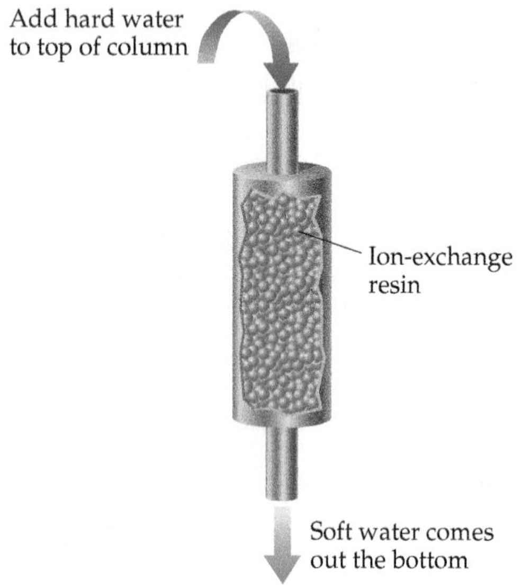

Add hard water to top of column

Ion-exchange resin

Soft water comes out the bottom

9.9 One mystery in environmental science is the imbalance in the "carbon dioxide budget." Considering only human activities, scientists have estimated that 1.6 billion metric tons of CO$_2$ is added to the atmosphere every year because of deforestation (plants use CO$_2$, and fewer plants will leave more CO$_2$ in the atmosphere). Another 5.5 billion tons per year is put into the atmosphere because of burning fossil fuels. It is further estimated (again, considering only human activities) that the atmosphere actually takes up about 3.3 billion tons of this CO$_2$ per year, while the oceans take up 2 billion tons per year, leaving about 1.8 billion tons of CO$_2$ per year unaccounted for. This "missing" CO$_2$ is assumed to be taken up by the "land." What do you think might be happening? [Sections 9.1–9.3]

EARTH'S ATMOSPHERE (section 9.1)

9.10 (a) What is the primary basis for the division of the atmosphere into different regions? (b) Name the regions of the atmosphere, indicating the altitude interval for each one.

9.11 (a) How are the boundaries between the regions of the atmosphere determined? (b) Explain why the stratosphere, which is more than 20 miles thick, has a smaller total mass than the troposphere, which is less than 10 miles thick.

9.12 Air pollution in the Mexico City metropolitan area is among the worst in the world. The concentration of ozone in Mexico City has been measured at 441 ppb (0.441 ppm). Mexico City sits at an altitude of 7400 feet, which means its atmospheric pressure is only 0.67 atm. (a) Calculate the partial pressure of ozone at 441 ppb if the atmospheric pressure is 0.67 atm. (b) How many ozone molecules are in 1.0 L of air in Mexico City? Assume $T = 25\,°C$.

9.13 From the data in Table 9.1, calculate the partial pressures of carbon dioxide and argon when the total atmospheric pressure is 1.05 bar.

9.14 The average concentration of carbon monoxide in air in an Ohio city in 2006 was 3.5 ppm. Calculate the number of CO molecules in 1.0 L of this air at a pressure of 759 torr and a temperature of 22 °C.

9.15 (a) From the data in Table 9.1, what is the concentration of neon in the atmosphere in ppm? (b) What is the concentration of neon in the atmosphere in molecules per L, assuming an atmospheric pressure of 730 torr and a temperature of 296 K?

9.16 The dissociation energy of a carbon–bromine bond is typically about 210 kJ/mol. (a) What is the maximum wavelength of photons that can cause C—Br bond dissociation? (b) Which kind of electromagnetic radiation—ultraviolet, visible, or infrared—does the wavelength you calculated in part (a) correspond to?

9.17 In CF$_3$Cl the C—Cl bond-dissociation energy is 339 kJ/mol. In CCl$_4$ the C—Cl bond-dissociation energy is 293 kJ/mol. What is the range of wavelengths of photons that can cause C—Cl bond rupture in one molecule but not in the other?

9.18 (a) Distinguish between *photodissociation* and *photoionization*. (b) Use the energy requirements of these two processes to explain why photodissociation of oxygen is more important than photoionization of oxygen at altitudes below about 90 km.

9.19 Why is the photodissociation of N$_2$ in the atmosphere relatively unimportant compared with the photodissociation of O$_2$?

HUMAN ACTIVITIES AND EARTH'S ATMOSPHERE (section 9.2)

9.20 Do the reactions involved in ozone depletion involve changes in oxidation state of the O atoms? Explain.

9.21 Explain how the reactions of ozone in the stratosphere are responsible for the relatively warm temperatures of the stratosphere.

9.22 (a) What is the difference between chlorofluorocarbons and hydrofluorocarbons? (b) Why are hydrofluorocarbons potentially less harmful to the ozone layer than CFCs?

9.23 Draw the Lewis structure for the chlorofluorocarbon CFC-11, $CFCl_3$. What chemical characteristics of this substance allow it to effectively deplete stratospheric ozone?

9.24 (a) Why is the fluorine present in chlorofluorocarbons not a major contributor to depletion of the ozone layer? (b) What are the chemical forms in which chlorine exists in the stratosphere following cleavage of the carbon–chlorine bond?

9.25 Would you expect the substance $CFBr_3$ to be effective in depleting the ozone layer, assuming that it is present in the stratosphere? Explain.

9.26 For each of the following gases, make a list of known or possible naturally occurring sources: (a) CH_4, (b) SO_2, (c) NO.

9.27 Why is rainwater naturally acidic, even in the absence of polluting gases such as SO_2?

9.28 (a) Write a chemical equation that describes the attack of acid rain on limestone, $CaCO_3$. (b) If a limestone sculpture were treated to form a surface layer of calcium sulfate, would this help to slow down the effects of acid rain? Explain.

9.29 The first stage in corrosion of iron upon exposure to air is oxidation to Fe^{2+}. (a) Write a balanced chemical equation to show the reaction of iron with oxygen and protons from acid rain. (b) Would you expect the same sort of reaction to occur with a silver surface? Explain.

9.30 Alcohol-based fuels for automobiles lead to the production of formaldehyde (CH_2O) in exhaust gases. Formaldehyde undergoes photodissociation, which contributes to photochemical smog:

$$CH_2O + h\nu \longrightarrow CHO + H$$

The maximum wavelength of light that can cause this reaction is 335 nm. (a) In what part of the electromagnetic spectrum is light with this wavelength found? (b) What is the maximum strength of a bond, in kJ/mol, that can be broken by absorption of a photon of 335-nm light? (c) Compare your answer from part (b) to the appropriate value from Table 3.4. What do you conclude about C—H bond energy in formaldehyde? (d) Write out the formaldehyde photodissociation reaction, showing Lewis-dot structures.

9.31 An important reaction in the formation of photochemical smog is the photodissociation of NO_2:

$$NO_2 + h\nu \longrightarrow NO(g) + O(g)$$

The maximum wavelength of light that can cause this reaction is 420 nm. (a) In what part of the electromagnetic spectrum is light with this wavelength found? (b) What is the maximum strength of a bond, in kJ/mol, that can be broken by absorption of a photon of 420-nm light? (c) Write out the photodissociation reaction showing Lewis-dot structures.

9.32 Explain why increasing concentrations of CO_2 in the atmosphere affect the quantity of energy leaving Earth but do not affect the quantity of energy entering from the Sun.

9.33 (a) With respect to absorption of radiant energy, what distinguishes a greenhouse gas from a nongreenhouse gas? (b) CH_4 is a greenhouse gas, but N_2 is not. How might the molecular structure of CH_4 explain why it is a greenhouse gas?

EARTH'S WATER (section 9.3)

9.34 What is the molarity of Na^+ in a solution of NaCl whose salinity is 5.6 if the solution has a density of 1.03 g/mol?

9.35 Phosphorus is present in seawater to the extent of 0.07 ppm by mass. If the phosphorus is present as phosphate, PO_4^{3-}, calculate the corresponding molar concentration of phosphate in seawater.

9.36 The enthalpy of evaporation of water is 40.67 kJ/mol. Sunlight striking Earth's surface supplies 168 W per square meter (1 W = 1 watt = 1 J/s). (a) Assuming that evaporation of water is only due to energy input from the Sun, calculate how many grams of water could be evaporated from a 1.00 square meter patch of ocean over a 12-hour day. (b) The specific heat capacity of liquid water is 4.184 J/g °C. If the initial temperature of a 1.00 square meter patch of ocean is 26 °C, what is its final temperature after being in sunlight for 12 hours, assuming no phase changes and assuming that sunlight penetrates uniformly to depth of 10.0 cm?

[9.37] The enthalpy of fusion of water is 6.01 kJ/mol. Sunlight striking Earth's surface supplies 168 W per square meter (1 W = 1 watt = 1 J/s). (a) Assuming that melting of ice is only due to energy input from the Sun, calculate how many grams of ice could be melted from a 1.00 square meter patch of ice over a 12-

hour day. (b) The specific heat capacity of ice is 2.032 J/g °C. If the initial temperature of a 1.00 square meter patch of ice is −5.0 °C, what is its final temperature after being in sunlight for 12 hours, assuming no phase changes and assuming that sunlight penetrates uniformly to a depth of 1.00 cm?

9.38 A first-stage recovery of magnesium from seawater is precipitation of $Mg(OH)_2$ with CaO:

$$Mg^{2+}(aq) + CaO(s) + H_2O(l) \longrightarrow Mg(OH)_2(s) + Ca^{2+}(aq)$$

What mass of CaO, in grams, is needed to precipitate 1000 lb of $Mg(OH)_2$?

9.39 Gold is found in seawater at very low levels, about 0.05 ppb by mass. Assuming that gold is worth about $800 per troy ounce, how many liters of seawater would you have to process to obtain $1,000,000 worth of gold? Assume the density of seawater is 1.03 g/mL and that your gold recovery process is 50% efficient.

9.40 (a) What is *groundwater*? (b) What is an *aquifer*?

9.41 The Ogallala aquifer is the largest in the United States, covering 450,000 km^2 across eight states, from South Dakota to Texas. This aquifer provides 82% of the drinking water for the people who live in this region, although most (>75%) of the water that is pumped from it is for irrigation. Irrigation withdrawals are approximately 18 billion gallons per day. **(a)** The Ogallala aquifer might run dry, according to some estimates, in 25 years. How many cubic kilometers of water would be withdrawn in a 25-year period? **(b)** Explain the processes that would recharge the aquifer.

HUMAN ACTIVITIES AND EARTH'S WATER (section 9.4)

9.42 Suppose that one wishes to use reverse osmosis to reduce the salt content of brackish water containing 0.22 M total salt concentration to a value of 0.01 M, thus rendering it usable for human consumption. What is the minimum pressure that needs to be applied in the permeators (Figure 9.19) to achieve this goal, assuming that the operation occurs at 298 K?

9.43 Assume that a portable reverse-osmosis apparatus operates on seawater, whose concentrations of constituent ions are listed in Table 9.5, and that the desalinated water output has an effective molarity of about 0.02 M. What minimum pressure must be applied by hand pumping at 297 K to cause reverse osmosis to occur?

9.44 List the common products formed when an organic material containing the elements carbon, hydrogen, oxygen, sulfur, and nitrogen decomposes **(a)** under aerobic conditions, **(b)** under anaerobic conditions.

9.45 **(a)** Explain why the concentration of dissolved oxygen in freshwater is an important indicator of the quality of the water. **(b)** How is the solubility of oxygen in water affected by increasing temperature?

9.46 The organic anion

$$H_3C-(CH_2)_9-\overset{\overset{\displaystyle H}{|}}{\underset{\underset{\displaystyle CH_3}{|}}{C}}-\langle\bigcirc\rangle-SO_3^-$$

is found in most detergents. Assume that the anion undergoes aerobic decomposition in the following manner:

$$2\,C_{18}H_{29}SO_3^-(aq) + 51\,O_2(aq) \longrightarrow$$
$$36\,CO_2(aq) + 28\,H_2O(l) + 2\,H^+(aq) + 2\,SO_4^{2-}(aq)$$

What is the total mass of O_2 required to biodegrade 10.0 g of this substance?

9.47 The average daily mass of O_2 taken up by sewage discharged in the United States is 59 g per person. How many liters of water at 9 ppm O_2 are totally depleted of oxygen in 1 day by a population of 1,200,000 people?

9.48 Write a balanced chemical equation to describe how magnesium ions are removed in water treatment by the addition of slaked lime, $Ca(OH)_2$.

9.49 **(a)** Which of the following ionic species could be responsible for hardness in a water supply: Ca^{2+}, K^+, Mg^{2+}, Fe^{2+}, Na^+? **(b)** What properties of an ion determine whether it will contribute to water hardness?

9.50 How many moles of $Ca(OH)_2$ and Na_2CO_3 should be added to soften 1200 L of water in which $[Ca^{2+}] = 5.0 \times 10^{-4}\,M$ and $[HCO_3^-] = 7.0 \times 10^{-4}\,M$?

9.51 The concentration of Ca^{2+} in a particular water supply is $5.7 \times 10^{-3}\,M$. The concentration of bicarbonate ion, HCO_3^-, in the same water is $1.7 \times 10^{-3}\,M$. What masses of $Ca(OH)_2$ and Na_2CO_3 must be added to 5.0×10^7 L of this water to reduce the level of Ca^{2+} to 20% of its original level?

9.52 Ferrous sulfate ($FeSO_4$) is often used as a coagulant in water purification. The iron(II) salt is dissolved in the water to be purified, then oxidized to the iron(III) state by dissolved oxygen, at which time gelatinous $Fe(OH)_3$ forms, assuming the pH is above approximately 6. Write balanced chemical equations for the oxidation of Fe^{2+} to Fe^{3+} by dissolved oxygen and for the formation of $Fe(OH)_3(s)$ by reaction of $Fe^{3+}(aq)$ with $HCO_3^-(aq)$.

9.53 What properties make a substance a good coagulant for water purification?

9.54 **(a)** What are *trihalomethanes* (THMs)? **(b)** Draw the Lewis structures of two example THMs.

9.55 If trihalomethanes are easily removed from water by aeration (bubbling with air), what does this imply about the vapor pressure of THMs compared to water?

ADDITIONAL EXERCISES

9.56 A friend of yours has seen each of the following items in newspaper articles and would like an explanation: **(a)** acid rain, **(b)** greenhouse gas, **(c)** photochemical smog, **(d)** ozone depletion. Give a brief explanation of each term and identify one or two of the chemicals associated with each.

9.57 Suppose that on another planet the atmosphere consists of 17% Kr, 38% CH_4, and 45% O_2. What is the average molar mass at the surface? What is the average molar mass at an altitude at which all the O_2 is photodissociated?

9.58 If an average O_3 molecule "lives" only 100–200 seconds in the stratosphere before undergoing dissociation, how can O_3 offer any protection from ultraviolet radiation?

9.59 Show how Equations 9.7 and 9.9 can be added to give Equation 9.10.

9.60 What properties of CFCs make them ideal for various commercial applications but also make them a long-term problem in the stratosphere?

9.61 *Halons* are fluorocarbons that contain bromine, such as $CBrF_3$. They are used extensively as foaming agents for fighting fires. Like CFCs, halons are very unreactive and ultimately can diffuse into the stratosphere. **(a)** Based on the data in Table 3.4, would you expect photodissociation of Br atoms to occur in the stratosphere? **(b)** Propose a mechanism by which the presence of halons in the stratosphere could lead to the depletion of stratospheric ozone.

9.62 It is estimated that the lifetime for HFCs in the stratosphere is 2–7 years. If HFCs have such long lifetimes, why are they being used to replace CFCs?

[**9.63**] The *hydroxyl radical*, OH, is formed at low altitudes via the reaction of excited oxygen atoms with water:

$$O^*(g) + H_2O(g) \longrightarrow 2\,OH(g)$$

(a) Write the Lewis structure for the hydroxyl radical. (*Hint:* It has one unpaired electron.)
Once produced, the hydroxyl radical is very reactive. Explain why each of the following series of reactions affects the pollution in the troposphere:

(b) $OH + NO_2 \longrightarrow HNO_3$

(c) $OH + CO + O_2 \longrightarrow CO_2 + OOH$
$OOH + NO \longrightarrow OH + NO_2$

(d) $OH + CH_4 \longrightarrow H_2O + CH_3$
$CH_3 + O_2 \longrightarrow OOCH_3$
$OOCH_3 + NO \longrightarrow OCH_3 + NO_2$

(e) The concentration of hydroxyl radicals in the troposphere is approximately 2×10^6 radicals per cm^3. This estimate is based on a method called long path absorption spectroscopy (LPAS), similar in principle to the Beer's law measurement discussed in the Closer Look essay on p. 564, except that the path length in the LPAS measurement is 20 km. Why must the path length be so large?

9.64 Explain, using Le Châtelier's principle, why the equilibrium constant for the formation of NO from N_2 and O_2 increases with increasing temperature, whereas the equilibrium constant for the formation of NO_2 from NO and O_2 decreases with increasing temperature.

9.65 Natural gas consists primarily of methane, $CH_4(g)$. (a) Write a balanced chemical equation for the complete combustion of methane to produce $CO_2(g)$ as the only carbon-containing product. (b) Write a balanced chemical equation for the incomplete combustion of methane to produce $CO(g)$ as the only carbon-containing product. (c) At 25 °C and 1.0 atm pressure, what is the minimum quantity of dry air needed to combust 1.0 L of $CH_4(g)$ completely to $CO_2(g)$?

9.66 One of the possible consequences of climate change is an increase in the temperature of ocean water. The oceans serve as a "sink" for CO_2 by dissolving large amounts of it. (a) How would the solubility of CO_2 in the oceans be affected by an increase in

the temperature of the water? (b) Discuss the implications of your answer to part (a) for the problem of climate change.

9.67 The rate of solar energy striking Earth averages 168 watts per square meter. The rate of energy radiated from Earth's surface averages 390 watts per square meter. Comparing these numbers, one might expect that the planet would cool quickly, yet it does not. Why not?

9.68 The solar power striking Earth every day averages 168 watts per square meter. The peak electrical power usage in New York City is 12,000 megawatts. Considering that present technology for solar energy conversion is only about 10% efficient, from how many square meters of land must sunlight be collected in order to provide this peak power? (For comparison, the total area of the city is 830 km².)

9.69 Write balanced chemical equations for each of the following reactions: (a) The nitric oxide molecule undergoes photodissociation in the upper atmosphere. (b) The nitric oxide molecule undergoes photoionization in the upper atmosphere. (c) Nitric oxide undergoes oxidation by ozone in the stratosphere. (d) Nitrogen dioxide dissolves in water to form nitric acid and nitric oxide.

9.70 (a) Explain why $Mg(OH)_2$ precipitates when $CO_3{}^{2-}$ ion is added to a solution containing Mg^{2+}. (b) Will $Mg(OH)_2$ precipitate when 4.0 g of Na_2CO_3 is added to 1.00 L of a solution containing 125 ppm of Mg^{2+}?

[**9.71**] It has been pointed out that there may be increased amounts of NO in the troposphere as compared with the past because of massive use of nitrogen-containing compounds in fertilizers. Assuming that NO can eventually diffuse into the stratosphere, how might it affect the conditions of life on Earth? Using the index to this text, look up the chemistry of nitrogen oxides. What chemical pathways might NO in the troposphere follow?

[**9.72**] As of the writing of this text, EPA standards limit atmospheric ozone levels in urban environments to 84 ppb. How many moles of ozone would there be in the air above Los Angeles County (area about 4000 square miles; consider a height of 10 m above the ground) if ozone was at this concentration?

INTEGRATIVE EXERCISES

9.73 The estimated average concentration of NO_2 in air in the United States in 2006 was 0.016 ppm. (a) Calculate the partial pressure of the NO_2 in a sample of this air when the atmospheric pressure is 755 torr (99.1 kPa). (b) How many molecules of NO_2 are present under these conditions at 20 °C in a room that measures $15 \times 14 \times 8$ ft?

[9.74] In 1986 an electrical power plant in Taylorsville, Georgia, burned 8,376,726 tons of coal, a national record at that time. (a) Assuming that the coal was 83% carbon and 2.5% sulfur and that combustion was complete, calculate the number of tons of carbon dioxide and sulfur dioxide produced by the plant during the year. (b) If 55% of the SO_2 could be removed by reaction with powdered CaO to form $CaSO_3$, how many tons of $CaSO_3$ would be produced?

9.75 The water supply for a midwestern city contains the following impurities: coarse sand, finely divided particulates, nitrate ion, trihalomethanes, dissolved phosphorus in the form of phosphates, potentially harmful bacterial strains, dissolved organic substances. Which of the following processes or agents, if any, is effective in removing each of these impurities: coarse sand filtration, activated carbon filtration, aeration, ozonization, precipitation with aluminum hydroxide?

9.76 An impurity in water has an extinction coefficient of $3.45 \times 10^3\,M^{-1}\,cm^{-1}$ at 280 nm, its absorption maximum (A Closer Look, p. 564). Below 50 ppb, the impurity is not a problem for human health. Given that most spectrometers cannot detect absorbances less than 0.0001 with good reliability, is measuring the absorbance of water at 280 nm a good way to detect concentrations of the impurity above the 50-ppb threshold?

9.77 The concentration of H_2O in the stratosphere is about 5 ppm. It undergoes photodissociation according to:

$$H_2O(g) \longrightarrow H(g) + OH(g)$$

(a) Write out the Lewis-dot structures for both products and reactant.

(b) Using Table 3.4, calculate the wavelength required to cause this dissociation.

(c) The hydroxyl radicals, OH, can react with ozone, giving the following reactions:

$$OH(g) + O_3(g) \longrightarrow HO_2(g) + O_2(g)$$
$$HO_2(g) + O(g) \longrightarrow OH(g) + O_2(g)$$

What overall reaction results from these two elementary reactions? What is the catalyst in the overall reaction? Explain.

9.78 Bioremediation is the process by which bacteria repair their environment in response, for example, to an oil spill. The efficiency of bacteria for "eating" hydrocarbons depends on the amount of oxygen in the system, pH, temperature, and many other factors. In a certain oil spill, hydrocarbons from the oil disappeared with a first-order rate constant of $2 \times 10^{-6}\,s^{-1}$. How many days did it take for the hydrocarbons to decrease to 10% of their initial value?

9.79 The standard enthalpies of formation of ClO and ClO_2 are 101 and 102 kJ/mol, respectively. Using these data and the thermodynamic data in Appendix C, calculate the overall enthalpy change for each step in the following catalytic cycle:

$$ClO(g) + O_3(g) \longrightarrow ClO_2(g) + O_2(g)$$
$$ClO_2(g) + O(g) \longrightarrow ClO(g) + O_2(g)$$

What is the enthalpy change for the overall reaction that results from these two steps?

9.80 The main reason that distillation is a costly method for purifying water is the high energy required to heat and vaporize water. (a) Using the density, specific heat, and heat of vaporization of water from Appendix B, calculate the amount of energy required to vaporize 1.00 gal of water beginning with water at 20 °C. (b) If the energy is provided by electricity costing $0.085 / kWh, calculate its cost. (c) If distilled water sells in a grocery store for $1.26 per gal, what percentage of the sales price is represented by the cost of the energy?

[9.81] A reaction that contributes to the depletion of ozone in the stratosphere is the direct reaction of oxygen atoms with ozone:

$$O(g) + O_3(g) \longrightarrow 2\,O_2(g)$$

At 298 K the rate constant for this reaction is $4.8 \times 10^5\,M^{-1}\,s^{-1}$. (a) Based on the units of the rate constant, write the likely rate law for this reaction. (b) Would you expect this reaction to occur via a single elementary process? Explain why or why not.

(c) From the magnitude of the rate constant, would you expect the activation energy of this reaction to be large or small? Explain. (d) Use ΔH_f° values from Appendix C to estimate the enthalpy change for this reaction. Would this reaction raise or lower the temperature of the stratosphere?

9.82 Nitrogen dioxide (NO_2) is the only important gaseous species in the lower atmosphere that absorbs visible light. (a) Write the Lewis structure(s) for NO_2. (b) How does this structure account for the fact that NO_2 dimerizes to form N_2O_4? Based on what you can find about this dimerization reaction in the text, would you expect to find the NO_2 that forms in an urban environment to be in the form of dimer? Explain. (c) What would you expect as products, if any, for the reaction of NO_2 with CO? (d) Would you expect NO_2 generated in an urban environment to migrate to the stratosphere? Explain.

9.83 The following data were collected for the destruction of O_3 by H ($O_3 + H \longrightarrow O_2 + OH$) at very low concentrations:

Trial	$[O_3]$ (M)	$[H]$ (M)	Initial Rate (M/s)
1	5.17×10^{-33}	3.22×10^{-26}	1.88×10^{-14}
2	2.59×10^{-33}	3.25×10^{-26}	9.44×10^{-15}
3	5.19×10^{-33}	6.46×10^{-26}	3.77×10^{-14}

(a) Write the rate law for the reaction.

(b) Calculate the rate constant.

9.84 The degradation of CF_3CH_2F (an HFC) by OH radicals in the troposphere is first order in each reactant and has a rate constant of $k = 1.6 \times 10^8\,M^{-1}s^{-1}$ at 4 °C. If the tropospheric concentrations of OH and CF_3CH_2F are 8.1×10^5 and 6.3×10^8 molecules/cm³, respectively, what is the rate of reaction at this temperature in M/s?

[9.85] The Henry's law constant for CO_2 in water at 25 °C is $3.1 \times 10^{-2}\,M$ atm^{-1}. (a) What is the solubility of CO_2 in water at this temperature if the solution is in contact with air at normal atmospheric pressure? (b) Assume that all of this CO_2 is in the form of H_2CO_3 produced by the reaction between CO_2 and H_2O:

$$CO_2(aq) + H_2O(l) \longrightarrow H_2CO_3(aq)$$

What is the pH of this solution?

[9.86] If the pH of a 1.0-in. rainfall over 1500 mi² is 3.5, how many kilograms of H_2SO_4 are present, assuming that it is the only acid contributing to the pH?

9.87 The precipitation of $Al(OH)_3$ ($K_{sp} = 1.3 \times 10^{-33}$) is sometimes used to purify water. (a) Estimate the pH at which precipitation of $Al(OH)_3$ will begin if 5.0 lb of $Al_2(SO_4)_3$ is added to 2000 gal of water. (b) Approximately how many pounds of CaO must be added to the water to achieve this pH?

WHAT'S AHEAD

10.1 THE NATURE OF ENERGY

We begin by considering the nature of *energy* and the forms it takes, notably *kinetic energy* and *potential energy*. We discuss the units used in measuring energy and the fact that energy can be used to do *work* or to transfer *heat*. To study energy changes, we focus on a particular part of the universe, which we call the *system*. Everything else is called the *surroundings*.

10.2 THE FIRST LAW OF THERMODYNAMICS

We then explore the *first law of thermodynamics*: Energy cannot be created or destroyed but can be transformed from one form to another or transferred between systems and surroundings. The energy possessed by a system is called its *internal energy*. Internal energy is a *state function,* a quantity whose value depends only on the current state of a system, not on how the system came to be in that state.

10.3 ENTHALPY

Next, we encounter a state function called *enthalpy* that is useful because the change in enthalpy measures the quantity of heat energy gained or lost by a system in a process occurring under constant pressure.

BIOENERGY. The sugars in sugarcane, produced from CO_2, H_2O, and sunshine via photosynthesis, can be converted into ethanol, which is used as an alternative to gasoline. In certain climates, such as that in Brazil, the sugarcane crop replenishes itself rapidly, making cane-based ethanol a *sustainable* fuel source.

10

10.4 ENTHALPIES OF REACTION
We see that the enthalpy change associated with a chemical reaction is the enthalpies of the products minus the enthalpies of the reactants. This quantity is directly proportional to the amount of reactant consumed in the reaction.

10.5 CALORIMETRY
We next examine *calorimetry*, an experimental technique used to measure heat changes in chemical processes.

10.6 HESS'S LAW
We observe that the enthalpy change for a given reaction can be calculated using appropriate enthalpy changes for related reactions. To do so, we apply *Hess's law*.

10.7 ENTHALPIES OF FORMATION
Then we discuss how to establish standard values for enthalpy changes in chemical reactions and how to use them to calculate enthalpy changes for reactions.

10.8 FOODS AND FUELS
Finally, we examine foods and fuels as sources of energy and discuss some related health and social issues.

THERMO-CHEMISTRY

CHANCES ARE YOU'VE HEARD THE word *energy* today, perhaps in one of your courses, in the news, in conversation, or possibly in all these instances. Our modern society depends on energy for its existence. The issues surrounding energy—its sources, production, distribution, and consumption—pervade a lot of our conversation, from science to politics to economics to environmental issues. The production of energy is a major factor in the growth of national economies, especially rapidly developing countries such as China, India, and Brazil. The chapter-opening photograph highlights the efforts in Brazil to use their bountiful and fast-growing sugarcane crop as a source of ethanol. A major part of the Brazilian economy has depended on the use of ethanol instead of petroleum-based fuels in transportation and industry.

With the exception of the energy from the Sun, most of the energy used in our daily lives comes from chemical reactions. The combustion of gasoline, the production of electricity from coal, the heating of homes by natural gas, and the use of batteries to power electronic devices are all examples of how chemistry is used to produce energy. In addition, chemical reactions provide the energy that sustains living systems. Plants, such as the sugarcane in the chapter-opening photograph, use solar energy to carry out photosynthesis, allowing them to grow. The plants in turn provide food from which we humans derive the energy needed to move, maintain body temperature, and carry out all other bodily functions. What exactly is energy, though, and what principles are involved in its production, consumption, and transformation from one form to another?

In this chapter we begin to explore energy and its changes. We are motivated not only by the impact of energy on so many aspects of our daily lives but also by the fact that if we are to properly understand chemistry, we must understand the energy changes that accompany chemical reactions.

The study of energy and its transformations is known as **thermodynamics** (Greek: *thérme-*, "heat"; *dy'namis,* "power"). This area of study began during the Industrial Revolution in order to develop the relationships among heat, work, and fuels in steam engines. In this chapter we will examine the relationships between chemical reactions and energy changes that involve heat. This portion of thermodynamics is called **thermochemistry**. We will discuss additional aspects of thermodynamics in Chapter 13.

10.1 | THE NATURE OF ENERGY

The concept of matter has always been easy to grasp because matter can be seen and touched. By contrast, although the concept of energy is a familiar one, it is challenging to deal with in a precise way. **Energy** is commonly defined as *the capacity to do work or transfer heat.* This definition requires us to understand the concepts of work and heat. **Work** is *the energy used to cause an object to move against a force,* and **heat** is *the energy used to cause the temperature of an object to increase* (◀ FIGURE 10.1). Let's begin our study of thermochemistry by examining the ways in which matter can possess energy and how that energy can be transferred from one piece of matter to another.

Kinetic Energy and Potential Energy

Objects, whether they are baseballs or molecules, can possess **kinetic energy**, the energy of *motion*. The magnitude of the kinetic energy, E_k, of an object depends on its mass, m, and speed, v:

$$E_k = \tfrac{1}{2}mv^2 \qquad [10.1]$$

We see that the kinetic energy of an object increases as its speed increases. For example, a car moving at 55 miles per hour (mph) has greater kinetic energy than it does at 25 mph. For a given speed the kinetic energy increases with increasing mass. Thus, a large truck traveling at 55 mph has greater kinetic energy than a small sedan traveling at the same speed because the truck has the greater mass. In chemistry, we are interested in the kinetic energy of atoms and molecules. Although too small to be seen, these particles have mass and are in motion and, therefore, possess kinetic energy.

All other kinds of energy—the energy stored in a stretched spring, in a weight held above your head, or in a chemical bond, for example—are potential energy. An object has **potential energy** by virtue of its position relative to other objects. Potential energy is, in essence, the "stored" energy that arises from the attractions and repulsions an object experiences in relation to other objects.

We are all familiar with instances in which potential energy is converted into kinetic energy. For example, think of a cyclist poised at the top of a hill (▶ FIGURE 10.2). Because of the attractive force of gravity, the potential energy of the cyclist and her bicycle is greater at the top of the hill than at the bottom. As a result, the bicycle easily moves down the hill with increasing speed. As it does so, the potential energy initially stored in it is converted into kinetic energy. The potential energy decreases as the bicycle rolls down the hill, but its kinetic energy increases as the speed increases (Equation 10.1).

We will soon see that this interconversion of energy, with one form decreasing while the other increases, is the first cornerstone of thermodynamics.

Gravitational forces play a negligible role in the ways that atoms and molecules interact with one another. Forces that arise from electrical charges are more important when dealing with atoms and molecules. One of the most important forms of potential energy in chemistry is *electrostatic potential energy*, E_{el}, which arises from the interactions between charged particles. This energy is proportional to the electrical charges on the

GO FIGURE

Why is a pitcher able to throw a baseball faster than he could throw a bowling ball?

Work done by pitcher on ball to make ball move

(a)

Heat added by burner to water makes water temperature rise

(b)

▲ **FIGURE 10.1 Work and heat, two forms of energy.** (a) *Work* is energy used to cause an object to move. (b) *Heat* is energy used to cause the temperature of an object to increase.

Suppose the bicyclist is coasting (not pedaling) at constant speed on a flat road and begins to go up a hill. If she does not start pedaling, what happens to her speed? Why?

High potential energy,
zero kinetic energy

Decreasing potential energy,
increasing kinetic energy

◀ FIGURE 10.2   **Potential energy and kinetic energy.** The potential energy initially stored in the motionless bicycle at the top of the hill is converted to kinetic energy as the bicycle moves down the hill and loses potential energy.

two interacting objects, Q_1 and Q_2, and inversely proportional to the distance, d, separating them:

$$E_{el} = \frac{\kappa Q_1 Q_2}{d}$$ [10.2]

Here κ is simply a constant of proportionality, 8.99×10^9 J-m/C². [C is the coulomb, a unit of electrical charge, and J is the joule, a unit of energy we will discuss soon.] At the molecular level, the electrical charges Q_1 and Q_2 are typically on the order of magnitude of the charge of the electron (1.60×10^{-19} C).

Equation 10.2 shows that the electrostatic potential energy goes to zero as d becomes infinite; in other words, the zero of electrostatic potential energy is defined as infinite separation of the charged particles. ▼ FIGURE 10.3 illustrates how E_{el} behaves

A positively charged particle and a negatively charged particle are initially far apart. What happens to their electrostatic potential energy as they are brought closer together?

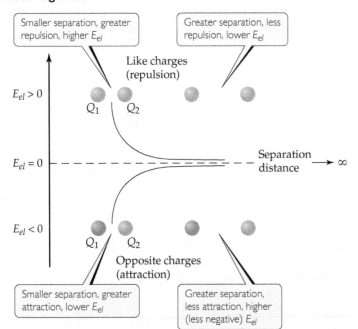

Smaller separation, greater repulsion, higher E_{el}

Greater separation, less repulsion, lower E_{el}

Like charges
(repulsion)

$E_{el} > 0$

Q_1 Q_2

$E_{el} = 0$

Separation
distance   ∞

$E_{el} < 0$

Q_1 Q_2

Opposite charges
(attraction)

Smaller separation, greater attraction, lower E_{el}

Greater separation, less attraction, higher (less negative) E_{el}

◀ FIGURE 10.3   **Electrostatic potential energy.** At finite separation distances for two charged particles, E_{el} is positive for like charges and negative for opposite charges. As the particles move farther apart, their electrostatic potential energy approaches zero.

for charges of the same and different sign. When Q_1 and Q_2 have the same sign (for example, both positive), the two charged particles repel each other, and a repulsive force pushes them apart. In this case, E_{el} is positive, and the potential energy decreases as the particles move farther and farther apart. When Q_1 and Q_2 have opposite signs, the particles attract each other, and an attractive force pulls them toward each other. In this case, E_{el} is negative, and the potential energy increases (becomes less negative) as the particles move apart.

These trends in electrostatic potential energy are used often in chemistry, as we will see later in the text.

One of our goals in chemistry is to relate the energy changes seen in the macroscopic world to the kinetic or potential energy of substances at the molecular level. Many substances—fuels, for example—release *chemical energy* when they react, energy due to the potential energy stored in the arrangements of their atoms. The energy a substance possesses because of its temperature (its *thermal energy*) is associated with the kinetic energy of the molecules in the substance.

GIVE IT SOME THOUGHT

When the cyclist and bicycle in Figure 10.2 come to a stop at the bottom of the hill, (a) is the potential energy the same as it was at the top of the hill? (b) Is the kinetic energy the same as it was at the top of the hill?

Units of Energy

The SI unit for energy is the **joule** (pronounced "jool"), J, in honor of James Joule (1818–1889), a British scientist who investigated work and heat: $1 \text{ J} = 1 \text{ kg-m}^2/\text{s}^2$. Equation 10.1 shows that a mass of 2 kg moving at a speed of 1 m/s possesses a kinetic energy of 1 J:

$$E_k = \tfrac{1}{2} mv^2 = \tfrac{1}{2}(2 \text{ kg})(1 \text{ m/s})^2 = 1 \text{ kg-m}^2/\text{s}^2 = 1 \text{ J}$$

Because a joule is not a large amount of energy, we often use *kilojoules* (kJ) in discussing the energies associated with chemical reactions.

Traditionally, energy changes accompanying chemical reactions have been expressed in calories, a non–SI unit still widely used in chemistry, biology, and biochemistry. A **calorie** (cal) was originally defined as the amount of energy required to raise the temperature of 1 g of water from 14.5 °C to 15.5 °C. A calorie is now defined in terms of the joule:

$$1 \text{ cal} = 4.184 \text{ J (exactly)}$$

A related energy unit used in nutrition is the nutritional *Calorie* (note the capital C): $1 \text{ Cal} = 1000 \text{ cal} = 1 \text{ kcal}$.

System and Surroundings

When analyzing energy changes, we need to focus on a limited and well-defined part of the universe to keep track of the energy changes that occur. The portion we single out for study is called the **system**; everything else is called the **surroundings**. When we study the energy change that accompanies a chemical reaction in the laboratory, the reactants and products constitute the system. The container and everything beyond it are considered the surroundings.

Systems may be open, closed, or isolated. An *open* system is one in which matter and energy can be exchanged with the surroundings. An uncovered pot of boiling water on a stove, such as in Figure 10.1(b), is an open system: Heat comes into the system from the stove, and water is released to the surroundings as steam.

The systems we can most readily study in thermochemistry are called *closed systems*—systems that can exchange energy but not matter with their surroundings. For example, consider a mixture of hydrogen gas, H_2, and oxygen gas, O_2, in a cylinder fitted with a piston (◀ **FIGURE 10.4**). The system is just the hydrogen and oxygen; the cylinder,

GO FIGURE

If the piston is pulled upward so that it sits halfway between the position shown and the top of the cylinder, is the system still closed?

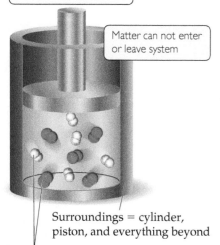

Energy can enter or leave system as heat or as work done on piston

Matter can not enter or leave system

Surroundings = cylinder, piston, and everything beyond

System = $H_2(g)$ and $O_2(g)$

▲ **FIGURE 10.4** **A closed system.**

piston, and everything beyond them (including us) are the surroundings. If the gases react to form water, energy is liberated:

$$2 H_2(g) + O_2(g) \longrightarrow 2 H_2O(g) + \text{energy}$$

Although the chemical form of the hydrogen and oxygen atoms in the system is changed by this reaction, the system has not lost or gained mass, which means it has not exchanged any matter with its surroundings. However, it can exchange energy with its surroundings in the form of *work* and *heat*.

An *isolated* system is one in which neither energy nor matter can be exchanged with the surroundings. An insulated thermos containing hot coffee approximates an isolated system. We know, however, that the coffee eventually cools, so it is not perfectly isolated.

 GIVE IT SOME THOUGHT

Is a human being an isolated, closed, or open system?

Transferring Energy: Work and Heat

Figure 10.1 illustrates the two ways we experience energy changes in our everyday lives—in the form of work and in the form of heat. In Figure 10.1(a) work is done as energy is transferred from the pitcher's arm to the ball, directing it toward the plate at high speed. In Figure 10.1(b) energy is transferred in the form of heat. Causing the motion of an object against a force and causing a temperature change are the two general ways that energy can be transferred into or out of a system.

A **force** is any push or pull exerted on an object. We define work, *w*, as the energy transferred when a force moves an object. The magnitude of this work equals the product of the force, *F*, and the distance, *d*, the object moves:

$$w = F \times d \qquad [10.3]$$

We perform work, for example, when we lift an object against the force of gravity. If we define the object as the system, then we—as part of the surroundings—are performing work on that system, transferring energy to it.

The other way in which energy is transferred is as heat. *Heat* is the energy transferred from a hotter object to a colder one. A combustion reaction, such as the burning of natural gas illustrated in Figure 10.1(b), releases the chemical energy stored in the molecules of the fuel. If we define the substances involved in the reaction as the system and everything else as the surroundings, we find that the released energy causes the temperature of the system to increase. Energy in the form of heat is then transferred from the hotter system to the cooler surroundings.

SAMPLE EXERCISE 10.1 **Describing and Calculating Energy Changes**

A bowler lifts a 5.4-kg (12-lb) bowling ball from ground level to a height of 1.6 m (5.2 ft) and then drops it. (**a**) What happens to the potential energy of the ball as it is raised? (**b**) What quantity of work, in J, is used to raise the ball? (**c**) After the ball is dropped, it gains kinetic energy. If all the work done in part (b) has been converted to kinetic energy by the time the ball strikes the ground, what is the ball's speed just before it hits the ground? (Note: The force due to gravity is $F = m \times g$, where *m* is the mass of the object and *g* is the gravitational constant; $g = 9.8 \text{ m/s}^2$.)

SOLUTION

Analyze We need to relate the potential energy of the bowling ball to its position relative to the ground. We then need to establish the relationship between work and the change in the ball's potential energy. Finally, we need to connect the change in potential energy when the ball is dropped with the kinetic energy attained by the ball.

Plan We can calculate the work done in lifting the ball by using Equation 10.3: $w = F \times d$. The kinetic energy of the ball just before it hits the ground equals its initial potential energy. We can use the kinetic energy and Equation 10.1 to calculate the speed, *v*, just before impact.

Solve

(a) Because the ball is raised above the ground, its potential energy relative to the ground increases.

(b) The ball has a mass of 5.4 kg and is lifted 1.6 m. To calculate the work performed to raise the ball, we use Equation 10.3 and $F = m \times g$ for the force that is due to gravity:

$$w = F \times d = m \times g \times d = (5.4\text{ kg})(9.8\text{ m/s}^2)(1.6\text{ m}) = 85\text{ kg-m}^2/\text{s}^2 = 85\text{ J}$$

Thus, the bowler has done 85 J of work to lift the ball to a height of 1.6 m.

(c) When the ball is dropped, its potential energy is converted to kinetic energy. We assume that the kinetic energy just before the ball hits the ground is equal to the work done in part (b), 85 J:

$$E_k = \tfrac{1}{2}\,mv^2 = 85\text{ J} = 85\text{ kg-m}^2/\text{s}^2$$

We can now solve this equation for v:

$$v^2 = \left(\frac{2E_k}{m}\right) = \left(\frac{2(85\text{ kg-m}^2/\text{s}^2)}{5.4\text{ kg}}\right) = 31.5\text{ m}^2/\text{s}^2$$

$$v = \sqrt{31.5\text{ m}^2/\text{s}^2} = 5.6\text{ m/s}$$

Check Work must be done in (b) to increase the potential energy of the ball, which is in accord with our experience. The units are appropriate in (b) and (c). The work is in units of J and the speed in units of m/s. In (c) we carry an additional digit in the intermediate calculation involving the square root, but we report the final value to only two significant figures, as appropriate.

Comment A speed of 1 m/s is roughly 2 mph, so the bowling ball has a speed greater than 10 mph just before impact.

PRACTICE EXERCISE

What is the kinetic energy, in J, of **(a)** an Ar atom moving at a speed of 650 m/s, **(b)** a mole of Ar atoms moving at 650 m/s? (*Hint:* 1 amu $= 1.66 \times 10^{-27}$ kg.)

Answers: **(a)** 1.4×10^{-20} J, **(b)** 8.4×10^3 J

10.2 | THE FIRST LAW OF THERMODYNAMICS

We have seen that the potential energy of a system can be converted into kinetic energy, and vice versa. We have also seen that energy can be transferred back and forth between a system and its surroundings in the forms of work and heat. All of these conversions and transfers proceed in accord with one of the most important observations in science: Energy can be neither created nor destroyed. Any energy that is lost by a system must be gained by the surroundings, and vice versa. This important observation—that *energy is conserved*—is known as the **first law of thermodynamics**. To apply this law quantitatively, let's first define the energy of a system more precisely.

Internal Energy

We will use the first law of thermodynamics to analyze energy changes in chemical systems. In order to do so, we must consider all the sources of kinetic and potential energy in the system we are studying. We define the **internal energy**, E, of a system as the sum of *all* the kinetic and potential energies of the components of the system. For the system in Figure 10.4, for example, the internal energy includes not only the motions and interactions of the H_2 and O_2 molecules but also the motions and interactions of the nuclei and electrons. We generally do not know the numerical value of a system's internal energy. In thermodynamics, we are mainly concerned with the *change* in E (and, as we shall see, changes in other quantities as well) that accompanies a change in the system.

Imagine that we start with a system with an initial internal energy E_{initial}. The system then undergoes a change, which might involve work being done or heat being transferred. After the change, the final internal energy of the system is E_{final}. We define

▲ GO FIGURE

What is the value of ΔE if E_{final} equals $E_{initial}$?

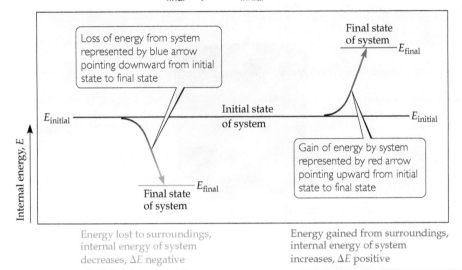

Loss of energy from system represented by blue arrow pointing downward from initial state to final state

Gain of energy by system represented by red arrow pointing upward from initial state to final state

Final state of system E_{final}

Initial state of system

$E_{initial}$

$E_{initial}$

Final state E_{final} of system

Internal energy, E

Energy lost to surroundings, internal energy of system decreases, ΔE negative

Energy gained from surroundings, internal energy of system increases, ΔE positive

◀ **FIGURE 10.5 Changes in internal energy.**

the *change* in internal energy, denoted ΔE (read "delta E"),* as the difference between E_{final} and $E_{initial}$:

$$\Delta E = E_{final} - E_{initial} \qquad [10.4]$$

We generally can't determine the actual values of E_{final} and $E_{initial}$ for any system of practical interest. Nevertheless, one of the beautiful aspects of the first law of thermodynamics is that we need only the value of ΔE in order to apply the law. We can often determine the value of ΔE even though we don't know the specific values of E_{final} and $E_{initial}$.

Thermodynamic quantities such as ΔE have three parts: (1) a number and (2) a unit, which together give the magnitude of the change, and (3) a sign that gives the direction. A *positive* value of ΔE results when $E_{final} > E_{initial}$, indicating that the system has gained energy from its surroundings. A *negative* value of ΔE results when $E_{final} < E_{initial}$, indicating that the system has lost energy to its surroundings. Notice that we are taking the point of view of the system rather than that of the surroundings in discussing the energy changes. We need to remember, however, that any increase in the energy of the system is accompanied by a decrease in the energy of the surroundings, and vice versa. These features of energy changes are summarized in ▲ **FIGURE 10.5**.

In a chemical reaction, the initial state of the system refers to the reactants and the final state refers to the products. In the reaction

$$2\,H_2(g) + O_2(g) \longrightarrow 2\,H_2O(l)$$

for instance, the initial state is the $2\,H_2(g) + O_2(g)$ and the final state is the $2\,H_2O(l)$. When hydrogen and oxygen form water at a given temperature, the system loses energy to the surroundings. Because energy is lost from the system, the internal energy of the products (final state) is less than that of the reactants (initial state), and ΔE for the process is negative. Thus, the *energy diagram* in ▶ **FIGURE 10.6** shows that the internal energy of the mixture of H_2 and O_2 is greater than that of the H_2O produced in the reaction.

Relating ΔE to Heat and Work

As we noted in Section 10.1, a system may exchange energy with its surroundings in two general ways: as heat or as work. The internal energy of a system changes in magnitude as heat is added to or removed from the system or as work is done on or by the system. If we think of internal energy as the system's bank account of energy, we see that deposits or withdrawals can be made either in increments of heat or in increments of

▲ GO FIGURE

The internal energy for Mg(s) and $Cl_2(g)$ is greater than that of $MgCl_2(s)$. Sketch an energy diagram that represents the reaction $MgCl_2(s) \longrightarrow Mg(s) + Cl_2(g)$.

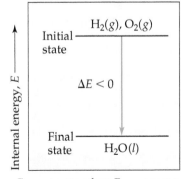

Initial state $H_2(g),\ O_2(g)$

$\Delta E < 0$

Final state $H_2O(l)$

Internal energy, E

$E_{initial}$ greater than E_{final}, energy released from system to surrounding during reaction, $\Delta E < 0$

▲ **FIGURE 10.6 Energy diagram for the reaction $2\,H_2(g) + O_2(g) \longrightarrow 2\,H_2O(l)$.**

*The symbol Δ is commonly used to denote *change*. For example, a change in height, h, can be represented by Δh.

◢ **GO FIGURE**

Suppose a system receives a "deposit" of work from the surroundings and loses a "withdrawal" of heat to the surroundings. Can we determine the sign of ΔE for this process?

System is interior of vault

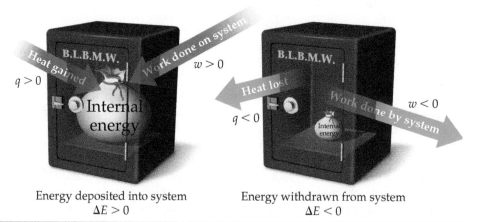

Energy deposited into system
$\Delta E > 0$

Energy withdrawn from system
$\Delta E < 0$

▶ **FIGURE 10.7 Sign conventions for heat and work.** Heat, q, gained by a system and work, w, done on a system are both positive quantities, corresponding to "deposits" of internal energy into the system. Conversely, heat transferred from the system to the surroundings and work done by the system on the surroundings are both "withdrawals" of internal energy from the system.

work. Deposits increase the energy of the system (positive ΔE), whereas withdrawals decrease the energy of the system (negative ΔE).

We can use these ideas to write a useful algebraic expression of the first law of thermodynamics. When a system undergoes any chemical or physical change, the accompanying change in internal energy, ΔE, is the sum of the heat added to or liberated from the system, q, and the work done on or by the system, w:

$$\Delta E = q + w \qquad [10.5]$$

When heat is added to a system or work is done on a system, its internal energy increases. Therefore, when heat is transferred to the system from the surroundings, q has a positive value. Adding heat to the system is like making a deposit to the energy account—the energy of the system increases (▲ FIGURE 10.7). Likewise, when work is done on the system by the surroundings, w has a positive value. Conversely, both the heat lost by the system to the surroundings and the work done by the system on the surroundings have negative values; that is, they lower the internal energy of the system. They are energy withdrawals and lower the amount of energy in the system's account.

The sign conventions for q, w, and ΔE are summarized in ▼ TABLE 10.1. Notice that any energy entering the system as either heat or work carries a positive sign.

TABLE 10.1 • Sign Conventions for q, w, and ΔE

For q	+ means system *gains* heat	− means system *loses* heat
For w	+ means work done *on* system	− means work done *by* system
For ΔE	+ means *net gain* of energy by system	− means *net loss* of energy by system

SAMPLE EXERCISE 10.2	Relating Heat and Work to Changes of Internal Energy

Gases A(g) and B(g) are confined in a cylinder-and-piston arrangement like that in Figure 10.4 and react to form a solid product C(s): A(g) + B(g) ⟶ C(s). As the reaction occurs, the system loses 1150 J of heat to the surroundings. The piston moves downward as the gases react to form a solid. As the volume of the gas decreases under the constant pressure of the atmosphere, the surroundings do 480 J of work on the system. What is the change in the internal energy of the system?

SOLUTION

Analyze The question asks us to determine ΔE, given information about q and w.

Plan We first determine the signs of q and w (Table 10.1) and then use Equation 10.5, $\Delta E = q + w$, to calculate ΔE.

Solve Heat is transferred from the system to the surroundings, and work is done on the system by the surroundings, so q is negative and w is positive: $q = -1150$ J and $w = 480$ kJ. Thus,

$$\Delta E = q + w = (-1150\ \text{J}) + (480\ \text{J}) = -670\ \text{J}$$

The negative value of ΔE tells us that a net quantity of 670 J of energy has been transferred from the system to the surroundings.

Comment You can think of this change as a decrease of 670 J in the net value of the system's energy bank account (hence, the negative sign); 1150 J is withdrawn in the form of heat while 480 J is deposited in the form of work. Notice that as the volume of the gases decreases, work is being done *on* the system *by* the surroundings, resulting in a deposit of energy.

PRACTICE EXERCISE

Calculate the change in the internal energy for a process in which a system absorbs 140 J of heat from the surroundings and does 85 J of work on the surroundings.

Answer: +55 J

Endothermic and Exothermic Processes

Because transfer of heat to and from the system is central to our discussion in this chapter, we have some special terminology to indicate the direction of transfer. When a process occurs in which the system absorbs heat, the process is called **endothermic** (*endo-* means "into"). During an endothermic process, such as the melting of ice, heat flows *into* the system from its surroundings [▶ FIGURE 10.8(a)]. If we, as part of the surroundings, touch a container in which ice is melting, the container feels cold to us because heat has passed from our hand to the container.

A process in which the system loses heat is called **exothermic** (*exo-* means "out of"). During an exothermic process, such as the combustion of gasoline, heat *exits* or flows *out* of the system into the surroundings [Figure 10.8(b)].

GIVE IT SOME THOUGHT

When H₂(g) and O₂(g) react to form H₂O(l), heat is released to the surroundings. Consider the reverse reaction, namely, the formation of H₂(g) and O₂(g) from H₂O(l): 2 H₂O(l) ⟶ 2 H₂(g) + O₂(g). Is this reaction exothermic or endothermic? (*Hint:* Refer to Figure 10.6)

State Functions

Although we usually have no way of knowing the precise value of the internal energy of a system, E, it does have a fixed value for a given set of conditions. The conditions that influence internal energy include the temperature and pressure. Furthermore, the internal energy of a system is proportional to the total quantity of matter in the system because energy is an extensive property.

Suppose we define our system as 50 g of water at 25 °C (▶ FIGURE 10.9). The system could have reached this state by cooling 50 g of water from 100 °C to 25 °C or by melting 50 g of ice and subsequently warming the water to 25 °C. The internal energy of

► **FIGURE 10.8 Endothermic and exothermic reactions.** (a) When ammonium thiocyanate and barium hydroxide octahydrate are mixed at room temperature, the temperature drops. (b) The reaction of powdered aluminum with Fe_2O_3 (the thermite reaction) proceeds vigorously, releasing heat and forming Al_2O_3 and molten iron.

System: reactants + products

Surroundings: solvent, initially at room temperature

Heat flows from surroundings into system (endothermic reaction), temperature of surroundings drops, thermometer reads temperature well below room temperature

(a)

System: reactants

Surroundings: air around reactants

Heat flows (violently) from system into surroundings (exothermic reaction), temperature of surroundings increases

(b)

► **FIGURE 10.9 Internal energy, *E*, a state function.** Any state function depends only on the present state of the system and not on the path by which the system arrived at that state.

50 g $H_2O(l)$ 100 °C

Initially hot water cools to water at 25 °C; once this temperature is reached, system has internal energy *E*

50 g $H_2O(l)$ 25 °C

Ice warms up to water at 25 °C; once this temperature is reached, system has internal energy *E*

50 g $H_2O(s)$ 0 °C

the water at 25 °C is the same in either case. Internal energy is an example of a **state function**, a property of a system that is determined by specifying the system's condition, or state (in terms of temperature, pressure, and so forth). *The value of a state function depends only on the present state of the system, not on the path the system took to reach that state.* Because *E* is a state function, ΔE depends only on the initial and final states of the system, not on how the change occurs.

An analogy may help you understand the difference between quantities that are state functions and those that are not. Suppose you drive from Chicago, which is 596 ft above sea level, to Denver, which is 5280 ft above sea level. No matter which route you take, the altitude change is 4684 ft. The distance you travel, however, depends on your route. Altitude is analogous to a state function because the change in altitude is independent of the path taken. Distance traveled is not a state function.

Some thermodynamic quantities, such as *E*, are state functions. Other quantities, such as *q* and *w*, are not. This means that, although $\Delta E = q + w$ does not depend on how the change occurs, the specific amounts of heat and work produced depend on the way in which the change occurs, analogous to the choice of travel route between Chicago and Denver. Nevertheless, if changing the path by which a system goes from an initial state to a final state increases the value of q, that path change will also decrease the value of w by exactly the same amount. The result is that ΔE is the same for the two paths.

We can illustrate this principle using a flashlight battery as our system. As the battery is discharged, its internal energy decreases as the energy stored in the battery is released to the surroundings. In ▶ FIGURE 10.10, we consider two possible ways of discharging the battery at constant temperature. If a wire shorts out the battery, no work is accomplished because nothing is moved against a force. All the energy lost from the battery is in the form of heat. (The wire gets warmer and releases heat to the surroundings.) If the battery is used to make a motor turn, the discharge produces work. Some heat is released, but not as much as when the battery is shorted out. We see that the magnitudes of q and w must be different for these two cases. If the initial and final states of the battery are identical in the two cases, however, then $\Delta E = q + w$ must be the same in both cases because ΔE is a state function. Remember: ΔE depends only on the initial and final states of the system, not on the specific path taken from the initial to the final state.

 GIVE IT SOME THOUGHT

In what ways is the balance in your checkbook a state function?

10.3 | ENTHALPY

The chemical and physical changes that occur around us, such as photosynthesis in the leaves of a plant, evaporation of water from a lake, or a reaction in an open beaker in a laboratory, occur under the essentially constant pressure of Earth's atmosphere. These changes can result in the release or absorption of heat and can be accompanied by work done by or on the system. In exploring these changes, we have a number of experimental means to measure the flow of heat into and out of the system, and we therefore focus much of our discussion on what we can learn from the heat flow. (Of course, in order to apply the first law of thermodynamics to these processes, we still need to account for any work that accompanies the process.)

A system that consists of a gas confined to a container can be characterized by several different properties. Among the most important are the *pressure* of the gas, P, and the *volume* of the container, V. Like internal energy E, both P and V are state functions—they depend only on the current state of the system and not on the path taken to that state.

We can combine these three state functions—E, P, and V—to define a new state function called **enthalpy** (from the Greek *enthalpein*, "to warm"). This new function is particularly useful for discussing heat flow in processes that occur under constant (or nearly constant) pressure. Enthalpy, which we denote by the symbol H, is defined as the internal energy plus the product of the pressure and volume of the system:

$$H = E + PV \qquad [10.6]$$

 GIVE IT SOME THOUGHT

Given the definition of enthalpy in Equation 10.6, why must H be a state function?

You might be asking yourself why it is convenient to define a new function H. To answer that question, recall from Equation 10.5 that ΔE involves not only the heat q added to or removed from the system but also the work w done by or on the system. Most commonly, the only kind of work produced by chemical or physical changes open to the atmosphere is the mechanical work associated with a change in volume. For example, when the reaction of zinc metal with hydrochloric acid solution,

$$Zn(s) + 2\,H^+(aq) \longrightarrow Zn^{2+}(aq) + H_2(g) \qquad [10.7]$$

▲ **GO FIGURE**

If the battery is defined as the system, what is the sign on *w* in part (b)?

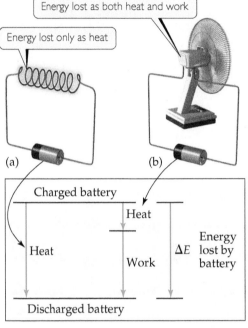

Energy lost as both heat and work

Energy lost only as heat

(a)   (b)

Charged battery

Heat

Heat

Work

ΔE

Energy lost by battery

Discharged battery

▲ **FIGURE 10.10 Internal energy is a state function, but heat and work are not.** (a) A battery shorted out by a wire loses energy to the surroundings only as heat; no work is performed. (b) A battery discharged through a motor loses energy as work (to make the fan turn) and also loses some energy as heat. The value of ΔE is the same for both processes even though the values of q and w in (a) are different from those in (b).

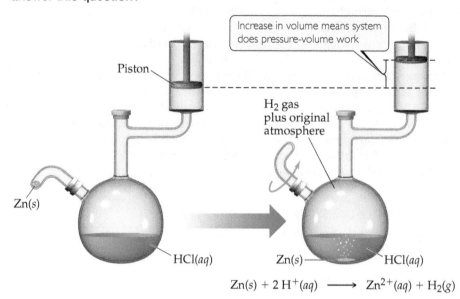

If the amount of zinc used in the reaction is increased, will more work be done by the system? Is there additional information you need in order to answer this question?

▲ **FIGURE 10.11 A system that does work on its surroundings.**

is run at constant pressure in the apparatus illustrated in ▲ **FIGURE 10.11**, the piston moves up or down to maintain a constant pressure in the vessel. If we assume for simplicity that the piston has no mass, the pressure in the apparatus is the same as atmospheric pressure. As the reaction proceeds, H_2 gas forms, and the piston rises. The gas within the flask is thus doing work on the surroundings by lifting the piston against the force of atmospheric pressure.

The work involved in the expansion or compression of gases is called **pressure-volume work** (or *P-V* work). When pressure is constant in a process, as in our preceding example, the sign and magnitude of the pressure-volume work are given by

$$w = -P\,\Delta V \qquad [10.8]$$

where P is pressure and $\Delta V = V_{\text{final}} - V_{\text{initial}}$ is the change in volume of the system. The negative sign in Equation 10.8 is necessary to conform to the sign conventions of Table 10.1. The pressure P is always either a positive number or zero. If the volume of the system expands, then ΔV is positive as well. Because the expanding system does work on the surroundings, w is negative—energy leaves the system as work. Notice that if the gas is compressed, ΔV is negative (the volume decreases), and Equation 10.8 indicates that w is positive, meaning work is done on the system by the surroundings. The "A Closer Look" box discusses pressure-volume work in detail, but all you need to keep in mind for now is Equation 10.8, which applies to processes occurring at constant pressure.

 GIVE IT SOME THOUGHT

If a system does not change its volume during the course of a process, does it do pressure-volume work?

Let's now return to our discussion of enthalpy. When a change occurs at constant pressure, the change in enthalpy, ΔH, is given by the relationship

$$\begin{aligned} \Delta H &= \Delta(E + PV) \\ &= \Delta E + P\Delta V \quad \text{(constant pressure)} \end{aligned} \qquad [10.9]$$

That is, the change in enthalpy equals the change in internal energy plus the product of the constant pressure times the change in volume.

Recall that $\Delta E = q + w$ (Equation 10.5) and that the work involved in the expansion or compression of a gas is $w = -P\,\Delta V$ (at constant pressure). Substituting $-w$ for $P\,\Delta V$ and $q + w$ for ΔE into Equation 10.9, we have

$$\Delta H = \Delta E + P\,\Delta V = (q_P + w) - w = q_P \qquad [10.10]$$

The subscript P on q indicates that the process occurs at constant pressure. Thus, *the change in enthalpy equals the heat q_P gained or lost at constant pressure.* Because q_P is something we can either measure or readily calculate and because so many physical and chemical changes of interest to us occur at constant pressure, enthalpy is a more useful function for most reactions than is internal energy. In addition, for most reactions the difference in ΔH and ΔE is small because $P\,\Delta V$ is small.

When ΔH is positive (that is, when q_P is positive), the system has gained heat from the surroundings (Table 10.1), which means the process is endothermic. When ΔH is negative, the system has released heat to the surroundings, which means the process is exothermic. To continue the bank analogy of Figure 10.7, under constant pressure an endothermic process deposits energy in the system in the form of heat and an exothermic process withdraws energy in the form of heat (▶ FIGURE 10.12).

Because H is a state function, ΔH (which equals q_P) depends only on the initial and final states of the system, not on how the change occurs. At first glance this statement might seem to contradict our discussion in Section 10.2, in which we said that q is *not* a state function. There is no contradiction, however, because the relationship between ΔH and q_P has the special limitations that only *P-V* work is involved and that the pressure is constant.

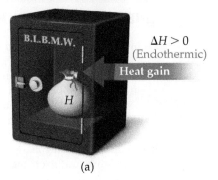

Constant pressure maintained in system

B.L.B.M.W.

H

$\Delta H > 0$ (Endothermic)

Heat gain

(a)

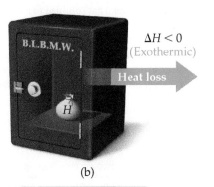

B.L.B.M.W.

H

$\Delta H < 0$ (Exothermic)

Heat loss

(b)

ΔH is amount of heat that flows into or out of system under constant pressure

▲ FIGURE 10.12 **Endothermic and exothermic processes.** (a) An endothermic process ($\Delta H > 0$) deposits heat into the system. (b) An exothermic process ($\Delta H < 0$) withdraws heat from the system.

 GIVE IT SOME THOUGHT

What common laboratory measuring device will we likely always use in experiments that measure enthalpy changes?

SAMPLE EXERCISE 10.3 **Determining the Sign of ΔH**

Indicate the sign of the enthalpy change, ΔH, in these processes carried out under atmospheric pressure and indicate whether each process is endothermic or exothermic: **(a)** An ice cube melts; **(b)** 1 g of butane (C_4H_{10}) is combusted in sufficient oxygen to give complete combustion to CO_2 and H_2O.

SOLUTION

Analyze Our goal is to determine whether ΔH is positive or negative for each process. Because each process occurs at constant pressure, the enthalpy change equals the quantity of heat absorbed or released, $\Delta H = q_P$.

Plan We must predict whether heat is absorbed or released by the system in each process. Processes in which heat is absorbed are endothermic and have a positive sign for ΔH; those in which heat is released are exothermic and have a negative sign for ΔH.

Solve In (a) the water that makes up the ice cube is the system. The ice cube absorbs heat from the surroundings as it melts, so ΔH is positive and the process is endothermic. In (b) the system is the 1 g of butane and the oxygen required to combust it. The combustion of butane in oxygen gives off heat, so ΔH is negative and the process is exothermic.

PRACTICE EXERCISE

Molten gold poured into a mold solidifies at atmospheric pressure. With the gold defined as the system, is the solidification an exothermic or endothermic process?

Answer: In order to solidify, the gold must cool to below its melting temperature. It cools by transferring heat to its surroundings. The air around the sample would feel hot because heat is transferred to it from the molten gold, meaning the process is exothermic.

You may notice that solidification of a liquid is the reverse of the melting we analyzed in the exercise. As we will see, reversing the direction of a process changes the sign of the heat transferred.

A CLOSER LOOK

ENERGY, ENTHALPY, AND *P-V* WORK

In chemistry we are interested mainly in two types of work: electrical work and mechanical work done by expanding gases. We focus here on the latter, called pressure-volume, or *P-V*, work. Expanding gases in the cylinder of an automobile engine do *P-V* work on the piston; this work eventually turns the wheels. Expanding gases from an open reaction vessel do *P-V* work on the atmosphere. This work accomplishes nothing in a practical sense, but we must keep track of all work, useful or not, when monitoring energy changes in a system.

Let's consider a gas confined to a cylinder with a movable piston of cross-sectional area A (▼ FIGURE 10.13). A downward force F acts on the piston. The *pressure, P,* on the gas is the force per area: $P = F/A$. We assume that the piston is massless and that the only pressure acting on it is the *atmospheric pressure* that is due to Earth's atmosphere, which we assume to be constant.

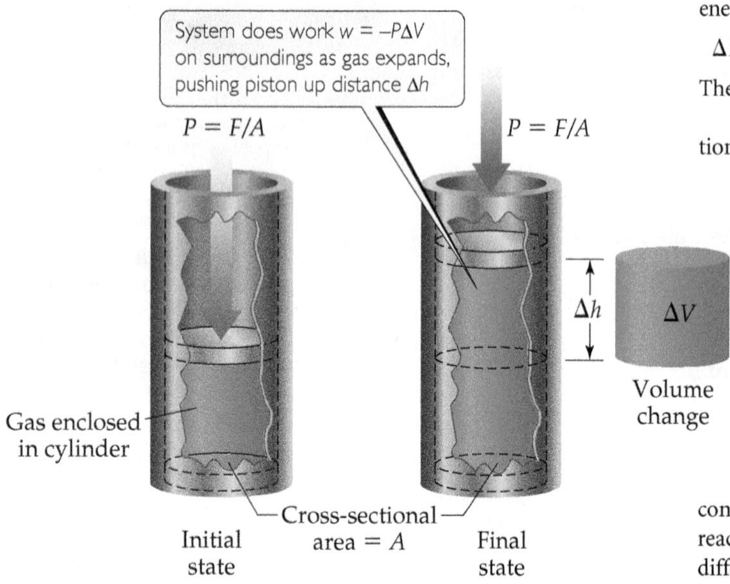

System does work $w = -P\Delta V$ on surroundings as gas expands, pushing piston up distance Δh

$P = F/A$ $P = F/A$

Δh ΔV

Volume change

Gas enclosed in cylinder

Cross-sectional area = A

Initial state   Final state

▲ FIGURE 10.13 **Pressure-volume work.** The amount of work done by the system on the surroundings is $w = -P\Delta V$.

Suppose the gas expands and the piston moves a distance Δh. From Equation 10.3, the magnitude of the work done by the system is

$$\text{Magnitude of work} = \text{force} \times \text{distance} = F \times \Delta h \quad [10.11]$$

We can rearrange the definition of pressure, $P = F/A$, to $F = P \times A$. The volume change, ΔV, resulting from the movement of the piston is the product of the cross-sectional area of the piston and the distance it moves: $\Delta V = A \times \Delta h$. Substituting into Equation 10.11 gives

$$\text{Magnitude of work} = F \times \Delta h = P \times A \times \Delta h$$
$$= P \times \Delta V$$

Because the system (the confined gas) does work on the surroundings, the work is a negative quantity:

$$w = -P\,\Delta V \quad [10.12]$$

Now, if *P-V* work is the only work that can be done, we can substitute Equation 10.12 into Equation 10.5 to give

$$\Delta E = q + w = q - P\,\Delta V \quad [10.13]$$

When a reaction is carried out in a constant-volume container ($\Delta V = 0$), therefore, the heat transferred equals the change in internal energy:

$$\Delta E = q - P\Delta V = q - P(0) = q_V \quad \text{(constant volume)}[10.14]$$

The subscript V indicates that the volume is constant.

Most reactions are run under constant pressure, so that Equation 10.13 becomes

$$\Delta E = q_P - P\,\Delta V$$
$$q_P = \Delta E + P\,\Delta V \quad \text{(constant pressure)} \quad [10.15]$$

We see from Equation 10.9 that the right side of Equation 10.15 is the enthalpy change under constant-pressure conditions. Thus, $\Delta H = q_P$, as we saw in Equation 10.10.

In summary, the change in internal energy is equal to the heat gained or lost at constant volume, and the change in enthalpy is equal to the heat gained or lost at constant pressure. The difference between ΔE and ΔH is the amount of *P-V* work done by the system when the process occurs at constant pressure, $-P\,\Delta V$. The volume change accompanying many reactions is close to zero, which makes $P\,\Delta V$ and, therefore, the difference between ΔE and ΔH small. Under most circumstances, it is generally satisfactory to use ΔH as the measure of energy changes during most chemical processes.

RELATED EXERCISES: 10.35, 10.36, 10.37, 10.38

10.4 | ENTHALPIES OF REACTION

Because $\Delta H = H_{\text{final}} - H_{\text{initial}}$, the enthalpy change for a chemical reaction is given by

$$\Delta H = H_{\text{products}} - H_{\text{reactants}} \quad [10.16]$$

The enthalpy change that accompanies a reaction is called either the **enthalpy of reaction** or the *heat of reaction* and is sometimes written ΔH_{rxn}, where "rxn" is a commonly used abbreviation for "reaction."

When we give a numerical value for ΔH_{rxn}, we must specify the reaction involved. For example, when 2 mol $H_2(g)$ burn to form 2 mol $H_2O(g)$ at a constant pressure, the system releases 483.6 kJ of heat. We can summarize this information as

$$2\,H_2(g) + O_2(g) \longrightarrow 2\,H_2O(g) \qquad \Delta H = -483.6\ \text{kJ} \quad [10.17]$$

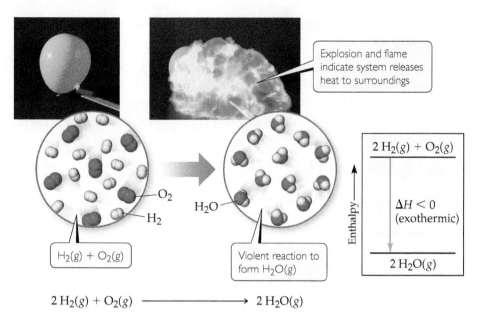

Exothermic reaction of hydrogen with oxygen. When a mixture of $H_2(g)$ and $O_2(g)$ is ignited to form $H_2O(g)$, the resultant explosion produces a ball of flame. Because the system releases heat to the surroundings, the reaction is exothermic as indicated in the enthalpy diagram.

Explosion and flame indicate system releases heat to surroundings

$2\ H_2(g) + O_2(g)$

$\Delta H < 0$ (exothermic)

$2\ H_2O(g)$

Enthalpy ⟶

O_2

H_2O

H_2

$H_2(g) + O_2(g)$

Violent reaction to form $H_2O(g)$

$$2\ H_2(g) + O_2(g) \longrightarrow 2\ H_2O(g)$$

The negative sign for ΔH tells us that this reaction is exothermic. Notice that ΔH is reported at the end of the balanced equation, without explicitly specifying the amounts of chemicals involved. In such cases the coefficients in the balanced equation represent the number of moles of reactants and products producing the associated enthalpy change. Balanced chemical equations that show the associated enthalpy change in this way are called *thermochemical equations*.

The exothermic nature of this reaction is also shown in the *enthalpy diagram* in ▲ FIGURE 10.14. Notice that the enthalpy of the reactants is greater (more positive) than the enthalpy of the products. Thus, $\Delta H = H_{products} - H_{reactants}$ is negative.

GIVE IT SOME THOUGHT

If the reaction to form water were written $H_2(g) + \frac{1}{2} O_2(g) \longrightarrow H_2O(g)$, would you expect the same value of ΔH as in Equation 10.17? Why or why not?

The reaction of hydrogen with oxygen is highly exothermic and occurs rapidly once it starts. It can occur with explosive violence, as demonstrated by the explosions of the German airship *Hindenburg* in 1937 (▼ FIGURE 10.15) and the U.S. space shuttle *Challenger* in 1986.

◀ FIGURE 10.15   **The burning of the hydrogen-filled airship *Hindenburg*.** This tragedy, in Lakehurst, New Jersey, on May 6, 1937, led to the discontinuation of hydrogen as a buoyant gas in such craft. Modern-day airships are filled with helium, which is not as buoyant as hydrogen but is not flammable.

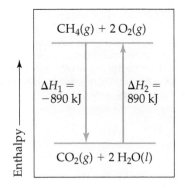

CH$_4$(g) + 2 O$_2$(g)

$\Delta H_1 =$ −890 kJ

$\Delta H_2 =$ 890 kJ

CO$_2$(g) + 2 H$_2$O(l)

Enthalpy

▲ **FIGURE 10.16** **ΔH for a reverse reaction.** Reversing a reaction changes the sign but not the magnitude of the enthalpy change: $\Delta H_2 = -\Delta H_1$.

The following guidelines are helpful when using thermochemical equations and enthalpy diagrams:

1. **Enthalpy is an extensive property.** The magnitude of ΔH is proportional to the amount of reactant consumed in the process. For example, 890 kJ of heat is produced when 1 mol of CH$_4$ is burned in a constant-pressure system:

$$CH_4(g) + 2 O_2(g) \longrightarrow CO_2(g) + 2 H_2O(l) \qquad \Delta H = -890 \text{ kJ} \qquad [10.18]$$

Because the combustion of 1 mol of CH$_4$ with 2 mol of O$_2$ releases 890 kJ of heat, the combustion of 2 mol of CH$_4$ with 4 mol of O$_2$ releases twice as much heat, 1780 kJ.

2. **The enthalpy change for a reaction is equal in magnitude, but opposite in sign, to ΔH for the reverse reaction.** For example, ΔH for the reverse of Equation 10.18 is +890 kJ:

$$CO_2(g) + 2 H_2O(l) \longrightarrow CH_4(g) + 2 O_2(g) \qquad \Delta H = +890 \text{ kJ} \qquad [10.19]$$

When we reverse a reaction, we reverse the roles of the products and the reactants. From Equation 10.16, we see that reversing the products and reactants leads to the same magnitude of ΔH but a change in sign (◀ **FIGURE 10.16**).

3. **The enthalpy change for a reaction depends on the states of the reactants and products.** If the product in Equation 10.18 were H$_2$O(g) instead of H$_2$O(l), ΔH_{rxn} would be −802 kJ instead of −890 kJ. Less heat would be available for transfer to the surroundings because the enthalpy of H$_2$O(g) is greater than that of H$_2$O(l). One way to see this is to imagine that the product is initially liquid water. The liquid water must be converted to water vapor, and the conversion of 2 mol H$_2$O(l) to 2 mol H$_2$O(g) is an endothermic process that absorbs 88 kJ:

$$2 H_2O(l) \longrightarrow 2 H_2O(g) \qquad \Delta H = +88 \text{ kJ} \qquad [10.20]$$

Thus, it is important to specify the states of the reactants and products in thermochemical equations. In addition, we will generally assume that the reactants and products are both at the same temperature, 25 °C, unless otherwise indicated.

SAMPLE EXERCISE 10.4 | **Relating ΔH to Quantities of Reactants and Products**

How much heat is released when 4.50 g of methane gas is burned in a constant-pressure system? (Use the information given in Equation 10.18.)

SOLUTION

Analyze Our goal is to use a thermochemical equation to calculate the heat produced when a specific amount of methane gas is combusted. According to Equation 10.18, 890 kJ is released by the system when 1 mol CH$_4$ is burned at constant pressure.

Plan Equation 10.18 provides us with a stoichiometric conversion factor: (1 mol CH$_4$ ≙ −890 kJ). Thus, we can convert moles of CH$_4$ to kJ of energy. First, however, we must convert grams of CH$_4$ to moles of CH$_4$. Thus, the conversion sequence is grams CH$_4$ (given) → moles CH$_4$ → kJ (unknown to be found).

Solve By adding the atomic weights of C and 4 H, we have 1 mol CH$_4$ = 16.0 CH$_4$. We can use the appropriate conversion factors to convert grams of CH$_4$ to moles of CH$_4$ to kilojoules:

$$\text{Heat} = (4.50 \text{ g CH}_4)\left(\frac{1 \text{ mol CH}_4}{16.0 \text{ g CH}_4}\right)\left(\frac{-890 \text{ kJ}}{1 \text{ mol CH}_4}\right) = -250 \text{ kJ}$$

The negative sign indicates that the system released 250 kJ into the surroundings.

PRACTICE EXERCISE

Hydrogen peroxide can decompose to water and oxygen by the reaction

$$2 H_2O_2(l) \longrightarrow 2 H_2O(l) + O_2(g) \qquad \Delta H = -196 \text{ kJ}$$

Calculate the quantity of heat released when 5.00 g of H$_2$O$_2$(l) decomposes at constant pressure.
Answer: −14.4 kJ

STRATEGIES IN CHEMISTRY

USING ENTHALPY AS A GUIDE

If you hold a brick in the air and let it go, you know what happens: It falls as the force of gravity pulls it toward Earth. A process that is thermodynamically favored to happen, such as a brick falling to the ground, is called a *spontaneous* process. A spontaneous process can be either fast or slow; the rate at which processes occur is not governed by thermodynamics.

Chemical processes can be thermodynamically favored, or spontaneous, too. By spontaneous, however, we do not mean that the reaction will form products without any intervention. That can be the case, but often some energy must be imparted to get the process started. The enthalpy change in a reaction gives one indication as to whether the reaction is likely to be spontaneous. The combustion of $H_2(g)$ and $O_2(g)$, for example, is highly exothermic:

$$H_2(g) + \tfrac{1}{2} O_2(g) \longrightarrow H_2O(g) \qquad \Delta H = -242 \text{ kJ}$$

Hydrogen gas and oxygen gas can exist together in a volume indefinitely without noticeable reaction occurring. Once the reaction is initiated, however, energy is rapidly transferred from the system (the reactants) to the surroundings as heat. The system thus loses enthalpy by transferring the heat to the surroundings. (Recall that the first law of thermodynamics tells us that the total energy of the system plus the surroundings does not change; energy is conserved.)

Enthalpy change is not the only consideration in the spontaneity of reactions, however, nor is it a foolproof guide. For example, even though ice melting is an endothermic process,

$$H_2O(s) \longrightarrow H_2O(l) \qquad \Delta H = +6.01 \text{ kJ}$$

this process is spontaneous at temperatures above the freezing point of water (0 °C). The reverse process, water freezing, is spontaneous at temperatures below 0 °C. Thus, we know that ice at room temperature melts and water put into a freezer at −20 °C turns into ice. Both processes are spontaneous under different conditions even though they are the reverse of one another. In Chapter 13 we will address the spontaneity of processes more fully. We will see why a process can be spontaneous at one temperature but not at another, as is the case for the conversion of water to ice.

Despite these complicating factors, you should pay attention to the enthalpy changes in reactions. As a general observation, when the enthalpy change is large, it is the dominant factor in determining spontaneity. Thus, reactions for which ΔH is *large* and *negative* tend to be spontaneous. Reactions for which ΔH is *large* and *positive* tend to be spontaneous only in the reverse direction.

RELATED EXERCISES: 10.47, 10.48

In many situations we will find it valuable to know the sign and magnitude of the enthalpy change associated with a given chemical process. As we see in the following sections, ΔH can be either determined directly by experiment or calculated from known enthalpy changes of other reactions.

10.5 | CALORIMETRY

The value of ΔH can be determined experimentally by measuring the heat flow accompanying a reaction at constant pressure. Typically, we can determine the magnitude of the heat flow by measuring the magnitude of the temperature change the heat flow produces. The measurement of heat flow is **calorimetry**; a device used to measure heat flow is a **calorimeter**.

Heat Capacity and Specific Heat

The more heat an object gains, the hotter it gets. All substances change temperature when they are heated, but the magnitude of the temperature change produced by a given quantity of heat varies from substance to substance. The temperature change experienced by an object when it absorbs a certain amount of heat is determined by its **heat capacity**, denoted C. The heat capacity of an object is the amount of heat required to raise its temperature by 1 K (or 1 °C). The greater the heat capacity, the greater the heat required to produce a given increase in temperature.

For pure substances the heat capacity is usually given for a specified amount of the substance. The heat capacity of one mole of a substance is called its **molar heat capacity**, C_m. The heat capacity of one gram of a substance is called its *specific heat capacity*, or merely its **specific heat**. The specific heat, C_s, of a substance can be determined experimentally by

Is the process shown in the figure

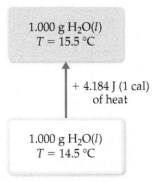

▲ FIGURE 10.17 **Specific heat of water.**

measuring the temperature change, ΔT, that a known mass m of the substance undergoes when it gains or loses a specific quantity of heat q:

$$\text{Specific heat} = \frac{(\text{quantity of heat transferred})}{(\text{grams of substance}) \times (\text{temperature change})}$$

$$C_s = \frac{q}{m \times \Delta T} \qquad [10.21]$$

For example, 209 J is required to increase the temperature of 50.0 g of water by 1.00 K. Thus, the specific heat of water is

$$C_s = \frac{209 \text{ J}}{(50.0 \text{ g})(1.00 \text{ K})} = 4.18 \text{ J/g-K}$$

A temperature change in kelvins is equal in magnitude to the temperature change in degrees Celsius: ΔT in $K = \Delta T$ in °C. Therefore, this specific heat for water can also be reported as 4.18 J/g-°C.

Because the specific heat values for a given substance can vary slightly with temperature, the temperature is often precisely specified. The 4.18 J/g-K value we use here for water, for instance, is for water initially at 14.5 °C (◄ FIGURE 10.17). Water's specific heat at this temperature is used to define the calorie at the value given in Section 10.1: 1 cal = 4.184 J exactly.

When a sample absorbs heat (positive q), its temperature increases (positive ΔT). Rearranging Equation 10.21, we get

$$q = C_s \times m \times \Delta T \qquad [10.22]$$

Thus, we can calculate the quantity of heat a substance gains or loses by using its specific heat together with its measured mass and temperature change.

▼ TABLE 10.2 lists the specific heats of several substances. Notice that the specific heat of liquid water is higher than those of the other substances listed. The high specific heat of water affects Earth's climate because it makes the temperatures of the oceans relatively resistant to change.

 GIVE IT SOME THOUGHT

Which substance in Table 10.2 undergoes the greatest temperature change when the same mass of each substance absorbs the same quantity of heat?

TABLE 10.2 • Specific Heats of Some Substances at 298 K			
Elements		**Compounds**	
Substance	**Specific Heat (J/g-K)**	**Substance**	**Specific Heat (J/g-K)**
$N_2(g)$	1.04	$H_2O(l)$	4.18
Al(s)	0.90	$CH_4(g)$	2.20
Fe(s)	0.45	$CO_2(g)$	0.84
Hg(l)	0.14	$CaCO_3(s)$	0.82

SAMPLE EXERCISE 10.5 Relating Heat, Temperature Change, and Heat Capacity

(a) How much heat is needed to warm 250 g of water (about 1 cup) from 22 °C (about room temperature) to 98 °C (near its boiling point)? (b) What is the molar heat capacity of water?

SOLUTION

Analyze In part (a) we must find the quantity of heat (q) needed to warm the water, given the mass of water (m), its temperature change (ΔT), and its specific heat (C_s). In part (b) we must calculate

the molar heat capacity (heat capacity per mole, C_m) of water from its specific heat (heat capacity per gram).

Plan (a) Given C_s, m, and ΔT, we can calculate the quantity of heat, q, using Equation 10.22. (b) We can use the molar mass of water and dimensional analysis to convert from heat capacity per gram to heat capacity per mole.

Solve

(a) The water undergoes a temperature change of

$$\Delta T = 98\ ^\circ\text{C} - 22\ ^\circ\text{C} = 76\ ^\circ\text{C} = 76\ \text{K}$$

Using Equation 10.22, we have

$$q = C_s \times m \times \Delta T$$
$$= (4.18\ \text{J/g-K})(250\ \text{g})(76\ \text{K}) = 7.9 \times 10^4\ \text{J}$$

(b) The molar heat capacity is the heat capacity of one mole of substance. Using the atomic weights of hydrogen and oxygen, we have

$$1\ \text{mol}\ H_2O = 18.0\ \text{g}\ H_2O$$

From the specific heat given in part (a), we have

$$C_m = \left(4.18\ \frac{\text{J}}{\text{g-K}}\right)\left(\frac{18.0\ \text{g}}{1\ \text{mol}}\right) = 75.2\ \text{J/mol-K}$$

PRACTICE EXERCISE

(a) Large beds of rocks are used in some solar-heated homes to store heat. Assume that the specific heat of the rocks is 0.82 J/g-K. Calculate the quantity of heat absorbed by 50.0 kg of rocks if their temperature increases by 12.0 °C. (b) What temperature change would these rocks undergo if they emitted 450 kJ of heat?

Answers: (a) 4.9×10^5 J, (b) 11 K decrease $=$ 11 °C decrease

Constant-Pressure Calorimetry

The techniques and equipment employed in calorimetry depend on the nature of the process being studied. For many reactions, such as those occurring in solution, it is easy to control pressure so that ΔH is measured directly. Although the calorimeters used for highly accurate work are precision instruments, a simple "coffee-cup" calorimeter (▶ FIGURE 10.18) is often used in general chemistry laboratories to illustrate the principles of calorimetry. Because the calorimeter is not sealed, the reaction occurs under the essentially constant pressure of the atmosphere.

Imagine adding two aqueous solutions, each containing a reactant, to a coffee-cup calorimeter. Once mixed, the reactants can react to form products. In this case there is no physical boundary between the system and the surroundings. The reactants and products of the reaction are the system, and the water in which they are dissolved is part of the surroundings. (The calorimeter apparatus is also part of the surroundings.) If we assume that the calorimeter is perfectly insulated, then any heat released or absorbed by the reaction will raise or lower the temperature of the water in the solution. Thus, we measure the temperature change of the solution and assume that any changes are due to heat transferred from the reaction to the water (for an exothermic process) or transferred from the water to the reaction (endothermic). In other words, by monitoring the temperature of the solution, we are seeing the flow of heat between the system (the reactants and products in the solution) and the surroundings (the water that forms the bulk of the solution).

For an exothermic reaction, heat is "lost" by the reaction and "gained" by the water in the solution, so the temperature of the solution rises. The opposite occurs for an endothermic reaction: Heat is gained by the reaction and lost by the water in the solution, and the temperature of the solution decreases. The heat gained or lost by the solution, q_{soln}, is therefore equal in magnitude but opposite in sign to the heat absorbed or released by the reaction, q_{rxn}: $q_{\text{soln}} = -q_{\text{rxn}}$. The value of q_{soln} is readily calculated from the mass of the solution, its specific heat, and the temperature change:

$$q_{\text{soln}} = (\text{specific heat of solution}) \times (\text{grams of solution}) \times \Delta T = -q_{\text{rxn}} \quad [10.23]$$

For dilute aqueous solutions we usually assume that the specific heat of the solution is the same as that of water, 4.18 J/g-K.

Equation 10.23 makes it possible to calculate q_{rxn} from the temperature change of the solution in which the reaction occurs. A temperature increase ($\Delta T > 0$) means the reaction is exothermic ($q_{\text{rxn}} < 0$).

GO FIGURE

Propose a reason for why two Styrofoam® cups are often used instead of just one.

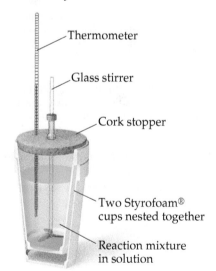

Thermometer

Glass stirrer

Cork stopper

Two Styrofoam® cups nested together

Reaction mixture in solution

▲ FIGURE 10.18 **Coffee-cup calorimeter.** This simple apparatus is used to measure temperature changes of reactions at constant pressure.

SAMPLE EXERCISE 10.6 | **Measuring ΔH Using a Coffee-Cup Calorimeter**

When a student mixes 50 mL of 1.0 M HCl and 50 mL of 1.0 M NaOH in a coffee-cup calorimeter, the temperature of the resultant solution increases from 21.0 °C to 27.5 °C. Calculate the enthalpy change for the reaction in kJ/mol HCl, assuming that the calorimeter loses only a negligible quantity of heat, that the total volume of the solution is 100 mL, that its density is 1.0 g/mL, and that its specific heat is 4.18 J/g-K.

SOLUTION

Analyze Mixing solutions of HCl and NaOH results in an acid–base reaction:

$$HCl(aq) + NaOH(aq) \longrightarrow H_2O(l) + NaCl(aq)$$

We need to calculate the heat produced per mole of HCl, given the temperature increase of the solution, the number of moles of HCl and NaOH involved, and the density and specific heat of the solution.

Plan The total heat produced can be calculated using Equation 10.23. The number of moles of HCl consumed in the reaction must be calculated from the volume and molarity of this substance, and this amount is then used to determine the heat produced per mol HCl.

Solve

Because the total volume of the solution is 100 mL, its mass is	$(100 \text{ mL})(1.0 \text{ g/mL}) = 100 \text{ g}$
The temperature change is	$\Delta T = 27.5 \,°C - 21.0 \,°C = 6.5 \,°C = 6.5 \text{ K}$
Using Equation 10.23, we have	$q_{rxn} = -C_s \times m \times \Delta T$
	$= -(4.18 \text{ J/g-K})(100 \text{ g})(6.5 \text{ K}) = -2.7 \times 10^3 \text{ J} = -2.7 \text{ kJ}$
Because the process occurs at constant pressure,	$\Delta H = q_P = -2.7 \text{ kJ}$
To express the enthalpy change on a molar basis, we use the fact that the number of moles of HCl is given by the product of the volume (50 mL = 0.050 L) and concentration (1.0 M = 1.0 mol/L) of the HCl solution:	$(0.050 \text{ L})(1.0 \text{ mol/L}) = 0.050 \text{ mol}$
Thus, the enthalpy change per mole of HCl is	$\Delta H = -2.7 \text{ kJ}/0.050 \text{ mol} = -54 \text{ kJ/mol}$

Check ΔH is negative (exothermic), which is expected for the reaction of an acid with a base and evidenced by the fact that the reaction causes the temperature of the solution to increase. The magnitude of the molar enthalpy change seems reasonable.

PRACTICE EXERCISE

When 50.0 mL of 0.100 M AgNO₃ and 50.0 mL of 0.100 M HCl are mixed in a constant-pressure calorimeter, the temperature of the mixture increases from 22.30 °C to 23.11 °C. The temperature increase is caused by the following reaction:

$$AgNO_3(aq) + HCl(aq) \longrightarrow AgCl(s) + HNO_3(aq)$$

Calculate ΔH for this reaction in kJ/mol AgNO₃, assuming that the combined solution has a mass of 100.0 g and a specific heat of 4.18 J/g °C.

Answer: −68,000 J/mol = −68 kJ/mol

Bomb Calorimetry (Constant-Volume Calorimetry)

An important type of reaction studied using calorimetry is combustion, in which a compound reacts completely with excess oxygen. Combustion reactions are most accurately studied using a **bomb calorimeter** (▶ FIGURE 10.19). The substance to be studied is placed in a small cup within an insulated sealed vessel called a *bomb*. The bomb, which is designed to withstand high pressures, has an inlet valve for adding oxygen and electrical leads. After the sample has been placed in the bomb, the bomb is sealed and pressurized with oxygen. It is then placed in the calorimeter and covered with an accurately measured quantity of water. The combustion reaction is initiated by passing an electrical current through a fine wire in contact with the sample. When the wire becomes sufficiently hot, the sample ignites.

The heat released when combustion occurs is absorbed by the water and the various components of the calorimeter (which all together make up the surroundings), causing the water temperature to rise. The change in water temperature caused by the reaction is measured very precisely.

To calculate the heat of combustion from the measured temperature increase, we must know the total heat capacity of the calorimeter, C_{cal}. This quantity is determined by combusting a sample that releases a known quantity of heat and measuring the temperature change. For example, combustion of exactly 1 g of benzoic acid, C_6H_5COOH, in a bomb calorimeter produces 26.38 kJ of heat. Suppose 1.000 g of benzoic acid is combusted in a calorimeter, leading to a temeperature increase of 4.857 °C. The heat capacity of the calorimeter is then $C_{cal} = 26.38\ kJ/4.857\ °C = 5.431\ kJ/°C$. Once we know C_{cal}, we can measure temperature changes produced by other reactions, and from these we can calculate the heat evolved in the reaction, q_{rxn}:

$$q_{rxn} = -C_{cal} \times \Delta T \qquad [10.24]$$

Measurements made with a bomb calorimeter are generally more precise than those made with a coffee-cup calorimeter.

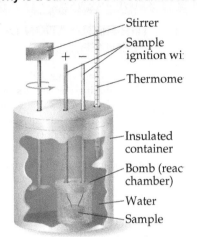

GO FIGURE

Why is a stirrer used in calorimeters?

Stirrer

Sample ignition wi:

Thermome

Insulated container

Bomb (reac chamber)

Water

Sample

▲ FIGURE 10.19 Bomb calorimeter.

SAMPLE EXERCISE 10.7 | **Measuring q_{rxn} Using a Bomb Calorimeter**

The combustion of methylhydrazine (CH_6N_2), a liquid rocket fuel, produces $N_2(g)$, $CO_2(g)$, and $H_2O(l)$:

$$2\ CH_6N_2(l) + 5\ O_2(g) \longrightarrow 2\ N_2(g) + 2\ CO_2(g) + 6\ H_2O(l)$$

When 4.00 g of methylhydrazine is combusted in a bomb calorimeter, the temperature of the calorimeter increases from 25.00 °C to 39.50 °C. In a separate experiment the heat capacity of the calorimeter is measured to be 7.794 kJ/°C. Calculate the heat of reaction for the combustion of a mole of CH_6N_2.

SOLUTION

Analyze We are given a temperature change and the total heat capacity of the calorimeter. We are also given the amount of reactant combusted. Our goal is to calculate the enthalpy change per mole for combustion of the reactant.

Plan We will first calculate the heat evolved for the combustion of the 4.00-g sample. We will then convert this heat to a molar quantity.

Solve

For combustion of the 4.00-g sample of methylhydrazine, the temperature change of the calorimeter is

$$\Delta T = (39.50\ °C - 25.00\ °C) = 14.50\ °C$$

We can use ΔT and the value for C_{cal} to calculate the heat of reaction (Equation 10.24):

$$q_{rxn} = -C_{cal} \times \Delta T = -(7.794\ kJ/°C)(14.50\ °C) = -113.0\ kJ$$

We can readily convert this value to the heat of reaction for a mole of CH_6N_2:

$$\left(\frac{-113.0\ kJ}{4.00\ g\ CH_6N_2}\right) \times \left(\frac{46.1\ g\ CH_6N_2}{1\ mol\ CH_6N_2}\right) = -1.30 \times 10^3\ kJ/mol\ CH_6N_2$$

Check The units cancel properly, and the sign of the answer is negative as it should be for an exothermic reaction. The magnitude of the answer seems reasonable.

PRACTICE EXERCISE

A 0.5865-g sample of lactic acid ($HC_3H_5O_3$) is burned in a calorimeter whose heat capacity is 4.812 kJ/°C. The temperature increases from 23.10 °C to 24.95 °C. Calculate the heat of combustion of lactic acid (a) per gram and (b) per mole.

Answers: (a) −15.2 kJ/g **(b)** −1370 kJ/mol

Because reactions in a bomb calorimeter are carried out at constant volume, the heat transferred corresponds to the change in internal energy, ΔE, rather than the change in enthalpy, ΔH (Equation 10.14). For most reactions, however, the difference between ΔE and ΔH is very small. For the reaction discussed in Sample Exercise 10.7, for example, the difference between ΔE and ΔH is about 1 kJ/mol—a difference of less than 0.1%. It is possible to correct the measured heat changes to obtain ΔH values, and these form the basis of the tables of enthalpy used in the following sections. We need not concern ourselves with how these small corrections are made.

CHEMISTRY AND LIFE

THE REGULATION OF BODY TEMPERATURE

For most of us, being asked the question "Are you running a fever?" was one of our first introductions to medical diagnosis. Indeed, a deviation in body temperature of only a few degrees indicates something amiss. In the laboratory you may have observed how difficult it is to maintain a solution at a constant temperature. Yet our bodies maintain a near-constant temperature in spite of widely varying weather, levels of physical activity, and periods of high metabolic activity (such as after a meal).

Maintaining a near-constant temperature is one of the primary physiological functions of the human body. Normal body temperature generally ranges from 35.8 °C to 37.2 °C (96.5 °F to 99 °F). This very narrow range is essential to proper muscle function and to control of the rates of the biochemical reactions in the body. You will learn more about the effects of temperature on reaction rates in Chapter 14.

The portion of the human brain stem called the *hypothalamus* regulates body temperature—in essence, the hypothalamus acts as a thermostat for the body. When body temperature rises above the normal range, the hypothalamus triggers mechanisms to lower the temperature. It likewise triggers mechanisms to increase the temperature if body temperature drops too low.

To understand how the body's heating and cooling mechanisms operate, we can view the body as a thermodynamic system. The body increases its internal energy content by ingesting foods from the surroundings. The foods, such as glucose ($C_6H_{12}O_6$), are metabolized—a process that is essentially controlled oxidation to CO_2 and H_2O:

$$C_6H_{12}O_6(s) \; + \; 6\,O_2(g) \longrightarrow 6\,CO_2(g) \; + \; 6\,H_2O(l)$$
$$\Delta H = -2803 \text{ kJ}$$

Roughly 40% of the energy produced is ultimately used to do work in the form of muscle contractions and nerve cell activities. The remainder is released as heat, part of which is used to maintain body temperature. When the body produces too much heat, as in times of heavy physical exertion, it dissipates the excess to the surroundings.

Heat is transferred from the body to its surroundings primarily by *radiation, convection,* and *evaporation.* Radiation is the direct loss of heat from the body to cooler surroundings, much as a hot stovetop radiates heat to its surroundings. Convection is heat loss by virtue of heating air that is in contact with the body. The heated air rises and is replaced with cooler air, and the process continues. Warm clothing, which usually consists of insulating layers of material with "dead air" in between, decreases convective heat loss in cold weather. Evaporative cooling occurs when perspiration is generated at the skin surface by the sweat glands (▶ FIGURE 10.20). Heat is removed from the body as the perspiration evaporates into the surroundings. Perspira-

▲ FIGURE 10.20 **Perspiration!**

tion is predominantly water, so the process is the endothermic conversion of liquid water into water vapor:

$$H_2O(l) \longrightarrow H_2O(g) \qquad \Delta H = +44.0 \text{ kJ}$$

The speed with which evaporative cooling occurs decreases as the atmospheric humidity increases, which is why we feel more sweaty and uncomfortable on hot, humid days.

When the hypothalamus senses that body temperature has risen too high, it increases heat loss from the body in two principal ways. First, it increases blood flow near the skin surface, which allows for increased radiational and convective cooling. The reddish, "flushed" appearance of a hot individual is the result of this increased subsurface blood flow. Second, the hypothalamus stimulates secretion of perspiration from the sweat glands, which increases evaporative cooling. During extreme activity, the amount of liquid secreted as perspiration can be as high as 2 to 4 liters per hour. As a result, the body's water supply must be replenished during these periods. If the body loses too much liquid through perspiration, it will no longer be able to cool itself and blood volume decreases, which can lead to either *heat exhaustion* or the more serious and potentially fatal *heat stroke,* during which the body temperature can rise to as high as 41 °C to 45 °C (106 °F to 113 °F). However, replenishing water without replenishing the electrolytes lost during perspiration can also lead to serious problems.

When body temperature drops too low, the hypothalamus decreases blood flow to the skin surface, thereby decreasing heat loss. It also triggers small involuntary contractions of the muscles; the biochemical reactions that generate the energy to do this work also generate heat for the body. When these contractions get large enough—as when the body feels a chill—a *shiver* results. If the body is unable to maintain a temperature above 35 °C (95 °F), the very dangerous condition called *hypothermia* can result.

The ability of the human body to maintain its temperature by "tuning" the amount of heat it transfers to and from its surroundings is truly remarkable. If you take courses in human anatomy and physiology, you will see many other applications of thermochemistry and thermodynamics to the ways in which the human body works.

10.6 | HESS'S LAW

It is often possible to calculate the ΔH for a reaction from the tabulated ΔH values of other reactions. Thus, it is not necessary to make calorimetric measurements for all reactions.

Because enthalpy is a state function, the enthalpy change, ΔH, associated with any chemical process depends only on the amount of matter that undergoes change and on the nature of the initial state of the reactants and the final state of the products. This means that whether a particular reaction is carried out in one step or in a series of steps, the sum of the enthalpy changes associated with the individual steps must be the same as the enthalpy change associated with the one-step process. As an example, combustion of methane gas, $CH_4(g)$, to form $CO_2(g)$ and $H_2O(l)$ can be thought of as occurring in one step, as represented on the left in ▶ FIGURE 10.21, or in two steps, as represented on the right in Figure 10.21: (1) combustion of $CH_4(g)$ to form $CO_2(g)$ and $H_2O(g)$ and (2) condensation of $H_2O(g)$ to form $H_2O(l)$. The enthalpy change for the overall process is the sum of the enthalpy changes for these two steps:

$$CH_4(g) + 2\,O_2(g) \longrightarrow CO_2(g) + 2\,H_2O(g) \qquad \Delta H = -802\ \text{kJ}$$

(Add) $\qquad\qquad 2\,H_2O(g) \longrightarrow 2\,H_2O(l) \qquad\qquad\qquad \Delta H = -\ 88\ \text{kJ}$

$$\overline{CH_4(g) + 2\,O_2(g) + 2\,H_2O(g) \longrightarrow CO_2(g) + 2\,H_2O(l) + 2\,H_2O(g)}$$

$$\Delta H = -890\ \text{kJ}$$

The net equation is

$$CH_4(g) + 2\,O_2(g) \longrightarrow CO_2(g) + 2\,H_2O(l) \qquad \Delta H = -890\ \text{kJ}$$

Hess's law states that *if a reaction is carried out in a series of steps, ΔH for the overall reaction equals the sum of the enthalpy changes for the individual steps.* The overall enthalpy change for the process is independent of the number of steps and independent of the path by which the reaction is carried out. This law is a consequence of the fact that enthalpy is a state function. We can therefore calculate ΔH for any process as long as we find a route for which ΔH is known for each step. This means that a relatively small number of experimental measurements can be used to calculate ΔH for a vast number of reactions.

Hess's law provides a useful means of calculating energy changes that are difficult to measure directly. For instance, it is impossible to measure directly the enthalpy for the combustion of carbon to form carbon monoxide. Combustion of 1 mol of carbon with 0.5 mol of O_2 produces both CO and CO_2, leaving some carbon unreacted. However, solid carbon and carbon monoxide can both be completely burned in O_2 to produce CO_2. We can therefore use the enthalpy changes of these reactions to calculate the heat of combustion of carbon.

GIVE IT SOME THOUGHT

What effect do these changes have on ΔH for a reaction:
a. reversing the reaction,
b. multiplying the coefficients of the equation for the reaction by 2?

GO FIGURE

What process corresponds to the -88 kJ enthalpy change?

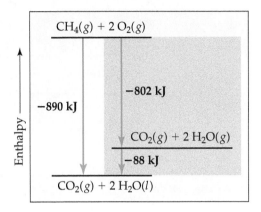

$CH_4(g) + 2\,O_2(g)$

-802 kJ

-890 kJ

$CO_2(g) + 2\,H_2O(g)$

-88 kJ

$CO_2(g) + 2\,H_2O(l)$

Enthalpy

▲ FIGURE 10.21 **Enthalpy diagram for combustion of 1 mol of methane.** The enthalpy change of the one-step reaction equals the sum of the enthalpy changes of the reaction run in two steps: -890 kJ $= -802$ kJ $+ (-88$ kJ).

SAMPLE EXERCISE 10.8 | **Using Hess's Law to Calculate ΔH**

The enthalpy of reaction for the combustion of C to CO_2 is -393.5 kJ/mol C, and the enthalpy for the combustion of CO to CO_2 is -283.0 kJ/mol CO:

(1) $\qquad C(s) + O_2(g) \longrightarrow CO_2(g) \qquad \Delta H = -393.5\ \text{kJ}$

(2) $\qquad CO(g) + \tfrac{1}{2}O_2(g) \longrightarrow CO_2(g) \qquad \Delta H = -283.0\ \text{kJ}$

Using these data, calculate the enthalpy for the combustion of C to CO:

(3) $\qquad C(s) + \tfrac{1}{2}O_2(g) \longrightarrow CO(g) \qquad \Delta H = ?$

SOLUTION

Analyze We are given two thermochemical equations, and our goal is to combine them in such a way as to obtain the third equation and its enthalpy change.

Plan We will use Hess's law. In doing so, we first note the numbers of moles of substances among the reactants and products in the target equation, (3). We then manipulate equations (1) and (2) to give the same number of moles of these substances, so that when the resulting equations are added, we obtain the target equation. At the same time, we keep track of the enthalpy changes, which we add.

Solve To use equations (1) and (2), we arrange them so that $C(s)$ is on the reactant side and $CO(g)$ is on the product side of the arrow, as in the target reaction, equation (3). Because equation (1) has $C(s)$ as a reactant, we can use that equation just as it is. We need to turn equation (2) around, however, so that $CO(g)$ is a product. Remember that when reactions are turned around, the sign of ΔH is reversed. We arrange the two equations so that they can be added to give the desired equation:

$$C(s) + O_2(g) \longrightarrow CO_2(g) \qquad\qquad \Delta H = -393.5 \text{ kJ}$$
$$\underline{CO_2(g) \longrightarrow CO(g) + \tfrac{1}{2}O_2(g) \qquad\qquad -\Delta H = 283.0 \text{ kJ}}$$
$$C(s) + \tfrac{1}{2}O_2(g) \longrightarrow CO(g) \qquad\qquad \Delta H = -110.5 \text{ kJ}$$

When we add the two equations, $CO_2(g)$ appears on both sides of the arrow and therefore cancels out. Likewise, $\tfrac{1}{2}O_2(g)$ is eliminated from each side.

PRACTICE EXERCISE

Carbon occurs in two forms, graphite and diamond. The enthalpy of the combustion of graphite is -393.5 kJ/mol, and that of diamond is -395.4 kJ/mol:

$$C(graphite) + O_2(g) \longrightarrow CO_2(g) \qquad \Delta H = -393.5 \text{ kJ}$$
$$C(diamond) + O_2(g) \longrightarrow CO_2(g) \qquad \Delta H = -395.4 \text{ kJ}$$

Calculate ΔH for the conversion of graphite to diamond:

$$C(graphite) \longrightarrow C(diamond) \qquad \Delta H = ?$$

Answer: $+1.9$ kJ

SAMPLE EXERCISE 10.9 | **Using Three Equations with Hess's Law to Calculate ΔH**

Calculate ΔH for the reaction

$$2\,C(s) + H_2(g) \longrightarrow C_2H_2(g)$$

given the following chemical equations and their respective enthalpy changes:

$$C_2H_2(g) + \tfrac{5}{2}O_2(g) \longrightarrow 2\,CO_2(g) + H_2O(l) \qquad \Delta H = -1299.6 \text{ kJ}$$
$$C(s) + O_2(g) \longrightarrow CO_2(g) \qquad\qquad\qquad \Delta H = -393.5 \text{ kJ}$$
$$H_2(g) + \tfrac{1}{2}O_2(g) \longrightarrow H_2O(l) \qquad\qquad\qquad \Delta H = -285.8 \text{ kJ}$$

SOLUTION

Analyze We are given a chemical equation and asked to calculate its ΔH using three chemical equations and their associated enthalpy changes.

Plan We will use Hess's law, summing the three equations or their reverses and multiplying each by an appropriate coefficient so that they add to give the net equation for the reaction of interest. At the same time, we keep track of the ΔH values, reversing their signs if the reactions are reversed and multiplying them by whatever coefficient is employed in the equation.

Solve Because the target equation has C_2H_2 as a product, we turn the first equation around; the sign of ΔH is therefore changed. The desired equation has $2\,C(s)$ as a reactant, so we multiply the second equation and its ΔH by 2. Because the target equation has H_2 as a reactant, we keep the third equation as it is. We then add the three equations and their enthalpy changes in accordance with Hess's law:

$$2\,CO_2(g) + H_2O(l) \longrightarrow C_2H_2(g) + \tfrac{5}{2}O_2(g) \qquad \Delta H = 1299.6 \text{ kJ}$$
$$2\,C(s) + 2\,O_2(g) \longrightarrow 2\,CO_2(g) \qquad\qquad\qquad \Delta H = -787.0 \text{ kJ}$$
$$\underline{H_2(g) + \tfrac{1}{2}O_2(g) \longrightarrow H_2O(l) \qquad\qquad\qquad \Delta H = -285.8 \text{ kJ}}$$
$$2\,C(s) + H_2(g) \longrightarrow C_2H_2(g) \qquad\qquad\qquad \Delta H = 226.8 \text{ kJ}$$

When the equations are added, there are 2 CO_2, $\frac{5}{2}O_2$, and H_2O on both sides of the arrow. These are canceled in writing the net equation.

Check The procedure must be correct because we obtained the correct net equation. In cases like this you should go back over the numerical manipulations of the ΔH values to ensure that you did not make an inadvertent error with signs.

PRACTICE EXERCISE

Calculate ΔH for the reaction

$$NO(g) + O(g) \longrightarrow NO_2(g)$$

given the following information:

$$NO(g) + O_3(g) \longrightarrow NO_2(g) + O_2(g) \qquad \Delta H = -198.9\,kJ$$
$$O_3(g) \longrightarrow \tfrac{3}{2}O_2(g) \qquad \Delta H = -142.3\,kJ$$
$$O_2(g) \longrightarrow 2\,O(g) \qquad \Delta H = 495.0\,kJ$$

Answer: -304.1 kJ

The key point of these examples is that H is a state function, so *for a particular set of reactants and products, ΔH is the same whether the reaction takes place in one step or in a series of steps.* We reinforce this point by giving one more example of an enthalpy diagram and Hess's law. Again we use combustion of methane to form CO_2 and H_2O, our reaction from Figure 10.21. This time we envision a different two-step path, with the initial formation of CO, which is then combusted to CO_2 (▶ **FIGURE 10.22**). Even though the two-step path is different from that in Figure 10.21, the overall reaction again has $\Delta H_1 = -890$ kJ. Because H is a state function, both paths *must* produce the same value of ΔH. In Figure 10.22, that means $\Delta H_1 = \Delta H_2 + \Delta H_3$. We will soon see that breaking up reactions in this way allows us to derive the enthalpy changes for reactions that are hard to carry out in the laboratory.

GO FIGURE

Suppose the overall reaction were modified to produce 2 $H_2O(g)$ rather than 2 $H_2O(l)$. Would any of the values of ΔH in the diagram stay the same?

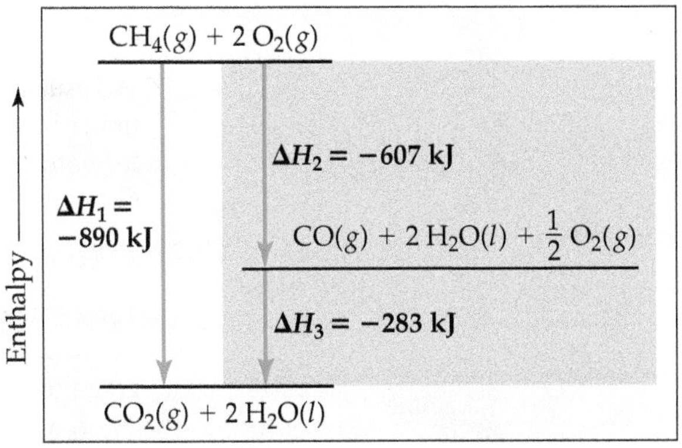

▲ **FIGURE 10.22 Enthalpy diagram illustrating Hess's law.** The net reaction is the same as in Figure 10.21, but here we imagine different reactions in our two-step version. As long as we can write a series of equations that add up to the equation we need, and as long as we know a value for ΔH for all intermediate reactions, we can calculate the overall ΔH.

10.7 | ENTHALPIES OF FORMATION

We can use the methods just discussed to calculate enthalpy changes for a great many reactions from tabulated ΔH values. For example, extensive tables exist of *enthalpies of vaporization* (ΔH for converting liquids to gases), *enthalpies of fusion* (ΔH for melting solids), *enthalpies of combustion* (ΔH for combusting a substance in oxygen), and so forth. A particularly important process used for tabulating thermochemical data is the formation of a compound from its constituent elements. The enthalpy change associated with this process is called the **enthalpy of formation** (or *heat of formation*), ΔH_f, where the subscript f indicates that the substance has been *formed* from its constituent elements.

The magnitude of any enthalpy change depends on the temperature, pressure, and state (gas, liquid, or solid crystalline form) of the reactants and products. To compare enthalpies of different reactions, we must define a set of conditions, called a *standard state*, at which most enthalpies are tabulated. The standard state of a substance is its pure form at atmospheric pressure (1 atm) and the temperature of interest, which we usually choose to be 298 K (25 °C).* The **standard enthalpy change** of a reaction is defined as the enthalpy change when all reactants and products are in their standard states. We denote a standard enthalpy change as $\Delta H°$, where the superscript ° indicates standard-state conditions.

The **standard enthalpy of formation** of a compound, $\Delta H_f°$, is the change in enthalpy for the reaction that forms one mole of the compound from its elements with all substances in their standard states:

If: elements (in standard state) $\longrightarrow$ compound (1 mol in standard state)
Then: $\Delta H = \Delta H_f°$

*The definition of the standard state for gases has been changed to 1 bar (1 atm = 1.013bar), a slightly lower pressure than 1 atm. For most purposes, this change makes very little difference in the standard enthalpy changes.

TABLE 10.3 • Standard Enthalpies of Formation, ΔH_f°, at 298 K

Substance	Formula	ΔH_f° (kJ/mol)	Substance	Formula	ΔH_f° (kJ/mol)
Acetylene	$C_2H_2(g)$	226.7	Hydrogen chloride	$HCl(g)$	−92.30
Ammonia	$NH_3(g)$	−46.19	Hydrogen fluoride	$HF(g)$	−268.60
Benzene	$C_6H_6(l)$	49.0	Hydrogen iodide	$HI(g)$	25.9
Calcium carbonate	$CaCO_3(s)$	−1207.1	Methane	$CH_4(g)$	−74.80
Calcium oxide	$CaO(s)$	−635.5	Methanol	$CH_3OH(l)$	−238.6
Carbon dioxide	$CO_2(g)$	−393.5	Propane	$C_3H_8(g)$	−103.85
Carbon monoxide	$CO(g)$	−110.5	Silver chloride	$AgCl(s)$	−127.0
Diamond	$C(s)$	1.88	Sodium bicarbonate	$NaHCO_3(s)$	−947.7
Ethane	$C_2H_6(g)$	−84.68	Sodium carbonate	$Na_2CO_3(s)$	−1130.9
Ethanol	$C_2H_5OH(l)$	−277.7	Sodium chloride	$NaCl(s)$	−410.9
Ethylene	$C_2H_4(g)$	52.30	Sucrose	$C_{12}H_{22}O_{11}(s)$	−2221
Glucose	$C_6H_{12}O_6(s)$	−1273	Water	$H_2O(l)$	−285.8
Hydrogen bromide	$HBr(g)$	−36.23	Water vapor	$H_2O(g)$	−241.8

We usually report ΔH_f° values at 298 K. If an element exists in more than one form under standard conditions, the most stable form of the element is usually used for the formation reaction. For example, the standard enthalpy of formation for ethanol, C_2H_5OH, is the enthalpy change for the reaction

$$2\,C(graphite) + 3\,H_2(g) + \tfrac{1}{2}\,O_2(g) \longrightarrow C_2H_5OH(l) \quad \Delta H_f^\circ = -277.7\text{ kJ} \qquad [10.25]$$

The elemental source of oxygen is O_2, not O or O_3, because O_2 is the stable form of oxygen at 298 K and atmospheric pressure. Similarly, the elemental source of carbon is graphite and not diamond because graphite is the more stable (lower-energy) form at 298 K and atmospheric pressure (see Practice Exercise 10.8). Likewise, the most stable form of hydrogen under standard conditions is $H_2(g)$, so this is used as the source of hydrogen in Equation 10.25.

The stoichiometry of formation reactions always indicates that one mole of the desired substance is produced, as in Equation 10.25. As a result, standard enthalpies of formation are reported in kJ/mol of the substance being formed. Some values are given in ▲ TABLE 10.3, and a more extensive table is provided in Appendix C.

By definition, *the standard enthalpy of formation of the most stable form of any element is zero* because there is no formation reaction needed when the element is already in its standard state. Thus, the values of ΔH_f° for C(graphite), $H_2(g)$, $O_2(g)$, and the standard states of other elements are zero by definition.

 GIVE IT SOME THOUGHT

Ozone, $O_3(g)$, is a form of elemental oxygen produced during electrical discharge. Is ΔH_f° for $O_3(g)$ necessarily zero?

SAMPLE EXERCISE 10.10   Equations Associated with Enthalpies of Formation

For which of these reactions at 25 °C does the enthalpy change represent a standard enthalpy of formation? For each that does not, what changes are needed to make it an equation whose ΔH is an enthalpy of formation?

(a) $2\,Na(s) + \tfrac{1}{2}\,O_2(g) \longrightarrow Na_2O(s)$

(b) $2\,K(l) + Cl_2(g) \longrightarrow 2\,KCl(s)$

(c) $C_6H_{12}O_6(s) \longrightarrow 6\,C(diamond) + 6\,H_2(g) + 3\,O_2(g)$

SOLUTION

Analyze The standard enthalpy of formation is represented by a reaction in which each reactant is an element in its standard state and the product is one mole of the compound.

Plan We need to examine each equation to determine (1) whether the reaction is one in which one mole of substance is formed from the elements, and (2) whether the reactant elements are in their standard states.

Solve In (a) 1 mol Na_2O is formed from the elements sodium and oxygen in their proper states, solid Na and O_2 gas, respectively. Therefore, the enthalpy change for reaction (a) corresponds to a standard enthalpy of formation.

In (b) potassium is given as a liquid. It must be changed to the solid form, its standard state at room temperature. Furthermore, two moles of product are formed, so the enthalpy change for the reaction as written is twice the standard enthalpy of formation of KCl(s). The equation for the formation reaction of 1 mol of KCl(s) is

$$K(s) + \tfrac{1}{2} Cl_2(g) \longrightarrow KCl(s)$$

Reaction (c) does not form a substance from its elements. Instead, a substance decomposes to its elements, so this reaction must be reversed. Next, the element carbon is given as diamond, whereas graphite is the standard state of carbon at room temperature and 1 atm pressure. The equation that correctly represents the enthalpy of formation of glucose from its elements is

$$6 \, C(graphite) + 6 \, H_2(g) + 3 \, O_2(g) \longrightarrow C_6H_{12}O_6(s)$$

PRACTICE EXERCISE

Write the equation corresponding to the standard enthalpy of formation of liquid carbon tetrachloride (CCl_4).

Answer: $C(graphite) + 2 \, Cl_2(g) \longrightarrow CCl_4(l)$

Using Enthalpies of Formation to Calculate Enthalpies of Reaction

We can use Hess's law and tabulations of ΔH_f° values, such as those in Table 10.3 and Appendix C, to calculate the standard enthalpy change for any reaction for which we know the ΔH_f° values for all reactants and products. For example, consider the combustion of propane gas, $C_3H_8(g)$, to $CO_2(g)$ and $H_2O(l)$ under standard conditions:

$$C_3H_8(g) + 5 \, O_2(g) \longrightarrow 3 \, CO_2(g) + 4 \, H_2O(l)$$

We can write this equation as the sum of three formation equations:

$C_3H_8(g) \longrightarrow 3 \, C(s) + 4 \, H_2(g)$	$\Delta H_1 = -\Delta H_f^\circ \, [C_3H_8(g)]$	[10.26]
$3 \, C(s) + 3 \, O_2(g) \longrightarrow 3 \, CO_2(g)$	$\Delta H_2 = 3\Delta H_f^\circ \, [CO_2(g)]$	[10.27]
$4 \, H_2(g) + 2 \, O_2(g) \longrightarrow 4 \, H_2O(l)$	$\Delta H_3 = 4\Delta H_f^\circ \, [H_2O(l)]$	[10.28]
$C_3H_8(g) + 5 \, O_2(g) \longrightarrow 3 \, CO_2(g) + 4 \, H_2O(l)$	$\Delta H_{rxn}^\circ = \Delta H_1 + \Delta H_2 + \Delta H_3$	[10.29]

(Note that it is sometimes useful to add subscripts to the enthalpy changes, as we have done here, to keep track of the associations between reactions and their ΔH values.)

Notice that we have used Hess's law to write the standard enthalpy change for Equation 10.29 as the sum of the enthalpy changes for Equations 10.26 through 10.28. We can use values from Table 10.3 to calculate ΔH_{rxn}°:

$$\begin{aligned}
\Delta H_{rxn}^\circ &= \Delta H_1 + \Delta H_2 + \Delta H_3 \\
&= -\Delta H_f^\circ \, [C_3H_8(g)] + 3\Delta H_f^\circ \, [CO_2(g)] + 4\Delta H_f^\circ \, [H_2O(l)] \\
&= -(-103.85 \text{ kJ}) + 3(-393.5 \text{ kJ}) + 4(-285.8 \text{ kJ}) = -2220 \text{ kJ} \quad [10.30]
\end{aligned}$$

▶ **FIGURE 10.23**, an enthalpy diagram for Equation 10.29, shows our propane combustion reaction broken down to the three reactions. Several aspects of this calculation depend on the guidelines we discussed in Section 10.4.

1. **Decomposition.** Equation 10.26 is the reverse of the formation reaction for $C_3H_8(g)$, so the enthalpy change for this decomposition reaction is the negative of the ΔH_f° value for the propane formation reaction: $-\Delta H_f^\circ \, [C_3H_8(g)]$.

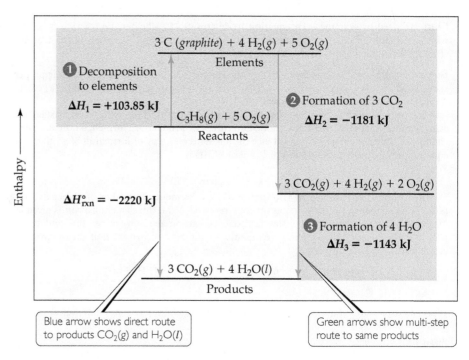

▲ FIGURE 10.23 **Enthalpy diagram for propane combustion.**

2. **Formation of CO_2.** Equation 10.27 is the formation reaction for 3 mol of $CO_2(g)$. Because enthalpy is an extensive property, the enthalpy change for this step is $3\Delta H_f^\circ [CO_2(g)]$.

3. **Formation of H_2O.** The enthalpy change for Equation 10.28, formation of 4 mol of H_2O, is $4\Delta H_f^\circ [H_2O(l)]$. The reaction specifies that $H_2O(l)$ is produced, so be careful to use the value of ΔH_f° for $H_2O(l)$ and not the value for $H_2O(g)$.

Note that in this analysis we assume that the stoichiometric coefficients in the balanced equation represent moles. For Equation 10.29, therefore, $\Delta H_{rxn}^\circ = -2220$ kJ represents the enthalpy change for the reaction of 1 mol C_3H_8 and 5 mol O_2 to form 3 mol CO_2 and 4 mol H_2O. The product of the number of moles and the enthalpy change in kJ/mol has the units kJ: (number of moles) $\times$ (ΔH_f° in kJ/mol) = kJ. We therefore report ΔH_{rxn}° in kJ.

We can break down any reaction into formation reactions as we have done here. When we do, we obtain the general result that the standard enthalpy change of a reaction is the sum of the standard enthalpies of formation of the products minus the standard enthalpies of formation of the reactants:

$$\Delta H_{rxn}^\circ = \Sigma n\Delta H_f^\circ(\text{products}) - \Sigma m\Delta H_f^\circ(\text{reactants}) \qquad [10.31]$$

The symbol Σ (sigma) means "the sum of," and n and m are the stoichiometric coefficients of the relevant chemical equation. The first term on the right in Equation 10.31 represents the formation reactions of the products, which are written in the "forward" direction in the chemical equation, that is, elements reacting to form products. This term is analogous to Equations 10.27 and 10.28. The second term on the right in Equation 10.31 represents the reverse of the formation reactions of the reactants, analogous to Equation 10.26, which is why this term is preceded by a minus sign.

SAMPLE EXERCISE 10.11 Calculating an Enthalpy of Reaction from Enthalpies of Formation

(a) Calculate the standard enthalpy change for the combustion of 1 mol of benzene, $C_6H_6(l)$, to $CO_2(g)$ and $H_2O(l)$. (b) Compare the quantity of heat produced by combustion of 1.00 g propane with that produced by 1.00 g benzene.

SOLUTION

Analyze (a) We are given a reaction [combustion of $C_6H_6(l)$ to form $CO_2(g)$ and $H_2O(l)$] and asked to calculate its standard enthalpy change, $\Delta H°$. (b) We then need to compare the quantity of heat produced by combustion of 1.00 g C_6H_6 with that produced by 1.00 g C_3H_8, whose combustion was treated previously in the text. (See Equations 10.29 and 10.30.)

Plan (a) We need to write the balanced equation for the combustion of C_6H_6. We then look up $\Delta H_f°$ values in Appendix C or in Table 10.3 and apply Equation 10.31 to calculate the enthalpy change for the reaction. (b) We use the molar mass of C_6H_6 to change the enthalpy change per mole to that per gram. We similarly use the molar mass of C_3H_8 and the enthalpy change per mole calculated in the text previously to calculate the enthalpy change per gram of that substance.

Solve

(a) We know that a combustion reaction involves $O_2(g)$ as a reactant. Thus, the balanced equation for the combustion reaction of 1 mol $C_6H_6(l)$ is

$$C_6H_6(l) + \tfrac{15}{2}O_2(g) \longrightarrow 6\,CO_2(g) + 3\,H_2O(l)$$

We can calculate $\Delta H°$ for this reaction by using Equation 10.31 and data in Table 10.3. Remember to multiply the $\Delta H_f°$ value for each substance in the reaction by that substance's stoichiometric coefficient. Recall also that $\Delta H_f° = 0$ for any element in its most stable form under standard conditions, so $\Delta H_f°[O_2(g)] = 0$:

$$\begin{aligned}\Delta H_{rxn}° &= [6\Delta H_f°(CO_2) + 3\Delta H_f°(H_2O)] - [\Delta H_f°(C_6H_6) + \tfrac{15}{2}\Delta H_f°(O_2)]\\ &= [6(-393.5\text{ kJ}) + 3(-285.8\text{ kJ})] - [(49.0\text{ kJ}) + \tfrac{15}{2}(0\text{ kJ})]\\ &= (-2361 - 857.4 - 49.0)\text{ kJ}\\ &= -3267\text{ kJ}\end{aligned}$$

(b) From the example worked in the text, $\Delta H° = -2220$ kJ for the combustion of 1 mol of propane. In part (a) of this exercise we determined that $\Delta H° = -3267$ kJ for the combustion of 1 mol benzene. To determine the heat of combustion per gram of each substance, we use the molar masses to convert moles to grams:

$C_3H_8(g)$: $(-2220\text{ kJ/mol})(1\text{ mol}/44.1\text{ g}) = -50.3\text{ kJ/g}$
$C_6H_6(l)$: $(-3267\text{ kJ/mol})(1\text{ mol}/78.1\text{ g}) = -41.8\text{ kJ/g}$

Comment Both propane and benzene are hydrocarbons. As a rule, the energy obtained from the combustion of a gram of hydrocarbon is between 40 and 50 kJ.

PRACTICE EXERCISE

Use Table 10.3 to calculate the enthalpy change for the combustion of 1 mol of ethanol:

$$C_2H_5OH(l) + 3\,O_2(g) \longrightarrow 2\,CO_2(g) + 3\,H_2O(l)$$

Answer: -1367 kJ

SAMPLE EXERCISE 10.12 Calculating an Enthalpy of Formation Using an Enthalpy of Reaction

The standard enthalpy change for the reaction $CaCO_3(s) \longrightarrow CaO(s) + CO_2(g)$ is 178.1 kJ. Use Table 10.3 to calculate the standard enthalpy of formation of $CaCO_3(s)$.

SOLUTION

Analyze Our goal is to obtain $\Delta H_f°[CaCO_3(s)]$.

Plan We begin by writing the expression for the standard enthalpy change for the reaction:

$$\Delta H_{rxn}° = \Delta H_f°[CaO(s)] + \Delta H_f°[CO_2(g)] - \Delta H_f°[CaCO_3(s)]$$

Solve Inserting the given $\Delta H_{rxn}°$ and the known $\Delta H_f°$ values from Table 10.3 or Appendix C, we have

$$178.1 = -635.5\text{ kJ} - 393.5\text{ kJ} - \Delta H_f°[CaCO_3(s)]$$

Solving for $\Delta H_f°[CaCO_3(s)]$ gives

$$\Delta H_f°[CaCO_3(s)] = -1207.1\text{ kJ/mol}$$

Check We expect the enthalpy of formation of a stable solid such as calcium carbonate to be negative, as obtained.

PRACTICE EXERCISE

Given the following standard enthalpy change, use the standard enthalpies of formation in Table 10.3 to calculate the standard enthalpy of formation of $CuO(s)$:

$$CuO(s) + H_2(g) \longrightarrow Cu(s) + H_2O(l) \qquad \Delta H° = -129.7\text{ kJ}$$

Answer: -156.1 kJ/mol

10.8 | FOODS AND FUELS

Most chemical reactions used for the production of heat are combustion reactions. The energy released when one gram of any substance is combusted is the **fuel value** of the substance. The fuel value of any food or fuel can be measured by calorimetry.

Foods

Most of the energy our bodies need comes from carbohydrates and fats. The carbohydrates known as starches are decomposed in the intestines into glucose, $C_6H_{12}O_6$. Glucose is soluble in blood, and in the human body it is known as blood sugar. It is transported by the blood to cells where it reacts with O_2 in a series of steps, eventually producing $CO_2(g)$, $H_2O(l)$, and energy:

$$C_6H_{12}O_6(s) + 6\ O_2(g) \longrightarrow 6\ CO_2(g) + 6\ H_2O(l) \qquad \Delta H° = -2803\text{ kJ}$$

Because carbohydrates break down rapidly, their energy is quickly supplied to the body. However, the body stores only a very small amount of carbohydrates. The average fuel value of carbohydrates is 17 kJ/g (4 kcal/g).*

Like carbohydrates, fats produce CO_2 and H_2O when metabolized. The reaction of tristearin, $C_{57}H_{110}O_6$, a typical fat, is

$$2\ C_{57}H_{110}O_6(s) + 163\ O_2(g) \longrightarrow 114\ CO_2(g) + 110\ H_2O(l) \quad \Delta H° = -75{,}520\text{ kJ}$$

The body uses the chemical energy from foods to maintain body temperature (see the "Chemistry and Life" box in Section 10.5), to contract muscles, and to construct and repair tissues. Any excess energy is stored as fats. Fats are well suited to serve as the body's energy reserve for at least two reasons: (1) They are insoluble in water, which facilitates storage in the body, and (2) they produce more energy per gram than either proteins or carbohydrates, which makes them efficient energy sources on a mass basis. The average fuel value of fats is 38 kJ/g (9 kcal/g).

The combustion of carbohydrates and fats in a bomb calorimeter gives the same products as when they are metabolized in the body. The metabolism of proteins produces less energy than combustion in a calorimeter because the products are different. Proteins contain nitrogen, which is released in the bomb calorimeter as N_2. In the body this nitrogen ends up mainly as urea, $(NH_2)_2CO$. Proteins are used by the body mainly as building materials for organ walls, skin, hair, muscle, and so forth. On average, the metabolism of proteins produces 17 kJ/g (4 kcal/g), the same as for carbohydrates.

Fuel values for some common foods are shown in ▼ TABLE 10.4. Labels on packaged foods show the amounts of carbohydrate, fat, and protein contained in an average serving, as well as the amount of energy supplied by a serving (◄ FIGURE 10.24).

GO FIGURE

Which value would change most if this label were for skim milk instead of whole milk: grams of fat, grams of total carbohydrate, or grams of protein?

▲ **FIGURE 10.24** **Nutrition label for whole milk.**

TABLE 10.4 • Compositions and Fuel Values of Some Common Foods

	Approximate Composition (% by mass)			Fuel Value	
	Carbohydrate	Fat	Protein	kJ/g	kcal/g (Cal/g)
Carbohydrate	100	—	—	17	4
Fat	—	100	—	38	9
Protein	—	—	100	17	4
Apples	13	0.5	0.4	2.5	0.59
Beer†	1.2	—	0.3	1.8	0.42
Bread	52	3	9	12	2.8
Cheese	4	37	28	20	4.7
Eggs	0.7	10	13	6.0	1.4
Fudge	81	11	2	18	4.4
Green beans	7.0	—	1.9	1.5	0.38
Hamburger	—	30	22	15	3.6
Milk (whole)	5.0	4.0	3.3	3.0	0.74
Peanuts	22	39	26	23	5.5

†Beer typically contains 3.5% ethanol, which has fuel value.

*Although fuel values represent the heat *released* in a combustion reaction, fuel values are reported as positive numbers.

The amount of energy our bodies require varies considerably, depending on such factors as weight, age, and muscular activity. About 100 kJ per kilogram of body mass per day is required to keep the body functioning at a minimal level. An average 70-kg (154-lb) person expends about 800 kJ/hr when doing light work, and strenuous activity often requires 2000 kJ/hr or more. When the fuel value, or caloric content, of the food we ingest exceeds the energy we expend, our body stores the surplus as fat.

GIVE IT SOME THOUGHT

Which releases the greatest amount of energy per gram when metabolized: carbohydrates, proteins, or fats?

SAMPLE EXERCISE 10.13 | Comparing Fuel Values

Celery contains carbohydrates in the form of starch and cellulose, which have essentially the same fuel values when combusted in a bomb calorimeter. When we eat celery, however, our bodies receive fuel value from the starch only. What can we conclude about the difference between starch and cellulose as foods?

SOLUTION

If cellulose does not provide fuel value, we must conclude that it is not converted in the body into CO_2 and H_2O, as starch is. A slight but critical difference in the structures of starch and cellulose explains why only starch is broken down into glucose in the body. Cellulose passes through without undergoing significant chemical change. It serves as fiber, or roughage, in the diet but provides no caloric value.

PRACTICE EXERCISE

The nutrition label on a bottle of canola oil indicates that 10 g of the oil has a fuel value of 86 kcal. A similar label on a bottle of pancake syrup indicates that 60 mL (about 60 g) has a fuel value of 200 kcal. Account for the difference.

Answer: The oil has a fuel value of 8.6 kcal/g, whereas the syrup has a fuel value of about 3.3 kcal/g. The higher fuel value for the canola oil arises because the oil is essentially pure fat, whereas the syrup is a solution of sugars (carbohydrates) in water. The oil has a higher fuel value per gram; in addition, the syrup is diluted by water.

SAMPLE EXERCISE 10.14 | Estimating the Fuel Value of a Food from Its Composition

(a) A 28-g (1-oz) serving of a popular breakfast cereal served with 120 mL of skim milk provides 8 g protein, 26 g carbohydrates, and 2 g fat. Using the average fuel values of these substances, estimate the fuel value (caloric content) of this serving. (b) A person of average weight uses about 100 Cal/mi when running or jogging. How many servings of this cereal provide the fuel value requirements to run 3 mi?

SOLUTION

(a) Analyze The fuel value of the serving will be the sum of the fuel values of the protein, carbohydrates, and fat.

Plan We are given the masses of the protein, carbohydrates, and fat contained in a serving. We can use the data in Table 10.4 to convert these masses to their fuel values, which we can sum to get the total fuel value.

Solve

$$(8 \text{ g protein})\left(\frac{17 \text{ kJ}}{1 \text{ g protein}}\right) + (26 \text{ g carbohydrate})\left(\frac{17 \text{ kJ}}{1 \text{ g carbohydrate}}\right) +$$

$$(2 \text{ g fat})\left(\frac{38 \text{ kJ}}{1 \text{ g fat}}\right) = 650 \text{ kJ (to two significant figures)}$$

This corresponds to 160 kcal:

$$(650 \text{ kJ})\left(\frac{1 \text{ kcal}}{4.18 \text{ kJ}}\right) = 160 \text{ kcal}$$

Recall that the dietary Calorie is equivalent to 1 kcal. Thus, the serving provides 160 Cal.

(b) Analyze Here we are faced with the reverse problem, calculating the quantity of food that provides a specific fuel value.

Plan The problem statement provides a conversion factor between Calories and miles. The answer to part (a) provides us with a conversion factor between servings and Calories.

Solve We can use these factors in a straightforward dimensional analysis to determine the number of servings needed, rounded to the nearest whole number:

$$\text{Servings} = (3 \text{ mi})\left(\frac{100 \text{ Cal}}{1 \text{ mi}}\right)\left(\frac{1 \text{ serving}}{160 \text{ Cal}}\right) = 2 \text{ servings}$$

PRACTICE EXERCISE

(a) Dry red beans contain 62% carbohydrate, 22% protein, and 1.5% fat. Estimate the fuel value of these beans. (b) During a very light activity, such as reading or watching television, the average adult expends about 7 kJ/min. How many minutes of such activity can be sustained by the energy provided by a serving of chicken noodle soup containing 13 g protein, 15 g carbohydrate, and 5 g fat?
Answers: (a) 15 kJ/g, (b) 100 min

Fuels

During the complete combustion of fuels, carbon is converted to CO_2 and hydrogen is converted to H_2O, both of which have large negative enthalpies of formation. Consequently, the greater the percentage of carbon and hydrogen in a fuel, the higher its fuel value. In ▼ TABLE 10.5, for example, compare the compositions and fuel values of bituminous coal and wood. The coal has a higher fuel value because of its greater carbon content.

In 2008 the United States consumed 1.05×10^{17} kJ of energy. This value corresponds to an average daily energy consumption per person of 9.4×10^5 kJ, roughly 100 times greater than the per capita food-energy needs. Although the population of the United States is only about 4.5% of the world's population, the United States accounts for nearly 20% of the world's total energy consumption. ◀ FIGURE 10.25 illustrates the sources of this energy.

Coal, petroleum, and natural gas, which are the world's major sources of energy, are known as **fossil fuels**. All have formed over millions of years from the decomposition of plants and animals and are being depleted far more rapidly than they are being formed.

Natural gas consists of gaseous hydrocarbons, compounds of hydrogen and carbon. It contains primarily methane (CH_4), with small amounts of ethane (C_2H_6), propane (C_3H_8), and butane (C_4H_{10}). We determined the fuel value of propane in Sample Exercise 10.11. **Petroleum** is a liquid composed of hundreds of compounds, most of which are hydrocarbons, with the remainder being chiefly organic compounds containing sulfur, nitrogen, or oxygen. **Coal**, which is solid, contains hydrocarbons of high molecular weight as well as compounds containing sulfur, oxygen, or nitrogen. Coal is the most abundant

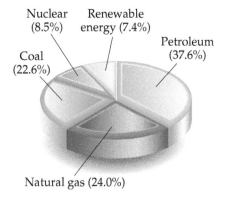

▲ **FIGURE 10.25** **Energy consumption in the United States.** In 2008 the United States consumed a total of 1.05×10^{17} kJ of energy.

TABLE 10.5 • Fuel Values and Compositions of Some Common Fuels

	Approximate Elemental Composition (mass %)			
	C	**H**	**O**	**Fuel Value (kJ/g)**
Wood (pine)	50	6	44	18
Anthracite coal (Pennsylvania)	82	1	2	31
Bituminous coal (Pennsylvania)	77	5	7	32
Charcoal	100	0	0	34
Crude oil (Texas)	85	12	0	45
Gasoline	85	15	0	48
Natural gas	70	23	0	49
Hydrogen	0	100	0	142

fossil fuel; current reserves are projected to last for well over 100 years at current consumption rates. However, the use of coal presents a number of problems.

Coal is a complex mixture of substances, and it contains components that cause air pollution. When coal is combusted, the sulfur it contains is converted mainly to sulfur dioxide, SO_2, a troublesome air pollutant. Because coal is a solid, recovery from its underground deposits is expensive and often dangerous. Furthermore, coal deposits are not always close to locations of high-energy use, so there are often substantial shipping costs.

Fossil fuels release energy in combustion reactions, which ideally produce only CO_2 and H_2O. The production of CO_2 has become a major issue that involves science and public policy because of concerns that increasing concentrations of atmospheric CO_2 are causing global climate changes. In December 2009 the United Nations held a Climate Change Conference in Copenhagen, Denmark, that attracted about 15,000 participants from nearly 200 countries, including many government leaders. Much of the discussion at this conference involved the impact of atmospheric CO_2 and ways in which alternative energy sources could be implemented.

 GIVE IT SOME THOUGHT

Much current research is directed toward using hydrogen gas, $H_2(g)$, as a fuel. What intrinsic advantage does hydrogen as a fuel have with respect to the current climate-change debate?

Other Energy Sources

Nuclear energy is the energy released in either the splitting or the fusion (combining) of atomic nuclei. Nuclear power is currently used to produce about 21% of the electric power in the United States and makes up about 8.5% of the total U.S. energy production (Figure 10.25). Nuclear energy is, in principle, free of the polluting emissions that are a major problem with fossil fuels. However, nuclear power plants produce radioactive waste products, and their use has therefore been controversial.

Fossil fuels and nuclear energy are *nonrenewable* sources of energy—they are limited resources that we are consuming at a much greater rate than they can be regenerated. Eventually these fuels will be expended, although estimates vary greatly as to when this will occur. Because nonrenewable energy sources will eventually be used up, a great deal of research is being conducted on **renewable energy sources**, sources that are essentially inexhaustible. Renewable energy sources include *solar energy* from the Sun, *wind energy* harnessed by windmills, *geothermal energy* from the heat stored inside Earth, *hydroelectric energy* from flowing rivers, and *biomass energy* from crops and biological waste matter. Currently, renewable sources provide about 7.4% of the U.S. annual energy consumption, with hydroelectric and biomass sources the major contributors.

Fulfilling our future energy needs will depend on developing technology to harness solar energy with greater efficiency. Solar energy is the world's largest energy source. On a clear day about 1 kJ of solar energy reaches each square meter of Earth's surface every second. The average solar energy falling on only 0.1% of U.S. land area is equivalent to all the energy this nation currently uses. Harnessing this energy is difficult because it is dilute (that is, distributed over a wide area) and varies with time of day and weather conditions. The effective use of solar energy will depend on the development of some means of storing and distributing it. Any practical means for doing this will almost certainly involve an endothermic chemical process that can be later reversed to release heat. One such reaction is

$$CH_4(g) + H_2O(g) + \text{heat} \longleftrightarrow CO(g) + 3\,H_2(g)$$

This reaction proceeds in the forward direction at high temperatures, which can be obtained in a solar furnace. The CO and H_2 formed in the reaction could then be stored and allowed to react later, with the heat released being put to useful work.

CHEMISTRY PUT TO WORK

The Scientific and Political Challenges of Biofuels

One of the biggest challenges facing us in the twenty-first century is production of abundant sources of energy, both food and fuels. World population more than doubled from 1960 to 2000, from about 3 billion to more than 6 billion people. It continues to grow at a rate of about 750 million per decade—at the end of 2009, the global population was about 6.8 billion people. A growing world population puts greater demands on the global food supply, especially in Asia and Africa, which together make up more than 75% of the world population.

A growing population also increases demands on the production of fuels for transportation, industry, electricity, heating, and cooling. Further, many of the most populous nations, such as China and India, have seen dramatic increases in the quality of life among their citizens. As these countries have modernized, their per capita consumption of energy—for automobiles, new industries, modern housing, and technology advances—has increased significantly. In China, for instance, per capita energy consumption roughly doubled between 1990 and 2010 (although it is still less than 20% of U.S. per capita energy consumption).

Global fuel energy consumption in 2009 was more than 5×10^{17} kJ, a staggeringly large number that is projected to grow to more than 7×10^{17} kJ by 2030. More than 80% of current energy requirements comes from combustion of nonrenewable fossil fuels, especially petroleum. Depletion has generally increased the cost of petroleum-based fuels. In addition, the exploration of new petroleum sources often involves environmentally sensitive regions, such as the Arctic National Wildlife Refuge. Thus, increasing the supplies of petroleum becomes a major political and economic issue.

Global dependence on petroleum is in large part because it provides liquid fuels, such as gasoline, that are critical to supplying transportation needs. One of the most promising—but controversial—alternatives to petroleum-based fuels is *biofuels*, liquid fuels derived from biological matter. The most common approach to producing biofuels is to transform plant sugars and other carbohydrates into combustible liquids. The energy stored in the carbohydrates produced in photosynthesis (Equation 10.32) is higher than the energy in H_2O and CO_2; thus, photosynthesis is a way to "store" solar energy in plants.

The most commonly produced biofuel is *bioethanol*, which is ethanol (C_2H_5OH) made from fermentation of plant carbohydrates. The fuel value of ethanol is about two-thirds that of gasoline and is therefore comparable to that of coal (Table 10.5). The United States and Brazil dominate bioethanol production, together supplying 85% of the world's total.

In the United States, nearly all the bioethanol currently produced is made from yellow feed corn (▶ FIGURE 10.26). Glucose ($C_6H_{12}O_6$) in the corn is converted to ethanol and CO_2:

$$C_6H_{12}O_6(s) \longrightarrow 2\,C_2H_5OH(l) + 2\,CO_2(g) \qquad \Delta H = 15.8 \text{ KJ}$$

Notice that this reaction is *anaerobic*—it does not involve $O_2(g)$—and that the enthalpy change is positive and much smaller in magnitude than for most combustion reactions. Other carbohydrates can be converted to ethanol in similar fashion.

Producing bioethanol from corn is controversial for two main reasons. First, growing and transporting corn are both energy-intensive processes, and growing it requires the use of fertilizers. It is estimated that the *energy return* on corn-based bioethanol is only 34%—that is, for each 1.00 J of energy expended to produce the corn, 1.34 J of energy is produced in the form of bioethanol. Second, the use of corn as a starting material for making bioethanol competes with its use as an important component of the food chain (the so-called "food versus fuel" debate). In particular, the diversion of corn crops to bioethanol production has led to higher prices for food, including beef (corn is used as feed for cattle). Much current research focuses on the formation of bioethanol from *cellulosic* plants, plants that contain the complex carbohydrate cellulose. Cellulose is not readily metabolized (Sample Exercise 10.13) and so does not compete with the food supply. However, the chemistry for converting cellulose to ethanol is much more complex than that for converting corn. Cellulosic bioethanol could be produced from very fast growing nonfood plants, such as prairie grasses and switchgrass, which readily renew themselves without the use of fertilizers.

As shown in the chapter-opening photograph, the Brazilian bioethanol industry uses sugarcane as its feedstock. Sugarcane grows much faster than corn and without the need for fertilizers or tending. Because of these differences, the energy return for sugarcane is much higher than the energy return for corn. It is estimated that for each 1.0 J of energy expended in growing and processing sugarcane, 8.0 J of energy is produced as bioethanol. Because the climate in Brazil is ideal for growing cane, the Brazilian government started investing in the 1970s in ways to utilize sugarcane as a major fuel source.

Other biofuels that are also becoming a major part of the world economy include *biodiesel,* a substitute for petroleum-derived diesel fuel. Biodiesel is typically produced from crops that have a high oil content, such as soybeans and canola. It can also be produced from animal fats and waste vegetable oil from the food and restaurant industry.

Biofuels are combusted in the presence of $O_2(g)$ to produce $CO_2(g)$, $H_2O(g)$, and energy in the form of heat, much as hydrocarbon fuels do. Because $CO_2(g)$ is a product, the use of biofuels is part of the international debate about carbon dioxide and climate change.

RELATED EXERCISES:
10.89, 10.90, 10.111, 10.119

▲ FIGURE 10.26 **Corn, a source of food and bioethanol.** The sugars in the kernels of feed corn can be used as food or as a feedstock for fermentation to ethanol.

Plants utilize solar energy in *photosynthesis,* the reaction in which the energy of sunlight is used to convert CO_2 and H_2O into carbohydrates and O_2. One common photosynthetic reaction produces the sugar glucose:

$$6\,CO_2(g) + 6\,H_2O(l) + \text{sunlight} \longrightarrow C_6H_{12}O_6(s) + 6\,O_2(g) \qquad [10.32]$$

In essence, photosynthesis is the reverse of combustion in that CO_2 and H_2O are consumed and O_2 and an organic molecule are produced. Photosynthesis is an important part of Earth's ecosystem because it replenishes atmospheric O_2, produces an energy-rich molecule that can be used as fuel, and consumes some atmospheric CO_2.

Perhaps the most direct way to use the Sun's energy is to convert it directly into electricity in photovoltaic devices, sometimes called *solar cells.* The efficiencies of such devices have increased dramatically during the past few years. Photovoltaics are vital to the generation of power for space vehicles, such as the International Space Station research facility currently orbiting Earth. Technological advances have led to solar panels that last longer and produce electricity with greater efficiency at steadily decreasing unit cost. Indeed, the future of solar energy is, like the Sun itself, very bright.

SAMPLE INTEGRATIVE EXERCISE | Putting Concepts Together

Trinitroglycerin, $C_3H_5N_3O_9$ (usually referred to simply as nitroglycerin), has been widely used as an explosive. Alfred Nobel used it to make dynamite in 1866. Rather surprisingly, it also is used as a medication, to relieve angina (chest pains resulting from partially blocked arteries to the heart) by dilating the blood vessels. At 1 atm pressure and 25 °C, the enthalpy of decomposition of trinitroglycerin to form nitrogen gas, carbon dioxide gas, liquid water, and oxygen gas is −1541.4 kJ/mol. **(a)** Write a balanced chemical equation for the decomposition of trinitroglycerin. **(b)** Calculate the standard heat of formation of trinitroglycerin. **(c)** A standard dose of trinitroglycerin for relief of angina is 0.60 mg. If the sample is eventually oxidized in the body (not explosively, though!) to nitrogen gas, carbon dioxide gas, and liquid water, what number of calories is released? **(d)** One common form of trinitroglycerin melts at about 3 °C. From this information and the formula for the substance, would you expect it to be a molecular or ionic compound? Explain. **(e)** Describe the various conversions of forms of energy when trinitroglycerin is used as an explosive to break rockfaces in highway construction.

SOLUTION

(a) The general form of the equation we must balance is

$$C_3H_5N_3O_9(l) \longrightarrow N_2(g) + CO_2(g) + H_2O(l) + O_2(g)$$

We go about balancing in the usual way. To obtain an even number of nitrogen atoms on the left, we multiply the formula for $C_3H_5N_3O_9$ by 2, which gives us 3 mol of N_2, 6 mol of CO_2 and 5 mol of H_2O. Everything is balanced except for oxygen. We have an odd number of oxygen atoms on the right. We can balance the oxygen by adding $\frac{1}{2}$ mol of O_2 on the right:

$$2\,C_3H_5N_3O_9(l) \longrightarrow 3\,N_2(g) + 6\,CO_2(g) + 5\,H_2O(l) + \tfrac{1}{2}\,O_2(g)$$

We multiply through by 2 to convert all coefficients to whole numbers:

$$4\,C_3H_5N_3O_9(l) \longrightarrow 6\,N_2(g) + 12\,CO_2(g) + 10\,H_2O(l) + O_2(g)$$

(At the temperature of the explosion, water is a gas. The rapid expansion of the gaseous products creates the force of an explosion.)

(b) The heat of formation is the enthalpy change in the balanced chemical equation:

$$3\,C(s) + \tfrac{3}{2}\,N_2(g) + \tfrac{5}{2}\,H_2(g) + \tfrac{9}{2}\,O_2(g) \longrightarrow C_3H_5N_3O_9(l) \qquad \Delta H_f^\circ = ?$$

We can obtain the value of ΔH_f° by using the equation for the heat of decomposition of trinitroglycerin:

$$4\,C_3H_5N_3O_9(l) \longrightarrow 6\,N_2(g) + 12\,CO_2(g) + 10\,H_2O(l) + O_2(g)$$

The enthalpy change in this reaction is $4(-1541.4\text{ kJ}) = -6165.6$ kJ. [We need to multiply by 4 because there are 4 mol of $C_3H_5N_3O_9(l)$ in the balanced equation.] This enthalpy change is given by the sum of the heats of formation of the products minus the heats of formation of the reactants, each multiplied by its coefficient in the balanced equation:

$$-6165.6\text{ kJ} = \left\{ 6\Delta H_f^\circ[N_2(g)] + 12\Delta H_f^\circ[CO_2(g)] + 10\Delta H_f^\circ[H_2O(l)] + \Delta H_f^\circ[O_2(g)] \right\}$$

$$-4\Delta H_f^\circ\,[C_3H_5N_3O_9(l)]$$

The ΔH_f° values for $N_2(g)$ and $O_2(g)$ are zero, by definition. We look up the values for $H_2O(l)$ and $CO_2(g)$ in Table 10.3 and find that

$$-6165.6 \text{ kJ} = 12(-393.5 \text{ kJ}) + 10(-285.8 \text{ kJ}) - 4\Delta H_f^\circ[C_3H_5N_3O_9(l)]$$
$$\Delta H_f^\circ[C_3H_5N_3O_9(l)] = -353.6 \text{ kJ/mol}$$

(c) We know that on oxidation 1 mol of $C_3H_5N_3O_9(l)$ yields 1541.4 kJ. We need to calculate the number of moles of $C_3H_5N_3O_9(l)$ in 0.60 mg:

$$(0.60 \times 10^{-3} \text{ g } C_3H_5N_3O_9)\left(\frac{1 \text{ mol } C_3H_5N_3O_9}{227 \text{ g } C_3H_5N_3O_9}\right)\left(\frac{1541.4 \text{ kJ}}{1 \text{ mol } C_3H_5N_3O_9}\right) = 4.1 \times 10^{-3} \text{ kJ}$$
$$= 4.1 \text{ J}$$

(d) Because trinitroglycerin melts below room temperature, we expect that it is a molecular compound. With few exceptions, ionic substances are generally hard, crystalline materials that melt at high temperatures. Also, the molecular formula suggests that it is likely to be a molecular substance. All the elements of which it is composed are nonmetals.

(e) The energy stored in trinitroglycerin is chemical potential energy. When the substance reacts explosively, it forms substances such as carbon dioxide, water, and nitrogen gas, which are of lower potential energy. In the course of the chemical transformation, energy is released in the form of heat; the gaseous reaction products are very hot. This very high heat energy is transferred to the surroundings; the gases expand against the surroundings, which may be solid materials. Work is done in moving the solid materials and imparting kinetic energy to them. For example, a chunk of rock might be impelled upward. It has been given kinetic energy by transfer of energy from the hot, expanding gases. As the rock rises, its kinetic energy is transformed into potential energy. Eventually, it again acquires kinetic energy as it falls to Earth. When it strikes Earth, its kinetic energy is converted largely to thermal energy, though some work may be done on the surroundings as well.

CHAPTER SUMMARY AND KEY TERMS

INTRODUCTION AND SECTION 10.1 **Thermodynamics** is the study of energy and its transformations. In this chapter we have focused on **thermochemistry**, the transformations of energy—especially heat—during chemical reactions.

An object can possess energy in two forms: (1) **kinetic energy** is the energy due to the motion of the object, and (2) **potential energy** is the energy that an object possesses by virtue of its position relative to other objects. An electron in motion near a proton, for example, has kinetic energy because of its motion and potential energy because of its electrostatic attraction to the proton. The SI unit of energy is the **joule** (J): $1 \text{ J} = 1 \text{ kg-m}^2/\text{s}^2$. Another common energy unit is the **calorie** (cal), which was originally defined as the quantity of energy necessary to increase the temperature of 1 g of water by $1 °C$: $1 \text{ cal} = 4.184 \text{ J}$.

When we study thermodynamic properties, we define a specific amount of matter as the **system**. Everything outside the system is the **surroundings**. When we study a chemical reaction, the system is generally the reactants and products. A closed system can exchange energy, but not matter, with the surroundings. Energy can be transferred between the system and the surroundings as work or heat. **Work** is the energy expended to move an object against a **force**. **Heat** is the energy that is transferred from a hotter object to a colder one. **Energy** is the capacity to do work or to transfer heat.

SECTION 10.2 The **internal energy** of a system is the sum of all the kinetic and potential energies of its component parts. The internal energy of a system can change because of energy transferred between the system and the surroundings. According to the **first law of thermodynamics**, the change in the internal energy of a system, ΔE, is the sum of the heat, q, transferred into or out of the system and the work, w, done on or by the system: $\Delta E = q + w$. Both q and w have a sign that indicates the direction of energy transfer. When heat is transferred

from the surroundings to the system, $q > 0$. Likewise, when the surroundings do work on the system, $w > 0$. In an **endothermic** process the system absorbs heat from the surroundings; in an **exothermic** process the system releases heat to the surroundings.

The internal energy, E, is a **state function**. The value of any state function depends only on the state or condition of the system and not on the details of how it came to be in that state. The heat, q, and the work, w, are not state functions; their values depend on the particular way by which a system changes its state.

SECTIONS 10.3 AND 10.4 When a gas is produced or consumed in a chemical reaction occurring at constant pressure, the system may perform **pressure-volume (P-V) work** against the prevailing pressure of the surroundings. For this reason, we define a new state function called **enthalpy**, H, which is related to energy: $H = E + PV$. In systems where only pressure-volume work is involved, the change in the enthalpy of a system, ΔH, equals the heat gained or lost by the system at constant pressure: $\Delta H = q_p$ (the subscript p denotes constant pressure). For an endothermic process, $\Delta H > 0$; for an exothermic process, $\Delta H < 0$.

In a chemical process, the **enthalpy of reaction** is the enthalpy of the products minus the enthalpy of the reactants: $\Delta H_{rxn} = H$ (products) $- H$ (reactants). Enthalpies of reaction follow some simple rules: (1) The enthalpy of reaction is proportional to the amount of reactant that reacts. (2) Reversing a reaction changes the sign of ΔH. (3) The enthalpy of reaction depends on the physical states of the reactants and products.

SECTION 10.5 The amount of heat transferred between the system and the surroundings is measured experimentally by **calorimetry**. A **calorimeter** measures the temperature change accompanying a process. The temperature change of a calorimeter depends on its **heat**

capacity, the amount of heat required to raise its temperature by 1 K. The heat capacity for one mole of a pure substance is called its **molar heat capacity**; for one gram of the substance, we use the term **specific heat**. Water has a very high specific heat, 4.18 J/g-K. The amount of heat, q, absorbed by a substance is the product of its specific heat (C_s), its mass, and its temperature change: $q = C_s \times m \times \Delta T$.

If a calorimetry experiment is carried out under a constant pressure, the heat transferred provides a direct measure of the enthalpy change of the reaction. Constant-volume calorimetry is carried out in a vessel of fixed volume called a **bomb calorimeter**. Bomb calorimeters are used to measure the heat evolved in combustion reactions. The heat transferred under constant-volume conditions is equal to ΔE. Corrections can be applied to ΔE values to yield enthalpies of combustion.

SECTION 10.6 Because enthalpy is a state function, ΔH depends only on the initial and final states of the system. Thus, the enthalpy change of a process is the same whether the process is carried out in one step or in a series of steps. **Hess's law** states that if a reaction is carried out in a series of steps, ΔH for the reaction will be equal to the sum of the enthalpy changes for the steps. We can therefore calculate ΔH for any process, as long as we can write the process as a series of steps for which ΔH is known.

SECTION 10.7 The **enthalpy of formation**, ΔH_f, of a substance is the enthalpy change for the reaction in which the substance is formed from its constituent elements. The **standard enthalpy change** of a reaction, $\Delta H°$, is the enthalpy change when all reactants and products are at 1 atm pressure and a specific temperature, usually 298 K (25 °C). Combining these ideas, the **standard enthalpy of formation**, $\Delta H_f°$, of a substance is the change in enthalpy for the reaction that forms one mole of the substance from its elements in their most stable form with all reactants and products at 1 atm pressure and usually 298 K. For any element in its most stable state at 298 K and 1 atm pressure, $\Delta H_f° = 0$. The standard enthalpy change for any reaction can be readily calculated from the standard enthalpies of formation of the reactants and products in the reaction:

$$\Delta H_{rxn}° = \Sigma n \Delta H_f°(\text{products}) - \Sigma m \Delta H_f°(\text{reactants})$$

SECTION 10.8 The **fuel value** of a substance is the heat released when one gram of the substance is combusted. Different types of foods have different fuel values and differing abilities to be stored in the body. The most common fuels are hydrocarbons that are found as **fossil fuels**, such as **natural gas**, **petroleum**, and **coal**. Coal is the most abundant fossil fuel, but the sulfur present in most coals causes air pollution. **Renewable energy sources** include solar energy, wind energy, biomass, and hydroelectric energy. Nuclear power does not utilize fossil fuels but does create controversial waste-disposal problems. The challenge of providing energy for the world has significant political and social implications in the areas of food supply and the environment.

KEY SKILLS

- Interconvert energy units. (Section 10.1)
- Distinguish between the system and the surroundings in thermodynamics. (Section 10.1)
- State the first law of thermodynamics. (Section 10.2)
- Understand the concept of a state function and be able to give examples. (Section 10.2)
- Express the relationships among the quantities q, w, ΔE, and ΔH. Learn their sign conventions, including how the signs of q and ΔH relate to whether a process is exothermic or endothermic. (Sections 10.2 and 10.3)
- Use thermochemical equations to relate the amount of heat energy transferred in reactions at constant pressure (ΔH) to the amount of substance involved in the reaction. (Section 10.4)
- Calculate the heat transferred in a process from temperature measurements together with heat capacities or specific heats (calorimetry). (Section 10.5)
- Use Hess's law to determine enthalpy changes for reactions. (Section 10.6)
- Use standard enthalpies of formation to calculate $\Delta H°$ for reactions. (Section 10.7)

KEY EQUATIONS

- $E_k = \frac{1}{2}mv^2$ [10.1]   Kinetic energy
- $\Delta E = E_{\text{final}} - E_{\text{initial}}$ [10.4]   The change in internal energy
- $\Delta E = q + w$ [10.5]   Relates the change in internal energy to heat and work (the first law of thermodynamics)
- $w = -P \Delta V$ [10.8]   The work done by an expanding gas at constant pressure
- $\Delta H = \Delta E + P \Delta V = q_P$ [10.10]   Enthalpy change at constant pressure
- $q = C_s \times m \times \Delta T$ [10.22]   Heat gained or lost based on specific heat, mass, and temperature change
- $\Delta H_{rxn}° = \Sigma n \Delta H_f°(\text{products}) - \Sigma m \Delta H_f°(\text{reactants})$ [10.31]   Standard enthalpy change of a reaction

EXERCISES

VISUALIZING CONCEPTS

10.1 Imagine a book that is falling from a shelf. At a particular moment during its fall, the book has a kinetic energy of 24 J and a potential energy with respect to the floor of 47 J. **(a)** How does the book's kinetic energy and its potential energy change as it continues to fall? **(b)** What is its total kinetic energy at the instant just before it strikes the floor? **(c)** If a heavier book fell from the same shelf, would it have the same kinetic energy when it strikes the floor? [Section 10.1]

10.2 The accompanying photo shows a pipevine swallowtail caterpillar climbing up a twig. **(a)** As the caterpillar climbs, its potential energy is increasing. What source of energy has been used to effect this change in potential energy? **(b)** If the caterpillar is the system, can you predict the sign of q as the caterpillar climbs? **(c)** Does the caterpillar do work in climbing the twig? Explain. **(d)** Does the amount of work done in climbing a 12-inch section of the twig depend on the speed of the caterpillar's climb? **(e)** Does the change in potential energy depend on the caterpillar's speed of climb? [Section 10.1]

10.3 Consider the accompanying energy diagram. **(a)** Does this diagram represent an increase or decrease in the internal energy of the system? **(b)** What sign is given to ΔE for this process? **(c)** If there is no work associated with the process, is it exothermic or endothermic? [Section 10.2]

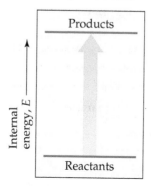

10.4 The contents of the closed box in each of the following illustrations represent a system, and the arrows show the changes to the system during some process. The lengths of the arrows represent the relative magnitudes of q and w. **(a)** Which of these processes is endothermic? **(b)** For which of these processes, if any, is $\Delta E < 0$? **(c)** For which process, if any, does the system experience a net gain in internal energy? [Section 10.2]

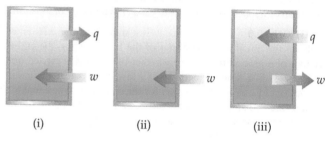

(i)　　　　　(ii)　　　　　(iii)

10.5 Imagine that you are climbing a mountain. **(a)** Is the distance you travel to the top a state function? Why or why not? **(b)** Is the change in elevation between your base camp and the peak a state function? Why or why not? [Section 10.2]

10.6 The diagram shows four states of a system, each with different internal energy, E. **(a)** Which of the states of the system has the greatest internal energy? **(b)** In terms of the ΔE values, write two expressions for the difference in internal energy between State A and State B. **(c)** Write an expression for the difference in energy between State C and State D. **(d)** Suppose there is another state of the system, State E, and that its energy relative to State A is $\Delta E = \Delta E_1 + \Delta E_4$. Where would State E be on the diagram? [Section 10.2]

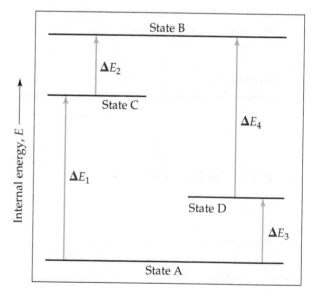

10.7 You may have noticed that when you compress the air in a bicycle pump, the body of the pump gets warmer. **(a)** Assuming the pump and the air in it comprise the system, what is the sign of w when you compress the air? **(b)** What is the sign of q for this process? **(c)** Based on your answers to parts (a) and (b), can you determine the sign of ΔE for compressing the air in the pump? If not, what would you expect for the sign of ΔE? What is your reasoning? [Section 10.2]

10.8 In the accompanying cylinder diagram a chemical process occurs at constant temperature and pressure. (a) Is the sign of w indicated by this change positive or negative? (b) If the process is endothermic, does the internal energy of the system within the cylinder increase or decrease during the change and is ΔE positive or negative? [Sections 10.2 and 10.3]

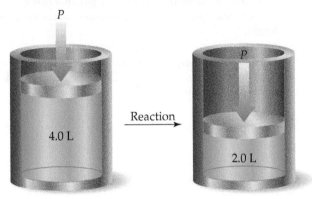

10.9 Imagine a container placed in a tub of water, as depicted in the accompanying diagram. (a) If the contents of the container are the system and heat is able to flow through the container walls, what qualitative changes will occur in the temperatures of the system and in its surroundings? What is the sign of q associated with each change? From the system's perspective, is the process exothermic or endothermic? (b) If neither the volume nor the pressure of the system changes during the process, how is the change in internal energy related to the change in enthalpy? [Sections 10.2 and 10.3]

10.10 The gas-phase reaction shown, between N_2 and O_2, was run in an apparatus designed to maintain a constant pressure. (a) Write a balanced chemical equation for the reaction depicted and predict whether w is positive, negative, or zero. (b) Using data from Appendix C, determine ΔH for the formation of one mole of the product. Why is this enthalpy change called the enthalpy of formation of the involved product? [Sections 10.3 and 10.7]

10.11 Consider the two diagrams that follow. (a) Based on (i), write an equation showing how ΔH_A is related to ΔH_B and ΔH_C. How do both diagram (i) and your equation relate to the fact that enthalpy is a state function? (b) Based on (ii), write an equation relating ΔH_Z to the other enthalpy changes in the diagram. (c) How do these diagrams relate to Hess's law? [Section 10.6]

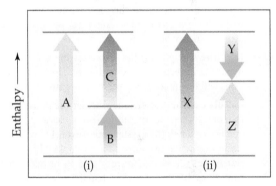

10.12 Consider the conversion of compound A into compound B: A $\longrightarrow$ B. For both compounds A and B, $\Delta H_f^\circ > 0$. (a) Sketch an enthalpy diagram for the reaction that is analogous to Figure 10.23. (b) Suppose the overall reaction is exothermic. What can you conclude? [Section 10.7]

THE NATURE OF ENERGY (section 10.1)

10.13 In what two ways can an object possess energy? How do these two ways differ from one another?

10.14 Suppose you toss a tennis ball upward. (a) Does the kinetic energy of the ball increase or decrease as it moves higher? (b) What happens to the potential energy of the ball as it moves higher? (c) If the same amount of energy were imparted to a ball the same size as a tennis ball but of twice the mass, how high would it go in comparison to the tennis ball? Explain your answers.

10.15 (a) Calculate the kinetic energy in joules of a 1200-kg automobile moving at 18 m/s. (b) Convert this energy to calories. (c) What happens to this energy when the automobile brakes to a stop?

10.16 (a) A baseball weighs 5.13 oz. What is the kinetic energy in joules of this baseball when it is thrown by a major-league pitcher at 95.0 mph? (b) By what factor will the kinetic energy change if the speed of the baseball is decreased to 55.0 mph? (c) What happens to the kinetic energy when the baseball is caught by the catcher? (d) What careful experimental measurement could (in principle) be made to confirm your answer to (c)?

10.17 The use of the British thermal unit (Btu) is common in much engineering work. A Btu is the amount of heat required to raise the temperature of 1 lb of water by 1 °F. Calculate the number of joules in a Btu.

10.18 A watt is a measure of power (the rate of energy change) equal to 1 J/s. (a) Calculate the number of joules in a kilowatt-hour. (b) An adult person radiates heat to the surroundings at about the same rate as a 100-watt electric incandescent lightbulb. What is the total amount of energy in kcal radiated to the surroundings by an adult in 24 hours?

10.19 (a) What is meant by the term *system* in thermodynamics? (b) What is a *closed system*? (c) What do we call the part of the universe that is not part of the system?

10.20 In a thermodynamic study a scientist focuses on the properties of a solution in an apparatus as illustrated. A solution is continuously flowing into the apparatus at the top and out at the bottom, such that the amount of solution in the apparatus is constant with time. (a) Is the solution in the apparatus a closed system, open system, or isolated system? Explain your choice. (b) If it is not a closed system, what could be done to make it a closed system?

10.21 (a) What is work? (b) How do we determine the amount of work done, given the force associated with the work?

10.22 (a) What is heat? (b) Under what conditions is heat transferred from one object to another?

10.23 Identify the force present and explain whether work is being performed in the following cases: (a) You lift a pencil off the top of a desk. (b) A spring is compressed to half its normal length.

10.24 Identify the force present and explain whether work is done when (a) a positively charged particle moves in a circle at a fixed distance from a negatively charged particle; (b) an iron nail is pulled off a magnet.

THE FIRST LAW OF THERMODYNAMICS (section 10.2)

10.25 (a) State the first law of thermodynamics. (b) What is meant by the *internal energy* of a system? (c) By what means can the internal energy of a closed system increase?

10.26 (a) Write an equation that expresses the first law of thermodynamics in terms of heat and work. (b) Under what conditions will the quantities q and w be negative numbers?

10.27 Calculate ΔE and determine whether the process is endothermic or exothermic for the following cases: (a) $q = 0.763$ kJ and $w = -840$ J; (b) a system releases 66.1 kJ of heat to its surroundings while the surroundings do 44.0 kJ of work on the system; (c) the system absorbs 7.25 kJ of heat from the surroundings while its volume remains constant (assume that only P-V work can be done).

10.28 For the following processes, calculate the change in internal energy of the system and determine whether the process is endothermic or exothermic: (a) A balloon is cooled by removing 0.655 kJ of heat. It shrinks on cooling, and the atmosphere does 382 J of work on the balloon. (b) A 100.0-g bar of gold is heated from 25 °C to 50 °C during which it absorbs 322 J of heat. Assume the volume of the gold bar remains constant. (c) The surroundings do 1.44 kJ of work compressing gas in a perfectly insulated cylinder.

10.29 A gas is confined to a cylinder fitted with a piston and an electrical heater, as shown here:

Suppose that current is supplied to the heater so that 100 J of energy is added. Consider two different situations. In case (1) the piston is allowed to move as the energy is added. In case (2) the piston is fixed so that it cannot move. (a) In which case does the gas have the higher temperature after addition of the electrical energy? Explain. (b) What can you say about the values of q and w in each case? (c) What can you say about the relative values of ΔE for the system (the gas in the cylinder) in the two cases?

10.30 Consider a system consisting of two oppositely charged spheres hanging by strings and separated by a distance r_1, as shown in the accompanying illustration. Suppose they are separated to a larger distance r_2, by moving them apart along a track. (a) What change, if any, has occurred in the potential energy of the system? (b) What effect, if any, does this process have on the value of ΔE? (c) What can you say about q and w for this process?

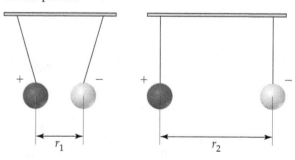

10.31 (a) What is meant by the term *state function*? (b) Give an example of a quantity that is a state function and one that is not. (c) Is the volume of the system a state function? Why or why not?

10.32 Indicate which of the following is independent of the path by which a change occurs: (a) the change in potential energy when a book is transferred from table to shelf, (b) the heat evolved when a cube of sugar is oxidized to $CO_2(g)$ and $H_2O(g)$, (c) the work accomplished in burning a gallon of gasoline.

ENTHALPY (sections 10.3 and 10.4)

10.33 **(a)** Why is the change in enthalpy usually easier to measure than the change in internal energy? **(b)** H is a state function, but q is not a state function. Explain. **(c)** For a given process at constant pressure, ΔH is positive. Is the process endothermic or exothermic?

10.34 **(a)** Under what condition will the enthalpy change of a process equal the amount of heat transferred into or out of the system? **(b)** During a constant-pressure process, the system releases heat to the surroundings. Does the enthalpy of the system increase or decrease during the process? **(c)** In a constant-pressure process, $\Delta H = 0$. What can you conclude about ΔE, q, and w?

10.35 You are given ΔH for a process that occurs at constant pressure. What additional information do you need to determine ΔE for the process?

10.36 Suppose that the gas-phase reaction $2\,NO(g) + O_2(g) \longrightarrow 2\,NO_2(g)$ were carried out in a constant-volume container at constant temperature. Would the measured heat change represent ΔH or ΔE? If there is a difference, which quantity is larger for this reaction? Explain.

10.37 A gas is confined to a cylinder under constant atmospheric pressure, as illustrated in Figure 10.4. When the gas undergoes a particular chemical reaction, it absorbs 824 J of heat from its surroundings and has 0.65 kJ of P-V work done on it by its surroundings. What are the values of ΔH and ΔE for this process?

10.38 A gas is confined to a cylinder under constant atmospheric pressure, as illustrated in Figure 10.4. When 0.49 kJ of heat is added to the gas, it expands and does 214 J of work on the surroundings. What are the values of ΔH and ΔE for this process?

10.39 The complete combustion of ethanol, $C_2H_5OH(l)$, to form $H_2O(g)$ and $CO_2(g)$ at constant pressure releases 1235 kJ of heat per mole of C_2H_5OH. **(a)** Write a balanced thermochemical equation for this reaction. **(b)** Draw an enthalpy diagram for the reaction.

10.40 The decomposition of *slaked lime*, $Ca(OH)_2(s)$, into *lime*, $CaO(s)$, and $H_2O(g)$ at constant pressure requires the addition of 109 kJ of heat per mole of $Ca(OH)_2$. **(a)** Write a balanced thermochemical equation for the reaction. **(b)** Draw an enthalpy diagram for the reaction.

10.41 Ozone, $O_3(g)$, is a form of elemental oxygen that is important in the absorption of ultraviolet radiation in the stratosphere. It decomposes to $O_2(g)$ at room temperature and pressure according to the following reaction:

$$2\,O_3(g) \longrightarrow 3\,O_2(g) \qquad \Delta H = -284.6\ kJ$$

(a) What is the enthalpy change for this reaction per mole of $O_3(g)$? **(b)** Which has the higher enthalpy under these conditions, $2\,O_3(g)$ or $3\,O_2(g)$?

10.42 Without referring to tables, predict which of the following has the higher enthalpy in each case: **(a)** 1 mol $CO_2(s)$ or 1 mol $CO_2(g)$ at the same temperature, **(b)** 2 mol of hydrogen atoms or 1 mol of H_2, **(c)** 1 mol $H_2(g)$ and 0.5 mol $O_2(g)$ at 25 °C or 1 mol $H_2O(g)$ at 25 °C, **(d)** 1 mol $N_2(g)$ at 100 °C or 1 mol $N_2(g)$ at 300 °C.

10.43 Consider the following reaction:

$$2\,Mg(s) + O_2(g) \longrightarrow 2\,MgO(s) \qquad \Delta H = -1204\ kJ$$

(a) Is this reaction exothermic or endothermic? **(b)** Calculate the amount of heat transferred when 3.55 g of $Mg(s)$ reacts at constant pressure. **(c)** How many grams of MgO are produced during an enthalpy change of −234 kJ? **(d)** How many kilojoules of heat are absorbed when 40.3 g of $MgO(s)$ is decomposed into $Mg(s)$ and $O_2(g)$ at constant pressure?

10.44 Consider the following reaction:

$$2\,CH_3OH(g) \longrightarrow 2\,CH_4(g) + O_2(g) \qquad \Delta H = +252.8\ kJ$$

(a) Is this reaction exothermic or endothermic? **(b)** Calculate the amount of heat transferred when 24.0 g of $CH_3OH(g)$ is decomposed by this reaction at constant pressure. **(c)** For a given sample of CH_3OH, the enthalpy change during the reaction is 82.1 kJ. How many grams of methane gas are produced? **(d)** How many kilojoules of heat are released when 38.5 g of $CH_4(g)$ reacts completely with $O_2(g)$ to form $CH_3OH(g)$ at constant pressure?

10.45 When solutions containing silver ions and chloride ions are mixed, silver chloride precipitates:

$$Ag^+(aq) + Cl^-(aq) \longrightarrow AgCl(s) \qquad \Delta H = -65.5\ kJ$$

(a) Calculate ΔH for production of 0.450 mol of AgCl by this reaction. **(b)** Calculate ΔH for the production of 9.00 g of AgCl. **(c)** Calculate ΔH when 9.25×10^{-4} mol of AgCl dissolves in water.

10.46 At one time, a common means of forming small quantities of oxygen gas in the laboratory was to heat $KClO_3$:

$$2\,KClO_3(s) \longrightarrow 2\,KCl(s) + 3\,O_2(g) \qquad \Delta H = -89.4\ kJ$$

For this reaction, calculate ΔH for the formation of **(a)** 1.36 mol of O_2 and **(b)** 10.4 g of KCl. **(c)** The decomposition of $KClO_3$ proceeds spontaneously when it is heated. Do you think that the reverse reaction, the formation of $KClO_3$ from KCl and O_2, is likely to be feasible under ordinary conditions? Explain your answer.

10.47 Consider the combustion of liquid methanol, $CH_3OH(l)$:

$$CH_3OH(l) + \tfrac{3}{2}O_2(g) \longrightarrow CO_2(g) + 2\,H_2O(l)$$
$$\Delta H = -726.5\ kJ$$

(a) What is the enthalpy change for the reverse reaction? **(b)** Balance the forward reaction with whole-number coefficients. What is ΔH for the reaction represented by this equation? **(c)** Which is more likely to be thermodynamically favored, the forward reaction or the reverse reaction? **(d)** If the reaction were written to produce $H_2O(g)$ instead of $H_2O(l)$, would you expect the magnitude of ΔH to increase, decrease, or stay the same? Explain.

10.48 Consider the decomposition of liquid benzene, $C_6H_6(l)$, to gaseous acetylene, $C_2H_2(g)$:

$$C_6H_6(l) \longrightarrow 3\,C_2H_2(g) \qquad \Delta H = +630\ kJ$$

(a) What is the enthalpy change for the reverse reaction? **(b)** What is ΔH for the formation of 1 mol of acetylene? **(c)** Which is more likely to be thermodynamically favored, the forward reaction or the reverse reaction? **(d)** If $C_6H_6(g)$ were consumed instead of $C_6H_6(l)$, would you expect the magnitude of ΔH to increase, decrease, or stay the same? Explain.

CALORIMETRY (section 10.5)

10.49 (a) What are the units of molar heat capacity? (b) What are the units of specific heat? (c) If you know the specific heat of copper, what additional information do you need to calculate the heat capacity of a particular piece of copper pipe?

10.50 Two solid objects, A and B, are placed in boiling water and allowed to come to temperature there. Each is then lifted out and placed in separate beakers containing 1000 g water at 10.0 °C. Object A increases the water temperature by 3.50 °C; B increases the water temperature by 2.60 °C. (a) Which object has the larger heat capacity? (b) What can you say about the specific heats of A and B?

10.51 (a) What is the specific heat of liquid water? (b) What is the molar heat capacity of liquid water? (c) What is the heat capacity of 185 g of liquid water? (d) How many kJ of heat are needed to raise the temperature of 10.00 kg of liquid water from 24.6 °C to 46.2 °C?

10.52 (a) Which substance in Table 10.2 requires the smallest amount of energy to increase the temperature of 50.0 g of that substance by 10 K? (b) Calculate the energy needed for this temperature change.

10.53 The specific heat of *octane*, $C_8H_{18}(l)$, is 2.22 J/g-K. (a) How many J of heat are needed to raise the temperature of 80.0 g of octane from 10.0 °C to 25.0 °C? (b) Which will require more heat, increasing the temperature of 1 mol of $C_8H_{18}(l)$ by a certain amount or increasing the temperature of 1 mol of $H_2O(l)$ by the same amount?

10.54 Consider the data about gold metal in Exercise 10.28(b). (a) Based on the data, calculate the specific heat of Au(s). (b) Suppose that the same amount of heat is added to two 10.0-g blocks of metal, both initially at the same temperature. One block is gold metal and one is iron metal. Which block will have the greater rise in temperature after the addition of the heat? (c) What is the molar heat capacity of Au(s)?

10.55 When a 6.50-g sample of solid sodium hydroxide dissolves in 100.0 g of water in a coffee-cup calorimeter (Figure 10.18), the temperature rises from 21.6 °C to 37.8 °C. Calculate ΔH (in kJ/mol NaOH) for the solution process

$$NaOH(s) \longrightarrow Na^+(aq) + OH^-(aq)$$

Assume that the specific heat of the solution is the same as that of pure water.

10.56 (a) When a 4.25-g sample of solid ammonium nitrate dissolves in 60.0 g of water in a coffee-cup calorimeter (Figure 10.18), the temperature drops from 22.0 °C to 16.9 °C. Calculate ΔH (in kJ/mol NH_4NO_3) for the solution process

$$NH_4NO_3(s) \longrightarrow NH_4^+(aq) + NO_3^-(aq)$$

Assume that the specific heat of the solution is the same as that of pure water. (b) Is this process endothermic or exothermic?

10.57 A 2.200-g sample of quinone ($C_6H_4O_2$) is burned in a bomb calorimeter whose total heat capacity is 7.854 kJ/°C. The temperature of the calorimeter increases from 23.44 °C to 30.57 °C. What is the heat of combustion per gram of quinone? Per mole of quinone?

10.58 A 1.800-g sample of phenol (C_6H_5OH) was burned in a bomb calorimeter whose total heat capacity is 11.66 kJ/°C. The temperature of the calorimeter plus contents increased from 21.36 °C to 26.37 °C. (a) Write a balanced chemical equation for the bomb calorimeter reaction. (b) What is the heat of combustion per gram of phenol? Per mole of phenol?

10.59 Under constant-volume conditions, the heat of combustion of glucose ($C_6H_{12}O_6$) is 15.57 kJ/g. A 3.500-g sample of glucose is burned in a bomb calorimeter. The temperature of the calorimeter increased from 20.94 °C to 24.72 °C. (a) What is the total heat capacity of the calorimeter? (b) If the size of the glucose sample had been exactly twice as large, what would the temperature change of the calorimeter have been?

10.60 Under constant-volume conditions, the heat of combustion of benzoic acid (C_6H_5COOH) is 26.38 kJ/g. A 2.760-g sample of benzoic acid is burned in a bomb calorimeter. The temperature of the calorimeter increases from 21.60 °C to 29.93 °C. (a) What is the total heat capacity of the calorimeter? (b) A 1.440-g sample of a new organic substance is combusted in the same calorimeter. The temperature of the calorimeter increases from 22.14 °C to 27.09 °C. What is the heat of combustion per gram of the new substance? (c) Suppose that in changing samples, a portion of the water in the calorimeter were lost. In what way, if any, would this change the heat capacity of the calorimeter?

HESS'S LAW (section 10.6)

10.61 What is the connection between Hess's law and the fact that H is a state function?

10.62 Consider the following hypothetical reactions:

$$A \longrightarrow B \qquad \Delta H = +30 \text{ kJ}$$
$$B \longrightarrow C \qquad \Delta H = +60 \text{ kJ}$$

(a) Use Hess's law to calculate the enthalpy change for the reaction A $\longrightarrow$ C. (b) Construct an enthalpy diagram for substances A, B, and C, and show how Hess's law applies.

10.63 Calculate the enthalpy change for the reaction

$$P_4O_6(s) + 2 O_2(g) \longrightarrow P_4O_{10}(s)$$

given the following enthalpies of reaction:

$$P_4(s) + 3 O_2(g) \longrightarrow P_4O_6(s) \qquad \Delta H = -1640.1 \text{ kJ}$$
$$P_4(s) + 5 O_2(g) \longrightarrow P_4O_{10}(s) \qquad \Delta H = -2940.1 \text{ kJ}$$

10.64 From the enthalpies of reaction

$$2 C(s) + O_2(g) \longrightarrow 2 CO(g) \qquad \Delta H = -221.0 \text{ kJ}$$
$$2 C(s) + O_2(g) + 4 H_2(g) \longrightarrow 2 CH_3OH(g) \qquad \Delta H = -402.4 \text{ kJ}$$

calculate ΔH for the reaction

$$CO(g) + 2 H_2(g) \longrightarrow CH_3OH(g)$$

10.65 From the enthalpies of reaction

$$H_2(g) + F_2(g) \longrightarrow 2 HF(g) \qquad \Delta H = -537 \text{ kJ}$$
$$C(s) + 2 F_2(g) \longrightarrow CF_4(g) \qquad \Delta H = -680 \text{ kJ}$$
$$2 C(s) + 2 H_2(g) \longrightarrow C_2H_4(g) \qquad \Delta H = +52.3 \text{ kJ}$$

calculate ΔH for the reaction of ethylene with F_2:

$$C_2H_4(g) + 6 F_2(g) \longrightarrow 2 CF_4(g) + 4 HF(g)$$

10.66 Given the data

$$N_2(g) + O_2(g) \longrightarrow 2\,NO(g) \qquad \Delta H = +180.7\ kJ$$
$$2\,NO(g) + O_2(g) \longrightarrow 2\,NO_2(g) \qquad \Delta H = -113.1\ kJ$$
$$2\,N_2O(g) \longrightarrow 2\,N_2(g) + O_2(g) \qquad \Delta H = -163.2\ kJ$$

use Hess's law to calculate ΔH for the reaction

$$N_2O(g) + NO_2(g) \longrightarrow 3\,NO(g)$$

ENTHALPIES OF FORMATION (section 10.7)

10.67 (a) What is meant by the term *standard conditions* with reference to enthalpy changes? (b) What is meant by the term *enthalpy of formation*? (c) What is meant by the term *standard enthalpy of formation*?

10.68 (a) Why are tables of standard enthalpies of formation so useful? (b) What is the value of the standard enthalpy of formation of an element in its most stable form? (c) Write the chemical equation for the reaction whose enthalpy change is the standard enthalpy of formation of sucrose (table sugar), $C_{12}H_{22}O_{11}(s)$, $\Delta H_f^\circ[C_{12}H_{22}O_{11}]$.

10.69 For each of the following compounds, write a balanced thermochemical equation depicting the formation of one mole of the compound from its elements in their standard states and use Appendix C to obtain the value of ΔH_f°: (a) $NO_2(g)$, (b) $SO_3(g)$, (c) $NaBr(s)$, (d) $Pb(NO_3)_2(s)$.

10.70 Write balanced equations that describe the formation of the following compounds from elements in their standard states, and use Appendix C to obtain the values of their standard enthalpies of formation: (a) $H_2O_2(g)$, (b) $CaCO_3(s)$, (c) $POCl_3(l)$, (d) $C_2H_5OH(l)$.

10.71 The following is known as the thermite reaction [Figure 10.8(b)]:

$$2\,Al(s) + Fe_2O_3(s) \longrightarrow Al_2O_3(s) + 2\,Fe(s)$$

This highly exothermic reaction is used for welding massive units, such as propellers for large ships. Using standard enthalpies of formation in Appendix C, calculate ΔH° for this reaction.

10.72 Many portable gas heaters and grills use propane, $C_3H_8(g)$, as a fuel. Using standard enthalpies of formation, calculate the quantity of heat produced when 10.0 g of propane is completely combusted in air under standard conditions.

10.73 Using values from Appendix C, calculate the standard enthalpy change for each of the following reactions:

(a) $2\,SO_2(g) + O_2(g) \longrightarrow 2\,SO_3(g)$
(b) $Mg(OH)_2(s) \longrightarrow MgO(s) + H_2O(l)$
(c) $N_2O_4(g) + 4\,H_2(g) \longrightarrow N_2(g) + 4\,H_2O(g)$
(d) $SiCl_4(l) + 2\,H_2O(l) \longrightarrow SiO_2(s) + 4\,HCl(g)$

10.74 Using values from Appendix C, calculate the value of ΔH° for each of the following reactions:

(a) $CaO(s) + 2\,HCl(g) \longrightarrow CaCl_2(s) + H_2O(g)$
(b) $4\,FeO(s) + O_2(g) \longrightarrow 2\,Fe_2O_3(s)$
(c) $2\,CuO(s) + NO(g) \longrightarrow Cu_2O(s) + NO_2(g)$
(d) $4\,NH_3(g) + O_2(g) \longrightarrow 2\,N_2H_4(g) + 2\,H_2O(l)$

10.75 Complete combustion of 1 mol of acetone (C_3H_6O) liberates 1790 kJ:

$$C_3H_6O(l) + 4\,O_2(g) \longrightarrow 3\,CO_2(g) + 3\,H_2O(l)$$
$$\Delta H^\circ = -1790\ kJ$$

Using this information together with data from Appendix C, calculate the enthalpy of formation of acetone.

10.76 Calcium carbide (CaC_2) reacts with water to form acetylene (C_2H_2) and $Ca(OH)_2$. From the following enthalpy of reaction data and data in Appendix C, calculate ΔH_f° for $CaC_2(s)$:

$$CaC_2(s) + 2\,H_2O(l) \longrightarrow Ca(OH)_2(s) + C_2H_2(g)$$
$$\Delta H^\circ = -127.2\ kJ$$

10.77 Gasoline is composed primarily of hydrocarbons, including many with eight carbon atoms, called *octanes*. One of the cleanest-burning octanes is a compound called 2,3,4-trimethylpentane, which has the following structural formula:

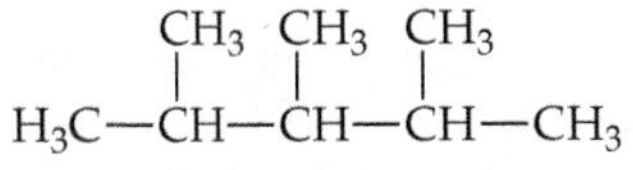

$$\begin{array}{c} CH_3 \quad CH_3 \quad CH_3 \\ | \qquad | \qquad | \\ H_3C-CH-CH-CH-CH_3 \end{array}$$

The complete combustion of one mole of this compound to $CO_2(g)$ and $H_2O(g)$ leads to $\Delta H^\circ = -5064.9$ kJ/mol. (a) Write a balanced equation for the combustion of 1 mol of $C_8H_{18}(l)$. (b) Write a balanced equation for the formation of $C_8H_{18}(l)$ from its elements. (c) By using the information in this problem and data in Table 10.3, calculate ΔH_f° for 2,3,4-trimethylpentane.

10.78 Diethyl ether, $C_4H_{10}O(l)$, a flammable compound that has long been used as a surgical anesthetic, has the structure

$$CH_3-CH_2-O-CH_2-CH_3$$

The complete combustion of 1 mol of $C_4H_{10}O(l)$ to $CO_2(g)$ and $H_2O(l)$ yields $\Delta H^\circ = -2723.7$ kJ. (a) Write a balanced equation for the combustion of 1 mol of $C_4H_{10}O(l)$. (b) Write a balanced equation for the formation of $C_4H_{10}O(l)$ from its elements. (c) By using the information in this problem and data in Table 10.3, calculate ΔH_f° for diethyl ether.

10.79 Ethanol (C_2H_5OH) is currently blended with gasoline as an automobile fuel. (a) Write a balanced equation for the combustion of liquid ethanol in air. (b) Calculate the standard enthalpy change for the reaction, assuming $H_2O(g)$ as a product. (c) Calculate the heat produced per liter of ethanol by combustion of ethanol under constant pressure. Ethanol has a density of 0.789 g/mL. (d) Calculate the mass of CO_2 produced per kJ of heat emitted.

10.80 Methanol (CH_3OH) is used as a fuel in race cars. (a) Write a balanced equation for the combustion of liquid methanol in air. (b) Calculate the standard enthalpy change for the reaction, assuming $H_2O(g)$ as a product. (c) Calculate the heat produced by combustion per liter of methanol. Methanol has a density of 0.791 g/mL. (d) Calculate the mass of CO_2 produced per kJ of heat emitted.

FOODS AND FUELS (section 10.8)

10.81 (a) What is meant by the term *fuel value*? (b) Which is a greater source of energy as food, 5 g of fat or 9 g of carbohydrate? (c) The metabolism of glucose produces $CO_2(g)$ and $H_2O(l)$. How does the human body expel these reaction products?

10.82 (a) Why are fats well suited for energy storage in the human body? (b) A particular chip snack food is composed of 12% protein, 14% fat, and the rest carbohydrate. What percentage of the calorie content of this food is fat? (c) How many grams of protein provide the same fuel value as 25 g of fat?

10.83 (a) A serving of a particular ready-to-serve chicken noodle soup contains 2.5 g fat, 14 g carbohydrate, and 7 g protein. Estimate the number of Calories in a serving. (b) According to its nutrition label, the same soup also contains 690 mg of sodium. Do you think the sodium contributes to the caloric content of the soup?

10.84 A pound of plain M&M® candies contains 96 g fat, 320 g carbohydrate, and 21 g protein. What is the fuel value in kJ in a 42-g (about 1.5 oz) serving? How many Calories does it provide?

10.85 The heat of combustion of fructose, $C_6H_{12}O_6$, is −2812 kJ/mol. If a fresh golden delicious apple weighing 4.23 oz (120 g) contains 16.0 g of fructose, what caloric content does the fructose contribute to the apple?

10.86 The heat of combustion of ethanol, $C_2H_5OH(l)$, is −1367 kJ/mol. A batch of Sauvignon Blanc wine contains 10.6% ethanol by mass. Assuming the density of the wine to be 1.0 g/mL, what is the caloric content due to the alcohol (ethanol) in a 6-oz glass of wine (177 mL)?

10.87 The standard enthalpies of formation of gaseous propyne (C_3H_4), propylene (C_3H_6), and propane (C_3H_8) are +185.4, +20.4, and −103.8 kJ/mol, respectively. (a) Calculate the heat evolved per mole on combustion of each substance to yield $CO_2(g)$ and $H_2O(g)$. (b) Calculate the heat evolved on combustion of 1 kg of each substance. (c) Which is the most efficient fuel in terms of heat evolved per unit mass?

10.88 It is interesting to compare the "fuel value" of a hydrocarbon in a world where fluorine rather than oxygen is the combustion agent. The enthalpy of formation of $CF_4(g)$ is −679.9 kJ/mol. Which of the following two reactions is the more exothermic?

$$CH_4(g) + 2 O_2(g) \longrightarrow CO_2(g) + 2 H_2O(g)$$
$$CH_4(g) + 4 F_2(g) \longrightarrow CF_4(g) + 4 HF(g)$$

[10.89] At the end of 2009, global population was about 6.8 billion people. What mass of glucose in kg would be needed to provide 1500 Cal/person/day of nourishment to the global population for one year? Assume that glucose is metabolized entirely to $CO_2(g)$ and $H_2O(l)$ according to the following thermochemical equation:

$$C_6H_{12}O_6(s) + 6 O_2(g) \longrightarrow 6 CO_2(g) + 6 H_2O(l)$$
$$\Delta H° = -2803 \text{ kJ}$$

[10.90] The automobile fuel called E85 consists of 85% ethanol and 15% gasoline. E85 can be used in so-called "flex-fuel" vehicles (FFVs), which can use gasoline, ethanol, or a mix as fuels. Assume that gasoline consists of a mixture of octanes (different isomers of C_8H_{18}), that the average heat of combustion of $C_8H_{18}(l)$ is 5400 kJ/mol, and that gasoline has an average density of 0.70 g/mL. The density of ethanol is 0.79 g/mL. (a) By using the information given as well as data in Appendix C, compare the energy produced by combustion of 1.0 L of gasoline and of 1.0 L of ethanol. (b) Assume that the density and heat of combustion of E85 can be obtained by using 85% of the values for ethanol and 15% of the values for gasoline. How much energy could be released by the combustion of 1.0 L of E85? (c) How many gallons of E85 would be needed to provide the same energy as 10 gal of gasoline? (d) If gasoline costs $3.10 per gallon in the United States, what is the break-even price per gallon of E85 if the same amount of energy is to be delivered?

ADDITIONAL EXERCISES

10.91 At 20 °C (approximately room temperature) the average velocity of N_2 molecules in air is 1050 mph. (a) What is the average speed in m/s? (b) What is the kinetic energy (in J) of an N_2 molecule moving at this speed? (c) What is the total kinetic energy of 1 mol of N_2 molecules moving at this speed?

10.92 Suppose an Olympic diver who weighs 52.0 kg executes a straight dive from a 10-m platform. At the apex of the dive, the diver is 10.8 m above the surface of the water. (a) What is the potential energy of the diver at the apex of the dive, relative to the surface of the water? (b) Assuming that all the potential energy of the diver is converted into kinetic energy at the surface of the water, at what speed in m/s will the diver enter the water? (c) Does the diver do work on entering the water? Explain.

10.93 The air bags that provide protection in autos in the event of an accident expand because of a rapid chemical reaction. From the viewpoint of the chemical reactants as the system, what do you expect for the signs of q and w in this process?

[10.94] An aluminum can of a soft drink is placed in a freezer. Later, you find that the can is split open and its contents frozen.

Work was done on the can in splitting it open. Where did the energy for this work come from?

[10.95] Consider a system consisting of the following apparatus, in which gas is confined in one flask and there is a vacuum in the other flask. The flasks are separated by a valve that, when opened, connects the two flasks. Assume that the flasks are perfectly insulated and will not allow the flow of heat into or out of the flasks to the surroundings. (a) When the valve is opened, gas flows from the filled flask to the evacuated one. Does that surprise you? (b) Is work performed during the expansion of the gas? Why or why not? (c) Can you determine the value of ΔE for the process? Does the answer surprise you? (We will talk about this system more in Chapter 13.)

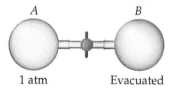

A   B

1 atm   Evacuated

[**10.96**] A sample of gas is contained in a cylinder-and-piston arrangement. It undergoes the change in state shown in the drawing. **(a)** Assume first that the cylinder and piston are perfect thermal insulators that do not allow heat to be transferred. What is the value of q for the state change? What is the sign of w for the state change? What can be said about ΔE for the state change? **(b)** Now assume that the cylinder and piston are made up of a thermal conductor such as a metal. During the state change, the cylinder gets warmer to the touch. What is the sign of q for the state change in this case? Describe the difference in the state of the system at the end of the process in the two cases. What can you say about the relative values of ΔE?

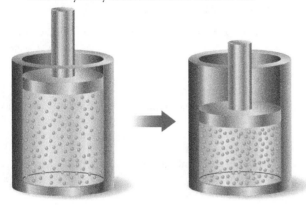

[**10.97**] Limestone stalactites and stalagmites are formed in caves by the following reaction:

$$Ca^{2+}(aq) + 2\,HCO_3^-(aq) \longrightarrow CaCO_3(s) + CO_2(g) + H_2O(l)$$

If 1 mol of $CaCO_3$ forms at 298 K under 1 atm pressure, the reaction performs 2.47 kJ of $P\text{-}V$ work, pushing back the atmosphere as the gaseous CO_2 forms. At the same time, 38.95 kJ of heat is absorbed from the environment. What are the values of ΔH and of ΔE for this reaction?

[**10.98**] Consider the systems shown in Figure 10.10. In one case the battery becomes completely discharged by running the current through a heater and in the other case by running a fan. Both processes occur at constant pressure. In both cases the change in state of the system is the same: The battery goes from being fully charged to being fully discharged. Yet in one case the heat evolved is large, and in the other it is small. Is the enthalpy change the same in the two cases? If not, how can enthalpy be considered a state function? If it is, what can you say about the relationship between enthalpy change and q in this case, as compared with others that we have considered?

10.99 A house is designed to have passive solar energy features. Brickwork incorporated into the interior of the house acts as a heat absorber. Each brick weighs approximately 1.8 kg. The specific heat of the brick is 0.85 J/g-K. How many bricks must be incorporated into the interior of the house to provide the same total heat capacity as 1.7×10^3 gal of water?

[**10.100**] A coffee-cup calorimeter of the type shown in Figure 10.18 contains 150.0 g of water at 25.1 °C. A 121.0-g block of copper metal is heated to 100.4 °C by putting it in a beaker of boiling water. The specific heat of $Cu(s)$ is 0.385 J/g-K. The Cu is added to the calorimeter, and after a time the contents of the cup reach a constant temperature of 30.1 °C. **(a)** Determine the amount of heat, in J, lost by the copper block. **(b)** Determine the amount of heat gained by the water. The specific heat of water is 4.18 J/g-K. **(c)** The difference between your answers for (a) and (b) is due to heat loss through the

Styrofoam® cups and the heat necessary to raise the temperature of the inner wall of the apparatus. The heat capacity of the calorimeter is the amount of heat necessary to raise the temperature of the apparatus (the cups and the stopper) by 1 K. Calculate the heat capacity of the calorimeter in J/K. **(d)** What would be the final temperature of the system if all the heat lost by the copper block were absorbed by the water in the calorimeter?

[**10.101**] **(a)** When a 0.235-g sample of benzoic acid is combusted in a bomb calorimeter (Figure 10.19), the temperature rises 1.642 °C. When a 0.265-g sample of caffeine, $C_8H_{10}O_2N_4$, is burned, the temperature rises 1.525 °C. Using the value 26.38 kJ/g for the heat of combustion of benzoic acid, calculate the heat of combustion per mole of caffeine at constant volume. **(b)** Assuming that there is an uncertainty of 0.002 °C in each temperature reading and that the masses of samples are measured to 0.001 g, what is the estimated uncertainty in the value calculated for the heat of combustion per mole of caffeine?

10.102 Meals-ready-to-eat (MREs) are military meals that can be heated on a flameless heater. The heat is produced by the following reaction: $Mg(s) + 2\,H_2O(l) \longrightarrow Mg(OH)_2(s) + H_2(g)$. **(a)** Calculate the standard enthalpy change for this reaction. **(b)** Calculate the number of grams of Mg needed for this reaction to release enough energy to increase the temperature of 75 mL of water from 21 °C to 79 °C.

10.103 Burning methane in oxygen can produce three different carbon-containing products: soot (very fine particles of graphite), $CO(g)$, and $CO_2(g)$. **(a)** Write three balanced equations for the reaction of methane gas with oxygen to produce these three products. In each case assume that $H_2O(l)$ is the only other product. **(b)** Determine the standard enthalpies for the reactions in part (a). **(c)** Why, when the oxygen supply is adequate, is $CO_2(g)$ the predominant carbon-containing product of the combustion of methane?

10.104 **(a)** Calculate the standard enthalpy of formation of gaseous diborane (B_2H_6) using the following thermochemical information:

$$4\,B(s) + 3\,O_2(g) \longrightarrow 2\,B_2O_3(s) \qquad \Delta H° = -2509.1\ \text{kJ}$$
$$2\,H_2(g) + O_2(g) \longrightarrow 2\,H_2O(l) \qquad \Delta H° = -571.7\ \text{kJ}$$
$$B_2H_6(g) + 3\,O_2(g) \longrightarrow B_2O_3(s) + 3\,H_2O(l) \qquad \Delta H° = -2147.5\ \text{kJ}$$

(b) Pentaborane (B_5H_9) is another boron hydride. What experiment or experiments would you need to perform to yield the data necessary to calculate the heat of formation of $B_5H_9(l)$? Explain by writing out and summing any applicable chemical reactions.

10.105 From the following data for three prospective fuels, calculate which could provide the most energy per unit volume:

Fuel	Density at 20 °C (g/cm^3)	Molar Enthalpy of Combustion (kJ/mol)
Nitroethane, $C_2H_5NO_2(l)$	1.052	-1368
Ethanol, $C_2H_5OH(l)$	0.789	-1367
Methylhydrazine, $CH_6N_2(l)$	0.874	-1307

10.106 The hydrocarbons acetylene (C_2H_2) and benzene (C_6H_6) have the same empirical formula. Benzene is an "aromatic" hydrocarbon, one that is unusually stable because of its structure. **(a)** By using the data in Appendix C, determine the standard enthalpy change for the reaction $3\,C_2H_2(g) \longrightarrow C_6H_6(l)$.

(b) Which has greater enthalpy, 3 mol of acetylene gas or 1 mol of liquid benzene? **(c)** Determine the fuel value in kJ/g for acetylene and benzene.

[**10.107**] Ammonia (NH_3) boils at -33 °C; at this temperature it has a density of 0.81 g/cm^3. The enthalpy of formation of $NH_3(g)$ is -46.2 kJ/mol, and the enthalpy of vaporization of $NH_3(l)$ is 23.2 kJ/mol. Calculate the enthalpy change when 1 L of liquid NH_3 is burned in air to give $N_2(g)$ and $H_2O(g)$. How does this compare with ΔH for the complete combustion of 1 L of liquid methanol, $CH_3OH(l)$? For $CH_3OH(l)$, the density at 25 °C is 0.792 g/cm^3, and $\Delta H_f^\circ = -239$ kJ/mol.

[**10.108**] Three common hydrocarbons that contain four carbons are listed here, along with their standard enthalpies of formation:

Hydrocarbon	Formula	ΔH_f° (kJ/mol)
1,3-Butadiene	$C_4H_6(g)$	111.9
1-Butene	$C_4H_8(g)$	1.2
n-Butane	$C_4H_{10}(g)$	-124.7

(a) For each of these substances, calculate the molar enthalpy of combustion to $CO_2(g)$ and $H_2O(l)$. **(b)** Calculate the fuel value in kJ/g for each of these compounds. **(c)** For each hydrocarbon, determine the percentage of hydrogen by mass. **(d)** By comparing your answers for parts (b) and (c), propose a relationship between hydrogen content and fuel value in hydrocarbons.

10.109 A 200-lb man decides to add to his exercise routine by walking up three flights of stairs (45 ft) 20 times per day. He figures that the work required to increase his potential energy in this way will permit him to eat an extra order of French fries, at 245 Cal, without adding to his weight. Is he correct in this assumption?

10.110 The Sun supplies about 1.0 kilowatt of energy for each square meter of surface area (1.0 kW/m^2, where a watt = 1 J/s). Plants produce the equivalent of about 0.20 g of sucrose ($C_{12}H_{22}O_{11}$) per hour per square meter. Assuming that the sucrose is produced as follows, calculate the percentage of sunlight used to produce sucrose.

$$12\ CO_2(g) + 11\ H_2O(l) \longrightarrow C_{12}H_{22}O_{11} + 12\ O_2(g)$$
$$\Delta H = 5645\ kJ$$

[**10.111**] It is estimated that the net amount of carbon dioxide fixed by photosynthesis on the landmass of Earth is 5.5×10^{16} g/yr of CO_2. Assume that all this carbon is converted into glucose. **(a)** Calculate the energy stored by photosynthesis on land per year in kJ. **(b)** Calculate the average rate of conversion of solar energy into plant energy in MW (1W = 1 J/s). A large nuclear power plant produces about 10^3 MW. The energy of how many such nuclear power plants is equivalent to the solar energy conversion?

INTEGRATIVE EXERCISES

10.112 Consider the combustion of a single molecule of $CH_4(g)$ forming $H_2O(l)$ as a product. **(a)** How much energy, in J, is produced during this reaction? **(b)** A typical X-ray light source has an energy of 8 keV. How does the energy of combustion compare to the energy of the X-ray?

10.113 Consider the following unbalanced oxidation-reduction reactions in aqueous solution:

$$Ag^+(aq) + Li(s) \longrightarrow Ag(s) + Li^+(aq)$$
$$Fe(s) + Na^+(aq) \longrightarrow Fe^{2+}(aq) + Na(s)$$
$$K(s) + H_2O(l) \longrightarrow KOH(aq) + H_2(g)$$

(a) Balance each of the reactions. **(b)** By using data in Appendix C, calculate ΔH° for each of the reactions. **(c)** Based on the values you obtain for ΔH°, which of the reactions would you expect to be thermodynamically favored? **(d)** Use the activity series to predict which of these reactions should occur. Are these results in accord with your conclusion in part (c) of this problem?

[**10.114**] Consider the following acid-neutralization reactions involving the strong base NaOH(aq):

$$HNO_3(aq) + NaOH(aq) \longrightarrow NaNO_3(aq) + H_2O(l)$$
$$HCl(aq) + NaOH(aq) \longrightarrow NaCl(aq) + H_2O(l)$$
$$NH_4^+(aq) + NaOH(aq) \longrightarrow NH_3(aq) + Na^+(aq) + H_2O(l)$$

(a) By using data in Appendix C, calculate ΔH° for each of the reactions. **(b)** Nitric acid and hydrochloric acid are strong acids. Write net ionic equations for the neutralization of these acids. **(c)** Compare the values of ΔH° for the first two reactions. What can you conclude? **(d)** In the third equation $NH_4^+(aq)$ is acting as an acid. Based on the value of ΔH° for this reaction, do you think it is a strong or a weak acid? Explain.

10.115 Consider two solutions, the first being 50.0 mL of 1.00 M $CuSO_4$ and the second 50.0 mL of 2.00 M KOH. When the two solutions are mixed in a constant-pressure calorimeter, a precipitate forms and the temperature of the mixture rises from 21.5 °C to 27.7 °C. **(a)** Before mixing, how many grams of Cu are present in the solution of $CuSO_4$? **(b)** Predict the identity of the precipitate in the reaction. **(c)** Write complete and net ionic equations for the reaction that occurs when the two solutions are mixed. **(d)** From the calorimetric data, calculate ΔH for the reaction that occurs on mixing. Assume that the calorimeter absorbs only a negligible quantity of heat, that the total volume of the solution is 100.0 mL, and that the specific heat and density of the solution after mixing are the same as that of pure water.

10.116 The precipitation reaction between $AgNO_3(aq)$ and NaCl(aq) proceeds as follows:

$$AgNO_3(aq) + NaCl(aq) \longrightarrow NaNO_3(aq) + AgCl(s)$$

(a) By using Appendix C, calculate ΔH° for the net ionic equation of this reaction. **(b)** What would you expect for the value of ΔH° of the overall molecular equation compared to that for the net ionic equation? Explain. **(c)** Use the results from (a) and (b) along with data in Appendix C to determine the value of ΔH_f° for $AgNO_3(aq)$.

[10.117] A sample of a hydrocarbon is combusted completely in $O_2(g)$ to produce 21.83 g $CO_2(g)$, 4.47 g $H_2O(g)$, and 311 kJ of heat. (a) What is the mass of the hydrocarbon sample that was combusted? (b) What is the empirical formula of the hydrocarbon? (c) Calculate the value of ΔH_f° per empirical-formula unit of the hydrocarbon. (d) Do you think that the hydrocarbon is one of those listed in Appendix C? Explain your answer.

10.118 World energy supplies are often measured in the unit of quadrillion British thermal units (10^{12} Btu), generally called a "quad." In 2015, world energy consumption is projected to be 5.81×10^{17} kJ. (a) With reference to Exercise 10.17, how many quads of energy does this quantity represent? (b) Current annual energy consumption in the United States is 99.5 quads. Assume that all this energy is to be generated by burning $CH_4(g)$ in the form of natural gas. If the combustion of the $CH_4(g)$ were complete and 100% efficient, how many moles of $CH_4(g)$ would need to be combusted in order to provide the U.S. energy demand? (c) How many kilograms of $CO_2(g)$ would be generated in the combustion in part (b)? (d) Compare your answer to part (c) with information given in Exercise 10.111. Do you think that photosynthesis is an adequate means to maintain a stable level of CO_2 in the atmosphere?

WHAT'S AHEAD

11.1 SELECT PROPERTIES OF LIQUIDS
We learn that the nature and strength of the intermolecular forces between molecules are largely responsible for many properties of liquids, including *viscosity* and *surface tension*.

11.2 PHASE CHANGES
We explore *phase changes*—the transitions of matter between the gaseous, liquid, and solid states—and their associated energies.

11.3 VAPOR PRESSURE
We examine the *dynamic equilibrium* that exists between a liquid and its gaseous state and introduce *vapor pressure*.

11.4 PHASE DIAGRAMS
We learn how to read *phase diagrams,* which are graphic representations of the equilibria among the gaseous, liquid, and solid phases.

CAVERNS SUCH AS THIS FORM when underground rivers erode limestone bedrock through to the surface. These caverns, called cenotes, are but one of many ways in which chemical reactions that occur in water shape our planet and impact our lives.

LIQUIDS

INTERMOLECULAR ATTRACTIONS CAN HELP us understand many familiar properties of liquids. In this section we examine two: viscosity and surface tension.

SAE 40
higher number
higher viscosity
slower pouring

SAE 10
lower number
lower viscosity
faster pouring

▲ **FIGURE 11.1** **Comparing viscosities.** The Society of Automotive Engineers (SAE) has established a numeric scale to indicate motor-oil viscosity.

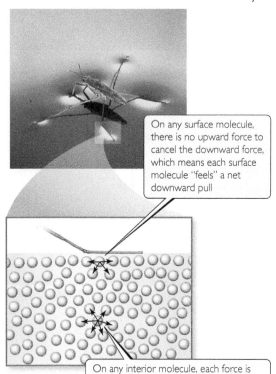

On any surface molecule, there is no upward force to cancel the downward force, which means each surface molecule "feels" a net downward pull

On any interior molecule, each force is balanced by a force pulling in the opposite direction, which means that interior molecules "feel" no net pull in any direction

▲ **FIGURE 11.2** **Molecular-level view of surface tension.** A water strider does not sink because of the high surface tension of water.

11.1 | SELECT PROPERTIES OF LIQUIDS

Some liquids, such as molasses and motor oil, flow very slowly; others, such as water and gasoline, flow easily. The resistance of a liquid to flow is called **viscosity**. The greater a liquid's viscosity, the more slowly it flows. Viscosity can be measured by timing how long it takes a certain amount of the liquid to flow through a thin vertical tube (◀ **FIGURE 11.1**). Viscosity can also be determined by measuring the rate at which steel balls fall through the liquid. The balls fall more slowly as the viscosity increases.

Viscosity is related to the ease with which the molecules of the liquid can move relative to one another. It depends on the attractive forces between molecules and on whether the shapes of the molecules are such that they tend to become entangled (for example, long molecules can become tangled like spaghetti). For a series of related compounds, viscosity increases with molecular weight, as illustrated in ▼ **TABLE 11.1**. The SI units for viscosity are kg/m-s. For any given substance, viscosity decreases with increasing temperature. Octane, for example, has a viscosity of 7.06×10^{-4} kg/m-s at 0 °C and 4.33×10^{-4} kg/m-s at 40 °C. At higher temperatures the greater average kinetic energy of the molecules overcomes the attractive forces between molecules.

The surface of water behaves almost as if it had an elastic skin, as evidenced by the ability of certain insects to "walk" on water. This behavior is due to an imbalance of intermolecular forces at the surface of the liquid. As shown in ◀ **FIGURE 11.2**, molecules in the interior are attracted equally in all directions, but those at the surface experience a net inward force. This net force tends to pull surface molecules toward the interior, thereby reducing the surface area and making the molecules at the surface pack closely together.

Because spheres have the smallest surface area for their volume, water droplets assume an almost spherical shape. This explains the tendency of water to "bead up" when it contacts a surface made of nonpolar molecules, like a lotus leaf or a newly waxed car.

A measure of the net inward force that must be overcome to expand the surface area of a liquid is given by its surface tension. **Surface tension** is the energy required to increase the surface area of a liquid by a unit amount. For example, the surface tension of water at 20 °C is 7.29×10^{-2} J/m^2, which means that an energy of 7.29×10^{-2} J must be supplied to increase the surface area of a given amount of water by 1 m^2. Water has a high surface tension because of its strong hydrogen bonds. The surface tension of mercury is even higher (4.6×10^{-1} J/m^2) because of even stronger metallic bonds between the atoms of mercury.

⚓ GIVE IT SOME THOUGHT

How do viscosity and surface tension change
a. as temperature increases,
b. as intermolecular forces of attraction become stronger?

TABLE 11.1 • Viscosities of a Series of Hydrocarbons at 20 °C		
Substance	**Formula**	**Viscosity (kg/m-s)**
Hexane	$CH_3CH_2CH_2CH_2CH_2CH_3$	3.26×10^{-4}
Heptane	$CH_3CH_2CH_2CH_2CH_2CH_2CH_3$	4.09×10^{-4}
Octane	$CH_3CH_2CH_2CH_2CH_2CH_2CH_2CH_3$	5.42×10^{-4}
Nonane	$CH_3CH_2CH_2CH_2CH_2CH_2CH_2CH_2CH_3$	7.11×10^{-4}
Decane	$CH_3CH_2CH_2CH_2CH_2CH_2CH_2CH_2CH_2CH_3$	1.42×10^{-3}

▲ GO FIGURE

If the inside surface of each tube were coated with wax, would the general shape of the water meniscus change? Would the general shape of the mercury meniscus change?

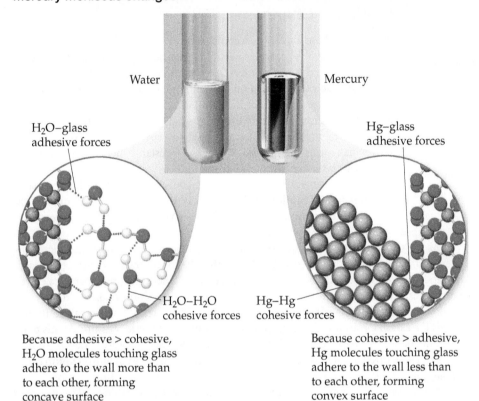

H_2O–glass
adhesive forces

Hg–glass
adhesive forces

H_2O–H_2O
cohesive forces

Hg–Hg
cohesive forces

Because adhesive > cohesive, H_2O molecules touching glass adhere to the wall more than to each other, forming concave surface

Because cohesive > adhesive, Hg molecules touching glass adhere to the wall less than to each other, forming convex surface

◀ FIGURE 11.3   **Meniscus shapes for water and mercury in glass tubes.**

Intermolecular forces that bind similar molecules to one another, such as the hydrogen bonding in water, are called *cohesive forces*. Intermolecular forces that bind a substance to a surface are called *adhesive forces*. Water placed in a glass tube adheres to the glass because the adhesive forces between the water and glass are greater than the cohesive forces between water molecules. The curved surface, or *meniscus*, of the water is therefore U-shaped (▲ FIGURE 11.3). For mercury, however, the situation is different. Mercury atoms can form bonds with one another but not with the glass. As a result the cohesive forces are much greater than the adhesive forces and the meniscus is shaped like an inverted U.

When a small-diameter glass tube, or capillary, is placed in water, water rises in the tube. The rise of liquids up very narrow tubes is called **capillary action**. The adhesive forces between the liquid and the walls of the tube tend to increase the surface area of the liquid. The surface tension of the liquid tends to reduce the area, thereby pulling the liquid up the tube. The liquid climbs until the force of gravity on the liquid balances the adhesive and cohesive forces. Capillary action helps water and dissolved nutrients move upward through plants.

11.2 | PHASE CHANGES

Liquid water left uncovered in a glass eventually evaporates. An ice cube left in a warm room quickly melts. Solid CO_2 (sold as a product called dry ice) *sublimes* at room temperature; that is, it changes directly from solid to gas. In general, each state of matter—solid,

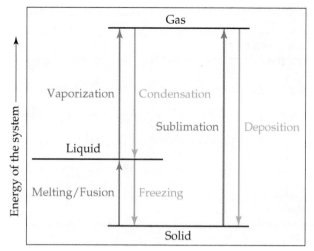

—— Endothermic process (energy added to substance)
—— Exothermic process (energy released from substance)

▲ FIGURE 11.4 **Phase changes and the names associated with them.**

liquid, gas—can transform into either of the other two states. ◄ FIGURE 11.4 shows the names associated with these transformations, which are called either **phase changes** or *changes of state*.

Energy Changes Accompanying Phase Changes

Every phase change is accompanied by a change in the energy of the system. In a solid, for example, the particles—either molecules, ions, or atoms—are in more or less fixed positions with respect to one another and closely arranged to minimize the energy of the system. As the temperature of the solid increases, the particles vibrate about their equilibrium positions with increasingly energetic motion. When the solid melts, the particles are freed to move relative to one another, which ordinarily means the average distance between particles increases.

Melting is called (somewhat confusingly) *fusion*. The increased freedom of motion of the particles comes at a price, measured by the **heat of fusion** or *enthalpy of fusion*, ΔH_{fus}. The heat of fusion of ice, for example, is 6.01 kJ/mol.

As the temperature of the liquid increases, the particles move about with increasing energy. One measure of this increasing energy is that the concentration of gas-phase particles above the liquid surface increases with temperature. These gas-phase particles exert a pressure called *vapor pressure*. We explore vapor pressure in Section 11.3. For now we just need to understand that vapor pressure increases with increasing temperature until it equals the external pressure above the liquid, typically atmospheric pressure. At this point the liquid boils—the particles move into the gaseous state where they are widely separated. The energy required to cause this transition is called either the **heat of vaporization** or the *enthalpy of vaporization*, ΔH_{vap}. For water, the heat of vaporization is 40.7 kJ/mol.

▼ FIGURE 11.5 shows ΔH_{fus} and ΔH_{vap} values for four substances. The values of ΔH_{vap} tend to be larger than the values of ΔH_{fus} because in the transition from liquid to gas, particles must essentially sever all their interparticle attractive interactions, whereas in the transition from solid to liquid, many of these attractive interactions remain operative.

The particles of a solid can move directly into the gaseous state. The enthalpy change required for this transition is called the **heat of sublimation**, denoted ΔH_{sub}. As illustrated in Figure 11.5, ΔH_{sub} is the sum of ΔH_{fus} and ΔH_{vap}. Thus, ΔH_{sub} for water is approximately 47 kJ/mol.

GO FIGURE

Is it possible to calculate the heat of sublimation for a substance given its heats of vaporization and fusion? If so, what is the relationship?

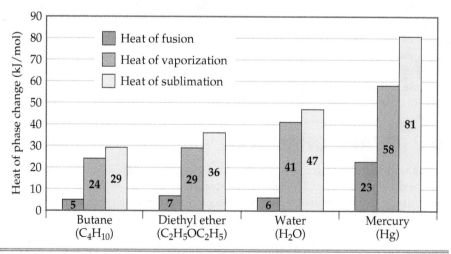

▶ FIGURE 11.5 **Heats of fusion, vaporization, and sublimation.**

Phase changes show up in important ways in our everyday experiences. When we use ice cubes to cool a drink, for instance, the heat of fusion of the ice cools the liquid. We feel cool when we step out of a swimming pool or a warm shower because the liquid water's heat of vaporization is drawn from our bodies as the water evaporates from our skin. Our bodies use this mechanism to regulate body temperature, especially when we exercise vigorously in warm weather. A refrigerator also relies on the cooling effects of vaporization. Its mechanism contains an enclosed gas that can be liquefied under pressure. The liquid absorbs heat as it subsequently evaporates, thereby cooling the interior of the refrigerator.

What happens to the heat absorbed when the liquid refrigerant vaporizes? According to the first law of thermodynamics ⚭(Section 10.2), this absorbed heat must be released when the gas condenses to liquid. As this phase change occurs, the heat released is dissipated through cooling coils in the back of the refrigerator. Just as for a given substance the heat of condensation is equal in magnitude to the heat of vaporization and has the opposite sign, so also the *heat of deposition* for a given substance is exothermic to the same degree that the heat of sublimation is endothermic; the *heat of freezing* is exothermic to the same degree that the heat of fusion is endothermic (see Figure 11.4).

 GIVE IT SOME THOUGHT

> What is the name of the phase change that occurs when ice left at room temperature changes to liquid water? Is this change exothermic or endothermic?

Heating Curves

When we heat an ice cube initially at −25 °C and 1 atm pressure, the temperature of the ice increases. As long as the temperature is below 0 °C, the ice cube remains in the solid state. When the temperature reaches 0 °C, the ice begins to melt. Because melting is an endothermic process, the heat we add at 0 °C is used to convert ice to liquid water, and *the temperature remains constant until all the ice has melted*. Once all the ice has melted, adding more heat causes the temperature of the liquid water to increase.

A graph of temperature versus amount of heat added is called a *heating curve*. ▶ FIGURE 11.6 shows the heating curve for transforming ice, $H_2O(s)$, initially at −25 °C to steam, $H_2O(g)$, at 125 °C. Heating the $H_2O(s)$ from −25 °C to 0 °C is represented by the line segment AB, and converting the $H_2O(s)$ at 0 °C to $H_2O(\ell)$ at 0 °C is the horizontal segment BC. Additional heat increases the temperature of the $H_2O(\ell)$ until the temperature reaches 100 °C (segment CD). The heat is then used to convert $H_2O(\ell)$ to $H_2O(g)$ at a constant temperature of 100 °C (segment DE). Once all the $H_2O(\ell)$ has been converted to $H_2O(g)$, the $H_2O(g)$ is heated to its final temperature of 125 °C (segment EF).

We can calculate the enthalpy change of the system for each segment of the heating curve. In segments AB, CD, and EF we are heating a single phase from one temperature to another. As we saw in Section 10.5, the amount of heat needed to raise the temperature of a substance is given by the product of the specific heat, mass, and temperature change (Equation 10.22). The greater the specific heat of a substance, the more heat we must add to accomplish a certain temperature increase. Because the specific heat of water is greater than that of ice, the slope of segment CD is less than that of segment AB. This lesser slope means the amount of heat we must add to a given mass of liquid water to achieve a 1 °C temperature change is greater than the amount we must add to achieve a 1 °C temperature change in the same mass of ice.

In segments BC and DE we are converting one phase to another at a constant temperature. The temperature remains constant during these phase changes because the added energy is used to overcome the attractive forces between molecules rather than to increase their average kinetic energy. For segment BC, the enthalpy change can be calculated by using ΔH_{fus}, and for segment DE we can use ΔH_{vap}.

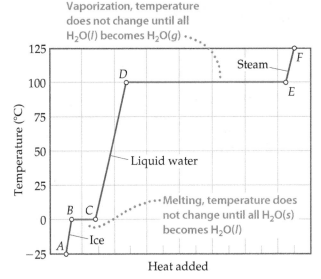

▲ FIGURE 11.6   **Heating curve for water.** Changes that occur when 1.00 mol of H_2O is heated from $H_2O(s)$ at −25 °C to $H_2O(g)$ at 125 °C at a constant pressure of 1 atm. Heat is added over the entire temperature range, but the temperature of the system increases only when the H_2O is either all solid or all liquid or all gas (blue lines). Even though heat is being added continuously, the system temperature does not change during the two phase changes (red lines).

SAMPLE EXERCISE 11.1 Calculating ΔH for Temperature and Phase Changes

Calculate the enthalpy change upon converting 1.00 mol of ice at −25 °C to steam at 125 °C under a constant pressure of 1 atm. The specific heats of ice, liquid water, and steam are 2.03 J/g-K, 4.18 J/g-K, and 1.84 J/g-K, respectively. For H_2O, $\Delta H_{fus} = 6.01$ kJ/mol and $\Delta H_{vap} = 40.67$ kJ/mol.

SOLUTION

Analyze Our goal is to calculate the total heat required to convert 1 mol of ice at −25 °C to steam at 125 °C.

Plan We can calculate the enthalpy change for each segment and then sum them to get the total enthalpy change (Hess's law, Section 10.6).

Solve: For segment *AB* in Figure 11.6, we are adding enough heat to ice to increase its temperature by 25 °C. A temperature change of 25 °C is the same as a temperature change of 25 K, so we can use the specific heat of ice to calculate the enthalpy change during this process:

AB: $\Delta H = (1.00\ \text{mol})(18.0\ \text{g/mol})(2.03\ \text{J/g-K})(25\ \text{K}) = 914\ \text{J} = 0.91\ \text{kJ}$

For segment *BC* in Figure 11.6, in which we convert ice to water at 0 °C , we can use the molar enthalpy of fusion directly:

BC: $\Delta H = (1.00\ \text{mol})(6.01\ \text{kJ/mol}) = 6.01\ \text{kJ}$

The enthalpy changes for segments *CD*, *DE*, and *EF* can be calculated in similar fashion:

CD: $\Delta H = (1.00\ \text{mol})(18.0\ \text{g/mol})(4.18\ \text{J/g-K})(100\ \text{K}) = 7520\ \text{J} = 7.52\ \text{kJ}$
DE: $\Delta H = (1.00\ \text{mol})(40.67\ \text{kJ/mol}) = 40.7\ \text{kJ}$
EF: $\Delta H = (1.00\ \text{mol})(18.0\ \text{g/mol})(1.84\ \text{J/g-K})(25\ \text{K}) = 830\ \text{J} = 0.83\ \text{kJ}$

The total enthalpy change is the sum of the changes of the individual steps:

$\Delta H = 0.91\ \text{kJ} + 6.01\ \text{kJ} + 7.52\ \text{kJ} + 40.7\ \text{kJ} + 0.83\ \text{kJ} = 56.0\ \text{kJ}$

Check The components of the total energy change are reasonable relative to the horizontal lengths (heat added) of the segments in Figure 11.6. Notice that the largest component is the heat of vaporization.

PRACTICE EXERCISE

What is the enthalpy change during the process in which 100.0 g of water at 50.0 °C is cooled to ice at −30.0 °C ? (Use the specific heats and enthalpies for phase changes given in Sample Exercise 11.1.)
Answer: −20.9 kJ − 33.4 kJ − 6.09 kJ = −60.4 kJ

If we start with 1 mole of steam at 125 °C and cool it, we move right to left across Figure 11.6. We first lower the temperature of the $H_2O(g)$ ($F \longrightarrow E$), then condense it ($E \longrightarrow D$) to $H_2O(\ell)$, and so forth.

Sometimes as we remove heat from a liquid, we can temporarily cool it below its freezing point without forming a solid. This phenomenon, called *supercooling*, occurs when the heat is removed so rapidly that the molecules have no time to assume the ordered structure of a solid. A supercooled liquid is unstable; particles of dust entering the solution or gentle stirring is often sufficient to cause the substance to solidify quickly.

Critical Temperature and Pressure

A gas normally liquefies at some point when pressure is applied. Suppose we have a cylinder fitted with a piston, and the cylinder contains water vapor at 100 °C. If we increase the pressure on the water vapor, liquid water will form when the pressure is 760 torr. However, if the temperature is 110 °C, the liquid phase does not form until the pressure is 1075 torr. At 374 °C the liquid phase forms only at 1.655×10^5 torr (217.7 atm). Above this temperature no amount of pressure causes a distinct liquid phase to form. Instead, as pressure increases, the gas becomes steadily more compressed. The highest temperature at which a distinct liquid phase can form is called the **critical temperature**. The **critical pressure** is the pressure required to bring about liquefaction at this critical temperature.

TABLE 11.2 • Critical Temperatures and Pressures of Selected Substances		
Substance	Critical Temperature (K)	Critical Pressure (atm)
Nitrogen, N_2	126.1	33.5
Argon, Ar	150.9	48.0
Oxygen, O_2	154.4	49.7
Methane, CH_4	190.0	45.4
Carbon dioxide, CO_2	304.3	73.0
Phosphine, PH_3	324.4	64.5
Propane, $CH_3CH_2CH_3$	370.0	42.0
Hydrogen sulfide, H_2S	373.5	88.9
Ammonia, NH_3	405.6	111.5
Water, H_2O	647.6	217.7

The critical temperature is the highest temperature at which a liquid can exist. Above the critical temperature, the kinetic energies of the molecules are greater than the attractive forces that lead to the liquid state regardless of how much the substance is compressed to bring the molecules closer together. The greater the intermolecular forces, the higher the critical temperature of a substance.

Several critical temperatures and pressures are listed in ▲ TABLE 11.2. Notice that nonpolar, low-molecular-weight substances, which have weak intermolecular attractions, have lower critical temperatures and pressures than substances that are polar or of higher molecular weight. Notice also that water and ammonia have exceptionally high critical temperatures and pressures as a consequence of strong intermolecular hydrogen-bonding forces.

Because they provide information about the conditions under which gases liquefy, critical temperatures and pressures are often of considerable importance to engineers and other people working with gases. Sometimes we want to liquefy a gas; other times we want to avoid liquefying it. It is useless to try to liquefy a gas by applying pressure if the gas is above its critical temperature. For example, O_2 has a critical temperature of 154.4 K. It must be cooled below this temperature before it can be liquefied by pressure. In contrast, ammonia has a critical temperature of 405.6 K. Thus, it can be liquefied at room temperature (approximately 295 K) by applying sufficient pressure.

When the temperature exceeds the critical temperature and the pressure exceeds the critical pressure, the liquid and gas phases are indistinguishable from each other, and the substance is in a state called a **supercritical fluid**. Like liquids, supercritical fluids can behave as solvents dissolving a wide range of substances. Using *supercritical fluid extraction,* the components of mixtures can be separated from one another. Supercritical fluid extraction has been successfully used to separate complex mixtures in the chemical, food, pharmaceutical, and energy industries. Supercritical CO_2 is a popular choice because it is relatively inexpensive and there are no problems associated with disposing of solvent, nor are there toxic residues resulting from the process.

11.3 | VAPOR PRESSURE

Molecules can escape from the surface of a liquid into the gas phase by evaporation. Suppose we place a quantity of ethanol (CH_3CH_2OH) in an evacuated, closed container, as in ▶ FIGURE 11.7. The ethanol quickly begins to evaporate. As a result, the pressure exerted by the vapor in the space above the liquid increases. After a short time the pressure of the vapor attains a constant value, which we call the **vapor pressure**.

At any instant, some of the ethanol molecules at the liquid surface possess sufficient kinetic energy to overcome the attractive forces of their neighbors and, therefore, escape into the gas phase. At any particular temperature, the movement of molecules from liquid phase to gas phase goes on continuously. As the number of gas-phase molecules

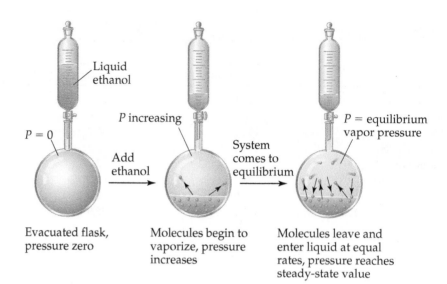

▶ **FIGURE 11.7 Equilibrium vapor pressure over a liquid.**

increases, however, the probability increases that a molecule in the gas phase will strike the liquid surface and be recaptured by the liquid, as shown in the flask on the right in Figure 11.7. Eventually, the rate at which molecules return to the liquid equals the rate at which they escape. The number of molecules in the gas phase then reaches a steady value, and the pressure exerted by the vapor becomes constant.

The condition in which two opposing processes occur simultaneously at equal rates is called **dynamic equilibrium** (or simply *equilibrium*). A liquid and its vapor are in dynamic equilibrium when evaporation and condensation occur at equal rates. It may appear that nothing is occurring at equilibrium because there is no net change in the system. In fact, though, a great deal is happening as molecules continuously pass from liquid state to gas state and from gas state to liquid state. *The vapor pressure of a liquid is the pressure exerted by its vapor when the liquid and vapor are in dynamic equilibrium.*

Volatility, Vapor Pressure, and Temperature

When vaporization occurs in an open container, as when water evaporates from a bowl, the vapor spreads away from the liquid. Little, if any, is recaptured at the surface of the liquid. Equilibrium never occurs, and the vapor continues to form until the liquid evaporates to dryness. Substances with high vapor pressure (such as gasoline) evaporate more quickly than substances with low vapor pressure (such as motor oil). Liquids that evaporate readily are said to be **volatile**.

Hot water evaporates more quickly than cold water because vapor pressure increases with increasing temperature. To see why this statement is true, we begin with the fact that the molecules of a liquid move at various speeds. ◀ **FIGURE 11.8** shows the distribution of kinetic energies of the molecules at the surface of a liquid at two temperatures. (The curves are like those shown for gases in Section 8.7.) As the temperature is increased, the molecules move more energetically and more of them can break free from their neighbors and enter the gas phase, increasing the vapor pressure.

◀ **FIGURE 11.9** depicts the variation in vapor pressure with temperature for four common substances that differ greatly in volatility. Note that the vapor pressure in all cases increases nonlinearly with increasing temperature. The weaker the intermolecular forces in the liquid, the more easily molecules can escape and, therefore, the higher the vapor pressure at a given temperature.

GO FIGURE

As the temperature increases, does the rate of molecules escaping into the gas phase increase or decrease?

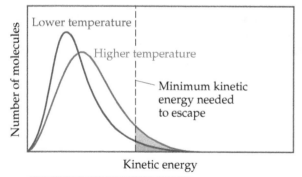

Blue area = number of molecules having enough energy to evaporate at lower temperature

Red + blue areas = number of molecules having enough energy to evaporate at higher temperature

▲ **FIGURE 11.8 The effect of temperature on the distribution of kinetic energies in a liquid.**

GIVE IT SOME THOUGHT

Which compound do you think is more volatile at 25 °C: CCl_4 or CBr_4?

Vapor Pressure and Boiling Point

A liquid boils when its vapor pressure equals the external pressure acting on the liquid surface. At this point, bubbles of vapor form within the liquid. The temperature at which a given liquid boils increases with increasing external pressure. The boiling point of a liquid at 1 atm (760 torr) pressure is called its **normal boiling point**. From Figure 11.9 we see that the normal boiling point of water is 100 °C.

The time required to cook food in boiling water depends on the water temperature. In an open container, that temperature is 100 °C, but it is possible to boil at higher temperatures. Pressure cookers work by allowing steam to escape only when it exceeds a predetermined pressure; the pressure above the water can therefore increase above atmospheric pressure. The higher pressure causes the water to boil at a higher temperature, thereby allowing the food to get hotter and to cook more rapidly.

The effect of pressure on boiling point also explains why it takes longer to cook food at high elevations than it does at sea level. The atmospheric pressure is lower at higher altitudes, so water boils at a temperature lower than 100 °C, and foods generally take longer to cook.

GO FIGURE

What is the vapor pressure of ethylene glycol at its normal boiling point?

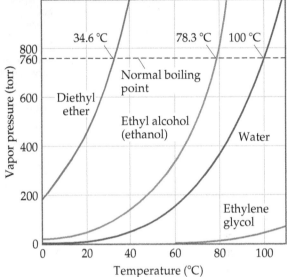

▲ FIGURE 11.9 **Vapor pressure for four liquids as a function of temperature.**

A CLOSER LOOK

THE CLAUSIUS–CLAPEYRON EQUATION

You might have noticed that the plots in Figure 11.9 have a distinct shape: For each substance, the vapor pressure curves sharply upward with increasing temperature. The relationship between vapor pressure and temperature is given by the *Clausius–Clapeyron equation*:

$$\ln P = \frac{-\Delta H_{vap}}{RT} + C \qquad [11.1]$$

where P is the vapor pressure, T is the absolute temperature, R is the gas constant (8.314 J/mol-K), ΔH_{vap} is the molar enthalpy of vaporization, and C is a constant. This equation predicts that a graph of $\ln P$ versus $1/T$ should give a straight line with a slope equal to $\Delta H_{vap}/R$. Thus, we can use such a plot to determine the enthalpy of vaporization of a substance by using the relationship

$$\Delta H_{vap} = -\text{slope} \times R$$

As an example of how we use the Clausius–Clapeyron equation, the vapor-pressure data for ethanol shown in Figure 11.9 are graphed as $\ln P$ versus $1/T$ in ▶ FIGURE 11.10. The data lie on a straight line with a negative slope. We can use the slope to determine ΔH_{vap} for ethanol, 38.56 kJ/mol. We can also extrapolate the line to obtain the vapor pressure of ethanol at temperatures above and below the temperature range for which we have data.

RELATED EXERCISES: 11.38, 11.39, 11.40

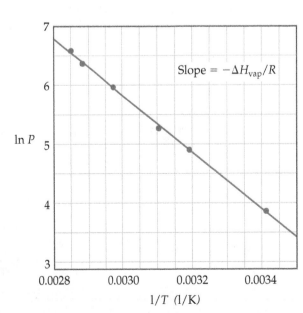

▲ FIGURE 11.10 **The natural logarithm of vapor pressure versus 1/T for ethanol.**

SAMPLE EXERCISE 11.2 Relating Boiling Point to Vapor Pressure

Use Figure 11.9 to estimate the boiling point of diethyl ether under an external pressure of 0.80 atm.

SOLUTION

Analyze We are asked to read a graph of vapor pressure versus temperature to determine the boiling point of a substance at a particular pressure. The boiling point is the temperature at which the vapor pressure is equal to the external pressure.

Plan We need to convert 0.80 atm to torr because that is the pressure scale on the graph. We estimate the location of that pressure on the graph, move horizontally to the vapor pressure curve, and then drop vertically from the curve to estimate the temperature.

Solve The pressure equals (0.80 atm)(760 torr/atm) = 610 torr. From Figure 11.9 we see that the boiling point at this pressure is about 27 °C, which is close to room temperature.

Comment We can make a flask of diethyl ether boil at room temperature by using a vacuum pump to lower the pressure above the liquid to about 0.8 atm.

PRACTICE EXERCISE

At what external pressure will ethanol have a boiling point of 60 °C?

Answer: about 340 torr (0.45 atm)

11.4 | PHASE DIAGRAMS

The equilibrium between a liquid and its vapor is not the only dynamic equilibrium that can exist between states of matter. Under appropriate conditions, a solid can be in equilibrium with its liquid or even with its vapor. A **phase diagram** is a graphic way to summarize the conditions under which equilibria exist between the different states of matter. Such a diagram also allows us to predict which phase of a substance is present at any given temperature and pressure.

The phase diagram for any substance that can exist in all three phases of matter is shown in ▼ FIGURE 11.11. The diagram contains three important curves, each of which represents the temperature and pressure at which the various phases can coexist

▲ **GO FIGURE**

If the pressure exerted on a liquid is increased, while the temperature is held constant, what type of phase transition will eventually occur?

▲ **FIGURE 11.11 Generic phase diagram for a pure substance.** The green line is the sublimation curve, the blue line is the melting curve, and the red line is the vapor pressure curve.

at equilibrium. The only substance present in the system is the one whose phase diagram is under consideration. The pressure shown in the diagram is either the pressure applied to the system or the pressure generated by the substance. The curves may be described as follows:

1. The red curve is the *vapor-pressure curve* of the liquid, representing equilibrium between the liquid and gas phases. The point on this curve where the vapor pressure is 1 atm is the normal boiling point of the substance. The vapor-pressure curve ends at the *critical point* (*C*), which corresponds to the critical temperature and critical pressure of the substance. Beyond the critical point, the liquid and gas phases are indistinguishable from each other, and the substance is a *supercritical fluid*.

2. The green curve, the *sublimation curve,* separates the solid phase from the gas phase and represents the change in the vapor pressure of the solid as it sublimes at different temperatures.

3. The blue curve, the *melting curve,* separates the solid phase from the liquid phase and represents the change in melting point of the solid with increasing pressure. This curve usually slopes slightly to the right as pressure increases because for most substances the solid form is denser than the liquid form. An increase in pressure usually favors the more compact solid phase; thus, higher temperatures are required to melt the solid at higher pressures. The melting point at 1 atm is the **normal melting point**.

Point *T*, where the three curves intersect, is the **triple point,** and here all three phases are in equilibrium. Any other point on any of the three curves represents equilibrium between two phases. Any point on the diagram that does not fall on one of the curves corresponds to conditions under which only one phase is present. The gas phase, for example, is stable at low pressures and high temperatures, whereas the solid phase is stable at low temperatures and high pressures. Liquids are stable in the region between the other two.

The Phase Diagrams of H_2O and CO_2

▼ FIGURE 11.12 shows the phase diagram of H_2O. Because of the large range of pressures covered in the diagram, a logarithmic scale is used to represent pressure. The melting curve (blue line) of H_2O is atypical, slanting slightly to the left with increasing pressure, indicating that for water the melting point *decreases* with increasing pressure. This unusual behavior occurs because water is among the very few substances whose liquid form is more compact than its solid form, as we learned in Section 5.2.

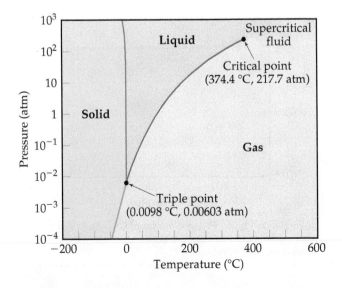

▶ FIGURE 11.12   **Phase diagram of H_2O.** Note that a linear scale is used to represent temperature and a logarithmic scale to represent pressure.

If the pressure is held constant at 1 atm, it is possible to move from the solid to liquid to gaseous regions of the phase diagram by changing the temperature, as we expect from our everyday encounters with water. The triple point of H_2O falls at a relatively low pressure, 0.00603 atm. Below this pressure, liquid water is not stable and ice sublimes to water vapor on heating. This property of water is used to "freeze-dry" foods and beverages. The food or beverage is frozen to a temperature below 0 °C. Next it is placed in a low-pressure chamber (below 0.00603 atm) and then warmed so that the water sublimes, leaving behind dehydrated food or beverage.

The phase diagram for CO_2 is shown in ▼ FIGURE 11.13. The melting curve (blue line) behaves typically, slanting to the right with increasing pressure, telling us that the melting point of CO_2 increases with increasing pressure. Because the pressure at the triple point is relatively high, 5.11 atm, CO_2 does not exist as a liquid at 1 atm, which means that solid CO_2 does not melt when heated, but instead sublimes. Thus, CO_2 does not have a normal melting point; instead, it has a normal sublimation point, −78.5 °C. Because CO_2 sublimes rather than melts as it absorbs energy at ordinary pressures, this makes solid CO_2 (dry ice) a convenient coolant.

SAMPLE EXERCISE 11.3 | Interpreting a Phase Diagram

Use the phase diagram for methane, CH_4, shown in ▼ FIGURE 11.14 to answer the following questions. (a) What are the approximate temperature and pressure of the critical point? (b) What are the approximate temperature and pressure of the triple point? (c) Is methane a solid, liquid, or gas at 1 atm and 0 °C? (d) If solid methane at 1 atm is heated while the pressure is held constant, will it melt or sublime? (e) If methane at 1 atm and 0 °C is compressed until a phase change occurs, in which state is the methane when the compression is complete?

SOLUTION

Analyze We are asked to identify key features of the phase diagram and to use it to deduce what phase changes occur when specific pressure and temperature changes take place.

Plan We must identify the triple and critical points on the diagram and also identify which phase exists at specific temperatures and pressures.

Solve
(a) The critical point is the point where the liquid, gaseous, and supercritical fluid phases coexist. It is marked point 3 in the phase diagram and located at approximately −80 °C and 50 atm.

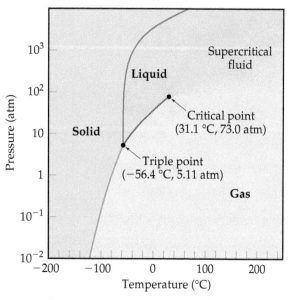

▲ FIGURE 11.13 **Phase diagram of CO₂.** Note that a linear scale is used to represent temperature and a logarithmic scale to represent pressure.

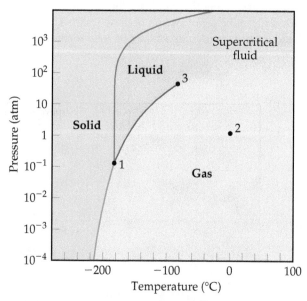

▲ FIGURE 11.14 **Phase diagram of CH₄.** Note that a linear scale is used to represent temperature and a logarithmic scale to represent pressure.

(b) The triple point is the point where the solid, liquid, and gaseous phases coexist. It is marked point 1 in the phase diagram and located at approximately −180 °C and 0.1 atm.

(c) The intersection of 0 °C and 1 atm is marked point 2 in the phase diagram. It is well within the gaseous region of the phase diagram.

(d) If we start in the solid region at $P = 1$ atm and move horizontally (this means we hold the pressure constant), we cross first into the liquid region, at $T \approx -180$ °C, and then into the gaseous region, at $T \approx -160$ °C. Therefore, solid methane melts when the pressure is 1 atm. (In order for methane to sublime, the pressure must be below the triple point pressure.)

(e) Moving vertically up from point 2, which is 1 atm and 0 °C, the first phase change we come to is from gas to supercritical fluid. This phase change happens when we exceed the critical pressure (~50 atm).

Check The pressure and temperature at the critical point are higher than those at the triple point, which is expected. Methane is the principal component of natural gas. So it seems reasonable that it exists as a gas at 1 atm and 0 °C.

PRACTICE EXERCISE

Use the phase diagram of methane to answer the following questions. **(a)** What is the normal boiling point of methane? **(b)** Over what pressure range does solid methane sublime? **(c)** Liquid methane does not exist above what temperature?

Answers: **(a)** −162 °C; **(b)** It sublimes whenever the pressure is less than 0.1 atm; **(c)** The highest temperature at which a liquid can exist is defined by the critical temperature. So we do not expect to find liquid methane when the temperature is higher than −80 °C.

CHAPTER SUMMARY AND KEY TERMS

SECTION 11.1 The stronger the intermolecular forces, the greater is the **viscosity**, or resistance to flow, of a liquid. The surface tension of a liquid also increases as intermolecular forces increase in strength. **Surface tension** is a measure of the tendency of a liquid to maintain a minimum surface area. The adhesion of a liquid to the walls of a narrow tube and the cohesion of the liquid account for **capillary action** and the formation of a meniscus at the surface of a liquid.

SECTION 11.2 A substance may exist in more than one state of matter, or phase. **Phase changes** are transformations from one phase to another. Changes of a solid to liquid (melting), solid to gas (sublimation), and liquid to gas (vaporization) are all endothermic processes. Thus, the **heat of fusion** (melting), the **heat of sublimation**, and the **heat of vaporization** are all positive quantities. The reverse processes (freezing, deposition, and condensation) are exothermic. A gas cannot be liquefied by application of pressure if the temperature is above its **critical temperature**. The pressure required to liquefy a gas at its critical temperature is called the **critical pressure**. When the temperature exceeds the critical temperature and the pressure exceeds the critical pressure, the liquid and gas phases cannot be distinguished and the substance is in a state called a **supercritical fluid**.

SECTION 11.3 The **vapor pressure** of a liquid indicates the tendency of the liquid to evaporate. The vapor pressure is the partial pressure of the vapor when it is in **dynamic equilibrium** with the liquid. At equilibrium the rate of transfer of molecules from the liquid to the vapor equals the rate of transfer from the vapor to the liquid. The higher the vapor pressure of a liquid, the more readily it evaporates and the more **volatile** it is. Vapor pressure increases nonlinearly with temperature. Boiling occurs when the vapor pressure equals the external pressure. The **normal boiling point** is the temperature at which the vapor pressure equals 1 atm.

SECTION 11.4 The equilibria between the solid, liquid, and gas phases of a substance as a function of temperature and pressure are displayed on a **phase diagram**. A line indicates equilibria between any two phases. The line through the melting point usually slopes slightly to the right as pressure increases, because the solid is usually more dense than the liquid. The melting point at 1 atm is the **normal melting point**. The point on the diagram at which all three phases coexist in equilibrium is called the **triple point**.

KEY SKILLS

- Explain the concepts of viscosity and surface tension in liquids. (Section 11.1)
- Know the names of the various changes of state for a pure substance. (Section 11.2)
- Interpret heating curves and be able to calculate quantities related to temperature and enthalpies of phase changes. (Section 11.2)
- Define critical pressure, critical temperature, vapor pressure, normal boiling point, normal melting point, critical point, and triple point. (Sections 11.3 and 11.4)
- Be able to interpret and sketch phase diagrams. Explain how water's phase diagram differs from most other substances, and why. (Section 11.4)

EXERCISES

VISUALIZING CONCEPTS

11.1 Do you expect the viscosity of glycerol, $C_3H_5(OH)_3$, to be larger or smaller than that of 1-propanol, C_3H_7OH? Explain. [Section 11.1]

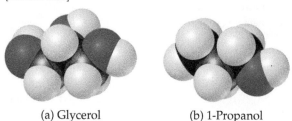

(a) Glycerol (b) 1-Propanol

11.2 If 42.0 kJ of heat is added to a 32.0-g sample of liquid methane under 1 atm of pressure at a temperature of -170 °C, what are the final state and temperature of the methane once the system equilibrates? Assume no heat is lost to the surroundings. The normal boiling point of methane is -161.5 °C. The specific heats of liquid and gaseous methane are 3.48 and 2.22 J/g-K, respectively. [Section 11.2]

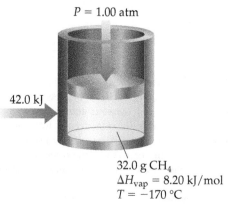

$P = 1.00$ atm

42.0 kJ

32.0 g CH_4
$\Delta H_{vap} = 8.20$ kJ/mol
$T = -170$ °C

11.3 Using this graph of CS_2 data,

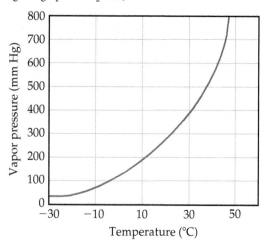

determine **(a)** the approximate vapor pressure of CS_2 at 30 °C, **(b)** the temperature at which the vapor pressure equals 300 torr, **(c)** the normal boiling point of CS_2. [Section 11.3]

11.4 The molecules

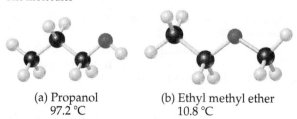

(a) Propanol   (b) Ethyl methyl ether
97.2 °C   10.8 °C

have the same molecular formula (C_3H_8O) but different normal boiling points, as shown. Rationalize the difference in boiling points. [Sections 11.2 and 11.3]

11.5 The phase diagram of a hypothetical substance is

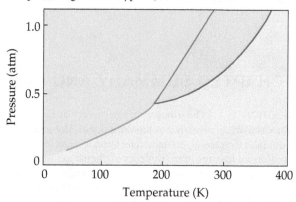

(a) Estimate the normal boiling point and freezing point of the substance.

(b) What is the physical state of the substance under the following conditions: (i) $T = 150$ K, $P = 0.2$ atm, (ii) $T = 100$ K, $P = 0.8$ atm, (iii) $T = 300$ K, $P = 1.0$ atm?

(c) What is the triple point of the substance? [Section 11.4]

SELECT PROPERTIES OF LIQUIDS (section 11.1)

11.6 **(a)** Explain why surface tension and viscosity decrease with increasing temperature. **(b)** Why do substances with high surface tensions also tend to have high viscosities?

11.7 **(a)** Distinguish between adhesive forces and cohesive forces. **(b)** What adhesive and cohesive forces are involved when a paper towel absorbs water? **(c)** Explain the cause for the U-shaped meniscus formed when water is in a glass tube.

11.8 Explain the following observations: (a) The surface tension of $CHBr_3$ is greater than that of $CHCl_3$. (b) As temperature increases, oil flows faster through a narrow tube. (c) Raindrops that collect on a waxed automobile hood take on a nearly spherical shape. (d) Oil droplets that collect on a waxed automobile hood take on a flat shape.

11.9 Hydrazine (H_2NNH_2), hydrogen peroxide (HOOH), and water (H_2O) all have exceptionally high surface tensions compared with other substances of comparable molecular weights. (a) Draw the Lewis structures for these three compounds. (b) What structural property do these substances have in common, and how might that account for the high surface tensions?

11.10 The boiling points, surface tensions, and viscosities of water and several alchohols are as follows:

	Boiling Point (°C)	Surface Tension (J/m²)	Viscosity (kg/m-s)
Water, H_2O	100	7.3×10^{-2}	0.9×10^{-3}
Ethanol, CH_3CH_2OH	78	2.3×10^{-2}	1.1×10^{-3}
Propanol, $CH_3CH_2CH_2OH$	97	2.4×10^{-2}	2.2×10^{-3}
n-Butanol, $CH_3CH_2CH_2CH_2OH$	117	2.6×10^{-2}	2.6×10^{-3}
Ethylene glycol, $HOCH_2CH_2OH$	197	4.8×10^{-2}	26×10^{-3}

(a) For ethanol, propanol, and n-butanol the boiling points, surface tensions, and viscosities all increase. What is the reason for this increase? (b) How do you explain the fact that propanol and ethylene glycol have similar molecular weights (60 versus 62 amu), yet the viscosity of ethylene glycol is more than 10 times larger than propanol? (c) How do you explain the fact that water has the highest surface tension but the lowest viscosity?

11.11 (a) Would you expect the viscosity of n-pentane, $CH_3CH_2CH_2CH_2CH_3$, to be larger or smaller than the viscosity of n-hexane (3.26×10^{-4} kg/m-s from Table 11.1)? (b) If you compared their viscosities at 270 K, would you expect the viscosity of neopentane, $(CH_3)_4C$, to be smaller or larger than n-pentane?

PHASE CHANGES (section 11.2)

11.12 Name the phase transition in each of the following situations and indicate whether it is exothermic or endothermic: (a) When ice is heated, it turns to water. (b) Wet clothes dry on a warm summer day. (c) Frost appears on a window on a cold winter day. (d) Droplets of water appear on a cold glass of beer.

11.13 Name the phase transition in each of the following situations and indicate whether it is exothermic or endothermic: (a) Bromine vapor turns to bromine liquid as it is cooled. (b) Crystals of iodine disappear from an evaporating dish as they stand in a fume hood. (c) Rubbing alcohol in an open container slowly disappears. (d) Molten lava from a volcano turns into solid rock.

11.14 Explain why any substance's heat of fusion is generally lower than its heat of vaporization.

11.15 Ethyl chloride (C_2H_5Cl) boils at 12 °C. When liquid C_2H_5Cl under pressure is sprayed on a room-temperature (25 °C) surface in air, the surface is cooled considerably. (a) What does this observation tell us about the specific heat of $C_2H_5Cl(g)$ as compared with $C_2H_5Cl(l)$? (b) Assume that the heat lost by the surface is gained by ethyl chloride. What enthalpies must you consider if you were to calculate the final temperature of the surface?

11.16 For many years drinking water has been cooled in hot climates by evaporating it from the surfaces of canvas bags or porous clay pots. How many grams of water can be cooled from 35 °C to 20 °C by the evaporation of 60 g of water? (The heat of vaporization of water in this temperature range is 2.4 kJ/g. The specific heat of water is 4.18 J/g-K.)

11.17 Compounds like CCl_2F_2 are known as chlorofluorocarbons, or CFCs. These compounds were once widely used as refrigerants but are now being replaced by compounds that are believed to be less harmful to the environment. The heat of vaporization of CCl_2F_2 is 289 J/g. What mass of this substance must evaporate to freeze 200 g of water initially at 15 °C? (The heat of fusion of water is 334 J/g; the specific heat of water is 4.18 J/g-K.)

11.18 Ethanol (C_2H_5OH) melts at −114 °C and boils at 78 °C. The enthalpy of fusion of ethanol is 5.02 kJ/mol, and its enthalpy of vaporization is 38.56 kJ/mol. The specific heats of solid and liquid ethanol are 0.97 J/g-K and 2.3 J/g-K, respectively. (a) How much heat is required to convert 42.0 g of ethanol at 35 °C to the vapor phase at 78 °C? (b) How much heat is required to convert the same amount of ethanol at −155 °C to the vapor phase at 78 °C?

11.19 The fluorocarbon compound $C_2Cl_3F_3$ has a normal boiling point of 47.6 °C. The specific heats of $C_2Cl_3F_3(l)$ and $C_2Cl_3F_3(g)$ are 0.91 J/g-K and 0.67 J/g-K, respectively. The heat of vaporization for the compound is 27.49 kJ/mol. Calculate the heat required to convert 35.0 g of $C_2Cl_3F_3$ from a liquid at 10.00 °C to a gas at 105.00 °C.

11.20 (a) What is the significance of the critical pressure of a substance? (b) What happens to the critical temperature of a series of compounds as the force of attraction between molecules increases? (c) Which of the substances listed in Table 11.2 can be liquefied at the temperature of liquid nitrogen (−196 °C)?

11.21 The critical temperatures (K) and pressures (atm) of a series of halogenated methanes are as follows:

Compound	CCl_3F	CCl_2F_2	$CClF_3$	CF_4
Critical temperature	471	385	302	227
Critical pressure	43.5	40.6	38.2	37.0

(a) List the intermolecular forces that occur for each compound. (b) Predict the order of increasing intermolecular attraction, from least to most, for this series of compounds. (c) Predict the critical temperature and pressure for CCl_4 based on the trends in this table. Look up the experimentally determined critical temperatures and pressures for CCl_4, using a source such as the *CRC Handbook of Chemistry and Physics*, and suggest a reason for any discrepancies.

VAPOR PRESSURE (section 11.3)

11.22 Explain how each of the following affects the vapor pressure of a liquid: (a) volume of the liquid, (b) surface area, (c) intermolecular attractive forces, (d) temperature, (e) density of the liquid.

11.23 Acetone, H_3CCOCH_3, has a boiling point of 56 °C. Based on the data given in Figure 11.9, would you expect acetone to have a higher or lower vapor pressure than ethanol at 25 °C?

11.24 (a) Place the following substances in order of increasing volatility: CH_4, CBr_4, CH_2Cl_2, CH_3Cl, $CHBr_3$, and CH_2Br_2. Explain. (b) How do the boiling points vary through this series?

11.25 True or false:
(a) CBr_4 is more volatile than CCl_4.
(b) CBr_4 has a higher boiling point than CCl_4.
(c) CBr_4 has weaker intermolecular forces than CCl_4.
(d) CBr_4 has a higher vapor pressure at the same temperature than CCl_4.

11.26 (a) Two pans of water are on different burners of a stove. One pan of water is boiling vigorously, while the other is boiling gently. What can be said about the temperature of the water in the two pans? (b) A large container of water and a small one are at the same temperature. What can be said about the relative vapor pressures of the water in the two containers?

11.27 Explain the following observations: (a) Water evaporates more quickly on a hot, dry day than on a hot, humid day. (b) It takes longer to cook an egg in boiling water at high altitudes than it does at lower altitudes.

11.28 Using the vapor-pressure curves in Figure 11.9, (a) estimate the boiling point of ethanol at an external pressure of 200 torr; (b) estimate the external pressure at which ethanol will boil at 60 °C; (c) estimate the boiling point of diethyl ether at 400 torr; (d) estimate the external pressure at which diethyl ether will boil at 40 °C.

11.29 Appendix B lists the vapor pressure of water at various external pressures.
(a) Plot the data in Appendix B, vapor pressure (torr) versus temperature (°C). From your plot, estimate the vapor pressure of water at body temperature, 37 °C.
(b) Explain the significance of the data point at 760.0 torr, 100 °C.
(c) A city at an altitude of 5000 ft above sea level has a barometric pressure of 633 torr. To what temperature would you have to heat water to boil it in this city?
(d) A city at an altitude of 500 ft below sea level would have a barometric pressure of 774 torr. To what temperature would you have to heat water to boil it in this city?
(e) For the two cities in parts (c) and (d), compare the average kinetic energies of the water molecules at their boiling points. Are the kinetic energies the same or different? Explain.

PHASE DIAGRAMS (section 11.4)

11.30 (a) What is the significance of the critical point in a phase diagram? (b) Why does the line that separates the gas and liquid phases end at the critical point?

11.31 (a) What is the significance of the triple point in a phase diagram? (b) Could you measure the triple point of water by measuring the temperature in a vessel in which water vapor, liquid water, and ice are in equilibrium under one atmosphere of air? Explain.

11.32 Referring to Figure 11.12, describe all the phase changes that would occur in each of the following cases: (a) Water vapor originally at 0.005 atm and −0.5 °C is slowly compressed at constant temperature until the final pressure is 20 atm. (b) Water originally at 100.0 °C and 0.50 atm is cooled at constant pressure until the temperature is −10 °C.

11.33 Referring to Figure 11.13, describe the phase changes (and the temperatures at which they occur) when CO_2 is heated from −80 °C to −20 °C at (a) a constant pressure of 3 atm, (b) a constant pressure of 6 atm.

11.34 The phase diagram for neon is

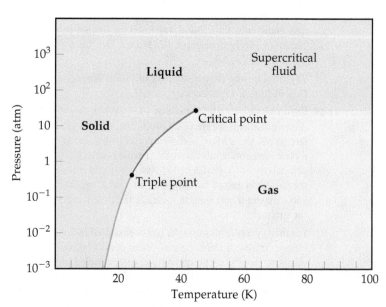

Use the phase diagram to answer the following questions. (a) What is the approximate value of the normal melting point?

(b) Over what pressure range will solid neon sublime? **(c)** At room temperature ($T = 25$ °C) can neon be liquefied by compressing it?

11.35 Use the phase diagram of neon to answer the following questions. **(a)** What is the approximate value of the normal boiling point? **(b)** What can you say about the strength of the intermolecular forces in neon and argon based on the critical points of Ne and Ar? (See Table 11.2.)

11.36 The fact that water on Earth can readily be found in all three states (solid, liquid, and gas) is in part a consequence of the fact that the triple point of water ($T = 0.01$ °C, $P = 0.006$ atm) falls within a range of temperatures and pressures found on Earth. Saturn's largest moon Titan has a considerable amount of methane in its atmosphere. The conditions on the surface of Titan are estimated to be $P = 1.6$ atm and $T = -178$ °C. As seen from the phase diagram of methane (Figure 11.14), these conditions are not far from the triple point of methane, raising the tantalizing possibility that solid, liquid, and gaseous methane can be found on Titan. **(a)** What state would you expect to find methane in on the surface of Titan? **(b)** On

moving upward through the atmosphere the pressure will decrease. If we assume that the temperature does not change, what phase change would you expect to see as we move away from the surface?

11.37 At 25 °C gallium is a solid with a density of 5.91 g/cm³. Its melting point, 29.8 °C, is low enough that you can melt it by holding it in your hand. The density of liquid gallium just above the melting point is 6.1 g/cm³. Based on this information, what unusual feature would you expect to find in the phase diagram of gallium?

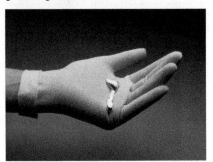

ADDITIONAL EXERCISES

11.38 **(a)** When you exercise vigorously, you sweat. How does this help your body cool? **(b)** A flask of water is connected to a vacuum pump. A few moments after the pump is turned on, the water begins to boil. After a few minutes, the water begins to freeze. Explain why these processes occur.

[11.39] The following table gives the vapor pressure of hexafluorobenzene (C_6F_6) as a function of temperature:

Temperature (K)	Vapor Pressure (torr)
280.0	32.42
300.0	92.47
320.0	225.1
330.0	334.4
340.0	482.9

(a) By plotting these data in a suitable fashion, determine whether the Clausius–Clapeyron equation (Equation 11.1) is obeyed. If it is obeyed, use your plot to determine ΔH_{vap} for C_6F_6. **(b)** Use these data to determine the boiling point of the compound.

[11.40] Suppose the vapor pressure of a substance is measured at two different temperatures. **(a)** By using the Clausius–Clapeyron equation (Equation 11.1) derive the following relationship between the vapor pressures, P_1 and P_2, and the absolute temperatures at which they were measured, T_1 and T_2:

$$\ln \frac{P_1}{P_2} = -\frac{\Delta H_{vap}}{R}\left(\frac{1}{T_1} - \frac{1}{T_2}\right)$$

(b) Gasoline is a mixture of hydrocarbons, a major component of which is octane, $CH_3CH_2CH_2CH_2CH_2CH_2CH_2CH_3$. Octane has a vapor pressure of 13.95 torr at 25 °C and a vapor pressure of 144.78 torr at 75 °C. Use these data and the equation in part (a) to calculate the heat of vaporization of octane. **(c)** By using the equation in part (a) and the data given in part (b), calculate the normal boiling point of octane. Compare your answer to the one you obtained from Exercise 5.42. **(d)** Calculate the vapor pressure of octane at −30 °C.

[11.41] The following data present the temperatures at which certain vapor pressures are achieved for dichloromethane (CH_2Cl_2) and methyl iodide (CH_3I):

(a) Which of the two substances is expected to have the greater dipole–dipole forces? Which is expected to have the greater dispersion forces? Based on your answers, explain why it is difficult to predict which compound would be more volatile. **(b)** Which

Vapor Pressure (torr):	10.0	40.0	100.0	400.0
T for CH_2Cl_2 (°C):	−43.3	−22.3	−6.3	24.1
T for CH_3I (°C):	−45.8	−24.2	−7.0	25.3

compound would you expect to have the higher boiling point? Check your answer in a reference book such as the *CRC Handbook of Chemistry and Physics*. **(c)** The order of volatility of these two substances changes as the temperature is increased. What quantity must be different for the two substances in order for this phenomenon to occur? **(d)** Substantiate your answer for part (c) by drawing an appropriate graph.

[11.42] A particular liquid crystalline substance has the phase diagram shown in the figure. By analogy with the phase diagram for a non–liquid crystalline substance, identify the phase present in each area.

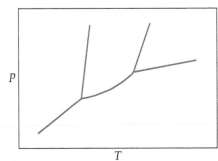

INTEGRATIVE EXERCISES

11.43 **(a)** At the molecular level, what factor is responsible for the steady increase in viscosity with increasing molecular weight in the hydrocarbon series shown in Table 11.1? **(b)** Although the viscosity varies over a factor of more than two in the series from hexane to nonane, the surface tension at 25 °C increases by only about 20% in the same series. How do you account for this? **(c)** *n*-Octyl alcohol, $CH_3(CH_2)_7OH$, has a viscosity of 1.01×10^{-2} kg/m-s, much higher than nonane, which has about the same molecular weight. What accounts for this difference? How does your answer relate to the difference in normal boiling points for these two substances?

11.44 The table shown here lists the molar heats of vaporization for several organic compounds. Use specific examples from this list to illustrate how the heat of vaporization varies with **(a)** molar mass, **(b)** molecular shape, **(c)** molecular polarity, **(d)** hydrogen-bonding interactions. Explain these comparisons in terms of the nature of the intermolecular forces at work. (You may find it helpful to draw out the structural formula for each compound.)

Compound	Heat of Vaporization (kJ/mol)
$CH_3CH_2CH_3$	19.0
$CH_3CH_2CH_2CH_2CH_3$	27.6
$CH_3CHBrCH_3$	31.8
CH_3COCH_3	32.0
$CH_3CH_2CH_2Br$	33.6
$CH_3CH_2CH_2OH$	47.3

11.45 Liquid butane, C_4H_{10}, is stored in cylinders to be used as a fuel. The normal boiling point of butane is listed as −0.5 °C.

(a) Suppose the tank is standing in the sun and reaches a temperature of 35 °C. Would you expect the pressure in the tank to be greater or less than atmospheric pressure? How does the pressure within the tank depend on how much liquid butane is in it? **(b)** Suppose the valve to the tank is opened and a few liters of butane are allowed to escape rapidly. What do you expect would happen to the temperature of the remaining liquid butane in the tank? Explain. **(c)** How much heat must be added to vaporize 250 g of butane if its heat of vaporization is 21.3 kJ/mol ? What volume does this much butane occupy at 755 torr and 35 °C?

[11.46] Using information in Appendices B and C, calculate the minimum number of grams of propane, $C_3H_8(g)$, that must be combusted to provide the energy necessary to convert 5.50 kg of ice at −20 °C to liquid water at 75 °C.

11.47 The vapor pressure of a volatile liquid can be determined by slowly bubbling a known volume of gas through it at a known temperature and pressure. In an experiment, 5.00 L of N_2 gas is passed through 7.2146 g of liquid benzene, C_6H_6, at 26.0 °C. The liquid remaining after the experiment weighs 5.1493 g. Assuming that the gas becomes saturated with benzene vapor and that the total gas volume and temperature remain constant, what is the vapor pressure of the benzene in torr?

11.48 The relative humidity of air equals the ratio of the partial pressure of water in the air to the equilibrium vapor pressure of water at the same temperature times 100%. If the relative humidity of the air is 58% and its temperature is 68 °F, how many molecules of water are present in a room measuring 12 ft × 10 ft × 8 ft?

TRAFFIC ENTERING AND LEAVING a city.

12

12.5 CALCULATING EQUILIBRIUM CONSTANTS
We see that the value of an equilibrium constant can be calculated from equilibrium concentrations of reactants and products.

12.6 APPLICATIONS OF EQUILIBRIUM CONSTANTS
We also see that equilibrium constants can be used to predict equilibrium concentrations of reactants and products and to determine the direction in which a reaction mixture must proceed to achieve equilibrium.

12.7 LE CHÂTELIER'S PRINCIPLE
We discuss *Le Châtelier's principle*, which predicts how a system at equilibrium responds to changes in concentration, volume, pressure, and temperature.

CHEMICAL EQUILIBRIUM

TO BE IN EQUILIBRIUM IS to be in a state of balance. A tug of war in which the two sides pull with equal force so that the rope does not move is an example of a *static* equilibrium, one in which an object is at rest. Equilibria can also be *dynamic*, as illustrated in the chapter-opening photograph, which shows cars traveling in both directions over a bridge that serves as the entry to a city. If the rate at which cars leave the city equals the rate at which they enter, the two opposing processes are in balance, and the net number of cars in the city is constant.

We have already encountered several instances of dynamic equilibrium. For example, the vapor above a liquid in a closed container is in equilibrium with the liquid phase ∞ (Section 11.3), which means that the rate at which molecules escape from the liquid into the gas phase equals the rate at which molecules in the gas phase become part of the liquid. Similarly, in a saturated sodium chloride solution in contact with undissolved sodium chloride, the solid is in equilibrium with the ions dispersed in water. The rate at which ions leave the solid surface equals the rate at which other ions leave the liquid and become part of the solid.

In this chapter we consider dynamic equilibria in chemical reactions. **Chemical equilibrium** *occurs when opposing reactions proceed at equal rates*: The rate at which the products form from the reactants equals the rate at which the reactants form from the products. As a result, concentrations cease to change, making the reaction appear to be stopped. Chemical equilibria are involved in many natural phenomena and play important roles in many industrial processes. In this and the next two chapters, we will explore chemical equilibrium in some detail. Later, in Chapter 13, we will learn how to relate chemical equilibria to thermodynamics. Here we learn how to express the equilibrium state of a reaction in quantitative terms and study the factors that determine the relative concentrations of reactants and products in equilibrium mixtures.

12.1 | THE CONCEPT OF EQUILIBRIUM

Let's examine a simple chemical reaction to see how it reaches an *equilibrium state*—a mixture of reactants and products whose concentrations no longer change with time. We begin with N_2O_4, a colorless substance that dissociates to form brown NO_2. ▼ FIGURE 12.1 shows a sample of frozen N_2O_4 inside a sealed tube. The solid N_2O_4 vaporizes as it is warmed above its boiling point (21.2 °C), and the gas turns darker as the colorless N_2O_4 gas dissociates into brown NO_2 gas. Eventually, even though there is still N_2O_4 in the tube, the color stops getting darker because the system reaches equilibrium. We are left with an *equilibrium mixture* of N_2O_4 and NO_2 in which the concentrations of the gases no longer change as time passes. Because the reaction is in a closed system, where no gases can escape, equilibrium will eventually be reached.

GO FIGURE

How can you tell if you are at equilibrium?

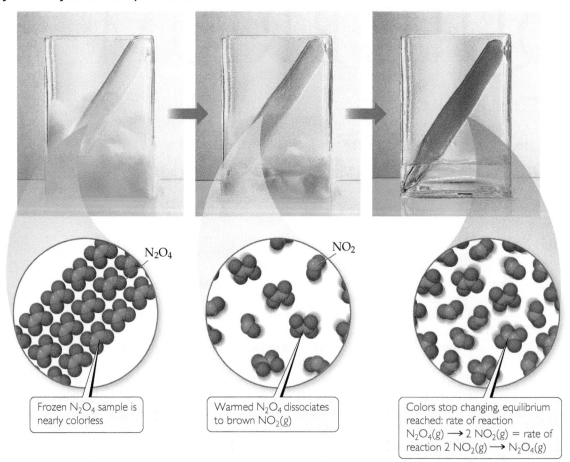

Frozen N_2O_4 sample is nearly colorless

Warmed N_2O_4 dissociates to brown $NO_2(g)$

Colors stop changing, equilibrium reached: rate of reaction $N_2O_4(g) \longrightarrow 2\ NO_2(g)$ = rate of reaction $2\ NO_2(g) \longrightarrow N_2O_4(g)$

▲ FIGURE 12.1 **The equilibrium between NO_2 and N_2O_4.**

The equilibrium mixture results because the reaction is *reversible*: N_2O_4 can form NO_2, and NO_2 can form N_2O_4. This situation is represented by writing the equation for the reaction with two half arrows pointing in opposite directions:

$$N_2O_4(g) \rightleftharpoons 2\ NO_2(g) \qquad\qquad [12.1]$$
$$\text{Colorless} \qquad\quad \text{Brown}$$

We can analyze this equilibrium using our knowledge of kinetics. Let's call the decomposition of N_2O_4 the forward reaction and the formation of N_2O_4 the reverse reaction. In this case, both the forward reaction and the reverse reaction are elementary reactions. The rate laws for elementary reactions can be written from their chemical equations:

$$\text{Forward reaction:}\quad N_2O_4(g) \longrightarrow 2\ NO_2(g) \qquad \text{Rate}_f = k_f[N_2O_4] \qquad [12.2]$$

$$\text{Reverse reaction:}\quad 2\ NO_2(g) \longrightarrow N_2O_4(g) \qquad \text{Rate}_r = k_r[NO_2]^2 \qquad [12.3]$$

At equilibrium, the rate at which NO_2 forms in the forward reaction equals the rate at which N_2O_4 forms in the reverse reaction:

$$\underbrace{k_f[N_2O_4]}_{\text{Forward reaction}} = \underbrace{k_r[NO_2]^2}_{\text{Reverse reaction}} \qquad\qquad [12.4]$$

Rearranging this equation gives

$$\frac{[NO_2]^2}{[N_2O_4]} = \frac{k_f}{k_r} = \text{a constant} \qquad\qquad [12.5]$$

From Equation 12.5 we see that the quotient of two rate constants is another constant. We also see that, at equilibrium, the ratio of the concentration terms equals this same constant. (We consider this constant, called the equilibrium constant, in Section 12.2.) It makes no difference whether we start with N_2O_4 or with NO_2, or even with some mixture of the two. At equilibrium, at a given temperature, the ratio equals a specific value. Thus, there is an important constraint on the proportions of N_2O_4 and NO_2 at equilibrium.

Once equilibrium is established, the concentrations of N_2O_4 and NO_2 no longer change, as shown in ▼ FIGURE 12.2(a). However, the fact that the composition of the equilibrium mixture remains constant with time does not mean that N_2O_4 and NO_2 stop reacting. On the contrary, the equilibrium is *dynamic*—which means some N_2O_4 is always converting to NO_2 and some NO_2 is always converting to N_2O_4. At equilibrium, however, the two processes occur at the same rate, as shown in Figure 12.2(b).

We learn several important lessons about equilibrium from this example:

- At equilibrium, the concentrations of reactants and products no longer change with time.

- For equilibrium to occur, neither reactants nor products can escape from the system.

- At equilibrium, a particular ratio of concentration terms equals a constant.

▲ GO FIGURE

At equilibrium, are the concentrations of NO_2 and N_2O_4 equal?

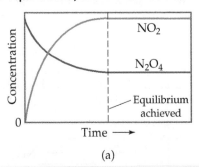

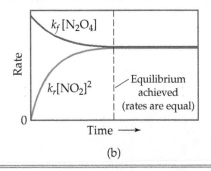

◄ FIGURE 12.2 **Achieving chemical equilibrium in the $N_2O_4(g) \rightleftharpoons 2\ NO_2(g)$ reaction.** Equilibrium occurs when the rate of the forward reaction equals the rate of the reverse reaction.

GIVE IT SOME THOUGHT

a. Which quantities are equal in a dynamic equilibrium?

b. If the rate constant for the forward reaction in Equation 12.1 is larger than the rate constant for the reverse reaction, will the constant in Equation 12.5 be greater than 1 or smaller than 1?

12.2 | THE EQUILIBRIUM CONSTANT

A reaction in which reactants convert to products and products convert to reactants in the same reaction vessel naturally leads to an equilibrium, regardless of how complicated the reaction is and regardless of the nature of the kinetic processes for the forward and reverse reactions. Consider the synthesis of ammonia from nitrogen and hydrogen:

$$N_2(g) + 3\,H_2(g) \rightleftharpoons 2\,NH_3(g) \qquad [12.6]$$

This reaction is the basis for the **Haber process**, which is critical for the production of fertilizers and therefore critical to the world's food supply. In the Haber process, N_2 and H_2 react at high pressure and temperature in the presence of a catalyst to form ammonia. In a closed system, however, the reaction does not lead to complete consumption of the N_2 and H_2. Rather, at some point the reaction appears to stop with all three components of the reaction mixture present at the same time.

How the concentrations of H_2, N_2, and NH_3 vary with time is shown in ▼ FIGURE 12.3. Notice that an equilibrium mixture is obtained regardless of whether we begin with N_2 and H_2 or with NH_3. *The equilibrium condition is reached from either direction.*

 GIVE IT SOME THOUGHT

How do we know when equilibrium has been reached in a chemical reaction?

An expression similar to Equation 12.5 governs the concentrations of N_2, H_2, and NH_3 at equilibrium. If we were to systematically change the relative amounts of the three gases in the starting mixture and then analyze each equilibrium mixture, we could determine the relationship among the equilibrium concentrations.

Chemists carried out studies of this kind on other chemical systems in the nineteenth century before Haber's work. In 1864, Cato Maximilian Guldberg (1836–1902) and Peter Waage (1833–1900) postulated their **law of mass action**, which expresses, for any reaction, the relationship between the concentrations of the reactants and products present at equilibrium. Suppose we have the general equilibrium equation

$$a\,A + b\,B \rightleftharpoons d\,D + e\,E \qquad [12.7]$$

where A, B, D, and E are the chemical species involved and a, b, d, and e are their coefficients in the balanced chemical equation. According to the law of mass action, the equilibrium condition is described by the expression

$$K_c = \frac{[D]^d[E]^e}{[A]^a[B]^b} \quad \begin{array}{l} \longleftarrow \text{products} \\ \longleftarrow \text{reactants} \end{array} \qquad [12.8]$$

We call this relationship the **equilibrium-constant expression** (or merely the *equilibrium expression*) for the reaction. The constant K_c, the **equilibrium constant**, is the numerical value obtained when we substitute molar equilibrium concentrations

▶ FIGURE 12.3 **The same equilibrium is reached whether we start with only reactants (N_2 and H_2) or with only product (NH_3).**

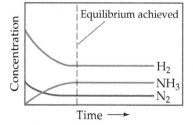

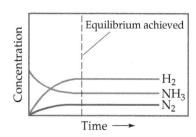

CHEMISTRY PUT TO WORK

The Haber Process

The quantity of food required to feed the ever-increasing human population far exceeds that provided by nitrogen-fixing plants. ◌◌◌ (Section 14.7) Therefore, human agriculture requires substantial amounts of ammonia-based fertilizers for croplands. Of all the chemical reactions that humans have learned to control for their own purposes, the synthesis of ammonia from hydrogen and atmospheric nitrogen is one of the most important.

In 1912 the German chemist Fritz Haber (1868–1934) developed the Haber process (Equation 12.6). The process is sometimes also called the *Haber–Bosch process* to honor Karl Bosch, the engineer who developed the industrial process on a large scale. The engineering needed to implement the Haber process requires the use of temperatures and pressures (approximately 500 °C and 200 to 600 atm) that were difficult to achieve at that time.

The Haber process provides a historically interesting example of the complex impact of chemistry on our lives. At the start of World War I, in 1914, Germany depended on nitrate deposits in Chile for the nitrogen-containing compounds needed to manufacture explosives. During the war, the Allied naval blockade of South America cut off this supply. However, by using the Haber reaction to fix nitrogen from air, Germany was able to continue to produce explosives. Experts have estimated that World War I would have ended before 1918 had it not been for the Haber process.

From these unhappy beginnings as a major factor in international warfare, the Haber process has become the world's principal source of fixed nitrogen. The same process that prolonged World War I has enabled the manufacture of fertilizers that have increased crop yields, thereby saving millions of people from starvation. About 40 billion pounds of ammonia are manufactured annually in the United States, mostly by the Haber process. The ammonia can be applied directly to the soil (▼ FIGURE 12.4), or it can be converted into ammonium salts that are also used as fertilizers.

Haber was a patriotic German who gave enthusiastic support to his nation's war effort. He served as chief of Germany's Chemical Warfare Service during World War I and developed the use of chlorine as a poison-gas weapon. Consequently, the decision to award him the Nobel Prize in Chemistry in 1918 was the subject of considerable controversy and criticism. The ultimate irony, however, came in 1933 when Haber was expelled from Germany because he was Jewish.

RELATED EXERCISES: 12.46 and 12.76

◀ FIGURE 12.4 **Liquid ammonia used as fertilizer by direct injection into soil.**

into the equilibrium-constant expression. The subscript c on the K indicates that concentrations expressed in molarity are used to evaluate the constant.

The numerator of the equilibrium-constant expression is the product of the concentrations of all substances on the product side of the equilibrium equation, each raised to a power equal to its coefficient in the balanced equation. The denominator is similarly derived from the reactant side of the equilibrium equation. Thus, for the Haber process, $N_2(g) + 3 H_2(g) \rightleftharpoons 2 NH_3(g)$, the equilibrium-constant expression is

$$K_c = \frac{[NH_3]^2}{[N_2][H_2]^3} \qquad [12.9]$$

Once we know the balanced chemical equation for a reaction that reaches equilibrium, we can write the equilibrium-constant expression even if we do not know the reaction mechanism. *The equilibrium-constant expression depends only on the stoichiometry of the reaction, not on its mechanism.*

The value of the equilibrium constant at any given temperature does not depend on the initial amounts of reactants and products. It also does not matter whether other substances are present, as long as they do not react with a reactant or a product. The value of K_c depends only on the particular reaction and on the temperature.

SAMPLE EXERCISE 12.1 **Writing Equilibrium-Constant Expressions**

Write the equilibrium expression for K_c for the following reactions:

(a) $2 O_3(g) \rightleftharpoons 3 O_2(g)$
(b) $2 NO(g) + Cl_2(g) \rightleftharpoons 2 NOCl(g)$
(c) $Ag^+(aq) + 2 NH_3(aq) \rightleftharpoons Ag(NH_3)_2^+(aq)$

SOLUTION

Analyze We are given three equations and are asked to write an equilibrium-constant expression for each.

Plan Using the law of mass action, we write each expression as a quotient having the product concentration terms in the numerator and the reactant concentration terms in the denominator. Each concentration term is raised to the power of its coefficient in the balanced chemical equation.

Solve

(a) $K_c = \dfrac{[O_2]^3}{[O_3]^2}$ **(b)** $K_c = \dfrac{[NOCl]^2}{[NO]^2[Cl_2]}$ **(c)** $K_c = \dfrac{[Ag(NH_3)_2^+]}{[Ag^+][NH_3]^2}$

PRACTICE EXERCISE

Write the equilibrium-constant expression K_c for **(a)** $H_2(g) + I_2(g) \rightleftharpoons 2 HI(g)$, **(b)** $Cd^{2+}(aq) + 4 Br^-(aq) \rightleftharpoons CdBr_4^{2-}(aq)$.

Answers: **(a)** $K_c = \dfrac{[HI]^2}{[H_2][I_2]}$ **(b)** $K_c = \dfrac{[CdBr_4^{2-}]}{[Cd^{2+}][Br^-]^4}$

Evaluating K_c

We can illustrate how the law of mass action was discovered empirically and demonstrate that the equilibrium constant is independent of starting concentrations by examining a series of experiments involving dinitrogen tetroxide and nitrogen dioxide:

$$N_2O_4(g) \rightleftharpoons 2 NO_2(g) \qquad K_c = \frac{[NO_2]^2}{[N_2O_4]} \qquad [12.10]$$

We start with several sealed tubes containing different concentrations of NO_2 and N_2O_4. The tubes are kept at 100 °C until equilibrium is reached. We then analyze the mixtures and determine the equilibrium concentrations of NO_2 and N_2O_4, which are shown in ▼ TABLE 12.1.

To evaluate K_c, we insert the equilibrium concentrations into the equilibrium-constant expression. For example, using Experiment 1 data, $[NO_2] = 0.0172\ M$ and $[N_2O_4] = 0.00140\ M$, we find

$$K_c = \frac{[NO_2]^2}{[N_2O_4]} = \frac{[0.0172]^2}{0.00140} = 0.211$$

TABLE 12.1 • Initial and Equilibrium Concentrations of $N_2O_4(g)$ and $NO_2(g)$ at 100 °C

Experiment	Initial $[N_2O_4]$ (M)	Initial $[NO_2]$ (M)	Equilibrium $[N_2O_4]$ (M)	Equilibrium $[NO_2]$ (M)	K_c
1	0.0	0.0200	0.00140	0.0172	0.211
2	0.0	0.0300	0.00280	0.0243	0.211
3	0.0	0.0400	0.00452	0.0310	0.213
4	0.0200	0.0	0.00452	0.0310	0.213

Proceeding in the same way, the values of K_c for the other samples are calculated. Note from Table 12.1 that the value for K_c is constant (within the limits of experimental error) even though the initial concentrations vary. Furthermore, Experiment 4 shows that equilibrium can be achieved beginning with N_2O_4 rather than with NO_2. That is, equilibrium can be approached from either direction. ▶ FIGURE 12.5 shows how Experiments 3 and 4 result in the same equilibrium mixture even though the two experiments start with very different NO_2 concentrations.

Notice that no units are given for K_c either in Table 12.1 or in the calculation we just did using Experiment 1 data. It is common practice to write equilibrium constants without units for reasons that we address later in this section.

Recall that we began our discussion of equilibrium in terms of rates. Equation 12.5 shows that K_c is equal to k_f/k_r, the ratio of the forward rate constant to the reverse rate constant. For the N_2O_4/NO_2 reaction, $K_c = 0.212$, which means that k_r is 4.72 times as large as k_f (since $1/0.212 = 4.72$). It is not possible to obtain the absolute value of either rate constant knowing only the value of K_c.

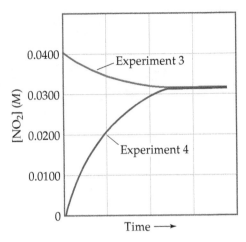

▲ FIGURE 12.5 **The same equilibrium mixture is produced regardless of the initial NO_2 concentration.** The concentration of NO_2 either increases or decreases until equilibrium is reached.

 GIVE IT SOME THOUGHT

How does the value of K_c in Equation 12.10 depend on the starting concentrations of NO_2 and N_2O_4?

Equilibrium Constants in Terms of Pressure, K_p

When the reactants and products in a chemical reaction are gases, we can formulate the equilibrium-constant expression in terms of partial pressures. When partial pressures in atmospheres are used in the expression, we denote the equilibrium constant K_p (where the subscript p stands for pressure). For the general reaction in Equation 12.7, we have

$$K_p = \frac{(P_D)^d (P_E)^e}{(P_A)^a (P_B)^b} \qquad [12.11]$$

where P_A is the partial pressure of A in atmospheres, P_B is the partial pressure of B in atmospheres, and so forth. For example, for our N_2O_4/NO_2 reaction we have

$$K_p = \frac{(P_{NO_2})^2}{P_{N_2O_4}}$$

 GIVE IT SOME THOUGHT

What is the difference between the equilibrium constant K_c and the equilibrium constant K_p?

For a given reaction, the numerical value of K_c is generally different from the numerical value of K_p. We must therefore take care to indicate, via subscript c or p, which constant we are using. It is possible, however, to calculate one from the other using the ideal-gas equation: ∞ (Section 8.4)

$$PV = nRT, \text{ so } P = \frac{n}{V}RT \qquad [12.12]$$

The usual units for n/V are mol/L, which equals molarity, M. For substance A in our generic reaction, we therefore see that

$$P_A = \frac{n_A}{V}RT = [A]RT \qquad [12.13]$$

When we substitute Equation 12.13 and like expressions for the other gaseous components of the reaction into Equation 12.11, we obtain a general expression relating K_p and K_c:

$$K_p = K_c(RT)^{\Delta n} \qquad [12.14]$$

The quantity Δn is the change in the number of moles of gas in the balanced chemical equation. It equals the sum of the coefficients of the gaseous products minus the sum of the coefficients of the gaseous reactants:

$$\Delta n = (\text{moles of gaseous product}) - (\text{moles of gaseous reactant}) \qquad [12.15]$$

For example, in the $N_2O_4(g) \rightleftharpoons 2\,NO_2(g)$ reaction, there are two moles of product NO_2 and one mole of reactant N_2O_4. Therefore, $\Delta n = 2 - 1 = 1$, and $K_p = K_c(RT)$ for this reaction.

From Equation 12.14, we see that $K_p = K_c$ only when the same number of moles of gas appears on both sides of the balanced chemical equation, so that $\Delta n = 0$.

SAMPLE EXERCISE 12.2 | **Converting between K_c and K_p**

For the Haber process,

$$N_2(g) + 3\,H_2(g) \rightleftharpoons 2\,NH_3(g)$$

$K_c = 9.60$ at 300 °C. Calculate K_p for this reaction at this temperature.

SOLUTION

Analyze We are given K_c for a reaction and asked to calculate K_p.

Plan The relationship between K_c and K_p is given by Equation 12.14. To apply that equation, we must determine Δn by comparing the number of moles of product with the number of moles of reactants (Equation 12.15).

Solve With 2 mol of gaseous products ($2\,NH_3$) and 4 mol of gaseous reactants ($1\,N_2 + 3\,H_2$), $\Delta n = 2 - 4 = -2$. (Remember that Δ functions are always based on *products minus reactants*.) The temperature is $273 + 300 = 573$ K. The value for the ideal-gas constant, R, is 0.08206 L-atm/mol-K. Using $K_c = 9.60$, we therefore have

$$K_p = K_c(RT)^{\Delta n} = (9.60)(0.08206 \times 573)^{-2} = \frac{(9.60)}{(0.08206 \times 573)^2} = 4.34 \times 10^{-3}$$

PRACTICE EXERCISE

For the equilibrium $2\,SO_3(g) \rightleftharpoons 2\,SO_2(g) + O_2(g)$, K_c is 4.08×10^{-3} at 1000 K. Calculate the value for K_p.

Answer: 0.335

Equilibrium Constants and Units

You may wonder why equilibrium constants are reported without units. The equilibrium constant is related to the kinetics of a reaction as well as to the thermodynamics. (We explore this latter connection in Chapter 13.) Equilibrium constants derived from thermodynamic measurements are defined in terms of *activities* rather than concentrations or partial pressures.

The activity of any substance in an *ideal* mixture is the ratio of the concentration or pressure of the substance either to a reference concentration (1 M) or to a reference pressure (1 atm). For example, if the concentration of a substance in an equilibrium mixture is 0.010 M, its activity is 0.010 M/1 M = 0.010. The units of such ratios always cancel and, consequently, activities have no units. Furthermore, the numerical value of the activity equals the concentration. For pure solids and pure liquids, the situation is even simpler because the activities then merely equal 1 (again with no units).

In real systems, activities are also ratios that have no units. Even though these activities may not be exactly numerically equal to concentrations, we will ignore the differences. All we need to know at this point is that activities have no units. As a result, the *thermodynamic equilibrium constants* derived from them also have no units. It is therefore common practice to write all types of equilibrium constants without units, a practice that we adhere to in this text. In more advanced chemistry courses, you may make more rigorous distinctions between concentrations and activities.

◢ **GIVE IT SOME THOUGHT**

If the concentration of N_2O_4 in an equilibrium mixture is 0.00140 M, what is its activity? (Assume the solution is ideal.)

12.3 | UNDERSTANDING AND WORKING WITH EQUILIBRIUM CONSTANTS

Before doing calculations with equilibrium constants, it is valuable to understand what the magnitude of an equilibrium constant can tell us about the relative concentrations of reactants and products in an equilibrium mixture. It is also useful to consider how the magnitude of any equilibrium constant depends on how the chemical equation is expressed.

The Magnitude of Equilibrium Constants

The magnitude of the equilibrium constant for a reaction gives us important information about the composition of the equilibrium mixture. For example, consider the experimental data for the reaction of carbon monoxide gas and chlorine gas at 100 °C to form phosgene ($COCl_2$), a toxic gas used in the manufacture of certain polymers and insecticides:

$$CO(g) + Cl_2(g) \rightleftharpoons COCl_2(g) \qquad K_c = \frac{[COCl_2]}{[CO][Cl_2]} = 4.56 \times 10^9$$

For the equilibrium constant to be so large, the numerator of the equilibrium-constant expression must be approximately a billion (10^9) times larger than the denominator. Thus, the equilibrium concentration of $COCl_2$ must be much greater than that of CO or Cl_2, and in fact this is just what we find experimentally. We say that this equilibrium *lies to the right* (that is, toward the product side). Likewise, a very small equilibrium constant indicates that the equilibrium mixture contains mostly reactants. We then say that the equilibrium *lies to the left*. In general,

If K ≫ 1 (large K):   Equilibrium lies to right, products predominate

If K ≪ 1 (small K):   Equilibrium lies to left, reactants predominate

These situations are summarized in ▶ FIGURE 12.6. Remember, it is forward and reverse *rates* that are equal at equilibrium, not concentrations.

GO FIGURE

What would this figure look like for a reaction in which *K* ≈ 1?

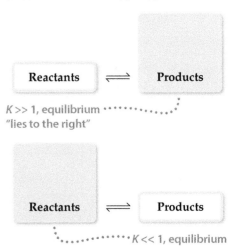

▲ FIGURE 12.6   **Relationship between magnitude of *K* and composition of an equilibrium mixture.**

SAMPLE EXERCISE 12.3   **Interpreting the Magnitude of an Equilibrium Constant**

The following diagrams represent three systems at equilibrium, all in the same-size containers. **(a)** Without doing any calculations, rank the systems in order of increasing K_c. **(b)** If the volume of the containers is 1.0 L and each sphere represents 0.10 mol, calculate K_c for each system.

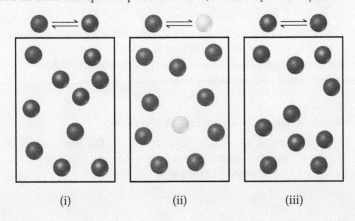

    (i)   (ii)   (iii)

SOLUTION

Analyze We are asked to judge the relative magnitudes of three equilibrium constants and then to calculate them.

Plan (a) The more product present at equilibrium, relative to reactant, the larger the equilibrium constant. **(b)** The equilibrium constant is given by Equation 12.8.

Solve

(a) Each box contains 10 spheres. The amount of product in each varies as follows: (i) 6, (ii) 1, (iii) 8. Therefore, the equilibrium constant varies in the order (ii) < (i) < (iii), from smallest (most reactant) to largest (most products).

(b) In (i) we have 0.60 mol/L product and 0.40 mol/L reactant, giving $K_c = 0.60/0.40 = 1.5$. (You will get the same result by merely dividing the number of spheres of each kind: 6 spheres/4 spheres = 1.5.) In (ii) we have 0.10 mol/L product and 0.90 mol/L reactant, giving $K_c = 0.10/0.90 = 0.11$ (or 1 sphere/9 spheres = 0.11). In (iii) we have 0.80 mol/L product and 0.20 mol/L reactant, giving $K_c = 0.80/0.20 = 4.0$ (or 8 spheres/2 spheres = 4.0). These calculations verify the order in (a).

Comment Imagine a drawing that represents a reaction with a very small or very large value of K_c. For example, what would the drawing look like if $K_c = 1 \times 10^{-5}$? In that case there would need to be 100,000 reactant molecules for only 1 product molecule. But then, that would be impractical to draw.

PRACTICE EXERCISE

For the reaction $H_2(g) + I_2(g) \rightleftharpoons 2\ HI(g)$, $K_p = 794$ at 298 K and $K_p = 55$ at 700 K. Is the formation of HI favored more at the higher or lower temperature?

Answer: at the lower temperature because K_p is larger at the lower temperature

The Direction of the Chemical Equation and *K*

We have seen that we can represent the N_2O_4/NO_2 equilibrium as

$$N_2O_4(g) \rightleftharpoons 2\ NO_2(g) \quad K_c = \frac{[NO_2]^2}{[N_2O_4]} = 0.212 \quad \text{(at 100 °C)} \quad [12.16]$$

We could equally well consider this equilibrium in terms of the reverse reaction:

$$2\ NO_2(g) \rightleftharpoons N_2O_4(g)$$

The equilibrium expression is then

$$K_c = \frac{[N_2O_4]}{[NO_2]^2} = \frac{1}{0.212} = 4.72 \quad \text{(at 100 °C)} \quad [12.17]$$

Equation 12.17 is the reciprocal of the expression in Equation 12.16. *The equilibrium-constant expression for a reaction written in one direction is the reciprocal of the expression for the reaction written in the reverse direction.* Consequently, the numerical value of the equilibrium constant for the reaction written in one direction is the reciprocal of that for the reverse reaction. Both expressions are equally valid, but it is meaningless to say that the equilibrium constant for the equilibrium between NO_2 and N_2O_4 is "0.212" or "4.72" unless we indicate how the equilibrium reaction is written and specify the temperature. Therefore, whenever you are using an equilibrium constant, you should always write the associated balanced chemical equation.

SAMPLE EXERCISE 12.4 | **Evaluating an Equilibrium Constant When an Equation Is Reversed**

For the reaction

$$N_2(g) + O_2(g) \rightleftharpoons 2\ NO(g)$$

that is run at 25 °C, $K_c = 1 \times 10^{-30}$. Use this information to write the equilibrium-constant expression and calculate the equilibrium constant for the reaction

$$2\ NO(g) \rightleftharpoons N_2(g) + O_2(g)$$

SOLUTION

Analyze We are asked to write the equilibrium-constant expression for a reaction and to determine the value of K_c given the chemical equation and equilibrium constant for the reverse reaction.

Plan The equilibrium-constant expression is a quotient of products over reactants, each raised to a power equal to its coefficient in the balanced equation. The value of the equilibrium constant is the reciprocal of that for the reverse reaction.

Solve
Writing products over reactants, we have

$$K_c = \frac{[N_2][O_2]}{[NO]^2}$$

Both the equilibrium-constant expression and the numerical value of the equilibrium constant are the reciprocals of those for the formation of NO from N_2 and O_2:

$$K_c = \frac{[N_2][O_2]}{[NO]^2} = \frac{1}{1 \times 10^{-30}} = 1 \times 10^{30}$$

Comment Regardless of the way we express the equilibrium among NO, N_2, and O_2, at 25 °C it lies on the side that favors N_2 and O_2. Thus, the equilibrium mixture will contain mostly N_2 and O_2 with very little NO present.

PRACTICE EXERCISE
For $N_2(g) + 3 H_2(g) \rightleftharpoons 2 NH_3(g)$, $K_p = 4.34 \times 10^{-3}$ at 300 °C. What is the value of K_p for the reverse reaction?
Answer: 2.30×10^2

Relating Chemical Equation Stoichiometry and Equilibrium Constants

There are many ways to write a balanced chemical equation for a given reaction. For example, if we multiply Equation 12.1, $N_2O_4(g) \rightleftharpoons 2 NO_2(g)$ by 2, we have

$$2 N_2O_4(g) \rightleftharpoons 4 NO_2(g)$$

This chemical equation is balanced and might be written this way in some contexts. Therefore, the equilibrium-constant expression for this equation is

$$K_c = \frac{[NO_2]^4}{[N_2O_4]^2}$$

which is the square of the equilibrium-constant expression given in Equation 12.10 for the reaction as written in Equation 12.1: $[NO_2]^2/[N_2O_4]$. Because the new equilibrium-constant expression equals the original expression squared, the new equilibrium constant K_c equals the original constant squared: $0.212^2 = 0.0449$ (at 100 °C). Once again, it is important to remember that you must relate each equilibrium constant you work with to a *specific* balanced chemical equation. The concentrations of the substances in the equilibrium mixture will be the same no matter how you write the chemical equation, but the value of K_c you calculate depends completely on how you write the reaction.

⏴ **GIVE IT SOME THOUGHT**
How does the magnitude of K_p for the reaction $2 HI(g) \rightleftharpoons H_2(g) + I_2(g)$ change if the equilibrium is written $6 HI(g) \rightleftharpoons 3 H_2(g) + 3 I_2(g)$?

It is also possible to calculate the equilibrium constant for a reaction if we know the equilibrium constants for other reactions that add up to give us the one we want, similar to Hess's law. ∞ (Section 10.6) For example, consider the following two reactions, their equilibrium-constant expressions, and their equilibrium constants at 100 °C:

1. $2 NOBr(g) \rightleftharpoons 2 NO(g) + Br_2(g)$ $K_c = \dfrac{[NO]^2[Br_2]}{[NOBr]^2} = 0.014$

2. $Br_2(g) + Cl_2(g) \rightleftharpoons 2 BrCl(g)$ $K_c = \dfrac{[BrCl]^2}{[Br_2][Cl_2]} = 7.2$

The net sum of these two equations is

3. $2 NOBr(g) + Cl_2(g) \rightleftharpoons 2 NO(g) + 2 BrCl(g)$

You can prove algebraically that the equilibrium-constant expression for reaction 3 is the product of the expressions for reactions 1 and 2:

$$K_c = \frac{[NO]^2[BrCl]^2}{[NOBr]^2[Cl_2]} = \frac{[NO]^2[Br_2]}{[NOBr]^2} \times \frac{[BrCl]^2}{[Br_2][Cl_2]}$$

Thus,

$$K_{c3} = (K_{c1})(K_{c2}) = (0.014)(7.2) = 0.10$$

To summarize:

1. The equilibrium constant of a reaction in the *reverse* direction is the *inverse* (or *reciprocal*) of the equilibrium constant of the reaction in the forward direction:

$$A + B \rightleftharpoons C + D \quad K_1$$
$$C + D \rightleftharpoons A + B \quad K = 1/K_1$$

2. The equilibrium constant of a reaction that has been *multiplied* by a number is equal to the original equilibrium constant raised to a *power* equal to that number.

$$A + B \rightleftharpoons C + D \quad K_1$$
$$nA + nB \rightleftharpoons nC + nD \quad K = K_1{}^n$$

3. The equilibrium constant for a net reaction made up of *two or more reactions* is the *product* of the equilibrium constants for the individual reactions:

$$1.\ A + B \rightleftharpoons C + D \quad K_1$$
$$2.\ C + F \rightleftharpoons G + A \quad K_2$$
$$\overline{3.\ B + F \rightleftharpoons D + G \quad K_3 = (K_1)(K_2)}$$

SAMPLE EXERCISE 12.5 | **Combining Equilibrium Expressions**

Given the reactions

$$HF(aq) \rightleftharpoons H^+(aq) + F^-(aq) \qquad K_c = 6.8 \times 10^{-4}$$

$$H_2C_2O_4(aq) \rightleftharpoons 2\,H^+(aq) + C_2O_4{}^{2-}(aq) \quad K_c = 3.8 \times 10^{-6}$$

determine the value of K_c for the reaction

$$2\,HF(aq) + C_2O_4{}^{2-}(aq) \rightleftharpoons 2\,F^-(aq) + H_2C_2O_4(aq)$$

SOLUTION

Analyze We are given two equilibrium equations and the corresponding equilibrium constants and are asked to determine the equilibrium constant for a third equation, which is related to the first two.

Plan We cannot simply add the first two equations to get the third. Instead, we need to determine how to manipulate the equations to come up with the steps that will add to give us the desired equation.

Solve

If we multiply the first equation by 2 and make the corresponding change to its equilibrium constant (raising to the power 2), we get

$$2\,HF(aq) \rightleftharpoons 2\,H^+(aq) + 2\,F^-(aq) \qquad\qquad K_c = (6.8 \times 10^{-4})^2 = 4.6 \times 10^{-7}$$

Reversing the second equation and again making the corresponding change to its equilibrium constant (taking the reciprocal) gives

$$2\,H^+(aq) + C_2O_4{}^{2-}(aq) \rightleftharpoons H_2C_2O_4(aq) \qquad K_c = \frac{1}{3.8 \times 10^{-6}} = 2.6 \times 10^5$$

Now we have two equations that sum to give the net equation, and we can multiply the individual K_c values to get the desired equilibrium constant.

$$2\,HF(aq) \rightleftharpoons 2\,H^+(aq) + 2\,F^-(aq) \qquad K_c = 4.6 \times 10^{-7}$$
$$\underline{2\,H^+(aq) + C_2O_4{}^{2-}(aq) \rightleftharpoons H_2C_2O_4(aq) \qquad\quad K_c = 2.5 \times 10^5}$$
$$2\,HF(aq) + C_2O_4{}^{2-}(aq) \rightleftharpoons 2\,F^-(aq) + H_2C_2O_4(aq) \quad K_c = (4.6 \times 10^{-7})(2.6 \times 10^5) = 0.12$$

PRACTICE EXERCISE

Given that, at 700 K, $K_p = 54.0$ for the reaction $H_2(g) + I_2(g) \rightleftharpoons 2\,HI(g)$ and $K_p = 1.04 \times 10^{-4}$ for the reaction $N_2(g) + 3\,H_2(g) \rightleftharpoons 2\,NH_3(g)$, determine the value of K_p for the reaction $2\,NH_3(g) + 3\,I_2(g) \rightleftharpoons 6\,HI(g) + N_2(g)$ at 700 K.

Answer: $\dfrac{(54.0)^3}{1.04 \times 10^{-4}} = 1.51 \times 10^9$

12.4 | HETEROGENEOUS EQUILIBRIA

Many equilibria involve substances that are all in the same phase, usually gas or liquid. Such equilibria are called **homogeneous equilibria**. In some cases, however, the substances in equilibrium are in different phases, giving rise to **heterogeneous equilibria**. As an example of the latter, consider the equilibrium that occurs when solid lead(II) chloride dissolves in water to form a saturated solution:

$$PbCl_2(s) \rightleftharpoons Pb^{2+}(aq) + 2\,Cl^-(aq) \qquad [12.18]$$

This system consists of a solid in equilibrium with two aqueous species. If we want to write the equilibrium-constant expression for this process, we encounter a problem we have not encountered previously: How do we express the concentration of a solid? Although we can express that concentration in moles per unit volume, it is unnecessary to do so in writing equilibrium-constant expressions. *Whenever a pure solid or a pure liquid is involved in a heterogeneous equilibrium, its concentration is not included in the equilibrium-constant expression.* Thus, the equilibrium-constant expression for the reaction of Equation 12.18 is

$$K_c = [Pb^{2+}][Cl^-]^2 \qquad [12.19]$$

Even though $PbCl_2(s)$ does not appear in the equilibrium-constant expression, it must be present for equilibrium to occur.

The fact that pure solids and pure liquids are excluded from equilibrium-constant expressions can be explained in two ways. First, the concentration of a pure solid or liquid has a constant value. If the mass of a solid is doubled, its volume also doubles. Thus, its concentration, which relates to the ratio of mass to volume, stays the same. Because equilibrium-constant expressions include terms only for reactants and products whose concentrations can change during a chemical reaction, the concentrations of pure solids and pure liquids are omitted.

The omission can also be rationalized in a second way. Recall from Section 12.2 that what is substituted into a thermodynamic equilibrium expression is the activity of each substance, which is a ratio of the concentration to a reference value. For a pure substance, the reference value is the concentration of the pure substance, so that the activity of any pure solid or liquid is always 1.

 GIVE IT SOME THOUGHT

Write the equilibrium-constant expression for the evaporation of water, $H_2O(l) \rightleftharpoons H_2O(g)$, in terms of partial pressures.

Decomposition of calcium carbonate is another example of a heterogeneous reaction:

$$CaCO_3(s) \rightleftharpoons CaO(s) + CO_2(g)$$

Omitting the concentrations of the solids from the equilibrium-constant expression gives

$$K_c = [CO_2] \quad \text{and} \quad K_p = P_{CO_2}$$

These equations tell us that at a given temperature, an equilibrium among $CaCO_3$, CaO, and CO_2 always leads to the same CO_2 partial pressure as long as all three components are present. As shown in ▶ FIGURE 12.7, we have the same CO_2 pressure regardless of the relative amounts of CaO and $CaCO_3$.

Imagine starting with only CaO in a bell jar and adding $CO_2(g)$ to make its pressure the same as it is in these two bell jars. How does the equilibrium concentration of $CO_2(g)$ in your jar compare with the $CO_2(g)$ equilibrium concentration in these two jars?

$$CaCO_3(s) \rightleftharpoons CaO(s) + CO_2(g)$$

CaCO₃   CaO

Large amount of $CaCO_3$, small amount of CaO, gas pressure P

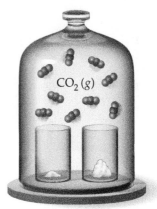

CaCO₃   CaO

Small amount of $CaCO_3$, large amount of CaO, gas pressure still P

▲ FIGURE 12.7 **At a given temperature, the equilibrium pressure of CO_2 in the bell jars is the same no matter how much of each solid is present.**

SAMPLE EXERCISE 12.6 | **Writing Equilibrium-Constant Expressions for Heterogeneous Reactions**

Write the equilibrium-constant expression K_c for

(a) $CO_2(g) + H_2(g) \rightleftharpoons CO(g) + H_2O(l)$

(b) $SnO_2(s) + 2\,CO(g) \rightleftharpoons Sn(s) + 2\,CO_2(g)$

SOLUTION

Analyze We are given two chemical equations, both for heterogeneous equilibria, and asked to write the corresponding equilibrium-constant expressions.

Plan We use the law of mass action, remembering to omit any pure solids and pure liquids from the expressions.

Solve
(a) The equilibrium-constant expression is

$$K_c = \frac{[CO]}{[CO_2][H_2]}$$

Because H_2O appears in the reaction as a liquid, its concentration does not appear in the equilibrium-constant expression.

(b) The equilibrium-constant expression is

$$K_c = \frac{[CO_2]^2}{[CO]^2}$$

Because SnO_2 and Sn are pure solids, their concentrations do not appear in the equilibrium-constant expression.

PRACTICE EXERCISE

Write the following equilibrium-constant expressions:

(a) K_c for $Cr(s) + 3\, Ag^+(aq) \rightleftharpoons Cr^{3+}(aq) + 3\, Ag(s)$
(b) K_p for $3\, Fe(s) + 4\, H_2O(g) \rightleftharpoons Fe_3O_4(s) + 4\, H_2(g)$

Answers: (a) $K_c = \dfrac{[Cr^{3+}]}{[Ag^+]^3}$ (b) $K_p = \dfrac{(P_{H_2})^4}{(P_{H_2O})^4}$

SAMPLE EXERCISE 12.7 **Analyzing a Heterogeneous Equilibrium**

Each of these mixtures was placed in a closed container and allowed to stand:

(a) $CaCO_3(s)$
(b) $CaO(s)$ and $CO_2(g)$ at a pressure greater than the value of K_p
(c) $CaCO_3(s)$ and $CO_2(g)$ at a pressure greater than the value of K_p
(d) $CaCO_3(s)$ and $CaO(s)$

Determine whether or not each mixture can attain the equilibrium

$$CaCO_3(s) \rightleftharpoons CaO(s) + CO_2(g)$$

SOLUTION

Analyze We are asked which of several combinations of species can establish an equilibrium between calcium carbonate and its decomposition products, calcium oxide and carbon dioxide.

Plan For equilibrium to be achieved, it must be possible for both the forward process and the reverse process to occur. For the forward process to occur, there must be some calcium carbonate present. For the reverse process to occur, there must be both calcium oxide and carbon dioxide. In both cases, either the necessary compounds may be present initially or they may be formed by reaction of the other species.

Solve Equilibrium can be reached in all cases except (c) as long as sufficient quantities of solids are present. (a) $CaCO_3$ simply decomposes, forming $CaO(s)$ and $CO_2(g)$ until the equilibrium pressure of CO_2 is attained. There must be enough $CaCO_3$, however, to allow the CO_2 pressure to reach equilibrium. (b) CO_2 continues to combine with CaO until the partial pressure of the CO_2 decreases to the equilibrium value. (c) There is no CaO present, so equilibrium cannot be attained because there is no way the CO_2 pressure can decrease to its equilibrium value (which would require some of the CO_2 to react with CaO). (d) The situation is essentially the same as in (a): $CaCO_3$ decomposes until equilibrium is attained. The presence of CaO initially makes no difference.

PRACTICE EXERCISE

When added to $Fe_3O_4(s)$ in a closed container, which one of the following substances — $H_2(g)$, $H_2O(g)$, $O_2(g)$ — allows equilibrium to be established in the reaction $3\, Fe(s) + 4\, H_2O(g) \rightleftharpoons Fe_3O_4(s) + 4\, H_2(g)$?
Answer: $H_2(g)$

When a solvent is a reactant or product in an equilibrium, its concentration is omitted from the equilibrium-constant expression, provided the concentrations of reactants and products are low, so that the solvent is essentially a pure substance. Applying this guideline to an equilibrium involving water as a solvent,

$$H_2O(l) + CO_3^{2-}(aq) \rightleftharpoons OH^-(aq) + HCO_3^-(aq) \qquad [12.20]$$

gives an equilibrium-constant expression that does not contain $[H_2O]$:

$$K_c = \frac{[OH^-][HCO_3^-]}{[CO_3^{2-}]} \qquad [12.21]$$

 GIVE IT SOME THOUGHT

Write the equilibrium-constant expression for the reaction $NH_3(aq) + H_2O(l) \rightleftharpoons NH_4^+(aq) + OH^-(aq)$

12.5 | CALCULATING EQUILIBRIUM CONSTANTS

If we can measure the equilibrium concentrations of all the reactants and products in a chemical reaction, as we did with the data in Table 12.1, calculating the value of the equilibrium constant is straightforward. We simply insert all the equilibrium concentrations into the equilibrium-constant expression for the reaction.

SAMPLE EXERCISE 12.8 | **Calculating K When All Equilibrium Concentrations Are Known**

After a mixture of hydrogen and nitrogen gases in a reaction vessel is allowed to attain equilibrium at 472 °C, it is found to contain 7.38 atm H_2, 2.46 atm N_2, and 0.166 atm NH_3. From these data, calculate the equilibrium constant K_p for the reaction

$$N_2(g) + 3\,H_2(g) \rightleftharpoons 2\,NH_3(g)$$

SOLUTION

Analyze We are given a balanced equation and equilibrium partial pressures and are asked to calculate the value of the equilibrium constant.

Plan Using the balanced equation, we write the equilibrium-constant expression. We then substitute the equilibrium partial pressures into the expression and solve for K_p.

Solve

$$K_p = \frac{(P_{NH_3})^2}{P_{N_2}(P_{H_2})^3} = \frac{(0.166)^2}{(2.46)(7.38)^3} = 2.79 \times 10^{-5}$$

PRACTICE EXERCISE

An aqueous solution of acetic acid is found to have the following equilibrium concentrations at 25 °C: $[CH_3COOH] = 1.65 \times 10^{-2}\,M$; $[H^+] = 5.44 \times 10^{-4}\,M$; and $[CH_3COO^-] = 5.44 \times 10^{-4}\,M$. Calculate the equilibrium constant K_c for the ionization of acetic acid at 25 °C. The reaction is

$$CH_3COOH(aq) \rightleftharpoons H^+(aq) + CH_3COO^-(aq)$$

Answer: 1.79×10^{-5}

Often we do not know the equilibrium concentrations of all species in an equilibrium mixture. If we know the equilibrium concentration of at least one species, however, we can generally use the stoichiometry of the reaction to deduce the equilibrium concentrations of the others. The following steps outline the procedure:

1. Tabulate all known initial and equilibrium concentrations of the species that appear in the equilibrium-constant expression.

2. For those species for which initial and equilibrium concentrations are known, calculate the change in concentration that occurs as the system reaches equilibrium.

3. Use the stoichiometry of the reaction (that is, the coefficients in the balanced chemical equation) to calculate the changes in concentration for all other species in the equilibrium-constant expression.

4. Use initial concentrations from step 1 and changes in concentration from step 3 to calculate any equilibrium concentrations not tabulated in step 1.

5. Determine the value of the equilibrium constant.

SAMPLE EXERCISE 12.9 | **Calculating K from Initial and Equilibrium Concentrations**

A closed system initially containing $1.000 \times 10^{-3} M$ H_2 and $2.000 \times 10^{-3} M$ I_2 at 448 °C is allowed to reach equilibrium, and at equilibrium the HI concentration is $1.87 \times 10^{-3} M$. Calculate K_c at 448 °C for the reaction taking place, which is

$$H_2(g) + I_2(g) \rightleftharpoons 2 HI(g)$$

SOLUTION

Analyze We are given the initial concentrations of H_2 and I_2 and the equilibrium concentration of HI. We are asked to calculate the equilibrium constant K_c for $H_2(g) + I_2(g) \rightleftharpoons 2 HI(g)$.

Plan We construct a table to find equilibrium concentrations of all species and then use the equilibrium concentrations to calculate the equilibrium constant.

Solve First, we tabulate the initial and equilibrium concentrations of as many species as we can. We also provide space in our table for listing the changes in concentrations. As shown, it is convenient to use the chemical equation as the heading for the table.

	$H_2(g)$	+	$I_2(g)$	$\rightleftharpoons$	$2 HI(g)$
Initial concentration (M)	1.000×10^{-3}		2.000×10^{-3}		0
Change in concentration (M)					
Equilibrium concentration (M)					1.87×10^{-3}

Second, we calculate the change in HI concentration, which is the difference between the equilibrium and initial values:

$$\text{Change in [HI]} = 1.87 \times 10^{-3} M - 0 = 1.87 \times 10^{-3} M$$

Third, we use the coefficients in the balanced equation to relate the change in [HI] to the changes in [H_2] and [I_2]:

$$\left(1.87 \times 10^{-3} \frac{\text{mol HI}}{\text{L}}\right)\left(\frac{1 \text{ mol } H_2}{2 \text{ mol HI}}\right) = 0.935 \times 10^{-3} \frac{\text{mol } H_2}{\text{L}}$$

$$\left(1.87 \times 10^{-3} \frac{\text{mol HI}}{\text{L}}\right)\left(\frac{1 \text{ mol } I_2}{2 \text{ mol HI}}\right) = 0.935 \times 10^{-3} \frac{\text{mol } I_2}{\text{L}}$$

Fourth, we calculate the equilibrium concentrations of H_2 and I_2, using initial concentrations and changes in concentration. The equilibrium concentration equals the initial concentration minus that consumed:

$$[H_2] = 1.000 \times 10^{-3} M - 0.935 \times 10^{-3} M = 0.065 \times 10^{-3} M$$

$$[I_2] = 2.000 \times 10^{-3} M - 0.935 \times 10^{-3} M = 1.065 \times 10^{-3} M$$

Our table now looks like this (with equilibrium concentrations in blue for emphasis):

	$H_2(g)$	+	$I_2(g)$	$\rightleftharpoons$	$2 HI(g)$
Initial concentration (M)	1.000×10^{-3}		2.000×10^{-3}		0
Change in concentration (M)	-0.935×10^{-3}		-0.935×10^{-3}		$+1.87 \times 10^{-3}$
Equilibrium concentration (M)	0.065×10^{-3}		1.065×10^{-3}		1.87×10^{-3}

Notice that the entries for the changes are negative when a reactant is consumed and positive when a product is formed.

Finally, we use the equilibrium-constant expression to calculate the equilibrium constant:

$$K_c = \frac{[HI]^2}{[H_2][I_2]} = \frac{(1.87 \times 10^{-3})^2}{(0.065 \times 10^{-3})(1.065 \times 10^{-3})} = 51$$

Comment The same method can be applied to gaseous equilibrium problems to calculate K_p, in which case partial pressures are used as table entries in place of molar concentrations. Your instructor may refer to this kind of table as an ICE chart, where ICE stands for Initial – Change – Equilibrium.

PRACTICE EXERCISE

Sulfur trioxide decomposes at high temperature in a sealed container: $2 SO_3(g) \rightleftharpoons 2 SO_2(g) + O_2(g)$. Initially, the vessel is charged at 1000 K with $SO_3(g)$ at a partial pressure of 0.500 atm. At equilibrium the SO_3 partial pressure is 0.200 atm. Calculate the value of K_p at 1000 K.

Answer: 0.338

12.6 | APPLICATIONS OF EQUILIBRIUM CONSTANTS

We have seen that the magnitude of K indicates the extent to which a reaction proceeds. If K is very large, the equilibrium mixture contains mostly substances on the product side of the equation for the reaction. (That is, the reaction proceeds far to the right.) If K is very small (that is, much less than 1), the equilibrium mixture contains mainly substances on the reactant side of the equation. The equilibrium constant also allows us to (1) predict the direction in which a reaction mixture achieves equilibrium and (2) calculate equilibrium concentrations of reactants and products.

Predicting the Direction of Reaction

For the formation of NH_3 from N_2 and H_2 (Equation 12.6), $K_c = 0.105$ at 472 °C. Suppose we place 2.00 mol of H_2, 1.00 mol of N_2, and 2.00 mol of NH_3 in a 1.00-L container at 472 °C. How will the mixture react to reach equilibrium? Will N_2 and H_2 react to form more NH_3, or will NH_3 decompose to N_2 and H_2?

To answer this question, we substitute the starting concentrations of N_2, H_2, and NH_3 into the equilibrium-constant expression and compare its value to the equilibrium constant:

$$\frac{[NH_3]^2}{[N_2][H_2]^3} = \frac{(2.00)^2}{(1.00)(2.00)^3} = 0.500 \quad \text{whereas} \quad K_c = 0.105 \qquad [12.22]$$

To reach equilibrium, the quotient $[NH_3]^2/[N_2][H_2]^3$ must decrease from the starting value of 0.500 to the equilibrium value of 0.105. Because the system is closed, this change can happen only if $[NH_3]$ decreases and $[N_2]$ and $[H_2]$ increase. Thus, the reaction proceeds toward equilibrium by forming N_2 and H_2 from NH_3; that is, the reaction as written in Equation 12.6 proceeds from right to left.

This approach can be formalized by defining a quantity called the reaction quotient. The **reaction quotient**, Q, *is a number obtained by substituting reactant and product concentrations or partial pressures at any point during a reaction into an equilibrium-constant expression.* Therefore, for the general reaction

$$a\,A + b\,B \rightleftharpoons d\,D + e\,E$$

the reaction quotient in terms of molar concentrations is

$$Q_c = \frac{[D]^d[E]^e}{[A]^a[B]^b} \qquad [12.23]$$

(A related quantity Q_p can be written for any reaction that involves gases by using partial pressures instead of concentrations.)

Although we use what looks like the equilibrium-constant expression to calculate the reaction quotient, the concentrations we use may or may not be the equilibrium concentrations. For example, when we substituted the starting concentrations into the equilibrium-constant expression of Equation 12.22, we obtained $Q_c = 0.500$ whereas $K_c = 0.105$. The equilibrium constant has only one value at each temperature. The reaction quotient, however, varies as the reaction proceeds.

Of what use is Q? One practical thing we can do with Q is tell whether our reaction really is at equilibrium, which is an especially valuable option when a reaction is very slow. We can take samples of our reaction mixture as the reaction proceeds, separate the components, and measure their concentrations. Then we insert these numbers into Equation 12.23 for our reaction. To determine whether or not we are at equilibrium, or in which direction the reaction proceeds to achieve equilibrium, we compare the values of Q_c and K_c or Q_p and K_p. Three possible situations arise:

- $Q = K$: The reaction quotient equals the equilibrium constant only if the system is at equilibrium.

At equilibrium

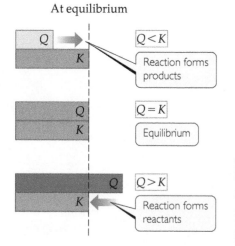

▲ **FIGURE 12.8** **Predicting the direction of a reaction by comparing _Q_ and _K_ at a given temperature.**

- $Q > K$: The concentration of products is too large and that of reactants too small. Substances on the right side of the chemical equation react to form substances on the left; the reaction proceeds from right to left to approach equilibrium.

- $Q < K$: The concentration of products is too small and that of reactants too large. The reaction achieves equilibrium by forming more products; it proceeds from left to right.

These relationships are summarized in ◀ **FIGURE 12.8**.

SAMPLE EXERCISE 12.10 | **Predicting the Direction of Approach to Equilibrium**

At 448 °C the equilibrium constant K_c for the reaction

$$H_2(g) + I_2(g) \rightleftharpoons 2\,HI(g)$$

is 50.5. Predict in which direction the reaction proceeds to reach equilibrium if we start with 2.0×10^{-2} mol of HI, 1.0×10^{-2} mol of H_2, and 3.0×10^{-2} mol of I_2 in a 2.00-L container.

SOLUTION

Analyze We are given a volume and initial molar amounts of the species in a reaction and asked to determine in which direction the reaction must proceed to achieve equilibrium.

Plan We can determine the starting concentration of each species in the reaction mixture. We can then substitute the starting concentrations into the equilibrium-constant expression to calculate the reaction quotient, Q_c. Comparing the magnitudes of the equilibrium constant, which is given, and the reaction quotient will tell us in which direction the reaction will proceed.

Solve
The initial concentrations are

$$[HI] = 2.0 \times 10^{-2} \text{ mol}/2.00 \text{ L} = 1.0 \times 10^{-2}\,M$$
$$[H_2] = 1.0 \times 10^{-2} \text{ mol}/2.00 \text{ L} = 5.0 \times 10^{-3}\,M$$
$$[I_2] = 3.0 \times 10^{-2} \text{ mol}/2.00 \text{ L} = 1.5 \times 10^{-2}\,M$$

The reaction quotient is therefore

$$Q_c = \frac{[HI]^2}{[H_2][I_2]} = \frac{(1.0 \times 10^{-2})^2}{(5.0 \times 10^{-3})(1.5 \times 10^{-2})} = 1.3$$

Because $Q_c < K_c$, the concentration of HI must increase and the concentrations of H_2 and I_2 must decrease to reach equilibrium; the reaction as written proceeds left to right to attain equilibrium.

PRACTICE EXERCISE

At 1000 K the value of K_p for the reaction $2\,SO_3(g) \rightleftharpoons 2\,SO_2(g) + O_2(g)$ is 0.338. Calculate the value for Q_p, and predict the direction in which the reaction proceeds toward equilibrium if the initial partial pressures are $P_{SO_3} = 0.16$ atm; $P_{SO_2} = 0.41$ atm; $P_{O_2} = 2.5$ atm.

Answer: $Q_p = 16$; $Q_p > K_p$, and so the reaction will proceed from right to left, forming more SO_3.

Calculating Equilibrium Concentrations

Chemists frequently need to calculate the amounts of reactants and products present at equilibrium in a reaction for which they know the equilibrium constant. The approach in solving problems of this type is similar to the one we used for evaluating equilibrium constants: We tabulate initial concentrations or partial pressures, changes in those concentrations or pressures, and final equilibrium concentrations or partial pressures. Usually we end up using the equilibrium-constant expression to derive an equation that must be solved for an unknown quantity, as demonstrated in Sample Exercise 12.11.

SAMPLE EXERCISE 12.11 **Calculating Equilibrium Concentrations**

For the Haber process, $N_2(g) + 3 H_2(g) \rightleftharpoons 2 NH_3(g)$, $K_p = 1.45 \times 10^{-5}$ at 500 °C. In an equilibrium mixture of the three gases at 500 °C, the partial pressure of H_2 is 0.928 atm and that of N_2 is 0.432 atm. What is the partial pressure of NH_3 in this equilibrium mixture?

SOLUTION

Analyze We are given an equilibrium constant, K_p, and the equilibrium partial pressures of two of the three substances in the equation (N_2 and H_2), and we are asked to calculate the equilibrium partial pressure for the third substance (NH_3).

Plan We can set K_p equal to the equilibrium-constant expression and substitute in the partial pressures that we know. Then we can solve for the only unknown in the equation.

Solve We tabulate the equilibrium pressures:

$$N_2(g) + 3 H_2(g) \rightleftharpoons 2 NH_3(g)$$

Equilibrium pressure (atm)	0.432	0.928	x

Because we do not know the equilibrium pressure of NH_3, we represent it with x. At equilibrium the pressures must satisfy the equilibrium-constant expression:

$$K_p = \frac{(P_{NH_3})^2}{P_{N_2}(P_{H_2})^3} = \frac{x^2}{(0.432)(0.928)^3} = 1.45 \times 10^{-5}$$

We now rearrange the equation to solve for x:

$$x^2 = (1.45 \times 10^{-5})(0.432)(0.928)^3 = 5.01 \times 10^{-6}$$

$$x = \sqrt{5.01 \times 10^{-6}} = 2.24 \times 10^{-3} \text{ atm} = P_{NH_3}$$

Check We can always check our answer by using it to recalculate the value of the equilibrium constant:

$$K_p = \frac{(2.24 \times 10^{-3})^2}{(0.432)(0.928)^3} = 1.45 \times 10^{-5}$$

PRACTICE EXERCISE

At 500 K the reaction $PCl_5(g) \rightleftharpoons PCl_3(g) + Cl_2(g)$ has $K_p = 0.497$. In an equilibrium mixture at 500 K, the partial pressure of PCl_5 is 0.860 atm and that of PCl_3 is 0.350 atm. What is the partial pressure of Cl_2 in the equilibrium mixture?

Answer: 1.22 atm

In many situations we know the value of the equilibrium constant and the initial amounts of all species. We must then solve for the equilibrium amounts. Solving this type of problem usually entails treating the change in concentration as a variable. The stoichiometry of the reaction gives us the relationship between the changes in the amounts of all the reactants and products, as illustrated in Sample Exercise 12.12. The calculations frequently involve the quadratic formula, as you will see in this exercise.

SAMPLE EXERCISE 12.12 **Calculating Equilibrium Concentrations from Initial Concentrations**

A 1.000-L flask is filled with 1.000 mol of $H_2(g)$ and 2.000 mol of $I_2(g)$ at 448 °C. The value of the equilibrium constant K_c for the reaction

$$H_2(g) + I_2(g) \rightleftharpoons 2 HI(g)$$

at 448 °C is 50.5. What are the equilibrium concentrations of H_2, I_2, and HI in moles per liter?

SOLUTION

Analyze We are given the volume of a container, an equilibrium constant, and starting amounts of reactants in the container and are asked to calculate the equilibrium concentrations of all species.

Plan In this case we are not given any of the equilibrium concentrations. We must develop some relationships that relate the initial concentrations to those at equilibrium. The procedure is similar in many regards to that outlined in Sample Exercise 12.9, where we calculated an equilibrium constant using initial concentrations.

Solve First, we note the initial concentrations of H_2 and I_2:

$$[H_2] = 1.000\ M \quad \text{and} \quad [I_2] = 2.000\ M$$

Second, we construct a table in which we tabulate the initial concentrations:

	$H_2(g)$ +	$I_2(g)$ $\rightleftharpoons$	2 HI(g)
Initial concentration (M)	1.000	2.000	0
Change in concentration (M)			
Equilibrium concentration (M)			

Third, we use the stoichiometry of the reaction to determine the changes in concentration that occur as the reaction proceeds to equilibrium. The H_2 and I_2 concentrations will decrease as equilibrium is established and that of HI will increase. Let's represent the change in concentration of H_2 by x. The balanced chemical equation tells us the relationship between the changes in the concentrations of the three gases. For each x mol of H_2 that reacts, x mol of I_2 are consumed and $2x$ mol of HI are produced:

Fourth, we use initial concentrations and changes in concentrations, as dictated by stoichiometry, to express the equilibrium concentrations. With all our entries, our table now looks like this:

Fifth, we substitute the equilibrium concentrations into the equilibrium-constant expression and solve for x:

If you have an equation-solving calculator, you can solve this equation directly for x. If not, expand this expression to obtain a quadratic equation in x:

Solving the quadratic equation (Appendix A.3) leads to two solutions for x:

When we substitute $x = 2.323$ into the expressions for the equilibrium concentrations, we find *negative* concentrations of H_2 and I_2. Because a negative concentration is not chemically meaningful, we reject this solution. We then use $x = 0.935$ to find the equilibrium concentrations:

Check We can check our solution by putting these numbers into the equilibrium-constant expression to assure that we correctly calculate the equilibrium constant:

	$H_2(g)$	$+$	$I_2(g)$	$\rightleftharpoons$	$2\,HI(g)$
Initial concentration (M)	1.000		2.000		0
Change in concentration (M)	$-x$		$-x$		$+2x$
Equilibrium concentration (M)					

	$H_2(g)$	$+$	$I_2(g)$	$\rightleftharpoons$	$2\,HI(g)$
Initial concentration (M)	1.000		2.000		0
Change in concentration (M)	$-x$		$-x$		$+2x$
Equilibrium concentration (M)	$1.000 - x$		$2.000 - x$		$2x$

$$K_c = \frac{[\text{HI}]^2}{[\text{H}_2][\text{I}_2]} = \frac{(2x)^2}{(1.000 - x)(2.000 - x)} = 50.5$$

$$4x^2 = 50.5(x^2 - 3.000x + 2.000)$$
$$46.5x^2 - 151.5x + 101.0 = 0$$

$$x = \frac{-(-151.5) \pm \sqrt{(-151.5)^2 - 4(46.5)(101.0)}}{2(46.5)} = 2.323 \text{ or } 0.935$$

$$[\text{H}_2] = 1.000 - x = 0.065 \ M$$
$$[\text{I}_2] = 2.000 - x = 1.065 \ M$$
$$[\text{HI}] = 2x = 1.87 \ M$$

$$K_c = \frac{[\text{HI}]^2}{[\text{H}_2][\text{I}_2]} = \frac{(1.87)^2}{(0.065)(1.065)} = 51$$

Comment Whenever you use a quadratic equation to solve an equilibrium problem, one of the solutions to the equation will give you a value that leads to negative concentrations and thus is not chemically meaningful. Reject this solution to the quadratic equation.

PRACTICE EXERCISE
For the equilibrium $PCl_5(g) \rightleftharpoons PCl_3(g) + Cl_2(g)$, the equilibrium constant K_p is 0.497 at 500 K. A gas cylinder at 500 K is charged with $PCl_5(g)$ at an initial pressure of 1.66 atm. What are the equilibrium pressures of PCl_5, PCl_3, and Cl_2 at this temperature?
Answer: $P_{PCl_5} = 0.967$ atm, $P_{PCl_3} = P_{Cl_2} = 0.693$ atm

12.7 | LE CHÂTELIER'S PRINCIPLE

Many of the products we use in everyday life are obtained from the chemical industry. Chemists and chemical engineers in industry spend a great deal of time and effort to maximize the yield of valuable products and minimize waste. For example, when Haber developed his process for making ammonia from N_2 and H_2, he examined how reaction conditions might be varied to increase yield. Using the values of the equilibrium constant at various temperatures, he calculated the equilibrium amounts of NH_3 formed under a variety of conditions. Some of Haber's results are shown in ▶ FIGURE 12.9.

GO FIGURE

At what combination of pressure and temperature should you run the reaction to maximize NH_3 yield?

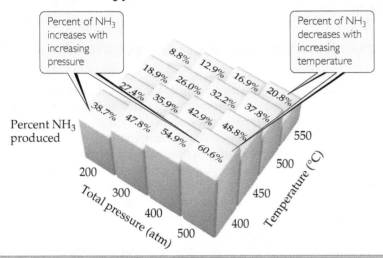

◄ **FIGURE 12.9   Effect of temperature and pressure on NH₃ yield in the Haber process.** Each mixture was produced by starting with a 3:1 molar mixture of H_2 and N_2.

Notice that the percent of NH_3 present at equilibrium decreases with increasing temperature and increases with increasing pressure.

We can understand these effects in terms of a principle first put forward by Henri-Louis Le Châtelier* (1850–1936), a French industrial chemist: *If a system at equilibrium is disturbed by a change in temperature, pressure, or a component concentration, the system will shift its equilibrium position so as to counteract the effect of the disturbance.*

Le Chatelier's Principle

If a system at equilibrium is disturbed by a change in **concentration, pressure,** or **temperature,** the system will shift its equilibrium position so as to counter the effect of the disturbance.

Concentration: adding or removing a reactant or product

If a substance is added to a system at equilibrium, the system reacts to consume some of the substance. If a substance is removed from a system, the system reacts to produce more of substance.

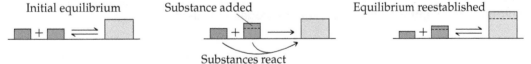

Pressure: changing the pressure by changing the volume

At constant temperature, reducing the volume of a gaseous equilibrium mixture causes the system to shift in the direction that reduces the number of moles of gas.

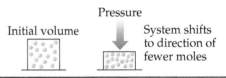

Temperature:

If the temperature of a system at equilibrium is increased, the system reacts as if we added a reactant to an endothermic reaction or a product to an exothermic reaction. The equilibrium shifts in the direction that consumes the "excess reactant," namely heat.

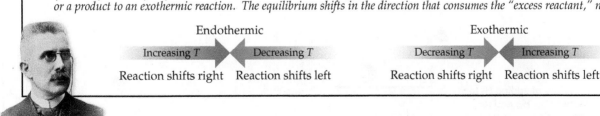

*Pronounced "le-SHOT-lee-ay."

In this section we use Le Châtelier's principle to make qualitative predictions about how a system at equilibrium responds to various changes in external conditions. We consider three ways in which a chemical equilibrium can be disturbed: (1) adding or removing a reactant or product, (2) changing the pressure by changing the volume, and (3) changing the temperature.

Change in Reactant or Product Concentration

A system at dynamic equilibrium is in a state of balance. When the concentrations of species in the reaction are altered, the equilibrium shifts until a new state of balance is attained. What does *shift* mean? It means that reactant and product concentrations change over time to accommodate the new situation. *Shift* does *not* mean that the equilibrium constant itself is altered; the equilibrium constant remains the same. Le Châtelier's principle states that the shift is in the direction that minimizes or reduces the effect of the change. Therefore, *if a chemical system is already at equilibrium and the concentration of any substance in the mixture is increased (either reactant or product), the system reacts to consume some of that substance. Conversely, if the concentration of a substance is decreased, the system reacts to produce some of that substance.*

There is no change in the equilibrium constant when we change the concentrations of reactants or products. As an example, consider our familiar equilibrium mixture of N_2, H_2, and NH_3:

$$N_2(g) + 3\,H_2(g) \rightleftharpoons 2\,NH_3(g)$$

Adding H_2 causes the system to shift so as to reduce the increased concentration of H_2 (▼ FIGURE 12.10). This change can occur only if the reaction consumes H_2 and simultaneously consumes N_2 to form more NH_3. Adding N_2 to the equilibrium mixture likewise causes the reaction to shift toward forming more NH_3. Removing NH_3 also causes a shift toward producing more NH_3, whereas *adding* NH_3 to the system at equilibrium causes the reaction to shift in the direction that reduces the increased NH_3 concentration: Some of the added ammonia decomposes to form N_2 and H_2.

In the Haber reaction, therefore, removing NH_3 from an equilibrium mixture of N_2, H_2, and NH_3 causes the reaction to shift right to form more NH_3. If the NH_3 can be removed continuously as it is produced, the yield can be increased dramatically. In the

GO FIGURE

Why does the nitrogen concentration decrease after hydrogen is added?

$$N_2(g) + 3\,H_2(g) \rightleftharpoons 2\,NH_3(g)$$

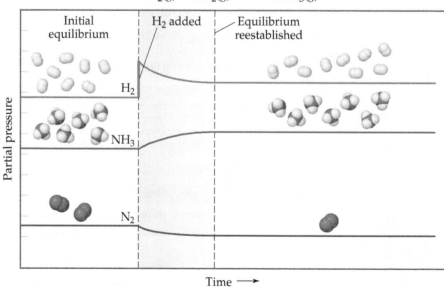

▶ **FIGURE 12.10 Effect of adding H_2 to an equilibrium mixture of N_2, H_2, and NH_3.** Adding H_2 causes the reaction as written to shift to the right, consuming some H_2 to produce more NH_3.

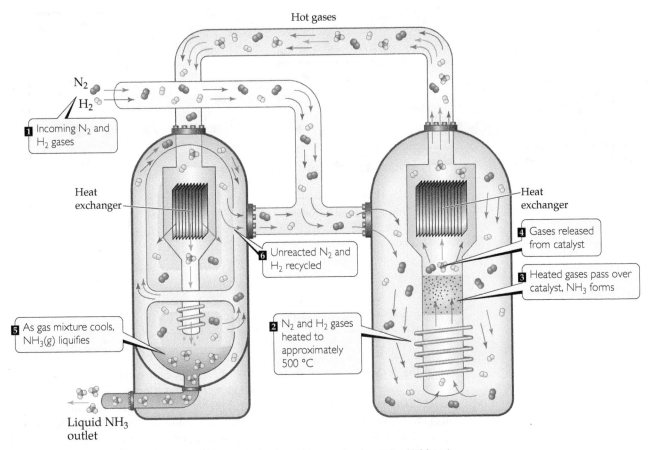

▲ **FIGURE 12.11** **Diagram of the industrial production of ammonia.** Incoming $N_2(g)$ and $H_2(g)$ are heated to approximately 500 °C and passed over a catalyst. When the resultant N_2, H_2, and NH_3 mixture is cooled, the NH_3 liquefies and is removed from the mixture, shifting the reaction to produce more NH_3.

industrial production of ammonia, the NH_3 is continuously removed by selectively liquefying it (▲ **FIGURE 12.11**). (The boiling point of NH_3, −33 °C, is much higher than those of N_2, −196 °C, and H_2, −253 °C.) The liquid NH_3 is removed, and the N_2 and H_2 are recycled to form more NH_3. As a result of the product being continuously removed, the reaction is driven essentially to completion.

 GIVE IT SOME THOUGHT

What happens to the equilibrium $2\,NO(g) + O_2(g) \rightleftharpoons 2\,NO_2(g)$ if
a. O_2 is added to the system,
b. NO is removed?

Effects of Volume and Pressure Changes

If a system containing one or more gases is at equilibrium and its volume is decreased, thereby increasing its total pressure, Le Châtelier's principle indicates that the system responds by shifting its equilibrium position to reduce the pressure. A system can reduce its pressure by reducing the total number of gas molecules (fewer molecules of gas exert a lower pressure). Thus, at constant temperature, *reducing the volume of a gaseous equilibrium mixture causes the system to shift in the direction that reduces the number of moles of gas*. Increasing the volume causes a shift in the direction that produces more gas molecules (▶ **FIGURE 12.12**).

GIVE IT SOME THOUGHT

What happens to the equilibrium $2\,SO_2(g) + O_2(g) \rightleftharpoons 2\,SO_3(g)$ if the volume of the system is increased?

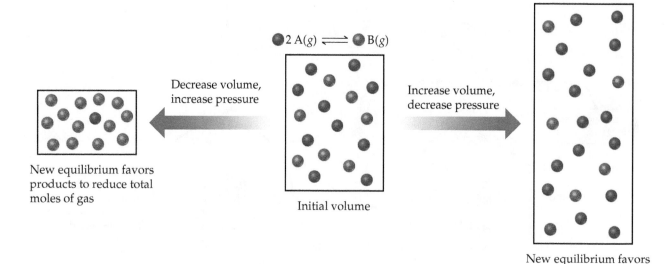

Decrease volume, increase pressure

2 A(g) ⇌ B(g)

Increase volume, decrease pressure

New equilibrium favors products to reduce total moles of gas

Initial volume

New equilibrium favors reactants to increase total moles of gas

▲ FIGURE 12.12 **Pressure and Le Châtelier's principle.**

In the reaction $N_2(g) + 3 H_2(g) \rightleftharpoons 2 NH_3(g)$, four molecules of reactant are consumed for every two molecules of product produced. Consequently, an increase in pressure (caused by a decrease in volume) shifts the reaction in the direction that produces fewer gas molecules, which leads to the formation of more NH_3, as indicated in Figure 12.9. In the reaction $H_2(g) + I_2(g) \rightleftharpoons 2 HI(g)$, the number of molecules of gaseous products (two) equals the number of molecules of gaseous reactants; therefore, changing the pressure does not influence the position of equilibrium.

Keep in mind that, as long as temperature remains constant, pressure-volume changes do *not* change the value of K. Rather, these changes alter the partial pressures of the gaseous substances. In Sample Exercise 12.8, we calculated $K_p = 2.79 \times 10^{-5}$ for the Haber reaction, $N_2(g) + 3 H_2(g) \rightleftharpoons 2 NH_3(g)$, in an equilibrium mixture at 472 °C containing 7.38 atm H_2, 2.46 atm N_2, and 0.166 atm NH_3. Consider what happens when we suddenly reduce the volume of the system by one-half. If there were no shift in equilibrium, this volume change would cause the partial pressures of all substances to double, giving $P_{H_2} = 14.76$ atm, $P_{N_2} = 4.92$ atm, and $P_{NH_3} = 0.332$ atm. The reaction quotient would then no longer equal the equilibrium constant:

$$Q_p = \frac{(P_{NH_3})^2}{P_{N_2}(P_{H_2})^3} = \frac{(0.332)^2}{(4.92)(14.76)^3} = 6.97 \times 10^{-6} \neq K_p$$

Because $Q_p < K_p$, the system would no longer be at equilibrium. Equilibrium would be reestablished by increasing P_{NH_3} and/or decreasing P_{N_2} and P_{H_2} until $Q_p = K_p = 2.79 \times 10^{-5}$. Therefore, the equilibrium shifts to the right in the reaction as written, as Le Châtelier's principle predicts.

It is possible to change the pressure of a system in which a chemical reaction is running without changing its volume. For example, pressure increases if additional amounts of any reacting components are added to the system. We have already seen how to deal with a change in concentration of a reactant or product. The total pressure in the reaction vessel might also be increased by adding a gas that is not involved in the equilibrium. For example, argon might be added to the ammonia equilibrium system. The argon would not alter the partial pressures of any of the reacting components and therefore would not cause a shift in equilibrium.

Effect of Temperature Changes

Changes in concentrations or partial pressures shift equilibria without changing the value of the equilibrium constant. In contrast, almost every equilibrium constant changes as the temperature changes. For example, consider the equilibrium established when cobalt(II) chloride ($CoCl_2$) is dissolved in hydrochloric acid, $HCl(aq)$, in the endothermic reaction

$$Co(H_2O)_6^{2+}(aq) + 4\,Cl^-(aq) \rightleftharpoons CoCl_4^{2-}(aq) + 6\,H_2O(l) \qquad \Delta H > 0 \qquad [12.24]$$
$$\text{\small Pale pink} \hspace{5cm} \text{\small Deep blue}$$

Because $Co(H_2O)_6^{2+}$ is pink and $CoCl_4^{2-}$ is blue, the position of this equilibrium is readily apparent from the color of the solution (▼ **FIGURE 12.13**). When the solution is heated it turns blue, indicating that the equilibrium has shifted to form more $CoCl_4^{2-}$. Cooling the solution leads to a pink solution, indicating that the equilibrium has shifted to produce more $Co(H_2O)_6^{2+}$. We can monitor this reaction by spectroscopic methods, measuring the concentration of all species at the different temperatures. ∞ (Section 14.2) We can then calculate the equilibrium constant at each temperature. How can we explain the fact that the equilibrium constants and therefore the position of equilibrium both depend on temperature?

We can deduce the rules for the relationship between K and temperature from Le Châtelier's principle. We do this by treating heat as a chemical reagent. In an *endothermic* (heat-absorbing) reaction, we consider heat a *reactant*, and in an *exothermic* (heat-releasing) reaction, we consider heat a *product*:

Endothermic: Reactants + *heat* $\rightleftharpoons$ products

Exothermic: Reactants $\rightleftharpoons$ products + *heat*

When the temperature of a system at equilibrium is increased, the system reacts as if we added a reactant to an endothermic reaction or a product to an exothermic reaction. The equilibrium shifts in the direction that consumes the excess reactant (or product), namely heat.

$\Delta H > 0$, endothermic reaction

$$\text{Heat} + Co(H_2O)_6^{2+}(aq) + 4\,Cl^-(aq) \rightleftharpoons CoCl_4^{2-}(aq) + 6\,H_2O(l)$$
$$\text{Pink} \hspace{5cm} \text{Blue}$$

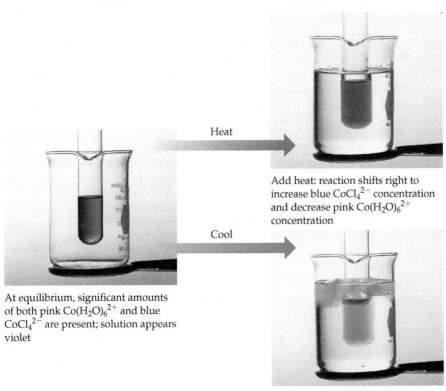

At equilibrium, significant amounts of both pink $Co(H_2O)_6^{2+}$ and blue $CoCl_4^{2-}$ are present; solution appears violet

Heat

Add heat: reaction shifts right to increase blue $CoCl_4^{2-}$ concentration and decrease pink $Co(H_2O)_6^{2+}$ concentration

Cool

Remove heat: reaction shifts left to decrease blue $CoCl_4^{2-}$ concentration and increase pink $Co(H_2O)_6^{2+}$ concentration

◀ **FIGURE 12.13   Temperature and Le Châtelier's principle.**

⬛ GIVE IT SOME THOUGHT

Use Le Châtelier's principle to explain why the equilibrium vapor pressure of a liquid increases with increasing temperature.

In an endothermic reaction, such as Equation 12.24, heat is absorbed as reactants are converted to products. Thus, increasing the temperature causes the equilibrium to shift to the right, in the direction of making more products, and K increases. In an exothermic reaction, the opposite occurs: Heat is produced as reactants are converted to products. Thus, increasing the temperature in this case causes the equilibrium to shift to the left, in the direction of making more reactants, and K decreases.

Endothermic: Increasing T results in higher K value

Exothermic: Increasing T results in lower K value

Cooling a reaction has the opposite effect. As we lower the temperature, the equilibrium shifts in the direction that produces heat. Thus, cooling an endothermic reaction shifts the equilibrium to the left, decreasing K, as shown in Figure 12.13, and cooling an exothermic reaction shifts the equilibrium to the right, increasing K.

SAMPLE EXERCISE 12.13 | **Using Le Châtelier's Principle to Predict Shifts in Equilibrium**

Consider the equilibrium

$$N_2O_4(g) \rightleftharpoons 2\,NO_2(g) \qquad \Delta H° = 58.0\ kJ$$

In which direction will the equilibrium shift when (**a**) N_2O_4 is added, (**b**) NO_2 is removed, (**c**) the pressure is increased by addition of $N_2(g)$, (**d**) the volume is increased, (**e**) the temperature is decreased?

SOLUTION

Analyze We are given a series of changes to be made to a system at equilibrium and are asked to predict what effect each change will have on the position of the equilibrium.

Plan Le Châtelier's principle can be used to determine the effects of each of these changes.

Solve
(**a**) The system will adjust to decrease the concentration of the added N_2O_4, so the equilibrium shifts to the right, in the direction of product.

(**b**) The system will adjust to the removal of NO_2 by shifting to the side that produces more NO_2; thus, the equilibrium shifts to the right.

(**c**) Adding N_2 will increase the total pressure of the system, but N_2 is not involved in the reaction. The partial pressures of NO_2 and N_2O_4 are therefore unchanged, and there is no shift in the position of the equilibrium.

(**d**) If the volume is increased, the system will shift in the direction that occupies a larger volume (more gas molecules); thus, the equilibrium shifts to the right.

(**e**) The reaction is endothermic, so we can imagine heat as a reagent on the reactant side of the equation. Decreasing the temperature will shift the equilibrium in the direction that produces heat, so the equilibrium shifts to the left, toward the formation of more N_2O_4. Note that only this last change also affects the value of the equilibrium constant, K.

PRACTICE EXERCISE

For the reaction

$$PCl_5(g) \rightleftharpoons PCl_3(g) + Cl_2(g) \qquad \Delta H° = 87.9\ kJ$$

in which direction will the equilibrium shift when (**a**) $Cl_2(g)$ is removed, (**b**) the temperature is decreased, (**c**) the volume of the reaction system is increased, (**d**) $PCl_3(g)$ is added?

Answers: (**a**) right, (**b**) left, (**c**) right, (**d**) left

SAMPLE EXERCISE 12.14 **Predicting the Effect of Temperature on K**

(a) Using the standard heat of formation data in Appendix C, determine the standard enthalpy change for the reaction

$$N_2(g) + 3\,H_2(g) \rightleftharpoons 2\,NH_3(g)$$

(b) Determine how the equilibrium constant for this reaction should change with temperature.

SOLUTION

Analyze We are asked to determine the standard enthalpy change of a reaction and how the equilibrium constant for the reaction varies with temperature.

Plan (a) We can use standard enthalpies of formation to calculate $\Delta H°$ for the reaction. (b) We can then use Le Châtelier's principle to determine what effect temperature will have on the equilibrium constant.

Solve

(a) Recall that the standard enthalpy change for a reaction is given by the sum of the standard molar enthalpies of formation of the products, each multiplied by its coefficient in the balanced chemical equation, less the same quantities for the reactants. ∞∞ (Section 10.7) At 25 °C, $\Delta H_f°$ for $NH_3(g)$ is -46.19 kJ/mol. The $\Delta H_f°$ values for $H_2(g)$ and $N_2(g)$ are zero by definition because the enthalpies of formation of the elements in their normal states at 25 °C are defined as zero. ∞∞ (Section 10.7) Because 2 mol of NH_3 is formed, the total enthalpy change is

$$(2\ \text{mol})(-46.19\ \text{kJ/mol}) - 0 = -92.38\ \text{kJ}$$

(b) Because the reaction in the forward direction is exothermic, we can consider heat a product of the reaction. An increase in temperature causes the reaction to shift in the direction of less NH_3 and more N_2 and H_2. This effect is seen in the values for K_p presented in ▶ TABLE 12.2. Notice that K_p changes markedly with changes in temperature and that it is larger at lower temperatures.

Comment The fact that K_p for the formation of NH_3 from N_2 and H_2 decreases with increasing temperature is a matter of great practical importance. To form NH_3 at a reasonable rate requires higher temperatures. At higher temperatures, however, the equilibrium constant is smaller, and so the percentage conversion to NH_3 is smaller. To compensate for this, higher pressures are needed because high pressure favors NH_3 formation.

PRACTICE EXERCISE

Using the thermodynamic data in Appendix C, determine the enthalpy change for the reaction

$$2\,POCl_3(g) \rightleftharpoons 2\,PCl_3(g) + O_2(g)$$

Use this result to determine how the equilibrium constant for the reaction should change with temperature.

Answer: $\Delta H° = 508.3$ kJ; the equilibrium constant will increase with increasing temperature

TABLE 12.2 • Variation in K_p with Temperature for $N_2 + 3\,H_2 \rightleftharpoons 2\,NH_3$

Temperature (°C)	K_p
300	4.34×10^{-3}
400	1.64×10^{-4}
450	4.51×10^{-5}
500	1.45×10^{-5}
550	5.38×10^{-6}
600	2.25×10^{-6}

The Effect of Catalysts

What happens if we add a catalyst to a chemical system that is at equilibrium? As shown in ▶ FIGURE 12.14, ∞∞ (Figure 14.23) a catalyst lowers the activation barrier between reactants and products. The activation energies for both the forward and reverse reactions are lowered. The catalyst thereby increases the rates of both forward and reverse reactions. Since K is the ratio of the forward and reverse rate constants for a reaction, you can predict, correctly, that the presence of a catalyst, even though it changes the reaction *rate,* does not affect the numeric value of K (Figure 12.14). As a result, *a catalyst increases the rate at which equilibrium is achieved but does not change the composition of the equilibrium mixture.*

The rate at which a reaction approaches equilibrium is an important practical consideration. As an example, let's again consider the synthesis of ammonia from N_2 and H_2. In designing his process, Haber had to deal with a rapid decrease in the equilibrium constant with increasing temperature (Table 12.2). At temperatures sufficiently high to

How much faster is the catalyzed reaction compared to the uncatalyzed reaction?

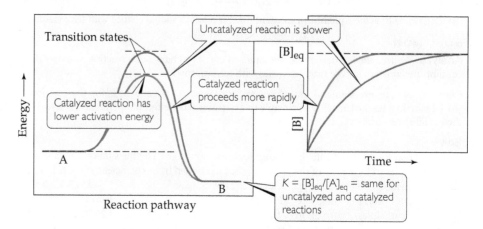

▲ FIGURE 12.14 **A catalyst increases the rate at which equilibrium is reached but does not change the overall composition of the mixture at equilibrium.**

give a satisfactory reaction rate, the amount of ammonia formed was too small. The solution to this dilemma was to develop a catalyst that would produce a reasonably rapid approach to equilibrium at a sufficiently low temperature, so that the equilibrium constant remained reasonably large. The development of a suitable catalyst thus became the focus of Haber's research efforts.

After trying different substances to see which would be most effective, Carl Bosch (see "Chemistry Put to Work: The Haber Process") settled on iron mixed with metal oxides, and variants of this catalyst formulation are still used today. These catalysts make it possible to obtain a reasonably rapid approach to equilibrium at around 400 to 500 °C and 200 to 600 atm. The high pressures are needed to obtain a satisfactory equilibrium amount of NH_3. If chemists and chemical engineers could identify a catalyst that leads to sufficiently rapid reaction at temperatures lower than 400 °C, it would be possible to obtain the same extent of equilibrium conversion at pressures much lower than 200 to 600 atm. This would result in great savings in the cost of the high-pressure equipment used in ammonia synthesis today.

As noted in Section 12.2, our need for nitrogen as fertilizer is growing globally, making the fixation of nitrogen a process of ever-increasing importance.

GIVE IT SOME THOUGHT

Does the addition of a catalyst have any effect on the position of an equilibrium?

SAMPLE INTEGRATIVE EXERCISE Putting Concepts Together

At temperatures near 800 °C, steam passed over hot coke (a form of carbon obtained from coal) reacts to form CO and H_2:

$$C(s) + H_2O(g) \rightleftharpoons CO(g) + H_2(g)$$

The mixture of gases that results is an important industrial fuel called *water gas*. (a) At 800 °C the equilibrium constant for this reaction is $K_p = 14.1$. What are the equilibrium partial pressures of H_2O, CO, and H_2 in the equilibrium mixture at this temperature if we start with solid carbon and 0.100 mol of H_2O in a 1.00-L vessel? (b) What is the minimum amount of carbon required to achieve equilibrium under these conditions? (c) What is the total pressure in the vessel at equilibrium? (d) At 25 °C the value of K_p for this reaction is 1.7×10^{-21}. Is the reaction exothermic or endothermic? (e) To produce the maximum amount of CO and H_2 at equilibrium, should the pressure of the system be increased or decreased?

SOLUTION

(a) To determine the equilibrium partial pressures, we use the ideal-gas equation, first determining the starting partial pressure of hydrogen.

$$P_{H_2O} = \frac{n_{H_2O}RT}{V} = \frac{(0.100 \text{ mol})(0.08206 \text{ L-atm/mol-K})(1073 \text{ K})}{1.00 \text{ L}} = 8.81 \text{ atm}$$

We then construct a table of initial partial pressures and their changes as equilibrium is achieved:

	C(s) +	H$_2$O(g) $\rightleftharpoons$	CO(g) +	H$_2$(g)
Initial partial pressure (atm)		8.81	0	0
Change in partial pressure (atm)		$-x$	$+x$	$+x$
Equilibrium partial pressure (atm)		$8.81 - x$	x	x

There are no entries in the table under C(s) because the reactant, being a solid, does not appear in the equilibrium-constant expression. Substituting the equilibrium partial pressures of the other species into the equilibrium-constant expression for the reaction gives

$$K_p = \frac{P_{CO}P_{H_2}}{P_{H_2O}} = \frac{(x)(x)}{(8.81 - x)} = 14.1$$

Multiplying through by the denominator gives a quadratic equation in x:

$$x^2 = (14.1)(8.81 - x)$$
$$x^2 + 14.1x - 124.22 = 0$$

Solving this equation for x using the quadratic formula yields $x = 6.14$ atm. Hence, the equilibrium partial pressures are $P_{CO} = x = 6.14$ atm, $P_{H_2} = x = 6.14$ atm, and $P_{H_2O} = (8.81 - x) = 2.67$ atm.

(b) Part (a) shows that $x = 6.14$ atm of H$_2$O must react for the system to achieve equilibrium. We can use the ideal-gas equation to convert this partial pressure into a mole amount.

$$n = \frac{PV}{RT} = \frac{(6.14 \text{ atm})(1.00 \text{ L})}{(0.08206 \text{ L-atm/mol-K})(1073 \text{ K})} = 0.0697 \text{ mol}$$

Thus, 0.0697 mol of H$_2$O and the same amount of C must react to achieve equilibrium. As a result, there must be at least 0.0697 mol of C (0.836 g C) present among the reactants at the start of the reaction.

(c) The total pressure in the vessel at equilibrium is simply the sum of the equilibrium partial pressures:

$$P_{total} = P_{H_2O} + P_{CO} + P_{H_2} = 2.67 \text{ atm} + 6.14 \text{ atm} + 6.14 \text{ atm} = 14.95 \text{ atm}$$

(d) In discussing Le Châtelier's principle, we saw that endothermic reactions exhibit an increase in K_p with increasing temperature. Because the equilibrium constant for this reaction increases as temperature increases, the reaction must be endothermic. From the enthalpies of formation given in Appendix C, we can verify our prediction by calculating the enthalpy change for the reaction, $\Delta H° = \Delta H_f°(CO(g)) + \Delta H_f°(H_2(g)) - \Delta H_f°(C(s, \text{graphite})) - \Delta H_f°(H_2O(g)) = +131.3$ KJ. The positive sign for $\Delta H°$ indicates that the reaction is endothermic.

(e) According to Le Châtelier's principle, a decrease in the pressure causes a gaseous equilibrium to shift toward the side of the equation with the greater number of moles of gas. In this case there are two moles of gas on the product side and only one on the reactant side. Therefore, the pressure should be decreased to maximize the yield of the CO and H$_2$.

CHEMISTRY PUT TO WORK

Controlling Nitric Oxide Emissions

The formation of NO from N_2 and O_2,

$$\tfrac{1}{2}N_2(g) + \tfrac{1}{2}O_2(g) \rightleftharpoons NO(g) \qquad \Delta H° = 90.4 \text{ kJ}$$

[12.25]

provides an interesting example of the practical importance of the fact that equilibrium constants and reaction rates change with temperature. By applying Le Châtelier's principle to this endothermic reaction and treating heat as a reactant, we deduce that an increase in temperature shifts the equilibrium in the direction of more NO. The equilibrium constant K_p for formation of 1 mol of NO from its elements at 300 K is only about 1×10^{-15} (▶ FIGURE 12.15). At 2400 K, however, the equilibrium constant is about 0.05, which is 10^{13} times larger than the 300 K value.

Figure 12.15 helps explain why NO is a pollution problem. In the cylinder of a modern high-compression automobile engine, the temperature during the fuel-burning part of the cycle is approximately 2400 K. Also, there is a fairly large excess of air in the cylinder. These conditions favor the formation of NO. After combustion, however, the gases cool quickly. As the temperature drops, the equilibrium in Equation 12.25 shifts to the left (because the reactant heat is being removed). The lower temperature also means that the reaction rate decreases, however, so the NO formed at 2400 K is essentially "frozen" in that form as the gas cools.

The gases exhausting from the cylinder are still quite hot, perhaps 1200 K. At this temperature, as shown in Figure 12.15, the equilibrium constant for formation of NO is about 5×10^{-4}, much smaller than the value at 2400 K. However, the rate of conversion of NO to N_2 and O_2 is too slow to permit much loss of NO before the gases are cooled further.

One of the goals of automotive catalytic converters is to achieve rapid conversion of NO to N_2 and O_2 at the temperature of the exhaust gas. Some catalysts developed for this reaction are reasonably effective under the grueling conditions in automotive exhaust systems. Nevertheless, scientists and engineers are continuously searching for new materials that provide even more effective catalysis of the decomposition of nitrogen oxides.

◀ **GO FIGURE**

Estimate the value of K_p at 1200 K, the exhaust gas temperature.

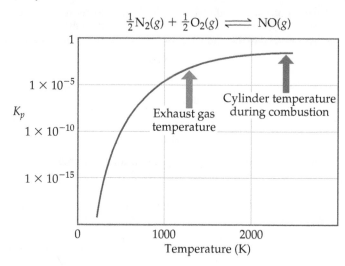

▲ **FIGURE 12.15 Equilibrium and temperature.** The equilibrium constant increases with increasing temperature because the reaction is endothermic. It is necessary to use a log scale for K_p because the values vary over such a large range.

CHAPTER SUMMARY AND KEY TERMS

INTRODUCTION AND SECTION 12.1 A chemical reaction can achieve a state in which the forward and reverse processes are occurring at the same rate. This condition is called **chemical equilibrium**, and it results in the formation of an equilibrium mixture of the reactants and products of the reaction. The composition of an equilibrium mixture does not change with time if temperature is held constant.

SECTION 12.2 An equilibrium that is used throughout this chapter is the reaction $N_2(g) + 3 H_2(g) \rightleftharpoons 2 NH_3(g)$. This reaction is the basis of the **Haber process** for the production of ammonia. The relationship between the concentrations of the reactants and products of a system at equilibrium is given by the **law of mass action**. For an equilibrium equation of the form $a A + b B \rightleftharpoons d D + e E$, the **equilibrium-constant expression** is written as

$$K_c = \frac{[D]^d[E]^e}{[A]^a[B]^b}$$

where K_c is a constant called the **equilibrium constant**. When the equilibrium system of interest consists of gases, it is often convenient to express the concentrations of reactants and products in terms of gas pressures:

$$K_p = \frac{(P_D)^d(P_E)^e}{(P_A)^a(P_B)^b}$$

K_c and K_p are related by the expression $K_p = K_c(RT)^{\Delta n}$.

SECTION 12.3 The value of the equilibrium constant changes with temperature. A large value of K_c indicates that the equilibrium mixture contains more products than reactants and therefore lies toward the product side of the equation. A small value for the equilibrium constant means that the equilibrium mixture contains less products than reactants and therefore lies toward the reactant side. The equilibrium-constant expression and the equilibrium constant of the reverse of a reaction are the reciprocals of those of the forward reaction. If a reaction is the sum of two or more reactions, its equilibrium constant will be the product of the equilibrium constants for the individual reactions.

SECTION 12.4 Equilibria for which all substances are in the same phase are called **homogeneous equilibria**; in **heterogeneous equilibria** two or more phases are present. The concentrations of pure solids and liquids are left out of the equilibrium-constant expression for a heterogeneous equilibrium.

SECTION 12.5 If the concentrations of all species in an equilibrium are known, the equilibrium-constant expression can be used to calculate the equilibrium constant. The changes in the concentrations of reactants and products on the way to achieving equilibrium are governed by the stoichiometry of the reaction.

SECTION 12.6 The **reaction quotient**, Q, is found by substituting reactant and product concentrations or partial pressures at any point during a reaction into the equilibrium-constant expression. If the system is at equilibrium, $Q = K$. If $Q \neq K$, however, the system is not at equilibrium. When $Q < K$, the reaction will move toward equilibrium by forming more products (the reaction proceeds from left to right); when $Q > K$, the reaction will proceed from right to left. Knowing the value of K makes it possible to calculate the equilibrium amounts of reactants and products, often by the solution of an equation in which the unknown is the change in a partial pressure or concentration.

SECTION 12.7 **Le Châtelier's principle** states that if a system at equilibrium is disturbed, the equilibrium will shift to minimize the disturbing influence. By this principle, if a reactant or product is added to a system at equilibrium, the equilibrium will shift to consume the added substance. The effects of removing reactants or products and of changing the pressure or volume of a reaction can be similarly deduced. For example, if the volume of the system is reduced, the equilibrium will shift in the direction that decreases the number of gas molecules. The enthalpy change for a reaction indicates how an increase in temperature affects the equilibrium: For an endothermic reaction, an increase in temperature shifts the equilibrium to the right; for an exothermic reaction, a temperature increase shifts the equilibrium to the left. Catalysts affect the speed at which equilibrium is reached but do not affect the magnitude of K.

KEY SKILLS

- Understand what is meant by chemical equilibrium and how it relates to reaction rates (Section 12.1).
- Write the equilibrium-constant expression for any reaction (Section 12.2).
- Relate K_c and K_p (Section 12.2).
- Relate the magnitude of an equilibrium constant to the relative amounts of reactants and products present in an equilibrium mixture (Section 12.3).
- Manipulate the equilibrium constant to reflect changes in the chemical equation (Section 12.3).
- Write the equilibrium-constant expression for a heterogeneous reaction (Section 12.4).
- Calculate an equilibrium constant from concentration measurements (Section 12.5).
- Predict the direction of a reaction given the equilibrium constant and the concentrations of reactants and products (Section 12.6).
- Calculate equilibrium concentrations given the equilibrium constant and all but one equilibrium concentration (Section 12.6).
- Calculate equilibrium concentrations, given the equilibrium constant and the starting concentrations (Section 12.6).
- Understand how changing the concentrations, volume, or temperature of a system at equilibrium affects the equilibrium position (Section 12.7).

KEY EQUATIONS

- $K_c = \dfrac{[D]^d[E]^e}{[A]^a[B]^b}$ [12.8]   The equilibrium-constant expression for a general reaction of the type $a\,A + b\,B \rightleftharpoons d\,D + e\,E$; the concentrations are equilibrium concentrations only

- $K_p = \dfrac{(P_D)^d(P_E)^e}{(P_A)^a(P_B)^b}$ [12.11]   The equilibrium-constant expression in terms of equilibrium partial pressures

- $K_p = K_c(RT)^{\Delta n}$ [12.14]   Relating the equilibrium constant based on pressures to the equilibrium constant based on concentration

- $Q_c = \dfrac{[D]^d[E]^e}{[A]^a[B]^b}$ [12.23]   The reaction quotient. The concentrations are for any time during a reaction. If the concentrations are equilibrium concentrations, then $Q_c = K_c$.

EXERCISES

VISUALIZING CONCEPTS

12.1 (a) Based on the following energy profile, predict whether $k_f > k_r$ or $k_f < k_r$. (b) Using Equation 12.5, predict whether the equilibrium constant for the process is greater than 1 or less than 1. [Section 12.1]

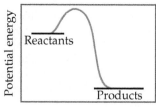

Reaction progress

12.2 The following diagrams represent a hypothetical reaction A $\longrightarrow$ B, with A represented by red spheres and B represented by blue spheres. The sequence from left to right represents the system as time passes. Do the diagrams indicate that the system reaches an equilibrium state? Explain. [Sections 12.1 and 12.2]

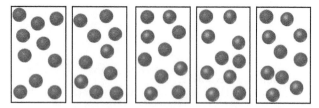

12.3 The following diagram represents an equilibrium mixture produced for a reaction of the type A + X $\rightleftharpoons$ AX. If the volume is 1 L, is K greater or smaller than 1? [Section 12.2]

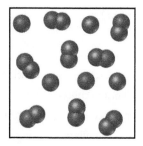

12.4 The following diagram represents a reaction shown going to completion. (a) Letting A = red spheres and B = blue spheres, write a balanced equation for the reaction. (b) Write the equilibrium-constant expression for the reaction. (c) Assuming that all of the molecules are in the gas phase, calculate Δn, the change in the number of gas molecules that accompanies the reaction. (d) How can you calculate K_p if you know K_c at a particular temperature? [Section 12.2]

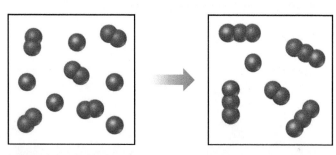

12.5 A friend says that the faster the reaction, the larger the equilibrium constant. Is your friend correct? Why or why not? [Sections 12.1 and 12.2]

12.6 A certain chemical reaction has $K_c = 1.5 \times 10^6$. Does this mean that at equilibrium there are 1.5×10^6 times as many product molecules as reactant molecules? Explain. [Sections 12.1 and 12.2]

12.7 Ethene (C_2H_4) reacts with halogens (X_2) by the following reaction:

$$C_2H_4(g) + X_2(g) \rightleftharpoons C_2H_4X_2(g)$$

The following figures represent the concentrations at equilibrium at the same temperature when X_2 is Cl_2 (green), Br_2 (brown), and I_2 (purple). List the equilibria from smallest to largest equilibrium constant. [Section 12.3]

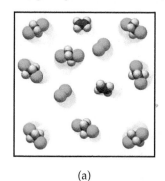
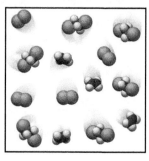

(a)   (b)

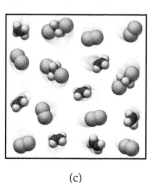

(c)

12.8 The reaction $A_2 + B_2 \rightleftharpoons 2\,AB$ has an equilibrium constant $K_c = 1.5$. The following diagrams represent reaction mixtures containing A_2 molecules (red), B_2 molecules (blue), and AB molecules. (a) Which reaction mixture is at equilibrium? (b) For those mixtures that are not at equilibrium, how will the reaction proceed to reach equilibrium? [Sections 12.5 and 12.6]

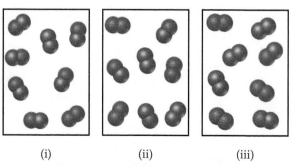

(i)   (ii)   (iii)

12.9 The reaction $A_2(g) + B(g) \rightleftharpoons A(g) + AB(g)$ has an equilibrium constant of $K_p = 2$. The accompanying diagram shows a mixture containing A atoms (red), A_2 molecules, and AB molecules (red and blue). How many B atoms should be added to the diagram to illustrate an equilibrium mixture? [Section 12.6]

12.10 The diagram shown here represents the equilibrium state for the reaction $A_2(g) + 2B(g) \rightleftharpoons 2AB(g)$. **(a)** Assuming the volume is 2 L, calculate the equilibrium constant K_c for the reaction. **(b)** If the volume of the equilibrium mixture is decreased, will the number of AB molecules increase or decrease? [Sections 12.5 and 12.7]

12.11 The following diagrams represent equilibrium mixtures for the reaction $A_2 + B \rightleftharpoons A + AB$ at (a) 300 K and (b) 500 K. The A atoms are red, and the B atoms are blue. Is the reaction exothermic or endothermic? [Section 12.7]

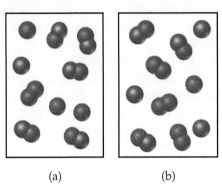

(a)   (b)

12.12 The following graph represents the yield of the compound AB at equilibrium in the reaction $A(g) + B(g) \longrightarrow AB(g)$ at two different pressures, x and y, as a function of temperature.

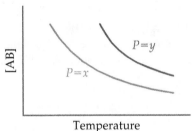

(a) Is this reaction exothermic or endothermic? **(b)** Is $P = x$ greater or smaller than $P = y$? [Section 12.7]

EQUILIBRIUM; THE EQUILIBRIUM CONSTANT (sections 12.1, 12.2, 12.3, 12.4)

12.13 Suppose that the gas-phase reactions $A \longrightarrow B$ and $B \longrightarrow A$ are both elementary processes with rate constants of $4.7 \times 10^{-3}\ s^{-1}$ and $5.8 \times 10^{-1}\ s^{-1}$, respectively. **(a)** What is the value of the equilibrium constant for the equilibrium $A(g) \rightleftharpoons B(g)$? **(b)** Which is greater at equilibrium, the partial pressure of A or the partial pressure of B? Explain.

12.14 Consider the reaction $A + B \rightleftharpoons C + D$. Assume that both the forward reaction and the reverse reaction are elementary processes and that the value of the equilibrium constant is very large. **(a)** Which species predominate at equilibrium, reactants or products? **(b)** Which reaction has the larger rate constant, the forward or the reverse? Explain.

12.15 Write the expression for K_c for the following reactions. In each case indicate whether the reaction is homogeneous or heterogeneous.
(a) $3NO(g) \rightleftharpoons N_2O(g) + NO_2(g)$
(b) $CH_4(g) + 2H_2S(g) \rightleftharpoons CS_2(g) + 4H_2(g)$
(c) $Ni(CO)_4(g) \rightleftharpoons Ni(s) + 4CO(g)$
(d) $HF(aq) \rightleftharpoons H^+(aq) + F^-(aq)$

(e) $2Ag(s) + Zn^{2+}(aq) \rightleftharpoons 2Ag^+(aq) + Zn(s)$
(f) $H_2O(l) \rightleftharpoons H^+(aq) + OH^-(aq)$
(g) $2H_2O(l) \rightleftharpoons 2H^+(aq) + 2OH^-(aq)$

12.16 Write the expressions for K_c for the following reactions. In each case indicate whether the reaction is homogeneous or heterogeneous.
(a) $2O_3(g) \rightleftharpoons 3O_2(g)$
(b) $Ti(s) + 2Cl_2(g) \rightleftharpoons TiCl_4(l)$
(c) $2C_2H_4(g) + 2H_2O(g) \rightleftharpoons 2C_2H_6(g) + O_2(g)$
(d) $C(s) + 2H_2(g) \rightleftharpoons CH_4(g)$
(e) $4HCl(aq) + O_2(g) \rightleftharpoons 2H_2O(l) + 2Cl_2(g)$
(f) $2C_8H_{18}(l) + 25O_2(g) \rightleftharpoons 16CO_2(g) + 18H_2O(g)$
(g) $2C_8H_{18}(l) + 25O_2(g) \rightleftharpoons 16CO_2(g) + 18H_2O(l)$

12.17 When the following reactions come to equilibrium, does the equilibrium mixture contain mostly reactants or mostly products?
(a) $N_2(g) + O_2(g) \rightleftharpoons 2NO(g); K_c = 1.5 \times 10^{-10}$
(b) $2SO_2(g) + O_2(g) \rightleftharpoons 2SO_3(g); K_p = 2.5 \times 10^9$

12.18 Which of the following reactions lies to the right, favoring the formation of products, and which lies to the left, favoring formation of reactants?

(a) $2 NO(g) + O_2(g) \rightleftharpoons 2 NO_2(g)$; $K_p = 5.0 \times 10^{12}$

(b) $2 HBr(g) \rightleftharpoons H_2(g) + Br_2(g)$; $K_c = 5.8 \times 10^{-18}$

12.19 Can the equilibrium constant ever be a negative number? Explain.

12.20 Can the equilibrium constant ever be zero? Explain.

12.21 If $K_c = 0.042$ for $PCl_3(g) + Cl_2(g) \rightleftharpoons PCl_5(g)$ at 500 K, what is the value of K_p for this reaction at this temperature?

12.22 Calculate K_c at 303 K for $SO_2(g) + Cl_2(g) \rightleftharpoons SO_2Cl_2(g)$ if $K_p = 34.5$ at this temperature.

12.23 The equilibrium constant for the reaction

$$2 NO(g) + Br_2(g) \rightleftharpoons 2 NOBr(g)$$

is $K_c = 1.3 \times 10^{-2}$ at 1000 K. (a) At this temperature does the equilibrium favor NO and Br_2, or does it favor NOBr? (b) Calculate K_c for $2 NOBr(g) \rightleftharpoons 2 NO(g) + Br_2(g)$. (c) Calculate K_c for $NOBr(g) : NO(g) + \frac{1}{2} Br_2(g)$.

12.24 Consider the following equilibrium:

$$2 H_2(g) + S_2(g) \rightleftharpoons 2 H_2S(g) \quad K_c = 1.08 \times 10^7 \text{ at } 700 \,°C$$

(a) Calculate K_p. (b) Does the equilibrium mixture contain mostly H_2 and S_2 or mostly H_2S? (c) Calculate the values of K_c and K_p if you rewrote the balanced chemical equation with 1 mol of $H_2(g)$ instead of 2 mol.

12.25 At 1000 K, $K_p = 1.85$ for the reaction

$$SO_2(g) + \frac{1}{2} O_2(g) \rightleftharpoons SO_3(g)$$

(a) What is the value of K_p for the reaction $SO_3(g) \rightleftharpoons SO_2(g) + \frac{1}{2} O_2(g)$? (b) What is the value of K_p for the reaction $2 SO_2(g) + O_2(g) \rightleftharpoons 2 SO_3(g)$? (c) What is the value of K_c for the reaction in part (b)?

12.26 Consider the following equilibrium, for which $K_p = 0.0752$ at 480 °C:

$$2 Cl_2(g) + 2 H_2O(g) \rightleftharpoons 4 HCl(g) + O_2(g)$$

(a) What is the value of K_p for the reaction $4 HCl(g) + O_2(g) \rightleftharpoons 2 Cl_2(g) + 2 H_2O(g)$? (b) What is the value of K_p for the reaction $Cl_2(g) + H_2O(g) \rightleftharpoons 2 HCl(g) + \frac{1}{2} O_2(g)$? (c) What is the value of K_c for the reaction in part (b)?

12.27 The following equilibria were attained at 823 K:

$$CoO(s) + H_2(g) \rightleftharpoons Co(s) + H_2O(g) \quad K_c = 67$$
$$CoO(s) + CO(g) \rightleftharpoons Co(s) + CO_2(g) \quad K_c = 490$$

Based on these equilibria, calculate the equilibrium constant for $H_2(g) + CO_2(g) \rightleftharpoons CO(g) + H_2O(g)$ at 823 K.

12.28 Consider the equilibrium

$$N_2(g) + O_2(g) + Br_2(g) \rightleftharpoons 2 NOBr(g)$$

Calculate the equilibrium constant K_p for this reaction, given the following information (at 298 K):

$$2 NO(g) + Br_2(g) \rightleftharpoons 2 NOBr(g) \quad K_c = 2.0$$
$$2 NO(g) \rightleftharpoons N_2(g) + O_2(g) \quad K_c = 2.1 \times 10^{30}$$

12.29 Explain why we normally exclude pure solids and liquids from equilibrium-constant expressions.

12.30 Explain why we normally exclude solvents from liquid-phase reactions in equilibrium-constant expressions.

12.31 Mercury(I) oxide decomposes into elemental mercury and elemental oxygen: $2 Hg_2O(s) \rightleftharpoons 4 Hg(l) + O_2(g)$. (a) Write the equilibrium-constant expression for this reaction in terms of partial pressures. (b) Suppose you run this reaction in a solvent that dissolves elemental mercury and elemental oxygen. Rewrite the equilibrium-constant expression in terms of molarities for the reaction, using (solv) to indicate solvation.

12.32 Consider the equilibrium $Na_2O(s) + SO_2(g) \rightleftharpoons Na_2SO_3(s)$. (a) Write the equilibrium-constant expression for this reaction in terms of partial pressures. (b) All the compounds in this reaction are soluble in water. Rewrite the equilibrium-constant expression in terms of molarities for the aqueous reaction.

CALCULATING EQUILIBRIUM CONSTANTS (section 12.5)

12.33 Methanol (CH_3OH) is produced commercially by the catalyzed reaction of carbon monoxide and hydrogen: $CO(g) + 2 H_2(g) \rightleftharpoons CH_3OH(g)$. An equilibrium mixture in a 2.00-L vessel is found to contain 0.0406 mol CH_3OH, 0.170 mol CO, and 0.302 mol H_2 at 500 K. Calculate K_c at this temperature.

12.34 Gaseous hydrogen iodide is placed in a closed container at 425 °C, where it partially decomposes to hydrogen and iodine: $2 HI(g) \rightleftharpoons H_2(g) + I_2(g)$. At equilibrium it is found that $[HI] = 3.53 \times 10^{-3} M$, $[H_2] = 4.79 \times 10^{-4} M$, and $[I_2] = 4.79 \times 10^{-4} M$. What is the value of K_c at this temperature?

12.35 The equilibrium $2 NO(g) + Cl_2(g) \rightleftharpoons 2 NOCl(g)$ is established at 500 K. An equilibrium mixture of the three gases has partial pressures of 0.095 atm, 0.171 atm, and 0.28 atm for NO, Cl_2, and NOCl, respectively. (a) Calculate K_p for this reaction at 500.0 K. (b) If the vessel has a volume of 5.00 L, calculate K_c at this temperature.

12.36 Phosphorus trichloride gas and chlorine gas react to form phosphorus pentachloride gas: $PCl_3(g) + Cl_2(g) \rightleftharpoons PCl_5(g)$. A 7.5-L gas vessel is charged with a mixture of $PCl_3(g)$ and $Cl_2(g)$, which is allowed to equilibrate at 450 K. At equilibrium the partial pressures of the three gases are $P_{PCl_3} = 0.124$ atm, $P_{Cl_2} = 0.157$ atm, and $P_{PCl_5} = 1.30$ atm. (a) What is the value of K_p at this temperature? (b) Does the equilibrium favor reactants or products? (c) Calculate K_c for this reaction at 450 K.

12.37 A mixture of 0.10 mol of NO, 0.050 mol of H_2, and 0.10 mol of H_2O is placed in a 1.0-L vessel at 300 K. The following equilibrium is established:

$$2 NO(g) + 2 H_2(g) \rightleftharpoons N_2(g) + 2 H_2O(g)$$

At equilibrium $[NO] = 0.062 M$. (a) Calculate the equilibrium concentrations of H_2, N_2, and H_2O. (b) Calculate K_c.

12.38 A mixture of 1.374 g of H_2 and 70.31 g of Br_2 is heated in a 2.00-L vessel at 700 K. These substances react according to

$$H_2(g) + Br_2(g) \rightleftharpoons 2 HBr(g)$$

At equilibrium the vessel is found to contain 0.566 g of H_2. (a) Calculate the equilibrium concentrations of H_2, Br_2, and HBr. (b) Calculate K_c.

12.39 A mixture of 0.2000 mol of CO_2, 0.1000 mol of H_2, and 0.1600 mol of H_2O is placed in a 2.000-L vessel. The following equilibrium is established at 500 K:

$$CO_2(g) + H_2(g) \rightleftharpoons CO(g) + H_2O(g)$$

(a) Calculate the initial partial pressures of CO_2, H_2, and H_2O. (b) At equilibrium $P_{H_2O} = 3.51$ atm. Calculate the equilibrium partial pressures of CO_2, H_2, and CO. (c) Calculate K_p for the reaction. (d) Calculate K_c for the reaction.

12.40 A flask is charged with 1.500 atm of $N_2O_4(g)$ and 1.00 atm $NO_2(g)$ at 25 °C, and the following equilibrium is achieved:

$$N_2O_4(g) \rightleftharpoons 2 NO_2(g)$$

After equilibrium is reached, the partial pressure of NO_2 is 0.512 atm. (a) What is the equilibrium partial pressure of N_2O_4? (b) Calculate the value of K_p for the reaction. (c) Calculate K_c for the reaction.

12.41 Two different proteins X and Y are dissolved in aqueous solution at 37 °C. The proteins bind in a 1:1 ratio to form XY. A solution that is initially 1.00 mM in each protein is allowed to reach equilibrium. At equilibrium, 0.20 mM of free X and 0.20 mM of free Y remain. What is K_c for the reaction?

[12.42] A chemist at a pharmaceutical company is measuring equilibrium constants for reactions in which drug candidate molecules bind to a protein involved in cancer. The drug molecules bind the protein in a 1:1 ratio to form a drug-protein complex. The protein concentration in aqueous solution at 25 °C is $1.50 \times 10^{-6} M$. Drug A is introduced into the protein solution at an initial concentration of $2.00 \times 10^{-6} M$. Drug B is introduced into a separate, identical protein solution at an initial concentration of $2.00 \times 10^{-6} M$. At equilibrium, the drug A-protein solution has an A-protein complex concentration of $1.00 \times 10^{-6} M$, and the drug B solution has a B-protein complex concentration of $1.40 \times 10^{-6} M$. Calculate the K_c value for the A-protein binding reaction and for the B-protein binding reaction. Assuming that the drug that binds more strongly will be more effective, which drug is the better choice for further research?

APPLICATIONS OF EQUILIBRIUM CONSTANTS (section 12.6)

12.43 (a) How does a reaction quotient differ from an equilibrium constant? (b) If $Q_c < K_c$, in which direction will a reaction proceed in order to reach equilibrium? (c) What condition must be satisfied so that $Q_c = K_c$?

12.44 (a) How is a reaction quotient used to determine whether a system is at equilibrium? (b) If $Q_c > K_c$, how must the reaction proceed to reach equilibrium? (c) At the start of a certain reaction, only reactants are present; no products have been formed. What is the value of Q_c at this point in the reaction?

12.45 At 100 °C the equilibrium constant for the reaction $COCl_2(g) \rightleftharpoons CO(g) + Cl_2(g)$ has the value $K_c = 2.19 \times 10^{-10}$. Are the following mixtures of $COCl_2$, CO, and Cl_2 at 100 °C at equilibrium? If not, indicate the direction that the reaction must proceed to achieve equilibrium. (a) $[COCl_2] = 2.00 \times 10^{-3} M$, $[CO] = 3.3 \times 10^{-6} M$, $[Cl_2] = 6.62 \times 10^{-6} M$; (b) $[COCl_2] = 4.50 \times 10^{-2} M$, $[CO] = 1.1 \times 10^{-7} M$, $[Cl_2] = 2.25 \times 10^{-6} M$; (c) $[COCl_2] = 0.0100 M$, $[CO] = [Cl_2] = 1.48 \times 10^{-6} M$

12.46 As shown in Table 12.2, K_p for the equilibrium

$$N_2(g) + 3 H_2(g) \rightleftharpoons 2 NH_3(g)$$

is 4.51×10^{-5} at 450 °C. For each of the mixtures listed here, indicate whether the mixture is at equilibrium at 450 °C. If it is not at equilibrium, indicate the direction (toward product or toward reactants) in which the mixture must shift to achieve equilibrium.
(a) 98 atm NH_3, 45 atm N_2, 55 atm H_2
(b) 57 atm NH_3, 143 atm N_2, no H_2
(c) 13 atm NH_3, 27 atm N_2, 82 atm H_2

12.47 At 100 °C, $K_c = 0.078$ for the reaction

$$SO_2Cl_2(g) \rightleftharpoons SO_2(g) + Cl_2(g)$$

In an equilibrium mixture of the three gases, the concentrations of SO_2Cl_2 and SO_2 are 0.108 M and 0.052 M, respectively. What is the partial pressure of Cl_2 in the equilibrium mixture?

12.48 At 900 K the following reaction has $K_p = 0.345$:

$$2 SO_2(g) + O_2(g) \rightleftharpoons 2 SO_3(g)$$

In an equilibrium mixture the partial pressures of SO_2 and O_2 are 0.135 atm and 0.455 atm, respectively. What is the equilibrium partial pressure of SO_3 in the mixture?

12.49 (a) At 1285 °C the equilibrium constant for the reaction $Br_2(g) \rightleftharpoons 2 Br(g)$ is $K_c = 1.04 \times 10^{-3}$. A 0.200-L vessel containing an equilibrium mixture of the gases has 0.245 g $Br_2(g)$ in it. What is the mass of Br(g) in the vessel? (b) For the reaction $H_2(g) + I_2(g) \rightleftharpoons 2 HI(g)$, $K_c = 55.3$ at 700 K. In a 2.00-L flask containing an equilibrium mixture of the three gases, there are 0.056 g H_2 and 4.36 g I_2. What is the mass of HI in the flask?

12.50 (a) At 800 K the equilibrium constant for $I_2(g) \rightleftharpoons 2 I(g)$ is $K_c = 3.1 \times 10^{-5}$. If an equilibrium mixture in a 10.0-L vessel contains 2.67×10^{-2} g of I(g), how many grams of I_2 are in the mixture? (b) For $2 SO_2(g) + O_2(g) \rightleftharpoons 2 SO_3(g)$, $K_p = 3.0 \times 10^4$ at 700 K. In a 2.00-L vessel the equilibrium mixture contains 1.17 g of SO_3 and 0.105 g of O_2. How many grams of SO_2 are in the vessel?

12.51 At 2000 °C the equilibrium constant for the reaction

$$2 NO(g) \rightleftharpoons N_2(g) + O_2(g)$$

is $K_c = 2.4 \times 10^3$. If the initial concentration of NO is 0.175 M, what are the equilibrium concentrations of NO, N_2, and O_2?

12.52 For the equilibrium

$$Br_2(g) + Cl_2(g) \rightleftharpoons 2 BrCl(g)$$

at 400 K, $K_c = 7.0$. If 0.25 mol of Br_2 and 0.55 mol of Cl_2 are introduced into a 3.0-L container at 400 K, what will be the equilibrium concentrations of Br_2, Cl_2, and BrCl?

12.53 At 373 K, $K_p = 0.416$ for the equilibrium

$$2 NOBr(g) \rightleftharpoons 2 NO(g) + Br_2(g)$$

If the pressures of NOBr(g) and NO(g) are equal, what is the equilibrium pressure of $Br_2(g)$?

12.54 At 218 °C, $K_c = 1.2 \times 10^{-4}$ for the equilibrium

$$NH_4SH(s) \rightleftharpoons NH_3(g) + H_2S(g)$$

Calculate the equilibrium concentrations of NH_3 and H_2S if a sample of solid NH_4SH is placed in a closed vessel at 218 °C and decomposes until equilibrium is reached.

12.55 Consider the reaction

$$CaSO_4(s) \rightleftharpoons Ca^{2+}(aq) + SO_4^{2-}(aq)$$

At 25 °C the equilibrium constant is $K_c = 2.4 \times 10^{-5}$ for this reaction. (a) If excess $CaSO_4(s)$ is mixed with water at 25 °C to produce a saturated solution of $CaSO_4$, what are the equilibrium concentrations of Ca^{2+} and SO_4^{2-}? (b) If the resulting solution has a volume of 1.4 L, what is the minimum mass of $CaSO_4(s)$ needed to achieve equilibrium?

12.56 At 80 °C, $K_c = 1.87 \times 10^{-3}$ for the reaction

$$PH_3BCl_3(s) \rightleftharpoons PH_3(g) + BCl_3(g)$$

(a) Calculate the equilibrium concentrations of PH_3 and BCl_3 if a solid sample of PH_3BCl_3 is placed in a closed vessel at 80 °C and decomposes until equilibrium is reached. (b) If the flask has a volume of 0.250 L, what is the minimum mass of $PH_3BCl_3(s)$ that must be added to the flask to achieve equilibrium?

12.57 For the reaction $I_2 + Br_2(g) \rightleftharpoons 2 IBr(g)$, $K_c = 280$ at 150 °C. Suppose that 0.500 mol IBr in a 2.00-L flask is allowed to reach equilibrium at 150 °C. What are the equilibrium concentrations of IBr, I_2, and Br_2?

12.58 At 25 °C the reaction

$$CaCrO_4(s) \rightleftharpoons Ca^{2+}(aq) + CrO_4^{2-}(aq)$$

has an equilibrium constant $K_c = 7.1 \times 10^{-4}$. What are the equilibrium concentrations of Ca^{2+} and CrO_4^{2-} in a saturated solution of $CaCrO_4$?

12.59 Methane, CH_4, reacts with I_2 according to the reaction $CH_4(g) + I_2(g) \rightleftharpoons CH_3I(g) + HI(g)$. At 630 K, K_p for this reaction is 2.26×10^{-4}. A reaction was set up at 630 K with initial partial pressures of methane of 105.1 torr and of 7.96 torr for I_2. Calculate the pressures, in torr, of all reactants and products at equilibrium.

12.60 The reaction of an organic acid with an alcohol, in organic solvent, to produce an ester and water is commonly done in the pharmaceutical industry. This reaction is catalyzed by strong acid (usually H_2SO_4). A simple example is the reaction of acetic acid with ethyl alcohol to produce ethyl acetate and water:

$$CH_3COOH(solv) + CH_3CH_2OH(solv) \rightleftharpoons$$
$$CH_3COOCH_2CH_3(solv) + H_2O(solv)$$

where "(solv)" indicates that all reactants and products are in solution but not an aqueous solution. The equilibrium constant for this reaction at 55 °C is 6.68. A pharmaceutical chemist makes up 12.0 L of a solution that is initially 0.275 M in acetic acid and 3.85 M in ethanol. At equilibrium, how many grams of ethyl acetate are formed?

LE CHÂTELIER'S PRINCIPLE (section 12.7)

12.61 Consider the following equilibrium for which $\Delta H < 0$

$$2 SO_2(g) + O_2(g) \rightleftharpoons 2 SO_3(g)$$

How will each of the following changes affect an equilibrium mixture of the three gases: (a) $O_2(g)$ is added to the system; (b) the reaction mixture is heated; (c) the volume of the reaction vessel is doubled; (d) a catalyst is added to the mixture; (e) the total pressure of the system is increased by adding a noble gas; (f) $SO_3(g)$ is removed from the system?

12.62 Consider $4 NH_3(g) + 5 O_2(g) \rightleftharpoons 4 NO(g) + 6 H_2O(g)$, $\Delta H = -904.4$ kJ. How does each of the following changes affect the yield of NO at equilibrium? Answer increase, decrease, or no change: (a) increase $[NH_3]$; (b) increase $[H_2O]$; (c) decrease $[O_2]$; (d) decrease the volume of the container in which the reaction occurs; (e) add a catalyst; (f) increase temperature.

12.63 How do the following changes affect the value of the equilibrium constant for a gas-phase exothermic reaction: (a) removal of a reactant (b) removal of a product, (c) decrease in the volume, (d) decrease in the temperature, (e) addition of a catalyst?

12.64 For a certain gas-phase reaction, the fraction of products in an equilibrium mixture is increased by either increasing the temperature or by increasing the volume of the reaction vessel. (a) Is the reaction exothermic or endothermic? (b) Does the balanced chemical equation have more molecules on the reactant side or product side?

12.65 Consider the following equilibrium between oxides of nitrogen

$$3 NO(g) \rightleftharpoons NO_2(g) + N_2O(g)$$

(a) Use data in Appendix C to calculate $\Delta H°$ for this reaction. (b) Will the equilibrium constant for the reaction increase or decrease with increasing temperature? Explain. (c) At constant temperature, would a change in the volume of the container affect the fraction of products in the equilibrium mixture?

12.66 Methanol (CH_3OH) can be made by the reaction of CO with H_2:

$$CO(g) + 2 H_2(g) \rightleftharpoons CH_3OH(g)$$

(a) Use thermochemical data in Appendix C to calculate $\Delta H°$ for this reaction. (b) To maximize the equilibrium yield of methanol, would you use a high or low temperature? (c) To maximize the equilibrium yield of methanol, would you use a high or low pressure?

12.67 Ozone, O_3, decomposes to molecular oxygen in the stratosphere according to the reaction $2 O_3(g) : 3 O_2(g)$. Would an increase in pressure favor the formation of ozone or of oxygen?

12.68 *Bioremediation* is the use of microorganisms to degrade environmental pollutants. Many pollutants contain only carbon and hydrogen (oil being one example). The chemical reactions are complicated, but in general the microorganisms react the pollutant hydrocarbon with O_2 to produce CO_2 and other carbon-containing compounds that are incorporated into the organism's biomass. How would increasing levels of CO_2 in the environment affect the bioremediation reaction?

ADDITIONAL EXERCISES

12.69 Both the forward reaction and the reverse reaction in the following equilibrium are believed to be elementary steps:

$$CO(g) + Cl_2(g) \rightleftharpoons COCl(g) + Cl(g)$$

At 25 °C the rate constants for the forward and reverse reactions are $1.4 \times 10^{-28}\ M^{-1}\,s^{-1}$ and $9.3 \times 10^{10}\ M^{-1}\,s^{-1}$, respectively. (**a**) What is the value for the equilibrium constant at 25 °C ? (**b**) Are reactants or products more plentiful at equilibrium? (**c**) What additional information would you need in order to decide whether the reaction as written is endothermic or exothermic?

12.70 If $K_c = 1$ for the equilibrium $2\,A(g) \rightleftharpoons B(g)$, what is the relationship between [A] and [B] at equilibrium?

12.71 A mixture of CH_4 and H_2O is passed over a nickel catalyst at 1000 K. The emerging gas is collected in a 5.00-L flask and is found to contain 8.62 g of CO, 2.60 g of H_2, 43.0 g of CH_4, and 48.4 g of H_2O. Assuming that equilibrium has been reached, calculate K_c and K_p for the reaction.

12.72 When 2.00 mol of SO_2Cl_2 is placed in a 2.00-L flask at 303 K, 56% of the SO_2Cl_2 decomposes to SO_2 and Cl_2:

$$SO_2Cl_2(g) \rightleftharpoons SO_2(g) + Cl_2(g)$$

(**a**) Calculate K_c for this reaction at this temperature. (**b**) Calculate K_p for this reaction at 303 K. (**c**) Repeat these calculations for 2.00 mol of SO_2Cl_2 in a 15.00-L vessel at 303 K.

12.73 A mixture of H_2, S, and H_2S is held in a 1.0-L vessel at 90 °C and reacts according to the equation:

$$H_2(g) + S(s) \rightleftharpoons H_2S(g)$$

At equilibrium the mixture contains 0.46 g of H_2S and 0.40 g H_2. (**a**) Write the equilibrium-constant expression for this reaction. (**b**) What is the value of K_c for the reaction at this temperature? (**c**) Why can we ignore the amount of S when doing the calculation in part (b)?

12.74 A sample of nitrosyl bromide (NOBr) decomposes according to the equation

$$2\,NOBr(g) \rightleftharpoons 2\,NO(g) + Br_2(g)$$

An equilibrium mixture in a 5.00-L vessel at 100 °C contains 3.22 g of NOBr, 3.08 g of NO, and 4.19 g of Br_2. (**a**) Calculate K_c. (**b**) What is the total pressure exerted by the mixture of gases? (**c**) What was the mass of the original sample of NOBr?

12.75 Consider the hypothetical reaction $A(g) \rightleftharpoons 2\,B(g)$. A flask is charged with 0.75 atm of pure A, after which it is allowed to reach equilibrium at 0 °C. At equilibrium the partial pressure of A is 0.36 atm. (**a**) What is the total pressure in the flask at equilibrium? (**b**) What is the value of K_p? (**c**) What could we do to maximize the yield of B?

12.76 As shown in Table 12.2, the equilibrium constant for the reaction $N_2(g) + 3\,H_2(g) \rightleftharpoons 2\,NH_3(g)$ is $K_p = 4.34 \times 10^{-3}$ at 300 °C. Pure NH_3 is placed in a 1.00-L flask and allowed to reach equilibrium at this temperature. There are 1.05 g NH_3 in the equilibrium mixture. (**a**) What are the masses of N_2 and H_2 in the equilibrium mixture? (**b**) What was the initial mass of ammonia placed in the vessel? (**c**) What is the total pressure in the vessel?

12.77 For the equilibrium

$$2\,IBr(g) \rightleftharpoons I_2(g) + Br_2(g)$$

$K_p = 8.5 \times 10^{-3}$ at 150 °C. If 0.025 atm of IBr is placed in a 2.0-L container, what is the partial pressure of all substances after equilibrium is reached?

12.78 For the equilibrium

$$PH_3BCl_3(s) \rightleftharpoons PH_3(g) + BCl_3(g)$$

$K_p = 0.052$ at 60 °C. (**a**) Calculate K_c. (**b**) After 3.00 g of solid PH_3BCl_3 is added to a closed 1.500-L vessel at 60 °C, the vessel is charged with 0.0500 g of $BCl_3(g)$. What is the equilibrium concentration of PH_3?

[12.79] Solid NH_4SH is introduced into an evacuated flask at 24 °C. The following reaction takes place:

$$NH_4SH(s) \rightleftharpoons NH_3(g) + H_2S(g)$$

At equilibrium the total pressure (for NH_3 and H_2S taken together) is 0.614 atm. What is K_p for this equilibrium at 24 °C?

[12.80] A 0.831-g sample of SO_3 is placed in a 1.00-L container and heated to 1100 K. The SO_3 decomposes to SO_2 and O_2:

$$2\,SO_3(g) \rightleftharpoons 2\,SO_2(g) + O_2(g)$$

At equilibrium the total pressure in the container is 1.300 atm. Find the values of K_p and K_c for this reaction at 1100 K.

12.81 Nitric oxide (NO) reacts readily with chlorine gas as follows:

$$2\,NO(g) + Cl_2(g) \rightleftharpoons 2\,NOCl(g)$$

At 700 K the equilibrium constant K_p for this reaction is 0.26. Predict the behavior of each of the following mixtures at this temperature and indicate whether or not the mixtures are at equilibrium. If not, state whether the mixture will need to produce more products or reactants to reach equilibrium. (**a**) $P_{NO} = 0.15$ atm, $P_{Cl_2} = 0.31$ atm, and $P_{NOCl} = 0.11$ atm; (**b**) $P_{NO} = 0.12$ atm, $P_{Cl_2} = 0.10$ atm, and $P_{NOCl} = 0.050$ atm; (**c**) $P_{NO} = 0.15$ atm, $P_{Cl_2} = 0.20$ atm, and $P_{NOCl} = 5.10 \times 10^{-3}$ atm.

12.82 At 900 °C, $K_c = 0.0108$ for the reaction

$$CaCO_3(s) \rightleftharpoons CaO(s) + CO_2(g)$$

A mixture of $CaCO_3$, CaO, and CO_2 is placed in a 10.0-L vessel at 900 °C. For the following mixtures, will the amount of $CaCO_3$ increase, decrease, or remain the same as the system approaches equilibrium? (**a**) 15.0 g $CaCO_3$, 15.0 g CaO, and 4.25 g CO_2 (**b**) 2.50 g $CaCO_3$, 25.0 g CaO, and 5.66 g CO_2 (**c**) 30.5 g $CaCO_3$, 25.5 g CaO, and 6.48 g CO_2

12.83 When 1.50 mol CO_2 and 1.50 mol H_2 are placed in a 3.00-L container at 395 °C, the following reaction occurs: $CO_2(g) + H_2(g) \rightleftharpoons CO(g) + H_2O(g)$. If $K_c = 0.802$, what are the concentrations of each substance in the equilibrium mixture?

12.84 The equilibrium constant K_c for $C(s) + CO_2(g) \rightleftharpoons 2\,CO(g)$ is 1.9 at 1000 K and 0.133 at 298 K. (**a**) If excess C is allowed to react with 25.0 g of CO_2 in a 3.00-L vessel at 1000 K, how many grams of CO are produced? (**b**) How many grams of C are consumed? (**c**) If a smaller vessel is used for the reaction, will the yield of CO be greater or smaller? (**d**) Is the reaction endothermic or exothermic?

12.85 NiO is to be reduced to nickel metal in an industrial process by use of the reaction

$$NiO(s) + CO(g) \rightleftharpoons Ni(s) + CO_2(g)$$

At 1600 K the equilibrium constant for the reaction is $K_p = 6.0 \times 10^2$. If a CO pressure of 150 torr is to be employed in the furnace and total pressure never exceeds 760 torr, will reduction occur?

12.86 Le Châtelier noted that many industrial processes of his time could be improved by an understanding of chemical equilibria. For example, the reaction of iron oxide with carbon monoxide was used to produce elemental iron and CO_2 according to the reaction

$$Fe_2O_3(s) + 3\ CO(g) \rightleftharpoons 2\ Fe(s) + 3\ CO_2(g)$$

Even in Le Châtelier's time, it was noted that a great deal of CO was wasted, expelled through the chimneys over the furnaces. Le Châtelier wrote, "Because this incomplete reaction was thought to be due to an insufficiently prolonged contact between carbon monoxide and the iron ore [oxide], the dimensions of the furnaces have been increased. In England they have been made as high as thirty meters. But the proportion of carbon monoxide escaping has not diminished, thus demonstrating, by an experiment costing several hundred thousand francs, that the reduction of iron oxide by carbon monoxide is a limited reaction. Acquaintance with the laws of chemical equilibrium would have permitted the same conclusion to be reached more rapidly and far more economically." What does this anecdote tell us about the equilibrium constant for this reaction?

[12.87] At 700 K the equilibrium constant for the reaction

$$CCl_4(g) \rightleftharpoons C(s) + 2\ Cl_2(g)$$

is $K_p = 0.76$. A flask is charged with 2.00 atm of CCl_4, which then reaches equilibrium at 700 K. (a) What fraction of the CCl_4 is converted into C and Cl_2? (b) What are the partial pressures of CCl_4 and Cl_2 at equilibrium?

[12.88] The reaction $PCl_3(g) + Cl_2(g) \rightleftharpoons PCl_5(g)$ has $K_p = 0.0870$ at 300 °C. A flask is charged with 0.50 atm PCl_3, 0.50 atm Cl_2, and 0.20 atm PCl_5 at this temperature. (a) Use the reaction quotient to determine the direction the reaction must proceed to reach equilibrium. (b) Calculate the equilibrium partial pressures of the gases. (c) What effect will increasing the volume of the system have on the mole fraction of Cl_2 in the equilibrium mixture? (d) The reaction is exothermic. What effect will increasing the temperature of the system have on the mole fraction of Cl_2 in the equilibrium mixture?

[12.89] An equilibrium mixture of H_2, I_2, and HI at 458 °C contains 0.112 mol H_2, 0.112 mol I_2, and 0.775 mol HI in a 5.00-L

vessel. What are the equilibrium partial pressures when equilibrium is reestablished following the addition of 0.200 mol of HI?

[12.90] Consider the hypothetical reaction $A(g) + 2\ B(g) \rightleftharpoons 2\ C(g)$, for which $K_c = 0.25$ at a certain temperature. A 1.00-L reaction vessel is loaded with 1.00 mol of compound C, which is allowed to reach equilibrium. Let the variable x represent the number of mol/L of compound A present at equilibrium. (a) In terms of x, what are the equilibrium concentrations of compounds B and C? (b) What limits must be placed on the value of x so that all concentrations are positive? (c) By putting the equilibrium concentrations (in terms of x) into the equilibrium-constant expression, derive an equation that can be solved for x. (d) The equation from part (c) is a cubic equation (one that has the form $ax^3 + bx^2 + cx + d = 0$). In general, cubic equations cannot be solved in closed form. However, you can estimate the solution by plotting the cubic equation in the allowed range of x that you specified in part (b). The point at which the cubic equation crosses the x-axis is the solution. (e) From the plot in part (d), estimate the equilibrium concentrations of A, B, and C. (*Hint:* You can check the accuracy of your answer by substituting these concentrations into the equilibrium expression.)

12.91 At 1200 K, the approximate temperature of automobile exhaust gases (Figure 12.15), K_p for the reaction

$$2\ CO_2(g) \rightleftharpoons 2\ CO(g) + O_2(g)$$

is about 1×10^{-13}. Assuming that the exhaust gas (total pressure 1 atm) contains 0.2% CO, 12% CO_2, and 3% O_2 by volume, is the system at equilibrium with respect to the CO_2 reaction? Based on your conclusion, would the CO concentration in the exhaust be decreased or increased by a catalyst that speeds up the CO_2 reaction?

12.92 Suppose that you worked at the U.S. Patent Office and a patent application came across your desk claiming that a newly developed catalyst was much superior to the Haber catalyst for ammonia synthesis because the catalyst led to much greater equilibrium conversion of N_2 and H_2 into NH_3 than the Haber catalyst under the same conditions. What would be your response?

INTEGRATIVE EXERCISES

12.93 Consider the reaction $IO_4^-(aq) + 2\ H_2O(l) \rightleftharpoons H_4IO_6^-(aq)$; $K_c = 3.5 \times 10^{-2}$. If you start with 25.0 mL of a 0.905 M solution of $NaIO_4$, and then dilute it with water to 500.0 mL, what is the concentration of $H_4IO_6^-$ at equilibrium?

[12.94] Silver chloride, AgCl(s), is an "insoluble" strong electrolyte. (a) Write the equation for the dissolution of AgCl(s) in $H_2O(l)$. (b) Write the expression for K_c for the reaction in part (a). (c) Based on the thermochemical data in Appendix C and Le Châtelier's principle, predict whether the solubility of AgCl in H_2O increases or decreases with increasing temperature. (d) The equilibrium constant for the dissolution of AgCl in water is 1.6×10^{-10} at 25 °C. In addition, $Ag^+(aq)$ can react with $Cl^-(aq)$ according to the reaction

$$Ag^+(aq) + 2\ Cl^-(aq) \longrightarrow AgCl_2^-(aq)$$

where $K_c = 1.8 \times 10^5$ at 25 °C. Although AgCl is "not soluble" in water, the complex $AgCl_2^-$ is soluble. At 25 °C, is the solubility of AgCl in a 0.100 M NaCl solution *greater* than the solubility of AgCl in pure water, due to the formation of soluble $AgCl_2^-$ ions? Or is the AgCl solubility in 0.100 M NaCl *less* than in pure water because of a Le Châtelier–type argument? Justify your answer with calculations. (*Hint:* Any form in which silver is in solution counts as "solubility.")

[12.95] Consider the equilibrium $A \rightleftharpoons B$ in which both the forward and reverse reactions are elementary (single-step) reactions. Assume that the only effect of a catalyst on the reaction is to lower the activation energies of the forward and reverse reactions, as shown in Figure 12.14. Using the Arrhenius equation (Section 14.5), prove that the equilibrium constant is the same for the catalyzed reaction as for the uncatalyzed one.

[12.96] The phase diagram for SO_2 is shown here. (a) What does this diagram tell you about the enthalpy change in the reaction $SO_2(l) \longrightarrow SO_2(g)$? (b) Calculate the equilibrium constant for this reaction at 100 °C and at 0 °C. (c) Why is it not possible to calculate an equilibrium constant between the gas and liquid phases in the supercritical region? (d) At which of the three points marked in red does $SO_2(g)$ most closely approach ideal-gas behavior? (e) At which of the three red points does $SO_2(g)$ behave least ideally?

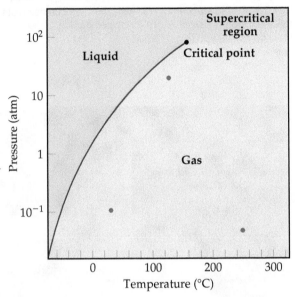

[12.97] Write the equilibrium-constant expression for the equilibrium

$$C(s) + CO_2(g) \rightleftharpoons 2\,CO(g)$$

The table that follows shows the relative mole percentages of $CO_2(g)$ and $CO(g)$ at a total pressure of 1 atm for several temperatures. Calculate the value of K_p at each temperature. Is the reaction exothermic or endothermic? Explain.

Temperature (°C)	CO₂ (mol %)	CO (mol %)
850	6.23	93.77
950	1.32	98.68
1050	0.37	99.63
1200	0.06	99.94

12.98 In Section 11.3 we defined the vapor pressure of a liquid in terms of an equilibrium. (a) Write the equation representing the equilibrium between liquid water and water vapor and the corresponding expression for K_p. (b) By using data in Appendix B, give the value of K_p for this reaction at 30 °C. (c) What is the value of K_p for any liquid in equilibrium with its vapor at the normal boiling point of the liquid?

12.99 Water molecules in the atmosphere can form hydrogen-bonded dimers, $(H_2O)_2$. The presence of these dimers is thought to be important in the nucleation of ice crystals in the atmosphere and in the formation of acid rain. (a) Using VSEPR theory, draw the structure of a water dimer, using dashed lines to indicate intermolecular interactions. (b) What kind of intermolecular forces are involved in water dimer formation? (c) The K_p for water dimer formation in the gas phase is 0.050 at 300 K and 0.020 at 350 K. Is water dimer formation endothermic or exothermic?

12.100 The protein hemoglobin (Hb) transports O_2 in mammalian blood. Each Hb can bind 4 O_2 molecules. The equilibrium constant for the O_2-binding reaction is higher in fetal hemoglobin than in adult hemoglobin. In discussing protein oxygen-binding capacity, biochemists use a measure called the *P50* value, defined as the partial pressure of oxygen at which 50% of the protein is saturated. Fetal hemoglobin has a P50 value of 19 torr, and adult hemoglobin has a P50 value of 26.8 torr. Use these data to estimate how much larger K_c is for the aqueous reaction $4\,O_2(g) + Hb(aq) \longrightarrow [Hb(O_2)_4(aq)]$.

WHAT'S AHEAD

13.1 SPONTANEOUS PROCESSES
We see that changes that occur in nature have a directional character. They move *spontaneously* in one direction but not in the reverse direction.

13.2 ENTROPY AND THE SECOND LAW OF THERMODYNAMICS
We discuss *entropy*, a thermodynamic state function that is important in determining whether a process is spontaneous. The *second law of thermodynamics* tells us that in any spontaneous process the entropy of the universe (system plus surroundings) increases.

13.3 MOLECULAR INTERPRETATION OF ENTROPY
On the molecular level, the entropy of a system is related to the number of accessible *microstates*. The entropy of the system increases as the randomness of the system increases. The *third law of thermodynamics* states that, at 0 K, the entropy of a perfect crystalline solid is zero.

13.4 ENTROPY CHANGES IN CHEMICAL REACTIONS
Using tabulated *standard molar entropies*, we can calculate the standard entropy changes for systems undergoing reaction.

THE SKYLINE OF HONG KONG The construction of our human environment entails the use of enormous amounts of energy to create complex ordered structures, such as modern skyscrapers.

13.5 GIBBS FREE ENERGY
We encounter another thermodynamic state function, *free energy* (or *Gibbs free energy*), a measure of how far removed a system is from equilibrium. The change in free energy measures the maximum amount of useful work obtainable from a process and tells us the direction in which a chemical reaction is spontaneous.

13.6 FREE ENERGY AND TEMPERATURE
We consider how the relationship among free-energy change, enthalpy change, and entropy change provides insight into how temperature affects the spontaneity of a process.

13.7 FREE ENERGY AND THE EQUILIBRIUM CONSTANT
Finally, we consider how the standard free-energy change for a chemical reaction can be used to calculate the equilibrium constant for the reaction.

CHEMICAL THERMO-DYNAMICS

HUMANKIND HAS LEARNED TO HARNESS Earth's resources to create impressive, highly ordered structures, such as the beautiful skyline in the chapter-opening photograph. Our modern society depends heavily on the design of chemical reactions that produce specific useful substances from natural and synthetic materials.

Two of the most important questions chemists ask when designing and using chemical reactions are "How fast is the reaction?" and "How far does it proceed?" The first question is addressed by chemical kinetics. The second question involves the equilibrium constant, the focus of Chapter 12. Let's briefly review how these concepts are related.

The rate of any chemical reaction is controlled largely by a factor related to energy, namely, the activation energy of the reaction. ∞ (Section 14.5) In general, the lower the activation energy, the faster a reaction proceeds. In Chapter 12 we saw that chemical equilibrium is reached when a given reaction and its reverse reaction occur at the same rate. ∞ (Section 12.1)

Because reaction rates are closely tied to energy, it is logical that equilibrium also depends in some way on energy. In this chapter we explore the connection between energy and the extent of a reaction. Doing so requires a deeper look at *chemical thermodynamics*, the area of chemistry that deals with energy relationships. We first encountered thermodynamics in Chapter 10, where we discussed the nature of energy, the first law of thermodynamics, and the concept of enthalpy. Recall that the enthalpy change for any system is the heat transferred between the system and its surroundings during a constant-pressure process. ∞(Section 10.3)

In the "Strategies in Chemistry" box in Section 10.4, we pointed out that the enthalpy change that takes place during a reaction is an important guide as to whether the reaction is likely to proceed. Now we will see that reactions involve not only changes in enthalpy but also changes in *entropy*—another important thermodynamic quantity. Our discussion of entropy will lead us to the second law of thermodynamics, which provides insight into why physical and chemical changes tend to favor one direction over another. We drop a brick, for example, and it falls to the ground. We do not expect the brick to spontaneously rise from the ground to our outstretched hand. We light a candle, and it burns down. We do not expect a half-consumed candle to regenerate itself spontaneously, even if we have captured all the gases produced when the candle burned. Thermodynamics helps us understand the significance of this directional character of processes, regardless of whether they are exothermic or endothermic.

13.1 | SPONTANEOUS PROCESSES

The first law of thermodynamics states that *energy is conserved*. ∞(Section 10.2) In other words, energy is neither created nor destroyed in any process, whether that process is a brick falling, a candle burning, or an ice cube melting. Energy can be transferred between a system and the surroundings and can be converted from one form to another, but the total energy of the universe remains constant. We expressed this law mathematically as $\Delta E = q + w$, where ΔE is the change in the internal energy of a system, q is the heat absorbed (or released) by the system from (or to) the surroundings, and w is the work done on the system by the surroundings, or on the surroundings by the system. Remember that $q > 0$ means that the system is absorbing heat from the surroundings, and $w > 0$ means that the surroundings are doing work on the system.

The first law helps us balance the books, so to speak, on the heat transferred between a system and its surroundings and the work done by or on a system. However, because energy is conserved, we can't simply use the value of ΔE to tell us whether a process is favored to occur because anything we do to lower the energy of the system raises the energy of the surroundings, and vice versa. Nevertheless, experience tells us that certain processes *always* occur, even though the energy of the universe is conserved. Water placed in a freezer turns into ice, for instance, and if you touch a hot object, heat is transferred to your hand. The first law guarantees that energy is conserved in these processes, and yet they occur without any outside intervention. We say they are *spontaneous*. A **spontaneous process** is one that proceeds on its own without any outside assistance.

A spontaneous process occurs in one direction only, and the reverse of any spontaneous process is always *nonspontaneous*. Drop an egg above a hard surface, for example, and it breaks on impact (◄ **FIGURE 13.1**). Now, imagine seeing a video clip in which a broken egg rises from the floor, reassembles itself, and ends up in someone's hand. You would conclude that the video is running in reverse because you know that broken eggs simply do not magically rise and reassemble themselves! An egg falling and breaking is spontaneous. The reverse process is *nonspontaneous*, even though energy is conserved in both processes.

We know other spontaneous and nonspontaneous processes that relate more directly to our study of chemistry. For example, a gas spontaneously expands into a vacuum (► **FIGURE 13.2**), but the reverse process, in which the gas moves back entirely into one of the flasks, does not happen. In other words, expansion of the gas is spontaneous, but the reverse process is nonspontaneous. In general, *processes that are spontaneous in one direction are nonspontaneous in the opposite direction.*

Experimental conditions, such as temperature and pressure, are often important in determining whether a process is spontaneous. We are all familiar with situations in which a forward process is spontaneous at one temperature but the reverse process is

Spontaneous Not spontaneous

▲ **FIGURE 13.1 A spontaneous process!**

spontaneous at a different temperature. Consider, for example, ice melting. At atmospheric pressure, when the temperature of the surroundings is above 0 °C, ice melts spontaneously, and the reverse process— liquid water turning into ice—is not spontaneous. However, when the temperature of the surroundings is below 0 °C, the opposite is true—liquid water turns to ice spontaneously, but the reverse process is *not* spontaneous (▼ FIGURE 13.3).

What happens at $T = 0$ °C, the normal melting point of water, when the flask of Figure 13.3 contains both water and ice? At the normal melting point of a substance, the solid and liquid phases are in equilibrium. ∞ (Section 11.4) At this temperature, the two phases are interconverting at the same rate and there is no preferred direction for the process.

It is important to realize that the fact that a process is spontaneous does not necessarily mean that it will occur at an observable rate. A chemical reaction is spontaneous if it occurs on its own accord, regardless of its speed. A spontaneous reaction can be very fast, as in the case of acid–base neutralization, or very slow, as in the rusting of iron. Thermodynamics tells us the *direction* and *extent* of a reaction but nothing about the *speed*.

 GIVE IT SOME THOUGHT

If a process is nonspontaneous, does that mean the process cannot occur under any circumstances?

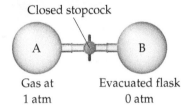
GO FIGURE

If flask B were smaller than flask A, would the final pressure after the stopcock is opened be greater than, equal to, or less than 0.5 atm?

Closed stopcock

A   B

Gas at   Evacuated flask
1 atm   0 atm

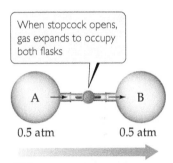

When stopcock opens, gas expands to occupy both flasks

A   B

0.5 atm   0.5 atm

This process is spontaneous

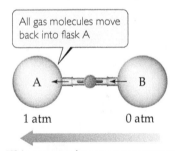

All gas molecules move back into flask A

A   B

1 atm   0 atm

This process is not spontaneous

▲ **FIGURE 13.2 Expansion of a gas into an evacuated space is a spontaneous process.** The reverse process—gas molecules initially distributed evenly in two flasks all moving into one flask—is not spontaneous.

 GO FIGURE

In which direction is this process exothermic?

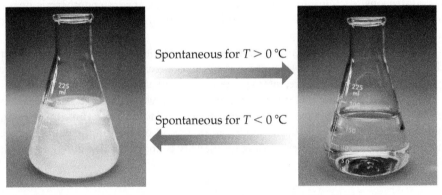

Spontaneous for $T > 0$ °C

Spontaneous for $T < 0$ °C

▲ **FIGURE 13.3 Spontaneity can depend on temperature.** At $T > 0$ °C, ice melts spontaneously to liquid water. At $T < 0$ °C, the reverse process, water freezing to ice, is spontaneous. At $T = 0$ °C the two states are in equilibrium.

SAMPLE EXERCISE 13.1 Identifying Spontaneous Processes

Predict whether each process is spontaneous as described, spontaneous in the reverse direction, or in equilibrium: **(a)** Water at 40 °C gets hotter when a piece of metal heated to 150 °C is added. **(b)** Water at room temperature decomposes into $H_2(g)$ and $O_2(g)$. **(c)** Benzene vapor, $C_6H_6(g)$, at a pressure of 1 atm condenses to liquid benzene at the normal boiling point of benzene, 80.1 °C.

SOLUTION

Analyze We are asked to judge whether each process is spontaneous in the direction indicated, in the reverse direction, or in neither direction.

Plan We need to think about whether each process is consistent with our experience about the natural direction of events or whether we expect the reverse process to occur.

Solve
(a) This process is spontaneous. Whenever two objects at different temperatures are brought into contact, heat is transferred from the hotter object to the colder one. ∞ (Section 10.1) Thus, heat is transferred from the hot metal to the cooler water. The final temperature, after the metal and water achieve the same temperature (thermal equilibrium), will be somewhere

between the initial temperatures of the metal and the water. **(b)** Experience tells us that this process is not spontaneous—we certainly have never seen hydrogen and oxygen gases spontaneously bubbling up out of water! Rather, the *reverse* process—the reaction of H_2 and O_2 to form H_2O—is spontaneous. **(c)** The normal boiling point is the temperature at which a vapor at 1 atm is in equilibrium with its liquid. Thus, this is an equilibrium situation. If the temperature were below 80.1 °C, condensation would be spontaneous.

PRACTICE EXERCISE

At 1 atm pressure, $CO_2(s)$ sublimes at −78 °C. Is this process spontaneous at −100 °C and 1 atm pressure?

Answer: No, the reverse process is spontaneous at this temperature.

Seeking a Criterion for Spontaneity

A marble rolling down an incline or a brick falling from your hand loses potential energy. The loss of some form of energy is a common feature of spontaneous change in mechanical systems. During the 1870s Marcellin Bertholet (1827–1907), a famous chemist of that era, suggested that the direction of spontaneous changes in chemical systems is determined by the loss of energy. He proposed that all spontaneous chemical and physical changes are exothermic. It takes only a few moments, however, to find exceptions to this generalization. For example, the melting of ice at room temperature is spontaneous and endothermic. Similarly, many spontaneous dissolution processes, such as the dissolving of NH_4NO_3, are endothermic. We conclude that although the majority of spontaneous reactions are exothermic, there are spontaneous endothermic ones as well. Clearly, some other factor must be at work in determining the natural direction of processes.

To understand why certain processes are spontaneous, we need to consider more closely the ways in which the state of a system can change. Recall from Section 10.2 that quantities such as temperature, internal energy, and enthalpy are *state functions*, properties that define a state and do not depend on how we reach that state. The heat transferred between a system and its surroundings, *q*, and the work done by or on the system, *w*, are *not* state functions—their values depend on the specific path taken between states. One key to understanding spontaneity is understanding differences in the paths between states.

Reversible and Irreversible Processes

In 1824 a 28-year-old French engineer named Sadi Carnot (1796–1832) published an analysis of the factors that determine how efficiently a steam engine can convert heat to work. Carnot considered what an *ideal engine*, one with the highest possible efficiency, would be like. He observed that it is impossible to convert the energy content of a fuel completely to work because a significant amount of heat is always lost to the surroundings. Carnot's analysis gave insight into how to build better, more efficient engines, and it was one of the earliest studies in what has developed into the discipline of thermodynamics.

An ideal engine operates under an ideal set of conditions in which all the processes are reversible. A **reversible process** is a specific way in which a system changes its state. In a reversible process, the change occurs in such a way that the system and surroundings can be restored to their original states by *exactly* reversing the change. In other words, we can restore the system to its original condition with no net change to either the system or its surroundings. An **irreversible process** is one that cannot simply be reversed to restore the system and its surroundings to their original states. What Carnot discovered is that the amount of work we can extract from any process depends on the manner in which the process is carried out. He concluded that *a reversible change produces the maximum amount of work that can be done by a system on its surroundings.*

If the flow of heat into or out of the system is to be reversible, what must be true of δT?

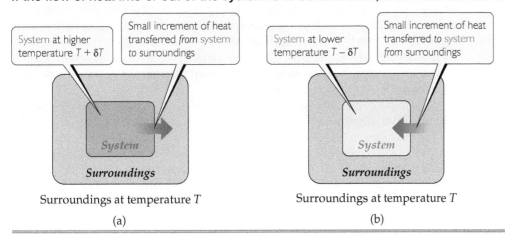

System at higher temperature $T + \delta T$

Small increment of heat transferred *from* system to surroundings

System at lower temperature $T - \delta T$

Small increment of heat transferred *to* system *from* surroundings

System

Surroundings

Surroundings at temperature T

(a)

System

Surroundings

Surroundings at temperature T

(b)

◀ **FIGURE 13.4 Reversible flow of heat.** Heat can flow reversibly between a system and its surroundings only if the two have an infinitesimally small difference in temperature δT. (a) Increasing the temperature of the system by δT causes heat to flow from the hotter system to the colder surroundings. (b) Decreasing the temperature of the system by δT causes heat to flow from the hotter surroundings to the colder system.

Suppose you have a system made up of water only, with the container and everything beyond being the surroundings. Consider a process in which the water is first evaporated and then condensed back into its original container. Is this two-step process necessarily reversible?

Let's next examine some aspects of reversible and irreversible processes, first with respect to the transfer of heat. When two objects at different temperatures are in contact, heat flows spontaneously from the hotter object to the colder one. Because it is impossible to make heat flow in the opposite direction, from colder object to hotter one, the flow of heat is an irreversible process. Given these facts, can we imagine any conditions under which heat transfer can be made reversible?

To answer this question, we must consider temperature differences that are infinitesimally small, as opposed to the discrete temperature differences with which we are most familiar. For example, consider a system and its surroundings at essentially the same temperature, with just an infinitesimal temperature difference δT between them (▲ **FIGURE 13.4**). If the surroundings are at temperature T and the system is at the infinitesimally higher temperature $T + \delta T$, then an infinitesimal amount of heat flows from system to surroundings. We can reverse the direction of heat flow by making an infinitesimal change of temperature in the opposite direction, lowering the system temperature to $T - \delta T$. Now the direction of heat flow is from surroundings to system. *Reversible processes are those that reverse direction whenever an infinitesimal change is made in some property of the system.**

Now let's consider another example, the expansion of an ideal gas at constant temperature (referred to as an **isothermal process**). In the cylinder-piston arrangement of ▼ **FIGURE 13.5**, when the partition is removed, the gas expands spontaneously to fill the

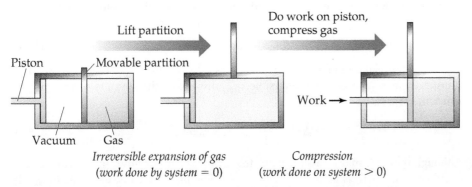

Lift partition

Do work on piston, compress gas

Piston

Movable partition

Work →

Vacuum Gas

Irreversible expansion of gas
(work done by system $= 0$)

Compression
(work done on system > 0)

◀ **FIGURE 13.5 An irreversible process.** Initially an ideal gas is confined to the right half of a cylinder. When the partition is removed, the gas spontaneously expands to fill the whole cylinder. No work is done by the system during this expansion. Using the piston to compress the gas back to its original state requires the surroundings to do work on the system.

*For a process to be truly reversible, the amounts of heat must be infinitesimally small and the transfer of heat must occur infinitely slowly; thus, no process that we can observe is truly reversible. The notion of infinitesimal amounts are related to the infinitesimals that you may have studied in a calculus course.

evacuated space. Can we determine whether this particular isothermal expansion is reversible or irreversible? Because the gas expands into a vacuum with no external pressure, it does no *P-V* work on the surroundings. ∞ (Section 10.3) Thus, for the expansion, $w = 0$. We can use the piston to compress the gas back to its original state, but doing so requires that the surroundings do work on the system, meaning that $w > 0$ for the compression. In other words, the path that restores the system to its original state requires a different value of w (and, by the first law, a different value of q) than the path by which the system was first changed. The fact that the same path can't be followed to restore the system to its original state indicates that the process is irreversible.

What might a *reversible* isothermal expansion of an ideal gas be? This process will occur only if initially, when the gas is confined to half the cylinder, the external pressure acting on the piston exactly balances the pressure exerted by the gas on the piston. If the external pressure is reduced infinitely slowly, the piston will move outward, allowing the pressure of the confined gas to readjust to maintain the pressure balance. This infinitely slow process in which the external pressure and internal pressure are always in equilibrium is reversible. If we reverse the process and compress the gas in the same infinitely slow manner, we can return the gas to its original volume. The complete cycle of expansion and compression in this hypothetical process, moreover, is accomplished without any net change to the surroundings.

Because real processes can at best only approximate the infinitely slow change associated with reversible processes, all real processes are irreversible. Further, as noted earlier in this discussion, the reverse of any spontaneous process is a nonspontaneous process. A nonspontaneous process can occur only if the surroundings do work on the system. Thus, *any spontaneous process is irreversible.* Even if we return the system to the original condition, the surroundings will have changed.

13.2 | ENTROPY AND THE SECOND LAW OF THERMODYNAMICS

How can we use the fact that any spontaneous process is irreversible to make predictions about the spontaneity of an unfamiliar process? Understanding spontaneity requires us to examine the thermodynamic quantity called **entropy**. In general, entropy is associated either with the extent of *randomness* in a system or with the extent to which energy is distributed among the various motions of the molecules of the system. In this section we consider how we can relate entropy changes to heat transfer and temperature. Our analysis will bring us to a profound statement about spontaneity that we call the second law of thermodynamics.

Entropy Change

The entropy, S, of a system is a state function just like internal energy, E, and enthalpy, H. As with these other quantities, the value of S is a characteristic of the state of a system. ∞ (Section 10.2) Thus, the change in entropy, ΔS, in a system depends only on the initial and final states of the system and not on the path taken from one state to the other:

$$\Delta S = S_{final} - S_{initial} \qquad [13.1]$$

For the special case of an isothermal process, ΔS is equal to the heat that would be transferred if the process were reversible, q_{rev}, divided by the absolute temperature at which the process occurs:

$$\Delta S = \frac{q_{rev}}{T} \qquad (\text{constant } T) \qquad [13.2]$$

Although there are many possible paths that can take the system from one state to another, only one path is associated with a reversible process. Thus, the value of q_{rev} is uniquely defined for any two states of the system. Because S is a state function, we can use Equation 13.2 to calculate ΔS for *any* isothermal process between states, not just the reversible one.

⚠ GIVE IT SOME THOUGHT

How do we reconcile the fact that S is a state function but ΔS depends on q, which is not a state function?

ΔS for Phase Changes

The melting of a substance at its melting point and the vaporization of a substance at its boiling point are isothermal processes. ∞ (Section 11.2) Consider the melting of ice. At 1 atm pressure, ice and liquid water are in equilibrium at 0 °C. Imagine melting 1 mol of ice at 0 °C, 1 atm to form 1 mol of liquid water at 0 °C, 1 atm. We can achieve this change by adding a certain amount of heat to the system from the surroundings: $q = \Delta H_{fusion}$. Now imagine that we add the heat infinitely slowly, raising the temperature of the surroundings only infinitesimally above 0 °C. When we make the change in this fashion, the process is reversible because we can reverse it by infinitely slowly removing the same amount of heat, ΔH_{fusion}, from the system, using immediate surroundings that are infinitesimally below 0 °C. Thus, $q_{rev} = \Delta H_{fusion}$ for the melting of ice at $T = 0\,°C = 273\,K$.

The enthalpy of fusion for H_2O is $\Delta H_{fusion} = 6.01\,kJ/mol$ (a positive value because melting is an endothermic process). Thus, we can use Equation 13.2 to calculate ΔS_{fusion} for melting 1 mol of ice at 273 K:

$$\Delta S_{fusion} = \frac{q_{rev}}{T} = \frac{\Delta H_{fusion}}{T} = \frac{(1\,mol)(6.01 \times 10^3\,J/mol)}{273\,K} = 22.0\,J/K$$

Notice (a) that we must use the absolute temperature in Equation 13.2 and (b) that the units for ΔS, J/K, are energy divided by absolute temperature, as we expect from Equation 13.2.

SAMPLE EXERCISE 13.2   **Calculating ΔS for a Phase Change**

Elemental mercury is a silver liquid at room temperature. Its normal freezing point is −38.9 °C, and its molar enthalpy of fusion is $\Delta H_{fusion} = 2.29\,kJ/mol$. What is the entropy change of the system when 50.0 g of Hg(l) freezes at the normal freezing point?

SOLUTION

Analyze We first recognize that freezing is an *exothermic* process, which means heat is transferred from system to surroundings and $q < 0$. The enthalpy of fusion refers to the process of melting. Because freezing is the reverse of melting, the enthalpy change that accompanies the freezing of 1 mol of Hg is $-\Delta H_{fusion} = -2.29\,kJ/mol$.

Plan We can use $-\Delta H_{fusion}$ and the atomic weight of Hg to calculate q for freezing 50.0 g of Hg. Then we use this value of q as q_{rev} in Equation 13.2 to determine ΔS for the system.

Solve
For q we have

$$q = (50.0\,g\,Hg)\left(\frac{1\,mol\,Hg}{200.59\,g\,Hg}\right)\left(\frac{-2.29\,kJ}{1\,mol\,Hg}\right)\left(\frac{1000\,J}{1\,kJ}\right) = -571$$

Before using Equation 13.2, we must first convert the given Celsius temperature to kelvins:

$$-38.9\,°C = (-38.9 + 273.15)\,K = 234.3\,K$$

We can now calculate ΔS_{sys}:

$$\Delta S_{sys} = \frac{q_{rev}}{T} = \frac{-571\,J}{234.3\,K} = -2.44\,J/K$$

Check The entropy change is negative because our q_{rev} value is negative, which it must be because heat flows out of the system in this exothermic process.

Comment This procedure can be used to calculate ΔS for other isothermal phase changes, such as the vaporization of a liquid at its boiling point.

PRACTICE EXERCISE

The normal boiling point of ethanol, C_2H_5OH, is 78.3 °C, and its molar enthalpy of vaporization is 38.56 kJ/mol. What is the change in entropy in the system when 68.3 g of $C_2H_5OH(g)$ at 1 atm condenses to liquid at the normal boiling point?

Answer: −163 J/K

A CLOSER LOOK

THE ENTROPY CHANGE WHEN A GAS EXPANDS ISOTHERMALLY

In general, the entropy of any system increases as the system becomes more random or more spread out. Thus, we expect the spontaneous expansion of a gas to result in an increase in entropy. To see how this entropy increase can be calculated, consider the expansion of an ideal gas that is initially constrained by a piston, as in the rightmost part of Figure 13.5. Imagine that we allow the gas to undergo a reversible isothermal expansion by infinitesimally decreasing the external pressure on the piston. The work done on the surroundings by the reversible expansion of the system against the piston can be calculated with the aid of calculus (we do not show the derivation):

$$w_{rev} = -nRT \ln \frac{V_2}{V_1}$$

In this equation, n is the number of moles of gas, R is the gas constant ∞ (Section 8.4), T is the absolute temperature, V_1 is the initial volume, and V_2 is the final volume. Notice that if $V_2 > V_1$, as it must be in our expansion, then $w_{rev} < 0$, meaning that the expanding gas does work on the surroundings.

One characteristic of an ideal gas is that its internal energy depends only on temperature, not on pressure. Thus, when an ideal gas expands isothermally, $\Delta E = 0$. Because $\Delta E = q_{rev} + w_{rev} = 0$, we see that $q_{rev} = -w_{rev} = nRT \ln(V_2/V_1)$. Then, using Equation 13.2, we can calculate the entropy change in the system:

$$\Delta S_{sys} = \frac{q_{rev}}{T} = \frac{nRT \ln \dfrac{V_2}{V_1}}{T} = nR \ln \frac{V_2}{V_1} \quad [13.3]$$

From the ideal-gas equation, we can calculate the number of moles in 1.00 L of an ideal gas at 1.00 atm and 0 °C by using the value 0.08206 L-atm/mol-K for R:

$$n = \frac{PV}{RT} = \frac{(1.00 \text{ atm})(1.00 \text{ L})}{(0.08206 \text{ L-atm/mol-K})(273 \text{ K})} = 4.46 \times 10^{-2} \text{ mol}$$

The gas constant, R, can also be expressed as 8.314 J/mol-K (Table 8.2), and this is the value we must use in Equation 13.3 because we want our answer to be expressed in terms of J rather than in L-atm. Thus, for the expansion of the gas from 1.00 L to 2.00 L, we have

$$\Delta S_{sys} = (4.46 \times 10^{-2} \text{ mol})\left(8.314 \frac{J}{\text{mol-K}}\right)\left(\ln \frac{2.00 \text{ L}}{1.00 \text{ L}}\right)$$

$$= 0.26 \text{ J/K}$$

In Section 13.3 we will see that this increase in entropy is a measure of the increased randomness of the molecules because of the expansion.

RELATED EXERCISES: 13.29, 13.30, and 13.106

The Second Law of Thermodynamics

The key idea of the first law of thermodynamics is that energy is conserved in any process. ∞ (Section 10.2) Entropy, however, is not conserved. For any spontaneous process, the total change in entropy, which is the sum of the entropy change of the system plus the entropy change of the surroundings, is greater than zero.

Let's illustrate this generalization by calculating the entropy change of a system and the entropy change of its surroundings when our system is 1 mol of ice (a piece roughly the size of an ice cube) melting in the palm of your hand, which is part of the surroundings. The process is not reversible because the system and surroundings are at different temperatures. Nevertheless, because ΔS is a state function, its value is the same regardless of whether the process is reversible or irreversible. We calculated the entropy change of the system just before Sample Exercise 13.2:

$$\Delta S_{sys} = \frac{q_{rev}}{T} = \frac{(1 \text{ mol})(6.01 \times 10^3 \text{ J/mol})}{273 \text{ K}} = 22.0 \text{ J/K}$$

The surroundings immediately in contact with the ice are your hand, which we assume is at body temperature, 37 °C = 310 K. The quantity of heat lost by your hand is -6.01×10^3 J/mol, which is equal in magnitude to the quantity of heat gained by the ice but has the opposite sign. Hence, the entropy change of the surroundings is

$$\Delta S_{surr} = \frac{q_{rev}}{T} = \frac{(1 \text{ mol})(-6.01 \times 10^3 \text{ J/mol})}{310 \text{ K}} = -19.4 \text{ J/K}$$

Thus, the total entropy change is positive:

$$\Delta S_{total} = \Delta S_{sys} + \Delta S_{surr} = (22.0 \text{ J/K}) + (-19.4 \text{ J/K}) = 2.6 \text{ J/K}$$

If the temperature of the surroundings were not 310 K but rather some temperature infinitesimally above 273 K, the melting would be reversible instead of irreversible. In that case the entropy change of the surroundings would equal -22.0 J/K and ΔS_{total} would be zero.

In general, any irreversible process results in an increase in total entropy, whereas any reversible process results in no overall change in entropy. This statement is known as the **second law of thermodynamics**.

The sum of the entropy of a system plus the entropy of the surroundings is everything there is, and so we refer to the total entropy change as the entropy change of the universe, ΔS_{univ}. We can therefore state the second law of thermodynamics in terms of two equations:

$$\text{Reversible Process: } \Delta S_{univ} = \Delta S_{sys} + \Delta S_{surr} = 0$$

$$\text{Irreversible Process: } \Delta S_{univ} = \Delta S_{sys} + \Delta S_{surr} > 0 \qquad [13.4]$$

Because spontaneous processes are irreversible, we can say that *the entropy of the universe increases in any spontaneous process.* This profound generalization is yet another way of expressing the second law of thermodynamics.

GIVE IT SOME THOUGHT

The rusting of iron is spontaneous and is accompanied by a decrease in the entropy of the system (the iron and oxygen). What can we conclude about the entropy change of the surroundings?

The second law of thermodynamics tells us the essential character of any spontaneous change—it is always accompanied by an increase in the entropy of the universe. We can use this criterion to predict whether a given process is spontaneous or not. Before seeing how this is done, however, we will find it useful to explore entropy from a molecular perspective.

A word on notation before we proceed. Throughout most of the remainder of this chapter, we will focus on systems rather than surroundings. To simplify the notation, we will usually refer to the entropy change of the system as ΔS rather than explicitly indicating ΔS_{sys}.

13.3 | MOLECULAR INTERPRETATION OF ENTROPY

As chemists, we are interested in molecules. What does entropy have to do with them and with their transformations? What molecular property does entropy reflect? Ludwig Boltzmann (1844–1906) gave conceptual meaning to the notion of entropy, and to understand his contribution, we need to examine the ways in which we can interpret entropy at the molecular level.

Expansion of a Gas at the Molecular Level

In discussing Figure 13.2, we talked about the expansion of a gas into a vacuum as a spontaneous process. We now understand that it is an irreversible process and that the entropy of the universe increases during the expansion. How can we explain the spontaneity of this process at the molecular level? We can get a sense of what makes this expansion spontaneous by envisioning the gas as a collection of particles in constant motion, as we did in discussing the kinetic-molecular theory of gases. ∞∞ (Section 8.7) When the stopcock in Figure 13.2 is opened, we can view the expansion of the gas as the ultimate result of the gas molecules moving randomly throughout the larger volume.

Let's look at this idea more closely by tracking two of the gas molecules as they move around. Before the stopcock is opened, both molecules are confined to the left flask, as shown in ▶ FIGURE 13.6(a). After the stopcock is opened, the molecules travel randomly throughout the entire apparatus. As Figure 13.6(b) shows, there are four possible arrangements for the two molecules once both flasks are available to them. Because the molecular motion is random, all four arrangements are equally likely. Note that now only one arrangement corresponds to the situation before the stopcock was opened: both molecules in the left flask.

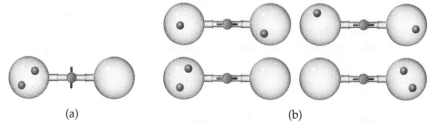

(a)

The two molecules are colored
red and blue to keep track of them.

(b)

Four possible arrangements (microstates)
once the stopcock is opened.

▲ FIGURE 13.6 **Possible arrangements of two gas molecules in two flasks.** (a) Before the stopcock is opened, both molecules are in the left flask. (b) After the stopcock is opened, there are four possible arrangements of the two molecules.

Figure 13.6(b) shows that with both flasks available to the molecules, the probability of the red molecule being in the left flask is two in four (top right and bottom left arrangements), and the probability of the blue molecule being in the left flask is the same (top left and bottom left arrangements). Because the probability is $^2/_4 = ^1/_2$ that each molecule is in the left flask, the probability that *both* are there is $(^1/_2)^2 = ^1/_4$. If we apply the same analysis to *three* gas molecules, we find that the probability that all three are in the left flask at the same time is $(^1/_2)^3 = 1/8$.

Now let's consider a *mole* of gas. The probability that all the molecules are in the left flask at the same time is $(^1/_2)^N$, where $N = 6.02 \times 10^{23}$. This is a vanishingly small number! Thus, there is essentially zero likelihood that all the gas molecules will be in the left flask at the same time. This analysis of the microscopic behavior of the gas molecules leads to the expected macroscopic behavior: The gas spontaneously expands to fill both the left and right flasks, and it does not spontaneously all go back in the left flask.

This molecular view of gas expansion shows the tendency of the molecules to "spread out" among the different arrangements they can take. Before the stopcock is opened, there is only one possible arrangement: all molecules in the left flask. When the stopcock is opened, the arrangement in which all the molecules are in the left flask is but one of an extremely large number of possible arrangements. The most probable arrangements by far are those in which there are essentially equal numbers of molecules in the two flasks. When the gas spreads throughout the apparatus, any given molecule can be in either flask rather than confined to the left flask. We say that with the stopcock opened, the arrangement of gas molecules is more random or disordered than when the molecules are all confined in the left flask.

We will see this notion of increasing randomness helps us understand entropy at the molecular level.

Boltzmann's Equation and Microstates

The science of thermodynamics developed as a means of describing the properties of matter in our macroscopic world without regard to microscopic structure. In fact, thermodynamics was a well-developed field before the modern view of atomic and molecular structure was even known. The thermodynamic properties of water, for example, addressed the behavior of bulk water (or ice or water vapor) as a substance without considering any specific properties of individual H_2O molecules.

To connect the microscopic and macroscopic descriptions of matter, scientists have developed the field of *statistical thermodynamics*, which uses the tools of statistics and probability to link the microscopic and macroscopic worlds. Here we show how entropy, which is a property of bulk matter, can be connected to the behavior of atoms and molecules. Because the mathematics of statistical thermodynamics is complex, our discussion will be largely conceptual.

In our discussion of two gas molecules in the two-flask system in Figure 13.6, we saw that the number of possible arrangements helped explain why the gas expands.

Suppose we now consider one mole of an ideal gas in a particular thermodynamic state, which we can define by specifying the temperature, T, and volume, V, of the gas. What is happening to this gas at the microscopic level, and how does what is going on at the microscopic level relate to the entropy of the gas?

Imagine taking a snapshot of the positions and speeds of all the molecules at a given instant. The speed of each molecule tells us its kinetic energy. That particular set of 6×10^{23} positions and kinetic energies of the individual gas molecules is what we call a *microstate* of the system. A **microstate** is a single possible arrangement of the positions and kinetic energies of the gas molecules when the gas is in a specific thermodynamic state. We could envision continuing to take snapshots of our system to see other possible microstates.

As you no doubt see, there would be such a staggeringly large number of microstates that taking individual snapshots of all of them is not feasible. Because we are examining such a large number of particles, however, we can use the tools of statistics and probability to determine the total number of microstates for the thermodynamic state. (That is where the *statistical* part of the name *statistical thermodynamics* comes in.) Each thermodynamic state has a characteristic number of microstates associated with it, and we will use the symbol W for that number.

▲ **FIGURE 13.7** **Ludwig Boltzmann's gravestone.** Boltzmann's gravestone in Vienna is inscribed with his famous relationship between the entropy of a state, S, and the number of available microstates, W. (In Boltzmann's time, "log" was used to represent the natural logarithm.)

Students sometimes have difficulty distinguishing between the state of a system and the microstates associated with the state. The difference is that *state* is used to describe the macroscopic view of our system as characterized, for example, by the pressure or temperature of a sample of gas. A *microstate* is a particular microscopic arrangement of the atoms or molecules of the system that corresponds to the given state of the system. Each of the snapshots we described is a microstate—the positions and kinetic energies of individual gas molecules will change from snapshot to snapshot, but each one is a possible arrangement of the collection of molecules corresponding to a single state. For macroscopically sized systems, such as a mole of gas, there is a very large number of microstates for each state—that is, W is generally an extremely large number.

The connection between the number of microstates of a system, W, and the entropy of the system, S, is expressed in a beautifully simple equation developed by Boltzmann and engraved on his tombstone (▶ **FIGURE 13.7**):

$$S = k \ln W \qquad [13.5]$$

In this equation, k is Boltzmann's constant, 1.38×10^{-23} J/K. Thus, *entropy is a measure of how many microstates are associated with a particular macroscopic state.*

GIVE IT SOME THOUGHT

What is the entropy of a system that has only a single microstate?

From Equation 13.5, we see that the entropy change accompanying any process is

$$\Delta S = k \ln W_{final} - k \ln W_{initial} = k \ln \frac{W_{final}}{W_{initial}} \qquad [13.6]$$

Any change in the system that leads to an increase in the number of microstates ($W_{final} > W_{initial}$) leads to a positive value of ΔS: *Entropy increases with the number of microstates of the system.*

Let's consider two modifications to our ideal-gas sample and see how the entropy changes in each case. First, suppose we increase the volume of the system, which is analogous to allowing the gas to expand isothermally. A greater volume means a greater number of positions available to the gas atoms and therefore a greater number of microstates. The entropy therefore increases as the volume increases, as we saw in the "A Closer Look" box in Section 13.2.

Second, suppose we keep the volume fixed but increase the temperature. How does this change affect the entropy of the system? Recall the distribution of molecular speeds presented in Figure 8.17(a). An increase in temperature increases the most probable speed of the molecules and also broadens the distribution of speeds. Hence, the molecules have a greater number of possible kinetic energies, and the number of microstates increases. Thus, the entropy of the system increases with increasing temperature.

Molecular Motions and Energy

When a substance is heated, the motion of its molecules increases. In Section 8.7, we found that the average kinetic energy of the molecules of an ideal gas is directly proportional to the absolute temperature of the gas. That means the higher the temperature, the faster the molecules move and the more kinetic energy they possess. Moreover, hotter systems have a *broader distribution* of molecular speeds, as Figure 8.17(a) shows.

The particles of an ideal gas are idealized points with no volume and no bonds, however, points that we visualize as flitting around through space. Any real molecule can undergo three kinds of more complex motion. The entire molecule can move in one direction, which is the simple motion we visualize for an ideal particle and see in a macroscopic object, such as a thrown baseball. We call such movement **translational motion**. The molecules in a gas have more freedom of translational motion than those in a liquid, which have more freedom of translational motion than the molecules of a solid.

A real molecule can also undergo **vibrational motion**, in which the atoms in the molecule move periodically toward and away from one another, and **rotational motion**, in which the molecule spins about an axis. ▼ FIGURE 13.8 shows the vibrational motions and one of the rotational motions possible for the water molecule. These different forms of motion are ways in which a molecule can store energy, and we refer to the various forms collectively as the *motional energy* of the molecule.

GIVE IT SOME THOUGHT
What kinds of motion can a molecule undergo that a single atom cannot?

The vibrational and rotational motions possible in real molecules lead to arrangements that a single atom can't have. A collection of real molecules therefore has a greater number of possible microstates than does the same number of ideal-gas particles. In general, *the number of microstates possible for a system increases with an increase in volume, an increase in temperature, or an increase in the number of molecules because any of these changes increases the possible positions and kinetic energies of the molecules making up the system.* We will also see that the number of microstates increases as the complexity of the molecule increases because there are more vibrational motions available.

Chemists have several ways of describing an increase in the number of microstates possible for a system and therefore an increase in the entropy for the system. Each way seeks to capture a sense of the increased freedom of motion that causes molecules to spread out when not restrained by physical barriers or chemical bonds.

GO FIGURE

Describe another possible rotational motion for this molecule.

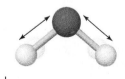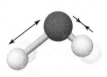

▶ FIGURE 13.8 **Vibrational and rotational motions in a water molecule.**

——— Vibrations ———   ——— Rotation ———

The most common way for describing an increase in entropy is as an increase in the *randomness*, or *disorder*, of the system. Another way likens an entropy increase to an increased *dispersion (spreading out) of energy* because there is an increase in the number of ways the positions and energies of the molecules can be distributed throughout the system. Each description (randomness or energy dispersal) is conceptually helpful if applied correctly.

Making Qualitative Predictions About ΔS

It is usually not difficult to estimate qualitatively how the entropy of a system changes during a simple process. As noted earlier, an increase in either the temperature or the volume of a system leads to an increase in the number of microstates, and hence an increase in the entropy. One more factor that correlates with number of microstates is the number of independently moving particles.

We can usually make qualitative predictions about entropy changes by focusing on these factors. For example, when water vaporizes, the molecules spread out into a larger volume. Because they occupy a larger volume, there is an increase in their freedom of motion, giving rise to a greater number of possible microstates, and hence an increase in entropy.

Now consider the phases of water. In ice, hydrogen bonding leads to the rigid structure shown in ▼ FIGURE 13.9. Each molecule in the ice is free to vibrate, but its translational and rotational motions are much more restricted than in liquid water. Although there are hydrogen bonds in liquid water, the molecules can more readily move about relative to one another (translation) and tumble around (rotation). During melting, therefore, the number of possible microstates increases and so does the entropy. In water vapor, the molecules are essentially independent of one another and have their full range of translational, vibrational, and rotational motions. Thus, water vapor has an even greater number of possible microstates and therefore a higher entropy than liquid water or ice.

GO FIGURE

In which phase are water molecules least able to have rotational motion?

Increasing entropy →

Ice	Liquid water	Water vapor
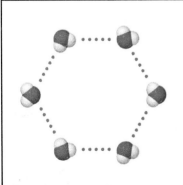		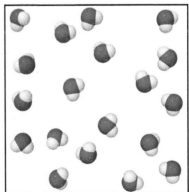

Rigid, crystalline structure

Motion restricted to **vibration** only

Smallest number of microstates

Increased freedom with respect to **translation**

Free to **vibrate** and **rotate**

Larger number of microstates

Molecules spread out, essentially independent of one another

Complete freedom for **translation**, **vibration**, and **rotation**

Largest number of microstates

▲ FIGURE 13.9   **Entropy and the phases of water.** The larger the number of possible microstates, the higher the entropy of the system.

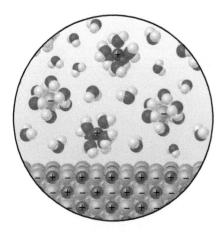

▲ **FIGURE 13.10** **Entropy changes when an ionic solid dissolves in water.** The ions become more spread out and disordered, but the water molecules that hydrate the ions become less disordered.

When an ionic solid dissolves in water, a mixture of water and ions replaces the pure solid and pure water, as shown for KCl in ◄ **FIGURE 13.10**. The ions in the liquid move in a volume that is larger than the volume in which they were able to move in the crystal lattice and so possess more motional energy. This increased motion might lead us to conclude that the entropy of the system has increased. We have to be careful, however, because some of the water molecules have lost some freedom of motion because they are now held around the ions as water of hydration. These water molecules are in a *more* ordered state than before because they are now confined to the immediate environment of the ions. Therefore, the dissolving of a salt involves both a disordering process (the ions become less confined) and an ordering process (some water molecules become more confined). The disordering processes are usually dominant, and so the overall effect is an increase in the randomness of the system when most salts dissolve in water.

The same ideas apply to chemical reactions. Consider the reaction between nitric oxide gas and oxygen gas to form nitrogen dioxide gas:

$$2\,NO(g) + O_2(g) \longrightarrow 2\,NO_2(g) \qquad [13.7]$$

which results in a decrease in the number of molecules—three molecules of gaseous reactants form two molecules of gaseous products (▶ **FIGURE 13.11**). The formation of new N—O bonds reduces the motions of the atoms in the system. The formation of new bonds decreases the *number of degrees of freedom*, or forms of motion, available to the atoms. That is, the atoms are less free to move in random fashion because of the formation of new bonds. The decrease in the number of molecules and the resultant decrease in motion result in fewer possible microstates and therefore a decrease in the entropy of the system.

In summary, we generally expect the entropy of a system to increase for processes in which

1. Gases form from either solids or liquids.

2. Liquids or solutions form from solids.

3. The number of gas molecules increases during a chemical reaction.

SAMPLE EXERCISE 13.3 | **Predicting the Sign of ΔS**

Predict whether ΔS is positive or negative for each process, assuming each occurs at constant temperature:

(a) $H_2O(l) \longrightarrow H_2O(g)$

(b) $Ag^+(aq) + Cl^-(aq) \longrightarrow AgCl(s)$

(c) $4\,Fe(s) + 3\,O_2(g) \longrightarrow 2\,Fe_2O_3(s)$

(d) $N_2(g) + O_2(g) \longrightarrow 2\,NO(g)$

SOLUTION

Analyze We are given four reactions and asked to predict the sign of ΔS for each.

Plan We expect ΔS to be positive if there is an increase in temperature, increase in volume, or increase in number of gas particles. The question states that the temperature is constant, and so we need to concern ourselves only with volume and number of particles.

Solve

(a) Evaporation involves a large increase in volume as liquid changes to gas. One mole of water (18 g) occupies about 18 mL as a liquid and if it could exist as a gas at STP it would occupy 22.4 L. Because the molecules are distributed throughout a much larger volume in the gaseous state, an increase in motional freedom accompanies vaporization and ΔS is positive.

(b) In this process, ions, which are free to move throughout the volume of the solution, form a solid, in which they are confined to a smaller volume and restricted to more highly constrained positions. Thus, ΔS is negative.

(c) The particles of a solid are confined to specific locations and have fewer ways to move (fewer microstates) than do the molecules of a gas. Because O_2 gas is converted into part of the solid product Fe_2O_3, ΔS is negative.

(d) The number of moles of reactant gases is the same as the number of moles of product gases, and so the entropy change is expected to be small. The sign of ΔS is impossible to predict based on our discussions thus far, but we can predict that ΔS will be close to zero.

PRACTICE EXERCISE

Indicate whether each process produces an increase or decrease in the entropy of the system:

(a) $CO_2(s) \longrightarrow CO_2(g)$

(b) $CaO(s) + CO_2(g) \longrightarrow CaCO_3(s)$

(c) $HCl(g) + NH_3(g) \longrightarrow NH_4Cl(s)$

(d) $2\,SO_2(g) + O_2(g) \longrightarrow 2\,SO_3(g)$

Answers: **(a)** increase, **(b)** decrease, **(c)** decrease, **(d)** decrease

---

SAMPLE EXERCISE 13.4 **Predicting Relative Entropies**

In each pair, choose the system that has greater entropy and explain your choice: **(a)** 1 mol of $NaCl(s)$ or 1 mol of $HCl(g)$ at 25 °C, **(b)** 2 mol of $HCl(g)$ or 1 mol of $HCl(g)$ at 25 °C, **(c)** 1 mol of $HCl(g)$ or 1 mol of $Ar(g)$ at 298 K.

SOLUTION

Analyze We need to select the system in each pair that has the greater entropy.

Plan We examine the state of each system and the complexity of the molecules it contains.

Solve
(a) $HCl(g)$ has the higher entropy because the particles in gases are more disordered and have more freedom of motion than the particles in solids. **(b)** When these two systems are at the same pressure, the sample containing 2 mol of HCl has twice the number of molecules as the sample containing 1 mol. Thus, the 2-mol sample has twice the number of microstates and twice the entropy. **(c)** The HCl system has the higher entropy because the number of ways in which an HCl molecule can store energy is greater than the number of ways in which an Ar atom can store energy. (Molecules can rotate and vibrate; atoms cannot.)

PRACTICE EXERCISE

Choose the system with the greater entropy in each case: **(a)** 1 mol of $H_2(g)$ at STP or 1 mol of $H_2(g)$ at 100 °C and 0.5 atm, **(b)** 1 mol of $H_2O(s)$ at 0 °C or 1 mol of $H_2O(l)$ at 25 °C, **(c)** 1 mol of $H_2(g)$ at STP or 1 mol of $SO_2(g)$ at STP, **(d)** 1 mol of $N_2O_4(g)$ at STP or 2 mol of $NO_2(g)$ at STP.

Answers: **(a)** 1 mol of $H_2(g)$ at 100 °C and 0.5 atm, **(b)** 1 mol of $H_2O(l)$ at 25 °C, **(c)** 1 mol of $SO_2(g)$ at STP, **(d)** 2 mol of $NO_2(g)$ at STP

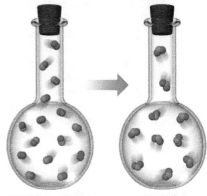

GO FIGURE

What major factor leads to a decrease in entropy as the reaction shown takes place?

$2\,NO(g) + O_2(g)$ $2\,NO_2(g)$

▲ **FIGURE 13.11** **Entropy decreases when NO(g) is oxidized by O$_2$(g) to NO$_2$(g).** A decrease in the number of gaseous molecules leads to a decrease in the entropy of the system.

The Third Law of Thermodynamics

If we decrease the thermal energy of a system by lowering the temperature, the energy stored in translational, vibrational, and rotational motion decreases. As less energy is stored, the entropy of the system decreases. If we keep lowering the temperature, do we reach a state in which these motions are essentially shut down, a point described by a single microstate? This question is addressed by the **third law of thermodynamics**, which states that *the entropy of a pure crystalline substance at absolute zero is zero*: $S(0\,K) = 0$.

Consider a pure crystalline solid. At absolute zero, the individual atoms or molecules in the lattice would be perfectly ordered and as well defined in position as they could be. Because none of them would have thermal motion, there is only one possible microstate. As a result, Equation 13.5 becomes $S = k \ln W = k \ln 1 = 0$. As the temperature is increased from absolute zero, the atoms or molecules in the crystal gain energy in the form of vibrational motion about their lattice positions. This means that the degrees of freedom and the entropy both increase. What happens to the entropy, however, as we continue to heat the crystal? We consider this important question in the next section.

GIVE IT SOME THOUGHT

If you are told that the entropy of a system is zero, what do you know about the system?

CHEMISTRY AND LIFE

ENTROPY AND HUMAN SOCIETY

The laws of thermodynamics have profound implications for our existence. In the "Chemistry Put to Work" box in chapter 10, we examined some of the scientific and political challenges of using biofuels as a major energy source to maintain our lifestyles. That discussion builds around the first law of thermodynamics, namely, that energy is conserved. We therefore have important decisions to make as to energy production and consumption.

The second law of thermodynamics is also relevant in discussions about our existence and about our ability and desire to advance as a civilization. Any living organism is a complex, highly organized, well-ordered system. Our entropy content is much lower than it would be if we were completely decomposed into carbon dioxide, water, and several other simple chemicals. Does this mean that our existence is a violation of the second law? No, because the thousands of chemical reactions necessary to produce and maintain human life have caused a very large increase in the entropy of the rest of the universe. Thus, as the second law requires, the overall entropy change during the lifetime of a human, or any other living system, is positive.

In addition to being complex living systems ourselves, we humans are masters of producing order in the world around us. As shown in the chapter-opening photograph, we build impressive, highly ordered structures and buildings. We manipulate and order matter at the nanoscale level in order to produce the technological breakthroughs that have become so commonplace in the twenty-first century (▶ FIGURE 13.12). We use tremendous quantities of raw materials to produce highly ordered materials—iron, copper, and a host of other metals from their ores, silicon for computer chips from sand, polymers from fossil fuel feedstocks, and so forth. In so doing, we expend a great deal of energy to, in essence, "fight" the second law of thermodynamics.

For every bit of order we produce, however, we produce an even greater amount of disorder. Petroleum, coal, and natural gas are burned to provide the energy necessary for us to achieve highly ordered structures, but their combustion increases the entropy of the universe by releasing $CO_2(g)$, $H_2O(g)$, and heat. Oxide and sulfide ores release $CO_2(g)$ and $SO_2(g)$ that spread throughout our atmosphere. Thus, even as we strive to create more impressive discoveries and greater order in our society, we drive the entropy of the universe higher, as the second law says we must.

We humans are, in effect, using up our storehouse of energy-rich materials to create order and advance technology. As noted in Chapter 10, we must learn to harness new energy sources, such as solar energy, before we exhaust the supplies of readily available energy of other kinds.

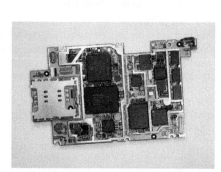

▲ FIGURE 13.12 **Fighting the second law.** Creating complex structures, such as the skyscrapers in the chapter-opening photograph, requires that we use energy to produce order while knowing that we are increasing the entropy of the universe. Modern cellular telephones, with their detailed displays and complex circuitry are an example on a smaller scale of the impressive order that human ingenuity achieves.

13.4 | ENTROPY CHANGES IN CHEMICAL REACTIONS

In Section 10.5 we discussed how calorimetry can be used to measure ΔH for chemical reactions. No comparable method exists for measuring ΔS for a reaction. However, because the third law establishes a zero point for entropy, we can use experimental measurements to determine the *absolute value of the entropy*, S. To see schematically how this is done, let's review in greater detail the variation in the entropy of a substance with temperature.

We know that the entropy of a pure crystalline solid at 0 K is zero and that the entropy increases as the temperature of the crystal is increased. ▶ FIGURE 13.13 shows that the entropy of the solid increases steadily with increasing temperature up to the melting point of the solid. When the solid melts, the atoms or molecules are free to move about the entire volume of the sample. The added degrees of freedom increase the randomness of the substance, thereby increasing its entropy. We therefore see a sharp increase in the entropy at the melting point. After all the solid has melted, the temperature again increases and with it, the entropy.

GO FIGURE

Why does the plot show vertical jumps at the melting and boiling points?

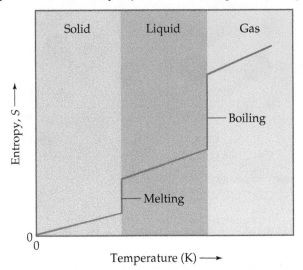

▲ FIGURE 13.13 **Entropy increases with increasing temperature.**

At the boiling point of the liquid, another abrupt increase in entropy occurs. We can understand this increase as resulting from the increased volume available to the atoms or molecules as they enter the gaseous state. When the gas is heated further, the entropy increases steadily as more energy is stored in the translational motion of the gas atoms or molecules.

Another change that occurs at higher temperatures is that the distribution of molecular speeds is skewed toward higher values. ∞ [Figure 8.17(a)] The expansion of the range of speeds leads to increased kinetic energy and increased disorder and, hence, increased entropy. The conclusions we reach in examining Figure 13.13 are consistent with what we noted earlier: Entropy generally increases with increasing temperature because the increased motional energy leads to a greater number of possible microstates.

Entropy plots such as Figure 13.13 can be obtained by carefully measuring how the heat capacity of a substance ∞ (Section 10.5) varies with temperature, and we can use the data to obtain the absolute entropies at different temperatures. (The theory and methods used for these measurements and calculations are beyond the scope of this text.) Entropies are usually tabulated as molar quantities, in units of joules per mole-kelvin (J/mol-K).

Molar entropies for substances in their standard states are known as **standard molar entropies** and denoted $S°$. The standard state for any substance is defined as the pure substance at 1 atm pressure.* ▶ TABLE 13.1 lists the values of $S°$ for a number of substances at 298 K; Appendix C gives a more extensive list.

We can make several observations about the $S°$ values in Table 13.1:

1. Unlike enthalpies of formation, standard molar entropies of elements at the reference temperature of 298 K are *not* zero.

2. The standard molar entropies of gases are greater than those of liquids and solids, consistent with our interpretation of experimental observations, as represented in Figure 13.13.

3. Standard molar entropies generally increase with increasing molar mass.

4. Standard molar entropies generally increase with an increasing number of atoms in the formula of a substance.

Point 4 is related to the molecular motion discussed in Section 13.3. In general, the number of degrees of freedom for a molecule increases with increasing number of

TABLE 13.1 • **Standard Molar Entropies of Selected Substances at 298 K**

Substance	$S°$ (J/mol-K)
$H_2(g)$	130.6
$N_2(g)$	191.5
$O_2(g)$	205.0
$H_2O(g)$	188.8
$NH_3(g)$	192.5
$CH_3OH(g)$	237.6
$C_6H_6(g)$	269.2
$H_2O(l)$	69.9
$CH_3OH(l)$	126.8
$C_6H_6(l)$	172.8
$Li(s)$	29.1
$Na(s)$	51.4
$K(s)$	64.7
$Fe(s)$	27.23
$FeCl_3(s)$	142.3
$NaCl(s)$	72.3

*The standard pressure used in thermodynamics is no longer 1 atm but rather is based on the SI unit for pressure, the pascal (Pa). The standard pressure is 10^5 Pa, a quantity known as a *bar*: 1 bar = 10^5 Pa = 0.987 atm. Because 1 bar differs from 1 atm by only 1.3%, we will continue to refer to the standard pressure as 1 atm.

GO FIGURE

What might you expect for the value of $S°$ for butane, C_4H_{10}?

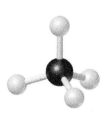 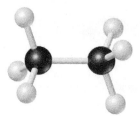 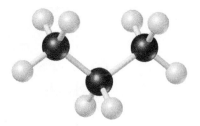

Methane, CH_4
$S° = 186.3$ J/mol-K

Ethane, C_2H_6
$S° = 229.6$ J/mol-K

Propane, C_3H_8
$S° = 270.3$ J/mol-K

▲ **FIGURE 13.14** **Entropy increases with increasing molecular complexity.**

atoms, and thus the number of possible microstates also increases. ▲ FIGURE 13.14 compares the standard molar entropies of three hydrocarbons in the gas phase. Notice how the entropy increases as the number of atoms in the molecule increases.

The entropy change in a chemical reaction equals the sum of the entropies of the products minus the sum of the entropies of the reactants:

$$\Delta S° = \sum nS°(\text{products}) - \sum mS°(\text{reactants}) \qquad [13.8]$$

As in Equation 10.31, the coefficients n and m are the coefficients in the balanced chemical equation for the reaction.

SAMPLE EXERCISE 13.5 **Calculating $\Delta S°$ from Tabulated Entropies**

Calculate the change in the standard entropy of the system, $\Delta S°$, for the synthesis of ammonia from $N_2(g)$ and $H_2(g)$ at 298 K:

$$N_2(g) + 3H_2(g) \longrightarrow 2NH_3(g)$$

SOLUTION

Analyze We are asked to calculate the standard entropy change for the synthesis of $NH_3(g)$ from its constituent elements.

Plan We can make this calculation using Equation 13.8 and the standard molar entropy values in Table 13.1 and Appendix C.

Solve
Using Equation 13.8, we have

$$\Delta S° = 2S°(NH_3) - [S°(N_2) + 3S°(H_2)]$$

Substituting the appropriate $S°$ values from Table 13.1 yields

$$\Delta S° = (2 \text{ mol})(192.5 \text{ J/mol-K}) - [(1 \text{ mol})(191.5 \text{ J/mol-K}) + (3 \text{ mol})(130.6 \text{ J/mol-K})]$$
$$= -198.3 \text{ J/K}$$

Check: The value for $\Delta S°$ is negative, in agreement with our qualitative prediction based on the decrease in the number of molecules of gas during the reaction.

PRACTICE EXERCISE

Using the standard molar entropies in Appendix C, calculate the standard entropy change, $\Delta S°$, for the following reaction at 298 K:

$$Al_2O_3(s) + 3H_2(g) \longrightarrow 2Al(s) + 3H_2O(g)$$

Answer: 180.39 J/K

Entropy Changes in the Surroundings

We can use tabulated absolute entropy values to calculate the standard entropy change in a system, such as a chemical reaction, as just described. But what about the entropy change in the surroundings? We encountered this situation in Section 13.2, but it is good to revisit it now that we are examining chemical reactions.

We should recognize that the surroundings for any system serve essentially as a large, constant-temperature heat source (or heat sink if the heat flows from the system to the surroundings). The change in entropy of the surroundings depends on how much heat is absorbed or given off by the system.

For an isothermal process, the entropy change of the surroundings is given by

$$\Delta S_{surr} = \frac{-q_{sys}}{T}$$

Because in a constant-pressure process, q_{sys} is simply the enthalpy change for the reaction, ΔH, we can write

$$\Delta S_{surr} = \frac{-\Delta H_{sys}}{T} \qquad [13.9]$$

For the reaction in Sample Exercise 13.5, q_{sys} is the enthalpy change for the reaction under standard conditions, $\Delta H°$, so the changes in entropy will be standard entropy changes, $\Delta S°$. Therefore, using the procedures described in Section 10.7, we have

$$\Delta H°_{rxn} = 2\Delta H°_f[NH_3(g)] - 3\Delta H°_f[H_2(g)] - \Delta H°_f[N_2(g)]$$
$$= 2(-46.19 \text{ kJ}) - 3(0 \text{ kJ}) - (0 \text{ kJ}) = -92.38 \text{ kJ}$$

The negative value tells us that at 298 K the formation of ammonia from $H_2(g)$ and $N_2(g)$ is exothermic. The surroundings absorb the heat given off by the system, which means an increase in the entropy of the surroundings:

$$\Delta S°_{surr} = \frac{92.38 \text{ kJ}}{298 \text{ K}} = 0.310 \text{ kJ/K} = 310 \text{ J/K}$$

Notice that the magnitude of the entropy gained by the surroundings is greater than that lost by the system, calculated as -198.3 J/K in Sample Exercise 13.5.

The overall entropy change for the reaction is

$$\Delta S°_{univ} = \Delta S°_{sys} + \Delta S°_{surr} = -198.3 \text{ J/K} + 310 \text{ J/K} = 112 \text{ J/K}$$

Because $\Delta S°_{univ}$ is positive for any spontaneous reaction, this calculation indicates that when $NH_3(g)$, $H_2(g)$, and $N_2(g)$ are together at 298 K in their standard states (each at 1 atm pressure), the reaction moves spontaneously toward formation of $NH_3(g)$.

Keep in mind that while the thermodynamic calculations indicate that formation of ammonia is spontaneous, they do not tell us anything about the rate at which ammonia is formed. Establishing equilibrium in this system within a reasonable period requires a catalyst, as discussed in Section 12.7.

◢ GIVE IT SOME THOUGHT

If a process is exothermic, does the entropy of the surroundings (1) always increase, (2) always decrease, or (3) sometimes increase and sometimes decrease, depending on the process?

13.5 | GIBBS FREE ENERGY

A spontaneous process that is endothermic must be accompanied by an increase in the entropy of the system. However, there are processes that are spontaneous and yet proceed with a *decrease* in the entropy of the system, such as the highly exothermic formation of sodium chloride from its constituent elements. ∞ (Section 3.2) Spontaneous processes that result in a decrease in the system's entropy are always exothermic. Thus, the spontaneity of a reaction seems to involve two thermodynamic concepts, enthalpy and entropy.

How can we use ΔH and ΔS to predict whether a given reaction occurring at constant temperature and pressure will be spontaneous? The means for doing so was first developed by the American mathematician J. Willard Gibbs (1839–1903). Gibbs (▶ FIGURE 13.15)

▲ FIGURE 13.15 **Josiah Willard Gibbs.** Gibbs was the first person to be awarded a Ph.D. in science from an American university (Yale, 1863). From 1871 until his death, he held the chair of mathematical physics at Yale. He developed much of the theoretical foundation that led to the development of chemical thermodynamics.

proposed a new state function, now called the **Gibbs free energy** (or just **free energy**), G, and defined as

$$G = H - TS \qquad [13.10]$$

where T is the absolute temperature. For an isothermal process, the change in the free energy of the system, ΔG, is

$$\Delta G = \Delta H - T\Delta S \qquad [13.11]$$

Under standard conditions, this equation becomes

$$\Delta G° = \Delta H° - T\Delta S° \qquad [13.12]$$

To see how the state function G relates to reaction spontaneity, recall that for a reaction occurring at constant temperature and pressure

$$\Delta S_{univ} = \Delta S_{sys} + \Delta S_{surr} = \Delta S_{sys} + \left(\frac{-\Delta H_{sys}}{T} \right)$$

where we have used Equation 13.9 to substitute for ΔS_{surr}. Multiplying both sides by $-T$ gives us

$$-T\Delta S_{univ} = \Delta H_{sys} - T\Delta S_{sys} \qquad [13.13]$$

Comparing Equations 13.11 and 13.13, we see that in a process occurring at constant temperature and pressure, the free-energy change, ΔG, is equal to $-T\Delta S_{univ}$. We know that for spontaneous processes, ΔS_{univ} is always positive and, therefore, $-T\Delta S_{univ}$ is always negative. Thus, the sign of ΔG provides us with extremely valuable information about the spontaneity of processes that occur at constant temperature and pressure. If both T and P are constant, the relationship between the sign of ΔG and the spontaneity of a reaction is as follows:

1. If $\Delta G < 0$, the reaction is spontaneous in the forward direction.
2. If $\Delta G = 0$, the reaction is at equilibrium.
3. If $\Delta G > 0$, the reaction in the forward direction is nonspontaneous (work must be done to make it occur) but the reverse reaction is spontaneous.

It is more convenient to use ΔG as a criterion for spontaneity than to use ΔS_{univ} because ΔG relates to the system alone and avoids the complication of having to examine the surroundings.

An analogy is often drawn between the free-energy change during a spontaneous reaction and the potential-energy change when a boulder rolls down a hill (◄ **FIGURE 13.16**). Potential energy in a gravitational field "drives" the boulder until it reaches a state of minimum potential energy in the valley. Similarly, the free energy of a chemical system decreases until it reaches a minimum value. When this minimum is reached, a state of equilibrium exists. *In any spontaneous process carried out at constant temperature and pressure, the free energy always decreases.*

To illustrate these ideas, let's return to the Haber process for the synthesis of ammonia from nitrogen and hydrogen, which we discussed extensively in Chapter 12:

$$N_2(g) + 3\,H_2(g) \rightleftharpoons 2\,NH_3(g)$$

Imagine that we have a reaction vessel that allows us to maintain a constant temperature and pressure and that we have a catalyst that allows the reaction to proceed at a reasonable rate. What happens when we charge the vessel with a certain number of moles of N_2 and three times that number of moles of H_2? As we saw in Figure 12.3, the N_2 and H_2 react spontaneously to form NH_3 until equilibrium is achieved. Similarly, Figure 12.3 shows that if we charge the vessel with pure NH_3, it decomposes spontaneously to N_2 and H_2 until equilibrium is reached. In each case the free energy of the system gets progressively lower and lower as the reaction moves toward equilibrium, which represents a minimum in the free energy. We illustrate these cases in ▶ **FIGURE 13.17**.

GO FIGURE

Are the processes that move a system toward equilibrium spontaneous or nonspontaneous?

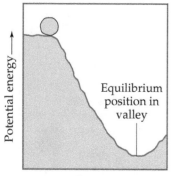

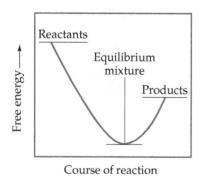

▲ **FIGURE 13.16 Potential energy and free energy.** An analogy is shown between the gravitational potential-energy change of a boulder rolling down a hill and the free-energy change in a spontaneous reaction.

GO FIGURE

GO FIGURE

Why are the spontaneous processes shown sometimes said to be "downhill" in free energy?

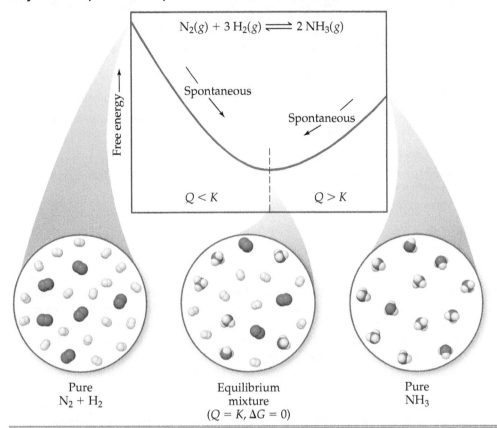

◀ **FIGURE 13.17   Free energy and approaching equilibrium.** In the reaction $N_2(g) + 3H_2(g) \rightleftharpoons 2NH_3(g)$, if the reaction mixture has too much N_2 and H_2 relative to NH_3 (left), the equilibrium lies too far to the left ($Q < K$) and NH_3 forms spontaneously. If there is too much NH_3 in the mixture (right), the equilibrium lies too far to the right ($Q > K$) and the NH_3 decomposes spontaneously into N_2 and H_2.

GIVE IT SOME THOUGHT

What are the criteria for spontaneity
a. in terms of entropy and
b. in terms of free energy?

This is a good time to remind ourselves of the significance of the reaction quotient, Q, for a system that is not at equilibrium. ∞ (Section 12.6) Recall that when $Q < K$, there is an excess of reactants relative to products and the reaction proceeds spontaneously in the forward direction to reach equilibrium, as noted in Figure 13.17. When $Q > K$, the reaction proceeds spontaneously in the reverse direction. At equilibrium $Q = K$.

SAMPLE EXERCISE 13.6	**Calculating Free-Energy Change from $\Delta H°$, T, and $\Delta S°$**

Calculate the standard free-energy change for the formation of NO(g) from $N_2(g)$ and $O_2(g)$ at 298 K:

$$N_2(g) + O_2(g) \longrightarrow 2NO(g)$$

given that $\Delta H° = 180.7$ kJ and $\Delta S° = 24.7$ J/K. Is the reaction spontaneous under these conditions?

SOLUTION

Analyze We are asked to calculate $\Delta G°$ for the indicated reaction (given $\Delta H°$, $\Delta S°$, and T) and to predict whether the reaction is spontaneous under standard conditions at 298 K.

Plan To calculate $\Delta G°$, we use Equation 13.12, $\Delta G° = \Delta H° - T\Delta S°$. To determine whether the reaction is spontaneous under standard conditions, we look at the sign of $\Delta G°$.

Solve

$$\Delta G° = \Delta H° - T\Delta S°$$

$$= 180.7 \text{ kJ} - (298 \text{ K})(24.7 \text{ J/K})\left(\frac{1 \text{ kJ}}{10^3 \text{ J}}\right)$$

$$= 180.7 \text{ kJ} - 7.4 \text{ kJ}$$

$$= 173.3 \text{ kJ}$$

Because $\Delta G°$ is positive, the reaction is not spontaneous under standard conditions at 298 K.

Comment Notice that we had to convert the units of the $T\Delta S°$ term to kJ so that they could be added to the $\Delta H°$ term, whose units are kJ.

PRACTICE EXERCISE

Calculate $\Delta G°$ for a reaction for which $\Delta H° = 24.6$ kJ and $\Delta S° = 132$ J/K at 298 K. Is the reaction spontaneous under these conditions?

Answer: $\Delta G° = -14.7$ kJ; the reaction is spontaneous.

Standard Free Energy of Formation

Recall that we defined *standard enthalpies of formation*, $\Delta H_f°$, as the enthalpy change when a substance is formed from its elements under defined standard conditions. ∞ (Section 10.7) We can define **standard free energies of formation**, $\Delta G_f°$, in a similar way. As is summarized in ◄ **TABLE 13.2**, standard state means 1 atm pressure for gases, the pure solid for solids, and the pure liquid for liquids. For substances in solution, the standard state is normally a concentration of 1 M. (In very accurate work it may be necessary to make certain corrections, but we need not worry about these.)

The temperature usually chosen for purposes of tabulating data is 25 °C, but we will calculate $\Delta G°$ at other temperatures as well. Just as for the standard heats of formation, the free energies of elements in their standard states are set to zero. This arbitrary choice of a reference point has no effect on the quantity in which we are interested, which is the *difference* in free energy between reactants and products.

A listing of standard free energies of formation is given in Appendix C.

TABLE 13.2 • Conventions Used in Establishing Standard Free Energies

State of Matter	Standard State
Solid	Pure solid
Liquid	Pure liquid
Gas	1 atm pressure
Solution	1 M concentration
Element	$\Delta G_f° = 0$ for element in standard state

GIVE IT SOME THOUGHT

What does the superscript ° indicate when associated with a thermodynamic quantity, as in $\Delta H°, \Delta S°,$ or $\Delta G°$?

Standard free energies of formation are useful in calculating the *standard free-energy change* for chemical processes. The procedure is analogous to the calculation of $\Delta H°$ (Equation 10.31) and $\Delta S°$ (Equation 13.8):

$$\Delta G° = \sum n\Delta G_f°(\text{products}) - \sum m\Delta G_f°(\text{reactants}) \qquad [13.14]$$

SAMPLE EXERCISE 13.7 | **Calculating Standard Free-Energy Change from Free Energies of Formation**

(a) Use data from Appendix C to calculate the standard free-energy change for the reaction $P_4(g) + 6 \text{ Cl}_2(g) \longrightarrow 4 \text{ PCl}_3(g)$ run at 298 K.
(b) What is $\Delta G°$ for the reverse of this reaction?

SOLUTION

Analyze We are asked to calculate the free-energy change for a reaction and then to determine the free-energy change for the reverse reaction.

Plan We look up the free-energy values for the products and reactants and use Equation 13.14: We multiply the molar quantities by the coefficients in the balanced equation and subtract the total for the reactants from that for the products.

Solve

(a) $Cl_2(g)$ is in its standard state, so ΔG_f° is zero for this reactant. $P_4(g)$, however, is not in its standard state, so ΔG_f° is not zero for this reactant. From the balanced equation and values from Appendix C, we have

$$\Delta G_{rxn}^\circ = 4\,\Delta G_f^\circ[PCl_3(g)] - \Delta G_f^\circ[P_4(g)] - 6\,\Delta G_f^\circ[Cl_2(g)]$$
$$= (4\text{ mol})(-269.6\text{ kJ/mol}) - (1\text{ mol})(24.4\text{ kJ/mol}) - 0$$
$$= -1102.8\text{ kJ}$$

That ΔG° is negative tells us that a mixture of $P_4(g)$, $Cl_2(g)$, and $PCl_3(g)$ at 25 °C, each present at a partial pressure of 1 atm, would react spontaneously in the forward direction to form more PCl_3. Remember, however, that the value of ΔG° tells us nothing about the rate at which the reaction occurs.

(b) When we reverse the reaction, we reverse the roles of the reactants and products. Thus, reversing the reaction changes the sign of ΔG in Equation 13.14, just as reversing the reaction changes the sign of ΔH. ∞ (Section 10.4) Hence, using the result from part (a), we have

$$4\,PCl_3(g) \longrightarrow P_4(g) + 6\,Cl_2(g) \quad \Delta G^\circ = +1102.8\text{ kJ}$$

PRACTICE EXERCISE

Use data from Appendix C to calculate ΔG° at 298 K for the combustion of methane: $CH_4(g) + 2\,O_2(g) \longrightarrow CO_2(g) + 2\,H_2O(g)$.

Answer: -800.7 kJ

SAMPLE EXERCISE 13.8   **Estimating and Calculating ΔG°**

In Section 10.7 we used Hess's law to calculate ΔH° for the combustion of propane gas at 298 K:

$$C_3H_8(g) + 5\,O_2(g) \longrightarrow 3\,CO_2(g) + 4\,H_2O(l) \quad \Delta H^\circ = -2220\text{ kJ}$$

(a) *Without using data from Appendix C*, predict whether ΔG° for this reaction is more negative or less negative than ΔH°. **(b)** Use data from Appendix C to calculate ΔG° for the reaction at 298 K. Is your prediction from part (a) correct?

SOLUTION

Analyze   In part (a) we must predict the value for ΔG° relative to that for ΔH° on the basis of the balanced equation for the reaction. In part (b) we must calculate the value for ΔG° and compare this value with our qualitative prediction.

Plan   The free-energy change incorporates both the change in enthalpy and the change in entropy for the reaction (Equation 13.11), so under standard conditions

$$\Delta G^\circ = \Delta H^\circ - T\Delta S^\circ$$

To determine whether ΔG° is more negative or less negative than ΔH°, we need to determine the sign of the term $T\Delta S^\circ$. Because T is the absolute temperature, 298 K, it is always a positive number. We can predict the sign of ΔS° by looking at the reaction.

Solve

(a) The reactants are six molecules of gas, and the products are three molecules of gas and four molecules of liquid. Thus, the number of molecules of gas has decreased significantly during the reaction. By using the general rules discussed in Section 13.3, we expect a decrease in the number of gas molecules to lead to a decrease in the entropy of the system—the products have fewer possible microstates than the reactants. We therefore expect ΔS° and $T\Delta S^\circ$ to be negative. Because we are subtracting $T\Delta S^\circ$, which is a negative number, we predict that ΔG° is *less negative* than ΔH°.

(b) Using Equation 13.14 and values from Appendix C, we have

$$\Delta G^\circ = 3\Delta G_f^\circ[CO_2(g)] + 4\Delta G_f^\circ[H_2O(l)] - \Delta G_f^\circ[C_3H_8(g)] - 5\Delta G_f^\circ[O_2(g)]$$
$$= 3\text{ mol}(-394.4\text{ kJ/mol}) + 4\text{ mol}(-237.13\text{ kJ/mol})-$$
$$\qquad\qquad 1\text{ mol}(-23.47\text{ kJ/mol}) - 5\text{ mol}(0\text{ kJ/mol}) = -2108\text{ kJ}$$

Notice that we have been careful to use the value of ΔG_f° for $H_2O(l)$. As in calculating ΔH values, the phases of the reactants and products are important. As we predicted, ΔG° is less negative than ΔH° because of the decrease in entropy during the reaction.

PRACTICE EXERCISE

For the combustion of propane at 298 K, $C_3H_8(g) + 5\,O_2(g) \longrightarrow 3\,CO_2(g) + 4\,H_2O(g)$, do you expect ΔG° to be more negative or less negative than ΔH°?

Answer: more negative

A CLOSER LOOK

WHAT'S "FREE" ABOUT FREE ENERGY?

The Gibbs free energy is a remarkable thermodynamic quantity. Because so many chemical reactions are carried out under conditions of near-constant pressure and temperature, chemists, biochemists, and engineers use the sign and magnitude of ΔG as exceptionally useful tools in the design of chemical and biochemical reactions. We will see examples of the usefulness of ΔG throughout the remainder of this chapter and this text.

Two common questions often arise when one first learns about the Gibbs free energy: Why does the sign of ΔG tell us about the spontaneity of reactions? And what is "free" about free energy? We address these two questions here by using concepts discussed in Chapter 10 and earlier in this chapter.

In Section 13.2 we saw that the second law of thermodynamics governs the spontaneity of processes. In order to apply the second law (Equation 13.4), however, we must determine ΔS_{univ}, which is often difficult to evaluate. When T and P are constant, however, we can relate ΔS_{univ} to the changes in entropy and enthalpy of just the *system* by substituting the Equation 13.9 expression for ΔS_{surr} in Equation 13.4:

$$\Delta S_{univ} = \Delta S_{sys} + \Delta S_{surr} = \Delta S_{sys} + \left(\frac{-\Delta H_{sys}}{T} \right) \quad [13.15]$$

$$(\text{constant } T, P)$$

Thus, at constant temperature and pressure, the second law becomes

Reversible process: $\quad \Delta S_{univ} = \Delta S_{sys} - \dfrac{\Delta H_{sys}}{T} = 0$

Irreversible process: $\quad \Delta S_{univ} = \Delta S_{sys} - \dfrac{\Delta H_{sys}}{T} > 0$ $\quad [13.16]$

$$(\text{constant } T, P)$$

Now we can see the relationship between ΔG_{sys} (which we call simply ΔG) and the second law. From Equation 13.11 we know that $\Delta G = \Delta H_{sys} - T\Delta S_{sys}$. If we multiply Equations 13.16 by $-T$ and rearrange, we reach the following conclusion:

Reversible process: $\Delta G = \Delta H_{sys} - T \Delta S_{sys} = 0$

Irreversible process: $\Delta G = \Delta H_{sys} - T \Delta S_{sys} < 0$ $\quad [13.17]$

$$(\text{constant } T, P)$$

Equations 13.17 allow us to use the sign of ΔG to conclude whether a reaction is spontaneous, nonspontaneous, or at equilibrium. When $\Delta G < 0$, a process is irreversible and, therefore, spontaneous. When $\Delta G = 0$, the process is reversible and, therefore, at equilibrium. If a process has $\Delta G > 0$, then the reverse process will have $\Delta G < 0$; thus, the process as written is nonspontaneous but its reverse reaction will be irreversible and spontaneous.

The magnitude of ΔG is also significant. A reaction for which ΔG is large and negative, such as the burning of gasoline, is much more capable of doing work on the surroundings than is a reaction for which ΔG is small and negative, such as ice melting at room temperature. In fact, thermodynamics tells us that *the change in free energy for a process, ΔG, equals the maximum useful work that can be done by the system on its surroundings in a spontaneous process occurring at constant temperature and pressure:*

$$\Delta G = -w_{max} \quad [13.18]$$

(Remember our sign convention from Table 10.1: Work done *by* a system is negative.) In other words, ΔG gives the theoretical limit to how much work can be done by a process.

The relationship in Equation 13.18 explains why ΔG is called *free* energy—it is the portion of the energy change of a spontaneous reaction that is free to do useful work. The remainder of the energy enters the environment as heat. For example, the theoretical maximum work obtained for the combustion of gasoline is given by the value of ΔG for the combustion reaction. On average, standard internal combustion engines are inefficient in utilizing this potential work—more than 60% of the potential work is lost (primarily as heat) in converting the chemical energy of the gasoline to mechanical energy to move the vehicle (▼ FIGURE 13.18). When other losses are considered—idling time, braking, aerodynamic drag, and so forth—only about 15% of the potential work from the gasoline is used to move the car. Advances in automobile design—such as hybrid technology, efficient diesel engines, and new lightweight materials—have the potential to increase the percentage of useful work obtained from the gasoline.

For nonspontaneous processes $(\Delta G > 0)$, the free-energy change is a measure of the *minimum* amount of work that must be done to cause the process to occur. In actuality, we always need to do more than this theoretical minimum amount because of the inefficiencies in the way the changes occur.

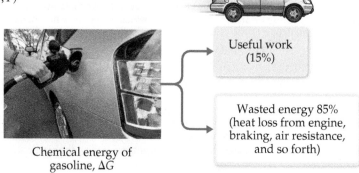

Useful work (15%)

Wasted energy 85% (heat loss from engine, braking, air resistance, and so forth)

Chemical energy of gasoline, ΔG

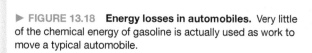

▶ FIGURE 13.18 **Energy losses in automobiles.** Very little of the chemical energy of gasoline is actually used as work to move a typical automobile.

13.6 | FREE ENERGY AND TEMPERATURE

Tabulations of ΔG_f°, such as those in Appendix C, make it possible to calculate ΔG° for reactions at the standard temperature of 25 °C, but we are often interested in examining reactions at other temperatures. To see how ΔG is affected by temperature, let's look again at Equation 13.11:

$$\Delta G = \Delta H - T\Delta S = \Delta H + (-T\Delta S)$$

$$\underset{\text{Enthalpy}\atop\text{term}}{} \qquad \underset{\text{Entropy}\atop\text{term}}{}$$

Notice that we have written the expression for ΔG as a sum of two contributions, an enthalpy term, ΔH, and an entropy term, $-T\Delta S$. Because the value of $-T\Delta S$ depends directly on the absolute temperature T, ΔG varies with temperature. We know that the enthalpy term, ΔH, can be either positive or negative and that T is positive at all temperatures other than absolute zero. The entropy term, $-T\Delta S$, can also be positive or negative. When ΔS is positive, which means the final state has greater randomness (a greater number of microstates) than the initial state, the term $-T\Delta S$ is negative. When ΔS is negative, $-T\Delta S$ is positive.

The sign of ΔG, which tells us whether a process is spontaneous, depends on the signs and magnitudes of ΔH and $-T\Delta S$. The various combinations of ΔH and $-T\Delta S$ signs are given in ▼ TABLE 13.3.

Note in Table 13.3 that when ΔH and $-T\Delta S$ have opposite signs, the sign of ΔG depends on the magnitudes of these two terms. In these instances temperature is an important consideration. Generally, ΔH and ΔS change very little with temperature. However, the value of T directly affects the magnitude of $-T\Delta S$. As the temperature increases, the magnitude of $-T\Delta S$ increases, and this term becomes relatively more important in determining the sign and magnitude of ΔG.

As an example, let's consider once more the melting of ice to liquid water at 1 atm:

$$H_2O(s) \longrightarrow H_2O(l) \quad \Delta H > 0, \Delta S > 0$$

This process is endothermic, which means that ΔH is positive. Because the entropy increases during the process, ΔS is positive, which makes $-T\Delta S$ negative. At temperatures below 0 °C (273 K), the magnitude of ΔH is greater than that of $-T\Delta S$. Hence, the positive enthalpy term dominates, and ΔG is positive. This positive value of ΔG means that ice melting is not spontaneous at $T < 0$ °C, just as our everyday experience tells us; rather, the reverse process, the freezing of liquid water into ice, is spontaneous at these temperatures.

What happens at temperatures greater than 0 °C? As T increases, so does the magnitude of $-T\Delta S$. When $T > 0$ °C, the magnitude of $-T\Delta S$ is greater than the magnitude of ΔH, which means that the $-T\Delta S$ term dominates and ΔG is negative. The negative value of ΔG tells us that ice melting is spontaneous at $T > 0$ °C.

At the normal melting point of water, $T = 0$ °C, the two phases are in equilibrium. Recall that $\Delta G = 0$ at equilibrium; at $T = 0$ °C, ΔH and $-T\Delta S$ are equal in magnitude and opposite in sign, so they cancel and give $\Delta G = 0$.

TABLE 13.3 • How Signs of ΔH and ΔS Affect Reaction Spontaneity

ΔH	ΔS	$-T\Delta S$	$\Delta G = \Delta H - T\Delta S$	Reaction Characteristics	Example
−	+	−	−	Spontaneous at all temperatures	$2\,O_3(g) \longrightarrow 3\,O_2(g)$
+	−	+	+	Nonspontaneous at all temperatures	$3\,O_2(g) \longrightarrow 2\,O_3(g)$
−	−	+	+ or −	Spontaneous at low T; nonspontaneous at high T	$H_2O(l) \longrightarrow H_2O(s)$
+	+	−	+ or −	Spontaneous at high T; nonspontaneous at low T	$H_2O(s) \longrightarrow H_2O(l)$

> ◢ GIVE IT SOME THOUGHT
>
> The normal boiling point of benzene is 80 °C. At 100 °C and 1 atm, which term is greater in magnitude for the vaporization of benzene, ΔH or $T\Delta S$?

Our discussion of the temperature dependence of ΔG is also relevant to standard free-energy changes. We can calculate the values of $\Delta H°$ and $\Delta S°$ at 298 K from the data in Appendix C. If we assume that these values do not change with temperature, we can then use Equation 13.12 to estimate $\Delta G°$ at temperatures other than 298 K.

SAMPLE EXERCISE 13.9 | **Determining the Effect of Temperature on Spontaneity**

The Haber process for the production of ammonia involves the equilibrium

$$N_2(g) + 3\,H_2(g) \rightleftharpoons 2\,NH_3(g)$$

Assume that $\Delta H°$ and $\Delta S°$ for this reaction do not change with temperature. (a) Predict the direction in which $\Delta G°$ for the reaction changes with increasing temperature. (b) Calculate $\Delta G°$ at 25 °C and 500 °C.

SOLUTION

Analyze In part (a) we are asked to predict the direction in which $\Delta G°$ changes as temperature increases. In part (b) we need to determine $\Delta G°$ for the reaction at two temperatures.

Plan We can answer part (a) by determining the sign of ΔS for the reaction and then using that information to analyze Equation 13.12. In part (b) we first calculate $\Delta H°$ and $\Delta S°$ for the reaction using data in Appendix C and then use Equation 13.12 to calculate $\Delta G°$.

Solve
(a) The temperature dependence of $\Delta G°$ comes from the entropy term in Equation 13.12, $\Delta G° = \Delta H° - T\Delta S°$. We expect $\Delta S°$ for this reaction to be negative because the number of molecules of gas is smaller in the products. Because $\Delta S°$ is negative, $-T\Delta S°$ is positive and increases with increasing temperature. As a result, $\Delta G°$ becomes less negative (or more positive) with increasing temperature. Thus, the driving force for the production of NH_3 becomes smaller with increasing temperature.

(b) We calculated $\Delta H°$ for this reaction in Sample Exercise 12.14 and $\Delta S°$ in Sample Exercise 13.5: $\Delta H° = -92.38$ kJ and $\Delta S° = -198.3$ J/K. If we assume that these values do not change with temperature, we can calculate $\Delta G°$ at any temperature by using Equation 13.12. At $T = 25\,°C = 298$ K, we have

$$\Delta G° = -92.38 \text{ kJ} - (298 \text{ K})(-198.3 \text{ J/K})\left(\frac{1 \text{ kJ}}{1000 \text{ J}}\right)$$

$$= -92.38 \text{ kJ} + 59.1 \text{ kJ} = -33.3 \text{ kJ}$$

At $T = 500\,°C = 773$ K, we have

$$\Delta G° = -92.38 \text{ kJ} - (773 \text{ K})\left(-198.3\,\frac{\text{J}}{\text{K}}\right)\left(\frac{1 \text{ kJ}}{1000 \text{ J}}\right)$$

$$= -92.38 \text{ kJ} + 153 \text{ kJ} = 61 \text{ kJ}$$

Notice that we had to convert the units of $-T\Delta S°$ to kJ in both calculations so that this term can be added to the $\Delta H°$ term, which has units of kJ.

Comment Increasing the temperature from 298 K to 773 K changes $\Delta G°$ from -33.3 kJ to $+61$ kJ. Of course, the result at 773 K assumes that $\Delta H°$ and $\Delta S°$ do not change with temperature. Although these values do change slightly with temperature, the result at 773 K should be a reasonable approximation.

The positive increase in $\Delta G°$ with increasing T agrees with our prediction in part (a). Our result indicates that in a mixture of $N_2(g)$, $H_2(g)$, and $NH_3(g)$, each present at a partial pressure of 1 atm, the $N_2(g)$ and $H_2(g)$ react spontaneously at 298 K to form more $NH_3(g)$. At 773 K, the positive value of $\Delta G°$ tells us that the reverse reaction is spontaneous. Thus, when the mixture of these gases, each at a partial pressure of 1 atm, is heated to 773 K, some of the $NH_3(g)$ spontaneously decomposes into $N_2(g)$ and $H_2(g)$.

PRACTICE EXERCISE

(a) Using standard enthalpies of formation and standard entropies in Appendix C, calculate $\Delta H°$ and $\Delta S°$ at 298 K for the reaction $2\,SO_2(g) + O_2(g) \longrightarrow 2\,SO_3(g)$. (b) Use your values from part (a) to estimate $\Delta G°$ at 400 K.
Answers: (a) $\Delta H° = -196.6$ kJ, $\Delta S° = -189.6$ J/K; (b) $\Delta G° = -120.8$ kJ

13.7 | FREE ENERGY AND THE EQUILIBRIUM CONSTANT

In Section 13.5 we saw a special relationship between ΔG and equilibrium: For a system at equilibrium, $\Delta G = 0$. We have also seen how to use tabulated thermodynamic data to calculate values of the standard free-energy change, $\Delta G°$. In this final section, we learn two more ways in which we can use free energy to analyze chemical reactions: using $\Delta G°$ to calculate ΔG under *nonstandard* conditions and relating the values of $\Delta G°$ and K for a reaction.

Free Energy Under Nonstandard Conditions

The set of standard conditions for which $\Delta G°$ values pertain is given in Table 13.2. Most chemical reactions occur under nonstandard conditions. For any chemical process, the relationship between the free-energy change under standard conditions, $\Delta G°$, and the free-energy change under any other conditions, ΔG, is given by

$$\Delta G = \Delta G° + RT \ln Q \qquad [13.19]$$

In this equation R is the ideal-gas constant, 8.314 J/mol-K; T is the absolute temperature; and Q is the reaction quotient for the reaction mixture of interest. ∞ (Section 12.6) Under standard conditions, the concentrations of all the reactants and products are equal to 1. Thus, under standard conditions $Q = 1$, $\ln Q = 0$, and Equation 13.19 reduces to $\Delta G = \Delta G°$ under standard conditions, as it should.

SAMPLE EXERCISE 13.10 Relating ΔG to a Phase Change at Equilibrium

(a) Write the chemical equation that defines the normal boiling point of liquid carbon tetrachloride, $CCl_4(l)$. **(b)** What is the value of $\Delta G°$ for the equilibrium in part (a)? **(c)** Use data from Appendix C and Equation 13.12 to estimate the normal boiling point of CCl_4.

SOLUTION

Analyze **(a)** We must write a chemical equation that describes the physical equilibrium between liquid and gaseous CCl_4 at the normal boiling point. **(b)** We must determine the value of $\Delta G°$ for CCl_4, in equilibrium with its vapor at the normal boiling point. **(c)** We must estimate the normal boiling point of CCl_4, based on available thermodynamic data.

Plan **(a)** The chemical equation is the change of state from liquid to gas. For **(b)**, we need to analyze Equation 13.19 at equilibrium ($\Delta G = 0$), and for **(c)** we can use Equation 13.12 to calculate T when $\Delta G = 0$.

Solve

(a) The normal boiling point is the temperature at which a pure liquid is in equilibrium with its vapor at a pressure of 1 atm:

$$CCl_4(l) \rightleftharpoons CCl_4(g) \quad P = 1 \text{ atm}$$

(b) At equilibrium, $\Delta G = 0$. In any normal boiling-point equilibrium, both liquid and vapor are in their standard state of pure liquid and vapor at 1 atm (Table 13.2). Consequently, $Q = 1$, $\ln Q = 0$, and $\Delta G = \Delta G°$ for this process. We conclude that $\Delta G° = 0$ for the equilibrium representing the normal boiling point of any liquid. (We would also find that $\Delta G° = 0$ for the equilibria relevant to normal melting points and normal sublimation points.)

(c) Combining Equation 13.12 with the result from part (b), we see that the equality at the normal boiling point, T_b, of $CCl_4(l)$ (or any other pure liquid) is

$$\Delta G° = \Delta H° - T_b \Delta S° = 0$$

Solving the equation for T_b, we obtain

$$T_b = \Delta H° / \Delta S°$$

Strictly speaking, we need the values of $\Delta H°$ and $\Delta S°$ for the $CCl_4(l)$–$CCl_4(g)$ equilibrium at the normal boiling point to do this calculation. However, we can *estimate* the boiling point by using the values of $\Delta H°$ and $\Delta S°$ for CCl_4 at 298 K, which we obtain from Appendix C and Equations 10.31 and 13.8:

$$\Delta H° = (1 \text{ mol})(-106.7 \text{ kJ/mol}) - (1 \text{ mol})(-139.3 \text{ kJ/mol}) = +32.6 \text{ kJ}$$
$$\Delta S° = (1 \text{ mol})(309.4 \text{ J/mol-K}) - (1 \text{ mol})(214.4 \text{ J/mol-K}) = +95.0 \text{ J/K}$$

As expected, the process is endothermic ($\Delta H > 0$) and produces a gas, thus increasing the entropy ($\Delta S > 0$). We now use these values to estimate T_b for $CCl_4(l)$:

$$T_b = \frac{\Delta H°}{\Delta S°} = \left(\frac{32.6 \text{ kJ}}{95.0 \text{ J/K}}\right)\left(\frac{1000 \text{ J}}{1 \text{ kJ}}\right) = 343 \text{ K} = 70 \text{ °C}$$

Note that we have used the conversion factor between joules and kilojoules to make the units of $\Delta H°$ and $\Delta S°$ match.

Check The experimental normal boiling point of $CCl_4(l)$ is 76.5 °C. The small deviation of our estimate from the experimental value is due to the assumption that $\Delta H°$ and $\Delta S°$ do not change with temperature.

PRACTICE EXERCISE

Use data in Appendix C to estimate the normal boiling point, in K, for elemental bromine, $Br_2(l)$. (The experimental value is given in Figure 5.5.)

Answer: 330 K

When the concentrations of reactants and products are nonstandard, we must calculate Q in order to determine ΔG. We illustrate how this is done in Sample Exercise 13.11. At this stage in our discussion, therefore, it becomes important to note the units used to calculate Q when using Equation 13.19. The convention used for standard states is used when applying this equation: In determining the value of Q, the concentrations of gases are always expressed as partial pressures in atmospheres and solutes are expressed as their concentrations in molarities.

SAMPLE EXERCISE 13.11 | **Calculating the Free-Energy Change under Nonstandard Conditions**

Calculate ΔG at 298 K for a mixture of 1.0 atm N_2, 3.0 atm H_2, and 0.50 atm NH_3 being used in the Haber process:

$$N_2(g) + 3\,H_2(g) \rightleftharpoons 2\,NH_3(g)$$

SOLUTION

Analyze We are asked to calculate ΔG under nonstandard conditions.

Plan We can use Equation 13.19 to calculate ΔG. Doing so requires that we calculate the value of the reaction quotient Q for the specified partial pressures, for which we use the partial-pressures form of Equation 12.23: $Q = [D]^d[E]^e/[A]^a[B]^b$. We then use a table of standard free energies of formation to evaluate $\Delta G°$.

Solve The partial-pressures form of Equation 12.23 gives

$$Q = \frac{P_{NH_3}^2}{P_{N_2}\,P_{H_2}^3} = \frac{(0.50)^2}{(1.0)(3.0)^3} = 9.3 \times 10^{-3}$$

In Sample Exercise 13.9 we calculated $\Delta G° = -33.3$ kJ for this reaction. We will have to change the units of this quantity in applying Equation 13.19, however. For the units in Equation 13.19 to work out, we will use kJ/mol as our units for $\Delta G°$, where "per mole" means "per mole of the reaction as written." Thus, $\Delta G° = -33.3$ kJ/mol implies per 1 mol of N_2, per 3 mol of H_2, and per 2 mol of NH_3.

We now use Equation 13.19 to calculate ΔG for these nonstandard conditions:

$$\begin{aligned}
\Delta G &= \Delta G° + RT \ln Q \\
&= (-33.3 \text{ kJ/mol}) + (8.314 \text{ J/mol-K})(298 \text{ K})(1\text{ kJ}/1000 \text{ J}) \ln(9.3 \times 10^{-3}) \\
&= (-33.3 \text{ kJ/mol}) + (-11.6 \text{ kJ/mol}) = -44.9 \text{ kJ/mol}
\end{aligned}$$

Comment We see that ΔG becomes more negative as the pressures of N_2, H_2, and NH_3 are changed from 1.0 atm (standard conditions, $\Delta G°$) to 1.0 atm, 3.0 atm, and 0.50 atm, respectively. The larger negative value for ΔG indicates a larger "driving force" to produce NH_3.

We would make the same prediction based on Le Châtelier's principle. ∞ (Section 12.7) Relative to standard conditions, we have increased the pressure of a reactant (H_2) and decreased the pressure of the product (NH_3). Le Châtelier's principle predicts that both changes shift the reaction to the product side, thereby forming more NH_3.

PRACTICE EXERCISE

Calculate ΔG at 298 K for the Haber reaction if the reaction mixture consists of 0.50 atm N_2, 0.75 atm H_2, and 2.0 atm NH_3.

Answer: −26.0 kJ/mol

Relationship Between $\Delta G°$ and K

We can now use Equation 13.19 to derive the relationship between $\Delta G°$ and the equilibrium constant, K. At equilibrium, $\Delta G = 0$ and $Q = K$. Thus, at equilibrium, Equation 13.19 transforms as follows:

$$\Delta G = \Delta G° + RT \ln Q$$

$$0 = \Delta G° + RT \ln K$$

$$\Delta G° = -RT \ln K \qquad \text{[13.20]}$$

By solving Equation 13.20 for K, we obtain an expression that allows us to calculate K if we know the value of $\Delta G°$:

$$\ln K = \frac{\Delta G°}{-RT}$$

$$K = e^{-\Delta G°/RT} \qquad \text{[13.21]}$$

As usual, we must be careful in our choice of units. In Equations 13.20 and 13.21 we again express $\Delta G°$ in kJ/mol. In the equilibrium-constant expression, we use atmospheres for gas pressures, molarities for solutions, and solids, liquids, and solvents do not appear in the expression. ∞ (Section 12.4) Thus, the equilibrium constant is K_p for gas-phase reactions and K_c for reactions in solution. ∞ (Section 12.2)

From Equation 13.20 we see that if $\Delta G°$ is negative, ln K must be positive, which means $K > 1$. Therefore, the more negative $\Delta G°$ is, the larger K is. Conversely, if $\Delta G°$ is positive, ln K is negative, which means $K < 1$. ▶ TABLE 13.4 summarizes these relationships.

TABLE 13.4 • Relationship between $\Delta G°$ and K at 298 K

$\Delta G°$ (kJ/mol)	K
+200	8.7×10^{-36}
+100	3.0×10^{-18}
+50	1.7×10^{-9}
+10	1.8×10^{-2}
+1.0	6.7×10^{-1}
0	1.0
−1.0	1.5
−10	5.7×10^{1}
−50	5.8×10^{8}
−100	3.4×10^{17}
−200	1.1×10^{35}

SAMPLE EXERCISE 13.12 | **Calculating an Equilibrium Constant from $\Delta G°$**

The standard free-energy change for the Haber process at 25 °C was obtained in Sample Exercise 13.9 for the Haber reaction:

$$N_2(g) + 3H_2(g) \rightleftharpoons 2NH_3(g) \qquad \Delta G° = -33.3 \text{ kJ/mol} = -33,300 \text{ J/mol}$$

Use this value of $\Delta G°$ to calculate the equilibrium constant for the process at 25 °C.

SOLUTION

Analyze We are asked to calculate K for a reaction, given $\Delta G°$.

Plan We can use Equation 13.21 to calculate K.

Solve Remembering to use the absolute temperature for T in Equation 13.21 and the form of R that matches our units, we have $\quad K = e^{-\Delta G°/RT} = e^{-(-33,300 \text{ J/mol})/(8.314 \text{ J/mol-K})(298 \text{ K})} = e^{13.4} = 7 \times 10^5$

Comment This is a large equilibrium constant, which indicates that the product, NH_3, is greatly favored in the equilibrium mixture at 25 °C. The equilibrium constants for the Haber reaction at temperatures in the range 300 °C to 600 °C, given in Table 12.2, are much smaller than the value at 25 °C. Clearly, a low-temperature equilibrium favors the production of ammonia more than a high-temperature one. Nevertheless, the Haber process is carried out at high temperatures because the reaction is extremely slow at room temperature.

Remember Thermodynamics can tell us the direction and extent of a reaction but tells us nothing about the rate at which it will occur. If a catalyst were found that would permit the reaction to proceed at a rapid rate at room temperature, high pressures would not be needed to force the equilibrium toward NH_3.

PRACTICE EXERCISE

Use data from Appendix C to calculate $\Delta G°$ and K at 298 K for the reaction $H_2(g) + Br_2(l) \rightleftharpoons 2HBr(g)$.

Answer: $\Delta G° = -106.4 \text{ kJ/mol}$, $K = 4 \times 10^{18}$

CHEMISTRY AND LIFE

DRIVING NONSPONTANEOUS REACTIONS

Many desirable chemical reactions, including a large number that are central to living systems, are nonspontaneous as written. For example, consider the extraction of copper metal from the mineral *chalcocite*, which contains Cu_2S. The decomposition of Cu_2S to its elements is nonspontaneous:

$$Cu_2S(s) \longrightarrow 2Cu(s) + S(s) \qquad \Delta G° = +86.2 \text{ kJ}$$

Because $\Delta G°$ is very positive, we cannot obtain $Cu(s)$ directly via this reaction. Instead, we must find some way to "do work" on the reaction to force it to occur as we wish. We can do this by coupling the reaction to another one so that the overall reaction *is* spontaneous. For example, we can envision the $S(s)$ reacting with $O_2(g)$ to form $SO_2(g)$:

$$S(s) + O_2(g) \longrightarrow SO_2(g) \qquad \Delta G° = -300.4 \text{ kJ}$$

By coupling these reactions, we can extract much of the copper metal via a spontaneous reaction:

$$Cu_2S(s) + O_2(g) \longrightarrow 2Cu(s) + SO_2(g)$$
$$\Delta G° = (+86.2 \text{ kJ}) + (-300.4 \text{ kJ}) = -214.2 \text{ kJ}$$

In essence, we have used the spontaneous reaction of $S(s)$ with $O_2(g)$ to provide the free energy needed to extract the copper metal from the mineral.

Biological systems employ the same principle of using spontaneous reactions to drive nonspontaneous ones. Many of the biochemical reactions that are essential for the formation and maintenance of highly ordered biological structures are not spontaneous. These necessary reactions are made to occur by coupling them with spontaneous reactions that release energy. The metabolism of food is the usual source of the free energy needed to do the work of maintaining biological systems. For example, complete oxidation of the sugar *glucose*, $C_6H_{12}O_6$, to CO_2 and H_2O yields substantial free energy:

$$C_6H_{12}O_6(s) + 6O_2(g) \longrightarrow 6CO_2(g) + 6H_2O(l)$$
$$\Delta G° = -2880 \text{ kJ}$$

This energy can be used to drive nonspontaneous reactions in the body. However, a means is necessary to transport the energy released by glucose metabolism to the reactions that require energy. One way, shown in ▼ FIGURE 13.19, involves the interconversion of adenosine triphosphate (ATP) and adenosine diphosphate (ADP), molecules that are related to the building blocks of nucleic acids. The conversion of ATP to ADP releases free energy ($\Delta G° = -30.5 \text{ kJ}$) that can be used to drive other reactions.

In the human body the metabolism of glucose occurs via a complex series of reactions, most of which release free energy. The free energy released during these steps is used in part to reconvert lower-energy ADP back to higher-energy ATP. Thus, the ATP–ADP interconversions are used to store energy during metabolism and to release it as needed to drive nonspontaneous reactions in the body. If you take a course in biochemistry, you will have the opportunity to learn more about the remarkable sequence of reactions used to transport free energy throughout the human body.

RELATED EXERCISES: 13.102 and 13.103

▶ **FIGURE 13.19 Schematic representation of free-energy changes during cell metabolism.** The oxidation of glucose to CO_2 and H_2O produces free energy that is then used to convert ADP into the more energetic ATP. The ATP is then used, as needed, as an energy source to drive nonspontaneous reactions, such as the conversion of simple molecules into more complex cell constituents.

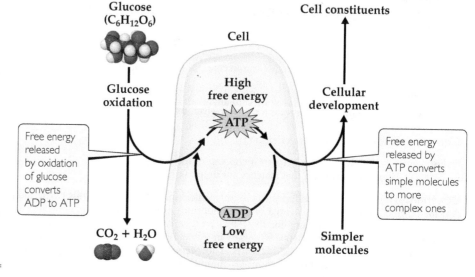

SAMPLE INTEGRATIVE EXERCISE   Putting Concepts Together

Consider the simple salts NaCl(s) and AgCl(s). We will examine the equilibria in which these salts dissolve in water to form aqueous solutions of ions:

$$NaCl(s) \rightleftharpoons Na^+(aq) + Cl^-(aq)$$

$$AgCl(s) \rightleftharpoons Ag^+(aq) + Cl^-(aq)$$

(a) Calculate the value of $\Delta G°$ at 298 K for each of the preceding reactions. (b) The two values from part (a) are very different. Is this difference primarily due to the enthalpy term or the entropy term of the standard free-energy change? (c) Use the values of $\Delta G°$ to calculate the K_{sp} values for the two salts at 298 K. (d) Sodium chloride is considered a soluble salt, whereas silver chloride is considered insoluble. Are these descriptions consistent with the answers to part (c)? (e) How will $\Delta G°$ for the solution process of these salts change with increasing T? What effect should this change have on the solubility of the salts?

SOLUTION

(a) We will use Equation 13.14 along with $\Delta G_f°$ values from Appendix C to calculate the $\Delta G_{soln}°$ values for each equilibrium. (We use the subscript "soln" to indicate that these are thermodynamic quantities for the formation of a solution.) We find

$$\Delta G_{soln}°(NaCl) = (-261.9 \text{ kJ/mol}) + (-131.2 \text{ kJ/mol}) - (-384.0 \text{ kJ/mol})$$

$$= -9.1 \text{ kJ/mol}$$

$$\Delta G_{soln}°(AgCl) = (+77.11 \text{ kJ/mol}) + (-131.2 \text{ kJ/mol}) - (-109.70 \text{ kJ/mol})$$

$$= +55.6 \text{ kJ/mol}$$

(b) We can write $\Delta G_{soln}°$ as the sum of an enthalpy term, $\Delta H_{soln}°$, and an entropy term, $-T\Delta S_{soln}°$: $\Delta G_{soln}° = \Delta H_{soln}° + (-T\Delta S_{soln}°)$. We can calculate the values of $\Delta H_{soln}°$ and $\Delta S_{soln}°$ by using Equations 10.31 and 13.8. We can then calculate $-T\Delta S_{soln}°$ at $T = 298$ K. All these calculations are now familiar to us. The results are summarized in the following table:

Salt	$\Delta H_{soln}°$	$\Delta S_{soln}°$	$T\Delta S_{soln}°$
NaCl	+3.6 kJ/mol	+43.2 kJ/mol-K	−12.9 kJ/mol
AgCl	+65.7 kJ/mol	+34.3 kJ/mol-K	−10.2 kJ/mol

The entropy terms for the solution of the two salts are very similar. That seems sensible because each solution process should lead to a similar increase in randomness as the salt dissolves, forming hydrated ions. In contrast, we see a very large difference in the enthalpy term for the solution of the two salts. The difference in the values of $\Delta G_{soln}°$ is dominated by the difference in the values of $\Delta H_{soln}°$.

(c) The solubility product, K_{sp}, is the equilibrium constant for the solution process. As such, we can relate K_{sp} directly to $\Delta G_{soln}°$ by using Equation 13.21:

$$K_{sp} = e^{-\Delta G_{soln}°/RT}$$

We can calculate the K_{sp} values in the same way we applied Equation 13.21 in Sample Exercise 13.12. We use the $\Delta G_{soln}°$ values we obtained in part (a), remembering to convert them from kJ/mol to J/mol:

NaCl: $K_{sp} = [Na^+(aq)][Cl^-(aq)] = e^{-(-9100)/[(8.314)(298)]} = e^{+3.7} = 40$

AgCl: $K_{sp} = [Ag^+(aq)][Cl^-(aq)] = e^{-(+55,600)/[(8.314)(298)]} = e^{-22.4} = 1.9 \times 10^{-10}$

The value calculated for the K_{sp} of AgCl is very close to that listed in Appendix D.

(d) A soluble salt is one that dissolves appreciably in water. The K_{sp} value for NaCl is greater than 1, indicating that NaCl dissolves to a great extent. The K_{sp} value for AgCl is very small, indicating that very little dissolves in water. Silver chloride should indeed be considered an insoluble salt.

(e) As we expect, the solution process has a positive value of ΔS for both salts (see the table in part b). As such, the entropy term of the free-energy change, $-T\Delta S_{soln}°$, is negative. If we assume that $\Delta H_{soln}°$ and $\Delta S_{soln}°$ do not change much with temperature, then an increase in T will serve to make $\Delta G_{soln}°$ more negative. Thus, the driving force for dissolution of the salts will increase with increasing T, and we therefore expect the solubility of the salts to increase with increasing T.

CHAPTER SUMMARY AND KEY TERMS

SECTION 13.1 Most reactions and chemical processes have an inherent directionality: They are **spontaneous** in one direction and nonspontaneous in the reverse direction. The spontaneity of a process is related to the thermodynamic path the system takes from the initial state to the final state. In a **reversible process**, both the system and its surroundings can be restored to their original state by exactly reversing the change. In an **irreversible process** the system cannot return to its original state without there being a permanent change in the surroundings. Any spontaneous process is irreversible. A process that occurs at a constant temperature is said to be **isothermal**.

SECTION 13.2 The spontaneous nature of processes is related to a thermodynamic state function called **entropy**, denoted S. For a process that occurs at constant temperature, the entropy change of the system is given by the heat absorbed by the system along a reversible path, divided by the temperature: $\Delta S = q_{rev}/T$. The way entropy controls the spontaneity of processes is given by the **second law of thermodynamics**, which governs the change in the entropy of the universe, $\Delta S_{univ} = \Delta S_{sys} + \Delta S_{surr}$. The second law states that in a reversible process $\Delta S_{univ} = 0$; in an irreversible (spontaneous) process $\Delta S_{univ} > 0$. Entropy values are usually expressed in units of joules per kelvin, J/K.

SECTION 13.3 A particular combination of motions and locations of the atoms and molecules of a system at a particular instant is called a **microstate**. The entropy of a system is a measure of its randomness or disorder. The entropy is related to the number of microstates, W, corresponding to the state of the system: $S = k \ln W$. Molecules can undergo three kinds of motion: In **translational motion** the entire molecule moves in space. Molecules can also undergo **vibrational motion**, in which the atoms of the molecule move toward and away from one another in periodic fashion, and **rotational motion**, in which the entire molecule spins like a top. The number of available microstates, and therefore the entropy, increases with an increase in volume, temperature, or motion of molecules because any of these changes increases the possible motions and locations of the molecules. As a result, entropy generally increases when liquids or solutions are formed from solids, gases are formed from either solids or liquids, or the number of molecules of gas increases during a chemical reaction. The **third law of thermodynamics** states that the entropy of a pure crystalline solid at 0 K is zero.

SECTION 13.4 The third law allows us to assign entropy values for substances at different temperatures. Under standard conditions the entropy of a mole of a substance is called its **standard molar entropy**, denoted $S°$. From tabulated values of $S°$, we can calculate the entropy change for any process under standard conditions. For an isothermal process, the entropy change in the surroundings is equal to $-\Delta H/T$.

SECTION 13.5 The **Gibbs free energy** (or just **free energy**), G, is a thermodynamic state function that combines the two state functions enthalpy and entropy: $G = H - TS$. For processes that occur at constant temperature, $\Delta G = \Delta H - T\Delta S$. For a process occurring at constant temperature and pressure, the sign of ΔG relates to the spontaneity of the process. When ΔG is negative, the process is spontaneous. When ΔG is positive, the process is nonspontaneous but the reverse process is spontaneous. At equilibrium the process is reversible and ΔG is zero. The free energy is also a measure of the maximum useful work that can be performed by a system in a spontaneous process. The standard free-energy change, $\Delta G°$, for any process can be calculated from tabulations of **standard free energies of formation**, $\Delta G_f°$, which are defined in a fashion analogous to standard enthalpies of formation, $\Delta G_f°$. The value of $\Delta G_f°$ for a pure element in its standard state is defined to be zero.

SECTIONS 13.6 AND 13.7 The values of ΔH and ΔS generally do not vary much with temperature. Therefore, the dependence of ΔG with temperature is governed mainly by the value of T in the expression $\Delta G = \Delta H - T\Delta S$. The entropy term $-T\Delta S$ has the greater effect on the temperature dependence of ΔG and, hence, on the spontaneity of the process. For example, a process for which $\Delta H > 0$ and $\Delta S > 0$, such as the melting of ice, can be nonspontaneous ($\Delta G > 0$) at low temperatures and spontaneous ($\Delta G < 0$) at higher temperatures. Under nonstandard conditions ΔG is related to $\Delta G°$ and the value of the reaction quotient, Q: $\Delta G = \Delta G° + RT \ln Q$. At equilibrium ($\Delta G = 0$, $Q = K$), $\Delta G° = -RT \ln K$. Thus, the standard free-energy change is directly related to the equilibrium constant for the reaction. This relationship expresses the temperature dependence of equilibrium constants.

KEY SKILLS

- Understand the meaning of spontaneous process, reversible process, irreversible process, and isothermal process. (Section 13.1)
- State the second law of thermodynamics. (Section 13.2)
- Explain how the entropy of a system is related to the number of possible microstates. (Section 13.3)
- Describe the kinds of molecular motion that a molecule can possess. (Section 13.3)
- Predict the sign of ΔS for physical and chemical processes. (Section 13.3)
- State the third law of thermodynamics. (Section 13.3)
- Calculate standard entropy changes for a system from standard molar entropies. (Section 13.4)
- Calculate entropy changes in the surroundings for isothermal processes. (Section 13.4)
- Calculate the Gibbs free energy from the enthalpy change and entropy change at a given temperature. (Section 13.5)
- Use free-energy changes to predict whether reactions are spontaneous. (Section 13.5)
- Calculate standard free-energy changes using standard free energies of formation. (Section 13.5)
- Predict the effect of temperature on spontaneity given ΔH and ΔS. (Section 13.6)
- Calculate ΔG under nonstandard conditions. (Section 13.7)
- Relate $\Delta G°$ and equilibrium constant. (Section 13.7)

KEY EQUATIONS

- $\Delta S = \dfrac{q_{rev}}{T}$ (constant T)

  [13.2]   Relating entropy change to the heat absorbed or released in a reversible process

- *Reversible process:* $\Delta S_{univ} = \Delta S_{sys} + \Delta S_{surr} = 0$
  Irreversible process: $\Delta S_{univ} = \Delta S_{sys} + \Delta S_{surr} > 0$ $\Bigg\}$

  [13.4]   The second law of thermodynamics

- $S = k \ln W$

  [13.5]   Relating entropy to the number of microstates

- $\Delta S° = \sum nS°(\text{products}) - \sum mS°(\text{reactants})$

  [13.8]   Calculating the standard entropy change from standard molar entropies

- $\Delta S_{surr} = \dfrac{-\Delta H_{sys}}{T}$

  [13.9]   The entropy change of the surroundings for a process at constant temperature and pressure

- $\Delta G = \Delta H - T\Delta S$

  [13.11]   Calculating the Gibbs free-energy change from enthalpy and entropy changes at constant temperature

- $\Delta G° = \sum n\Delta G_f°(\text{products}) - \sum m\Delta G_f°(\text{reactants})$

  [13.14]   Calculating the standard free-energy change from standard free energies of formation

- *Reversible process:* $\Delta G = \Delta H_{sys} - T\Delta S_{sys} = 0$
  Irreversible process: $\Delta G = \Delta H_{sys} - T\Delta S_{sys} < 0$ $\Bigg\}$

  [13.17]   Relating the free-energy change to the reversibility of a process at constant temperature and pressure

- $\Delta G = -w_{max}$

  [13.18]   Relating the free-energy change to the maximum work a process can perform

- $\Delta G = \Delta G° + RT \ln Q$

  [13.19]   Calculating free-energy change under nonstandard conditions

- $\Delta G° = -RT \ln K$

  [13.20]   Relating the standard free-energy change and the equilibrium constant

EXERCISES

VISUALIZING CONCEPTS

13.1 Two different gases occupy the two bulbs shown here. Consider the process that occurs when the stopcock is opened, assuming the gases behave ideally. (a) Draw the final (equilibrium) state. (b) Predict the signs of ΔH and ΔS for the process. (c) Is the process that occurs when the stopcock is opened a reversible one? (d) How does the process affect the entropy of the surroundings? [Sections 13.1 and 13.2]

13.2 As shown here, one type of computer keyboard cleaner contains liquefied 1,1-difluoroethane ($C_2H_4F_2$), which is a gas at atmospheric pressure. When the nozzle is squeezed, the 1,1-difluoroethane vaporizes out of the nozzle at high pressure, blowing dust out of objects. (a) Based on your experience, is the vaporization a spontaneous process at room temperature? (b) Defining the 1,1-difluoroethane as the system, do you expect q_{sys} for the process to be positive or negative? Explain. (c) Predict whether ΔS is positive or negative for this process. (d) Given your answers to (a), (b), and (c), do you think the operation of this product depends more on heat flow or more on entropy change?

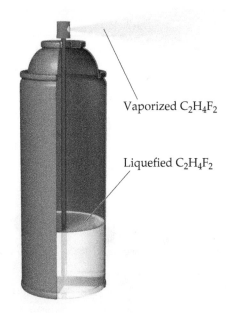

Vaporized $C_2H_4F_2$

Liquefied $C_2H_4F_2$

13.3 (a) What are the signs of ΔS and ΔH for the process depicted here? (b) How might temperature affect the sign of ΔG? (c) If energy can flow in and out of the system to maintain a constant temperature during the process, what can you say about the entropy change of the surroundings as a result of this process? [Sections 13.2 and 13.5]

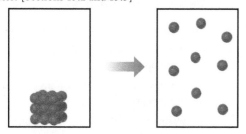

13.4 Predict the sign of ΔS accompanying this reaction. Explain your choice. [Section 13.3]

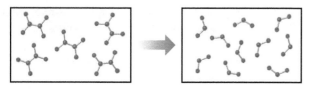

13.5 The accompanying diagram shows how entropy varies with temperature for a substance that is a gas at the highest temperature shown. (a) What processes correspond to the entropy increases along the vertical lines labeled 1 and 2? (b) Why is the entropy change for 2 larger than that for 1? [Section 13.3]

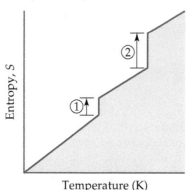

13.6 *Isomers* are molecules that have the same chemical formula but different arrangements of atoms, as shown here for two isomers of pentane, C_5H_{12}. (a) Do you expect a significant difference in the enthalpy of combustion of the two isomers? Explain. (b) Which isomer do you expect to have the higher standard molar entropy? Explain. [Section 13.4]

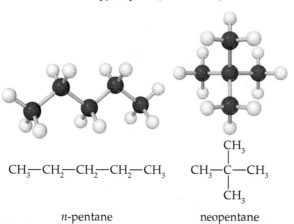

$$CH_3{-}CH_2{-}CH_2{-}CH_2{-}CH_3 \qquad CH_3{-}\underset{\underset{CH_3}{|}}{\overset{\overset{CH_3}{|}}{C}}{-}CH_3$$

n-pentane   neopentane

13.7 The accompanying diagram shows how ΔH (red line) and $T\Delta S$ (blue line) change with temperature for a hypothetical reaction. (a) What is the significance of the point at 300 K, where ΔH and $T\Delta S$ are equal? (b) In what temperature range is this reaction spontaneous? [Section 13.6]

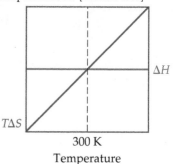

Temperature

13.8 The accompanying diagram shows how ΔG for a hypothetical reaction changes as temperature changes. (a) At what temperature is the system at equilibrium? (b) In what temperature range is the reaction spontaneous? (c) Is ΔH positive or negative? (d) Is ΔS positive or negative? [Sections 13.5 and 13.6]

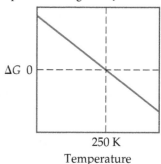

Temperature

13.9 Consider a reaction $A_2(g) + B_2(g) \rightleftharpoons 2\,AB(g)$, with atoms of A shown in red in the diagram and atoms of B shown in blue. (a) If $K_c = 1$, which box represents the system at equilibrium? (b) What is the sign of ΔG for any process in which the contents of a reaction vessel move to equilibrium? (c) Rank the boxes in order of increasing magnitude of ΔG for the reaction. [Sections 13.5 and 13.7]

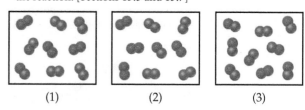

(1)   (2)   (3)

13.10 The accompanying diagram shows how the free energy, G, changes during a hypothetical reaction $A(g) + B(g) \longrightarrow C(g)$. On the left are pure reactants, each at 1 atm, and on the right is the pure product, also at 1 atm. (a) What is the significance of the minimum in the plot? (b) What does the quantity x, shown on the right side of the diagram, represent? [Section 13.7]

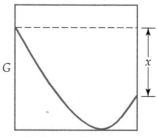

Progress of reaction

SPONTANEOUS PROCESSES (section 13.1)

13.11 Which of the following processes are spontaneous and which are nonspontaneous: (a) the ripening of a banana, (b) dissolution of sugar in a cup of hot coffee, (c) the reaction of nitrogen atoms to form N_2 molecules at 25 °C and 1 atm, (d) lightning, (e) formation of CH_4 and O_2 molecules from CO_2 and H_2O at room temperature and 1 atm of pressure?

13.12 Which of the following processes are spontaneous: (a) the melting of ice cubes at −10 °C and 1 atm pressure; (b) separating a mixture of N_2 and O_2 into two separate samples, one that is pure N_2 and one that is pure O_2; (c) alignment of iron filings in a magnetic field; (d) the reaction of hydrogen gas with oxygen gas to form water vapor; (e) the dissolution of $HCl(g)$ in water to form concentrated hydrochloric acid?

13.13 (a) Give two examples of endothermic processes that are spontaneous. (b) Give an example of a process that is spontaneous at one temperature but nonspontaneous at a different temperature.

13.14 The crystalline hydrate $Cd(NO_3)_2 \cdot 4\,H_2O(s)$ loses water when placed in a large, closed, dry vessel:

$$Cd(NO_3)_2 \cdot 4\,H_2O(s) \longrightarrow Cd(NO_3)_2(s) + 4\,H_2O(g)$$

This process is spontaneous and ΔH is positive. Is this process an exception to Bertholet's generalization that all spontaneous changes are exothermic? Explain.

13.15 Consider the vaporization of liquid water to steam at a pressure of 1 atm. (a) Is this process endothermic or exothermic? (b) In what temperature range is it a spontaneous process? (c) In what temperature range is it a nonspontaneous process? (d) At what temperature are the two phases in equilibrium?

13.16 The normal freezing point of n-octane (C_8H_{18}) is −57 °C. (a) Is the freezing of n-octane an endothermic or exothermic process? (b) In what temperature range is the freezing of n-octane a spontaneous process? (c) In what temperature range is it a nonspontaneous process? (d) Is there any temperature at which liquid n-octane and solid n-octane are in equilibrium? Explain.

13.17 (a) What is special about a *reversible* process? (b) Suppose a reversible process is reversed, restoring the system to its original state. What can be said about the surroundings after the process is reversed? (c) Under what circumstances will the vaporization of water to steam be a reversible process? (d) Are any of the processes that occur in the world around us reversible in nature? Explain.

13.18 (a) What is meant by calling a process *irreversible*? (b) After a particular irreversible process, the system is restored to its original state. What can be said about the condition of the surroundings after the system is restored to its original state? (c) Under what conditions will the condensation of a liquid be an irreversible process?

13.19 Consider a process in which an ideal gas changes from state 1 to state 2 in such a way that its temperature changes from 300 K to 200 K. (a) Describe how this change might be carried out while keeping the volume of the gas constant. (b) Describe how it might be carried out while keeping the pressure of the gas constant. (c) Does the change in ΔE depend on the particular pathway taken to carry out this change of state? Explain.

13.20 A system goes from state 1 to state 2 and back to state 1. (a) What is the relationship between the value of ΔE for going from state 1 to state 2 to that for going from state 2 back to state 1? (b) Without further information, can you conclude anything about the amount of heat transferred to the system as it goes from state 1 to state 2 as compared to that upon going from state 2 back to state 1? (c) Suppose the changes in state are reversible processes. Can you conclude anything about the work done by the system upon going from state 1 to state 2 as compared to that upon going from state 2 back to state 1?

13.21 Consider a system consisting of an ice cube. (a) Under what conditions can the ice cube melt reversibly? (b) If the ice cube melts reversibly, is ΔE zero for the process? Explain.

13.22 Consider what happens when a sample of the explosive TNT (Section 3.8: "Chemistry Put to Work: Explosives and Alfred Nobel") is detonated under atmospheric pressure. (a) Is the detonation a spontaneous process? (b) What is the sign of q for this process? (c) Can you determine whether w is positive, negative, or zero for the process? Explain. (d) Can you determine the sign of ΔE for the process? Explain.

ENTROPY AND THE SECOND LAW OF THERMODYNAMICS (section 13.2)

13.23 (a) How can we calculate ΔS for an isothermal process? (b) Does ΔS for a process depend on the path taken from the initial state to the final state of the system? Explain.

13.24 Suppose we vaporize a mole of liquid water at 25 °C and another mole of water at 100 °C. (a) Assuming that the enthalpy of vaporization of water does not change much between 25 °C and 100 °C, which process involves the larger change in entropy? (b) Does the entropy change in either process depend on whether we carry out the process reversibly or not? Explain.

13.25 The normal boiling point of $Br_2(l)$ is 58.8 °C, and its molar enthalpy of vaporization is $\Delta H_{vap} = 29.6$ kJ/mol. (a) When $Br_2(l)$ boils at its normal boiling point, does its entropy increase or decrease? (b) Calculate the value of ΔS when 1.00 mol of $Br_2(l)$ is vaporized at 58.8 °C.

13.26 The element gallium (Ga) freezes at 29.8 °C, and its molar enthalpy of fusion is $\Delta H_{fus} = 5.59$ kJ/mol. (a) When molten gallium solidifies to Ga(s) at its normal melting point, is ΔS positive or negative? (b) Calculate the value of ΔS when 60.0 g of Ga(l) solidifies at 29.8 °C.

13.27 (a) Express the second law of thermodynamics in words. (b) If the entropy of the system increases during a reversible process, what can you say about the entropy change of the surroundings? (c) In a certain spontaneous process the system undergoes an entropy change, $\Delta S = 42$ J/K. What can you conclude about ΔS_{surr}?

13.28 (a) Express the second law of thermodynamics as a mathematical equation. (b) In a particular spontaneous process the entropy of the system decreases. What can you conclude about the sign and magnitude of ΔS_{surr}? (c) During a certain reversible process, the surroundings undergo an entropy change, $\Delta S_{surr} = -78$ J/K. What is the entropy change of the system for this process?

13.29 **(a)** What sign for ΔS do you expect when the volume of 0.200 mol of an ideal gas at 27 °C is increased isothermally from an initial volume of 10.0 L? **(b)** If the final volume is 18.5 L, calculate the entropy change for the process. **(c)** Do you need to specify the temperature to calculate the entropy change? Explain.

13.30 **(a)** What sign for ΔS do you expect when the pressure on 0.600 mol of an ideal gas at 350 K is increased isothermally from an initial pressure of 0.750 atm? **(b)** If the final pressure on the gas is 1.20 atm, calculate the entropy change for the process. **(c)** Do you need to specify the temperature to calculate the entropy change? Explain.

THE MOLECULAR INTERPRETATION OF ENTROPY (section 13.3)

13.31 For the isothermal expansion of a gas into a vacuum, $\Delta E = 0$, $q = 0$, and $w = 0$. **(a)** Is this a spontaneous process? **(b)** Explain why no work is done by the system during this process. **(c)** In thermodynamics, what is the "driving force" for the expansion of the gas?

13.32 **(a)** What is the difference between a *state* and a *microstate* of a system? **(b)** As a system goes from state A to state B, its entropy decreases. What can you say about the number of microstates corresponding to each state? **(c)** In a particular spontaneous process, the number of microstates available to the system decreases. What can you conclude about the sign of ΔS_{surr}?

13.33 How would each of the following changes affect the number of microstates available to a system: **(a)** increase in temperature, **(b)** decrease in volume, **(c)** change of state from liquid to gas?

13.34 **(a)** Using the heat of vaporization in Appendix B, calculate the entropy change for the vaporization of water at 25 °C and at 100 °C. **(b)** From your knowledge of microstates and the structure of liquid water, explain the difference in these two values.

13.35 **(a)** What do you expect for the sign of ΔS in a chemical reaction in which two moles of gaseous reactants are converted to three moles of gaseous products? **(b)** For which of the processes in Exercise 13.11 does the entropy of the system increase?

13.36 **(a)** In a chemical reaction two gases combine to form a solid. What do you expect for the sign of ΔS? **(b)** How does the entropy of the system change in the processes described in Exercise 13.12?

13.37 How does the entropy of the system change when **(a)** a solid melts, **(b)** a gas liquefies, **(c)** a solid sublimes?

13.38 How does the entropy of the system change when **(a)** the temperature of the system increases, **(b)** the volume of a gas increases, **(c)** equal volumes of ethanol and water are mixed to form a solution?

13.39 **(a)** State the third law of thermodynamics. **(b)** Distinguish between translational motion, vibrational motion, and

rotational motion of a molecule. **(c)** Illustrate these three kinds of motion with sketches for the HCl molecule.

13.40 **(a)** If you are told that the entropy of a certain system is zero, what do you know about the system and the temperature? **(b)** The energy of a gas is increased by heating it. Using CO_2 as an example, illustrate the different ways in which additional energy can be distributed among the molecules of the gas. **(c)** $CO_2(g)$ and $Ar(g)$ have nearly the same molar mass. At a given temperature, will they have the same number of microstates? Explain.

13.41 For each of the following pairs, choose the substance with the higher entropy per mole at a given temperature: **(a)** Ar(l) or Ar(g), **(b)** He(g) at 3 atm pressure or He(g) at 1.5 atm pressure, **(c)** 1 mol of Ne(g) in 15.0 L or 1 mol of Ne(g) in 1.50 L, **(d)** $CO_2(g)$ or $CO_2(s)$.

13.42 For each of the following pairs, indicate which substance possesses the larger standard entropy: **(a)** 1 mol of $P_4(g)$ at 300 °C, 0.01 atm, or 1 mol of $As_4(g)$ at 300 °C, 0.01 atm; **(b)** 1 mol of $H_2O(g)$ at 100 °C, 1 atm, or 1 mol of $H_2O(l)$ at 100 °C, 1 atm; **(c)** 0.5 mol of $N_2(g)$ at 298 K, 20-L volume, or 0.5 mol $CH_4(g)$ at 298 K, 20-L volume; **(d)** 100 g $Na_2SO_4(s)$ at 30 °C or 100 g $Na_2SO_4(aq)$ at 30 °C.

13.43 Predict the sign of the entropy change of the system for each of the following reactions:
(a) $N_2(g) + 3 H_2(g) \longrightarrow 2 NH_3(g)$
(b) $CaCO_3(s) \longrightarrow CaO(s) + CO_2(g)$
(c) $3 C_2H_2(g) \longrightarrow C_6H_6(g)$
(d) $Al_2O_3(s) + 3 H_2(g) \longrightarrow 2 Al(s) + 3 H_2O(g)$

13.44 Predict the sign of ΔS_{sys} for each of the following processes: **(a)** Molten gold solidifies. **(b)** Gaseous Cl_2 dissociates in the stratosphere to form gaseous Cl atoms. **(c)** Gaseous CO reacts with gaseous H_2 to form liquid methanol, CH_3OH. **(d)** Calcium phosphate precipitates upon mixing $Ca(NO_3)_2(aq)$ and $(NH_4)_3PO_4(aq)$.

ENTROPY CHANGES IN CHEMICAL REACTIONS (section 13.4)

13.45 **(a)** Using Figure 13.13 as a model, sketch how the entropy of water changes as it is heated from −50 °C to 110 °C at sea level. Show the temperatures at which there are vertical increases in entropy. **(b)** Which process has the larger entropy change: melting ice or boiling water? Explain.

13.46 Propanol (C_3H_7OH) melts at −126.5 °C and boils at 97.4 °C. Draw a qualitative sketch of how the entropy changes as propanol vapor at 150 °C and 1 atm is cooled to solid propanol at −150 °C and 1 atm.

13.47 In each of the following pairs, which compound would you expect to have the higher standard molar entropy: **(a)** $C_2H_2(g)$ or $C_2H_6(g)$, **(b)** $CO_2(g)$ or $CO(g)$? Explain.

13.48 Cyclopropane and propylene are isomers (see Exercise 13.6) that both have the formula C_3H_6. Based on the molecular structures shown, which of these isomers would you expect to have the higher standard molar entropy at 25 °C?

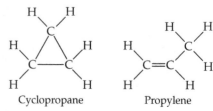

Cyclopropane   Propylene

13.49 Use Appendix C to compare the standard entropies at 25 °C for the following pairs of substances: (a) Sc(s) and Sc(g), (b) NH$_3$(g) and NH$_3$(aq), (c) 1 mol P$_4$(g) and 2 mol P$_2$(g), (d) C(graphite) and C(diamond). In each case explain the difference in the entropy values.

13.50 Using Appendix C, compare the standard entropies at 25 °C for the following pairs of substances: (a) CuO(s) and Cu$_2$O(s), (b) 1 mol N$_2$O$_4$(g) and 2 mol NO$_2$(g), (c) SiO$_2$(s) and CO$_2$(g), (d) CO(g) and CO$_2$(g). For each pair, explain the difference in the entropy values.

[13.51] The standard entropies at 298 K for certain of the group 4A elements are as follows: C(s, diamond) = 2.43 J/mol-K, Si(s) = 18.81 J/mol-K, Ge(s) = 31.09 J/mol-K, and Sn(s) = 51.818 J/mol-K. All but Sn have the diamond structure. How do you account for the trend in the $S°$ values?

[13.52] Three of the forms of elemental carbon are graphite, diamond, and buckminsterfullerene. The entropies at 298 K for graphite and diamond are listed in Appendix C. (a) Account

for the difference in the $S°$ values of graphite and diamond in light of their structures (Figure 7.3). (b) What would you expect for the $S°$ value of buckminsterfullerene (Figure 7.20) relative to the values for graphite and diamond? Explain.

13.53 Using $S°$ values from Appendix C, calculate $\Delta S°$ values for the following reactions. In each case account for the sign of $\Delta S°$.
(a) C$_2$H$_4$(g) + H$_2$(g) $\longrightarrow$ C$_2$H$_6$(g)
(b) N$_2$O$_4$(g) $\longrightarrow$ 2 NO$_2$(g)
(c) Be(OH)$_2$(s) $\longrightarrow$ BeO(s) + H$_2$O(g)
(d) 2 CH$_3$OH(g) + 3 O$_2$(g) $\longrightarrow$ 2 CO$_2$(g) + 4 H$_2$O(g)

13.54 Calculate $\Delta S°$ values for the following reactions by using tabulated $S°$ values from Appendix C. In each case explain the sign of $\Delta S°$.
(a) HNO$_3$(g) + NH$_3$(g) $\longrightarrow$ NH$_4$NO$_3$(s)
(b) 2 Fe$_2$O$_3$(s) $\longrightarrow$ 4 Fe(s) + 3 O$_2$(g)
(c) CaCO$_3$(s, calcite) + 2HCl(g) $\longrightarrow$
 CaCl$_2$(s) + CO$_2$(g) + H$_2$O(l)
(d) 3 C$_2$H$_6$(g) $\longrightarrow$ C$_6$H$_6$(l) + 6 H$_2$(g)

GIBBS FREE ENERGY (sections 13.5 and 13.6)

13.55 (a) For a process that occurs at constant temperature, express the change in Gibbs free energy in terms of changes in the enthalpy and entropy of the system. (b) For a certain process that occurs at constant T and P, the value of ΔG is positive. What can you conclude? (c) What is the relationship between ΔG for a process and the rate at which it occurs?

13.56 (a) What is the meaning of the standard free-energy change, $\Delta G°$, as compared with ΔG? (b) For any process that occurs at constant temperature and pressure, what is the significance of $\Delta G = 0$? (c) For a certain process, ΔG is large and negative. Does this mean that the process necessarily occurs rapidly?

13.57 For a certain chemical reaction, $\Delta H° = -35.4$ kJ and $\Delta S° = -85.5$ J/K. (a) Is the reaction exothermic or endothermic? (b) Does the reaction lead to an increase or decrease in the randomness or disorder of the system? (c) Calculate $\Delta G°$ for the reaction at 298 K. (d) Is the reaction spontaneous at 298 K under standard conditions?

13.58 A certain reaction has $\Delta H° = +23.7$ kJ and $\Delta S° = +52.4$ J/K. (a) Is the reaction exothermic or endothermic? (b) Does the reaction lead to an increase or decrease in the randomness or disorder of the system? (c) Calculate $\Delta G°$ for the reaction at 298 K. (d) Is the reaction spontaneous at 298 K under standard conditions?

13.59 Using data in Appendix C, calculate $\Delta H°$, $\Delta S°$, and $\Delta G°$ at 298 K for each of the following reactions. In each case show that $\Delta G° = \Delta H° - T\Delta S°$.
(a) H$_2$(g) + F$_2$(g) $\longrightarrow$ 2 HF(g)
(b) C(s, graphite) + 2 Cl$_2$(g) $\longrightarrow$ CCl$_4$(g)
(c) 2 PCl$_3$(g) + O$_2$(g) $\longrightarrow$ 2 POCl$_3$(g)
(d) 2 CH$_3$OH(g) + H$_2$(g) $\longrightarrow$ C$_2$H$_6$(g) + 2 H$_2$O(g)

13.60 Use data in Appendix C to calculate $\Delta H°$, $\Delta S°$, and $\Delta G°$ at 25 °C for each of the following reactions. In each case show that $\Delta G° = \Delta H° - T\Delta S°$.
(a) 2 Cr(s) + 3 O$_2$(g) $\longrightarrow$ 2 CrO$_3$(s)
(b) BaCO$_3$(s) $\longrightarrow$ BaO(s) + CO$_2$(g)
(c) 2 P(s) + 10 HF(g) $\longrightarrow$ 2 PF$_5$(g) + 5 H$_2$(g)
(d) K(s) + O$_2$(g) $\longrightarrow$ KO$_2$(s)

13.61 Using data from Appendix C, calculate $\Delta G°$ for the following reactions. Indicate whether each reaction is spontaneous at 298 K under standard conditions.
(a) 2 SO$_2$(g) + O$_2$(g) $\longrightarrow$ 2 SO$_3$(g)
(b) NO$_2$(g) + N$_2$O(g) $\longrightarrow$ 3 NO(g)
(c) 6 Cl$_2$(g) + 2 Fe$_2$O$_3$(s) $\longrightarrow$ 4 FeCl$_3$(s) + 3 O$_2$(g)
(d) SO$_2$(g) + 2 H$_2$(g) $\longrightarrow$ S(s) + 2 H$_2$O(g)

13.62 Using data from Appendix C, calculate the change in Gibbs free energy for each of the following reactions. In each case indicate whether the reaction is spontaneous at 298 K under standard conditions.
(a) 2 Ag(s) + Cl$_2$(g) $\longrightarrow$ 2 AgCl(s)
(b) P$_4$O$_6$(s) + 12 H$_2$(g) $\longrightarrow$ 4 PH$_3$(g) + 6 H$_2$O(g)
(c) CH$_4$(g) + 4 F$_2$(g) $\longrightarrow$ CF$_4$(g) + 4 HF(g)
(d) 2 H$_2$O$_2$(l) $\longrightarrow$ 2 H$_2$O(l) + O$_2$(g)

13.63 Octane (C$_8$H$_{18}$) is a liquid hydrocarbon at room temperature that is the primary constituent of gasoline. (a) Write a balanced equation for the combustion of C$_8$H$_{18}$(l) to form CO$_2$(g) and H$_2$O(l). (b) Without using thermochemical data, predict whether $\Delta G°$ for this reaction is more negative or less negative than $\Delta H°$.

13.64 Sulfur dioxide reacts with strontium oxide as follows:

$$\text{SO}_2(g) + \text{SrO}(s) \longrightarrow \text{SrSO}_3(s)$$

(a) Without using thermochemical data, predict whether $\Delta G°$ for this reaction is more negative or less negative than $\Delta H°$. (b) If you had only standard enthalpy data for this reaction, how would you go about making a rough estimate of the value of $\Delta G°$ at 298 K, using data from Appendix C on other substances?

13.65 Classify each of the following reactions as one of the four possible types summarized in Table 13.3:
(a) N$_2$(g) + 3 F$_2$(g) $\longrightarrow$ 2 NF$_3$(g)
 $\Delta H° = -249$ kJ; $\Delta S° = -278$ J/K
(b) N$_2$(g) + 3 Cl$_2$(g) $\longrightarrow$ 2 NCl$_3$(g)
 $\Delta H° = 460$ kJ; $\Delta S° = -275$ J/K
(c) N$_2$F$_4$(g) $\longrightarrow$ 2 NF$_2$(g)
 $\Delta H° = 85$ kJ; $\Delta S° = 198$ J/K

13.66 From the values given for $\Delta H°$ and $\Delta S°$, calculate $\Delta G°$ for each of the following reactions at 298 K. If the reaction is not spontaneous under standard conditions at 298 K, at what temperature (if any) would the reaction become spontaneous?
  (a) $2\,PbS(s) + 3\,O_2(g) \longrightarrow 2\,PbO(s) + 2\,SO_2(g)$
  $$\Delta H° = -844 \text{ kJ}; \Delta S° = -165 \text{ J/K}$$
  (b) $2\,POCl_3(g) \longrightarrow 2\,PCl_3(g) + O_2(g)$
  $$\Delta H° = 572 \text{ kJ}; \Delta S° = 179 \text{ J/K}$$

13.67 A particular constant-pressure reaction is spontaneous at 390 K. The enthalpy change for the reaction is +23.7 kJ. What can you conclude about the sign and magnitude of ΔS for the reaction?

13.68 A certain constant-pressure reaction is nonspontaneous at 45 °C. The entropy change for the reaction is 72 J/K. What can you conclude about the sign and magnitude of ΔH?

13.69 For a particular reaction, $\Delta H = -32$ kJ and $\Delta S = -98$ J/K. Assume that ΔH and ΔS do not vary with temperature. (a) At what temperature will the reaction have $\Delta G = 0$? (b) If T is increased from that in part (a), will the reaction be spontaneous or nonspontaneous?

13.70 Reactions in which a substance decomposes by losing CO are called *decarbonylation* reactions. The decarbonylation of acetic acid proceeds as follows:
  $$CH_3COOH(l) \longrightarrow CH_3OH(g) + CO(g)$$
  By using data from Appendix C, calculate the minimum temperature at which this process will be spontaneous under standard conditions. Assume that $\Delta H°$ and $\Delta S°$ do not vary with temperature.

13.71 Consider the following reaction between oxides of nitrogen:
  $$NO_2(g) + N_2O(g) \longrightarrow 3\,NO(g)$$
  (a) Use data in Appendix C to predict how $\Delta G°$ for the reaction varies with increasing temperature. (b) Calculate $\Delta G°$ at 800 K, assuming that $\Delta H°$ and $\Delta S°$ do not change with temperature. Under standard conditions is the reaction spontaneous at 800 K? (c) Calculate $\Delta G°$ at 1000 K. Is the reaction spontaneous under standard conditions at this temperature?

13.72 Methanol (CH_3OH) can be made by the controlled oxidation of methane:
  $$CH_4(g) + \tfrac{1}{2}O_2(g) \longrightarrow CH_3OH(g)$$
  (a) Use data in Appendix C to calculate $\Delta H°$ and $\Delta S°$ for this reaction. (b) How is $\Delta G°$ for the reaction expected to vary with increasing temperature? (c) Calculate $\Delta G°$ at 298 K. Under standard conditions, is the reaction spontaneous at this temperature? (d) Is there a temperature at which the reaction would be at equilibrium under standard conditions and that is low enough so that the compounds involved are likely to be stable?

13.73 (a) Use data in Appendix C to estimate the boiling point of benzene, $C_6H_6(l)$. (b) Use a reference source, such as the *CRC Handbook of Chemistry and Physics*, to find the experimental boiling point of benzene. How do you explain any deviation between your answer in part (a) and the experimental value?

13.74 (a) Using data in Appendix C, estimate the temperature at which the free-energy change for the transformation from $I_2(s)$ to $I_2(g)$ is zero. What assumptions must you make in arriving at this estimate? (b) Use a reference source, such as Web Elements (www.webelements.com), to find the experimental melting and boiling points of I_2. (c) Which of the values in part (b) is closer to the value you obtained in part (a)? Can you explain why this is so?

13.75 Acetylene gas, $C_2H_2(g)$, is used in welding. (a) Write a balanced equation for the combustion of acetylene gas to $CO_2(g)$ and $H_2O(l)$. (b) How much heat is produced in burning 1 mol of C_2H_2 under standard conditions if both reactants and products are brought to 298 K? (c) What is the maximum amount of useful work that can be accomplished under standard conditions by this reaction?

13.76 The fuel in high-efficiency natural gas vehicles consists primarily of methane (CH_4). (a) How much heat is produced in burning 1 mol of $CH_4(g)$ under standard conditions if reactants and products are brought to 298 K and $H_2O(l)$ is formed? (b) What is the maximum amount of useful work that can be accomplished under standard conditions by this system?

FREE ENERGY AND EQUILIBRIUM (section 13.7)

13.77 Explain qualitatively how ΔG changes for each of the following reactions as the partial pressure of O_2 is increased:
  (a) $2\,CO(g) + O_2(g) \longrightarrow 2\,CO_2(g)$
  (b) $2\,H_2O_2(l) \longrightarrow 2\,H_2O(l) + O_2(g)$
  (c) $2\,KClO_3(s) \longrightarrow 2\,KCl(s) + 3\,O_2(g)$

13.78 Indicate whether ΔG increases, decreases, or does not change when the partial pressure of H_2 is increased in each of the following reactions:
  (a) $N_2(g) + 3\,H_2(g) \longrightarrow 2\,NH_3(g)$
  (b) $2\,HBr(g) \longrightarrow H_2(g) + Br_2(g)$
  (c) $2\,H_2(g) + C_2H_2(g) \longrightarrow C_2H_6(g)$

13.79 Consider the reaction $2\,NO_2(g) \longrightarrow N_2O_4(g)$. (a) Using data from Appendix C, calculate $\Delta G°$ at 298 K. (b) Calculate ΔG at 298 K if the partial pressures of NO_2 and N_2O_4 are 0.40 atm and 1.60 atm, respectively.

13.80 Consider the reaction $3\,CH_4(g) \longrightarrow C_3H_8(g) + 2\,H_2(g)$. (a) Using data from Appendix C, calculate $\Delta G°$ at 298 K. (b) Calculate ΔG at 298 K if the reaction mixture consists of 40.0 atm of CH_4, 0.0100 atm of $C_3H_8(g)$, and 0.0180 atm of H_2.

13.81 Use data from Appendix C to calculate the equilibrium constant, K, at 298 K for each of the following reactions:
  (a) $H_2(g) + I_2(g) \rightleftharpoons 2\,HI(g)$
  (b) $C_2H_5OH(g) \rightleftharpoons C_2H_4(g) + H_2O(g)$
  (c) $3\,C_2H_2(g) \rightleftharpoons C_6H_6(g)$

13.82 Using data from Appendix C, write the equilibrium-constant expression and calculate the value of the equilibrium constant for these reactions at 298 K:
  (a) $NaHCO_3(s) \rightleftharpoons NaOH(s) + CO_2(g)$
  (b) $2\,HBr(g) + Cl_2(g) \rightleftharpoons 2\,HCl(g) + Br_2(g)$
  (c) $2\,SO_2(g) + O_2(g) \rightleftharpoons 2\,SO_3(g)$

13.83 Consider the decomposition of barium carbonate:
  $$BaCO_3(s) \rightleftharpoons BaO(s) + CO_2(g)$$
  Using data from Appendix C, calculate the equilibrium pressure of CO_2 at (a) 298 K and (b) 1100 K.

13.84 Consider the reaction
  $$PbCO_3(s) \rightleftharpoons PbO(s) + CO_2(g)$$
  Using data in Appendix C, calculate the equilibrium pressure of CO_2 in the system at (a) 400 °C and (b) 180 °C.

13.85 The value of K_a for nitrous acid (HNO_2) at 25 °C is given in Appendix D. **(a)** Write the chemical equation for the equilibrium that corresponds to K_a. **(b)** By using the value of K_a, calculate $\Delta G°$ for the dissociation of nitrous acid in aqueous solution. **(c)** What is the value of ΔG at equilibrium? **(d)** What is the value of ΔG when $[H^+] = 5.0 \times 10^{-2}\ M$, $[NO_2^-] = 6.0 \times 10^{-4}\ M$, and $[HNO_2] = 0.20\ M$?

13.86 The K_b for methylamine (CH_3NH_2) at 25 °C is given in Appendix D. **(a)** Write the chemical equation for the equilibrium that corresponds to K_b. **(b)** By using the value of K_b, calculate $\Delta G°$ for the equilibrium in part (a). **(c)** What is the value of ΔG at equilibrium? **(d)** What is the value of ΔG when $[H^+] = 6.7 \times 10^{-9}\ M$, $[CH_3NH_3^+] = 2.4 \times 10^{-3}\ M$, and $[CH_3NH_2] = 0.098\ M$?

ADDITIONAL EXERCISES

13.87 **(a)** Which of the thermodynamic quantities T, E, q, w, and S are state functions? **(b)** Which depend on the path taken from one state to another? **(c)** How many *reversible* paths are there between two states of a system? **(d)** For a reversible isothermal process, write an expression for ΔE in terms of q and w and an expression for ΔS in terms of q and T.

13.88 Indicate whether each of the following statements is true or false. If it is false, correct it. **(a)** The feasibility of manufacturing NH_3 from N_2 and H_2 depends entirely on the value of ΔH for the process $N_2(g) + 3\,H_2(g) \longrightarrow 2\,NH_3(g)$. **(b)** The reaction of $Na(s)$ with $Cl_2(g)$ to form $NaCl(s)$ is a spontaneous process. **(c)** A spontaneous process can in principle be conducted reversibly. **(d)** Spontaneous processes in general require that work be done to force them to proceed. **(e)** Spontaneous processes are those that are exothermic and that lead to a higher degree of order in the system.

13.89 For each of the following processes, indicate whether the signs of ΔS and ΔH are expected to be positive, negative, or about zero. **(a)** A solid sublimes. **(b)** The temperature of a sample of $Co(s)$ is lowered from 60 °C to 25 °C. **(c)** Ethyl alcohol evaporates from a beaker. **(d)** A diatomic molecule dissociates into atoms. **(e)** A piece of charcoal is combusted to form $CO_2(g)$ and $H_2O(g)$.

13.90 The reaction $2\,Mg(s) + O_2(g) \longrightarrow 2\,MgO(s)$ is highly spontaneous and has a negative value for $\Delta S°$. The second law of thermodynamics states that in any spontaneous process there is always an increase in the entropy of the universe. Is there an inconsistency between this reaction and the second law?

[13.91] Suppose four gas molecules are placed in the left flask in Figure 13.6(a). Initially, the right flask is evacuated and the stopcock is closed. **(a)** After the stopcock is opened, how many different arrangements of the molecules are possible? **(b)** How many of the arrangements from part (a) have all the molecules in the left flask? **(c)** How does the answer to part (b) explain the spontaneous expansion of the gas?

[13.92] Consider a system that consists of two standard playing dice, with the state of the system defined by the sum of the values shown on the top faces. **(a)** The two arrangements of top faces shown here can be viewed as two possible microstates of the system. Explain. **(b)** To which state does each microstate correspond? **(c)** How many possible states are there for the system? **(d)** Which state or states have the highest entropy? Explain. **(e)** Which state or states have the lowest entropy? Explain.

13.93 Ammonium nitrate dissolves spontaneously and endothermally in water at room temperature. What can you deduce about the sign of ΔS for this solution process?

[13.94] A standard air conditioner involves a *refrigerant* that is typically now a fluorinated hydrocarbon, such as CH_2F_2. An air-conditioner refrigerant has the property that it readily vaporizes at atmospheric pressure and is easily compressed to its liquid phase under increased pressure. The operation of an air conditioner can be thought of as a closed system made up of the refrigerant going through the two stages shown here (the air circulation is not shown in this diagram).

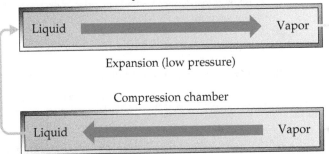

During *expansion*, the liquid refrigerant is released into an expansion chamber at low pressure, where it vaporizes. The vapor then undergoes *compression* at high pressure back to its liquid phase in a compression chamber. **(a)** What is the sign of q for the expansion? **(b)** What is the sign of q for the compression? **(c)** In a central air-conditioning system, one chamber is inside the home and the other is outside. Which chamber is where, and why? **(d)** Imagine that a sample of liquid refrigerant undergoes expansion followed by compression, so that it is back to its original state. Would you expect that to be a reversible process? **(e)** Suppose that a house and its exterior are both initially at 31 °C. Some time after the air conditioner is turned on, the house is cooled to 24 °C. Is this process spontaneous or nonspontaneous?

[13.95] *Trouton's rule* states that for many liquids at their normal boiling points, the standard molar entropy of vaporization is about 88 J/mol-K. **(a)** Estimate the normal boiling point of bromine, Br_2, by determining $\Delta H°_{vap}$ for Br_2 using data from Appendix C. Assume that $\Delta H°_{vap}$ remains constant with temperature and that Trouton's rule holds. **(b)** Look up the normal boiling point of Br_2 in a chemistry handbook or at the WebElements Web site (www.webelements.com).

[13.96] For the majority of the compounds listed in Appendix C, the value of $\Delta G°_f$ is more positive (or less negative) than the value of $\Delta H°_f$. **(a)** Explain this observation, using $NH_3(g)$, $CCl_4(l)$, and $KNO_3(s)$ as examples. **(b)** An exception to this observation is $CO(g)$. Explain the trend in the $\Delta H°_f$ and $\Delta G°_f$ values for this molecule.

13.97 Consider the following three reactions:

(i) $Ti(s) + 2 Cl_2(g) \longrightarrow TiCl_4(g)$

(ii) $C_2H_6(g) + 7 Cl_2(g) \longrightarrow 2 CCl_4(g) + 6 HCl(g)$

(iii) $BaO(s) + CO_2(g) \longrightarrow BaCO_3(s)$

(a) For each of the reactions, use data in Appendix C to calculate $\Delta H°$, $\Delta G°$, and $\Delta S°$ at 25 °C. (b) Which of these reactions are spontaneous under standard conditions at 25 °C? (c) For each of the reactions, predict the manner in which the change in free energy varies with an increase in temperature.

13.98 Using the data in Appendix C and given the pressures listed, calculate $\Delta G°$ for each of the following reactions:

(a) $N_2(g) + 3 H_2(g) \longrightarrow 2 NH_3(g)$
$P_{N_2} = 2.6$ atm, $P_{H_2} = 5.9$ atm, $P_{NH_3} = 1.2$ atm

(b) $2 N_2H_4(g) + 2 NO_2(g) \longrightarrow 3 N_2(g) + 4 H_2O(g)$
$P_{N_2H_4} = P_{NO_2} = 5.0 \times 10^{-2}$ atm,
$P_{N_2} = 0.5$ atm, $P_{H_2O} = 0.3$ atm

(c) $N_2H_4(g) \longrightarrow N_2(g) + 2 H_2(g)$
$P_{N_2H_4} = 0.5$ atm, $P_{N_2} = 1.5$ atm, $P_{H_2} = 2.5$ atm

13.99 (a) For each of the following reactions, predict the sign of $\Delta H°$ and $\Delta S°$ and discuss briefly how these factors determine the magnitude of K. (b) Based on your general chemical knowledge, predict which of these reactions will have $K > 0$. (c) In each case indicate whether K should increase or decrease with increasing temperature.

(i) $2 Mg(s) + O_2(g) \rightleftharpoons 2 MgO(s)$

(ii) $2 KI(s) \rightleftharpoons 2 K(g) + I_2(g)$

(iii) $Na_2(g) \rightleftharpoons 2 Na(g)$

(iv) $2 V_2O_5(s) \rightleftharpoons 4 V(s) + 5 O_2(g)$

13.100 Acetic acid can be manufactured by combining methanol with carbon monoxide, an example of a *carbonylation* reaction:

$$CH_3OH(l) + CO(g) \longrightarrow CH_3COOH(l)$$

(a) Calculate the equilibrium constant for the reaction at 25 °C. (b) Industrially, this reaction is run at temperatures above 25 °C. Will an increase in temperature produce an increase or decrease in the mole fraction of acetic acid at equilibrium? Why are elevated temperatures used? (c) At what temperature will this reaction have an equilibrium constant equal to 1? (You may assume that $\Delta H°$ and $\Delta S°$ are temperature independent, and you may ignore any phase changes that might occur.)

13.101 The oxidation of glucose ($C_6H_{12}O_6$) in body tissue produces CO_2 and H_2O. In contrast, anaerobic decomposition, which occurs during fermentation, produces ethanol (C_2H_5OH) and CO_2. (a) Using data given in Appendix C, compare the equilibrium constants for the following reactions:

$$C_6H_{12}O_6(s) + 6 O_2(g) \rightleftharpoons 6 CO_2(g) + 6 H_2O(l)$$

$$C_6H_{12}O_6(s) \rightleftharpoons 2 C_2H_5OH(l) + 2 CO_2(g)$$

(b) Compare the maximum work that can be obtained from these processes under standard conditions.

[13.102] The conversion of natural gas, which is mostly methane, into products that contain two or more carbon atoms, such as ethane (C_2H_6), is a very important industrial chemical process. In principle, methane can be converted into ethane and hydrogen:

$$2 CH_4(g) \longrightarrow C_2H_6(g) + H_2(g)$$

In practice, this reaction is carried out in the presence of oxygen:

$$2 CH_4(g) + \tfrac{1}{2} O_2(g) \longrightarrow C_2H_6(g) + H_2O(g)$$

(a) Using the data in Appendix C, calculate K for these reactions at 25 °C and 500 °C. (b) Is the difference in $\Delta G°$ for the two reactions due primarily to the enthalpy term (ΔH) or the entropy term ($-T\Delta S$)? (c) Explain how the preceding reactions are an example of driving a nonspontaneous reaction, as discussed in the "Chemistry and Life" box in Section 13.7. (d) The reaction of CH_4 and O_2 to form C_2H_6 and H_2O must be carried out carefully to avoid a competing reaction. What is the most likely competing reaction?

[13.103] Cells use the hydrolysis of adenosine triphosphate (ATP) as a source of energy (Figure 13.19). The conversion of ATP to ADP has a standard free-energy change of −30.5 kJ/mol. If all the free energy from the metabolism of glucose,

$$C_6H_{12}O_6(s) + 6 O_2(g) \longrightarrow 6 CO_2(g) + 6 H_2O(l)$$

goes into the conversion of ADP to ATP, how many moles of ATP can be produced for each mole of glucose?

[13.104] The potassium-ion concentration in blood plasma is about 5.0×10^{-3} M, whereas the concentration in muscle-cell fluid is much greater (0.15 M). The plasma and intracellular fluid are separated by the cell membrane, which we assume is permeable only to K^+. (a) What is ΔG for the transfer of 1 mol of K^+ from blood plasma to the cellular fluid at body temperature 37 °C? (b) What is the minimum amount of work that must be used to transfer this K^+?

[13.105] The relationship between the temperature of a reaction, its standard enthalpy change, and the equilibrium constant at that temperature can be expressed as the following linear equation:

$$\ln K = \frac{-\Delta H°}{RT} + \text{constant}$$

(a) Explain how this equation can be used to determine $\Delta H°$ experimentally from the equilibrium constants at several different temperatures. (b) Derive the preceding equation using relationships given in this chapter. To what is the constant equal?

[13.106] One way to derive Equation 13.3 depends on the observation that at constant T the number of ways, W, of arranging m ideal-gas particles in a volume V is proportional to the volume raised to the m power:

$$W \propto V^m$$

Use this relationship and Boltzmann's relationship between entropy and number of arrangements (Equation 13.5) to derive the equation for the entropy change for the isothermal expansion or compression of n moles of an ideal gas.

[13.107] About 86% of the world's electrical energy is produced by using steam turbines, a form of heat engine. In his analysis of an ideal heat engine, Sadi Carnot concluded that the maximum possible efficiency is defined by the total work that could be done by the engine, divided by the quantity of heat available to do the work (for example, from hot steam produced by combustion of a fuel such as coal or methane). This efficiency is given by the ratio $(T_{high} - T_{low})/T_{high}$, where T_{high} is the temperature of the heat going into the engine and T_{low} is that of the heat leaving the engine. (a) What is the maximum possible efficiency of a heat engine operating between an input temperature of 700 K and an exit temperature of 288 K? (b) Why is it important that electrical power plants be located near bodies of relatively cool water? (c) Under what conditions could a heat engine operate at or near 100% efficiency? (d) It is often said that if the energy of combustion of a fuel such as methane were captured in an electrical fuel cell instead of by burning the fuel in a heat engine, a greater fraction of the energy could be put to useful work. Make a qualitative drawing like that in Figure 10.10 that illustrates the fact that in principle the fuel cell route will produce more useful work than the heat engine route from combustion of methane.

INTEGRATIVE EXERCISES

13.108 Most liquids follow Trouton's rule, which states that the molar entropy of vaporization lies in the range of 88 ± 5 J/mol-K. The normal boiling points and enthalpies of vaporization of several organic liquids are as follows:

Substance	Normal Boiling Point (°C)	ΔH_{vap} (kJ/mol)
Acetone, $(CH_3)_2CO$	56.1	29.1
Dimethyl ether, $(CH_3)_2O$	−24.8	21.5
Ethanol, C_2H_5OH	78.4	38.6
Octane, C_8H_{18}	125.6	34.4
Pyridine, C_5H_5N	115.3	35.1

(a) Calculate ΔS_{vap} for each of the liquids. Do all the liquids obey Trouton's rule? **(b)** With reference to intermolecular forces (Section 5.2), can you explain any exceptions to the rule? **(c)** Would you expect water to obey Trouton's rule? By using data in Appendix B, check the accuracy of your conclusion. **(d)** Chlorobenzene (C_6H_5Cl) boils at 131.8 °C. Use Trouton's rule to estimate ΔH_{vap} for this substance.

13.109 In chemical kinetics the *entropy of activation* is the entropy change for the process in which the reactants reach the activated complex. The entropy of activation for bimolecular processes is usually negative. Explain this observation with reference to Figure 14.17.

13.110 The following processes were all discussed in Chapter 9, "Chemistry of the Environment." Estimate whether the entropy of the system increases or decreases during each process: **(a)** photodissociation of $O_2(g)$, **(b)** formation of ozone from oxygen molecules and oxygen atoms, **(c)** diffusion of CFCs into the stratosphere, **(d)** desalination of water by reverse osmosis.

13.111 Carbon disulfide (CS_2) is a toxic, highly flammable substance. The following thermodynamic data are available for $CS_2(l)$ and $CS_2(g)$ at 298 K:

	ΔH_f° (kJ/mol)	ΔG_f° (kJ/mol)
$CS_2(l)$	89.7	65.3
$CS_2(g)$	117.4	67.2

(a) Draw the Lewis structure of the molecule. What do you predict for the bond order of the C—S bonds? **(b)** Use the VSEPR method to predict the structure of the CS_2 molecule. **(c)** Liquid CS_2 burns in O_2 with a blue flame, forming $CO_2(g)$ and $SO_2(g)$. Write a balanced equation for this reaction. **(d)** Using the data in the preceding table and in Appendix C, calculate ΔH° and ΔG° for the reaction in part (c). Is the reaction exothermic? Is it spontaneous at 298 K? **(e)** Use the data in the table to calculate ΔS° at 298 K for the vaporization of $CS_2(l)$. Is the sign of ΔS° as you would expect for a vaporization? **(f)** Using data in the table and your answer to part (e), estimate the boiling point of $CS_2(l)$. Do you predict that the substance will be a liquid or a gas at 298 K and 1 atm?

[13.112] The following data compare the standard enthalpies and free energies of formation of some crystalline ionic substances and aqueous solutions of the substances:

Substance	ΔH_f° (kJ/mol)	ΔG_f° (kJ/mol)
$AgNO_3(s)$	−124.4	−33.4
$AgNO_3(aq)$	−101.7	−34.2
$MgSO_4(s)$	−1283.7	−1169.6
$MgSO_4(aq)$	−1374.8	−1198.4

(a) Write the formation reaction for $AgNO_3(s)$. Based on this reaction, do you expect the entropy of the system to increase or decrease upon the formation of $AgNO_3(s)$? **(b)** Use ΔH_f° and ΔG_f° of $AgNO_3(s)$ to determine the entropy change upon formation of the substance. Is your answer consistent with your reasoning in part (a)? **(c)** Is dissolving $AgNO_3$ in water an exothermic or endothermic process? What about dissolving $MgSO_4$ in water? **(d)** For both $AgNO_3$ and $MgSO_4$, use the data to calculate the entropy change when the solid is dissolved in water. **(e)** Discuss the results from part (d) with reference to material presented in this chapter and in the "A Closer Look" box on page 540.

[13.113] Consider the following equilibrium:

$$N_2O_4(g) \rightleftharpoons 2 NO_2(g)$$

Thermodynamic data on these gases are given in Appendix C. You may assume that ΔH° and ΔS° do not vary with temperature. **(a)** At what temperature will an equilibrium mixture contain equal amounts of the two gases? **(b)** At what temperature will an equilibrium mixture of 1 atm total pressure contain twice as much NO_2 as N_2O_4? **(c)** At what temperature will an equilibrium mixture of 10 atm total pressure contain twice as much NO_2 as N_2O_4? **(d)** Rationalize the results from parts (b) and (c) by using Le Châtelier's principle. [Section 12.7]

[13.114] The reaction

$$SO_2(g) + 2 H_2S(g) \rightleftharpoons 3 S(s) + 2 H_2O(g)$$

is the basis of a suggested method for removal of SO_2 from power-plant stack gases. The standard free energy of each substance is given in Appendix C. **(a)** What is the equilibrium constant for the reaction at 298 K? **(b)** In principle, is this reaction a feasible method of removing SO_2? **(c)** If $P_{SO_2} = P_{H_2S}$ and the vapor pressure of water is 25 torr, calculate the equilibrium SO_2 pressure in the system at 298 K. **(d)** Would you expect the process to be more or less effective at higher temperatures?

13.115 When most elastomeric polymers (e.g., a rubber band) are stretched, the molecules become more ordered, as illustrated here:

Suppose you stretch a rubber band. **(a)** Do you expect the entropy of the system to increase or decrease? **(b)** If the rubber band were stretched isothermally, would heat need to be absorbed or emitted to maintain constant temperature? **(c)** Try this experiment: Stretch a rubber band and wait a moment. Then place the stretched rubber band on your upper lip, and let it return suddenly to its unstretched state (remember to keep holding on). What do you observe? Are your observations consistent with your answer to part (b)?

WHAT'S AHEAD

14.1 FACTORS THAT AFFECT REACTION RATES
We explore four variables that affect reaction rates: concentration, physical states of reactants, temperature, and presence of catalysts. These factors can be understood in terms of the collisions among reactant molecules that lead to reaction.

14.2 REACTION RATES
We consider how to express *reaction rates* and how reactant disappearance rates and product appearance rates are related to the reaction stoichiometry.

14.3 CONCENTRATION AND RATE LAWS
We then show that the effect of concentration on rate is expressed quantitatively by *rate laws* and show how rate laws and *rate constants* are determined experimentally.

14.4 THE CHANGE OF CONCENTRATION WITH TIME
We learn that rate equations can be written to express how concentrations change with time and look at several examples of rate equations: *zero-order*, *first-order*, and *second-order* reactions.

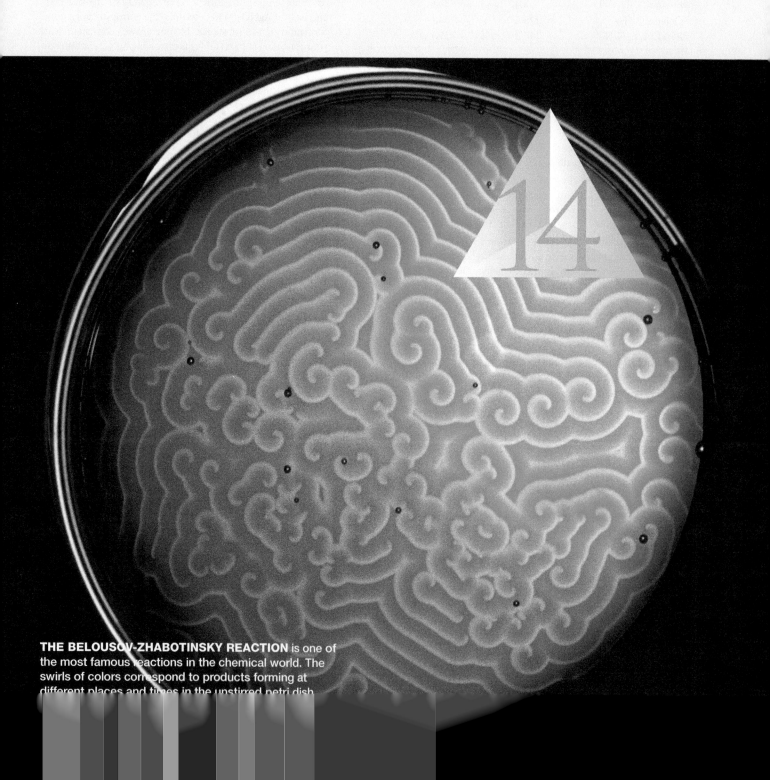

THE BELOUSOV-ZHABOTINSKY REACTION is one of the most famous reactions in the chemical world. The swirls of colors correspond to products forming at different places and times in the unstirred petri dish.

14.5 TEMPERATURE AND RATE
We next consider the effect of temperature on rate. In order to occur, most reactions require a minimum input of energy called the *activation energy*.

14.6 REACTION MECHANISMS
We then examine *reaction mechanisms,* the step-by-step molecular pathways leading from reactants to products.

14.7 CATALYSIS
We end the chapter with a discussion of how *catalysts* increase reaction rates, including a discussion of biological catalysts called *enzymes*.

CHEMICAL KINETICS

CHEMICAL REACTIONS CONVERT SUBSTANCES that have well-defined properties into other substances that have different properties. The chapter-opening photograph, for instance, shows that we can watch complex reactions as they happen in time by observing the different colors of reactants and products. In this particular case, multiple redox reactions are occurring, with the products of one reaction becoming the reactants in other reactions.

So far, we have been concerned with the beginning and end of chemical reactions: We start with certain reactants and see what products they yield. This view is useful but does not tell us what happens in the middle, that is, which chemical bonds are broken, which are formed, and in what order these events occur. The speed at which a chemical reaction occurs is called the **reaction rate**. To investigate how reactions happen, we must examine the reaction rates and the factors that influence them. Experimental information on the rate of a given reaction provides important evidence that helps us formulate a *reaction mechanism*, which is a step-by-step, molecular-level view of the pathway from reactants to products.

Some chemical reactions are complete within a fraction of a second, such as explosions, whereas others can take thousands or even millions of years, such as the formation of minerals in Earth's crust (▶ **FIGURE 14.1**).

10^{-15} s   1 s 10^9 s
(30 years) 10^{15} s
(30 million years)

Time scale

▲ **FIGURE 14.1** **Reaction rates span an enormous range of time scales.** The absorption of light by an atom or molecule is complete within one femtosecond; explosions occur within seconds; corrosion can occur over years; and the weathering of rocks can occur over millions of years.

The area of chemistry concerned with the speeds, or rates, of reactions is **chemical kinetics**. Chemical kinetics relates to how quickly a medicine works in the body, to whether the processes that form and deplete ozone in the atmosphere are in balance, and to such industrial challenges as the development of new *catalysts*, materials that speed up reactions.

Our goal in this chapter is to understand how to determine reaction rates and to consider the factors that control these rates. What factors determine how rapidly food spoils, for instance, or how does one design a fast-setting material for dental fillings? What determines the rate at which steel rusts, or how can we remove hazardous pollutants in automobile exhaust before the exhaust leaves the tailpipe? Although we will not address these specific questions, we will see that the rates of all chemical reactions are subject to the same principles.

Steel wool heated in air (about 20% O_2) glows red-hot but oxidizes to Fe_2O_3 slowly

Red-hot steel wool in 100% O_2 burns vigorously, forming Fe_2O_3 quickly

▲ **FIGURE 14.2** **Effect of concentration on reaction rate.** The difference in behavior is due to the different concentrations of O_2 in the two environments.

14.1 | FACTORS THAT AFFECT REACTION RATES

Four factors allow us to change the rate at which any particular reaction occurs:

1. **Physical state of the reactants.** Reactants must come together to react. The more readily reactant molecules collide with one another, the more rapidly they react. Most of the reactions we consider are homogeneous, involving either all gases or all liquids. When reactants are in different phases, however, we have heterogeneous conditions, and the reaction is limited by the area of contact of the reactants. Thus, heterogeneous reactions that involve solids tend to proceed faster if the surface area of the solid is increased. For example, a medicine in the form of a fine powder dissolves in the stomach and enters the blood more quickly than the same medicine in the form of a tablet.

2. **Reactant concentrations.** Most chemical reactions proceed faster if the concentration of one or more reactants is increased. For example, steel wool burns only slowly in air, which contains 20% O_2, but bursts into flame in pure oxygen (◄ **FIGURE 14.2**). As reactant concentration increases, the frequency with which the reactant molecules collide increases, leading to increased rates.

3. **Reaction temperature.** Reaction rates generally increase as temperature is increased. The bacterial reactions that spoil milk, for instance, proceed more rapidly at room temperature than at the lower temperature of a refrigerator. Increasing temperature increases the kinetic energies of molecules. ∞ (Section 8.7) As molecules move more rapidly, they collide more frequently and with higher energy, leading to increased reaction rates.

4. **The presence of a catalyst.** *Catalysts* are agents that increase reaction rates without themselves being used up. They affect the kinds of collisions (and therefore alter the mechanism) that lead to reaction. Catalysts play many crucial roles in living organisms, including ourselves.

On a molecular level, reaction rates depend on the frequency of collisions between molecules. The greater the frequency of collisions, the higher the reaction rate. For a collision to lead to a reaction, however, it must occur with sufficient energy to break bonds and with suitable orientation for new bonds to form in the proper locations. We will consider these factors as we proceed through this chapter.

> ⚠ **GIVE IT SOME THOUGHT**
>
> In a reaction involving reactants in the gas state, how does increasing the partial pressures of the gases affect the reaction rate?

14.2 | REACTION RATES

The *speed* of an event is defined as the *change* that occurs in a given *time* interval, which means that whenever we talk about speed, we necessarily bring in the notion of time. For example, the speed of a car is expressed as the change in the car's position over a certain time interval. The units of this speed are usually miles per hour—that is, the quantity that is changing (position measured in miles) divided by a time interval (measured in hours).

Similarly, the speed of a chemical reaction—its reaction rate—is the change in the concentration of reactants or products per unit of time. The units for reaction rate are usually molarity per second (M/s)—that is, the change in concentration measured in molarity divided by a time interval measured in seconds.

Let's consider the hypothetical reaction A $\longrightarrow$ B, depicted in ▼ FIGURE 14.3. Each red sphere represents 0.01 mol of A, each blue sphere represents 0.01 mol of B, and the container has a volume of 1.00 L. At the beginning of the reaction, there is 1.00 mol A, so the concentration is 1.00 mol/L $= 1.00\ M$. After 20 s the concentration of A has fallen to 0.54 M and the concentration of B has risen to 0.46 M. The sum of the concentrations is still 1.00 M because 1 mol of B is produced for each mole of A that reacts. After 40 s the concentration of A is 0.30 M and that of B is 0.70 M.

> ⚠ **GO FIGURE**
>
> If A converts completely to B, what type of molecules will the container hold?

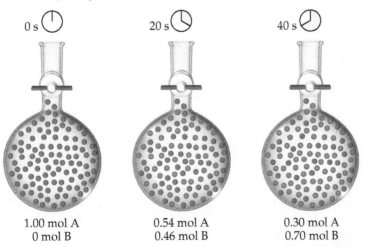

| 1.00 mol A | 0.54 mol A | 0.30 mol A |
| 0 mol B | 0.46 mol B | 0.70 mol B |

▲ **FIGURE 14.3   Progress of a hypothetical reaction A $\longrightarrow$ B.**

The rate of this reaction can be expressed either as the rate of disappearance of reactant A or as the rate of appearance of product B. The *average* rate of appearance of B over a particular time interval is given by the change in concentration of B divided by the change in time:

$$\text{Average rate of appearance of B} = \frac{\text{change in concentration of B}}{\text{change in time}}$$

$$= \frac{[B] \text{ at } t_2 - [B] \text{ at } t_1}{t_2 - t_1} = \frac{\Delta[B]}{\Delta t} \quad [14.1]$$

We use brackets around a chemical formula, as in [B], to indicate molarity. The Greek letter delta, Δ, is read "change in" and is always equal to a final value minus an initial value. ∞ (Section 10.2) The average rate of appearance of B over the 20-s interval from the beginning of the reaction ($t_1 = 0$ s to $t_2 = 20$ s) is

$$\text{Average rate} = \frac{0.46 \, M - 0.00 \, M}{20 \, \text{s} - 0 \, \text{s}} = 2.3 \times 10^{-2} \, M/\text{s}$$

We could equally well express the reaction rate in term of the reactant, A. In this case we would be describing the rate of disappearance of A, which we express as

$$\text{Average rate of disappearance of A} = -\frac{\text{change in concentration of A}}{\text{change in time}}$$

$$= -\frac{\Delta[A]}{\Delta t} \quad [14.2]$$

Notice the minus sign in this equation, which we use to indicate that the concentration of A decreases. By convention, *rates are always expressed as positive quantities.* Because [A] decreases, $\Delta[A]$ is a negative number. The minus sign we put in the equation converts the negative $\Delta[A]$ to a positive rate of disappearance.

Because one molecule of A is consumed for every molecule of B that forms, the average rate of disappearance of A equals the average rate of appearance of B:

$$\text{Average rate} = -\frac{\Delta[A]}{\Delta t} = -\frac{0.54 \, M - 1.00 \, M}{20 \, \text{s} - 0 \, \text{s}} = 2.3 \times 10^{-2} \, M/\text{s}$$

SAMPLE EXERCISE 14.1 | Calculating an Average Rate of Reaction

From the data in Figure 14.3, calculate the average rate at which A disappears over the time interval from 20 s to 40 s.

SOLUTION

Analyze We are given the concentration of A at 20 s (0.54 *M*) and at 40 s (0.30 *M*) and asked to calculate the average rate of reaction over this time interval.

Plan The average rate is given by the change in concentration, $\Delta[A]$, divided by the change in time, Δt. Because A is a reactant, a minus sign is used in the calculation to make the rate a positive quantity.

Solve $\text{Average rate} = -\frac{\Delta[A]}{\Delta t} = -\frac{0.30 \, M - 0.54 \, M}{40 \, \text{s} - 20 \, \text{s}} = 1.2 \times 10^{-2} \, M/\text{s}$

PRACTICE EXERCISE

Use the data in Figure 14.3 to calculate the average rate of appearance of B over the time interval from 0 s to 40 s.

Answer: $1.8 \times 10^{-2} \, M/\text{s}$

TABLE 14.1 • Rate Data for Reaction of C_4H_9Cl with Water		
Time, $t(s)$	**$[C_4H_9Cl](M)$**	**Average Rate (M/s)**
0.0	0.1000	1.9×10^{-4}
50.0	0.0905	1.7×10^{-4}
100.0	0.0820	1.6×10^{-4}
150.0	0.0741	1.4×10^{-4}
200.0	0.0671	1.22×10^{-4}
300.0	0.0549	1.01×10^{-4}
400.0	0.0448	0.80×10^{-4}
500.0	0.0368	0.560×10^{-4}
800.0	0.0200	
10,000	0	

Change of Rate with Time

Now let's consider the reaction between butyl chloride (C_4H_9Cl) and water to form butyl alcohol (C_4H_9OH) and hydrochloric acid:

$$C_4H_9Cl(aq) + H_2O(l) \longrightarrow C_4H_9OH(aq) + HCl(aq) \qquad [14.3]$$

Suppose we prepare a 0.1000-M aqueous solution of C_4H_9Cl and then measure the concentration of C_4H_9Cl at various times after time zero (which is the instant at which the reactants are mixed, thereby initiating the reaction). We can use the resulting data, shown in the first two columns of ▲ TABLE 14.1, to calculate the average rate of disappearance of C_4H_9Cl over various time intervals; these rates are given in the third column. Notice that the average rate decreases over each 50-s interval for the first several measurements and continues to decrease over even larger intervals through the remaining measurements. *It is typical for rates to decrease as a reaction proceeds because the concentration of reactants decreases.* The change in rate as the reaction proceeds is also seen in a graph of $[C_4H_9Cl]$ versus time (▶ FIGURE 14.4). Notice how the steepness of the curve decreases with time, indicating a decreasing reaction rate.

Instantaneous Rate

Graphs showing how the concentration of a reactant or product changes with time, such as Figure 14.4, allow us to evaluate the **instantaneous rate** of a reaction, which is the rate at a particular instant during the reaction. The instantaneous rate is determined from the slope of the curve at a particular point in time. We have drawn two tangent lines in Figure 14.4, a dashed line running through the point at $t = 0$ s and a solid line running through the point at $t = 600$ s. The slopes of these tangent lines give the instantaneous rates at these two time points.* To determine the instantaneous rate at 600 s, we construct horizontal and vertical lines to form the blue right triangle in Figure 14.4. The slope of the tangent line is the ratio of the height of the vertical side to the length of the horizontal side:

$$\text{Instantaneous rate} = -\frac{\Delta[C_4H_9Cl]}{\Delta t} = -\frac{(0.017 - 0.042)\ M}{(800 - 400)s}$$
$$= 6.3 \times 10^{-5}\ M/s$$

GO FIGURE

How does the instantaneous rate of reaction change as the reaction proceeds?

$$C_4H_9Cl(aq) + H_2O(l) \longrightarrow C_4H_9OH(aq) + HCl(aq)$$

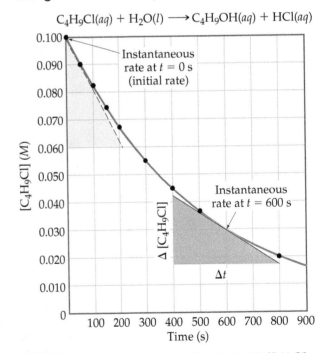

▲ FIGURE 14.4   **Concentration of butyl chloride (C_4H_9Cl) as a function of time.**

*You may wish to review graphical determination of slopes in Appendix A. If you are familiar with calculus, you may recognize that the average rate approaches the instantaneous rate as the time interval approaches zero. This limit, in the notation of calculus, is represented as $-d[C_4H_9Cl]/dt$.

In discussions that follow, the term *rate* means instantaneous rate unless indicated otherwise. The instantaneous rate at $t = 0$ is called the *initial rate* of the reaction. To understand the difference between average and instantaneous rates, imagine you have just driven 98 mi in 2.0 hr. Your average speed for the trip is 49 mi/hr, but your instantaneous speed at any moment during the trip is the speedometer reading at that moment.

SAMPLE EXERCISE 14.2 | **Calculating an Instantaneous Rate of Reaction**

Using Figure 14.4, calculate the instantaneous rate of disappearance of C_4H_9Cl at $t = 0$ s (the initial rate).

SOLUTION

Analyze We are asked to determine an instantaneous rate from a graph of reactant concentration versus time.

Plan To obtain the instantaneous rate at $t = 0$ s, we must determine the slope of the curve at $t = 0$. The tangent is drawn on the graph as the hypotenuse of the tan triangle. The slope of this straight line equals the change in the vertical axis divided by the corresponding change in the horizontal axis (that is, change in molarity over change in time).

Solve The tangent line falls from $[C_4H_9Cl] = 0.100$ M to 0.060 M in the time change from 0 s to 210 s. Thus, the initial rate is

$$\text{Rate} = -\frac{\Delta[C_4H_9Cl]}{\Delta t} = -\frac{(0.060 - 0.100)\ M}{(210 - 0)\ s} = 1.9 \times 10^{-4}\ M/s$$

PRACTICE EXERCISE

Using Figure 14.4, determine the instantaneous rate of disappearance of C_4H_9Cl at $t = 300$ s.

Answer: $1.1 \times 10^{-4}\ M/s$

 GIVE IT SOME THOUGHT

What is the difference between average rate and instantaneous rate? In a given reaction, can these two rates ever have the same numeric value?

Reaction Rates and Stoichiometry

During our discussion of the hypothetical reaction A $\longrightarrow$ B, we saw that the stoichiometry requires that the rate of disappearance of A equal the rate of appearance of B. Likewise, the stoichiometry of Equation 14.3 indicates that 1 mol of C_4H_9OH is produced for each mole of C_4H_9Cl consumed. Therefore, the rate of appearance of C_4H_9OH equals the rate of disappearance of C_4H_9Cl:

$$\text{Rate} = -\frac{\Delta[C_4H_9Cl]}{\Delta t} = \frac{\Delta[C_4H_9OH]}{\Delta t}$$

What happens when the stoichiometric relationships are not one-to-one? For example, consider the reaction $2\ HI(g) \rightarrow H_2(g) + I_2(g)$. We can measure either the rate of disappearance of HI or the rate of appearance of either H_2 or I_2. Because 2 mol of HI disappear for each mole of H_2 or I_2 that forms, the rate of disappearance of HI is twice the rate of appearance of either H_2 or I_2. How do we decide which number to use for the rate of the reaction? Depending on whether we monitor HI, I_2, or H_2, the rates can differ by a factor of two. To fix this problem, we need to take into account the reaction stoichiometry. To arrive at a number for the reaction rate that does not depend on which component we measured, we must divide the rate of disappearance of HI by 2 (its coefficient in the balanced chemical equation):

$$\text{Rate} = -\frac{1}{2}\frac{\Delta[HI]}{\Delta t} = \frac{\Delta[H_2]}{\Delta t} = \frac{\Delta[I_2]}{\Delta t}$$

In general, for the reaction

$$a\,A + b\,B \longrightarrow c\,C + d\,D$$

the rate is given by

$$\text{Rate} = -\frac{1}{a}\frac{\Delta[A]}{\Delta t} = -\frac{1}{b}\frac{\Delta[B]}{\Delta t} = \frac{1}{c}\frac{\Delta[C]}{\Delta t} = \frac{1}{d}\frac{\Delta[D]}{\Delta t} \qquad [14.4]$$

When we speak of the rate of a reaction without specifying a particular reactant or product, we mean the rate in this sense.*

SAMPLE EXERCISE 14.3 | **Relating Rates at Which Products Appear and Reactants Disappear**

(a) How is the rate at which ozone disappears related to the rate at which oxygen appears in the reaction $2\,O_3(g) \longrightarrow 3\,O_2(g)$?
(b) If the rate at which O_2 appears, $\Delta[O_2]/\Delta t$, is $6.0 \times 10^{-5}\ M/s$ at a particular instant, at what rate is O_3 disappearing at this same time, $-\Delta[O_3]/\Delta t$?

SOLUTION

Analyze We are given a balanced chemical equation and asked to relate the rate of appearance of the product to the rate of disappearance of the reactant.

Plan We can use the coefficients in the chemical equation as shown in Equation 14.4 to express the relative rates of reactions.

Solve

(a) Using the coefficients in the balanced equation and the relationship given by Equation 14.4, we have:

$$\text{Rate} = -\frac{1}{2}\frac{\Delta[O_3]}{\Delta t} = \frac{1}{3}\frac{\Delta[O_2]}{\Delta t}$$

(b) Solving the equation from part (a) for the rate at which O_3 disappears, $-\Delta[O_3]/\Delta t$, we have:

$$-\frac{\Delta[O_3]}{\Delta t} = \frac{2}{3}\frac{\Delta[O_2]}{\Delta t} = \frac{2}{3}(6.0 \times 10^{-5}\ M/s) = 4.0 \times 10^{-5}\ M/s$$

Check We can apply a stoichiometric factor to convert the O_2 formation rate to the O_3 disappearance rate:

$$-\frac{\Delta[O_3]}{\Delta t} = \left(6.0 \times 10^{-5}\frac{\text{mol }O_2/L}{s}\right)\left(\frac{2\text{ mol }O_3}{3\text{ mol }O_2}\right) = 4.0 \times 10^{-5}\frac{\text{mol }O_3/L}{s}$$
$$= 4.0 \times 10^{-5}\ M/s$$

PRACTICE EXERCISE

If the rate of decomposition of N_2O_5 in the reaction $2\,N_2O_5(g) \longrightarrow 4\,NO_2(g) + O_2(g)$ at a particular instant is $4.2 \times 10^{-7}\ M/s$, what is the rate of appearance of (a) NO_2 and (b) O_2 at that instant?

Answers: (a) $8.4 \times 10^{-7}\ M/s$, (b) $2.1 \times 10^{-7}\ M/s$

14.3 | CONCENTRATION AND RATE LAWS

One way of studying the effect of concentration on reaction rate is to determine the way in which the initial rate of a reaction depends on the initial concentrations. For example, we might study the rate of the reaction

$$NH_4^+(aq) + NO_2^-(aq) \longrightarrow N_2(g) + 2\,H_2O(l)$$

by measuring the concentration of NH_4^+ or NO_2^- as a function of time or by measuring the volume of N_2 collected as a function of time. Because the stoichiometric coefficients on NH_4^+, NO_2^-, and N_2 are the same, all of these rates are the same.

▼ TABLE 14.2 shows that changing the initial concentration of either reactant changes the initial reaction rate. If we double $[NH_4^+]$ while holding $[NO_2^-]$ constant,

TABLE 14.2 • Rate Data for the Reaction of Ammonium and Nitrite Ions in Water at 25 °C

Experiment Number	Initial NH_4^+ Concentration (M)	Initial NO_2^- Concentration (M)	Observed Initial Rate (M/s)
1	0.0100	0.200	5.4×10^{-7}
2	0.0200	0.200	10.8×10^{-7}
3	0.0400	0.200	21.5×10^{-7}
4	0.200	0.0202	10.8×10^{-7}
5	0.200	0.0404	21.6×10^{-7}
6	0.200	0.0808	43.3×10^{-7}

---

*Equation 14.4 does not hold true if substances other than C and D are formed in significant amounts. For example, sometimes intermediate substances build in concentration before forming the final products. In that case, the relationship between the rate of disappearance of reactants and the rate of appearance of products is not given by Equation 14.4. All reactions whose rates we consider in this chapter obey Equation 14.4.

the rate doubles (compare experiments 1 and 2). If we increase $[NH_4^+]$ by a factor of 4 but leave $[NO_2^-]$ unchanged (experiments 1 and 3), the rate changes by a factor of 4, and so forth. These results indicate that the initial reaction rate is proportional to $[NH_4^+]$. When $[NO_2^-]$ is similarly varied while $[NH_4^+]$ is held constant, the rate is affected in the same manner. Thus, the rate is also directly proportional to the concentration of NO_2^-.

A CLOSER LOOK

USING SPECTROSCOPIC METHODS TO MEASURE REACTION RATES

A variety of techniques can be used to monitor reactant and product concentration during a reaction, including spectroscopic methods, which rely on the ability of substances to absorb (or emit) light. Spectroscopic kinetic studies are often performed with the reaction mixture in the sample compartment of a *spectrometer*, an instrument that measures the amount of light transmitted or absorbed by a sample at different wavelengths. For kinetic studies, the spectrometer is set to measure the light absorbed at a wavelength characteristic of one of the reactants or products. In the decomposition of $HI(g)$ into $H_2(g)$ and $I_2(g)$, for example, both HI and H_2 are colorless, whereas I_2 is violet. During the reaction, the violet color of the reaction mixture gets deeper as I_2 forms. Thus, visible light of appropriate wavelength can be used to monitor the reaction (▶ FIGURE 14.5).

▼ FIGURE 14.6 shows the components of a spectrometer. The spectrometer measures the amount of light absorbed by the sample by comparing the intensity of the light emitted from the light source with the intensity of the light transmitted through the sample, for various wavelengths. As the concentration of I_2 increases and its color becomes more intense, the amount of light absorbed by the reaction mixture increases, as Figure 14.5 shows, causing less light to reach the detector.

Beer's law relates the amount of light absorbed to the concentration of the absorbing substance:

$$A = \epsilon bc \qquad [14.5]$$

In this equation, A is the measured absorbance, ϵ is the extinction coefficient (a characteristic of the substance being monitored at a given wavelength of light), b is the path length through which the

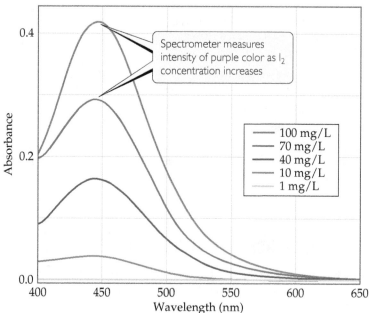

Spectrometer measures intensity of purple color as I_2 concentration increases

— 100 mg/L
— 70 mg/L
— 40 mg/L
— 10 mg/L
— 1 mg/L

▲ FIGURE 14.5 **Visible spectra of I_2 at different concentrations.**

light passes, and c is the molar concentration of the absorbing substance. Thus, the concentration is directly proportional to absorbance. Many chemical and pharmaceutical companies routinely use Beer's law to calculate the concentration of purified solutions of the compounds that they make.

RELATED EXERCISES: 14.107, 14.108

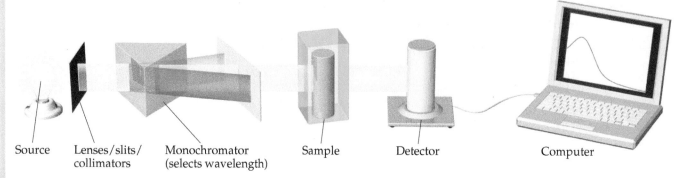

Source   Lenses/slits/   Monochromator   Sample   Detector   Computer
          collimators   (selects wavelength)

▲ FIGURE 14.6 **Components of a spectrometer.**

We express the way in which the rate depends on the reactant concentrations by the equation

$$\text{Rate} = k[\text{NH}_4^+][\text{NO}_2^-] \qquad [14.6]$$

An equation such as Equation 14.6, which shows how the rate depends on reactant concentrations, is called a **rate law**. For the general reaction

$$a\,\text{A} + b\,\text{B} \longrightarrow c\,\text{C} + d\,\text{D}$$

the rate law generally has the form

$$\text{Rate} = k[\text{A}]^m[\text{B}]^n \qquad [14.7]$$

The constant k is called the **rate constant**. The magnitude of k changes with temperature and therefore determines how temperature affects rate, as we will see in Section 14.5. The exponents m and n are typically small whole numbers. As we will learn shortly, if we know m and n for a reaction, we can gain great insight into the individual steps that occur during the reaction.

 GIVE IT SOME THOUGHT
How do reaction rate, rate constant, and rate law differ?

Once we know the rate law for a reaction and the reaction rate for a set of reactant concentrations, we can calculate the value of k. For example, using the values for experiment 1 in Table 14.2, we can substitute into Equation 14.6:

$$5.4 \times 10^{-7}\ M/s = k(0.0100\ M)(0.200\ M)$$

$$k = \frac{5.4 \times 10^{-7}\ M/s}{(0.0100\ M)(0.200\ M)} = 2.7 \times 10^{-4}\ M^{-1}\text{s}^{-1}$$

You may wish to verify that this same value of k is obtained using any of the other experimental results in Table 14.2.

Once we have both the rate law and the k value for a reaction, we can calculate the reaction rate for any set of concentrations. For example, using Equation 14.7 with $k = 2.7 \times 10^{-4}\ M^{-1}\,\text{s}^{-1}$, $m = 1$, and $n = 1$, we can calculate the rate for $[\text{NH}_4^+] = 0.100\ M$ and $[\text{NO}_2^-] = 0.100\ M$:

$$\text{Rate} = (2.7 \times 10^{-4}\ M^{-1}\,\text{s}^{-1})(0.100\ M)\,(0.100\ M) = 2.7 \times 10^{-6}\ M/s$$

GIVE IT SOME THOUGHT
Does the rate constant have the same units as the rate? Explain your answer.

Reaction Orders: The Exponents in the Rate Law

The rate law for most reactions has the form

$$\text{Rate} = k[\text{reactant 1}]^m[\text{reactant 2}]^n \ldots \qquad [14.8]$$

The exponents m and n are called **reaction orders**. For example, consider again the rate law for the reaction of NH_4^+ with NO_2^-:

$$\text{Rate} = k[\text{NH}_4^+][\text{NO}_2^-]$$

Because the exponent of $[\text{NH}_4^+]$ is 1, the rate is *first order* in NH_4^+. The rate is also first order in NO_2^-. (The exponent 1 is not shown in rate laws.) The **overall reaction order** is the sum of the orders with respect to each reactant represented in the rate law. Thus, for the $\text{NH}_4^+ - \text{NO}_2^-$ reaction, the rate law has an overall reaction order of $1 + 1 = 2$, and the reaction is *second order overall*.

The exponents in a rate law indicate how the rate is affected by each reactant concentration. Because the rate at which NH_4^+ reacts with NO_2^- depends on $[\text{NH}_4^+]$ raised to the first power, the rate doubles when $[\text{NH}_4^+]$ doubles, triples when $[\text{NH}_4^+]$ triples, and so forth. Doubling or tripling $[\text{NO}_2^-]$ likewise doubles or triples the rate. If a rate law is second order with respect to a reactant, $[A]^2$, then doubling the concentration of that substance causes the reaction rate to quadruple because $[2]^2 = 4$, whereas tripling the concentration causes the rate to increase ninefold: $[3]^2 = 9$.

The following are some additional examples of experimentally determined rate laws:

$$2\,N_2O_5(g) \longrightarrow 4\,NO_2(g) + O_2(g) \quad \text{Rate} = k[N_2O_5] \qquad [14.9]$$

$$CHCl_3(g) + Cl_2(g) \longrightarrow CCl_4(g) + HCl(g) \quad \text{Rate} = k[CHCl_3][Cl_2]^{1/2} \qquad [14.10]$$

$$H_2(g) + I_2(g) \longrightarrow 2\,HI(g) \qquad \text{Rate} = k[H_2][I_2] \qquad [14.11]$$

Although the exponents in a rate law are sometimes the same as the coefficients in the balanced equation, this is not necessarily the case, as Equations 14.9 and 14.10 show. For any reaction, *the rate law must be determined experimentally*. In most rate laws, reaction orders are 0, 1, or 2. However, we also occasionally encounter rate laws in which the reaction order is fractional (such as Equation 14.10) or even negative.

GIVE IT SOME THOUGHT

The experimentally determined rate law for the reaction $2\,NO(g) + 2\,H_2(g) \longrightarrow N_2(g) + 2\,H_2O(g)$ is rate = $k[NO]^2[H_2]$.
a. What are the reaction orders in this rate law?
b. Does doubling the concentration of NO have the same effect on rate as doubling the concentration of H_2?

SAMPLE EXERCISE 14.4	Relating a Rate Law to the Effect of Concentration on Rate

Consider a reaction $A + B \longrightarrow C$ for which rate = $k[A][B]^2$. Each of the following boxes represents a reaction mixture in which A is shown as red spheres and B as purple ones. Rank these mixtures in order of increasing rate of reaction.

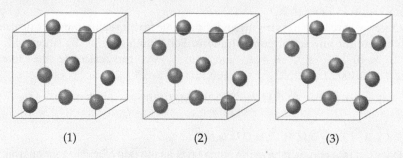

(1)   (2)   (3)

SOLUTION

Analyze We are given three boxes containing different numbers of spheres representing mixtures containing different reactant concentrations. We are asked to use the given rate law and the compositions of the boxes to rank the mixtures in order of increasing reaction rates.

Plan Because all three boxes have the same volume, we can put the number of spheres of each kind into the rate law and calculate the rate for each box.

Solve

Box 1 contains 5 red spheres and 5 purple spheres, giving the following rate:

$$\text{Box 1: Rate} = k(5)(5)^2 = 125k$$

Box 2 contains 7 red spheres and 3 purple spheres:

$$\text{Box 2: Rate} = k(7)(3)^2 = 63k$$

Box 3 contains 3 red spheres and 7 purple spheres:

$$\text{Box 3: Rate} = k(3)(7)^2 = 147k$$

The slowest rate is $63k$ (box 2), and the highest is $147k$ (box 3). Thus, the rates vary in the order $2 < 1 < 3$.

Check Each box contains 10 spheres. The rate law indicates that in this case [B] has a greater influence on rate than [A] because B has a higher reaction order. Hence, the mixture with the highest concentration of B (most purple spheres) should react fastest. This analysis confirms the order $2 < 1 < 3$.

PRACTICE EXERCISE
Assuming that rate $= k[A][B]$, rank the mixtures represented in this Sample Exercise in order of increasing rate.
Answer: $2 = 3 < 1$

Magnitudes and Units of Rate Constants

If chemists want to compare reactions to evaluate which ones are relatively fast and which ones are relatively slow, the quantity of interest is the rate constant. A good general rule is that a large value of k ($\sim 10^9$ or higher) means a fast reaction and a small value of k (10 or lower) means a slow reaction.

 GIVE IT SOME THOUGHT
What does it mean if k is 0?

The units of the rate constant depend on the overall reaction order of the rate law. In a reaction that is second order overall, for example, the units of the rate constant must satisfy the equation:

$$\text{Units of rate} = (\text{units of rate constant})(\text{units of concentration})^2$$

Hence, in our usual units of molarity for concentration and seconds for time, we have

$$\text{Units of rate constant} = \frac{\text{units of rate}}{(\text{units of concentration})^2} = \frac{M/s}{M^2} = M^{-1}\,s^{-1}$$

SAMPLE EXERCISE 14.5 **Determining Reaction Orders and Units for Rate Constants**

(a) What are the overall reaction orders for the reactions described in Equations 14.9 and 14.10? **(b)** What are the units of the rate constant for the rate law in Equation 14.9?

SOLUTION

Analyze We are given two rate laws and asked to express **(a)** the overall reaction order for each and **(b)** the units for the rate constant for the first reaction.

Plan The overall reaction order is the sum of the exponents in the rate law. The units for the rate constant, k, are found by using the normal units for rate (M/s) and concentration (M) in the rate law and applying algebra to solve for k.

Solve
(a) The rate of the reaction in Equation 14.9 is first order in N_2O_5 and first order overall. The reaction in Equation 14.10 is first order in $CHCl_3$ and one-half order in Cl_2. The overall reaction order is three halves.

(b) For the rate law for Equation 14.9, we have

$$\text{Units of rate} = (\text{units of rate constant})(\text{units of concentration})$$

so

$$\text{Units of rate constant} = \frac{\text{units of rate}}{\text{units of concentration}} = \frac{M/s}{M} = s^{-1}$$

Notice that the units of the rate constant change as the overall order of the reaction changes.

PRACTICE EXERCISE
(a) What is the reaction order of the reactant H_2 in Equation 14.11? **(b)** What are the units of the rate constant for Equation 14.11?
Answers: (a) 1, **(b)** $M^{-1}\,s^{-1}$

Using Initial Rates to Determine Rate Laws

We have seen that the rate law for most reactions has the general form

$$\text{Rate} = k[\text{reactant 1}]^m[\text{reactant 2}]^n \ldots$$

Thus, the task of determining the rate law becomes one of determining the reaction orders, m and n. In most reactions the reaction orders are 0, 1, or 2. If a reaction is zero order in a particular reactant, changing the concentration of that reactant has no effect on rate (as long as some of the reactant is present) because any concentration raised to the zero power equals 1. On the other hand, when a reaction is first order in a reactant, changes in the concentration of that reactant produce proportional changes in the rate. Thus, doubling the concentration will double the rate, and so forth. Finally, when the rate law is second order in a particular reactant, doubling its concentration increases the rate by a factor of $2^2 = 4$, tripling its concentration causes the rate to increase by a factor of $3^2 = 9$, and so forth.

In working with rate laws, it is important to realize that the *rate* of a reaction depends on concentration but the *rate constant* does not. As we will see later in this chapter, the rate constant (and hence the reaction rate) are affected by temperature and by the presence of a catalyst.

SAMPLE EXERCISE 14.6 | **Determining a Rate Law from Initial Rate Data**

The initial rate of a reaction $A + B \longrightarrow C$ was measured for several different starting concentrations of A and B, and the results are as follows:

Experiment Number	[A] (M)	[B] (M)	Initial Rate (M/s)
1	0.100	0.100	4.0×10^{-5}
2	0.100	0.200	4.0×10^{-5}
3	0.200	0.100	16.0×10^{-5}

Using these data, determine (a) the rate law for the reaction, (b) the rate constant, (c) the rate of the reaction when [A] = 0.050 M and [B] = 0.100 M.

SOLUTION

Analyze We are given a table of data that relates concentrations of reactants with initial rates of reaction and asked to determine (a) the rate law, (b) the rate constant, and (c) the rate of reaction for a set of concentrations not listed in the table.

Plan

(a) We assume that the rate law has the following form: Rate = $k[A]^m[B]^n$. So we must use the given data to deduce the reaction orders m and n by determining how changes in the concentration change the rate. (b) Once we know m and n, we can use the rate law and one of the sets of data to determine the rate constant k. (c) Now that we know both the rate constant and the reaction orders, we can use the rate law with the given concentrations to calculate rate.

Solve

(a) If we compare experiments 1 and 2, we see that [A] is held constant and [B] is doubled. Thus, this pair of experiments shows how [B] affects the rate, allowing us to deduce the order of the rate law with respect to B. Because the rate remains the same when [B] is doubled, the concentration of B has no effect on the reaction rate. The rate law is therefore zero order in B (that is, $n = 0$).

In experiments 1 and 3, [B] is held constant, so these data show how [A] affects rate. Holding [B] constant while doubling [A] increases the rate fourfold. This result indicates that rate is proportional to $[A]^2$ (that is, the reaction is second order in A). Hence, the rate law is

$$\text{Rate} = k[A]^2[B]^0 = k[A]^2$$

(b) Using the rate law and the data from experiment 1, we have

$$k = \frac{\text{rate}}{[A]^2} = \frac{4.0 \times 10^{-5}\,M/s}{(0.100\,M)^2} = 4.0 \times 10^{-3}\,M^{-1}\,s^{-1}$$

(c) Using the rate law from part (a) and the rate constant from part (b), we have

$$\text{Rate} = k[A]^2 = (4.0 \times 10^{-3}\,M^{-1}\,s^{-1})(0.050\,M)^2 = 1.0 \times 10^{-5}\,M/s$$

Because [B] is not part of the rate law, it is irrelevant to the rate if there is at least some B present to react with A.

Check A good way to check our rate law is to use the concentrations in experiment 2 or 3 and see if we can correctly calculate the rate. Using data from experiment 3, we have

$$\text{Rate} = k[A]^2 = (4.0 \times 10^{-3}\ M^{-1}\ s^{-1})(0.200\ M)^2 = 1.6 \times 10^{-4}\ M/s$$

Thus, the rate law correctly reproduces the data, giving both the correct number and the correct units for the rate.

PRACTICE EXERCISE

The following data were measured for the reaction of nitric oxide with hydrogen:

$$2\ NO(g) + 2\ H_2(g) \longrightarrow N_2(g) + 2\ H_2O(g)$$

Experiment Number	[NO] (M)	[H₂] (M)	Initial Rate (M/s)
1	0.10	0.10	1.23×10^{-3}
2	0.10	0.20	2.46×10^{-3}
3	0.20	0.10	4.92×10^{-3}

(a) Determine the rate law for this reaction. **(b)** Calculate the rate constant. **(c)** Calculate the rate when [NO] = 0.050 M and [H₂] = 0.150 M.
Answers: **(a)** rate = $k[NO]^2[H_2]$, **(b)** $k = 1.2\ M^{-2}\ s^{-1}$ **(c)** rate = $4.5 \times 10^{-4}\ M/s$

14.4 | THE CHANGE OF CONCENTRATION WITH TIME

The rate laws we have examined so far enable us to calculate the rate of a reaction from the rate constant and reactant concentrations. These rate laws can also be converted into equations that show the relationship between concentrations of reactants or products and time. The mathematics required to accomplish this conversion involves calculus. We do not expect you to be able to perform the calculus operations, but you should be able to use the resulting equations. We will apply this conversion to three of the simplest rate laws: those that are first order overall, those that are second order overall, and those that are zero order overall.

First-Order Reactions

A **first-order reaction** is one whose rate depends on the concentration of a single reactant raised to the first power. For a reaction of the type A → products, the rate law may be first order:

$$\text{Rate} = -\frac{\Delta[A]}{\Delta t} = k[A]$$

This form of a rate law, which expresses how rate depends on concentration, is called the *differential rate law*. Using an operation from calculus called integration, this relationship can be transformed into an equation that relates the initial concentration of A, $[A]_0$, to its concentration at any other time t, $[A]_t$:

$$\ln[A]_t - \ln[A]_0 = -kt \qquad \text{or} \qquad \ln\frac{[A]_t}{[A]_0} = -kt \qquad [14.12]$$

This form of the rate law is called the *integrated rate law*. The function "ln" in Equation 14.12 is the natural logarithm (Appendix A.2). Equation 14.12 can also be rearranged to

$$\ln[A]_t = -kt + \ln[A]_0 \qquad [14.13]$$

Equations 14.12 and 14.13 can be used with any concentration units as long as the units are the same for both $[A]_t$ and $[A]_0$.

For a first-order reaction, Equation 14.12 or 14.13 can be used in several ways. Given any three of the following quantities, we can solve for the fourth: k, t, $[A]_0$, and $[A]_t$. Thus, you can use these equations to determine (1) the concentration of a reactant remaining at any time after the reaction has started, (2) the time interval required for a given fraction of a sample to react, or (3) the time interval required for a reactant concentration to fall to a certain level.

SAMPLE EXERCISE 14.7 | **Using the Integrated First-Order Rate Law**

The decomposition of a certain insecticide in water at 12 °C follows first-order kinetics with a rate constant of 1.45 yr^{-1}. A quantity of this insecticide is washed into a lake on June 1, leading to a concentration of 5.0×10^{-7} g/cm^3. Assume that the average temperature of the lake is 12 °C. **(a)** What is the concentration of the insecticide on June 1 of the following year? **(b)** How long will it take for the insecticide concentration to decrease to 3.0×10^{-7} g/cm^3?

SOLUTION

Analyze We are given the rate constant for a reaction that obeys first-order kinetics, as well as information about concentrations and times, and asked to calculate how much reactant (insecticide) remains after one year. We must also determine the time interval needed to reach a particular insecticide concentration. Because the exercise gives time in (a) and asks for time in (b), we know that the integrated rate law, Equation 14.13, is required.

Plan

(a) We are given $k = 1.45$ yr^{-1}, $t = 1.00$ yr and $[\text{insecticide}]_0 = 5.0 \times 10^{-7}$ g/cm^3, and so Equation 14.13 can be solved for $[\text{insecticide}]_t$. **(b)** We have $k = 1.45$ yr^{-1}, $[\text{insecticide}]_0 = 5.0 \times 10^{-7}$ g/cm^3, and $[\text{insecticide}]_t = 3.0 \times 10^{-7}$ g/cm^3, and so we can solve Equation 14.13 for time, t.

Solve

(a) Substituting the known quantities into Equation 14.13, we have

$$\ln[\text{insecticide}]_{t=1\,\text{yr}} = -(1.45\,\text{yr}^{-1})(1.00\,\text{yr}) + \ln(5.0 \times 10^{-7})$$

We use the ln function on a calculator to evaluate the second term on the right, giving

$$\ln[\text{insecticide}]_{t=1\,\text{yr}} = -1.45 + (-14.51) = -15.96$$

To obtain $[\text{insecticide}]_{t=1\,\text{yr}}$, we use the inverse natural logarithm, or e^x, function on the calculator:

$$[\text{insecticide}]_{t=1\,\text{yr}} = e^{-15.96} = 1.2 \times 10^{-7}\,\text{g/cm}^3$$

Note that the concentration units for $[A]_t$ and $[A]_0$ must be the same.

(b) Again substituting into Equation 14.13, with $[\text{insecticide}]_t = 3.0 \times 10^{-7}$ g/cm^3, gives

$$\ln(3.0 \times 10^{-7}) = -(1.45\,\text{yr}^{-1})(t) + \ln(5.0 \times 10^{-7})$$

Solving for t gives

$$t = -[\ln(3.0 \times 10^{-7}) - \ln(5.0 \times 10^{-7})]/1.45\,\text{yr}^{-1}$$
$$= -(-15.02 + 14.51)/1.45\,\text{yr}^{-1} = 0.35\,\text{yr}$$

Check In part **(a)** the concentration remaining after 1.00 yr (that is, 1.2×10^{-7} g/cm^3) is less than the original concentration (5.0×10^{-7} g/cm^3), as it should be. In **(b)** the given concentration (3.0×10^{-7} g/cm^3) is greater than that remaining after 1.00 yr, indicating that the time must be less than a year. Thus, $t = 0.35$ yr is a reasonable answer.

PRACTICE EXERCISE

The decomposition of dimethyl ether, $(CH_3)_2O$, at 510 °C is a first-order process with a rate constant of 6.8×10^{-4} s^{-1}:

$$(CH_3)_2O(g) \longrightarrow CH_4(g) + H_2(g) + CO(g)$$

If the initial pressure of $(CH_3)_2O$ is 135 torr, what is its pressure after 1420 s?

Answer: 51 torr

Equation 14.13 can be used to verify whether a reaction is first order and to determine its rate constant. This equation has the form of the general equation for a straight line, $y = mx + b$, in which m is the slope and b is the y-intercept of the line (Appendix A.4):

$$\ln[A]_t = -kt + \ln[A]_0$$
$$y = mx + b$$

For a first-order reaction, therefore, a graph of $\ln[A]_t$ versus time gives a straight line with a slope of $-k$ and a y-intercept of $\ln[A]_0$. A reaction that is not first order will not yield a straight line.

As an example, consider the conversion of methyl isonitrile (CH_3NC) to its isomer acetonitrile (CH_3CN) (▶ FIGURE 14.7). Because experiments show that the reaction is first order, we can write the rate equation:

$$\ln[CH_3NC]_t = -kt + \ln[CH_3NC]_0$$

We run the reaction at a temperature at which methyl isonitrile is a gas (199 °C), and ▼ FIGURE 14.8(a) shows how the pressure of this gas varies with time. We can use pressure as a unit of concentration for a gas because we know from the ideal-gas law the pressure is directly proportional to the number of moles per unit volume. Figure 14.8(b) shows that a plot of the natural logarithm of the pressure versus time is a straight line. The slope of this line is $-5.1 \times 10^{-5} \, s^{-1}$. (You should verify this for yourself, remembering that your result may vary slightly from ours because of inaccuracies associated with reading the graph.) Because the slope of the line equals $-k$, the rate constant for this reaction equals $5.1 \times 10^{-5} \, s^{-1}$.

Second-Order Reactions

A **second-order reaction** is one whose rate depends either on a reactant concentration raised to the second power or on the concentrations of two reactants each raised to the first power. For simplicity, let's consider reactions of the type A ⟶ products or A + B ⟶ products that are second order in just one reactant, A:

$$\text{Rate} = -\frac{\Delta[A]}{\Delta t} = k[A]^2$$

With the use of calculus, this differential rate law can be used to derive the integrated rate law

$$\frac{1}{[A]_t} = kt + \frac{1}{[A]_0} \qquad [14.14]$$

This equation, like Equation 14.13, has four variables, k, t, $[A]_0$, and $[A]_t$, and any one of these can be calculated knowing the other three. Equation 14.14 also has the form of a straight line ($y = mx + b$). If the reaction is second order, a plot of $1/[A]_t$ versus t yields a straight line with slope k and y-intercept $1/[A]_0$. One way to distinguish between first- and second-order rate laws is to graph both $\ln[A]_t$ and $1/[A]_t$ against t. If the $\ln[A]_t$ plot is linear, the reaction is first order; if the $1/[A]_t$ plot is linear, the reaction is second order.

Methyl isonitrile

Acetonitrile

▲ FIGURE 14.7   **The first-order reaction of CH_3NC conversion into CH_3CN.**

⚠ GO FIGURE

What can you conclude from the fact that the plot of ln *P* versus *t* is linear?

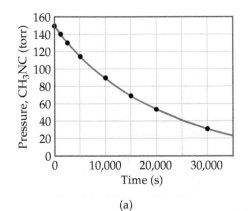

(a)

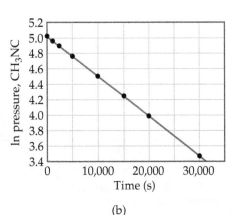

(b)

◀ FIGURE 14.8   **Kinetic data for conversion of methyl isonitrile into acetonitrile.**

| SAMPLE EXERCISE 14.8 | Determining Reaction Order from the Integrated Rate Law |

The following data were obtained for the gas-phase decomposition of nitrogen dioxide at 300 °C, $NO_2(g) \longrightarrow NO(g) + \frac{1}{2} O_2(g)$:

Time (s)	$[NO_2]$ (M)
0.0	0.01000
50.0	0.00787
100.0	0.00649
200.0	0.00481
300.0	0.00380

Is the reaction first or second order in NO_2?

SOLUTION

Analyze We are given the concentrations of a reactant at various times during a reaction and asked to determine whether the reaction is first or second order.

Plan We can plot $\ln[NO_2]$ and $1/[NO_2]$ against time. One or the other will be linear, indicating whether the reaction is first or second order.

Solve To graph $\ln[NO_2]$ and $1/[NO_2]$ against time, we will first prepare the following table from the data given:

Time (s)	$[NO_2]$ (M)	$\ln[NO_2]$	$1/[NO_2]$
0.0	0.01000	−4.605	100
50.0	0.00787	−4.845	127
100.0	0.00649	−5.037	154
200.0	0.00481	−5.337	208
300.0	0.00380	−5.573	263

As ▼ FIGURE 14.9 shows, only the plot of $1/[NO_2]$ versus time is linear. Thus, the reaction obeys a second-order rate law: Rate $= k[NO_2]^2$. From the slope of this straight-line graph, we determine that $k = 0.543\ M^{-1}\ s^{-1}$ for the disappearance of NO_2.

PRACTICE EXERCISE

The decomposition of NO_2 discussed in the Sample Exercise is second order in NO_2 with $k = 0.543\ M^{-1}\ s^{-1}$. If the initial concentration of NO_2 in a closed vessel is 0.0500, what is the concentration of this reactant after 0.500 hr?
Answer: $[NO_2] = 1.00 \times 10^{-3}\ M$

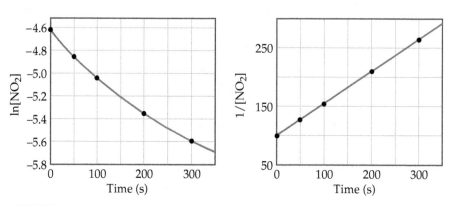

▲ FIGURE 14.9   **Kinetic data for decomposition of NO_2.**

Zero-Order Reactions

We've seen that in a first-order reaction the concentration of a reactant A decreases non-linearly, as shown by the red curve in ▶ FIGURE 14.10. As [A] declines, the *rate* at which it disappears declines in proportion. A **zero-order reaction** is one in which the rate of disappearance of A is *independent* of [A]. The rate law for a zero-order reaction is

$$\text{Rate} = \frac{-\Delta[A]}{\Delta t} = k$$

The integrated rate law for a zero-order reaction is

$$[A]_t = -kt + [A]_0$$

where $[A]_t$ is the concentration of A at time t and $[A]_0$ is the initial concentration. This is the equation for a straight line with vertical intercept $[A]_0$ and slope $-kt$, as shown in the blue curve in Figure 14.10.

The most common type of zero-order reaction occurs when a gas undergoes decomposition on the surface of a solid. If the surface is completely covered by decomposing molecules, the rate of reaction is constant because the number of reacting surface molecules is constant, so long as there is some gas-phase substance left.

Half-Life

The **half-life** of a reaction, $t_{1/2}$, is the time required for the concentration of a reactant to reach half its initial value, $[A]_{t_{1/2}} = \frac{1}{2}[A]_0$. Half-life is a convenient way to describe how fast a reaction occurs, especially if it is a first-order process. A fast reaction has a short half-life.

We can determine the half-life of a first-order reaction by substituting $[A]_{t_{1/2}} = \frac{1}{2}[A]_0$ for $[A]_t$ and $t_{1/2}$ for t in Equation 14.12:

$$\ln \frac{\frac{1}{2}[A]_0}{[A]_0} = -kt_{1/2}$$

$$\ln \frac{1}{2} = -kt_{1/2}$$

$$t_{1/2} = -\frac{\ln \frac{1}{2}}{k} = \frac{0.693}{k} \qquad [14.15]$$

From Equation 14.15, we see that $t_{1/2}$ for a first-order rate law does not depend on the initial concentration of any reactant. Consequently, the half-life remains constant throughout the reaction. If, for example, the concentration of a reactant is 0.120 M at some instant in the reaction, it will be $\frac{1}{2}(0.120\ M) = 0.060\ M$ after one half-life. After one more half-life passes, the concentration will drop to 0.030 M, and so on. Equation 14.15 also indicates that, for a first-order reaction, we can calculate $t_{1/2}$ if we know k and calculate k if we know $t_{1/2}$.

The change in concentration over time for the first-order rearrangement of gaseous methyl isonitrile at 199 °C is graphed in ▶ FIGURE 14.11. Because the concentration of this gas is directly proportional to its pressure during the reaction, we have chosen to plot pressure rather than concentration in this graph. The first half-life occurs at 13,600 s (3.78 hr). At a time 13,600 s later, the methyl isonitrile pressure (and therefore, concentration) has decreased to half of one-half, or one-fourth, of the initial value. *In a first-order reaction, the concentration of the reactant decreases by one-half in each of a series of regularly spaced time intervals, each interval equal to $t_{1/2}$.*

△ **GIVE IT SOME THOUGHT**

If a solution containing 10.0 g of a substance reacts by first-order kinetics, how many grams remain after 3 half-lives?

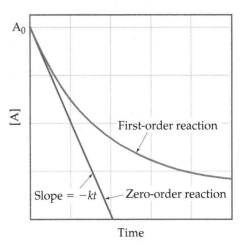

GO FIGURE

At which times during the reaction would you have trouble distinguishing a zero-order reac-

▲ **FIGURE 14.10 Comparison of first-order and zero-order reactions for the disappearance of reactant A with time.**

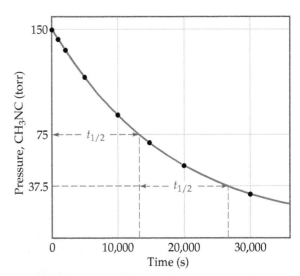

▲ **FIGURE 14.11 Kinetic data for the rearrangment of methyl isonitrile to acetonitrile at 199 °C, showing the half-life of the reaction.**

CHEMISTRY PUT TO WORK

Methyl Bromide in the Atmosphere

The compounds known as chlorofluorocarbons (CFCs) are well-known agents responsible for the destruction of Earth's protective ozone layer. Another simple molecule that has the potential to destroy the stratospheric ozone layer is methyl bromide, CH_3Br (▼ FIGURE 14.12). Because this substance has a wide range of uses, including antifungal treatment of plant seeds, it has been produced in large quantities in the past (about 150 million pounds per year worldwide in 1997, at the height of its production). In the stratosphere, the C—Br bond is broken through absorption of short-wavelength radiation. The resultant Br atoms then catalyze decomposition of O_3.

Methyl bromide is removed from the lower atmosphere by a variety of mechanisms, including a slow reaction with ocean water:

$$CH_3Br(g) + H_2O(l) \longrightarrow CH_3OH(aq) + HBr(aq) \quad [14.16]$$

Stratosphere

Diffusion to stratosphere

Troposphere

50% decomposes in 0.8 years

Lower atmosphere

Methyl bromide applied as antifungal treatment

To determine the potential importance of CH_3Br in destruction of the ozone layer, it is important to know how rapidly the reaction in Equation 14.16 and all other reactions remove CH_3Br from the lower atmosphere before it can diffuse into the stratosphere.

The average lifetime of CH_3Br in Earth's lower atmosphere is difficult to measure because the conditions that exist in the atmosphere are too complex to be simulated in the laboratory. Instead, scientists analyzed nearly 4000 atmospheric samples collected above the Pacific Ocean for the presence of several trace organic substances, including methyl bromide. From these measurements, it was possible to estimate the *atmospheric residence time* for CH_3Br.

The atmospheric residence time is related to the half-life for CH_3Br in the lower atmosphere, assuming the CH_3Br decomposes by a first-order process. From the experimental data, the half-life for methyl bromide in the lower atmosphere is estimated to be 0.8 ± 0.1 year. That is, a collection of CH_3Br molecules present at any given time will, on average, be 50% decomposed after 0.8 year, 75% decomposed after 1.6 years, and so on. A half-life of 0.8 year, while comparatively short, is still sufficiently long so that CH_3Br contributes significantly to the destruction of the ozone layer.

In 1997 an international agreement was reached to phase out use of methyl bromide in developed countries by 2005. However, in recent years exemptions for critical agricultural use have been requested and granted. Nevertheless, worldwide production was down to 25 million pounds in 2009, two-thirds of which is used in the United States.

RELATED EXERCISE: 14.124

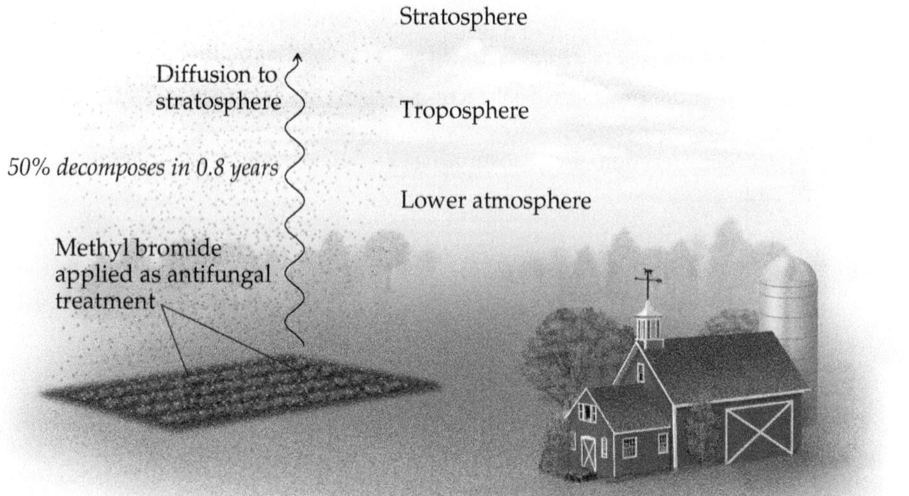

◄ FIGURE 14.12 **Distribution and fate of methyl bromide in Earth's atmosphere.**

SAMPLE EXERCISE 14.9 | **Determining the Half-Life of a First-Order Reaction**

The reaction of C_4H_9Cl with water is a first-order reaction. (**a**) Use Figure 14.4 to estimate the half-life for this reaction. (**b**) Use the half-life from (a) to calculate the rate constant.

SOLUTION

Analyze We are asked to estimate the half-life of a reaction from a graph of concentration versus time and then to use the half-life to calculate the rate constant for the reaction.

Plan
(**a**) To estimate a half-life, we can select a concentration and then determine the time required for the concentration to decrease to half of that value. (**b**) Equation 14.15 is used to calculate the rate constant from the half-life.

Solve

(a) From the graph, we see that the initial value of $[C_4H_9Cl]$ is 0.100 M. The half-life for this first-order reaction is the time required for $[C_4H_9Cl]$ to decrease to 0.050 M, which we can read off the graph. This point occurs at approximately 340 s.

(b) Solving Equation 14.15 for k, we have

$$k = \frac{0.693}{t_{1/2}} = \frac{0.693}{340 \text{ s}} = 2.0 \times 10^{-3} \text{ s}^{-1}$$

Check At the end of the second half-life, which should occur at 680 s, the concentration should have decreased by yet another factor of 2, to 0.025. Inspection of the graph shows that this is indeed the case.

PRACTICE EXERCISE

(a) Using Equation 14.15, calculate $t_{1/2}$ for the decomposition of the insecticide described in Sample Exercise 14.7. **(b)** How long does it take for the concentration of the insecticide to reach one-quarter of the initial value?

Answers: **(a)** 0.478 yr = 1.51×10^7 s, **(b)** it takes two half-lives, 2(0.478 yr) = 0.956 yr

The half-life for second-order and other reactions depends on reactant concentrations and therefore changes as the reaction progresses. We obtained Equation 14.15 for the half-life for a first-order reaction by substituting $[A]_{t_{1/2}} = \frac{1}{2}[A]_0$ for $[A]_t$ and $t_{1/2}$ for t in Equation 14.12. We find the half-life of a second-order reaction by making the same substitutions into Equation 14.14:

$$\frac{1}{\frac{1}{2}[A]_0} = kt_{1/2} + \frac{1}{[A]_0}$$

$$\frac{2}{[A]_0} - \frac{1}{[A]_0} = kt_{1/2}$$

$$t_{1/2} = \frac{1}{k[A]_0} \qquad [14.17]$$

In this case the half-life depends on the initial concentration of reactant—the lower the initial concentration, the longer the half-life.

 GIVE IT SOME THOUGHT

How does the half-life of a second-order reaction change as the reaction proceeds?

14.5 | TEMPERATURE AND RATE

The rates of most chemical reactions increase as the temperature rises. For example, dough rises faster at room temperature than when refrigerated, and plants grow more rapidly in warm weather than in cold. We can see the effect of temperature on reaction rate by observing a chemiluminescence reaction (one that produces light). The characteristic glow of fireflies is a familiar example of chemiluminescence. Another is the light produced by Cyalume® light sticks, which contain chemicals that produce chemiluminescence when mixed. As seen in ▶ FIGURE 14.13, these light sticks produce a brighter light at higher temperature. The amount of light produced is greater because the rate of the reaction is faster at the higher temperature. Although the light stick glows more brightly initially, its luminescence also dies out more rapidly at the higher temperature.

▶ FIGURE 14.13   **Temperature affects the rate of the chemiluminescence reaction in light sticks.**

Hot water   Cold water

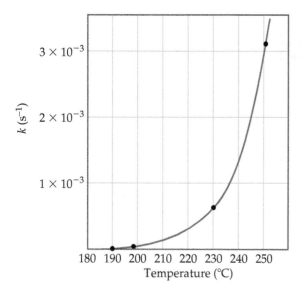

▲ **FIGURE 14.14 Temperature dependence of the rate constant for methyl isonitrile conversion to acetonitrile.** The four points indicated are used in Sample Exercise 14.11.

How is this experimentally observed temperature effect reflected in the rate law? The faster rate at higher temperature is due to an increase in the rate constant with increasing temperature. For example, let's reconsider the first-order reaction $CH_3NC \longrightarrow CH_3CN$. ◄ **FIGURE 14.14** shows the rate constant for this reaction as a function of temperature. The rate constant and, hence, the rate of the reaction increase rapidly with temperature, approximately doubling for each 10 °C rise.

The Collision Model

Reaction rates are affected both by reactant concentrations and by temperature. The **collision model**, based on the kinetic-molecular theory ∞ (Section 8.7), accounts for both of these effects at the molecular level. The central idea of the collision model is that molecules must collide to react. The greater the number of collisions per second, the greater the reaction rate. As reactant concentration increases, therefore, the number of collisions increases, leading to an increase in reaction rate. According to the kinetic-molecular theory of gases, increasing the temperature increases molecular speeds. As molecules move faster, they collide more forcefully (with more energy) and more frequently, increasing reaction rates.

For a reaction to occur, though, more is required than simply a collision. For most reactions, only a tiny fraction of collisions leads to a reaction. For example, in a mixture of H_2 and I_2 at ordinary temperatures and pressures, each molecule undergoes about 10^{10} collisions per second. If every collision between H_2 and I_2 resulted in the formation of HI, the reaction would be over in much less than a second. Instead, at room temperature the reaction proceeds very slowly because only about one in every 10^{13} collisions produces a reaction. What keeps the reaction from occurring more rapidly?

The Orientation Factor

In most reactions, molecules must be oriented in a certain way during collision for a reaction to occur. The relative orientations of the molecules during collision determine whether the atoms are suitably positioned to form new bonds. For example, consider the reaction

$$Cl + NOCl \longrightarrow NO + Cl_2$$

which takes place if the collision brings Cl atoms together to form Cl_2, as shown at the top in ▼ **FIGURE 14.15**. In contrast, the collision shown at the bottom in this figure is ineffective and does not yield products.

▼ **FIGURE 14.15 Molecular collisions may or may not lead to a chemical reaction between Cl and NOCl.**

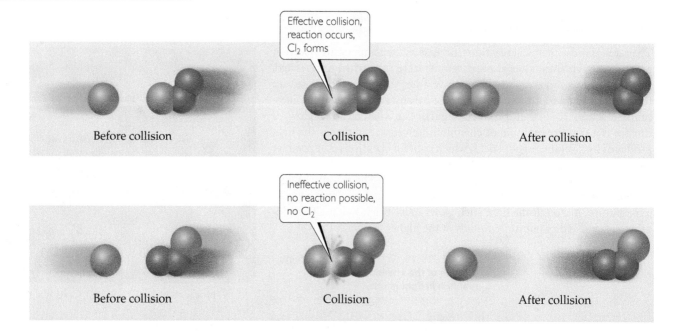

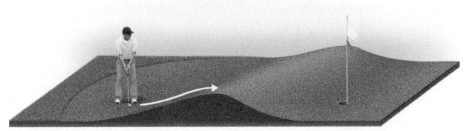

Activation Energy

In addition to molecular orientation during collisions, another factor is usually even more important in determining whether a particular collision results in reaction. In 1888 the Swedish chemist Svante Arrhenius suggested that molecules must possess a certain minimum amount of energy to react. According to the collision model, this energy comes from the kinetic energies of the colliding molecules. Upon collision, the kinetic energy of the molecules can be used to stretch, bend, and ultimately break bonds, leading to chemical reactions. That is, the kinetic energy is used to change the potential energy of the molecule. If molecules are moving too slowly—in other words, with too little kinetic energy— they merely bounce off one another without changing. The minimum energy required to initiate a chemical reaction is called the **activation energy**, E_a, and its value varies from reaction to reaction.

The situation during reactions is analogous to that shown in ▲ **FIGURE 14.16**. The player needs to move his ball over the hill in the direction of the cup. The hill is a *barrier* between ball and cup. To reach the cup, the player must impart enough kinetic energy with the putter to move the ball to the top of the barrier. If he does not impart enough energy, the ball will roll partway up the hill and then back down toward him. In the same way, molecules require a certain minimum energy to break existing bonds during a chemical reaction. We can think of this minimum energy as an *energy barrier*. In the rearrangement of methyl isonitrile to acetonitrile, for example, we might imagine the reaction passing through an intermediate state in which the $N \equiv C$ portion of the methyl isonitrile molecule is sideways:

$$H_3C-N\equiv C: \longrightarrow \left[H_3C \cdots \overset{C}{\underset{N}{\vert\vert\vert}} \right] \longrightarrow H_3C-C\equiv N:$$

▶ **FIGURE 14.17** shows that energy must be supplied to stretch the bond between the H_3C group and the $N\equiv C$ group to allow the $N\equiv C$ group to rotate. After the $N\equiv C$ group has twisted sufficiently, the $C-C$ bond begins to form, and the energy of the molecule drops. Thus, the barrier to formation of acetonitrile represents the energy necessary to force the molecule through the relatively unstable intermediate state, analogous to forcing the ball in Figure 14.16 over the hill. The difference between the energy of the starting molecule and the highest energy along the reaction pathway is the activation energy, E_a. The molecule having the arrangement of atoms shown at the top of the barrier is called either the **activated complex** or the **transition state**.

The conversion of $H_3C-N\equiv C$ to $H_3C-C\equiv N$ is exothermic. Figure 14.17 therefore shows the product as having a lower energy than the reactant. The energy change for the reaction, ΔE, has no effect on reaction rate, however. *The rate depends on the magnitude of E_a; generally, the lower the value of E_a is, the faster the reaction.*

Notice that the reverse reaction is endothermic. The activation energy for the reverse reaction is equal to the energy that must be overcome if approaching the barrier from the right: $\Delta E + E_a$.

△ **GO FIGURE**

How does the energy needed to overcome the energy barrier compare with the overall change in energy for this reaction?

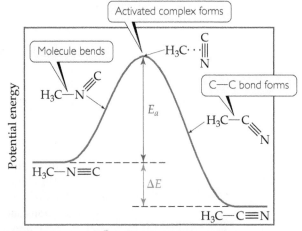

▲ **FIGURE 14.17** Energy profile for conversion of methyl isonitrile (H_3CNC) to its isomer acetonitrile (H_3CCN).

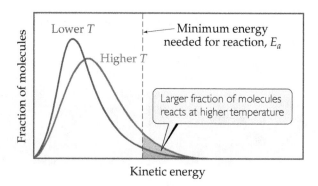

► FIGURE 14.18 **The effect of temperature on the distribution of kinetic energies of molecules in a sample.**

Any particular methyl isonitrile molecule acquires sufficient energy to overcome the energy barrier through collisions with other molecules. Recall from the kinetic-molecular theory of gases that, at any instant, gas molecules are distributed in energy over a wide range. ∞ (Section 8.7) ▲ FIGURE 14.18 shows the distribution of kinetic energies for two temperatures, comparing them with the minimum energy needed for reaction, E_a. At the higher temperature a much greater fraction of the molecules have kinetic energy greater than E_a, which leads to a greater rate of reaction.

 GIVE IT SOME THOUGHT

Suppose we have two reactions, A ⟶ B and B ⟶ C. You can isolate B, and it is stable. Is B the transition state for the reaction A ⟶ C?

The fraction of molecules that have an energy equal to or greater than E_a is given by the expression

$$f = e^{-E_a/RT} \qquad [14.18]$$

In this equation R is the gas constant (8.314 J/mol-K) and T is the absolute temperature. To get an idea of the magnitude of f, let's suppose that E_a is 100 kJ/mol, a value typical of many reactions, and that T is 300 K. The calculated value of f is 3.9×10^{-18}, an extremely small number! At 310 K, $f = 1.4 \times 10^{-17}$. Thus, a 10-degree increase in temperature produces a 3.6-fold increase in the fraction of molecules possessing at least 100 kJ/mol of energy.

GIVE IT SOME THOUGHT

In a chemical reaction, why does not every collision between reactant molecules result in formation of a product molecule?

The Arrhenius Equation

Arrhenius noted that for most reactions the increase in rate with increasing temperature is nonlinear (Figure 14.14). He found that most reaction-rate data obeyed an equation based on (a) the fraction of molecules possessing energy E_a or greater, (b) the number of collisions per second, and (c) the fraction of collisions that have the appropriate orientation. These three factors are incorporated into the **Arrhenius equation:**

$$k = Ae^{-E_a/RT} \qquad [14.19]$$

In this equation k is the rate constant, E_a is the activation energy, R is the gas constant (8.314 J/mol-K), and T is the absolute temperature. The **frequency factor**, A, is constant, or nearly so, as temperature is varied. This factor is related to the frequency of collisions and the probability that the collisions are favorably oriented for reaction.* As the magnitude of E_a increases, k decreases because the fraction of molecules that possess the required energy is smaller. Thus, *reaction rates decrease as E_a increases.*

*Because collision frequency increases with temperature, A also has some temperature dependence, but this dependence is much smaller than the exponential term. Therefore, A is considered approximately constant.

SAMPLE EXERCISE 14.10   **Relating Energy Profiles to Activation Energies and Speeds of Reaction**

Consider a series of reactions having these energy profiles:

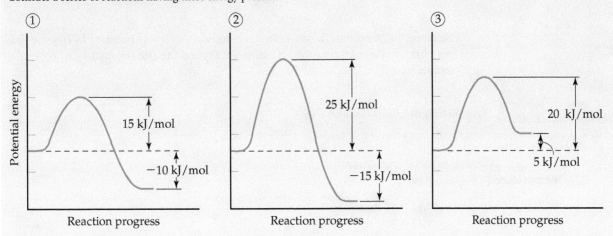

Rank the reactions from slowest to fastest assuming that they have nearly the same value for the frequency factor A.

SOLUTION

The lower the activation energy, the faster the reaction. The value of ΔE does not affect the rate. Hence, the order from slowest reaction to fastest is $2 < 3 < 1$.

PRACTICE EXERCISE

Rank the reverse reactions from slowest to fastest.

Answer: $2 < 1 < 3$ because, if you approach the barrier from the right, the E_a values are 40 kJ/mol for reverse reaction 2, 25 kJ/mol for reverse reaction 1, and 15 kJ/mol for reverse reaction 3.

Determining the Activation Energy

We can calculate the activation energy for a reaction by manipulating the Arrhenius equation. Taking the natural log of both sides of Equation 14.19, we obtain

$$\ln k = -\frac{E_a}{RT} + \ln A$$

[14.20]

$$y = mx + b$$

which has the form of the equation for a straight line. A graph of $\ln k$ versus $1/T$ is a line with a slope equal to $-E_a/R$ and a y-intercept equal to $\ln A$. Thus, the activation energy can be determined by measuring k at a series of temperatures, graphing $\ln k$ versus $1/T$, and calculating E_a from the slope of the resultant line.

We can also use Equation 14.20 to evaluate E_a in a nongraphical way if we know the rate constant of a reaction at two or more temperatures. For example, suppose that at two different temperatures T_1 and T_2 a reaction has rate constants k_1 and k_2. For each condition, we have

$$\ln k_1 = -\frac{E_a}{RT_1} + \ln A \quad \text{and} \quad \ln k_2 = -\frac{E_a}{RT_2} + \ln A$$

Subtracting $\ln k_2$ from $\ln k_1$ gives

$$\ln k_1 - \ln k_2 = \left(-\frac{E_a}{RT_1} + \ln A\right) - \left(-\frac{E_a}{RT_2} + \ln A\right)$$

Simplifying this equation and rearranging give

$$\ln \frac{k_1}{k_2} = \frac{E_a}{R}\left(\frac{1}{T_2} - \frac{1}{T_1}\right)$$ [14.21]

Equation 14.21 provides a convenient way to calculate a rate constant k_1 at some temperature T_1 when we know the activation energy and the rate constant k_2 at some other temperature T_2.

SAMPLE EXERCISE 14.11 | Determining the Activation Energy

The following table shows the rate constants for the rearrangement of methyl isonitrile at various temperatures (these are the data points in Figure 14.14):

Temperature (°C)	k (s^{-1})
189.7	2.52×10^{-5}
198.9	5.25×10^{-5}
230.3	6.30×10^{-4}
251.2	3.16×10^{-3}

(a) From these data, calculate the activation energy for the reaction. **(b)** What is the value of the rate constant at 430.0 K?

SOLUTION

Analyze We are given rate constants, k, measured at several temperatures and asked to determine the activation energy, E_a, and the rate constant, k, at a particular temperature.

Plan We can obtain E_a from the slope of a graph of $\ln k$ versus $1/T$. Once we know E_a, we can use Equation 14.21 together with the given rate data to calculate the rate constant at 430.0 K.

Solve
(a) We must first convert the temperatures from degrees Celsius to kelvins. We then take the inverse of each temperature, $1/T$, and the natural log of each rate constant, $\ln k$. This gives us the table shown at the right:

T (K)	$1/T$ (K^{-1})	$\ln k$
462.9	2.160×10^{-3}	-10.589
472.1	2.118×10^{-3}	-9.855
503.5	1.986×10^{-3}	-7.370
524.4	1.907×10^{-3}	-5.757

A graph of $\ln k$ versus $1/T$ is a straight line (▶ **FIGURE 14.19**).

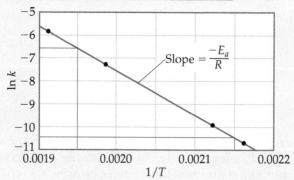

▲ **FIGURE 14.19** Graphical determination of activation energy E_a.

The slope of the line is obtained by choosing any two well-separated points and using the coordinates of each:

$$\text{Slope} = \frac{\Delta y}{\Delta x} = \frac{-6.6 - (-10.4)}{0.00195 - 0.00215} = -1.9 \times 10^4$$

Because logarithms have no units, the numerator in this equation is dimensionless. The denominator has the units of $1/T$, namely, K^{-1}. Thus, the overall units for the slope are K. The slope equals $-E_a/R$. We use the value for the gas constant R in units of J/mol-K (Table 8.2). We thus obtain

$$\text{Slope} = -\frac{E_a}{R}$$

$$E_a = -(\text{slope})(R) = -(-1.9 \times 10^4 \text{ K})\left(8.314 \frac{\text{J}}{\text{mol-K}}\right)\left(\frac{1 \text{ kJ}}{1000 \text{ J}}\right)$$

$$= 1.6 \times 10^2 \text{ kJ/mol} = 160 \text{ kJ/mol}$$

We report the activation energy to only two significant figures because we are limited by the precision with which we can read the graph in Figure 14.19.

(b) To determine the rate constant, k_1, at $T_1 = 430.0$ K, we can use Equation 14.21 with $E_a = 160$ kJ/mol and one of the rate constants and temperatures from the given data, such as $k_2 = 2.52 \times 10^{-5}$ s^{-1} and $T_2 = 462.9$ K:

$$\ln\left(\frac{k_1}{2.52 \times 10^{-5}\,\text{s}^{-1}}\right) = \left(\frac{160\,\text{kJ/mol}}{8.314\,\text{J/mol-K}}\right)\left(\frac{1}{462.9\,\text{K}} - \frac{1}{430.0\,\text{K}}\right)\left(\frac{1000\,\text{J}}{1\,\text{kJ}}\right) = -3.18$$

Thus,

$$\frac{k_1}{2.52 \times 10^{-5}\,\text{s}^{-1}} = e^{-3.18} = 4.15 \times 10^{-2}$$

$$k_1 = (4.15 \times 10^{-2})(2.52 \times 10^{-5}\,\text{s}^{-1}) = 1.0 \times 10^{-6}\,\text{s}^{-1}$$

Note that the units of k_1 are the same as those of k_2.

PRACTICE EXERCISE

Using the data in Sample Exercise 14.11, calculate the rate constant for the rearrangement of methyl isonitrile at 280 °C.

Answer: $2.2 \times 10^{-2}\,\text{s}^{-1}$

14.6 | REACTION MECHANISMS

A balanced equation for a chemical reaction indicates the substances present at the start of the reaction and those present at the end of the reaction. It provides no information, however, about the detailed steps that occur at the molecular level as the reactants are turned into products. The steps by which a reaction occurs is called the **reaction mechanism**. At the most sophisticated level, a reaction mechanism describes the order in which bonds are broken and formed and the changes in relative positions of the atoms in the course of the reaction.

Elementary Reactions

We have seen that reactions take place because of collisions between reacting molecules. For example, the collisions between molecules of methyl isonitrile (CH$_3$NC) can provide the energy to allow the CH$_3$NC to rearrange to acetonitrile:

Similarly, the reaction of NO and O$_3$ to form NO$_2$ and O$_2$ appears to occur as a result of a single collision involving suitably oriented and sufficiently energetic NO and O$_3$ molecules:

$$\text{NO}(g) + \text{O}_3(g) \longrightarrow \text{NO}_2(g) + \text{O}_2(g) \qquad [14.22]$$

Both reactions occur in a single event or step and are called **elementary reactions**.

The number of molecules that participate as reactants in an elementary reaction defines the **molecularity** of the reaction. If a single molecule is involved, the reaction is **unimolecular**. The rearrangement of methyl isonitrile is a unimolecular process. Elementary reactions involving the collision of two reactant molecules are **bimolecular**. The reaction between NO and O$_3$ is bimolecular. Elementary reactions involving the simultaneous collision of three molecules are **termolecular**. Termolecular reactions are far less probable than unimolecular or bimolecular processes and are rarely encountered. The chance that four or more molecules will collide simultaneously with any regularity is even more remote; consequently, such collisions are never proposed as part of a reaction mechanism.

GIVE IT SOME THOUGHT

What is the molecularity of the elementary reaction?

$$\text{NO}(g) + \text{Cl}_2(g) \longrightarrow \text{NOCl}(g) + \text{Cl}(g)$$

Multistep Mechanisms

The net change represented by a balanced chemical equation often occurs by a *multistep mechanism* consisting of a sequence of elementary reactions. For example, below 225 °C, the reaction

$$NO_2(g) + CO(g) \longrightarrow NO(g) + CO_2(g) \qquad [14.23]$$

appears to proceed in two elementary reactions (or two *elementary steps*), each of which is bimolecular. First, two NO_2 molecules collide, and an oxygen atom is transferred from one to the other. The resultant NO_3 then collides with a CO molecule and transfers an oxygen atom to it:

$$NO_2(g) + NO_2(g) \longrightarrow NO_3(g) + NO(g)$$

$$NO_3(g) + CO(g) \longrightarrow NO_2(g) + CO_2(g)$$

Thus, we say that the reaction occurs by a two-step mechanism.

The chemical equations for the elementary reactions in a multistep mechanism must always add to give the chemical equation of the overall process. In the present example the sum of the two elementary reactions is

$$2\,NO_2(g) + NO_3(g) + CO(g) \longrightarrow NO_2(g) + NO_3(g) + NO(g) + CO_2(g)$$

Simplifying this equation by eliminating substances that appear on both sides gives Equation 14.23, the net equation for the process.

Because NO_3 is neither a reactant nor a product of the reaction—it is formed in one elementary reaction and consumed in the next—it is called an **intermediate**. Multistep mechanisms involve one or more intermediates. Intermediates are not the same as transition states, as shown in ▼ FIGURE 14.20. Intermediates can be stable and can therefore sometimes be identified and even isolated. Transition states, on the other hand, are always inherently unstable and as such can never be isolated. Nevertheless, the use of advanced "ultrafast" techniques sometimes allows us to characterize them.

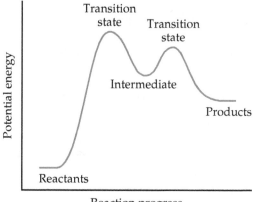

▶ FIGURE 14.20 **The energy profile of a reaction, showing transition states and an intermediate.**

SAMPLE EXERCISE 14.12 | **Determining Molecularity and Identifying Intermediates**

It has been proposed that the conversion of ozone into O_2 proceeds by a two-step mechanism:

$$O_3(g) \longrightarrow O_2(g) + O(g)$$

$$O_3(g) + O(g) \longrightarrow 2\,O_2(g)$$

(a) Describe the molecularity of each elementary reaction in this mechanism.
(b) Write the equation for the overall reaction. (c) Identify the intermediate(s).

SOLUTION

Analyze We are given a two-step mechanism and asked for (a) the molecularities of each of the two elementary reactions, (b) the equation for the overall process, and (c) the intermediate.

Plan The molecularity of each elementary reaction depends on the number of reactant molecules in the equation for that reaction. The overall equation is the sum of the equations for the elementary reactions. The intermediate is a substance formed in one step of the mechanism and used in another and therefore not part of the equation for the overall reaction.

Solve

(a) The first elementary reaction involves a single reactant and is consequently unimolecular. The second reaction, which involves two reactant molecules, is bimolecular.

(b) Adding the two elementary reactions gives

$$2\,O_3(g) + O(g) \longrightarrow 3\,O_2(g) + O(g)$$

Because $O(g)$ appears in equal amounts on both sides of the equation, it can be eliminated to give the net equation for the chemical process:

$$2\,O_3(g) \longrightarrow 3\,O_2(g)$$

(c) The intermediate is $O(g)$. It is neither an original reactant nor a final product but is formed in the first step of the mechanism and consumed in the second.

PRACTICE EXERCISE

For the reaction

$$Mo(CO)_6 + P(CH_3)_3 \longrightarrow Mo(CO)_5\,P(CH_3)_3 + CO$$

the proposed mechanism is

$$Mo(CO)_6 \longrightarrow Mo(CO)_5 + CO$$

$$Mo(CO)_5 + P(CH_3)_3 \longrightarrow Mo(CO)_5\,P(CH_3)_3$$

(a) Is the proposed mechanism consistent with the equation for the overall reaction? (b) What is the molecularity of each step of the mechanism? (c) Identify the intermediate(s).

Answers: (a) Yes, the two equations add to yield the equation for the reaction. (b) The first elementary reaction is unimolecular, and the second one is bimolecular. (c) $Mo(CO)_5$

Rate Laws for Elementary Reactions

In Section 14.3 we stressed that rate laws must be determined experimentally; they cannot be predicted from the coefficients of balanced chemical equations. We are now in a position to understand why this is so. Every reaction is made up of a series of one or more elementary steps, and the rate laws and relative speeds of these steps dictate the overall rate law for the reaction. Indeed, the rate law for a reaction can be determined from its mechanism, as we will see shortly, and compared with the experimental rate law. Thus, our next challenge in kinetics is to arrive at reaction mechanisms that lead to rate laws consistent with those observed experimentally. We start by examining the rate laws of elementary reactions.

Elementary reactions are significant in a very important way: *If a reaction is elementary, its rate law is based directly on its molecularity.* For example, consider the unimolecular reaction

$$A \longrightarrow products$$

As the number of A molecules increases, the number that react in a given time interval increases proportionally. Thus, the rate of a unimolecular process is first order:

$$Rate = k[A]$$

For bimolecular elementary steps, the rate law is second order, as in the reaction

$$A + B \longrightarrow products \qquad Rate = k[A][B]$$

The second-order rate law follows directly from collision theory. If we double the concentration of A, the number of collisions between molecules of A and B doubles; likewise, if we double [B], the number of collisions between A and B doubles. Therefore, the rate law is first order in both [A] and [B] and second order overall.

The rate laws for all feasible elementary reactions are given in ▶ TABLE 14.3. Notice how each rate law follows directly from the molecularity of the reaction. It is important to remember, however, that we cannot tell by merely looking at a balanced, overall chemical equation whether the reaction involves one or several elementary steps.

TABLE 14.3 • **Elementary Reactions and Their Rate Laws**

Molecularity	Elementary Reaction	Rate Law
Unimolecular	A $\longrightarrow$ products	Rate = $k[A]$
Bimolecular	A + A $\longrightarrow$ products	Rate = $k[A]^2$
Bimolecular	A + B $\longrightarrow$ products	Rate = $k[A][B]$
Termolecular	A + A + A $\longrightarrow$ products	Rate = $k[A]^3$
Termolecular	A + A + B $\longrightarrow$ products	Rate = $k[A]^2[B]$
Termolecular	A + B + C $\longrightarrow$ products	Rate = $k[A][B][C]$

SAMPLE EXERCISE 14.13 | **Predicting the Rate Law for an Elementary Reaction**

If the following reaction occurs in a single elementary reaction, predict its rate law:

$$H_2(g) + Br_2(g) \longrightarrow 2\,HBr(g)$$

SOLUTION

Analyze We are given the equation and asked for its rate law, assuming that it is an elementary process.

Plan Because we are assuming that the reaction occurs as a single elementary reaction, we are able to write the rate law using the coefficients for the reactants in the equation as the reaction orders.

Solve The reaction is bimolecular, involving one molecule of H_2 and one molecule of Br_2. Thus, the rate law is first order in each reactant and second order overall:

$$Rate = k[H_2][Br_2]$$

Comment Experimental studies of this reaction show that the reaction actually has a very different rate law:

$$Rate = k[H_2][Br_2]^{1/2}$$

Because the experimental rate law differs from the one obtained by assuming a single elementary reaction, we can conclude that the mechanism cannot occur by a single elementary step. It must, therefore, involve two or more elementary steps.

PRACTICE EXERCISE

Consider the following reaction: $2\,NO(g) + Br_2(g) \longrightarrow 2\,NOBr(g)$. **(a)** Write the rate law for the reaction, assuming it involves a single elementary reaction. **(b)** Is a single-step mechanism likely for this reaction?

Answers: **(a)** Rate = $k[NO]^2[Br_2]$, **(b)** No, because termolecular reactions are very rare.

The Rate-Determining Step for a Multistep Mechanism

As with the reaction in Sample Exercise 14.13, most reactions occur by mechanisms that involve two or more elementary reactions. Each step of the mechanism has its own rate constant and activation energy. Often one step is much slower than the others, and the overall rate of a reaction cannot exceed the rate of the slowest elementary step. Because the slow step limits the overall reaction rate, it is called the **rate-determining step** (or *rate-limiting step*).

To understand the concept of the rate-determining step for a reaction, consider a toll road with two toll plazas (▶ **FIGURE 14.21**). Cars enter the toll road at point 1 and pass through toll plaza A. They then pass an intermediate point 2 before passing through toll plaza B and arriving at point 3. We can envision this trip along the toll road as occurring in two elementary steps:

Step 1: Point 1 $\longrightarrow$ Point 2   (through toll plaza A)

Step 2: Point 2 $\longrightarrow$ Point 3   (through toll plaza B)

Overall: Point 1 $\longrightarrow$ Point 3   (through both toll plazas)

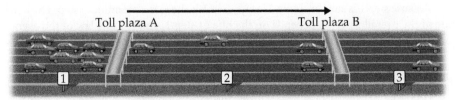

(a) Cars slowed at toll plaza A, rate-determining step is passage through A

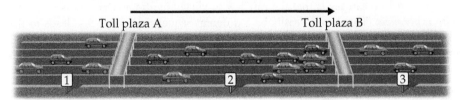

(b) Cars slowed at toll plaza B, rate-determining step is passage through B

◀ **FIGURE 14.21 Rate-determining steps in traffic flow on a toll road.**

Now suppose that one or more gates at toll plaza A are malfunctioning, so that traffic backs up behind the gates, as depicted in Figure 14.21(a). The rate at which cars can get to point 3 is limited by the rate at which they can get through the traffic jam at plaza A. Thus, step 1 is the rate-determining step of the journey along the toll road. If, however, all gates at A are functioning but one or more at B are not, traffic flows quickly through A but gets backed up at B, as depicted in Figure 14.21(b). In this case step 2 is the rate-determining step.

In the same way, *the slowest step in a multistep reaction limits the overall rate.* By analogy to Figure 14.21(a), the rate of a fast step following the rate-determining step does not speed up the overall rate. If the slow step is not the first one, as is the case in Figure 14.21(b), the faster preceding steps produce intermediate products that accumulate before being consumed in the slow step. In either case, *the rate-determining step governs the rate law for the overall reaction.*

 GIVE IT SOME THOUGHT

Why can't the rate law for a reaction generally be deduced from the balanced equation for the reaction?

Mechanisms with a Slow Initial Step

We can most easily see the relationship between the slow step in a mechanism and the rate law for the overall reaction by considering an example in which the first step in a multistep mechanism is the rate-determining step. Consider the reaction of NO_2 and CO to produce NO and CO_2 (Equation 14.23). Below 225 °C, it is found experimentally that the rate law for this reaction is second order in NO_2 and zero order in CO: Rate $= k[NO_2]^2$. Can we propose a reaction mechanism consistent with this rate law? Consider the two-step mechanism:*

Step 1: $NO_2(g) + NO_2(g) \xrightarrow{k_1} NO_3(g) + NO(g)$ (slow)

Step 2: $NO_3(g) + CO(g) \xrightarrow{k_2} NO_2(g) + CO_2(g)$ (fast)

Overall: $NO_2(g) + CO(g) \longrightarrow NO(g) + CO_2(g)$

Step 2 is much faster than step 1; that is, $k_2 \gg k_1$, telling us that the intermediate $NO_3(g)$ is slowly produced in step 1 and immediately consumed in step 2.

---

*Note the rate constants k_1 and k_2 written above the reaction arrows. The subscript on each rate constant identifies the elementary step involved. Thus, k_1 is the rate constant for step 1, and k_2 is the rate constant for step 2. A negative subscript refers to the rate constant for the reverse of an elementary step. For example, k_{-1} is the rate constant for the reverse of the first step.

Because step 1 is slow and step 2 is fast, step 1 is the rate-determining step. Thus, the rate of the overall reaction depends on the rate of step 1, and the rate law of the overall reaction equals the rate law of step 1. Step 1 is a bimolecular process that has the rate law

$$\text{Rate} = k_1[NO_2]^2$$

Thus, the rate law predicted by this mechanism agrees with the one observed experimentally. The reactant CO is absent from the rate law because it reacts in a step that follows the rate-determining step.

A scientist would not, at this point, say that we have "proved" that this mechanism is correct. All we can say is that the rate law predicted by the mechanism is *consistent with experiment*. There could easily be a different sequence of steps that leads to the same rate law. If, however, the predicted rate law of the proposed mechanism disagrees with experiment, we know for certain that the mechanism cannot be correct.

SAMPLE EXERCISE 14.14 | **Determining the Rate Law for a Multistep Mechanism**

The decomposition of nitrous oxide, N_2O, is believed to occur by a two-step mechanism:

$$N_2O(g) \longrightarrow N_2(g) + O(g) \quad \text{(slow)}$$
$$N_2O(g) + O(g) \longrightarrow N_2(g) + O_2(g) \quad \text{(fast)}$$

(a) Write the equation for the overall reaction. **(b)** Write the rate law for the overall reaction.

SOLUTION

Analyze Given a multistep mechanism with the relative speeds of the steps, we are asked to write the overall reaction and the rate law for that overall reaction.

Plan **(a)** Find the overall reaction by adding the elementary steps and eliminating the intermediates. **(b)** The rate law for the overall reaction will be that of the slow, rate-determining step.

Solve **(a)** Adding the two elementary reactions gives

$$2 N_2O(g) + O(g) \longrightarrow 2 N_2(g) + 2 O_2(g) + O(g)$$

Omitting the intermediate, $O(g)$, which occurs on both sides of the equation, gives the overall reaction:

$$2 N_2O(g) \longrightarrow 2 N_2(g) + O_2(g)$$

(b) The rate law for the overall reaction is just the rate law for the slow, rate-determining elementary reaction. Because that slow step is a unimolecular elementary reaction, the rate law is first order:

$$\text{Rate} = k[N_2O]$$

PRACTICE EXERCISE

Ozone reacts with nitrogen dioxide to produce dinitrogen pentoxide and oxygen:

$$O_3(g) + 2 NO_2(g) \longrightarrow N_2O_5(g) + O_2(g)$$

The reaction is believed to occur in two steps:

$$O_3(g) + NO_2(g) \longrightarrow NO_3(g) + O_2(g)$$
$$NO_3(g) + NO_2(g) \longrightarrow N_2O_5(g)$$

The experimental rate law is rate $= k[O_3][NO_2]$. What can you say about the relative rates of the two steps of the mechanism?

Answer: Because the rate law conforms to the molecularity of the first step, that must be the rate-determining step. The second step must be much faster than the first one.

Mechanisms with a Fast Initial Step

It is less straightforward to derive the rate law for a mechanism in which an intermediate is a reactant in the rate-determining step. This situation arises in multistep mechanisms when the first step is fast and therefore *not* the rate-determining step. Let's consider one example: the gas-phase reaction of nitric oxide (NO) with bromine (Br_2):

$$2 NO(g) + Br_2(g) \longrightarrow 2 NOBr(g) \qquad [14.24]$$

The experimentally determined rate law for this reaction is second order in NO and first order in Br_2:

$$Rate = k[NO]^2[Br_2] \qquad [14.25]$$

We seek a reaction mechanism that is consistent with this rate law. One possibility is that the reaction occurs in a single termolecular step:

$$NO(g) + NO(g) + Br_2(g) \longrightarrow 2\,NOBr(g) \qquad Rate = k[NO]^2[Br_2] \qquad [14.26]$$

As noted in Practice Exercise 14.13, this does not seem likely because termolecular processes are so rare.

GIVE IT SOME THOUGHT

Why are termolecular elementary steps rare in gas-phase reactions?

Let's consider an alternative mechanism that does not involve a termolecular step:

Step 1: $\qquad NO(g) + Br_2(g) \underset{k_{-1}}{\overset{k_1}{\rightleftharpoons}} NOBr_2(g)$ (fast)

$$[14.27]$$

Step 2: $\quad NOBr_2(g) + NO(g) \xrightarrow{k_2} 2\,NOBr(g)$ (slow)

In this mechanism, step 1 involves two processes: a forward reaction and its reverse.

Because step 2 is the rate-determining step, the rate law for that step governs the rate of the overall reaction:

$$Rate = k_2[NOBr_2][NO] \qquad [14.28]$$

However, $NOBr_2$ is an intermediate generated in the forward reaction of step 1. Intermediates are usually unstable and have a low, unknown concentration. Thus, the rate law of Equation 14.28 depends on the unknown concentration of an intermediate. This is not desirable. Instead, in general, we want to express the rate law for any reaction in terms of the reactants, or the products if necessary, of the reaction.

With the aid of some assumptions, we can express the concentration of the intermediate $NOBr_2$ in terms of the concentrations of the starting reactants NO and Br_2. We first assume that $NOBr_2$ is unstable and does not accumulate to any significant extent in the reaction mixture. Once formed, $NOBr_2$ can be consumed either by reacting with NO to form NOBr or by re-forming NO and Br_2. The first of these possibilities is step 2 of our alternative mechanism, a slow process. The second is the reverse of step 1, a unimolecular process:

$$NOBr_2(g) \xrightarrow{k_{-1}} NO(g) + Br_2(g)$$

Because step 2 is slow, we assume that most of the $NOBr_2$ falls apart according to this reaction. Thus, we have both the forward and reverse reactions of step 1 occurring much faster than step 2. Because they occur rapidly relative to step 2, the forward and reverse reactions of step 1 establish an equilibrium. As in any other dynamic equilibrium, the rate of the forward reaction equals that of the reverse reaction:

$$\underset{\text{Rate of forward reaction}}{k_1[NO][Br_2]} = \underset{\text{Rate of reverse reaction}}{k_{-1}[NOBr_2]}$$

Solving for $[NOBr_2]$, we have

$$[NOBr_2] = \frac{k_1}{k_{-1}}[NO][Br_2]$$

Substituting this relationship into Equation 14.28, we have

$$Rate = k_2\frac{k_1}{k_{-1}}[NO][Br_2][NO] = k[NO]^2[Br_2]$$

where the experimental rate constant k equals k_2k_1/k_{-1}. This expression is consistent with the experimental rate law (Equation 14.25). Thus, our alternative mechanism

(Equation 14.27), which involves two steps but only unimolecular and bimolecular processes, is far more probable than the single-step termolecular mechanism of Equation 14.26.

In general, *whenever a fast step precedes a slow one, we can solve for the concentration of an intermediate by assuming that an equilibrium is established in the fast step.*

SAMPLE EXERCISE 14.15 **Deriving the Rate Law for a Mechanism with a Fast Initial Step**

Show that the following mechanism for Equation 14.24 also produces a rate law consistent with the experimentally observed one:

Step 1: $NO(g) + NO(g) \underset{k_{-1}}{\overset{k_1}{\rightleftharpoons}} N_2O_2(g)$ (fast, equilibrium)

Step 2: $N_2O_2(g) + Br_2(g) \xrightarrow{k_2} 2\, NOBr(g)$ (slow)

SOLUTION

Analyze We are given a mechanism with a fast initial step and asked to write the rate law for the overall reaction.

Plan The rate law of the slow elementary step in a mechanism determines the rate law for the overall reaction. Thus, we first write the rate law based on the molecularity of the slow step. In this case the slow step involves the intermediate N_2O_2 as a reactant. Experimental rate laws, however, do not contain the concentrations of intermediates; instead they are expressed in terms of the concentrations of starting substances. Thus, we must relate the concentration of N_2O_2 to the concentration of NO by assuming that an equilibrium is established in the first step.

Solve The second step is rate determining, so the overall rate is

$$Rate = k_2[N_2O_2][Br_2]$$

We solve for the concentration of the intermediate N_2O_2 by assuming that an equilibrium is established in step 1; thus, the rates of the forward and reverse reactions in step 1 are equal:

$$k_1[NO]^2 = k_{-1}[N_2O_2]$$

Solving for the concentration of the intermediate, N_2O_2, gives

$$[N_2O_2] = \frac{k_1}{k_{-1}}[NO]^2$$

Substituting this expression into the rate expression gives

$$Rate = k_2 \frac{k_1}{k_{-1}}[NO]^2[Br_2] = k[NO]^2[Br_2]$$

Thus, this mechanism also yields a rate law consistent with the experimental one.

PRACTICE EXERCISE

The first step of a mechanism involving the reaction of bromine is

$$Br_2(g) \underset{k_{-1}}{\overset{k_1}{\rightleftharpoons}} 2\, Br(g) \quad \text{(fast, equilibrium)}$$

What is the expression relating the concentration of Br(g) to that of $Br_2(g)$?

Answer: $[Br] = \left(\dfrac{k_1}{k_{-1}}[Br_2] \right)^{1/2}$

So far we have considered only three reaction mechanisms: one for a reaction that occurs in a single elementary step and two for simple multistep reactions where there is one rate-determining step. There are other more complex mechanisms, however. If you take a biochemistry class, for example, you will learn about cases in which you have to assume that the concentration of an intermediate cannot be neglected in deriving the rate law. Furthermore, some mechanisms require a large number of steps, sometimes 35 or more, to arrive at a rate law that agrees with experimental data!

14.7 | CATALYSIS

A **catalyst** is a substance that changes the speed of a chemical reaction without undergoing a permanent chemical change itself. Most reactions in the body, the atmosphere, and the oceans occur with the help of catalysts. Much industrial chemical research is devoted to the search for more effective catalysts for reactions of commercial importance. Extensive research efforts also are devoted to finding means of inhibiting or removing certain catalysts that promote undesirable reactions, such as those that corrode metals, age our bodies, and cause tooth decay.

Homogeneous Catalysis

A catalyst that is present in the same phase as the reactants in a reaction mixture is called a **homogeneous catalyst**. Examples abound both in solution and in the gas phase. Consider, for example, the decomposition of aqueous hydrogen peroxide, $H_2O_2(aq)$, into water and oxygen:

$$2\,H_2O_2(aq) \longrightarrow 2\,H_2O(l) + O_2(g) \qquad [14.29]$$

In the absence of a catalyst, this reaction occurs extremely slowly. Many substances are capable of catalyzing the reaction, however, including bromide ion, which reacts with hydrogen peroxide in acidic solution, forming aqueous bromine and water (▼ FIGURE 14.22):

$$2\,Br^-(aq) + H_2O_2(aq) + 2\,H^+ \longrightarrow Br_2(aq) + 2\,H_2O(l) \qquad [14.30]$$

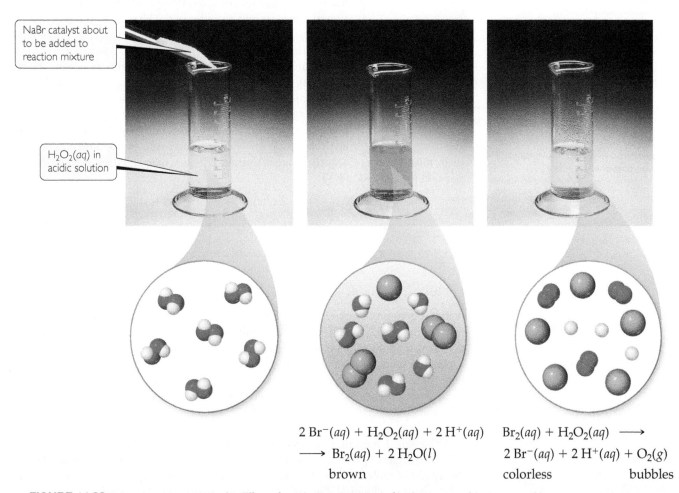

$2\,Br^-(aq) + H_2O_2(aq) + 2\,H^+(aq)$
$\longrightarrow Br_2(aq) + 2\,H_2O(l)$
brown

$Br_2(aq) + H_2O_2(aq) \longrightarrow$
$2\,Br^-(aq) + 2\,H^+(aq) + O_2(g)$
colorless   bubbles

▲ FIGURE 14.22 **Homogeneous catalysis.** Effect of catalyst on the speed of hydrogen peroxide decomposition to water and oxygen gas.

If this were the complete reaction, bromide ion would not be a catalyst because it undergoes chemical change during the reaction. However, hydrogen peroxide also reacts with the $Br_2(aq)$ generated in Equation 14.30:

$$Br_2(aq) + H_2O_2(aq) \longrightarrow 2\,Br^-(aq) + 2\,H^+(aq) + O_2(g) \qquad [14.31]$$

The sum of Equations 14.30 and 14.31 is just Equation 14.29, a result which you can check for yourself.

When the H_2O_2 has been completely decomposed, we are left with a colorless solution of $Br^-(aq)$, which means that this ion is indeed a catalyst of the reaction because it speeds up the reaction without itself undergoing any net change. In contrast, Br_2 is an intermediate because it is first formed (Equation 14.30) and then consumed (Equation 14.31). Neither the catalyst nor the intermediate appears in the equation for the overall reaction. Notice, however, that *the catalyst is there at the start of the reaction, whereas the intermediate is formed during the course of the reaction.*

How does a catalyst work? If we think about the general form of rate laws (Equation 14.7, rate = $k[A]^m[B]^n$), we must conclude that the catalyst must affect the numerical value of k, the rate constant. On the basis of the Arrhenius equation (Equation 14.19, $k = Ae^{-E_a/RT}$), k is determined by the activation energy (E_a) and the frequency factor (A). A catalyst may affect the rate of reaction by altering the value of either E_a or A. We can envision this happening in two ways: The catalyst could provide a new mechanism for the reaction that has an E_a value lower than the E_a value for the uncatalyzed reaction, or the catalyst could assist in the orientation of reactants and so increase A. The most dramatic catalytic effects come from lowering E_a. As a general rule, *a catalyst lowers the overall activation energy for a chemical reaction.*

A catalyst can lower the activation energy for a reaction by providing a different mechanism for the reaction. In the decomposition of hydrogen peroxide, for example, two successive reactions of H_2O_2, first with bromide and then with bromine, take place. Because these two reactions together serve as a catalytic pathway for hydrogen peroxide decomposition, *both* of them must have significantly lower activation energies than the uncatalyzed decomposition ($\blacktriangleleft$ **FIGURE 14.23**).

GO FIGURE

Where are the intermediates and transition states in this diagram?

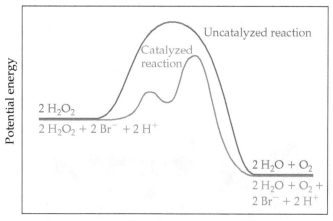

▲ **FIGURE 14.23** **Energy profiles for the uncatalyzed and bromide-catalyzed decomposition of H_2O_2.**

▲ **GIVE IT SOME THOUGHT**

How does a catalyst increase the rate of a reaction?

Heterogeneous Catalysis

A **heterogeneous catalyst** is one that exists in a phase different from the phase of the reactant molecules, usually as a solid in contact with either gaseous reactants or with reactants in a liquid solution. Many industrially important reactions are catalyzed by the surfaces of solids. For example, hydrocarbon molecules are rearranged to form gasoline with the aid of what are called "cracking" catalysts. Heterogeneous catalysts are often composed of metals or metal oxides. Because the catalyzed reaction occurs on the surface, special methods are often used to prepare catalysts so that they have very large surface areas.

The initial step in heterogeneous catalysis is usually **adsorption** of reactants. *Adsorption* refers to the binding of molecules to a surface, whereas *absorption* refers to the uptake of molecules into the interior of a substance. Adsorption occurs because the atoms or ions at the surface of a solid are extremely reactive. Unlike their counterparts in the interior of the substance, surface atoms and ions have unused bonding capacity that can be used to bond molecules from the gas or solution phase to the surface of the solid.

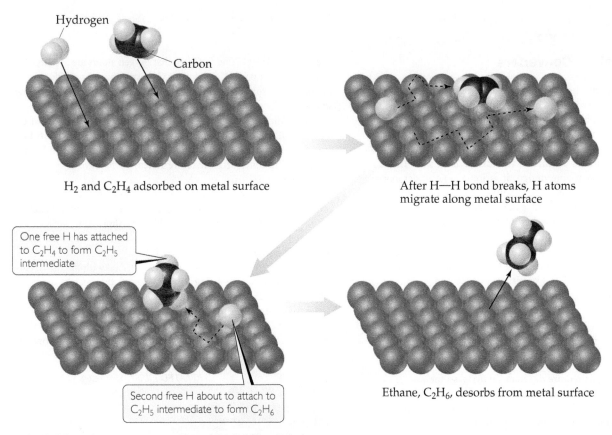

▲ **FIGURE 14.24   Heterogeneous catalysis.** Mechanism for reaction of ethylene with hydrogen on a catalytic surface.

The reaction of hydrogen gas with ethylene gas to form ethane gas provides an example of heterogeneous catalysis:

$$\underset{\text{Ethylene}}{C_2H_4(g)} + H_2(g) \longrightarrow \underset{\text{Ethane}}{C_2H_6(g)} \quad \Delta H° = -137 \text{ kJ/mol} \qquad [14.32]$$

Even though this reaction is exothermic, it occurs very slowly in the absence of a catalyst. In the presence of a finely powdered metal, however, such as nickel, palladium, or platinum, the reaction occurs easily at room temperature via the mechanism diagrammed in ▲ **FIGURE 14.24.** Both ethylene and hydrogen are adsorbed on the metal surface. Upon adsorption, the H—H bond of H_2 breaks, leaving two H atoms initially bonded to the metal surface but relatively free to move. When a hydrogen encounters an adsorbed ethylene molecule, it can form a σ bond to one of the carbon atoms, effectively destroying the C—C π bond and leaving an *ethyl group* (C_2H_5) bonded to the surface via a metal-to-carbon σ bond . This σ bond is relatively weak, so when the other carbon atom also encounters a hydrogen atom, a sixth C—H σ bond is readily formed, and an ethane molecule (C_2H_6) is released from the metal surface.

 GIVE IT SOME THOUGHT

How does a homogeneous catalyst compare with a heterogeneous one regarding the ease of recovery of the catalyst from the reaction mixture?

Enzymes

The human body is characterized by an extremely complex system of interrelated chemical reactions, all of which must occur at carefully controlled rates to maintain life. A large number of marvelously efficient biological catalysts known as **enzymes** are necessary for many of these reactions to occur at suitable rates. Most enzymes are large

CHEMISTRY PUT TO WORK

Catalytic Converters

Heterogeneous catalysis plays a major role in the fight against urban air pollution. Two components of automobile exhausts that help form photochemical smog are nitrogen oxides and unburned hydrocarbons. In addition, automobile exhaust may contain considerable quantities of carbon monoxide. Even with the most careful attention to engine design, it is impossible under normal driving conditions to reduce the quantity of these pollutants to an acceptable level in the exhaust gases. It is therefore necessary to remove them from the exhaust before they are vented to the air. This removal is accomplished in the *catalytic converter*.

The catalytic converter, which is part of an automobile's exhaust system, must perform two functions: (1) oxidation of CO and unburned hydrocarbons (C_xH_y) to carbon dioxide and water, and (2) reduction of nitrogen oxides to nitrogen gas:

$$CO, C_xH_y \xrightarrow{O_2} CO_2 + H_2O$$

$$NO, NO_2 \longrightarrow N_2$$

These two functions require different catalysts, so the development of a successful catalyst system is a difficult challenge. The catalysts must be effective over a wide range of operating temperatures. They must continue to be active despite the fact that various components of the exhaust can block the active sites of the catalyst. And the catalysts must be sufficiently rugged to withstand exhaust gas turbulence and the mechanical shocks of driving under various conditions for thousands of miles.

Catalysts that promote the combustion of CO and hydrocarbons are, in general, the transition-metal oxides and the noble metals. These materials are supported on a structure (▶ FIGURE 14.25) that allows the best possible contact between the flowing exhaust gas and the catalyst surface. A honeycomb structure made from alumina (Al_2O_3) and impregnated with the catalyst is employed. Such catalysts operate by first adsorbing oxygen gas present in the exhaust gas. This adsorption weakens the O—O bond in O_2, so that oxygen atoms are available for reaction with adsorbed CO to form CO_2. Hydrocarbon oxidation probably proceeds somewhat similarly, with the hydrocarbons first being adsorbed followed by rupture of a C—H bond.

Transition-metal oxides and noble metals are also the most effective catalysts for reduction of NO to N_2 and O_2. The catalysts that are most effective in one reaction, however, are usually much less effective in the other. It is therefore necessary to have two catalytic components.

Catalytic converters contain remarkably efficient heterogeneous catalysts. The automotive exhaust gases are in contact with the catalyst for only 100 to 400 ms, but in this very short time, 96% of the hydrocarbons and CO is converted to CO_2 and H_2O, and the emission of nitrogen oxides is reduced by 76%.

There are costs as well as benefits associated with the use of catalytic converters, one being that some of the metals are very expensive. Catalytic converters currently account for about 35% of the platinum, 65% of the palladium, and 95% of the rhodium used annually. All of these metals, which come mainly from Russia and South Africa, can be far more expensive than gold.

RELATED EXERCISES: 14.64, 14.87, 14.88

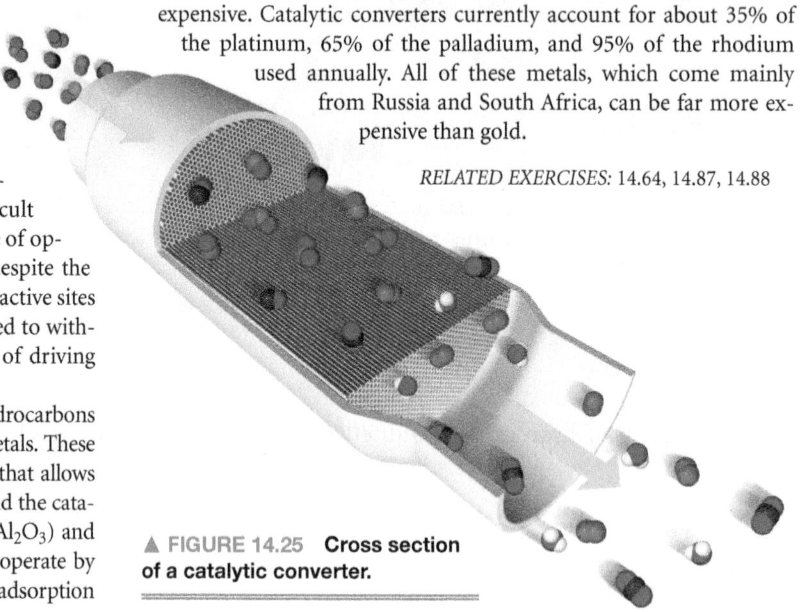

▲ FIGURE 14.25 **Cross section of a catalytic converter.**

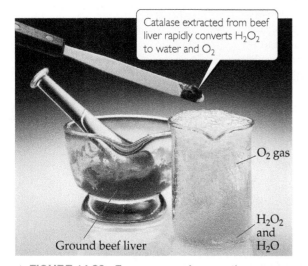

Catalase extracted from beef liver rapidly converts H_2O_2 to water and O_2

O_2 gas

Ground beef liver

H_2O_2 and H_2O

▲ FIGURE 14.26 **Enzymes speed up reactions.**

protein molecules with molecular weights ranging from about 10,000 to about 1 million amu. They are very selective in the reactions they catalyze, and some are absolutely specific, operating for only one substance in only one reaction. The decomposition of hydrogen peroxide, for example, is an important biological process. Because hydrogen peroxide is strongly oxidizing, it can be physiologically harmful. For this reason, the blood and liver of mammals contain an enzyme, *catalase*, that catalyzes the decomposition of hydrogen peroxide into water and oxygen (Equation 14.29). ◀ FIGURE 14.26 shows the dramatic acceleration of this chemical reaction by the catalase in beef liver.

Which molecules must bind more tightly to the active site, substrates or products?

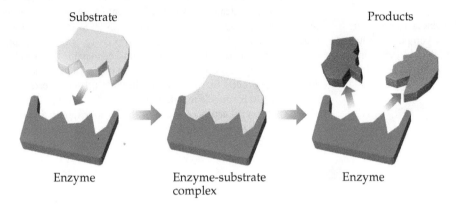

Substrate   Products

Enzyme   Enzyme-substrate   Enzyme
                    complex

▲ FIGURE 14.27   **Lock-and-key model for enzyme action.**

The reaction any given enzyme catalyzes takes place at a specific location in the enzyme, the **active site**. The substances that react at this site are called **substrates**. The **lock-and-key model** provides a simple explanation for the specificity of an enzyme (▲ FIGURE 14.27). The substrate is pictured as fitting neatly into the active site, much like a key fits into a lock. Although this model oversimplifies the situation, since enzymes can "wiggle" to adjust the shape and size of the active site, the lock-and-key model is a good place to start understanding enzyme activity.

▶ FIGURE 14.28 shows a model of the enzyme lysozyme without and with a bound substrate molecule.

The combination of enzyme and substrate is called the *enzyme-substrate complex*. Although Figure 14.27 shows both the active site and its substrate as having a fixed shape, the active site is often fairly flexible and so may change shape as it binds the substrate. The binding between substrate and active site involves dipole–dipole attractions, hydrogen bonds, and dispersion forces. ⚭ (Section 5.2)

As substrate molecules enter the active site, they are somehow activated so that they are capable of reacting rapidly. This activation process may occur, for example, by the withdrawal or donation of electron density from a particular bond or group of atoms in the enzyme's active site. In addition, the substrate may become distorted in the process of fitting into the active site and made more reactive. Once the reaction occurs, the products depart from the active site, allowing another substrate molecule to enter.

The activity of an enzyme is destroyed if some molecule other than the substrate specific to that enzyme binds to the active site and blocks entry of the substrate. Such substances are called *enzyme inhibitors*. Nerve poisons and certain toxic metal ions, such as lead and mercury, are believed to act in this way to inhibit enzyme activity. Some other poisons act by attaching elsewhere on the enzyme, thereby distorting the active site so that the substrate no longer fits.

Enzymes are enormously more efficient than nonbiochemical catalysts. The number of individual catalyzed reaction events occurring at a particular active site, called the *turnover number*, is generally in the range of 10^3 to 10^7 per second. Such large turnover numbers correspond to very low activation energies. Compared with a simple chemical catalyst, enzymes can increase the rate constant for a given reaction by a million-fold or more.

▲ FIGURE 14.28   **Molecular model of lysozyme without and with a bound substrate molecule (yellow).**

◢ GIVE IT SOME THOUGHT

Is it reasonable to say that enzymes stabilize the transition state for a reaction? Explain your answer.

CHEMISTRY AND LIFE

NITROGEN FIXATION AND NITROGENASE

Nitrogen is one of the most essential elements in living organisms, found in many compounds vital to life, including proteins, nucleic acids, vitamins, and hormones. Nitrogen is continually cycling through the biosphere in various forms, as shown in ◀ FIGURE 14.29. For example, certain microorganisms convert the nitrogen in animal waste and dead plants and animals into $N_2(g)$, which then returns to the atmosphere. For the food chain to be sustained, there must be a means of converting atmospheric $N_2(g)$ in a form plants can use. For this reason, if a chemist were asked to name the most important chemical reaction in the world, she might easily say *nitrogen fixation*, the process by which atmospheric $N_2(g)$ is converted into compounds suitable for plant use. Some fixed nitrogen results from the action of lightning on the atmosphere, and some is produced industrially using a process we discussed in Chapter 12. About 60% of fixed nitrogen, however, is a consequence of the action of the remarkable and complex enzyme *nitrogenase*. This enzyme is *not* present in humans or other animals; rather, it is found in bacteria that live in the root nodules of certain plants, such as the legumes clover and alfalfa.

Nitrogenase converts N_2 into NH_3, a process that, in the absence of a catalyst, has a very large activation energy. This process is a *reduction* reaction in which the oxidation state of N is reduced from 0 in N_2 to -3 in NH_3. The mechanism by which nitrogenase reduces N_2 is not fully understood. Like many other enzymes, including catalase, the active site of nitrogenase contains transition-metal atoms; such enzymes are called *metalloenzymes*. Because transition metals can readily change oxidation state, metalloenzymes are especially useful for effecting transformations in which substrates are either oxidized or reduced.

It has been known for nearly 30 years that a portion of nitrogenase contains iron and molybdenum atoms. This portion, called the *FeMo-cofactor*, is thought to serve as the active site of the enzyme. The FeMo-cofactor of nitrogenase is a cluster of seven Fe atoms and one Mo atom, all linked by sulfur atoms (◀ FIGURE 14.30).

It is one of the wonders of life that simple bacteria can contain beautifully complex and vitally important enzymes such as nitrogenase. Because of this enzyme, nitrogen is continually cycled between its comparatively inert role in the atmosphere and its critical role in living organisms. Without nitrogenase, life as we know it could not exist on Earth.

RELATED EXERCISES: 14.91, 14.126

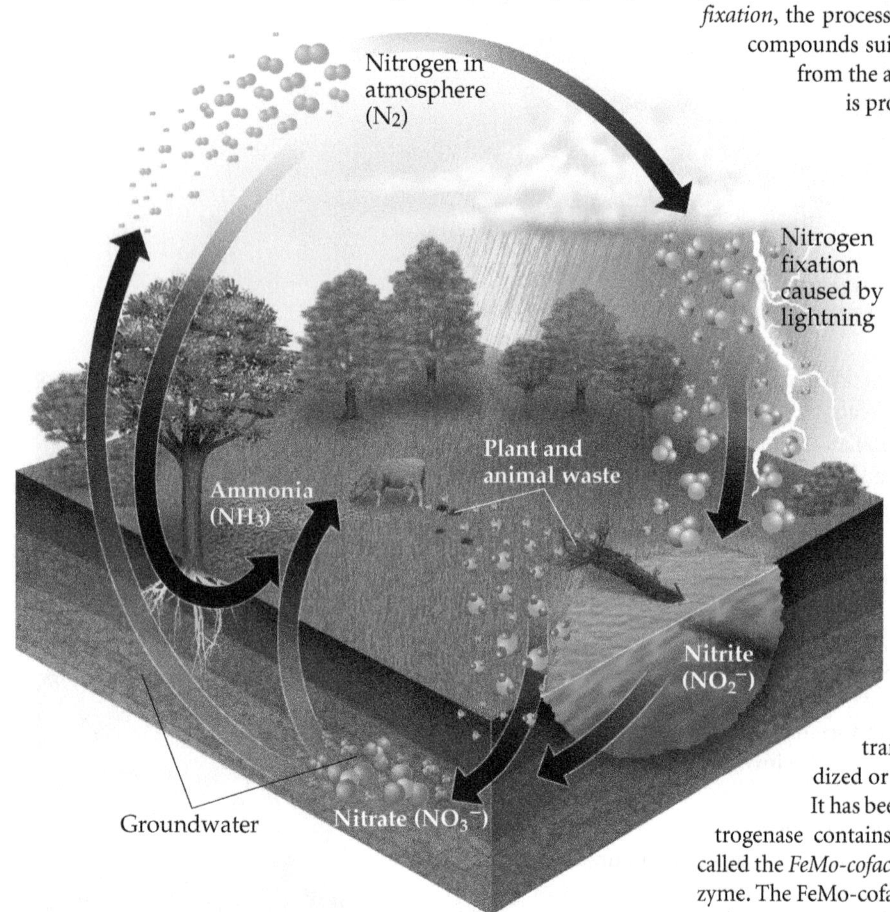

▲ FIGURE 14.29 **Simplified picture of the nitrogen cycle.**

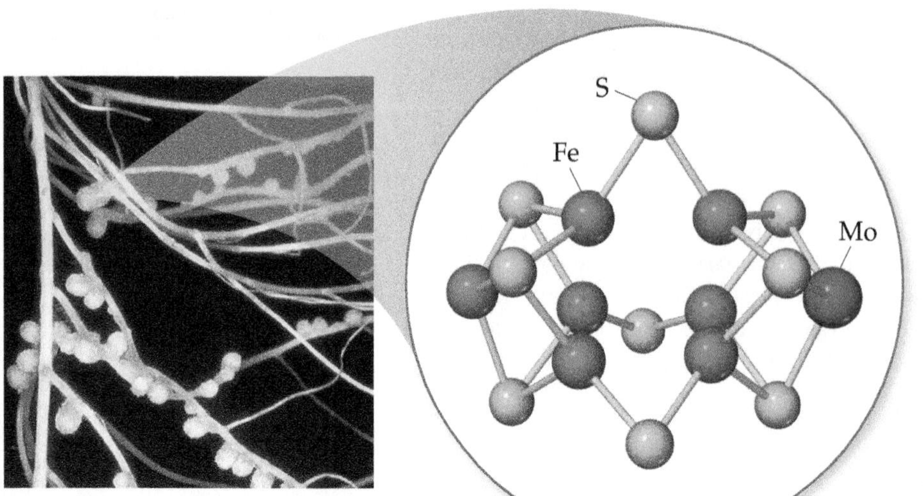

◀ FIGURE 14.30 **The FeMo-cofactor of nitrogenase.** Nitrogenase is found in nodules in the roots of certain plants, such as the white clover roots shown at the left. The cofactor, which is thought to be the active site of the enzyme, contains seven Fe atoms and one Mo atom, linked by sulfur atoms. The molecules on the outside of the cofactor connect it to the rest of the protein.

SAMPLE INTEGRATIVE EXERCISE **Putting Concepts Together**

Formic acid (HCOOH) decomposes in the gas phase at elevated temperatures as follows:

$$HCOOH(g) \longrightarrow CO_2(g) + H_2(g)$$

The uncatalyzed decomposition reaction is determined to be first order. A graph of the partial pressure of HCOOH versus time for decomposition at 838 K is shown as the red curve in ▶ FIGURE 14.31. When a small amount of solid ZnO is added to the reaction chamber, the partial pressure of acid versus time varies as shown by the blue curve in Figure 14.31.

(a) Estimate the half-life and first-order rate constant for formic acid decomposition.

(b) What can you conclude from the effect of added ZnO on the decomposition of formic acid?

(c) The progress of the reaction was followed by measuring the partial pressure of formic acid vapor at selected times. Suppose that, instead, we had plotted the concentration of formic acid in units of mol/L. What effect would this have had on the calculated value of k?

(d) The pressure of formic acid vapor at the start of the reaction is 3.00×10^2 torr. Assuming constant temperature and ideal-gas behavior, what is the pressure in the system at the end of the reaction? If the volume of the reaction chamber is 436 cm³, how many moles of gas occupy the reaction chamber at the end of the reaction?

(e) The standard heat of formation of formic acid vapor is $\Delta H_f^\circ = -378.6$ kJ/mol. Calculate ΔH° for the overall reaction. If the activation energy (E_a) for the reaction is 184 kJ/mol, sketch an approximate energy profile for the reaction, and label E_a, ΔH°, and the transition state.

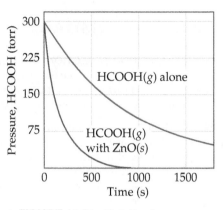

▲ FIGURE 14.31 **Variation in pressure of HCOOH(g) as a function of time at 838 K.**

SOLUTION

(a) The initial pressure of HCOOH is 3.00×10^2 torr. On the graph we move to the level at which the partial pressure of HCOOH is 1.50×10^2 torr, half the initial value. This corresponds to a time of about 6.60×10^2 s, which is therefore the half-life. The first-order rate constant is given by Equation 14.15: $k = 0.693/t_{1/2} = 0.693/660$ s $= 1.05 \times 10^{-3}$ s^{-1}.

(b) The reaction proceeds much more rapidly in the presence of solid ZnO, so the surface of the oxide must be acting as a catalyst for the decomposition of the acid. This is an example of heterogeneous catalysis.

(c) If we had graphed the concentration of formic acid in units of moles per liter, we would still have determined that the half-life for decomposition is 660 s, and we would have computed the same value for k. Because the units for k are s^{-1}, the value for k is independent of the units used for concentration.

(d) According to the stoichiometry of the reaction, two moles of product are formed for each mole of reactant. When reaction is completed, therefore, the pressure will be 600 torr, just twice the initial pressure, assuming ideal-gas behavior. (Because we are working at quite high temperature and fairly low gas pressure, assuming ideal-gas behavior is reasonable.) The number of moles of gas present can be calculated using the ideal-gas equation: ∞ (Section 8.4)

$$n = \frac{PV}{RT} = \frac{(600/760 \text{ atm})(0.436 \text{ L})}{(0.08206 \text{ L-atm/mol-K})(838 \text{ K})} = 5.00 \times 10^{-3} \text{ mole}$$

(e) We first calculate the overall change in energy, ΔH° (∞ Section 10.7 and Appendix C), as in

$$\Delta H^\circ = \Delta H_f^\circ(CO_2(g)) + \Delta H_f^\circ(H_2(g)) - \Delta H_f^\circ(HCOOH(g))$$
$$= -393.5 \text{ kJ/mol} + 0 - (-378.6 \text{ kJ/mol})$$
$$= -14.9 \text{ kJ/mol}$$

From this and the given value for E_a, we can draw an approximate energy profile for the reaction, in analogy to Figure 14.17.

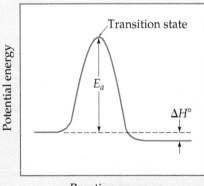

CHAPTER SUMMARY AND KEY TERMS

INTRODUCTION AND SECTION 14.1 **Chemical kinetics** is the area of chemistry in which **reaction rates** are studied. Factors that affect reaction rate are the physical state of the reactants; concentration; temperature; and the presence of catalysts.

SECTION 14.2 Reaction rate are usually expressed as changes in concentration per unit time: Typically, for reactions in solution, rates are given in units of molarity per second M/s. For most reactions, a plot of molarity versus time shows that the rate slows down as the reaction proceeds. The **instantaneous rate** is the slope of a line drawn tangent to the concentration-versus-time curve at a specific time. Rates can be written in terms of the appearance of products or the disappearance of reactants; the stoichiometry of the reaction dictates the relationship between rates of appearance and disappearance.

SECTION 14.3 The quantitative relationship between rate and concentration is expressed by a **rate law**, which usually has the following form:

$$\text{Rate} = k[\text{reactant 1}]^m[\text{reactant 2}]^n \ldots$$

The constant k in the rate law is called the **rate constant**; the exponents m, n, and so forth are called **reaction orders** for the reactants. The sum of the reaction orders gives the **overall reaction order**. Reaction orders must be determined experimentally. The units of the rate constant depend on the overall reaction order. For a reaction in which the overall reaction order is 1, k has units of s^{-1}; for one in which the overall reaction order is 2, k has units of $M^{-1}\,s^{-1}$. Spectroscopy is one technique that can be used to monitor the course of a reaction. According to Beer's law, the absorption of electromagnetic radiation by a substance at a particular wavelength is directly proportional to its concentration.

SECTION 14.4 Rate laws can be used to determine the concentrations of reactants or products at any time during a reaction. In a **first-order reaction** the rate is proportional to the concentration of a single reactant raised to the first power: Rate $= k[A]$. In such cases the integrated form of the rate law is $\ln[A]_t = -kt + \ln[A]_0$, where $[A]_t$ is the concentration of reactant A at time t, k is the rate constant, and $[A]_0$ is the initial concentration of A. Thus, for a first-order reaction, a graph of $\ln[A]$ versus time yields a straight line of slope $-k$.

A **second-order reaction** is one for which the overall reaction order is 2. If a second-order rate law depends on the concentration of only one reactant, then rate $= k[A]^2$, and the time dependence of $[A]$ is given by the integrated form of the rate law: $1/[A]_t = 1/[A]_0 + kt$. In this case a graph of $1/[A]_t$ versus time yields a straight line. A **zero-order reaction** is one for which the overall reaction order is 0. Rate $= k$ if the reaction is zero order.

The **half-life** of a reaction, $t_{1/2}$, is the time required for the concentration of a reactant to drop to one-half of its original value. For a first-order reaction, the half-life depends only on the rate constant and not on the initial concentration: $t_{1/2} = 0.693/k$. The half-life of a second-order reaction depends on both the rate constant and the initial concentration of A: $t_{1/2} = 1/k[A]_0$.

SECTION 14.5 The **collision model**, which assumes that reactions occur as a result of collisions between molecules, helps explain why the magnitudes of rate constants increase with increasing temperature.

The greater the kinetic energy of the colliding molecules, the greater is the energy of collision. The minimum energy required for a reaction to occur is called the **activation energy**, E_a. A collision with energy E_a or greater can cause the atoms of the colliding molecules to reach the **activated complex** (or **transition state**), which is the highest energy arrangement in the pathway from reactants to products. Even if a collision is energetic enough, it may not lead to reaction; the reactants must also be correctly oriented relative to one another in order for a collision to be effective.

Because the kinetic energy of molecules depends on temperature, the rate constant of a reaction is very dependent on temperature. The relationship between k and temperature is given by the **Arrhenius equation**: $k = Ae^{-E_a/RT}$. The term A is called the **frequency factor**; it relates to the number of collisions that are favorably oriented for reaction. The Arrhenius equation is often used in logarithmic form: $\ln k = \ln A - E_a/RT$. Thus, a graph of $\ln k$ versus $1/T$ yields a straight line with slope $-E_a/R$.

SECTION 14.6 A **reaction mechanism** details the individual steps that occur in the course of a reaction. Each of these steps, called **elementary reactions**, has a well-defined rate law that depends on the number of molecules (the **molecularity**) of the step. Elementary reactions are defined as either **unimolecular**, **bimolecular**, or **termolecular**, depending on whether one, two, or three reactant molecules are involved, respectively. Termolecular elementary reactions are very rare. Unimolecular, bimolecular, and termolecular reactions follow rate laws that are first order overall, second order overall, and third order overall, respectively. Many reactions occur by a multistep mechanism, involving two or more elementary reactions, or steps. An **intermediate** is produced in one elementary step, is consumed in a later elementary step, and therefore does not appear in the overall equation for the reaction. When a mechanism has several elementary steps, the overall rate is limited by the slowest elementary step, called the **rate-determining step**. A fast elementary step that follows the rate-determining step will have no effect on the rate law of the reaction. A fast step that precedes the rate-determining step often creates an equilibrium that involves an intermediate. For a mechanism to be valid, the rate law predicted by the mechanism must be the same as that observed experimentally.

SECTION 14.7 A **catalyst** is a substance that increases the rate of a reaction without undergoing a net chemical change itself. It does so by providing a different mechanism for the reaction, one that has a lower activation energy. A **homogeneous catalyst** is one that is in the same phase as the reactants. A **heterogeneous catalyst** has a different phase from the reactants. Finely divided metals are often used as heterogeneous catalysts for solution- and gas-phase reactions. Reacting molecules can undergo binding, or **adsorption**, at the surface of the catalyst. The adsorption of a reactant at specific sites on the surface makes bond breaking easier, lowering the activation energy. Catalysis in living organisms is achieved by **enzymes**, large protein molecules that usually catalyze a very specific reaction. The specific reactant molecules involved in an enzymatic reaction are called **substrates**. The site of the enzyme where the catalysis occurs is called the **active site**. In the **lock-and-key model** for enzyme catalysis, substrate molecules bind very specifically to the active site of the enzyme, after which they can undergo reaction.

KEY SKILLS

- Understand the factors that affect the rate of chemical reactions. (Section 14.1)
- Determine the rate of a reaction given time and concentration. (Section 14.2)
- Relate the rate of formation of products and the rate of disappearance of reactants given the balanced chemical equation for the reaction. (Section 14.2)
- Understand the form and meaning of a rate law including the ideas of reaction order and rate constant. (Section 14.3)
- Determine the rate law and rate constant for a reaction from a series of experiments given the measured rates for various concentrations of reactants. (Section 14.3)
- Use the integrated form of a rate law to determine the concentration of a reactant at a given time. (Section 14.4)
- Explain how the activation energy affects a rate and be able to use the Arrhenius equation. (Section 14.5)
- Predict a rate law for a reaction having a multistep mechanism given the individual steps in the mechanism. (Section 14.6)
- Explain how a catalyst works. (Section 14.7)

KEY EQUATIONS

- $\text{Rate} = -\dfrac{1}{a}\dfrac{\Delta[A]}{\Delta t} = -\dfrac{1}{b}\dfrac{\Delta[B]}{\Delta t} = \dfrac{1}{c}\dfrac{\Delta[C]}{\Delta t} = \dfrac{1}{d}\dfrac{\Delta[D]}{\Delta t}$ [14.4]   Relating rates to the components of the balanced chemical equation $a\,A + b\,B \longrightarrow c\,C + d\,D$

- $\text{Rate} = k[A]^m[B]^n$ [14.7]   General form of a rate law for the reaction $A + B \longrightarrow$ products

- $\ln[A]_t - \ln[A]_0 = -kt \quad \text{or} \quad \ln\dfrac{[A]_t}{[A]_0} = -kt$ [14.12]   The integrated form of a first-order rate law for the reaction $A \longrightarrow$ products

- $\dfrac{1}{[A]_t} = kt + \dfrac{1}{[A]_0}$ [14.14]   The integrated form of the second-order rate law for the reaction $A \longrightarrow$ products

- $t_{1/2} = \dfrac{0.693}{k}$ [14.15]   Relating the half-life and rate constant for a first-order reaction

- $k = Ae^{-E_a/RT}$ [14.19]   The Arrhenius equation, which expresses how the rate constant depends on temperature

- $\ln k = -\dfrac{E_a}{RT} + \ln A$ [14.20]   Linear form of the Arrhenius equation

EXERCISES

VISUALIZING CONCEPTS

14.1 For which one of the following vessels for the reaction $A + B \longrightarrow C$ is the reaction the fastest? Assume all vessels are at the same temperature. [Section 4.1]

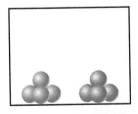
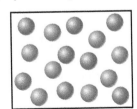
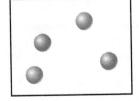

14.2 Consider the following graph of the concentration of a substance over time. (a) Is X a reactant or product of the reaction? (b) Is the reaction speeding up, slowing down, or not changing its rate as time progresses? (c) Why is the average rate of the reaction different between points 1 and 2 than between points 2 and 3? [Section 14.2]

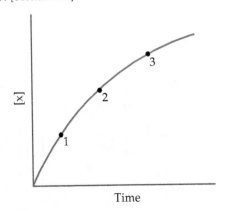

14.3 You study the rate of a reaction, measuring both the concentration of the reactant and the concentration of the product as a function of time, and obtain the following results:

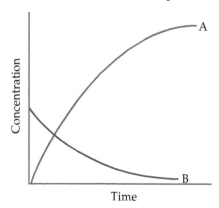

Which chemical equation is consistent with these data: (a) A ⟶ B, (b) B ⟶ A, (c) A ⟶ 2 B, (d) B ⟶ 2 A? Explain your choice. [Section 14.2]

14.4 You perform the reaction K + L → M, monitor the production of M over time, and then plot this graph from your data:

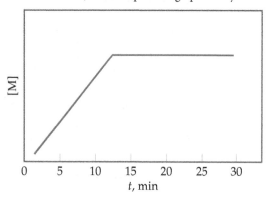

(a) Is the reaction occurring at a constant rate from $t = 0$ to $t = 15$ min? Explain. (b) Is the reaction completed at $t = 15$ min? Explain.

14.5 You perform a series of experiments for the reaction A ⟶ B + C and find that the rate law has the form rate $= k[A]^x$. Determine the value of x in each of the following cases: (a) There is no rate change when $[A]_0$ is tripled. (b) The rate increases by a factor of 9 when $[A]_0$ is tripled. (c) When $[A]_0$ is doubled, the rate increases by a factor of 8. [Section 14.3]

14.6 The following diagrams represent mixtures of NO(g) and $O_2(g)$. These two substances react as follows:

$$2 NO(g) + O_2(g) \longrightarrow 2 NO_2(g)$$

It has been determined experimentally that the rate is second order in NO and first order in O_2. Based on this fact, which of the following mixtures will have the fastest initial rate? [Section 14.3]

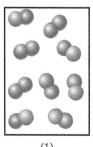   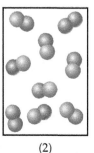   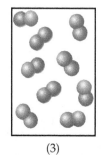

(1)   (2)   (3)

14.7 A friend studies a first-order reaction and obtains the following three graphs for experiments done at two different temperatures. (a) Which two graphs represent experiments done at the same temperature? What accounts for the difference in these two graphs? In what way are they the same? (b) Which two graphs represent experiments done with the same starting concentration but at different temperatures? Which graph probably represents the lower temperature? How do you know? [Section 14.4]

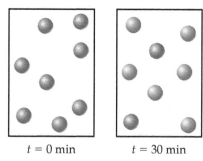

14.8 (a) Given the following diagrams at $t = 0$ min and $t = 30$ min, what is the half-life of the reaction if it follows first-order kinetics?

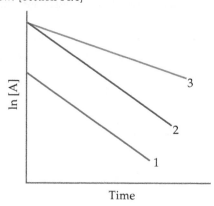

$t = 0$ min $t = 30$ min

(b) After four half-life periods for a first-order reaction, what fraction of reactant remains? [Section 14.4]

14.9 The following diagram shows the reaction profile of a reaction. Label the components indicated by the boxes. [Section 14.5]

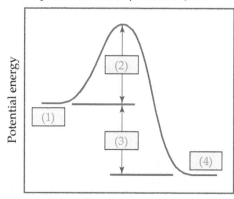

Reaction progress

14.10 You study the effect of temperature on the rate of two reactions and graph the natural logarithm of the rate constant for each reaction as a function of $1/T$. How do the two graphs compare (a) if the activation energy of the second reaction is higher than the activation energy of the first reaction but the two reactions have the same frequency factor, and (b) if the frequency factor of the second reaction is higher than the frequency factor of the first reaction but the two reactions have the same activation energy? [Section 14.5]

14.11 The following graph shows two different reaction pathways for the same overall reaction at the same temperature. (a) Which pathway is slower? Why? (b) How can there be two different reaction pathways for the same reaction at the same temperature? Discuss. [Section 14.6]

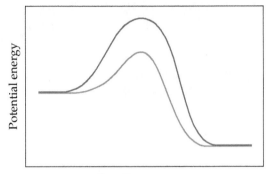

Reaction progress

14.12 Consider the diagram that follows, which represents two steps in an overall reaction. The red spheres are oxygen, the blue ones nitrogen, and the green ones fluorine. (a) Write the chemical equation for each step in the reaction. (b) Write the equation for the overall reaction. (c) Identify the intermediate in the mechanism. (d) Write the rate law for the overall reaction if the first step is the slow, rate-determining step. [Section 14.6]

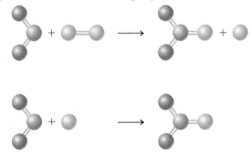

14.13 Based on the following reaction profile, how many intermediates are formed in the reaction A ⟶ C? How many transition states are there? Which step is the fastest? Is the reaction A ⟶ C exothermic or endothermic? [Section 14.6]

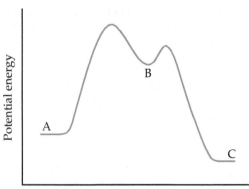

Reaction progress

14.14 Draw a possible transition state for the bimolecular reaction depicted here. (The blue spheres are nitrogen atoms, and the red ones are oxygen atoms.) Use dashed lines to represent the bonds that are in the process of being broken or made in the transition state. [Section 14.6]

14.15 The following diagram represents an imaginary two-step mechanism. Let the red spheres represent element A, the green ones element B, and the blue ones element C. (a) Write the equation for the net reaction that is occurring. (b) Identify the intermediate. (c) Identify the catalyst. [Sections 14.6 and 14.7]

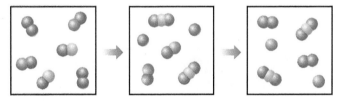

14.16 Draw a graph showing the reaction pathway for an overall exothermic reaction with two intermediates that are produced at different rates. On your graph indicate the reactants, products, intermediates, transition states, and activation energies. [Sections 14.6 and 14.7]

REACTION RATES (sections 14.1 and 14.2)

14.17 (a) What is meant by the term *reaction rate*? (b) Name three factors that can affect the rate of a chemical reaction. (c) Is the rate of disappearance of reactants always the same as the rate of appearance of products? Explain.

14.18 (a) What are the units usually used to express the rates of reactions occurring in solution? (b) From your everyday experience, give two examples of the effects of temperature on the rates of reactions. (c) What is the difference between average rate and instantaneous rate?

14.19 Consider the following hypothetical aqueous reaction: $A(aq) \longrightarrow B(aq)$. A flask is charged with 0.065 mol of A in a total volume of 100.0 mL. The following data are collected:

Time (min)	0	10	20	30	40
Moles of A	0.065	0.051	0.042	0.036	0.031

(a) Calculate the number of moles of B at each time in the table, assuming that there are no molecules of B at time zero, and that A cleanly converts to B with no intermediates. (b) Calculate the average rate of disappearance of A for each 10-min interval in units of M/s. (c) Between $t = 10$ min and $t = 30$ min, what is the average rate of appearance of B in units of M/s? Assume that the volume of the solution is constant.

14.20 A flask is charged with 0.100 mol of A and allowed to react to form B according to the hypothetical gas-phase reaction $A(g) \longrightarrow B(g)$. The following data are collected:

Time (s)	0	40	80	120	160
Moles of A	0.100	0.067	0.045	0.030	0.020

(a) Calculate the number of moles of B at each time in the table, assuming that A is cleanly converted to B with no intermediates. (b) Calculate the average rate of disappearance of A for each 40-s interval in units of mol/s. (c) What additional information would be needed to calculate the rate in units of concentration per time?

14.21 The isomerization of methyl isonitrile (CH_3NC) to acetonitrile (CH_3CN) was studied in the gas phase at 215 °C, and the following data were obtained:

Time (s)	[CH₃NC] (M)
0	0.0165
2,000	0.0110
5,000	0.00591
8,000	0.00314
12,000	0.00137
15,000	0.00074

(a) Calculate the average rate of reaction, in M/s, for the time interval between each measurement. (b) Calculate the average rate of reaction over the entire time of the data from $t = 0$ to $t = 15,000\,s$. (c) Graph [CH_3NC] versus time and determine the instantaneous rates in M/s at $t = 5000\,s$ and $t = 8000\,s$.

14.22 The rate of disappearance of HCl was measured for the following reaction:

$$CH_3OH(aq) + HCl(aq) \longrightarrow CH_3Cl(aq) + H_2O(l)$$

The following data were collected:

Time (min)	[HCl] (M)
0.0	1.85
54.0	1.58
107.0	1.36
215.0	1.02
430.0	0.580

(a) Calculate the average rate of reaction, in M/s, for the time interval between each measurement. (b) Calculate the average rate of reaction for the entire time for the data from $t = 0.0$ min to $t = 430.0$ min.

(c) Graph [HCl] versus time and determine the instantaneous rates in $M/$min and M/s at $t = 75.0$ min and $t = 250$ min.

14.23 For each of the following gas-phase reactions, indicate how the rate of disappearance of each reactant is related to the rate of appearance of each product:

(a) $H_2O_2(g) \longrightarrow H_2(g) + O_2(g)$

(b) $2\,N_2O(g) \longrightarrow 2\,N_2(g) + O_2(g)$

(c) $N_2(g) + 3\,H_2(g) \longrightarrow 2\,NH_3(g)$

(d) $C_2H_5NH_2(g) \longrightarrow C_2H_4(g) + NH_3(g)$

14.24 For each of the following gas-phase reactions, write the rate expression in terms of the appearance of each product and disappearance of each reactant:

(a) $2\,H_2O(g) \longrightarrow 2\,H_2(g) + O_2(g)$

(b) $2\,SO_2(g) + O_2(g) \longrightarrow 2\,SO_3(g)$

(c) $2\,NO(g) + 2\,H_2(g) \longrightarrow N_2(g) + 2\,H_2O(g)$

(d) $N_2(g) + 2\,H_2(g) \longrightarrow N_2H_4(g)$

14.25 (a) Consider the combustion of $H_2(g): 2\,H_2(g) + O_2(g) \longrightarrow 2\,H_2O(g)$. If hydrogen is burning at the rate of 0.48 mol/s, what is the rate of consumption of oxygen? What is the rate of formation of water vapor? (b) The reaction $2\,NO(g) + Cl_2(g) \longrightarrow 2\,NOCl(g)$ is carried out in a closed vessel. If the partial pressure of NO is decreasing at the rate of 56 torr/min, what is the rate of change of the total pressure of the vessel?

14.26 (a) Consider the combustion of ethylene, $C_2H_4(g) + 3\,O_2(g) \longrightarrow 2\,CO_2(g) + 2\,H_2O(g)$. If the concentration of C_2H_4 is decreasing at the rate of 0.036 M/s, what are the rates of change in the concentrations of CO_2 and H_2O? (b) The rate of decrease in N_2H_4 partial pressure in a closed reaction vessel from the reaction $N_2H_4(g) + H_2(g) \longrightarrow 2\,NH_3(g)$ is 74 torr per hour. What are the rates of change of NH_3 partial pressure and total pressure in the vessel?

RATE LAWS (section 14.3)

14.27 A reaction $A + B \longrightarrow C$ obeys the following rate law: Rate $= k[B]^2$. (a) If [A] is doubled, how will the rate change? Will the rate constant change? Explain. (b) What are the reaction orders for A and B? What is the overall reaction order? (c) What are the units of the rate constant?

14.28 Consider a hypothetical reaction between A, B, and C that is first order in A, zero order in B, and second order in C. (a) Write the rate law for the reaction. (b) How does the rate change when [A] is doubled and the other reactant concentrations are held constant? (c) How does the rate change when [B] is tripled and the other reactant concentrations are held constant? (d) How does the rate change when [C] is tripled and the other reactant concentrations are held constant? (e) By what factor does the rate change when the concentrations of all three reactants are tripled? (f) By what factor does the rate change when the concentrations of all three reactants are cut in half?

14.29 The decomposition reaction of N_2O_5 in carbon tetrachloride is $2\,N_2O_5 \longrightarrow 4\,NO_2 + O_2$. The rate law is first order in N_2O_5. At 64 °C the rate constant is $4.82 \times 10^{-3}\,s^{-1}$. (a) Write the rate law for the reaction. (b) What is the rate of reaction when [N_2O_5] $= 0.0240\,M$? (c) What happens to the rate when the concentration of N_2O_5 is doubled to $0.0480\,M$? (d) What happens to the rate when the concentration of N_2O_5 is halved to $0.0120\,M$?

14.30 Consider the following reaction:

$$2\,NO(g) + 2\,H_2(g) \longrightarrow N_2(g) + 2\,H_2O(g)$$

(a) The rate law for this reaction is first order in H_2 and second order in NO. Write the rate law. (b) If the rate constant for this reaction at 1000 K is $6.0 \times 10^4\,M^{-2}\,s^{-1}$, what is the reaction rate when [NO] $= 0.035\,M$ and [H_2] $= 0.015\,M$? (c) What is the reaction rate at 1000 K when the concentration of NO is increased to $0.10\,M$, while the concentration of H_2 is $0.010\,M$?

(d) What is the reaction rate at 1000 K if [NO] is decreased to 0.010 M and [H_2] is increased to 0.030 M?

14.31 Consider the following reaction:

$$CH_3Br(aq) + OH^-(aq) \longrightarrow CH_3OH(aq) + Br^-(aq)$$

The rate law for this reaction is first order in CH_3Br and first order in OH^-. When [CH_3Br] is 5.0×10^{-3} M and [OH^-] is 0.050 M, the reaction rate at 298 K is 0.0432 M/s. **(a)** What is the value of the rate constant? **(b)** What are the units of the rate constant? **(c)** What would happen to the rate if the concentration of OH^- were tripled? **(d)** What would happen to the rate if the concentration of both reactants were tripled?

14.32 The reaction between ethyl bromide (C_2H_5Br) and hydroxide ion in ethyl alcohol at 330 K, $C_2H_5Br(alc) + OH^-(alc) \longrightarrow C_2H_5OH(l) + Br^-(alc)$, is first order each in ethyl bromide and hydroxide ion. When [C_2H_5Br] is 0.0477 M and [OH^-] is 0.100 M, the rate of disappearance of ethyl bromide is 1.7×10^{-7} M/s. **(a)** What is the value of the rate constant? **(b)** What are the units of the rate constant? **(c)** How would the rate of disappearance of ethyl bromide change if the solution were diluted by adding an equal volume of pure ethyl alcohol to the solution?

14.33 The iodide ion reacts with hypochlorite ion (the active ingredient in chlorine bleaches) in the following way: $OCl^- + I^- \longrightarrow OI^- + Cl^-$. This rapid reaction gives the following rate data:

[OCl⁻] (M)	[I⁻] (M)	Initial Rate (M/s)
1.5×10^{-3}	1.5×10^{-3}	1.36×10^{-4}
3.0×10^{-3}	1.5×10^{-3}	2.72×10^{-4}
1.5×10^{-3}	3.0×10^{-3}	2.72×10^{-4}

(a) Write the rate law for this reaction. **(b)** Calculate the rate constant with proper units. **(c)** Calculate the rate when [OCl^-] = 2.0×10^{-3} M and [I^-] = 5.0×10^{-4} M.

14.34 The reaction $2 ClO_2(aq) + 2 OH^-(aq) \longrightarrow ClO_3^-(aq) + ClO_2^-(aq) + H_2O(l)$ was studied with the following results:

Experiment	[ClO₂] (M)	[OH⁻] (M)	Initial Rate (M/s)
1	0.060	0.030	0.0248
2	0.020	0.030	0.00276
3	0.020	0.090	0.00828

(a) Determine the rate law for the reaction. **(b)** Calculate the rate constant with proper units. **(c)** Calculate the rate when [ClO_2] = 0.100 M and [OH^-] = 0.050 M.

14.35 The following data were measured for the reaction $BF_3(g) + NH_3(g) \longrightarrow F_3BNH_3(g)$:

Experiment	[BF₃] (M)	[NH₃] (M)	Initial Rate (M/s)
1	0.250	0.250	0.2130
2	0.250	0.125	0.1065
3	0.200	0.100	0.0682
4	0.350	0.100	0.1193
5	0.175	0.100	0.0596

(a) What is the rate law for the reaction? **(b)** What is the overall order of the reaction? **(c)** Calculate the rate constant with proper units? **(d)** What is the rate when [BF_3] = 0.100 M and [NH_3] = 0.500 M?

14.36 The following data were collected for the rate of disappearance of NO in the reaction $2 NO(g) + O_2(g) \longrightarrow 2 NO_2(g)$:

Experiment	[NO] (M)	[O₂] (M)	Initial Rate (M/s)
1	0.0126	0.0125	1.41×10^{-2}
2	0.0252	0.0125	5.64×10^{-2}
3	0.0252	0.0250	1.13×10^{-1}

(a) What is the rate law for the reaction? **(b)** What are the units of the rate constant? **(c)** What is the average value of the rate constant calculated from the three data sets? **(d)** What is the rate of disappearance of NO when [NO] = 0.0750 M and [O_2] = 0.0100 M? **(e)** What is the rate of disappearance of O_2 at the concentrations given in part (d)?

[14.37] Consider the gas-phase reaction between nitric oxide and bromine at 273 °C: $2 NO(g) + Br_2(g) \longrightarrow 2 NOBr(g)$. The following data for the initial rate of appearance of NOBr were obtained:

Experiment	[NO] (M)	[Br₂] (M)	Initial Rate (M/s)
1	0.10	0.20	24
2	0.25	0.20	150
3	0.10	0.50	60
4	0.35	0.50	735

(a) Determine the rate law. **(b)** Calculate the average value of the rate constant for the appearance of NOBr from the four data sets. **(c)** How is the rate of appearance of NOBr related to the rate of disappearance of Br_2? **(d)** What is the rate of disappearance of Br_2 when [NO] = 0.075 M and [Br_2] = 0.25 M?

[14.38] Consider the reaction of peroxydisulfate ion ($S_2O_8^{2-}$) with iodide ion (I^-) in aqueous solution:

$$S_2O_8^{2-}(aq) + 3 I^-(aq) \longrightarrow 2 SO_4^{2-}(aq) + I_3^-(aq)$$

At a particular temperature the initial rate of disappearance of $S_2O_8^{2-}$ varies with reactant concentrations in the following manner:

Experiment	[S₂O₈²⁻] (M)	[I⁻] (M)	Initial Rate (M/s)
1	0.018	0.036	2.6×10^{-6}
2	0.027	0.036	3.9×10^{-6}
3	0.036	0.054	7.8×10^{-6}
4	0.050	0.072	1.4×10^{-5}

(a) Determine the rate law for the reaction and state the units of the rate constant. **(b)** What is the average value of the rate constant for the disappearance of $S_2O_8^{2-}$ based on the four sets of data? **(c)** How is the rate of disappearance of $S_2O_8^{2-}$ related to the rate of disappearance of I^-? **(d)** What is the rate of disappearance of I^- when [$S_2O_8^{2-}$] = 0.025 M and [I^-] = 0.050 M?

CHANGE OF CONCENTRATION WITH TIME (section 14.4)

14.39 (a) Define the following symbols that are encountered in rate equations for the generic reaction A $\longrightarrow$ B: $[A]_0$, $t_{1/2}$ $[A]_t$, k. (b) What quantity, when graphed versus time, will yield a straight line for a first-order reaction? (c) How can you calculate the rate constant for a first-order reaction from the graph you made in part (b)?

14.40 (a) For a generic second-order reaction A $\longrightarrow$ B, what quantity, when graphed versus time, will yield a straight line? (b) What is the slope of the straight line from part (a)? (c) How do the half-lives of first-order and second-order reactions differ?

14.41 For the generic reaction A $\longrightarrow$ B that is zero order in A, what would you graph in order to obtain the rate constant?

14.42 Sketch a graph for the generic first-order reaction A $\longrightarrow$ B that has concentration of A on the vertical axis and time on the horizontal axis. (a) Is this graph linear? Explain. (b) Indicate on your graph the half-life for the reaction.

14.43 (a) The gas-phase decomposition of SO_2Cl_2, $SO_2Cl_2(g)$ $\longrightarrow$ $SO_2(g) + Cl_2(g)$, is first order in SO_2Cl_2. At 600 K the half-life for this process is 2.3×10^5 s. What is the rate constant at this temperature? (b) At 320 °C the rate constant is 2.2×10^{-5} s^{-1}. What is the half-life at this temperature?

14.44 Molecular iodine, $I_2(g)$, dissociates into iodine atoms at 625 K with a first-order rate constant of 0.271 s^{-1}. (a) What is the half-life for this reaction? (b) If you start with 0.050 M I_2 at this temperature, how much will remain after 5.12 s assuming that the iodine atoms do not recombine to form I_2?

14.45 As described in Exercise 14.43, the decomposition of sulfuryl chloride (SO_2Cl_2) is a first-order process. The rate constant for the decomposition at 660 K is 4.5×10^{-2} s^{-1}. (a) If we begin with an initial SO_2Cl_2 pressure of 450 torr, what is the pressure of this substance after 60 s? (b) At what time will the pressure of SO_2Cl_2 decline to one-tenth its initial value?

14.46 The first-order rate constant for the decomposition of N_2O_5, $2 N_2O_5(g)$ $\longrightarrow$ $4 NO_2(g) + O_2(g)$, at 70 °C is 6.82×10^{-3} s^{-1}. Suppose we start with 0.0250 mol of $N_2O_5(g)$ in a volume of 2.0 L. (a) How many moles of N_2O_5 will remain after 5.0 min? (b) How many minutes will it take for the quantity of N_2O_5 to drop to 0.010 mol? (c) What is the half-life of N_2O_5 at 70 °C ?

14.47 The reaction

$$SO_2Cl_2(g) \longrightarrow SO_2(g) + Cl_2(g)$$

is first order in SO_2Cl_2. Using the following kinetic data, determine the magnitude and units of the first-order rate constant:

Time (s)	Pressure SO₂Cl₂ (atm)
0	1.000
2,500	0.947
5,000	0.895
7,500	0.848
10,000	0.803

14.48 From the following data for the first-order gas-phase isomerization of CH_3NC at 215 °C, calculate the first-order rate constant and half-life for the reaction:

Time (s)	Pressure CH₃NC (torr)
0	502
2,000	335
5,000	180
8,000	95.5
12,000	41.7
15,000	22.4

14.49 Consider the data presented in Exercise 14.19. (a) By using appropriate graphs, determine whether the reaction is first order or second order. (b) What is the rate constant for the reaction? (c) What is the half-life for the reaction?

14.50 Consider the data presented in Exercise 14.20. (a) Determine whether the reaction is first order or second order. (b) What is the rate constant? (c) What is the half-life?

14.51 The gas-phase decomposition of NO_2, $2 NO_2(g)$ $\longrightarrow$ $2 NO(g) + O_2(g)$, is studied at 383 °C, giving the following data:

Time (s)	[NO₂] (M)
0.0	0.100
5.0	0.017
10.0	0.0090
15.0	0.0062
20.0	0.0047

(a) Is the reaction first order or second order with respect to the concentration of NO_2? (b) What is the rate constant? (c) If you used the method of initial rates to obtain the order for NO_2, predict what reaction rates you would measure in the beginning of the reaction for initial concentrations of 0.200 M, 0.100 M, and 0.050 M NO_2.

14.52 Sucrose ($C_{12}H_{22}O_{11}$), commonly known as table sugar, reacts in dilute acid solutions to form two simpler sugars, glucose and fructose, both of which have the formula $C_6H_{12}O_6$. At 23 °C and in 0.5 M HCl, the following data were obtained for the disappearance of sucrose:

Time (min)	[C₁₂H₂₂O₁₁] (M)
0	0.316
39	0.274
80	0.238
140	0.190
210	0.146

(a) Is the reaction first order or second order with respect to $[C_{12}H_{22}O_{11}]$? (b) What is the rate constant? (c) Using this rate constant, calculate the concentration of sucrose at 39, 80, 140, and 210 min if the initial sucrose concentration was 0.316 M and the reaction was zero order in sucrose.

TEMPERATURE AND RATE (section 14.5)

14.53 (a) What factors determine whether a collision between two molecules will lead to a chemical reaction? (b) According to the collision model, why does temperature affect the value of the rate constant? (c) Does the rate constant for a reaction generally increase or decrease with an increase in reaction temperature?

14.54 (a) In which of the following reactions would you expect the orientation factor to be least important in leading to reaction: $NO + O \longrightarrow NO_2$ or $H + Cl \longrightarrow HCl$? (b) How does the kinetic-molecular theory help us understand the temperature dependence of chemical reactions?

14.55 Calculate the fraction of atoms in a sample of argon gas at 400 K that has an energy of 10.0 kJ or greater.

14.56 (a) The activation energy for the isomerization of methyl isonitrile (Figure 14.7) is 160 kJ/mol. Calculate the fraction of methyl isonitrile molecules that has an energy of 160.0 kJ or greater at 500 K. (b) Calculate this fraction for a temperature of 520 K. What is the ratio of the fraction at 520 K to that at 500 K?

14.57 The gas-phase reaction $Cl(g) + HBr(g) \longrightarrow HCl(g) + Br(g)$ has an overall enthalpy change of −66 kJ. The activation energy for the reaction is 7 kJ. (a) Sketch the energy profile for the reaction, and label E_a and ΔE. (b) What is the activation energy for the reverse reaction?

14.58 For the elementary process $N_2O_5(g) \longrightarrow NO_2(g) + NO_3(g)$ the activation energy (E_a) and overall ΔE are 154 kJ/mol and 136 kJ/mol, respectively. (a) Sketch the energy profile for this reaction, and label E_a and ΔE. (b) What is the activation energy for the reverse reaction?

14.59 Indicate whether each statement is true or false. If it is false, rewrite it so that it is true.
(a) If you compare two reactions with similar collision factors, the one with the larger activation energy will be faster.
(b) A reaction that has a small rate constant must have a small frequency factor.
(c) Increasing the reaction temperature increases the fraction of successful collisions between reactants.

14.60 Indicate whether each statement is true or false. If it is false, rewrite it so that it is true.
(a) If you measure the rate constant for a reaction at different temperatures, you can calculate the overall enthalpy change for the reaction.
(b) Exothermic reactions are faster than endothermic reactions.
(c) If you double the temperature for a reaction, you cut the activation energy in half.

14.61 Based on their activation energies and energy changes and assuming that all collision factors are the same, which of the following reactions would be fastest and which would be slowest? Explain your answer.
(a) $E_a = 45$ kJ/mol; $\Delta E = -25$ kJ/mol
(b) $E_a = 35$ kJ/mol; $\Delta E = -10$ kJ/mol
(c) $E_a = 55$ kJ/mol; $\Delta E = 10$ kJ/mol

14.62 Which of the reactions in Exercise 14.61 will be fastest in the reverse direction? Which will be slowest? Explain.

14.63 (a) A certain first-order reaction has a rate constant of $2.75 \times 10^{-2}\,s^{-1}$ at 20 °C. What is the value of k at 60 °C if $E_a = 75.5$ kJ/mol? (b) Another first-order reaction also has a rate constant of $2.75 \times 10^{-2}\,s^{-1}$ at 20 °C. What is the value of k at 60 °C if $E_a = 125$ kJ/mol? (c) What assumptions do you need to make in order to calculate answers for parts (a) and (b)?

14.64 Understanding the high-temperature behavior of nitrogen oxides is essential for controlling pollution generated in automobile engines. The decomposition of nitric oxide (NO) to N_2 and O_2 is second order with a rate constant of $0.0796\,M^{-1}\,s^{-1}$ at 737 °C and $0.0815\,M^{-1}\,s^{-1}$ at 947 °C. Calculate the activation energy for the reaction.

14.65 The rate of the reaction

$$CH_3COOC_2H_5(aq) + OH^-(aq) \longrightarrow$$
$$CH_3COO^-(aq) + C_2H_5OH(aq)$$

was measured at several temperatures, and the following data were collected:

Temperature (°C)	k ($M^{-1}\,s^{-1}$)
15	0.0521
25	0.101
35	0.184
45	0.332

Calculate the value of E_a by constructing an appropriate graph.

14.66 The temperature dependence of the rate constant for a reaction is tabulated as follows:

Temperature (K)	k ($M^{-1}\,s^{-1}$)
600	0.028
650	0.22
700	1.3
750	6.0
800	23

Calculate E_a and A.

[14.67] The activation energy of a certain reaction is 65.7 kJ/mol. How many times faster will the reaction occur at 50 °C than at 0 °C? State the assumptions you need to make in order to perform this calculation.

[14.68] The following is a quote from an article in the August 18, 1998, issue of *The New York Times* about the breakdown of cellulose and starch: "A drop of 18 degrees Fahrenheit [from 77 °F to 59 °F] lowers the reaction rate six times; a 36-degree drop [from 77 °F to 41 °F] produces a fortyfold decrease in the rate." (a) Calculate activation energies for the breakdown process based on the two estimates of the effect of temperature on rate. Are the values consistent? (b) Assuming the value of E_a calculated from the 36-degree drop and that the rate of breakdown is first order with a half-life at 25 °C of 2.7 years, calculate the half-life for breakdown at a temperature of −15 °C.

REACTION MECHANISMS (section 14.6)

14.69 (a) What is meant by the term *elementary reaction*? (b) What is the difference between a *unimolecular* and a *bimolecular* elementary reaction? (c) What is a *reaction mechanism*?

14.70 (a) What is meant by the term *molecularity*? (b) Why are termolecular elementary reactions so rare? (c) What is an *intermediate* in a mechanism?

14.71 What are the differences between an intermediate and a transition state?

14.72 What is meant by the term *rate-determining step*?

14.73 What is the molecularity of each of the following elementary reactions? Write the rate law for each.
(a) $Cl_2(g) \longrightarrow 2\,Cl(g)$
(b) $OCl^-(aq) + H_2O(l) \longrightarrow HOCl(aq) + OH^-(aq)$
(c) $NO(g) + Cl_2(g) \longrightarrow NOCl_2(g)$

14.74 What is the molecularity of each of the following elementary reactions? Write the rate law for each.
(a) $2\,NO(g) \longrightarrow N_2O_2(g)$
(b) $H_2C \overset{\displaystyle CH_2}{\frown} CH_2(g) \longrightarrow CH_2 {=} CH{-}CH_3(g)$
(c) $SO_3(g) \longrightarrow SO_2(g) + O(g)$

14.75 (a) Based on the following reaction profile, how many intermediates are formed in the reaction $A \longrightarrow D$? (b) How many transition states are there? (c) Which step is the fastest? (d) Is the reaction $A \longrightarrow D$ exothermic or endothermic?

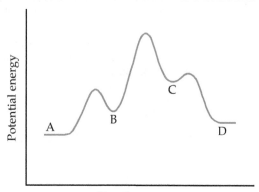

Reaction progress

14.76 Consider the following energy profile.

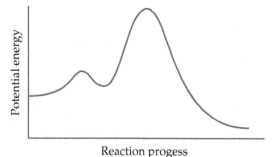

Reaction progess

(a) How many elementary reactions are in the reaction mechanism? (b) How many intermediates are formed in the reaction? (c) Which step is rate limiting? (d) Is the overall reaction exothermic or endothermic?

14.77 The following mechanism has been proposed for the gas-phase reaction of H_2 with ICl:
$$H_2(g) + ICl(g) \longrightarrow HI(g) + HCl(g)$$
$$HI(g) + ICl(g) \longrightarrow I_2(g) + HCl(g)$$
(a) Write the balanced equation for the overall reaction. (b) Identify any intermediates in the mechanism. (c) If the first step is slow and the second one is fast, which rate law do you expect to be observed for the overall reaction?

14.78 The decomposition of hydrogen peroxide is catalyzed by iodide ion. The catalyzed reaction is thought to proceed by a two-step mechanism:
$$H_2O_2(aq) + I^-(aq) \longrightarrow H_2O(l) + IO^-(aq) \quad \text{(slow)}$$
$$IO^-(aq) + H_2O_2(aq) \longrightarrow H_2O(l) + O_2(g) + I^-(aq) \quad \text{(fast)}$$
(a) Write the chemical equation for the overall process. (b) Identify the intermediate, if any, in the mechanism. (c) Assuming that the first step of the mechanism is rate determining, predict the rate law for the overall process.

14.79 The reaction $2\,NO(g) + Cl_2(g) \longrightarrow 2\,NOCl(g)$ was performed and the following data obtained:

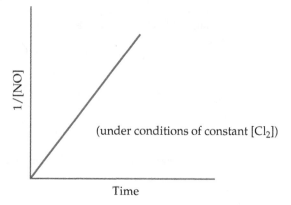

(under conditions of constant $[Cl_2]$)

Is the following mechanism consistent with the data? Explain.
$$NO(g) + Cl_2(g) \longrightarrow NOCl_2(g)$$
$$NOCl_2(g) + NO(g) \longrightarrow 2\,NOCl(g)$$

14.80 You have studied the gas-phase oxidation of HBr by O_2:
$$4\,HBr(g) + O_2(g) \longrightarrow 2\,H_2O(g) + 2\,Br_2(g)$$
You find the reaction to be first order with respect to HBr and first order with respect to O_2. You propose the following mechanism:
$$HBr(g) + O_2(g) \longrightarrow HOOBr(g)$$
$$HOOBr(g) + HBr(g) \longrightarrow 2\,HOBr(g)$$
$$HOBr(g) + HBr(g) \longrightarrow H_2O(g) + Br_2(g)$$
(a) Confirm that the elementary reactions add to give the overall reaction. (b) Based on the experimentally determined rate law, which step is rate determining? (c) What are the intermediates in this mechanism? (d) If you are unable to detect HOBr or HOOBr among the products, does this disprove your mechanism?

CATALYSIS (section 14.7)

14.81 (a) What is a catalyst? (b) What is the difference between a homogeneous and a heterogeneous catalyst? (c) Do catalysts affect the overall enthalpy change for a reaction, the activation energy, or both?

14.82 (a) Most commercial heterogeneous catalysts are extremely finely divided solid materials. Why is particle size important? (b) What role does adsorption play in the action of a heterogeneous catalyst?

[14.83] Platinum nanoparticles of diameter ~2 nm are important catalysts in carbon monoxide oxidation to carbon dioxide. Platinum crystallizes in a face-centered cubic arrangement with an edge length of 3.924 Å. (a) Estimate how many platinum atoms would fit into a 2.0-nm sphere; the volume of a sphere is $(4/3)\pi r^3$. Recall that $1 Å = 1 \times 10^{-10}$ m and 1 nm $= 1 \times 10^{-9}$ m. (b) Estimate how many platinum atoms are on the surface of a 2.0-nm Pt sphere, using the surface area of a sphere $(4\pi r^2)$ and assuming that the "footprint" of one Pt atom can be estimated from its atomic diameter of 2.8 Å. (c) Using your results from (a) and (b), calculate the percentage of Pt atoms that are on the surface of a 2.0-nm nanoparticle. (d) Repeat these calculations for a 5.0-nm platinum nanoparticle. (e) Which size of nanoparticle would you expect to be more catalytically active and why?

14.84 In solution, chemical species as simple as H^+ and OH^- can serve as catalysts for reactions. Imagine you could measure the $[H^+]$ of a solution containing an acid-catalyzed reaction as it occurs. Assume the reactants and products themselves are neither acids nor bases. Sketch the $[H^+]$ concentration profile you would measure as a function of time for the reaction, assuming $t = 0$ is when you add a drop of acid to the reaction.

14.85 The oxidation of SO_2 to SO_3 is catalyzed by NO_2. The reaction proceeds according to:

$$NO_2(g) + SO_2(g) \longrightarrow NO(g) + SO_3(g)$$
$$2 NO(g) + O_2(g) \longrightarrow 2 NO_2(g)$$

(a) Show that the two reactions can be summed to give the overall oxidation of SO_2 by O_2 to give SO_3. (b) Why do we consider NO_2 a catalyst and not an intermediate in this reaction? (c) Is this an example of homogeneous catalysis or heterogeneous catalysis?

14.86 NO catalyzes the decomposition of N_2O, possibly by the following mechanism:

$$NO(g) + N_2O(g) \longrightarrow N_2(g) + NO_2(g)$$
$$2 NO_2(g) \longrightarrow 2 NO(g) + O_2(g)$$

(a) What is the chemical equation for the overall reaction? Show how the two steps can be added to give the overall equation. (b) Why is NO considered a catalyst and not an intermediate? (c) If experiments show that during the decomposition of N_2O, NO_2 does not accumulate in measurable quantities, does this rule out the proposed mechanism? If you think not, suggest what might be going on.

14.87 Many metallic catalysts, particularly the precious-metal ones, are often deposited as very thin films on a substance of high surface area per unit mass, such as alumina (Al_2O_3) or silica (SiO_2). (a) Why is this an effective way of utilizing the catalyst material compared to having powdered metals? (b) How does the surface area affect the rate of reaction?

14.88 (a) If you were going to build a system to check the effectiveness of automobile catalytic converters on cars, what substances would you want to look for in the car exhaust? (b) Automobile catalytic converters have to work at high temperatures, as hot exhaust gases stream through them. In what ways could this be an advantage? In what ways a disadvantage? (c) Why is the rate of flow of exhaust gases over a catalytic converter important?

14.89 When D_2 reacts with ethylene (C_2H_4) in the presence of a finely divided catalyst, ethane with two deuteriums, CH_2D-CH_2D, is formed. (Deuterium, D, is an isotope of hydrogen of mass 2). Very little ethane forms in which two deuteriums are bound to one carbon (for example, CH_3-CHD_2). Use the sequence of steps involved in the reaction (Figure 14.24) to explain why this is so.

14.90 Heterogeneous catalysts that perform hydrogenation reactions, as illustrated in Figure 14.24, are subject to "poisoning," which shuts down their catalytic ability. Compounds of sulfur are often poisons. Suggest a mechanism by which such compounds might act as poisons.

14.91 (a) Explain the importance of enzymes in biological systems. (b) What chemical transformations are catalyzed (*i*) by the enzyme catalase, (*ii*) by nitrogenase? (c) Many enzymes follow this generic reaction mechanism, where E is enzyme, S is substrate, ES is the enzyme-substrate complex (where the substrate is bound to the enzyme's active site), and P is the product:

1. $E + S \rightleftharpoons ES$

2. $ES \longrightarrow E + P$

What assumptions are made in this model with regard to the rate of the bound substrate being chemically transformed into bound product in the active site?

14.92 There are literally thousands of enzymes at work in complex living systems such as human beings. What properties of enzymes give rise to their ability to distinguish one substrate from another?

14.93 The enzyme carbonic anhydrase catalyzes the reaction $CO_2(g) + H_2O(l) \longrightarrow HCO_3^-(aq) + H^+(aq)$. In water, without the enzyme, the reaction proceeds with a rate constant of 0.039 s^{-1} at 25 °C. In the presence of the enzyme in water, the reaction proceeds with a rate constant of $1.0 \times 10^6 s^{-1}$ at 25 °C. Assuming the collision factor is the same for both situations, calculate the difference in activation energies for the uncatalyzed versus enzyme-catalyzed reaction.

14.94 The enzyme urease catalyzes the reaction of urea, (NH_2CONH_2), with water to produce carbon dioxide and ammonia. In water, without the enzyme, the reaction proceeds with a first-order rate constant of $4.15 \times 10^{-5} s^{-1}$ at 100 °C. In the presence of the enzyme in water, the reaction proceeds with a rate constant of $3.4 \times 10^4 s^{-1}$ at 21 °C. (a) Write out the balanced equation for the reaction catalyzed by urease. (b) Assuming the collision factor is the same for both situations, estimate the difference in activation energies for the uncatalyzed versus enzyme-catalyzed reaction.

[14.95] The activation energy of an uncatalyzed reaction is 95 kJ/mol. The addition of a catalyst lowers the activation energy to 55 kJ/mol. Assuming that the collision factor remains the same, by what factor will the catalyst increase the rate of the reaction at (a) 25 °C, (b) 125 °C?

[14.96] Suppose that a certain biologically important reaction is quite slow at physiological temperature (37 °C) in the absence of a catalyst. Assuming that the collision factor remains the same, by how much must an enzyme lower the activation energy of the reaction in order to achieve a 1×10^5-fold increase in the reaction rate?

ADDITIONAL EXERCISES

14.97 Explain why rate laws generally cannot be written from balanced equations. Under what circumstance is the rate law related directly to the balanced equation for a reaction?

14.98 Hydrogen sulfide (H_2S) is a common and troublesome pollutant in industrial wastewaters. One way to remove H_2S is to treat the water with chlorine, in which case the following reaction occurs:

$$H_2S(aq) + Cl_2(aq) \longrightarrow S(s) + 2\,H^+(aq) + 2\,Cl^-(aq)$$

The rate of this reaction is first order in each reactant. The rate constant for the disappearance of H_2S at 28 °C is $3.5 \times 10^{-2}\,M^{-1}\,s^{-1}$. If at a given time the concentration of H_2S is $2.0 \times 10^{-4}\,M$ and that of Cl_2 is $0.025\,M$, what is the rate of formation of Cl^-?

14.99 The reaction $2\,NO(g) + O_2(g) \longrightarrow 2\,NO_2(g)$ is second order in NO and first order in O_2. When $[NO] = 0.040\,M$ and $[O_2] = 0.035\,M$, the observed rate of disappearance of NO is $9.3 \times 10^{-5}\,M/s$. (a) What is the rate of disappearance of O_2 at this moment? (b) What is the value of the rate constant? (c) What are the units of the rate constant? (d) What would happen to the rate if the concentration of NO were increased by a factor of 1.8?

14.100 Consider the following reaction between mercury(II) chloride and oxalate ion:

$$2\,HgCl_2(aq) + C_2O_4^{2-}(aq) \longrightarrow$$
$$2\,Cl^-(aq) + 2\,CO_2(g) + Hg_2Cl_2(s)$$

The initial rate of this reaction was determined for several concentrations of $HgCl_2$ and $C_2O_4^{2-}$, and the following rate data were obtained for the rate of disappearance of $C_2O_4^{2-}$:

Experiment	[HgCl$_2$] (M)	[C$_2$O$_4$$^{2-}$] (M)	Rate (M/s)
1	0.164	0.15	3.2×10^{-5}
2	0.164	0.45	2.9×10^{-4}
3	0.082	0.45	1.4×10^{-4}
4	0.246	0.15	4.8×10^{-5}

(a) What is the rate law for this reaction? (b) What is the value of the rate constant with proper units? (c) What is the reaction rate when the initial concentration of $HgCl_2$ is $0.100\,M$ and that of $(C_2O_4^{2-})$ is $0.25\,M$ if the temperature is the same as that used to obtain the data shown?

14.101 The reaction $2\,NO_2 \longrightarrow 2\,NO + O_2$ has the rate constant $k = 0.63\,M^{-1}\,s^{-1}$. Based on the units for k, is the reaction first or second order in NO_2? If the initial concentration of NO_2 is $0.100\,M$, how would you determine how long it would take for the concentration to decrease to $0.025\,M$?

14.102 Consider two reactions. Reaction (1) has a constant half-life, whereas reaction (2) has a half-life that gets longer as the reaction proceeds. What can you conclude about the rate laws of these reactions from these observations?

[14.103] When chemists are performing kinetics experiments, the general rule of thumb is to allow the reaction to proceed for 4 half-lives. (a) Explain how you would be able to tell that the reaction has proceeded for 4 half-lives. (b) Let us suppose a reaction $A \longrightarrow B$ takes 6 days to proceed for 4 half-lives and is first order in A. However, when your lab partner performs this reaction for the first time, he does not realize how long it takes, and he stops taking kinetic data, monitoring the loss of A, after only 2 hours. Your lab partner concludes the reaction is zero order in A based on the data. Sketch a graph of [A] versus time to convince your lab partner the two of you need to be in the lab for a few days to obtain the proper rate law for the reaction.

14.104 (a) The reaction $H_2O_2(aq) \longrightarrow H_2O(l) + \frac{1}{2}O_2(g)$ is first order. Near room temperature, the rate constant equals $7.0 \times 10^{-4}\,s^{-1}$. Calculate the half-life at this temperature. (b) At 415 °C, $(CH_2)_2O$ decomposes in the gas phase, $(CH_2)_2O(g) \longrightarrow CH_4(g) + CO(g)$. If the reaction is first order with a half-life of 56.3 min at this temperature, calculate the rate constant in s^{-1}.

14.105 Americium-241 is used in smoke detectors. It has a first order rate constant for radioactive decay of $k = 1.6 \times 10^{-3}\,yr^{-1}$. By contrast, iodine-125, which is used to test for thyroid functioning, has a rate constant for radioactive decay of $k = 0.011\,day^{-1}$. (a) What are the half-lives of these two isotopes? (b) Which one decays at a faster rate? (c) How much of a 1.00-mg sample of each isotope remains after 3 half-lives? (d) How much of a 1.00-mg sample of each isotope remains after 4 days?

14.106 Urea (NH_2CONH_2) is the end product in protein metabolism in animals. The decomposition of urea in $0.1\,M$ HCl occurs according to the reaction

$$NH_2CONH_2(aq) + H^+(aq) + 2\,H_2O(l) \longrightarrow$$
$$2\,NH_4^+(aq) + HCO_3^-(aq)$$

The reaction is first order in urea and first order overall. When $[NH_2CONH_2] = 0.200\,M$, the rate at 61.05 °C is $8.56 \times 10^{-5}\,M/s$. (a) What is the rate constant, k? (b) What is the concentration of urea in this solution after $4.00 \times 10^3\,s$ if the starting concentration is $0.500\,M$? (c) What is the half-life for this reaction at 61.05 °C?

14.107 The rate of a first-order reaction is followed by spectroscopy, monitoring the absorbance of a colored reactant at 520 nm. The reaction occurs in a 1.00-cm sample cell, and the only colored species in the reaction has an extinction coefficient of $5.60 \times 10^3\,M^{-1}\,cm^{-1}$ at 520 nm. (a) Calculate the initial concentration of the colored reactant if the absorbance is 0.605 at the beginning of the reaction. (b) The absorbance falls to 0.250 at 30.0 min. Calculate the rate constant in units of s^{-1}. (c) Calculate the half-life of the reaction. (d) How long does it take for the absorbance to fall to 0.100?

[14.108] A colored dye compound decomposes to give a colorless product. The original dye absorbs at 608 nm and has an extinction coefficient of $4.7 \times 10^4\ M^{-1}cm^{-1}$ at that wavelength. You perform the decomposition reaction in a 1-cm cuvette in a spectrometer and obtain the following data:

Time (min)	Absorbance at 608 nm
0	1.254
30	0.941
60	0.752
90	0.672
120	0.545

From these data, determine the rate law for the reaction "dye $\longrightarrow$ product" and determine the rate constant.

14.109 Cyclopentadiene (C_5H_6) reacts with itself to form dicyclopentadiene ($C_{10}H_{12}$). A 0.0400 M solution of C_5H_6 was monitored as a function of time as the reaction $2\ C_5H_6 \longrightarrow C_{10}H_{12}$ proceeded. The following data were collected:

Time (s)	[C₅H₆] (M)
0.0	0.0400
50.0	0.0300
100.0	0.0240
150.0	0.0200
200.0	0.0174

Plot $[C_5H_6]$ versus time, ln $[C_5H_6]$ versus time, and $1/[C_5H_6]$ versus time. What is the order of the reaction? What is the value of the rate constant?

14.110 (a) Two reactions have identical values for E_a. Does this ensure that they will have the same rate constant if run at the same temperature? Explain. (b) Two similar reactions have the same rate constant at 25 °C, but at 35 °C one of the reactions has a larger rate constant than the other. Account for these observations.

14.111 The first-order rate constant for reaction of a particular organic compound with water varies with temperature as follows:

Temperature (K)	Rate Constant (s⁻¹)
300	3.2×10^{-11}
320	1.0×10^{-9}
340	3.0×10^{-8}
355	2.4×10^{-7}

From these data, calculate the activation energy in units of kJ/mol.

14.112 The following mechanism has been proposed for the reaction of NO with H_2 to form N_2O and H_2O:

$$NO(g) + NO(g) \longrightarrow N_2O_2(g)$$
$$N_2O_2(g) + H_2(g) \longrightarrow N_2O(g) + H_2O(g)$$

(a) Show that the elementary reactions of the proposed mechanism add to provide a balanced equation for the reaction. (b) Write a rate law for each elementary reaction in the mechanism. (c) Identify any intermediates in the mechanism. (d) The observed rate law is rate = $k[NO]^2[H_2]$. If the proposed mechanism is correct, what can we conclude about the relative speeds of the first and second reactions?

14.113 Ozone in the upper atmosphere can be destroyed by the following two-step mechanism:

$$Cl(g) + O_3(g) \longrightarrow ClO(g) + O_2(g)$$
$$ClO(g) + O(g) \longrightarrow Cl(g) + O_2(g)$$

(a) What is the overall equation for this process? (b) What is the catalyst in the reaction? How do you know? (c) What is the intermediate in the reaction? How do you distinguish it from the catalyst?

14.114 Using Figure 14.23 as your basis, draw the energy profile for the bromide–catalyzed decomposition of hydrogen peroxide. (a) Label the curve with the activation energies for reactions [14.30] and [14.31]. (b) Notice from Figure 14.22 that when $Br^-(aq)$ is first added, Br_2 accumulates to some extent during the reaction and the solution turns brown. What does this tell us about the relative rates of the reactions represented by Equations 14.30 and 14.31?

[14.115] The following mechanism has been proposed for the gas-phase reaction of chloroform ($CHCl_3$) and chlorine:

$$\text{Step 1:}\quad Cl_2(g) \underset{k_{-1}}{\overset{k_1}{\rightleftharpoons}} 2\ Cl(g)\quad \text{(fast)}$$

$$\text{Step 2:}\quad Cl(g) + CHCl_3(g) \overset{k_2}{\longrightarrow} HCl(g) + CCl_3(g)\quad \text{(slow)}$$

$$\text{Step 3:}\quad Cl(g) + CCl_3(g) \overset{k_3}{\longrightarrow} CCl_4\quad \text{(fast)}$$

(a) What is the overall reaction? (b) What are the intermediates in the mechanism? (c) What is the molecularity of each of the elementary reactions? (d) What is the rate-determining step? (e) What is the rate law predicted by this mechanism? (*Hint:* The overall reaction order is not an integer.)

[14.116] In a hydrocarbon solution, the gold compound $(CH_3)_3AuPH_3$ decomposes into ethane (C_2H_6) and a different gold compound, $(CH_3)AuPH_3$. The following mechanism has been proposed for the decomposition of $(CH_3)_3AuPH_3$:

$$\text{Step 1:}\quad (CH_3)_3\ AuPH_3 \underset{k_{-1}}{\overset{k_1}{\rightleftharpoons}} (CH_3)_3Au + PH_3\quad \text{(fast)}$$

$$\text{Step 2:}\quad (CH_3)_3\ Au \overset{k_2}{\longrightarrow} C_2H_6 + (CH_3)Au\quad \text{(slow)}$$

$$\text{Step 3:}\quad (CH_3)Au + PH_3 \overset{k_3}{\longrightarrow} (CH_3)AuPH_3\quad \text{(fast)}$$

(a) What is the overall reaction? (b) What are the intermediates in the mechanism? (c) What is the molecularity of each of the elementary steps? (d) What is the rate-determining step? (e) What is the rate law predicted by this mechanism? (f) What would be the effect on the reaction rate of adding PH_3 to the solution of $(CH_3)_3AuPH_3$?

14.117 One of the many remarkable enzymes in the human body is carbonic anhydrase, which catalyzes the interconversion of carbon dioxide and water with bicarbonate ion and protons. If it were not for this enzyme, the body could not rid itself rapidly enough of the CO_2 accumulated by cell metabolism. The enzyme catalyzes the dehydration (release to air) of up to 10^7 CO_2 molecules per second. Which components of this description correspond to the terms *enzyme*, *substrate*, and *turnover number*?

14.118 Enzymes are often described as following the two-step mechanism:

$$E + S \rightleftharpoons ES \quad (fast)$$
$$ES \longrightarrow E + P \quad (slow)$$

where E = enzyme, S = substrate, ES = enzyme-substrate complex, and P = product.

(a) If an enzyme follows this mechanism, what rate law is expected for the reaction? **(b)** Molecules that can bind to the active site of an enzyme but are not converted into product are called *enzyme inhibitors*. Write an additional elementary step to add into the preceding mechanism to account for the reaction of E with I, an inhibitor.

INTEGRATIVE EXERCISES

14.119 Dinitrogen pentoxide (N_2O_5) decomposes in chloroform as a solvent to yield NO_2 and O_2. The decomposition is first order with a rate constant at 45 °C of 1.0×10^{-5} s^{-1}. Calculate the partial pressure of O_2 produced from 1.00 L of 0.600 M N_2O_5 solution at 45 °C over a period of 20.0 hr if the gas is collected in a 10.0-L container. (Assume that the products do not dissolve in chloroform.)

[14.120] The reaction between ethyl iodide and hydroxide ion in ethanol (C_2H_5OH) solution, $C_2H_5I(alc) + OH^-(alc) \longrightarrow C_2H_5OH(l) + I^-(alc)$, has an activation energy of 86.8 kJ/mol and a frequency factor of 2.10×10^{11} M^{-1} s^{-1}. **(a)** Predict the rate constant for the reaction at 35 °C. **(b)** A solution of KOH in ethanol is made up by dissolving 0.335 g KOH in ethanol to form 250.0 mL of solution. Similarly, 1.453 g of C_2H_5I is dissolved in ethanol to form 250.0 mL of solution. Equal volumes of the two solutions are mixed. Assuming the reaction is first order in each reactant, what is the initial rate at 35 °C ? **(c)** Which reagent in the reaction is limiting, assuming the reaction proceeds to completion? **(d)** Assuming the frequency factor and activation energy do not change as a function of temperature, calculate the rate constant for the reaction at 50 °C.

[14.121] You obtain kinetic data for a reaction at a set of different temperatures. You plot ln k versus $1/T$ and obtain the following graph:

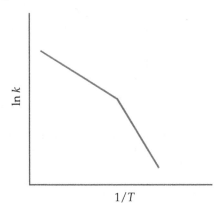

Suggest a molecular-level interpretation of these unusual data.

14.122 The gas-phase reaction of NO with F_2 to form NOF and F has an activation energy of $E_a = 6.3$ kJ/mol and a frequency factor of $A = 6.0 \times 10^8$ M^{-1} s^{-1}. The reaction is believed to be bimolecular:

$$NO(g) + F_2(g) \longrightarrow NOF(g) + F(g)$$

(a) Calculate the rate constant at 100 °C. **(b)** Draw the Lewis structures for the NO and the NOF molecules, given that the chemical formula for NOF is misleading because the nitrogen atom is actually the central atom in the molecule. **(c)** Predict the shape for the NOF molecule. **(d)** Draw a possible transition state for the formation of NOF, using dashed lines to indicate the weak bonds that are beginning to form. **(e)** Suggest a reason for the low activation energy for the reaction.

14.123 The mechanism for the oxidation of HBr by O_2 to form 2 H_2O and Br_2 is shown in Exercise 14.80. **(a)** Calculate the overall standard enthalpy change for the reaction process. **(b)** HBr does not react with O_2 at a measurable rate at room temperature under ordinary conditions. What can you infer from this about the magnitude of the activation energy for the rate-determining step? **(c)** Draw a plausible Lewis structure for the intermediate HOOBr. To what familiar compound of hydrogen and oxygen does it appear similar?

[14.124] The rates of many atmospheric reactions are accelerated by the absorption of light by one of the reactants. For example, consider the reaction between methane and chlorine to produce methyl chloride and hydrogen chloride:

Reaction 1: $CH_4(g) + Cl_2(g) \longrightarrow CH_3Cl(g) + HCl(g)$

This reaction is very slow in the absence of light. However, $Cl_2(g)$ can absorb light to form Cl atoms:

Reaction 2: $Cl_2(g) + h\nu \longrightarrow 2 Cl(g)$

Once the Cl atoms are generated, they can catalyze the reaction of CH_4 and Cl_2, according to the following proposed mechanism:

Reaction 3: $CH_4(g) + Cl(g) \longrightarrow CH_3(g) + HCl(g)$

Reaction 4: $CH_3(g) + Cl_2(g) \longrightarrow CH_3Cl(g) + Cl(g)$

The enthalpy changes and activation energies for these two reactions are tabulated as follows:

Reaction	$\Delta H°$ (kJ/mol)	E_a (kJ/mol)
3	+4	17
4	−109	4

(a) By using the bond enthalpy for Cl_2 (Table 3.4), determine the longest wavelength of light that is energetic enough to cause reaction 2 to occur. In which portion of the electromagnetic spectrum is this light found? (b) By using the data tabulated here, sketch a quantitative energy profile for the catalyzed reaction represented by reactions 3 and 4. (c) By using bond enthalpies, estimate where the reactants, $CH_4(g) + Cl_2(g)$, should be placed on your diagram in part (b). Use this result to estimate the value of E_a for the reaction $CH_4(g) + Cl_2(g) \longrightarrow CH_3(g) + HCl(g) + Cl(g)$. (d) The species $Cl(g)$ and $CH_3(g)$ in reactions 3 and 4 are radicals, that is, atoms or molecules with unpaired electrons. Draw a Lewis structure of CH_3, and verify that it is a radical. (e) The

sequence of reactions 3 and 4 comprises a radical chain mechanism. Why do you think this is called a "chain reaction"? Propose a reaction that will terminate the chain reaction.

[14.125] Many primary amines, RNH_2, where R is a carbon-containing fragment such as CH_3, CH_3CH_2, and so on, undergo reactions where the transition state is tetrahedral. (a) Draw a hybrid orbital picture to visualize the bonding at the nitrogen in a primary amine (just use a C atom for "R"). (b) What kind of reactant with a primary amine can produce a tetrahedral intermediate?

[14.126] The NO_x waste stream from automobile exhaust includes species such as NO and NO_2. Catalysts that convert these species to N_2 are desirable to reduce air pollution. (a) Draw the Lewis dot and VSEPR structures of NO, NO_2, and N_2. (b) Using a resource such as Table 3.4, look up the energies of the bonds in these molecules. In what region of the electromagnetic spectrum are these energies? (c) Design a spectroscopic experiment to monitor the conversion of NO_x into N_2, describing what wavelengths of light need to be monitored as a function of time.

MATHEMATICAL OPERATIONS

A.1 | EXPONENTIAL NOTATION

The numbers used in chemistry are often either extremely large or extremely small. Such numbers are conveniently expressed in the form

$$N \times 10^n$$

where N is a number between 1 and 10, and n is the exponent. Some examples of this *exponential notation*, which is also called *scientific notation*, follow.

1,200,000 is 1.2×10^6 (read "one point two times ten to the sixth power")

0.000604 is 6.04×10^{-4} (read "six point zero four times ten to the negative fourth power")

A positive exponent, as in the first example, tells us how many times a number must be multiplied by 10 to give the long form of the number:

$$1.2 \times 10^6 = 1.2 \times 10 \times 10 \times 10 \times 10 \times 10 \times 10 \quad \text{(six tens)}$$
$$= 1,200,000$$

It is also convenient to think of the *positive exponent* as the number of places the decimal point must be moved to the *left* to obtain a number greater than 1 and less than 10. For example, if we begin with 3450 and move the decimal point three places to the left, we end up with 3.45×10^3.

In a related fashion, a negative exponent tells us how many times we must divide a number by 10 to give the long form of the number.

$$6.04 \times 10^{-4} = \frac{6.04}{10 \times 10 \times 10 \times 10} = 0.000604$$

It is convenient to think of the *negative exponent* as the number of places the decimal point must be moved to the *right* to obtain a number greater than 1 but less than 10. For example, if we begin with 0.0048 and move the decimal point three places to the right, we end up with 4.8×10^{-3}.

In the system of exponential notation, with each shift of the decimal point one place to the right, the exponent *decreases* by 1:

$$4.8 \times 10^{-3} = 48 \times 10^{-4}$$

Similarly, with each shift of the decimal point one place to the left, the exponent *increases* by 1:

$$4.8 \times 10^{-3} = 0.48 \times 10^{-2}$$

Many scientific calculators have a key labeled EXP or EE, which is used to enter numbers in exponential notation. To enter the number 5.8×10^3 on such a calculator, the key sequence is

$$\boxed{5} \; \boxed{\cdot} \; \boxed{8} \; \boxed{\text{EXP}} \; (\text{or} \; \boxed{\text{EE}}) \; \boxed{3}$$

On some calculators the display will show 5.8, then a space, followed by 03, the exponent. On other calculators, a small 10 is shown with an exponent 3.

To enter a negative exponent, use the key labeled $+/-$. For example, to enter the number 8.6×10^{-5}, the key sequence is

$$\boxed{8}\;\boxed{\cdot}\;\boxed{6}\;\boxed{\text{EXP}}\;\boxed{+/-}\;\boxed{5}$$

When entering a number in exponential notation, do not key in the 10 if you use the EXP or EE button.

In working with exponents, it is important to recall that $10^0 = 1$. The following rules are useful for carrying exponents through calculations.

1. **Addition and Subtraction** In order to add or subtract numbers expressed in exponential notation, the powers of 10 must be the same.

$$(5.22 \times 10^4) + (3.21 \times 10^2) = (522 \times 10^2) + (3.21 \times 10^2)$$
$$= 525 \times 10^2 \quad \text{(3 significant figures)}$$
$$= 5.25 \times 10^4$$
$$(6.25 \times 10^{-2}) - (5.77 \times 10^{-3}) = (6.25 \times 10^{-2}) - (0.577 \times 10^{-2})$$
$$= 5.67 \times 10^{-2} \quad \text{(3 significant figures)}$$

When you use a calculator to add or subtract, you need not be concerned with having numbers with the same exponents because the calculator automatically takes care of this matter.

2. **Multiplication and Division** When numbers expressed in exponential notation are multiplied, the exponents are added; when numbers expressed in exponential notation are divided, the exponent of the denominator is subtracted from the exponent of the numerator.

$$(5.4 \times 10^2)(2.1 \times 10^3) = (5.4)(2.1) \times 10^{2+3}$$
$$= 11 \times 10^5$$
$$= 1.1 \times 10^6$$
$$(1.2 \times 10^5)(3.22 \times 10^{-3}) = (1.2)(3.22) \times 10^{5+(-3)} = 3.9 \times 10^2$$
$$\frac{3.2 \times 10^5}{6.5 \times 10^2} = \frac{3.2}{6.5} \times 10^{5-2} = 0.49 \times 10^3 = 4.9 \times 10^2$$
$$\frac{5.7 \times 10^7}{8.5 \times 10^{-2}} = \frac{5.7}{8.5} \times 10^{7-(-2)} = 0.67 \times 10^9 = 6.7 \times 10^8$$

3. **Powers and Roots** When numbers expressed in exponential notation are raised to a power, the exponents are multiplied by the power. When the roots of numbers expressed in exponential notation are taken, the exponents are divided by the root.

$$(1.2 \times 10^5)^3 = (1.2)^3 \times 10^{5 \times 3}$$
$$= 1.7 \times 10^{15}$$
$$\sqrt[3]{2.5 \times 10^6} = \sqrt[3]{2.5} \times 10^{6/3}$$
$$= 1.3 \times 10^2$$

Scientific calculators usually have keys labeled x^2 and $\sqrt{x}$ for squaring and taking the square root of a number, respectively. To take higher powers or roots, many calculators have y^x and $\sqrt[x]{y}$ (or INV y^x) keys. For example, to perform the operation $\sqrt[3]{7.5 \times 10^{-4}}$ on such a calculator, you would key in 7.5×10^{-4}, press the $\sqrt[x]{y}$ key (or the INV and then the y^x keys), enter the root, 3, and finally press $=$. The result is 9.1×10^{-2}.

SAMPLE EXERCISE 1 **Using Exponential Notation**

Perform each of the following operations, using your calculator where possible:

(a) Write the number 0.0054 in standard exponential notation.

(b) $(5.0 \times 10^{-2}) + (4.7 \times 10^{-3})$

(c) $(5.98 \times 10^{12})(2.77 \times 10^{-5})$

(d) $\sqrt[4]{1.75 \times 10^{-12}}$

SOLUTION

(a) Because we move the decimal point three places to the right to convert 0.0054 to 5.4, the exponent is -3:

$$5.4 \times 10^{-3}$$

Scientific calculators are generally able to convert numbers to exponential notation using one or two keystrokes; frequently "SCI" for "scientific notation" will convert a number into exponential notation. Consult your instruction manual to see how this operation is accomplished on your calculator.

(b) To add these numbers longhand, we must convert them to the same exponent.

$$(5.0 \times 10^{-2}) + (0.47 \times 10^{-2}) = (5.0 + 0.47) \times 10^{-2} = 5.5 \times 10^{-2}$$

(Note that the result has only two significant figures.) To perform this operation on a calculator, we enter the first number, strike the $+$ key, then enter the second number and strike the $=$ key.

(c) Performing this operation longhand, we have

$$(5.98 \times 2.77) \times 10^{12-5} = 16.6 \times 10^7 = 1.66 \times 10^8$$

On a scientific calculator, we enter 5.98×10^{12}, press the $\times$ key, enter 2.77×10^{-5}, and press the $=$ key.

(d) To perform this operation on a calculator, we enter the number, press the $\sqrt[x]{y}$ key (or the INV and y^x keys), enter 4, and press the $=$ key. The result is 1.15×10^{-3}.

PRACTICE EXERCISE

Perform the following operations:

(a) Write 67,000 in exponential notation, showing two significant figures.

(b) $(3.378 \times 10^{-3}) - (4.97 \times 10^{-5})$

(c) $(1.84 \times 10^{15})(7.45 \times 10^{-2})$

(d) $(6.67 \times 10^{-8})^3$

Answers: (a) 6.7×10^4, (b) 3.328×10^{-3}, (c) 2.47×10^{16}, (d) 2.97×10^{-22}

A.2 | LOGARITHMS

Common Logarithms

The common, or base-10, logarithm (abbreviated log) of any number is the power to which 10 must be raised to equal the number. For example, the common logarithm of 1000 (written log 1000) is 3 because raising 10 to the third power gives 1000.

$$10^3 = 1000, \text{ therefore, log } 1000 = 3$$

Further examples are

$$\log 10^5 = 5$$
$$\log 1 = 0 \qquad \text{Remember that } 10^0 = 1$$
$$\log 10^{-2} = -2$$

In these examples the common logarithm can be obtained by inspection. However, it is not possible to obtain the logarithm of a number such as 31.25 by inspection. The logarithm of 31.25 is the number x that satisfies the following relationship:

$$10^x = 31.25$$

Most electronic calculators have a key labeled LOG that can be used to obtain logarithms. For example, on many calculators we obtain the value of log 31.25 by entering 31.25 and pressing the LOG key. We obtain the following result:

$$\log 31.25 = 1.4949$$

Notice that 31.25 is greater than 10 (10^1) and less than 100 (10^2). The value for log 31.25 is accordingly between log 10 and log 100, that is, between 1 and 2.

Significant Figures and Common Logarithms

For the common logarithm of a measured quantity, the number of digits after the decimal point equals the number of significant figures in the original number. For example, if 23.5 is a measured quantity (three significant figures), then log 23.5 = 1.371 (three significant figures after the decimal point).

Antilogarithms

The process of determining the number that corresponds to a certain logarithm is known as obtaining an *antilogarithm*. It is the reverse of taking a logarithm. For example, we saw previously that log 23.5 = 1.371. This means that the antilogarithm of 1.371 equals 23.5.

$$\log 23.5 = 1.371$$
$$\text{antilog } 1.371 = 23.5$$

The process of taking the antilog of a number is the same as raising 10 to a power equal to that number.

$$\text{antilog } 1.371 = 10^{1.371} = 23.5$$

Many calculators have a key labeled 10^x that allows you to obtain antilogs directly. On others, it will be necessary to press a key labeled INV (for *inverse*), followed by the LOG key.

Natural Logarithms

Logarithms based on the number e are called natural, or base e, logarithms (abbreviated ln). The natural log of a number is the power to which e (which has the value 2.71828...) must be raised to equal the number. For example, the natural log of 10 equals 2.303.

$$e^{2.303} = 10, \text{ therefore } \ln 10 = 2.303$$

Your calculator probably has a key labeled LN that allows you to obtain natural logarithms. For example, to obtain the natural log of 46.8, you enter 46.8 and press the LN key.

$$\ln 46.8 = 3.846$$

The natural antilog of a number is e raised to a power equal to that number. If your calculator can calculate natural logs, it will also be able to calculate natural antilogs. On some calculators there is a key labeled e^x that allows you to calculate natural antilogs directly; on others, it will be necessary to first press the INV key followed by the LN key. For example, the natural antilog of 1.679 is given by

$$\text{Natural antilog } 1.679 = e^{1.679} = 5.36$$

The relation between common and natural logarithms is as follows:

$$\ln a = 2.303 \log a$$

Notice that the factor relating the two, 2.303, is the natural log of 10, which we calculated earlier.

Mathematical Operations Using Logarithms

Because logarithms are exponents, mathematical operations involving logarithms follow the rules for the use of exponents. For example, the product of z^a and z^b (where z is any number) is given by

$$z^a \cdot z^b = z^{(a+b)}$$

Similarly, the logarithm (either common or natural) of a product equals the *sum* of the logs of the individual numbers.

$$\log ab = \log a + \log b \qquad \ln ab = \ln a + \ln b$$

For the log of a quotient,

$$\log(a/b) = \log a - \log b \qquad \ln(a/b) = \ln a - \ln b$$

Using the properties of exponents, we can also derive the rules for the logarithm of a number raised to a certain power.

$$\log a^n = n \log a \qquad\qquad \ln a^n = n \ln a$$
$$\log a^{1/n} = (1/n) \log a \qquad \ln a^{1/n} = (1/n) \ln a$$

pH Problems

One of the most frequent uses for common logarithms in general chemistry is in working pH problems. The pH is defined as $-\log[H^+]$, where $[H^+]$ is the hydrogen ion concentration of a solution. The following sample exercise illustrates this application.

SAMPLE EXERCISE 2   **Using Logarithms**

(a) What is the pH of a solution whose hydrogen ion concentration is 0.015 M?

(b) If the pH of a solution is 3.80, what is its hydrogen ion concentration?

SOLUTION

1. We are given the value of $[H^+]$. We use the LOG key of our calculator to calculate the value of $\log[H^+]$. The pH is obtained by changing the sign of the value obtained. (Be sure to change the sign *after* taking the logarithm.)

$$[H^+] = 0.015$$
$$\log[H^+] = -1.82 \qquad \text{(2 significant figures)}$$
$$pH = -(-1.82) = 1.82$$

2. To obtain the hydrogen ion concentration when given the pH, we must take the antilog of $-pH$.

$$pH = -\log[H^+] = 3.80$$
$$\log[H^+] = -3.80$$
$$[H^+] = \text{antilog}(-3.80) = 10^{-3.80} = 1.6 \times 10^{-4}\ M$$

PRACTICE EXERCISE

Perform the following operations: (a) $\log(2.5 \times 10^{-5})$, (b) $\ln 32.7$, (c) antilog -3.47, (d) $e^{-1.89}$.
Answers: (a) -4.60, (b) 3.487, (c) 3.4×10^{-4}, (d) 1.5×10^{-1}

A.3 | QUADRATIC EQUATIONS

An algebraic equation of the form $ax^2 + bx + c = 0$ is called a *quadratic equation*. The two solutions to such an equation are given by the quadratic formula:

$$x = \frac{-b \pm \sqrt{b^2 - 4ac}}{2a}$$

Many calculators today can calculate the solutions to a quadratic equation with one or two keystrokes. Most of the time, x corresponds to the concentration of a chemical species in solution. Only one of the solutions will be a positive number, and that is the one you should use; a "negative concentration" has no physical meaning.

SAMPLE EXERCISE 3 **Using the Quadratic Formula**

Find the values of x that satisfy the equation $2x^2 + 4x = 1$.

SOLUTION

To solve the given equation for x, we must first put it in the form

$$ax^2 + bx + c = 0$$

and then use the quadratic formula. If

$$2x^2 + 4x = 1$$

then

$$2x^2 + 4x - 1 = 0$$

Using the quadratic formula, where $a = 2$, $b = 4$, and $c = -1$, we have

$$x = \frac{-4 \pm \sqrt{(4)(4) - 4(2)(-1)}}{2(2)}$$

$$= \frac{-4 \pm \sqrt{16 + 8}}{4} = \frac{-4 \pm \sqrt{24}}{4} = \frac{-4 \pm 4.899}{4}$$

The two solutions are

$$x = \frac{0.899}{4} = 0.225 \quad \text{and} \quad x = \frac{-8.899}{4} = -2.225$$

If this was a problem in which x represented a concentration, we would say $x = 0.225$ (in the appropriate units), since a negative number for concentration has no physical meaning.

A.4 | GRAPHS

Often the clearest way to represent the interrelationship between two variables is to graph them. Usually, the variable that is being experimentally varied, called the *independent variable*, is shown along the horizontal axis (x-axis). The variable that responds to the change in the independent variable, called the *dependent variable*, is then shown along the vertical axis (y-axis). For example, consider an experiment in which we vary the temperature of an enclosed gas and measure its pressure. The independent variable is temperature, and the dependent variable is pressure. The data shown in ▶ TABLE A.1 can be obtained by means of this experiment. These data are shown graphically in ▶ FIGURE A.1. The relationship between temperature and pressure is linear. The equation for any straight-line graph has the form

$$y = mx + b$$

where m is the slope of the line and b is the intercept with the y-axis. In the case of Figure A.1, we could say that the relationship between temperature and pressure takes the form

$$P = mT + b$$

where P is pressure in atm and T is temperature in °C. As shown in Figure A.1, the slope is 4.10×10^{-4} atm/°C, and the intercept—the point where the line crosses the y-axis—is 0.112 atm. Therefore, the equation for the line is

$$P = \left(4.10 \times 10^{-4} \frac{\text{atm}}{°\text{C}}\right) T + 0.112 \text{ atm}$$

TABLE A.1 • Interrelation between Pressure and Temperature

Temperature (°C)	Pressure (atm)
20.0	0.120
30.0	0.124
40.0	0.128
50.0	0.132

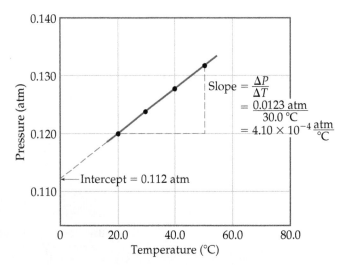

▲ FIGURE A.1 A graph of pressure versus temperature yields a straight line for the data.

A.5 | STANDARD DEVIATION

The standard deviation from the mean, s, is a common method for describing precision in experimentally determined data. We define the standard deviation as

$$s = \sqrt{\frac{\sum_{i=1}^{N}(x_i - \bar{x})^2}{N - 1}}$$

where N is the number of measurements, $\bar{x}$ is the average (also called the mean) of the measurements, and x_i represents the individual measurements. Electronic calculators with built-in statistical functions can calculate s directly by inputting the individual measurements.

A smaller value of s indicates a higher precision, meaning that the data are more closely clustered around the average. The standard deviation has statistical significance. If a large number of measurements is made, 68% of the measured values is expected to be within one standard deviation of the average, assuming only random errors are associated with the measurements.

SAMPLE EXERCISE 4 | Calculating an Average and Standard Deviation

The percent carbon in a sugar is measured four times: 42.01%, 42.28%, 41.79%, and 42.25%. Calculate (a) the average and (b) the standard deviation for these measurements.

SOLUTION

(a) The average is found by adding the quantities and dividing by the number of measurements:

$$\bar{x} = \frac{42.01 + 42.28 + 41.79 + 42.25}{4} = \frac{168.33}{4} = 42.08$$

(b) The standard deviation is found using the preceding equation:

$$s = \sqrt{\frac{\sum_{i=1}^{N}(x_i - \bar{x})^2}{N - 1}}$$

Let's tabulate the data so the calculation of $\sum_{i=1}^{N}(x_i - \bar{x})^2$ can be seen clearly.

Percent C	Difference between Measurement and Average, $(x_i - \bar{x})$	Square of Difference, $(x_i - \bar{x})^2$
42.01	$42.01 - 42.08 = -0.07$	$(-0.07)^2 = 0.005$
42.28	$42.28 - 42.08 = 0.20$	$(0.20)^2 = 0.040$
41.79	$41.79 - 42.08 = -0.29$	$(-0.29)^2 = 0.084$
42.25	$42.25 - 42.08 = 0.17$	$(0.17)^2 = 0.029$

The sum of the quantities in the last column is

$$\sum_{i=1}^{N}(x_i - \bar{x})^2 = 0.005 + 0.040 + 0.084 + 0.029 = 0.16$$

Thus, the standard deviation is

$$s = \sqrt{\frac{\sum_{i=1}^{N}(x_i - \bar{x})^2}{N - 1}} = \sqrt{\frac{0.16}{4 - 1}} = \sqrt{\frac{0.16}{3}} = \sqrt{0.053} = 0.23$$

Based on these measurements, it would be appropriate to represent the measured percent carbon as 42.08 ± 0.23.

PROPERTIES OF WATER

Density:	0.99987 g/mL at 0 °C
	1.00000 g/mL at 4 °C
	0.99707 g/mL at 25 °C
	0.95838 g/mL at 100 °C
Heat (enthalpy) of fusion:	6.008 kJ/mol at 0 °C
Heat (enthalpy) of vaporization:	44.94 kJ/mol at 0 °C
	44.02 kJ/mol at 25 °C
	40.67 kJ/mol at 100 °C
Ion-product constant, K_w:	1.14×10^{-15} at 0 °C
	1.01×10^{-14} at 25 °C
	5.47×10^{-14} at 50 °C
Specific heat:	2.092 J/g-K = 2.092 J/g·°C for ice at -3 °C
	4.184 J/g-K = 4.184 J/g·°C for water at 25 °C
	1.841 J/g-K = 1.841 J/g·°C for steam at 100 °C

Vapor Pressure (torr) at Different Temperatures

T(°C)	P	T(°C)	P	T(°C)	P	T(°C)	P
0	4.58	21	18.65	35	42.2	92	567.0
5	6.54	22	19.83	40	55.3	94	610.9
10	9.21	23	21.07	45	71.9	96	657.6
12	10.52	24	22.38	50	92.5	98	707.3
14	11.99	25	23.76	55	118.0	100	760.0
16	13.63	26	25.21	60	149.4	102	815.9
17	14.53	27	26.74	65	187.5	104	875.1
18	15.48	28	28.35	70	233.7	106	937.9
19	16.48	29	30.04	80	355.1	108	1004.4
20	17.54	30	31.82	90	525.8	110	1074.6

APPENDIX C

THERMODYNAMIC QUANTITIES FOR SELECTED SUBSTANCES AT 298.15 K (25 °C)

Substance	ΔH_f° (kJ/mol)	ΔG_f° (kJ/mol)	S° (J/mol-K)	Substance	ΔH_f° (kJ/mol)	ΔG_f° (kJ/mol)	S° (J/mol-K)
Aluminum				$C_2H_4(g)$	52.30	68.11	219.4
Al(s)	0	0	28.32	$C_2H_6(g)$	−84.68	−32.89	229.5
$AlCl_3(s)$	−705.6	−630.0	109.3	$C_3H_8(g)$	−103.85	−23.47	269.9
$Al_2O_3(s)$	−1669.8	−1576.5	51.00	$C_4H_{10}(g)$	−124.73	−15.71	310.0
				$C_4H_{10}(l)$	−147.6	−15.0	231.0
Barium				$C_6H_6(g)$	82.9	129.7	269.2
Ba(s)	0	0	63.2	$C_6H_6(l)$	49.0	124.5	172.8
$BaCO_3(s)$	−1216.3	−1137.6	112.1	$CH_3OH(g)$	−201.2	−161.9	237.6
BaO(s)	−553.5	−525.1	70.42	$CH_3OH(l)$	−238.6	−166.23	126.8
				$C_2H_5OH(g)$	−235.1	−168.5	282.7
Beryllium				$C_2H_5OH(l)$	−277.7	−174.76	160.7
Be(s)	0	0	9.44	$C_6H_{12}O_6(s)$	−1273.02	−910.4	212.1
BeO(s)	−608.4	−579.1	13.77	CO(g)	−110.5	−137.2	197.9
$Be(OH)_2(s)$	−905.8	−817.9	50.21	$CO_2(g)$	−393.5	−394.4	213.6
				$CH_3COOH(l)$	−487.0	−392.4	159.8
Bromine							
Br(g)	111.8	82.38	174.9	**Cesium**			
$Br^-(aq)$	−120.9	−102.8	80.71	Cs(g)	76.50	49.53	175.6
$Br_2(g)$	30.71	3.14	245.3	Cs(l)	2.09	0.03	92.07
$Br_2(l)$	0	0	152.3	Cs(s)	0	0	85.15
HBr(g)	−36.23	−53.22	198.49	CsCl(s)	−442.8	−414.4	101.2
Calcium				**Chlorine**			
Ca(g)	179.3	145.5	154.8	Cl(g)	121.7	105.7	165.2
Ca(s)	0	0	41.4	Cl(aq)	−167.2	−131.2	56.5
$CaCO_3$(s, calcite)	−1207.1	−1128.76	92.88	$Cl_2(g)$	0	0	222.96
$CaCl_2(s)$	−795.8	−748.1	104.6	HCl(aq)	−167.2	−131.2	56.5
$CaF_2(s)$	−1219.6	−1167.3	68.87	HCl(g)	−92.30	−95.27	186.69
CaO(s)	−635.5	−604.17	39.75				
$Ca(OH)_2(s)$	−986.2	−898.5	83.4	**Chromium**			
$CaSO_4(s)$	−1434.0	−1321.8	106.7	Cr(g)	397.5	352.6	174.2
				Cr(s)	0	0	23.6
Carbon				$Cr_2O_3(s)$	−1139.7	−1058.1	81.2
C(g)	718.4	672.9	158.0				
C(s, diamond)	1.88	2.84	2.43	**Cobalt**			
C(s, graphite)	0	0	5.69	Co(g)	439	393	179
$CCl_4(g)$	−106.7	−64.0	309.4	Co(s)	0	0	28.4
$CCl_4(l)$	−139.3	−68.6	214.4				
$CF_4(g)$	−679.9	−635.1	262.3	**Copper**			
$CH_4(g)$	−74.8	−50.8	186.3	Cu(g)	338.4	298.6	166.3
$C_2H_2(g)$	226.77	209.2	200.8	Cu(s)	0	0	33.30

Substance	ΔH_f° (kJ/mol)	ΔG_f° (kJ/mol)	S° (J/mol-K)	Substance	ΔH_f° (kJ/mol)	ΔG_f° (kJ/mol)	S° (J/mol-K)
$CuCl_2(s)$	−205.9	−161.7	108.1	$MgO(s)$	−601.8	−569.6	26.8
$CuO(s)$	−156.1	−128.3	42.59	$Mg(OH)_2(s)$	−924.7	−833.7	63.24
$Cu_2O(s)$	−170.7	−147.9	92.36	**Manganese**			
Fluorine				$Mn(g)$	280.7	238.5	173.6
$F(g)$	80.0	61.9	158.7	$Mn(s)$	0	0	32.0
$F(aq)$	−332.6	−278.8	−13.8	$MnO(s)$	−385.2	−362.9	59.7
$F_2(g)$	0	0	202.7	$MnO_2(s)$	−519.6	−464.8	53.14
$HF(g)$	−268.61	−270.70	173.51	$MnO_4^-(aq)$	−541.4	−447.2	191.2
Hydrogen				**Mercury**			
$H(g)$	217.94	203.26	114.60	$Hg(g)$	60.83	31.76	174.89
$H^+(aq)$	0	0	0	$Hg(l)$	0	0	77.40
$H^+(g)$	1536.2	1517.0	108.9	$HgCl_2(s)$	−230.1	−184.0	144.5
$H_2(g)$	0	0	130.58	$Hg_2Cl_2(s)$	−264.9	−210.5	192.5
Iodine				**Nickel**			
$I(g)$	106.60	70.16	180.66	$Ni(g)$	429.7	384.5	182.1
$I^-(aq)$	−55.19	−51.57	111.3	$Ni(s)$	0	0	29.9
$I_2(g)$	62.25	19.37	260.57	$NiCl_2(s)$	−305.3	−259.0	97.65
$I_2(s)$	0	0	116.73	$NiO(s)$	−239.7	−211.7	37.99
$HI(g)$	25.94	1.30	206.3	**Nitrogen**			
Iron				$N(g)$	472.7	455.5	153.3
$Fe(g)$	415.5	369.8	180.5	$N_2(g)$	0	0	191.50
$Fe(s)$	0	0	27.15	$NH_3(aq)$	−80.29	−26.50	111.3
$Fe^{2+}(aq)$	−87.86	−84.93	113.4	$NH_3(g)$	−46.19	−16.66	192.5
$Fe^{3+}(aq)$	−47.69	−10.54	293.3	$NH_4^+(aq)$	−132.5	−79.31	113.4
$FeCl_2(s)$	−341.8	−302.3	117.9	$N_2H_4(g)$	95.40	159.4	238.5
$FeCl_3(s)$	−400	−334	142.3	$NH_4CN(s)$	0.0	—	—
$FeO(s)$	−271.9	−255.2	60.75	$NH_4Cl(s)$	−314.4	−203.0	94.6
$Fe_2O_3(s)$	−822.16	−740.98	89.96	$NH_4NO_3(s)$	−365.6	−184.0	151
$Fe_3O_4(s)$	−1117.1	−1014.2	146.4	$NO(g)$	90.37	86.71	210.62
$FeS_2(s)$	−171.5	−160.1	52.92	$NO_2(g)$	33.84	51.84	240.45
Lead				$N_2O(g)$	81.6	103.59	220.0
$Pb(s)$	0	0	68.85	$N_2O_4(g)$	9.66	98.28	304.3
$PbBr_2(s)$	−277.4	−260.7	161	$NOCl(g)$	52.6	66.3	264
$PbCO_3(s)$	−699.1	−625.5	131.0	$HNO_3(aq)$	−206.6	−110.5	146
$Pb(NO_3)_2(aq)$	−421.3	−246.9	303.3	$HNO_3(g)$	−134.3	−73.94	266.4
$Pb(NO_3)_2(s)$	−451.9	—	—	**Oxygen**			
$PbO(s)$	−217.3	−187.9	68.70	$O(g)$	247.5	230.1	161.0
Lithium				$O_2(g)$	0	0	205.0
$Li(g)$	159.3	126.6	138.8	$O_3(g)$	142.3	163.4	237.6
$Li(s)$	0	0	29.09	$OH^-(aq)$	−230.0	−157.3	−10.7
$Li^+(aq)$	−278.5	−273.4	12.2	$H_2O(g)$	−241.82	−228.57	188.83
$Li^+(g)$	685.7	648.5	133.0	$H_2O(l)$	−285.83	−237.13	69.91
$LiCl(s)$	−408.3	−384.0	59.30	$H_2O_2(g)$	−136.10	−105.48	232.9
Magnesium				$H_2O_2(l)$	−187.8	−120.4	109.6
$Mg(g)$	147.1	112.5	148.6	**Phosphorus**			
$Mg(s)$	0	0	32.51	$P(g)$	316.4	280.0	163.2
$MgCl_2(s)$	−641.6	−592.1	89.6	$P_2(g)$	144.3	103.7	218.1

Substance	ΔH_f° (kJ/mol)	ΔG_f° (kJ/mol)	S° (J/mol-K)	Substance	ΔH_f° (kJ/mol)	ΔG_f° (kJ/mol)	S° (J/mol-K)
$P_4(g)$	58.9	24.4	280	$AgNO_3(s)$	−124.4	−33.41	140.9
$P_4(s, red)$	−17.46	−12.03	22.85	**Sodium**			
$P_4(s, white)$	0	0	41.08	$Na(g)$	107.7	77.3	153.7
$PCl_3(g)$	−288.07	−269.6	311.7	$Na(s)$	0	0	51.45
$PCl_3(l)$	−319.6	−272.4	217	$Na^+(aq)$	−240.1	−261.9	59.0
$PF_5(g)$	−1594.4	−1520.7	300.8	$Na^+(g)$	609.3	574.3	148.0
$PH_3(g)$	5.4	13.4	210.2	$NaBr(aq)$	−360.6	−364.7	141.00
$P_4O_6(s)$	−1640.1	—	—	$NaBr(s)$	−361.4	−349.3	86.82
$P_4O_{10}(s)$	−2940.1	−2675.2	228.9	$Na_2CO_3(s)$	−1130.9	−1047.7	136.0
$POCl_3(g)$	−542.2	−502.5	325	$NaCl(aq)$	−407.1	−393.0	115.5
$POCl_3(l)$	−597.0	−520.9	222	$NaCl(g)$	−181.4	−201.3	229.8
$H_3PO_4(aq)$	−1288.3	−1142.6	158.2	$NaCl(s)$	−410.9	−384.0	72.33
Potassium				$NaHCO_3(s)$	−947.7	−851.8	102.1
$K(g)$	89.99	61.17	160.2	$NaNO_3(aq)$	−446.2	−372.4	207
$K(s)$	0	0	64.67	$NaNO_3(s)$	−467.9	−367.0	116.5
$KCl(s)$	−435.9	−408.3	82.7	$NaOH(aq)$	−469.6	−419.2	49.8
$KClO_3(s)$	−391.2	−289.9	143.0	$NaOH(s)$	−425.6	−379.5	64.46
$KClO_3(aq)$	−349.5	−284.9	265.7	$Na_2SO_4(s)$	−1387.1	−1270.2	149.6
$K_2CO_3(s)$	−1150.18	−1064.58	155.44	**Strontium**			
$KNO_3(s)$	−492.70	−393.13	132.9	$SrO(s)$	−592.0	−561.9	54.9
$K_2O(s)$	−363.2	−322.1	94.14	$Sr(g)$	164.4	110.0	164.6
$KO_2(s)$	−284.5	−240.6	122.5	**Sulfur**			
$K_2O_2(s)$	−495.8	−429.8	113.0	$S(s, rhombic)$	0	0	31.88
$KOH(s)$	−424.7	−378.9	78.91	$S_8(g)$	102.3	49.7	430.9
$KOH(aq)$	−482.4	−440.5	91.6	$SO_2(g)$	−296.9	−300.4	248.5
Rubidium				$SO_3(g)$	−395.2	−370.4	256.2
$Rb(g)$	85.8	55.8	170.0	$SO_4^{2-}(aq)$	−909.3	−744.5	20.1
$Rb(s)$	0	0	76.78	$SOCl_2(l)$	−245.6	—	—
$RbCl(s)$	−430.5	−412.0	92	$H_2S(g)$	−20.17	−33.01	205.6
$RbClO_3(s)$	−392.4	−292.0	152	$H_2SO_4(aq)$	−909.3	−744.5	20.1
Scandium				$H_2SO_4(l)$	−814.0	−689.9	156.1
$Sc(g)$	377.8	336.1	174.7	**Titanium**			
$Sc(s)$	0	0	34.6	$Ti(g)$	468	422	180.3
Selenium				$Ti(s)$	0	0	30.76
$H_2Se(g)$	29.7	15.9	219.0	$TiCl_4(g)$	−763.2	−726.8	354.9
Silicon				$TiCl_4(l)$	−804.2	−728.1	221.9
$Si(g)$	368.2	323.9	167.8	$TiO_2(s)$	−944.7	−889.4	50.29
$Si(s)$	0	0	18.7	**Vanadium**			
$SiC(s)$	−73.22	−70.85	16.61	$V(g)$	514.2	453.1	182.2
$SiCl_4(l)$	−640.1	−572.8	239.3	$V(s)$	0	0	28.9
$SiO_2(s, quartz)$	−910.9	−856.5	41.84	**Zinc**			
Silver				$Zn(g)$	130.7	95.2	160.9
$Ag(s)$	0	0	42.55	$Zn(s)$	0	0	41.63
$Ag^+(aq)$	105.90	77.11	73.93	$ZnCl_2(s)$	−415.1	−369.4	111.5
$AgCl(s)$	−127.0	−109.70	96.11	$ZnO(s)$	−348.0	−318.2	43.9
$Ag_2O(s)$	−31.05	−11.20	121.3				

AQUEOUS EQUILIBRIUM CONSTANTS

TABLE D.1 · Dissociation Constants for Acids at 25 °C

Name	Formula	K_{a1}	K_{a2}	K_{a3}
Acetic acid	CH_3COOH (or $HC_2H_3O_2$)	1.8×10^{-5}		
Arsenic acid	H_3AsO_4	5.6×10^{-3}	1.0×10^{-7}	3.0×10^{-12}
Arsenous acid	H_3AsO_3	5.1×10^{-10}		
Ascorbic acid	$H_2C_6H_6O_6$	8.0×10^{-5}	1.6×10^{-12}	
Benzoic acid	C_6H_5COOH (or $HC_7H_5O_2$)	6.3×10^{-5}		
Boric acid	H_3BO_3	5.8×10^{-10}		
Butanoic acid	C_3H_7COOH (or $HC_4H_7O_2$)	1.5×10^{-5}		
Carbonic acid	H_2CO_3	4.3×10^{-7}	5.6×10^{-11}	
Chloroacetic acid	$CH_2ClCOOH$ (or $HC_2H_2O_2Cl$)	1.4×10^{-3}		
Chlorous acid	$HClO_2$	1.1×10^{-2}		
Citric acid	$HOOCC(OH)(CH_2COOH)_2$ (or $H_3C_6H_5O_7$)	7.4×10^{-4}	1.7×10^{-5}	4.0×10^{-7}
Cyanic acid	$HCNO$	3.5×10^{-4}		
Formic acid	$HCOOH$ (or $HCHO_2$)	1.8×10^{-4}		
Hydroazoic acid	HN_3	1.9×10^{-5}		
Hydrocyanic acid	HCN	4.9×10^{-10}		
Hydrofluoric acid	HF	6.8×10^{-4}		
Hydrogen chromate ion	$HCrO_4^-$	3.0×10^{-7}		
Hydrogen peroxide	H_2O_2	2.4×10^{-12}		
Hydrogen selenate ion	$HSeO_4^-$	2.2×10^{-2}		
Hydrogen sulfide	H_2S	9.5×10^{-8}	1×10^{-19}	
Hypobromous acid	$HBrO$	2.5×10^{-9}		
Hypochlorous acid	$HClO$	3.0×10^{-8}		
Hypoiodous acid	HIO	2.3×10^{-11}		
Iodic acid	HIO_3	1.7×10^{-1}		
Lactic acid	$CH_3CH(OH)COOH$ (or $HC_3H_5O_3$)	1.4×10^{-4}		
Malonic acid	$CH_2(COOH)_2$ (or $H_2C_3H_2O_4$)	1.5×10^{-3}	2.0×10^{-6}	
Nitrous acid	HNO_2	4.5×10^{-4}		
Oxalic acid	$(COOH)_2$ (or $H_2C_2O_4$)	5.9×10^{-2}	6.4×10^{-5}	
Paraperiodic acid	H_5IO_6	2.8×10^{-2}	5.3×10^{-9}	
Phenol	C_6H_5OH (or HC_6H_5O)	1.3×10^{-10}		
Phosphoric acid	H_3PO_4	7.5×10^{-3}	6.2×10^{-8}	4.2×10^{-13}
Propionic acid	C_2H_5COOH (or $HC_3H_5O_2$)	1.3×10^{-5}		
Pyrophosphoric acid	$H_4P_2O_7$	3.0×10^{-2}	4.4×10^{-3}	2.1×10^{-7}
Selenous acid	H_2SeO_3	2.3×10^{-3}	5.3×10^{-9}	
Sulfuric acid	H_2SO_4	Strong acid	1.2×10^{-2}	
Sulfurous acid	H_2SO_3	1.7×10^{-2}	6.4×10^{-8}	
Tartaric acid	$HOOC(CHOH)_2COOH$ (or $H_2C_4H_4O_6$)	1.0×10^{-3}		

TABLE D.2 • Dissociation Constants for Bases at 25 °C

Name	Formula	K_b
Ammonia	NH_3	1.8×10^{-5}
Aniline	$C_6H_5NH_2$	4.3×10^{-10}
Dimethylamine	$(CH_3)_2NH$	5.4×10^{-4}
Ethylamine	$C_2H_5NH_2$	6.4×10^{-4}
Hydrazine	H_2NNH_2	1.3×10^{-6}
Hydroxylamine	$HONH_2$	1.1×10^{-8}
Methylamine	CH_3NH_2	4.4×10^{-4}
Pyridine	C_5H_5N	1.7×10^{-9}
Trimethylamine	$(CH_3)_3N$	6.4×10^{-5}

TABLE D.3 • Solubility-Product Constants for Compounds at 25 °C

Name	Formula	K_{sp}	Name	Formula	K_{sp}
Barium carbonate	$BaCO_3$	5.0×10^{-9}	Lead(II) fluoride	PbF_2	3.6×10^{-8}
Barium chromate	$BaCrO_4$	2.1×10^{-10}	Lead(II) sulfate	$PbSO_4$	6.3×10^{-7}
Barium fluoride	BaF_2	1.7×10^{-6}	Lead(II) sulfide*	PbS	3×10^{-28}
Barium oxalate	BaC_2O_4	1.6×10^{-6}	Magnesium hydroxide	$Mg(OH)_2$	1.8×10^{-11}
Barium sulfate	$BaSO_4$	1.1×10^{-10}	Magnesium carbonate	$MgCO_3$	3.5×10^{-8}
Cadmium carbonate	$CdCO_3$	1.8×10^{-14}	Magnesium oxalate	MgC_2O_4	8.6×10^{-5}
Cadmium hydroxide	$Cd(OH)_2$	2.5×10^{-14}	Manganese(II) carbonate	$MnCO_3$	5.0×10^{-10}
Cadmium sulfide*	CdS	8×10^{-28}	Manganese(II) hydroxide	$Mn(OH)_2$	1.6×10^{-13}
Calcium carbonate (calcite)	$CaCO_3$	4.5×10^{-9}	Manganese(II) sulfide*	MnS	2×10^{-53}
Calcium chromate	$CaCrO_4$	4.5×10^{-9}	Mercury(I) chloride	Hg_2Cl_2	1.2×10^{-18}
Calcium fluoride	CaF_2	3.9×10^{-11}	Mercury(I) iodide	Hg_2I_2	$1.1 \times 10^{-1.1}$
Calcium hydroxide	$Ca(OH)_2$	6.5×10^{-6}	Mercury(II) sulfide*	HgS	2×10^{-53}
Calcium phosphate	$Ca_3(PO_4)_2$	2.0×10^{-29}	Nickel(II) carbonate	$NiCO_3$	1.3×10^{-7}
Calcium sulfate	$CaSO_4$	2.4×10^{-5}	Nickel(II) hydroxide	$Ni(OH)_2$	6.0×10^{-16}
Chromium(III) hydroxide	$Cr(OH)_3$	1.6×10^{-30}	Nickel(II) sulfide*	NiS	3×10^{-20}
Cobalt(II) carbonate	$CoCO_3$	1.0×10^{-10}	Silver bromate	$AgBrO_3$	5.5×10^{-13}
Cobalt(II) hydroxide	$Co(OH)_2$	1.3×10^{-15}	Silver bromide	$AgBr$	5.0×10^{-13}
Cobalt(II) sulfide*	CoS	5×10^{-22}	Silver carbonate	Ag_2CO_3	8.1×10^{-12}
Copper(I) bromide	$CuBr$	5.3×10^{-9}	Silver chloride	$AgCl$	1.8×10^{-10}
Copper(II) carbonate	$CuCO_3$	2.3×10^{-10}	Silver chromate	Ag_2CrO_4	1.2×10^{-12}
Copper(II) hydroxide	$Cu(OH)_2$	4.8×10^{-20}	Silver iodide	AgI	8.3×10^{-17}
Copper(II) sulfide*	CuS	6×10^{-37}	Silver sulfate	Ag_2SO_4	1.5×10^{-5}
Iron(II) carbonate	$FeCO_3$	2.1×10^{-11}	Silver sulfide*	Ag_2S	6×10^{-51}
Iron(II) hydroxide	$Fe(OH)_2$	7.9×10^{-16}	Strontium carbonate	$SrCO_3$	9.3×10^{-10}
Lanthanum fluoride	LaF_3	2×10^{-19}	Tin(II) sulfide*	SnS	1×10^{-26}
Lanthanum iodate	$La(IO_3)_3$	7.4×10^{-14}	Zinc carbonate	$ZnCO_3$	1.0×10^{-10}
Lead(II) carbonate	$PbCO_3$	7.4×10^{-14}	Zinc hydroxide	$Zn(OH)_2$	3.0×10^{-16}
Lead(II) chloride	$PbCl_2$	1.7×10^{-5}	Zinc oxalate	ZnC_2O_4	2.7×10^{-8}
Lead(II) chromate	$PbCrO_4$	2.8×10^{-13}	Zinc sulfide*	ZnS	2×10^{-25}

*For a solubility equilibrium of the type $MS(s) + H_2O(l) \rightleftharpoons M^{2+}(aq) + HS^-(aq) + OH^-(aq)$

STANDARD REDUCTION POTENTIALS AT 25 °C

Half-Reaction	$E°$(V)
$Ag^+(aq) + e^- \longrightarrow Ag(s)$	+0.799
$AgBr(s) + e^- \longrightarrow Ag(s) + Br^-(aq)$	+0.095
$AgCl(s) + e^- \longrightarrow Ag(s) + Cl^-(aq)$	+0.222
$Ag(CN)_2^-(aq) + e^- \longrightarrow Ag(s) + 2\,CN^-(aq)$	−0.31
$Ag_2CrO_4(s) + 2\,e^- \longrightarrow 2\,Ag(s) + CrO_4^{2-}(aq)$	+0.446
$AgI(s) + e^- \longrightarrow Ag(s) + I^-(aq)$	−0.151
$Ag(S_2O_3)_2^{3-}(aq) + e^- \longrightarrow Ag(s) + 2\,S_2O_3^{2-}(aq)$	+0.01
$Al^{3+}(aq) + 3\,e^- \longrightarrow Al(s)$	−1.66
$H_3AsO_4(aq) + 2\,H^+(aq) + 2\,e^- \longrightarrow$ $H_3AsO_3(aq) + H_2O(l)$	+0.559
$Ba^{2+}(aq) + 2\,e^- \longrightarrow Ba(s)$	−2.90
$BiO^+(aq) + 2\,H^+(aq) + 3\,e^- \longrightarrow Bi(s) + H_2O(l)$	+0.32
$Br_2(l) + 2\,e^- \longrightarrow 2\,Br^-(aq)$	+1.065
$2\,BrO_3^-(aq) + 12\,H^+(aq) + 10\,e^- \longrightarrow$ $Br_2(l) + 6\,H_2O(l)$	+1.52
$2\,CO_2(g) + 2\,H^+(aq) + 2\,e^- \longrightarrow H_2C_2O_4(aq)$	−0.49
$Ca^{2+}(aq) + 2\,e^- \longrightarrow Ca(s)$	−2.87
$Cd^{2+}(aq) + 2\,e^- \longrightarrow Cd(s)$	−0.403
$Ce^{4+}(aq) + e^- \longrightarrow Ce^{3+}(aq)$	+1.61
$Cl_2(g) + 2\,e^- \longrightarrow 2\,Cl^-(aq)$	+1.359
$2\,HClO(aq) + 2\,H^+(aq) + 2\,e^- \longrightarrow$ $Cl_2(g) + 2\,H_2O(l)$	+1.63
$ClO^-(aq) + H_2O(l) + 2\,e^- \longrightarrow$ $Cl^-(aq) + 2\,OH^-(aq)$	+0.89
$2\,ClO_3^-(aq) + 12\,H^+(aq) + 10\,e^- \longrightarrow$ $Cl_2(g) + 6\,H_2O(l)$	+1.47
$Co^{2+}(aq) + 2\,e^- \longrightarrow Co(s)$	−0.277
$Co^{3+}(aq) + e^- \longrightarrow Co^{2+}(aq)$	+1.842
$Cr^{3+}(aq) + 3\,e^- \longrightarrow Cr(s)$	−0.74
$Cr^{3+}(aq) + e^- \longrightarrow Cr^{2+}(aq)$	−0.41
$CrO_7^{2-}(aq) + 14\,H^+(aq) + 6\,e^- \longrightarrow$ $2\,Cr^{3+}(aq) + 7\,H_2O(l)$	+1.33
$CrO_4^{2-}(aq) + 4\,H_2O(l) + 3\,e^- \longrightarrow$ $Cr(OH)_3(s) + 5\,OH^-(aq)$	−0.13
$Cu^{2+}(aq) + 2\,e^- \longrightarrow Cu(s)$	+0.337
$Cu^{2+}(aq) + e^- \longrightarrow Cu^+(aq)$	+0.153
$Cu^+(aq) + e^- \longrightarrow Cu(s)$	+0.521
$CuI(s) + e^- \longrightarrow Cu(s) + I^-(aq)$	−0.185
$F_2(g) + 2\,e^- \longrightarrow 2\,F^-(aq)$	+2.87
$Fe^{2+}(aq) + 2\,e^- \longrightarrow Fe(s)$	−0.440
$Fe^{3+}(aq) + e^- \longrightarrow Fe^{2+}(aq)$	+0.771
$Fe(CN)_6^{3-}(aq) + e^- \longrightarrow Fe(CN)_6^{4-}(aq)$	+0.36
$2\,H^+(aq) + 2\,e^- \longrightarrow H_2(g)$	0.000

Half-Reaction	$E°$(V)
$2\,H_2O(l) + 2\,e^- \longrightarrow H_2(g) + 2\,OH^-(aq)$	−0.83
$HO_2^-(aq) + H_2O(l) + 2\,e^- \longrightarrow 3\,OH^-(aq)$	+0.88
$H_2O_2(aq) + 2\,H^+(aq) + 2\,e^- \longrightarrow 2\,H_2O(l)$	+1.776
$Hg_2^{2+}(aq) + 2\,e^- \longrightarrow 2\,Hg(l)$	+0.789
$2\,Hg^{2+}(aq) + 2\,e^- \longrightarrow Hg_2^{2+}(aq)$	+0.920
$Hg^{2+}(aq) + 2\,e^- \longrightarrow Hg(l)$	+0.854
$I_2(s) + 2\,e^- \longrightarrow 2\,I^-(aq)$	+0.536
$2\,IO_3^-(aq) + 12\,H^+(aq) + 10\,e^- \longrightarrow$ $I_2(s) + 6\,H_2O(l)$	+1.195
$K^+(aq) + e^- \longrightarrow K(s)$	−2.925
$Li^+(aq) + e^- \longrightarrow Li(s)$	−3.05
$Mg^{2+}(aq) + 2\,e^- \longrightarrow Mg(s)$	−2.37
$Mn^{2+}(aq) + 2\,e^- \longrightarrow Mn(s)$	−1.18
$MnO_2(s) + 4\,H^+(aq) + 2\,e^- \longrightarrow$ $Mn^{2+}(aq) + 2\,H_2O(l)$	+1.23
$MnO_4^-(aq) + 8\,H^+(aq) + 5\,e^- \longrightarrow$ $Mn^{2+}(aq) + 4\,H_2O(l)$	+1.51
$MnO_4^-(aq) + 2\,H_2O(l) + 3\,e^- \longrightarrow$ $MnO_2(s) + 4\,OH^-(aq)$	+0.59
$HNO_2(aq) + H^+(aq) + e^- \longrightarrow NO(g) + H_2O(l)$	+1.00
$N_2(g) + 4\,H_2O(l) + 4\,e^- \longrightarrow 4\,OH^-(aq) + N_2H_4(aq)$	−1.16
$N_2(g) + 5\,H^+(aq) + 4\,e^- \longrightarrow N_2H_5^+(aq)$	−0.23
$NO_3^-(aq) + 4\,H^+(aq) + 3\,e^- \longrightarrow NO(g) + 2\,H_2O(l)$	+0.96
$Na^+(aq) + e^- \longrightarrow Na(s)$	−2.71
$Ni^{2+}(aq) + 2\,e^- \longrightarrow Ni(s)$	−0.28
$O_2(g) + 4\,H^+(aq) + 4\,e^- \longrightarrow 2\,H_2O(l)$	+1.23
$O_2(g) + 2\,H_2O(l) + 4\,e^- \longrightarrow 4\,OH^-(aq)$	+0.40
$O_2(g) + 2\,H^+(aq) + 2\,e^- \longrightarrow H_2O_2(aq)$	+0.68
$O_3(g) + 2\,H^+(aq) + 2\,e^- \longrightarrow O_2(g) + H_2O(l)$	+2.07
$Pb^{2+}(aq) + 2\,e^- \longrightarrow Pb(s)$	−0.126
$PbO_2(s) + HSO_4^-(aq) + 3\,H^+(aq) + 2\,e^- \longrightarrow$ $PbSO_4(s) + 2\,H_2O(l)$	+1.685
$PbSO_4(s) + H^+(aq) + 2\,e^- \longrightarrow Pb(s) + HSO_4^-(aq)$	−0.356
$PtCl_4^{2-}(aq) + 2\,e^- \longrightarrow Pt(s) + 4\,Cl^-(aq)$	+0.73
$S(s) + 2\,H^+(aq) + 2\,e^- \longrightarrow H_2S(g)$	+0.141
$H_2SO_3(aq) + 4\,H^+(aq) + 4\,e^- \longrightarrow S(s) + 3\,H_2O(l)$	+0.45
$HSO_4^-(aq) + 3\,H^+(aq) + 2\,e^- \longrightarrow$ $H_2SO_3(aq) + H_2O(l)$	+0.17
$Sn^{2+}(aq) + 2\,e^- \longrightarrow Sn(s)$	−0.136
$Sn^{4+}(aq) + 2\,e^- \longrightarrow Sn^{2+}(aq)$	+0.154
$VO_2^+(aq) + 2\,H^+(aq) + e^- \longrightarrow VO^{2+}(aq) + H_2O(l)$	+1.00
$Zn^{2+}(aq) + 2\,e^- \longrightarrow Zn(s)$	−0.763

CHAPTER 1

1.2 (a) 0.1 m or 10 cm (b) No. Visible radiation has wavelengths much shorter than 0.1 m. (c) Energy and wavelength are inversely proportional. Photons of the longer 0.1-m radiation have less energy than visible photons. (d) Radiation with $\lambda = 0.1$ m is in the low-energy portion of the microwave region. The appliance is probably a microwave oven. **1.5** (a) Increase (b) decrease (c) the light from the hydrogen discharge tube is a line spectrum, so not all visible wavelengths will be in our "hydrogen discharge rainbow." Starting on the inside, the rainbow will be violet, then blue and blue-green. After a gap, the final band will be red. **1.8** (a) 1 (b) p (c) For the $n = 4$ shell, the lobes in the contour representation would extend farther along the y-axis. **1.11** (a) Meters (b) 1/second (c) meters/second **1.13** (a) True (b) False. Ultraviolet light has shorter wavelengths than visible light. (c) False. X-rays travel at the same speed as microwaves. (d) False. Electromagnetic radiation and sound waves travel at different speeds. **1.15** Wavelength of X-rays < ultraviolet < green light < red light < infrared < radio waves **1.17** (a) 3.0×10^{13} s^{-1} (b) 5.45×10^{-7} m = 545 nm (c) The radiation in (b) is visible; the radiation in (a) is not. (d) 1.50×10^{4} m **1.19** 5.64×10^{14} s^{-1}; green. **1.21** Quantization means that energy changes can happen only in certain allowed increments. If the human growth quantum is one foot, growth occurs instantaneously in one-foot increments. The child experiences growth spurts of one foot; her height can change only by one-foot increments. **1.23** (a) 4.47×10^{-21} J (b) 6.17×10^{-19} J (c) 69.2 nm **1.25** (a) $\lambda = 3.3\ \mu$m, $E = 6.0 \times 10^{-20}$ J; $\lambda = 0.154$ nm, $E = 1.29 \times 10^{-15}$ J (b) The 3.3-μm photon is in the infrared region and the 0.154-nm photon is in the X-ray region; the X-ray photon has the greater energy. **1.27** (a) 6.11×10^{-19} J/photon (b) 368 kJ/mol (c) 1.64×10^{15} photons (d) 368 kJ/mol **1.29** (a) The $\sim 1 \times 10^{-6}$ m radiation is in the infrared portion of the spectrum. (b) 8.1×10^{16} photons/s **1.31** (a) $E_{min} = 7.22 \times 10^{-19}$ J (b) $\lambda = 275$ nm (c) $E_{120} = 1.66 \times 10^{-18}$ J. The excess energy of the 120-nm photon is converted into the kinetic energy of the emitted electron. $E_k = 9.3 \times 10^{-19}$ J/electron. **1.33** When applied to atoms, the notion of quantized energies means that only certain values of ΔE are allowed. These are represented by the lines in the emission spectra of excited atoms. **1.35** (a) Emitted (b) absorbed (c) emitted **1.37** (a) $E_2 = -5.45 \times 10^{-19}$ J; $E_6 = -0.606 \times 10^{-19}$ J; $\Delta E = 4.84 \times 10^{-19}$ J; $\lambda = 410$ nm (b) visible, violet **1.39** (a) Only lines with $n_f = 2$ represent ΔE values and wavelengths that lie in the visible portion of the spectrum. Lines with $n_f = 1$ have shorter wavelengths and lines with $n_f > 2$ have longer wavelengths than visible radiation. (b) $n_i = 3, n_f = 2; \lambda = 6.56 \times 10^{-7}$ m; this is the red line at 656 nm. $n_i = 4, n_f = 2; \lambda = 4.86 \times 10^{-7}$ m; this is the blue-green line at 486 nm. $n_i = 5, n_f = 2; \lambda = 4.34 \times 10^{-7}$ m; this is the blue-violet line at 434 nm. **1.41** (a) Ultraviolet region (b) $n_i = 6, n_f = 1$ **1.43** (a) $\lambda = 5.6 \times 10^{-37}$ m (b) $\lambda = 2.65 \times 10^{-34}$ m (c) $\lambda = 2.3 \times 10^{-13}$ m (d) $\lambda = 1.51 \times 10^{-11}$ m **1.45** 4.14×10^{3} m/s **1.47** (a) $\Delta x \geq 4 \times 10^{-27}$ m (b) $\Delta x \geq 3 \times 10^{-10}$ m **1.49** (a) The uncertainty principle states that there is a limit to how precisely we can simultaneously know the position and momentum (a quantity related to energy) of an electron. The Bohr model states that electrons move about the nucleus in precisely circular orbits of known radius and energy. This violates the uncertainty principle. (b) De Broglie stated that electrons demonstrate the properties of both particles and waves and that each moving particle has a wave associated with it. A wave function is the mathematical description of the matter wave of an electron. (c) Although we cannot predict the exact location of an electron in an allowed energy state, we can determine the probability of finding an electron at a particular position. This statistical knowledge of electron location is the

probability density and is a function of Ψ^2, the square of the wave function Ψ. **1.51** (a) $n = 4, l = 3, 2, 1, 0$ (b) $l = 2, m_l = -2, -1, 0, 1, 2$ (c) $m_l = 2, l \geq 2$ or $l = 2, 3$ or 4 **1.53** (a) 3p: $n = 3, l = 1$ (b) 2s: $n = 2, l = 0$ (c) 4f: $n = 4, l = 3$ (d) 5d: $n = 5, l = 2$ **1.55** (a) impossible, 1p (b) possible (c) possible (d) impossible, 2d

1.57 (a)   (b)   (c)

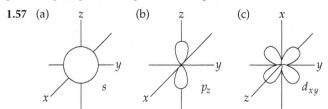

1.59 (a) The hydrogen atom 1s and 2s orbitals have the same overall spherical shape, but the 2s orbital has a larger radial extension and one more node than the 1s orbital. (b) A single 2p orbital is directional in that its electron density is concentrated along one of the three Cartesian axes of the atom. The $d_{x^2-y^2}$ orbital has electron density along both the x- and y-axes, while the p_x orbital has density only along the x-axis. (c) The average distance of an electron from the nucleus in a 3s orbital is greater than for an electron in a 2s orbital. (d) $1s < 2p < 3d < 4f < 6s$ **1.61** (a) In the hydrogen atom, orbitals with the same principal quantum number, n, have the same energy. (b) In a many-electron atom, for a given n value, orbital energy increases with increasing l value: $s < p < d < f$. **1.63** (a) There are two main pieces of experimental evidence for electron "spin." The Stern-Gerlach experiment shows that atoms with a single unpaired electron interact differently with an inhomogeneous magnetic field. Examination of the fine details of emission line spectra of multi-electron atoms reveals that each line is really a close pair of lines. Both observations can be rationalized if electrons have the property of spin.

(b)   (c)

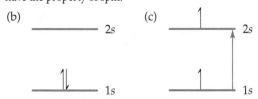

1.65 (a) 6 (b) 10 (c) 2 (d) 14 **1.67** (a) "Valence electrons" are those involved in chemical bonding. They are part or all of the outer-shell electrons listed after the core. (b) "Core electrons" are inner-shell electrons that have the electron configuration of the nearest noble-gas element. (c) Each box represents an orbital. (d) Each half-arrow in an orbital diagram represents an electron. The direction of the half-arrow represents electron spin. **1.69** (a) Cs, [Xe]$6s^1$ (b) Ni, [Ar]$4s^2 3d^8$ (c) Se, [Ar]$4s^2 3d^{10} 4p^4$ (d) Cd, [Kr]$5s^2 4d^{10}$ (e) U, [Rn]$5f^3 6d^1 7s^2$ (f) Pb, [Xe]$6s^2 4f^{14} 5d^{10} 6p^2$ **1.71** (a) Be, 0 unpaired electrons (b) O, 2 unpaired electrons (c) Cr, 6 unpaired electrons (d) Te, 2 unpaired electrons **1.73** (a) The fifth electron would fill the 2p subshell before the 3s. (b) Either the core is [He], or the outer electron configuration should be $3s^2 3p^3$. (c) The 3p subshell would fill before the 3d. **1.75** (a) $\lambda_A = 3.6 \times 10^{-8}$ m, $\lambda_B = 8.0 \times 10^{-8}$ m (b) $\nu_A = 8.4 \times 10^{15}$ s^{-1}, $\nu_B = 3.7 \times 10^{15}$ s^{-1} (c) A, ultraviolet; B, ultraviolet **1.78** 66.7 min **1.82** 1.6×10^{7} photons/s, 5.1×10^{-12} J/s **1.85** (a) The Paschen series lies in the infrared. (b) $n_i = 4, \lambda = 1.87 \times 10^{-6}$ m; $n_i = 5, \lambda = 1.28 \times 10^{-6}$ m; $n_i = 6, \lambda = 1.09 \times 10^{-6}$ m **1.90** (a) l (b) n and l (c) m_s (d) m_l **1.92** (a) The nodal plane of the p_z orbital is the xy-plane. (b) The two nodal planes of the d_{xy} orbital are the ones where $x = 0$ and $y = 0$. These are the yz- and xz-planes. (c) The two nodal planes of the $d_{x^2-y^2}$ orbital are the ones that bisect the x- and y-axes and contain the z-axis. **1.94** If m_s had three allowed values instead of two, each orbital would hold three electrons instead of two. Assuming that there is no change in the n, l, and m_l values, the number of elements in each of the first four rows would be 1st row, 3 elements; 2nd row, 12 elements; 3rd row, 12 elements; 4th row, 27 elements **1.97** (a) 1.7×10^{28} photons (b) 34 s **1.101** (a) Bohr's theory was based on the Rutherford nuclear model of the atom: a dense positive charge at the center and a diffuse negative charge surrounding it. Bohr's theory then specified the nature of the diffuse negative charge. The prevailing theory before the nuclear model was Thomson's plum pudding model: discrete electrons scattered about a diffuse positive charge cloud. Bohr's theory could not have been based on the Thomson model of the atom. (b) De Broglie's hypothesis is that electrons exhibit both particle and wave properties. Thomson's conclusion that electrons have mass is a particle property, while the nature of cathode rays is a wave property. De Broglie's hypothesis actually rationalizes these two seemingly contradictory observations about the properties of electrons.

CHAPTER 2

2.3 (a) The bonding atomic radius of A, r_A, is $d_1/2$; $r_X = d_2 - (d_1/2)$. (b) The length of the X—X bond is $2r_X$ or $2d_2 - d_1$. **2.6** The number of columns in the various blocks of the periodic chart corresponds to the maximum number of electrons that can occupy the various kinds of atomic orbitals: 2 columns on the left for 2 electrons in s orbitals, 10 columns in the transition metals for 10 electrons in d orbitals, 6 columns on the right for 6 electrons in p orbitals, 14-member rows below for 14 electrons in f orbitals. The order of blocks corresponds to the filling order of atomic orbitals, and the row number corresponds to the principal quantum number of the valence electrons of elements in that row, ns, np, $(n-1)d$, $(n-2)f$. **2.8** In general, elements are discovered according to their ease of isolation in elemental form. **2.10** (a) *Effective nuclear charge*, Z_{eff}, is a representation of the average electrical field experienced by a single electron. It is the average environment created by the nucleus and the other electrons in the molecule, expressed as a net positive charge at the nucleus. (b) Going from left to right across a period, effective nuclear charge increases. **2.12** (a) For both Na and K, $Z_{eff} = 1$. (b) For both Na and K, $Z_{eff} = 2.2$. (c) Slater's rules give values closer to the detailed calculations: Na, 2.51; K, 3.49. (d) Both approximations give the same value of Z_{eff} for Na and K; neither accounts for the gradual increase in Z_{eff} moving down a group. (e) Following the trend from detailed calculations, we predict a Z_{eff} value of approximately 4.5. **2.14** The $n = 3$ electrons in Kr experience a greater effective nuclear charge and thus have a greater probability of being closer to the nucleus. **2.16** (a) Atomic radii are determined by measuring distances between atoms in various situations. (b) Bonding radii are calculated from the internuclear separation of two atoms joined by a covalent chemical bond. Nonbonding radii are calculated from the internuclear separation between two gaseous atoms that collide and move apart but do not bond. (c) For a given element, the nonbonding radius is always larger than the bonding radius. (d) If a free atom reacts to become part of a covalent molecule, its radius changes from nonbonding to bonding and the atom gets smaller. **2.18** (a) 1.37 Å (b) The distance between W atoms will decrease. **2.20** From the sum of the atomic radii, As—I = 2.52 Å. This is very close to the experimental value of 2.55 Å. **2.22** (a) Decrease (b) increase (c) O < Si < Ge < I **2.24** (a) Cs > K > Li (b) Pb > Sn > Si (c) N > O > F **2.26** (a) False (b) true (c) false **2.28** The red sphere is a metal; its size decreases on reaction, characteristic of the change in radius when a metal atom forms a cation. The blue sphere is a nonmetal; its size increases on reaction, characteristic of the change in radius when a nonmetal atom forms an anion. **2.30** (a) An isoelectronic series is a group of atoms or ions that have the same number of electrons and the same electron configuration. (b) Ga^{3+}: Ar; Zr^{4+}: Kr; Mn^{7+}: Ar; I^-: Xe; Pb^{2+}: Hg **2.32** (a) Ar (b) Ar (c) There is no neutral atom isoelectronic with Fe^{2+}. Because transition metals fill the s subshell first but also lose s electrons first when they form ions, many transition metal ions do not have isoelectronic neutral atoms. (d) No

isoelectronic neutral atom; same reason as part (c). (e) No isoelectronic neutral atom; same reason as part (c). **2.34** (a) K^+ is smaller. (b) Cl^-, $Z_{eff} = 7$; K^+, $Z_{eff} = 9$ (c) Cl^-: $Z_{eff} = 5.75$; K^+, $Z_{eff} = 7.75$ (d) For isoelectronic ions, as nuclear charge (Z) increases, effective nuclear charge (Z_{eff}) increases and ionic radius decreases. **2.36** (a) Se < Se^{2-} < Te^{2-} (b) Co^{3+} < Fe^{3+} < Fe^{2+} (c) Ti^{4+} < Sc^{3+} < Ca (d) Be^{2+} < Na^+ < Ne **2.38** $Al(g) \longrightarrow Al^+(g) + 1e^-$; $Al^+(g) \longrightarrow Al^{2+}(g) + 1e^-$; $Al^{2+}(g) \longrightarrow Al^{3+}(g) + 1e^-$. The process for the first ionization energy requires the least amount of energy. **2.40** (a) False. Ionization energies are always positive quantities. (b) False. F has a greater first ionization energy than O. (c) True. **2.42** (a) The smaller the atom, the larger its first ionization energy. (b) Of the nonradioactive elements, He has the largest and Cs the smallest first ionization energy. **2.44** (a) Cl (b) Ca (c) K (d) Ge (e) Sn **2.46** (a) Fe^{2+}, $[Ar]3d^6$ (b) Hg^{2+}, $[Xe]4f^{14}5d^{10}$ (c) Mn^{2+}, $[Ar]3d^5$ (d) Pt^{2+}, $[Xe]4f^{14}5d^8$ (e) P^{3-}, $[Ne]3s^23p^6$ **2.48** Ni^{2+}, $[Ar]3d^8$; Pd^{2+}, $[Kr]4d^8$; Pt^{2+}, $[Xe]4f^{14}5d^8$ **2.50** (a) Positive, endothermic, values for ionization energy and electron affinity mean that energy is required to either remove or add electrons. Valence electrons in Ar experience the largest Z_{eff} of any element in the third row, resulting in a large, positive ionization energy. When an electron is added to Ar, the $n = 3$ electrons become core electrons that screen the extra electron so effectively that Ar^- has a higher energy than an Ar atom and a free electron. This results in a large positive electron affinity. (b) kJ/mol **2.52** Electron affinity of Br: $Br(g) + 1e^- \longrightarrow Br^-(g)$; $[Ar]4s^23d^{10}4p^5 \longrightarrow [Ar]4s^23d^{10}4p^6$; electron affinity of Kr: $Kr(g) + 1e^- \longrightarrow Kr^-(g)$; $[Ar]4s^23d^{10}4p^6 \longrightarrow [Ar]4s^23d^{10}4p^65s^1$. Br^- adopts the stable electron configuration of Kr; the added electron experiences essentially the same Z_{eff} and stabilization as the other valence electrons and electron affinity is negative. In Kr^- ion, the added electron occupies the higher energy $5s$ orbital. A $5s$ electron is farther from the nucleus, effectively shielded by the spherical Kr core and not stabilized by the nucleus; electron affinity is positive. **2.54** (a) Ionization energy (I_1) of Ne: $Ne(g) \longrightarrow Ne^+(g) + 1e^-$; $[He]2s^22p^6 \longrightarrow [He]2s^22p^5$; electron affinity ($E_1$) of F: $F(g) + 1e^- \longrightarrow F^-(g)$; $[He]2s^22p^5 \longrightarrow [He]2s^22p^6$. (b) I_1 of Ne is positive; E_1 of F is negative. (c) One process is apparently the reverse of the other, with one important difference. Ne has a greater Z and Z_{eff}, so we expect I_1 for Ne to be somewhat greater in magnitude and opposite in sign to E_1 for F. **2.56** Up to $Z = 82$, there are three instances where atomic weights are reversed relative to atomic numbers: Ar and K; Co and Ni; Te and I. In each case the most abundant isotope of the element with the larger atomic number has one more proton but fewer neutrons than the element with the smaller atomic number. The smaller number of neutrons causes the element with the larger Z to have a smaller than expected atomic weight. **2.58** (a) 5+ (b) 4.8+ (c) Shielding is greater for $3p$ electrons, owing to penetration by $3s$ electrons, so Z_{eff} for $3p$ electrons is less than that for $3s$ electrons. (d) The first electron lost is a $3p$ electron because it has a smaller Z_{eff} and experiences less attraction for the nucleus than a $3s$ electron does. **2.61** (a) The estimated distances are a bit longer than the measured distances. This probably shows a systematic bias in either the estimated radii or in the method of obtaining the measured values. (b) The principal quantum number of the outer electrons and thus the average distance of these electrons from the nucleus increase from $P(n = 3)$ to $As(n = 4)$ to $Sb(n = 5)$. This causes the systematic increase in M – H distance. **2.65** (a) $2 Sr(s) + O_2(g) \longrightarrow 2 SrO(s)$ (b) Based on ionic radii, the length of the side of the cube is 5.16 Å. (c) There are four SrO units in the cube.

2.68 (a) O, $[He]2s^22p^4$

↑↓	↑↓	↑	↑

$2s$ $2p$

O^{2-}, $[He]2s^22p^6 = [Ne]$

↑↓	↑↓	↑↓	↑↓

$2s$ $2p$

(b) O^{3-}, $[Ne]3s^1$. The third electron would be added to the $3s$ orbital, which is farther from the nucleus and more strongly shielded by the [Ne] core. The overall attraction of this $3s$ electron for the oxygen nucleus is not large enough for O^{3-} to be a stable particle. **2.71** (a) For both H and the alkali metals, the added electron will complete an ns

subshell, so shielding and repulsion effects will be similar. For the halogens, the electron is added to an np subshell, so the energy change is likely to be quite different. (b) True. The electron configuration of H is $1s^1$. The single $1s$ electron experiences no repulsion from other electrons and feels the full unshielded nuclear charge. The outer electrons of all other elements that form compounds are shielded by a spherical inner core of electrons and are less strongly attracted to the nucleus, resulting in larger bonding atomic radii. (c) Both H and the halogens have large ionization energies. The relatively large effective nuclear charge experienced by np electrons of the halogens is similar to the unshielded nuclear charge experienced by the H $1s$ electron. For the alkali metals, the ns electron being removed is effectively shielded by the core electrons, so ionization energies are low. (d) ionization energy of hydride, $H^-(g) \longrightarrow H(g) + 1 e^-$ (e) electron affinity of hydrogen, $H(g) + 1 e^- \longrightarrow H^-(g)$. The value for the ionization energy of hydride is equal in magnitude but opposite in sign to the electron affinity of hydrogen. **2.76** Electron configuration, $[Rn]7s^25f^46d^{10}7p^5$; first ionization energy, 805 kJ/mol; electron affinity, -235 kJ/mol; atomic size, 1.65 Å; common oxidation state, -1 **2.79** (a) Li, $[He]2s^1$; $Z_{eff} \approx 1+$ (b) $I_1 \approx 5.45 \times 10^{-19}$ J/mol ≈ 328 kJ/mol (c) The estimated value of 328 kJ/mol is less than the Table 2.4 value of 520 kJ/mol. Our estimate for Z_{eff} was a lower limit; the [He] core electrons do not perfectly shield the $2s$ electron from the nuclear charge. (d) Based on the experimental ionization energy, $Z_{eff} = 1.26$. This value is greater than the estimate from part (a) but agrees well with the "Slater" value of 1.3 and is consistent with the explanation in part (c). **2.81** (a) 9.8902 Å. (b) For Hg, the first ionization energy is 1007 kJ/mol, while the XPS energy of the $4f$ electron is 10,100 kJ/mol. The energy required to remove a $4f$ core electron is 10 times the energy required to remove a $6s$ valence electron. For O, the first ionization energy is 1314 kJ/mol, while the XPS energy of a $1s$ electron is 51,200 kJ/mol. The energy required to remove a $1s$ core electron is 40 times that required to remove a $2p$ valence electron. (c) Hg^{2+}, $[Xe]4f^{14}5d^{10}$; valence electrons are $5d$. O^{2-}, $[He]2s^22p^6$ or [Ne]; valence electrons are $2p$ (d) $Hg^{2+}5d$, $Z_{eff} = 18.85$; $Hg^{2+}4f$, $Z_{eff} = 43.85$; $O^{2-}4f$, $Z_{eff} = 3.85$.

CHAPTER 3

3.1 (a) Group 4A or 14 (b) Group 2A or 2 (c) Group 5A or 15 **3.4** (a) Ru (b) $[Kr]5s^24d^6$. **3.7** (a) Moving from left to right along the molecule, the first C needs 2 H atoms, the second needs 1, the third needs none, and the fourth needs 1. (b) In order of increasing bond length: $3 < 1 < 2$ (c) In order of increasing bond enthalpy: $2 < 1 < 3$ **3.9** (a) Valence electrons are those that take part in chemical bonding. This usually means the electrons beyond the core noble-gas configuration of the atom, although it is sometimes only the outer-shell electrons. (b) A nitrogen atom has 5 valence electrons. (c) The atom (Si) has 4 valence electrons. **3.11** Si, $1s^22s^22p^63s^23p^2$. The $n = 3$ electrons are valence electrons; the others are nonvalence electrons. Valence electrons participate in chemical bonding; the others do not.

3.13 (a) $\cdot \dot{Al} \cdot$ (b) $:\ddot{Br}:$ (c) $:\ddot{Ar}:$ (d) $\cdot Sr$

3.15 $\overset{\frown}{Mg} + :\ddot{O}: \longrightarrow Mg^{2+} + \left[:\ddot{O}:\right]^{2-}$

3.17 (a) AlF_3 (b) K_2S (c) Y_2O_3 (d) Mg_3N_2 **3.19** (a) Sr^{2+}, $[Ar]4s^23d^{10}4p^6 = [Kr]$, noble-gas configuration (b) Ti^{2+}, $[Ar]3d^2$ (c) Se^{2-}, $[Ar]4s^23d^{10}4p^6 = [Kr]$, noble-gas configuration (d) Ni^{2+}, $[Ar]3d^8$ (e) Br^-, $[Ar]4s^23d^{10}4p^6 = [Kr]$, noble-gas configuration (f) Mn^{3+}, $[Ar]3d^4$ **3.21** (a) *Lattice energy* is the energy required to totally separate one mole of solid ionic compound into its gaseous ions. (b) The magnitude of the lattice energy depends on the magnitudes of the charges of the two ions, their radii, and the arrangement of ions in the lattice. **3.23** KF, 808 kJ/mol; CaO, 3414 kJ/mol; ScN, 7547 kJ/mol. The interionic distances in the three compounds are similar. For compounds with similar ionic separations, the lattice energies should be related as the product of the charges of the ions. The lattice energies above are approximately related as $1:4:9$. Slight variations are due to the small differences in ionic separations.

3.25 Since the ionic charges are the same in the two compounds, the K—Br and Cs—Cl separations must be approximately equal. **3.27** The large attractive energy between oppositely charged Ca^{2+} and O^{2-} more than compensates for the energy required to form Ca^{2+} and O^{2-} from the neutral atoms. **3.29** The lattice energy of RbCl(s) is $+692$ kJ/mol. This value is smaller than the lattice energy for NaCl because Rb^+ has a larger ionic radius than Na^+ and therefore cannot approach Cl^- as closely as Na^+ can. **3.31** (a) A *covalent bond* is the bond formed when two atoms share one or more pairs of electrons. (b) Any simple compound whose component atoms are nonmetals, such as H_2, SO_2, and CCl_4, are molecular and have covalent bonds between atoms. (c) Covalent, because it is a gas at room temperature and below.

3.33

3.35 (a) $\ddot{O}=\ddot{O}$ (b) A double bond is required because there are not enough electrons to satisfy the octet rule with single bonds and unshared pairs. (c) The greater the number of shared electron pairs between two atoms, the shorter the distance between the atoms. An $O=O$ double bond is shorter than an $O—O$ single bond. **3.37** (a) *Electronegativity* is the ability of an atom in a molecule to attract electrons to itself. (b) The range of electronegativities on the Pauling scale is 0.7–4.0. (c) Fluorine is the most electronegative element. (d) Cesium is the least electronegative element that is not radioactive. **3.39** (a) Mg (b) S (c) C (d) As **3.41** The bonds in (a), (c), and (d) are polar. The more electronegative element in each polar bond is (a) F (c) O (d) I. **3.43** (a) The calculated charge on H and Br is 0.12e. (b) From Sample Exercise 3.5, the calculated charge on H and Cl in HCl is 0.178e. HBr has a smaller dipole moment and longer bond length than HCl; these properties both contribute to the smaller charge separation in HBr. **3.45** (a) $SiCl_4$, molecular, silicon tetrachloride; LaF_3, ionic, lanthanum(III) fluoride (b) $FeCl_2$, ionic, iron(II) chloride; $ReCl_6$, molecular (metal in high oxidation state), rhenium hexachloride. (c) $PbCl_4$, molecular (by contrast to the distinctly ionic RbCl), lead tetrachloride; RbCl, ionic, rubidium chloride

3.47 (a) (b) $:C\equiv O:$

(c) $:\ddot{F}-\ddot{S}-\ddot{F}:$ (d)

(e) $\left[:\ddot{O}-\ddot{Cl}-\ddot{O}:\right]^-$ (f)

3.49 (a) *Formal charge* is the charge on each atom in a molecule, assuming all atoms have the same electronegativity. (b) Formal charges are not actual charges. They are a bookkeeping system that assumes perfect covalency, one extreme for the possible electron distribution in a molecule. (c) Oxidation numbers are a bookkeeping system that assumes the more electronegative element holds all electrons in a bond. The true electron distribution is some composite of the two extremes. **3.51** Formal charges are shown on the Lewis structures; oxidation numbers are listed below each structure.

(a) $\ddot{O}=C=\ddot{S}$ (b)

O, -2; C, $+4$; S, -2 S, $+4$; Cl, -1; O, -2

(c) $\left[-1 :\overset{..}{\underset{..}{O}}-\overset{\overset{\overset{-1}{..}}{\overset{..}{O}}}{\underset{+2}{Br}}-\overset{..}{\underset{..}{O}}: -1 \right]^{1-}$ Br, +5; O, −2

(d) $^0 H-\overset{..}{\underset{..}{O}}-\overset{..}{\underset{..}{Cl}}-\overset{..}{\underset{..}{O}}: -1$ Cl, +3; H, +1; O, −2
$\,_0\,_{+1}$

3.53 (a) $\left[\overset{..}{O}=\overset{..}{N}-\overset{..}{\underset{..}{O}}: \right]^- \longleftrightarrow \left[:\overset{..}{\underset{..}{O}}-\overset{..}{N}=\overset{..}{O} \right]^-$

(b) O_3 is isoelectronic with NO_2^-; both have 18 valence electrons. (c) Since each N—O bond has partial double-bond character, the N—O bond length in NO_2^- should be shorter than an N—O single bond. **3.55** The more electron pairs shared by two atoms, the shorter the bond. Thus, the C—O bond lengths vary in the order $CO < CO_2 < CO_3^{2-}$. **3.57** (a) Two equally valid Lewis structures can be drawn for benzene.

The concept of resonance dictates that the true description of bonding is some hybrid or blend of these two Lewis structures. The most obvious blend of these two resonance structures is a molecule with six equivalent C—C bonds with equal lengths. (b) This model predicts a uniform C—C bond length that is shorter than a single bond but longer than a double bond. **3.59** (a) The octet rule states that atoms will gain, lose, or share electrons until they are surrounded by eight valence electrons. (b) The octet rule applies to atoms in a covalent compound and the individual ions in an ionic compound. In the covalent compound CCl_4, the atoms share electrons in order to surround themselves with an octet. In the ionic compound $MgCl_2$, Mg loses 2 e⁻ to become Mg^{2+} with the electron configuration of Ne. Each Cl atom gains one electron to form Cl⁻ with the electron configuration of Ar. **3.61** No chlorine oxide will obey the octet rule. Chlorine has seven valence electrons, and oxygen has six. For neutral chlorine oxides, regardless of the number of oxygen atoms in the molecule, the total number of valence electrons will be an (odd + even) sum, which is always an odd number.

3.63

(a) $\left[:\overset{..}{\underset{..}{O}}-\overset{..}{\underset{:\overset{..}{\underset{..}{O}}:}{S}}-\overset{..}{\underset{..}{O}}: \right]^{2-}$

Other resonance structures that minimize formal charges but violate the octet rule can be drawn. The octet rule versus formal charge debate is ongoing.

(b) $H-\overset{\overset{\textstyle |}{Al}}{\underset{\textstyle |}{}}-H$ 6 electrons around Al

H

(c) $\left[:N\equiv N-\overset{..}{\underset{..}{N}}: \right]^- \longleftrightarrow \left[:\overset{..}{\underset{..}{N}}-N\equiv N: \right]^- \longleftrightarrow$
$\left[:\overset{..}{N}=N=\overset{..}{N}: \right]^-$

(d) $:\overset{..}{\underset{..}{Cl}}-\overset{\overset{\textstyle :\overset{..}{\underset{..}{Cl}}:}{|}}{\underset{\textstyle |}{C}}-H$
H

(e) $:\overset{..}{\underset{..}{F}}-\overset{\overset{\textstyle :\overset{..}{\underset{..}{F}}:}{|}}{\underset{\textstyle |}{\underset{:\overset{..}{\underset{..}{F}}:}{Sb}}}\overset{..}{\underset{..}{F}}:$ 10 electrons around Sb

3.65 (a) $:\overset{..}{\underset{..}{Cl}}-Be-\overset{..}{\underset{..}{Cl}}:$
$\,_0\,_0\,_0$

This structure violates the octet rule.

(b) $\overset{..}{\underset{..}{Cl}}=Be=\overset{..}{\underset{..}{Cl}} \longleftrightarrow :\overset{..}{\underset{..}{Cl}}-Be\equiv Cl \longleftrightarrow Cl\equiv Be-\overset{..}{\underset{..}{Cl}}:$
$\,_{+1}\,_{-2}\,_{+1}\,_0\,_{-2}\,_{+2}\,_{+2}\,_{-2}\,_0$

(c) Formal charges are minimized on the structure that violates the octet rule; this form is probably dominant. **3.67** Three resonance structures for HSO_3^- are shown here. Because the ion has a 1− charge, the sum of the formal charges of the atoms is −1.

$\left[H-\overset{0}{\underset{}{O}}-\overset{+1}{\underset{:\overset{}{\underset{-1}{O}}:}{S}}-\overset{-1}{\underset{}{O}}: \right]^{1-}$ $\left[H-\overset{0}{\underset{}{O}}-\overset{0}{\underset{:\overset{}{\underset{-1}{O}}:}{S}}=\overset{0}{\underset{}{O}} \right]^{1-}$

$\left[H-\overset{0}{\underset{}{O}}-\overset{-1}{\underset{:\overset{}{\underset{0}{O}}:}{S}}=\overset{0}{\underset{}{O}}: \right]^{1-}$

The structure with no double bonds obeys the octet rule for all atoms, but does not lead to minimized formal charges. The structures with one and two double bonds both minimize formal charge but do not obey the octet rule. Of these two, the structure with one double bond is preferred because the formal charge is localized on the more electronegative oxygen atom. **3.69** (a) $\Delta H = -304$ kJ (b) $\Delta H = -82$ kJ (c) $\Delta H = -467$ kJ **3.71** (a) $\Delta H = -321$ kJ (b) $\Delta H = -103$ kJ (c) $\Delta H = -203$ kJ **3.73** (a) −97 kJ; exothermic (b) The ΔH calculated from bond enthalpies (−97 kJ) is slightly more exothermic (more negative) than that obtained using ΔH_f° values (−92.38 kJ). **3.75** The average Ti—Cl bond enthalpy is 430 kJ/mol. **3.77** (a) Six (nonradioactive) elements. Yes, they are in the same family, assuming H is placed with the alkali metals. The Lewis symbol represents the number of valence electrons of an element, and all elements in the same family have the same number of valence electrons. By definition of a family, all elements with the same Lewis symbol must be in the same family. **3.81** The charge on M is likely to be 3+. The range of lattice energies for ionic compounds with the general formula MX and a charge of 2+ on the metal is $3\text{-}4 \times 10^3$ kJ/mol. The lattice energy of 6×10^3 kJ/mol indicates that the charge on M must be greater than 2+. **3.85** (a) B—O. The most polar bond will be formed by the two elements with the greatest difference in electronegativity. (b) Te—I. These elements have the two largest covalent radii among this group. (c) TeI_2. The octet rule is be satisfied for all three atoms. (d) P_2O_3. Each P atom needs to share 3 e⁻ and each O atom 2 e⁻ to achieve an octet. And B_2O_3. Although this is not a purely ionic compound, it can be understood in terms of gaining and losing electrons to achieve a noble-gas configuration. If each B atom were to lose 3 e⁻ and each O atom were to gain 2 e⁻, charge balance and the octet rule would be satisfied. **3.90** (a) +1 (b) −1 (c) +1 (assuming the odd electron is on N) (d) 0 (e) +3 **3.95** An experimentally determined molecular structure will reveal bond lengths and angles of the B—A=B molecule. If resonance structures are important, the two B—A bond lengths will be identical. If the molecule features one single and one double bond, the lengths will be significantly different. **3.98** (a) $\Delta H = 7.85$ kJ/g nitroglycerine (b) $4 C_7H_5N_3O_6(s) \longrightarrow 6 N_2(g) + 7 CO_2(g) + 10 H_2O(g) + 21 C(s)$ **3.101** (a) Ti^{2+}, $[Ar]3d^2$; Ca, $[Ar]4s^2$. Yes. The 2 valence electrons in Ti^{2+} and Ca are in different principal quantum levels and different subshells. (b) In Ca the 4s is lower in energy than the 3d, while in Ti^{2+} the 3d is lower in energy than the 4s. (c) No. There is only one 4s orbital, so the 2 valence electrons in Ca are paired; there are 5 degenerate 3d orbitals, so the 2 valence electrons in Ti^{2+} are unpaired. **3.107** (a) Azide ion is N_3^-. (b) Resonance structures with formal charges are shown.

$\left[:\overset{..}{N}=N=\overset{..}{N}: \right]^- \longleftrightarrow \left[:N\equiv N-\overset{..}{\underset{..}{N}}: \right]^- \longleftrightarrow$
$\,_{-1}\,_{+1}\,_{-1}\qquad\,_0\,_{+1}\,_{-2}$

$\left[:\overset{..}{\underset{..}{N}}-N\equiv N: \right]^-$
$\,_{-2}\,_{+1}\,_0$

(c) The structure with two double bonds minimizes formal charges and is probably the main contributor. (d) The N—N distances will be equal and have the approximate length of a N—N double bond, 1.24 Å. **3.112** (a) $D(Br—Br)(l) = 223.6$ kJ; $D(Br—Br)(g) = 193$ kJ (b) $D(C—Cl)(l) = 336.1$ kJ; $D(C—Cl)(g) = 328$ kJ (c) $D(O—O)(l) = 192.7$ kJ; $D(O—O)(g) = 146$ kJ (d) Breaking bonds in the liquid requires more energy than breaking bonds in the gas phase. Bond dissociation in the liquid phase can be thought of in two steps, vaporization of the liquid followed by bond dissociation in the gas phase. The greater bond dissociation enthalpy in the liquid phase is due to the contribution from the enthalpy of vaporization.

CHAPTER 4

4.1 Removing an atom from the equatorial plane of the trigonal bipyramid in Figure 4.3 creates a seesaw shape. **4.3** (a) 2 electron-domain geometries, linear and trigonal bipyramidal (b) 1 electron-domain geometry, trigonal bipyramidal (c) 1 electron-domain geometry, octahedral (c) 1 electron-domain geometry, octahedral (d) 1 electron domain geometry, octahedral (e) 1 electron domain geometry, octahedral (f) 1 electron-domain geometry, trigonal bipyramidal (This triangular pyramid is an unusual molecular geometry not listed in Table 4.3. It could occur if the equatorial substituents on the trigonal bipyramid were extremely bulky, causing the nonbonding electron pair to occupy an axial position.) **4.5** (a) Zero energy corresponds to two separate, noninteracting Cl atoms. This infinite Cl—Cl distance is beyond the right extreme of the horizontal axis on the diagram. (b) According to the valence bond model, valence orbitals on the approaching atoms overlap, allowing two electrons to mutually occupy space between the two nuclei and be stabilized by two nuclei rather than one. (c) The Cl—Cl distance at the energy minimum on the plot is the Cl—Cl bond length. (d) At interatomic separations shorter than the bond distance, the two nuclei begin to repel each other, increasing the overall energy of the system. (e) The y-coordinate of the minimum point on the plot is a good estimate of the Cl—Cl bond energy or bond strength. **4.6** $SiCl_4$, 109°; PF_3, 107°; SF_2, 105°. Each molecule has tetrahedral electron domain geometry, but the number of nonbonding electron pairs increases from 0 to 2, respectively. Because nonbonding electron pairs occupy more space than bonding pairs, we expect the bond angles to decrease in the series. **4.9** (a) Yes. The stated shape defines the bond angle and the bond length tells the size. (b) No. Atom A could have 2, 3, or 4 nonbonding electron pairs. **4.11** A molecule with tetrahedral molecular geometry has an atom at each vertex of the tetrahedron. A trigonal-pyramidal molecule has one vertex of the tetrahedron occupied by a nonbonding electron pair rather than an atom. **4.13** (a) An *electron domain* is a region in a molecule where electrons are most likely to be found. (b) Like the balloons in Figure 4.5, each electron domain occupies a finite volume of space, so they also adopt an arrangement where repulsions are minimized. **4.15** (a) The number of electron domains in a molecule or ion is the number of bonds (double and triple bonds count as one domain) plus the number of nonbonding electron pairs. (b) A *bonding electron domain* is a region between two bonded atoms that contains one or more pairs of bonding electrons. A *nonbonding electron domain* is localized on a single atom and contains one pair of nonbonding electrons. **4.17** (a) No effect on molecular shape (b) 1 nonbonding pair on P influences molecular shape (c) no effect (d) no effect (e) 1 nonbonding pair on S influences molecular shape **4.19** (a) 2 (b) 1 (c) none (d) 3 **4.21** The electron-domain geometry indicated by VSEPR describes the arrangement of all bonding and nonbonding electron domains. The molecular geometry describes just the atomic positions. In H_2O there are 4 electron domains around oxygen, so the electron-domain geometry is tetrahedral. Because there are 2 bonding and 2 nonbonding domains, the molecular geometry is bent. We make this distinction because all electron domains must be considered when describing the atomic arrangement

and bond angles in a molecule but the molecular geometry or shape is a description of just the atom positions. **4.23** (a) Tetrahedral, tetrahedral (b) trigonal bipyramidal, T-shaped (c) octahedral, square pyramidal (d) octahedral, square planar **4.25** (a) Linear, linear (b) tetrahedral, trigonal pyramidal (c) trigonal bipyramidal, seesaw (d) octahedral, octahedral (e) tetrahedral, tetrahedral (f) linear, linear **4.27** (a) i, trigonal planar; ii, tetrahedral; iii, trigonal bipyramidal (b) i, 0; ii, 1; iii, 2 (c) N and P (d) Cl (or Br or I). This T-shaped molecular geometry arises from a trigonal-bipyramidal electron-domain geometry with 2 nonbonding domains. Assuming each F atom has 3 nonbonding domains and forms only single bonds with A, A must have 7 valence electrons and be in or below the third row of the periodic table to produce these electron-domain and molecular geometries. **4.29** (a) 1—109°, 2—109° (b) 3—109°, 4—109° (c) 5—180° (d) 6—120°, 7—109°, 8—109° **4.31** The two molecules with trigonal-bipyramidal electron-domain geometry, PF_5 and SF_4, have more than one F—A—F bond angle. **4.33** (a) Although both ions have 4 bonding electron domains, the 6 total domains around Br require octahedral domain geometry and square-planar molecular geometry, while the 4 total domains about B lead to tetrahedral domain and molecular geometry. (b) The less electronegative the central atom, the larger the nonbonding electron domain, and the greater the effect of repulsive forces on adjacent bonding domains. The less electronegative the central atom, the greater the deviation from ideal tetrahedral angles. The angles will vary as $H_2O > H_2S > H_2Se$. **4.35** A bond dipole is the asymmetric charge distribution between two bonded atoms with unequal electronegativities. A molecular dipole moment is the three-dimensional sum of all the bond dipoles in a molecule. **4.37** (a) Yes. The net dipole moment vector points along the Cl—S—Cl angle bisector. (b) No, $BeCl_2$ does not have a dipole moment. **4.39** (a) In Exercise 4.29, molecules (ii) and (iii) will have nonzero dipole moments. Molecule (i) has no nonbonding electron pairs on A, and the 3 A—F bond dipoles are oriented so that they cancel. Molecules (ii) and (iii) have nonbonding electron pairs on A and their bond dipoles do not cancel. (b) In Exercise 4.30, molecules (i) and (ii) have a zero dipole moment. **4.41** (a) IF (d) PCl_3 and (f) IF_5 are polar.

4.43 (a) Lewis structures

Molecular geometries

| Polar | Nonpolar | Polar |

(b) The middle isomer has a zero net dipole moment. (c) C_2H_3Cl has only one isomer, and it has a dipole moment. **4.45** (a) *Orbital overlap* occurs when valence atomic orbitals on two adjacent atoms share the same region of space. (b) A chemical bond is a concentration of electron density between the nuclei of two atoms. This concentration can take place because orbitals on the two atoms overlap. **4.47** (a) H—Mg—H, linear electron domain and molecular geometry (b) The linear electron-domain geometry in MgH_2 requires *sp* hybridization.

(c)

4.49

Molecule	Electron-Domain Geometry	Hybridization of Central Atom	Dipole Moment? Yes or No
CO_2	Linear	sp	No
NH_3	Tetrahedral	sp^3	Yes
CH_4	Tetrahedral	sp^3	No
BH_3	Trigonal planar	sp^2	No
SF_4	Trigonal bipyramidal	Not applicable	Yes
SF_6	Octahedral	Not applicable	No
H_2CO	Trigonal planar	sp^2	Yes
PF_5	Trigonal bipyramidal	Not applicable	No
XeF_2	Trigonal bipyramidal	Not applicable	No

4.51 (a) B, $[He]2s^22p^1$. One 2s electron is "promoted" to an empty $2p$ orbital. The 2s and two 2p orbitals that each contain one electron are hybridized to form three equivalent hybrid orbitals in a trigonal-planar arrangement. (b) sp^2 (d) A single $2p$ orbital is unhybridized. It lies perpendicular to the trigonal plane of the sp^2 hybrid orbitals. **4.53** (a) sp^2 (b) sp^3 (c) sp (d) sp^3 **4.57** No hybrid orbitals discussed in this chapter form angles of 90° with each other; p atomic orbitals are perpendicular to each other. 109.5°, sp^3; 120°, sp^2

4.57 (a)   (b)

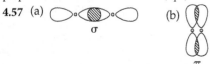

(c) A σ bond is generally stronger than a π bond because there is more extensive orbital overlap. (d) No. Overlap of two s orbitals results in electron density along the internuclear axis, while a π bond has none.

4.59 (a)

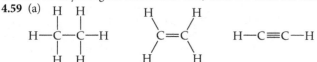

(b) sp^3, sp^2, sp (c) nonplanar, planar, planar (d) 7σ, 0π; 5σ, 1π; 3σ, 2π (e) The Si analogs would have the same hybridization as the C compounds given in part (b). That Si is in the row below C means it has a larger bonding atomic radius and atomic orbitals than C. The close approach of Si atoms required to form strong, stable π bonds in Si_2H_4 and Si_2H_2 is not possible and these Si analogs do not readily form. **4.61** (a) 18 valence electrons (b) 16 valence electrons form σ bonds. (c) 2 valence electrons form π bonds. (d) No valence electrons are nonbonding. (e) The left and central C atoms are sp^2 hybridized; the right C atom is sp^3 hybridized. **4.63** (a) ~109° about the leftmost C, sp^3; ~120° about the right-hand C, sp^2 (b) The doubly bonded O can be viewed as sp^2, and the other as sp^3; the nitrogen is sp^3 with approximately 109° bond angles. (c) nine σ bonds, one π bond **4.65** (a) In a localized π bond, the electron density is concentrated between the two atoms forming the bond. In a delocalized π bond, the electron density is spread over all the atoms that contribute p orbitals to the network. (b) The existence of more than one resonance form is a good indication that a molecule will have delocalized π bonding. (c) delocalized **4.67** (a) Linear (b) The two central C atoms each have trigonal planar geometry with ~120° bond angles about them. The C and O atoms lie in a plane with the H atoms free to rotate in and out of this plane. (c) The molecule is planar with ~120° bond angles about the two N atoms. **4.69** (a) Hybrid orbitals are mixtures of atomic orbitals from a single atom and remain localized on that atom. Molecular orbitals are combinations of atomic orbitals from two or more atoms and are delocalized over at least two atoms. (b) Each MO can hold a maximum of two electrons. (c) Antibonding molecular orbitals can have electrons in them.
4.71 (a)

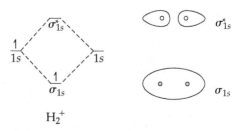

H_2^+

(b) There is one electron in H_2^+. (c) σ_{1s}^1 (d) BO = $\frac{1}{2}$ (e) Fall apart. If the single electron in H_2^+ is excited to the σ_{1s}^* orbital, its energy is higher than the energy of an H 1s atomic orbital and H_2^+ will decompose into a hydrogen atom and a hydrogen ion.

4.73

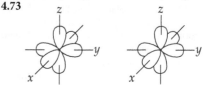

(a) 1 σ bond (b) 2 π bonds (c) 1 σ^* and 2 π^* **4.74** In the electron-sea model, valence electrons move about the metallic lattice, while metal atoms remain more or less fixed in position. Under the influence of an applied potential, the electrons are free to move throughout the structure, giving rise to thermal and electrical conductivity.

4.76

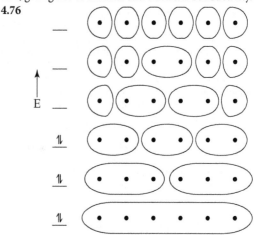

(a) Six AOs require six MOs (b) zero nodes in the lowest energy orbital (c) five nodes in highest energy orbital (d) two nodes in the HOMO (e) three nodes in the LUMO. **4.78** (a) Ag (b) Zn. Ductility decreases as the strength of metal–metal bonding increases, producing a stiffer lattice, less susceptible to distortion. **4.80** Moving from Y to Mo, the number of valence electrons, occupancy of the bonding band, and strength of metallic bonding increase. Stronger metallic bonding requires more energy to break bonds and mobilize atoms, resulting in higher melting points. **4.84** SiF_4 is tetrahedral, SF_4 is seesaw, XeF_4 is square planar. The shapes are different because the number of non-bonding electron domains is different in each molecule, even though all have four bonding electron domains. Bond angles and thus molecular shape are determined by the total number of electron domains. **4.87** (a) 2 σ bonds, 2 π bonds (b) 3 σ bonds, 4 π bonds (c) 3 σ bonds, 1 π bond (d) 4 σ bonds, 1 π bond **4.89** BF_3 is trigonal planar, the B—F bond dipoles cancel and the molecule is nonpolar. PF_3 has a tetrahedral electron-domain geometry with one position occupied by a nonbonding electron pair. The nonbonding electron pair ensures an asymmetrical electron distribution and the molecule is polar.

4.94

(a) The molecule is nonplanar. (b) Allene has no dipole moment. (c) The bonding in allene would not be described as delocalized. The π electron clouds of the two adjacent C$=$C are mutually perpendicular, so there is no overlap and no delocalization of π electrons. **4.96** (a) All O atoms have sp^2 hybridization. (b) The two σ bonds are formed by overlap of sp^2 hybrid orbitals, the π bond is formed by overlap of atomic p orbitals, one nonbonded pair is in a p atomic orbital and the other five nonbonded pairs are in sp^2 hybrid orbitals. (c) unhybridized p atomic orbitals (d) four, two from the π bond and two from the nonbonded pair in the p atomic orbital **4.99** (a) $2\,SF_4(g) + O_2(g) \longrightarrow 2\,OSF_4(g)$

(b)

$$\begin{array}{c} :\!\ddot{O}\!: \\ \| \\ :\!\ddot{F}\!-\!S\!-\!\ddot{F}\!: \\ \diagup\ \diagdown \\ :\!\ddot{F}\!: \quad :\!\ddot{F}\!: \end{array}$$

(c) $\Delta H = -551$ kJ, exothermic (d) The electron-domain geometry is trigonal bipyramidal. The O atom can be either equatorial or axial. (e) Since F is more electronegative than O, the structure that minimizes 90° F$-$S$-$F angles, the one with O axial, is preferred.

CHAPTER 5

5.1 The diagram best describes a liquid. The particles are close together, mostly touching, but there is no regular arrangement or order. This rules out a gaseous sample, where the particles are far apart, and a crystalline solid, which has a regular repeating structure in all three directions. **5.3** (a) Solid < liquid < gas (b) gas < liquid < solid (c) Matter in the gaseous state is most easily compressed because particles are far apart and there is much empty space. **5.5** Ar < CCl$_4$ < Si **5.7** (a) The molar volumes of Cl$_2$ and NH$_3$ are nearly the same because they are both gases. (b) On cooling to 160 K, both compounds condense from the gas phase to the solid-state, so we expect a significant decrease in the molar volume. (c) The molar volumes are 0.0351 L/mol Cl$_2$ and 0.0203 L/mol NH$_3$ (d) Solid-state molar volumes are not as similar as those in the gaseous state, because most of the empty space is gone and molecular characteristics determine properties. Cl$_2(s)$ is heavier, has a longer bond distance and weaker intermolecular forces, so it has a significantly larger molar volume than NH$_3(s)$. (e) There is little empty space between molecules in the liquid state, so we expect their molar volumes to be closer to those in the solid state than those in the gaseous state. **5.9** (a) London dispersion forces (b) dipole–dipole and London dispersion forces (c) dipole–dipole forces and in certain cases hydrogen bonding **5.11** (a) SO$_2$, dipole–dipole and London dispersion forces (b) CH$_3$COOH, London dispersion, dipole–dipole, and hydrogen bonding (c) H$_2$Se, dipole–dipole and London dispersion forces (but not hydrogen bonding) **5.13** (a) *Polarizability* is the ease with which the charge distribution in a molecule can be distorted to produce a transient dipole. (b) Sb is most polarizable because its valence electrons are farthest from the nucleus and least tightly held. (c) in order of increasing polarizability: CH$_4$ < SiH$_4$ < SiCl$_4$ < GeCl$_4$ < GeBr$_4$ (d) The magnitudes of London dispersion forces and thus the boiling points of molecules increase as polarizability increases. The order of increasing boiling points is the order of increasing polarizability given in (c). **5.15** (a) H$_2$S (b) CO$_2$ (c) GeH$_4$ **5.17** Both rodlike butane molecules and spherical 2-methylpropane molecules experience dispersion forces. The larger contact surface between butane molecules facilitates stronger forces and produces a higher boiling point. **5.19** (a) A molecule must contain H atoms, bound to either N, O, or F atoms, in order to participate in hydrogen bonding with like molecules. (b) CH$_3$NH$_2$ and CH$_3$OH **5.21** (a) Replacing a hydroxyl hydrogen with a CH$_3$ group eliminates hydrogen bonding in that part of the molecule. This reduces the strength of intermolecular forces and leads to a lower boiling point. (b) CH$_3$OCH$_2$CH$_2$OCH$_3$ is a larger, more polarizable molecule with stronger London dispersion forces and thus a higher boiling point.

5.23

Physical Property	H$_2$O	H$_2$S
Normal boiling point, °C	100.00	−60.7
Normal melting point, °C	0.00	−85.5

(a) Based on its much higher normal melting point and boiling point, H$_2$O has much stronger intermolecular forces. H$_2$O has hydrogen bonding, while H$_2$S has dipole–dipole forces. (b) H$_2$S is probably a typical compound with less empty space in the ordered solid than the liquid, so that the solid is denser than the liquid. For H$_2$O, maximizing the number of hydrogen bonds to each molecule in the solid requires more empty space than in the liquid, and the solid is less dense. (c) Specific heat is the energy required to raise the temperature of one gram of the substance one degree Celsius. Hydrogen bonding in water is such a strong attractive interaction that the energy required to disrupt it and increase molecular motion is large. **5.25** SO$_4^{2-}$ has a greater negative charge than BF$_4^-$, so ion–ion electrostatic attractions are greater in sulfate salts and they are less likely to form liquids. **5.27** In a nematic liquid crystalline phase, molecules are aligned along their long axes, but the molecular ends are not aligned. Molecules are free to translate in all dimensions, but they cannot tumble or rotate out of the molecular plane, or the order of the nematic phase is lost and the sample becomes an ordinary liquid. In an ordinary liquid, molecules are randomly oriented and free to move in any direction. **5.29** The presence of polar groups or nonbonded electron pairs leads to relatively strong dipole–dipole interactions between molecules. These are a significant part of the orienting forces necessary for liquid crystal formation. **5.31** Because order is maintained in at least one dimension, the molecules in a liquid-crystalline phase are not totally free to change orientation. This makes the liquid-crystalline phase more resistant to flow, more viscous, than the isotropic liquid. **5.33** Melting provides kinetic energy sufficient to disrupt molecular alignment in one dimension in the solid, producing a smectic phase with ordering in two dimensions. Additional heating of the smectic phase provides kinetic energy sufficient to disrupt alignment in another dimension, producing a nematic phase with one-dimensional order. **5.35** (a) Decrease (b) increase (c) increase (d) increase (e) increase (f) increase (g) increase **5.39** When a halogen is substituted for H in benzene, molar mass, polarizability and strength of dispersion forces increase; the order of increasing molar mass is the order of increasing boiling points for the first three compounds. C$_6$H$_5$OH experiences hydrogen bonding, the strongest force between neutral molecules, so it has the highest boiling point. **5.44** At low Antarctic temperatures, molecules in the liquid crystalline phase have less kinetic energy due to temperature, and the applied voltage may not be sufficient to overcome orienting forces among the ends of molecules. If some or all of the molecules do not rotate when the voltage is applied, the display will not function properly.

CHAPTER 6

6.1 Molecules (c) and (d) are the same molecule. **6.4** Compound (b), which has hydrogen bonding, has the highest boiling point. **6.6** (a) sp^3 (b) sp^2 (c) sp^2 (d) sp **6.8** Numbering from the right on the condensed structural formula, C1 has trigonal-planar electron-domain geometry, 120° bond angles, and sp^2 hybridization; C2 and C5 have tetrahedral electron-domain geometry, 109° bond angles, and sp^3 hybridization; C3 and C4 have linear electron-domain geometry, 180° bond angles, and sp hybridization. **6.10** NH$_3$ and CO are not typical organic molecules. NH$_3$ contains no carbon atoms. Carbon monoxide contains a C atom that does not form four bonds. **6.12** (a) A straight-chain alkane has all carbon atoms connected in a continuous chain. A carbon atom is bound to no more than two other carbon atoms and forms only σ bonds. A branched-chain hydrocarbon has a branch; at least one carbon atom is bound to three or more car-

bon atoms. (b) An alkane is a complete molecule composed of carbon and hydrogen in which all bonds are σ bonds. An alkyl group is a substituent formed by removing a hydrogen atom from an alkane. **6.14** (a) 2-methylhexane (b) 4-ethyl-2,4-dimethyldecane
(c) $CH_3CH_2CH_2CH_2CH_2CH(CH_3)_2$

(d) $CH_3CH_2CH_2CH_2CH(CH_2CH_3)CH(CH_3)CH(CH_3)_2$

(e)

or

6.16 (a) 2,3-dimethylheptane (b) $CH_3CH_2CH_2C(CH_3)_3$
(c)

(d) 2,2,5-trimethylhexane (e) methylcyclobutane   **6.18** 65
6.20 (a) Alkanes are said to be saturated because they cannot undergo addition reactions, such as those characteristic of carbon–carbon double bonds. (b) No. The compound C_4H_6 does not contain the maximum possible number of hydrogen atoms and is unsaturated.
6.22 (a) C_5H_{12} (b) C_5H_{10} (c) C_5H_{10} (d) C_5H_8; saturated: (a), (b); unsaturated: (c), (d)   **6.24** One possible structure is

$CH{\equiv}C{-}CH{=}CH{-}C{\equiv}CH$

6.26 There are at least 46 structural isomers with the formula C_6H_{10}. A few of them are

$CH_3CH_2CH_2CH_2C{\equiv}CH$ $CH_3CH_2CH_2C{\equiv}CCH_3$

6.29 (a)

(b)

(c) *cis*-6-methyl-3-octene (d) *para*-dibromobenzene (e) 4,4-dimethyl-1-hexyne   **6.30** Geometric isomerism in alkenes is the result of restricted rotation about the double bond. In alkanes bonding sites are interchangeable by free rotation about the C—C single bonds. In alkynes there is only one additional bonding site on a triply bound carbon, so no isomerism results.

6.32 (a) No

(b)

(c) no (d) no   **6.35** (a) An addition reaction is the addition of some reagent to the two atoms that form a multiple bond. In a substitution reaction one atom or group of atoms replaces another atom. Alkenes typically undergo addition, while aromatic hydrocarbons usually undergo substitution.
(b)

$CH_3CH_2CH{=}CH{-}CH_3 + Br_2 \longrightarrow$
     2-pentene
                    $CH_3CH_2CH(Br)CH(Br)CH_3$
                    2, 3-dibromopentane

(c)

$C_6H_6 + Cl_2 \xrightarrow{FeCl_3} C_6H_4Cl_2$

6.36 (a) The 60° C—C—C angles in the cyclopropane ring cause strain that provides a driving force for reactions that result in ring opening. There is no comparable strain in the five-or six-membered rings.   (b) $C_2H_4(g) + HBr(g) \longrightarrow CH_3CH_2Br(l)$;
$C_6H_6(l) + CH_3CH_2Br(l) \xrightarrow{AlCl_3} C_6H_5CH_2CH_3(l) + HBr(g)$
6.38 Not necessarily. That the two rate laws are first order in both reactants and second order overall indicates that the activated complex in the rate-determining step in each mechanism is bimolecular and contains one molecule of each reactant. This is usually an indication that the mechanisms are the same, but it does not rule out the possibility of different fast steps or a different order of elementary steps.
6.40 $\Delta H_{comb}/mol\ CH_2$ for   cyclopropane = 696.3 kJ,   for cyclopentane = 663.4 kJ. $\Delta H_{comb}/CH_2$ group for cyclopropane is greater because C_3H_6 contains a strained ring. When combustion occurs, the strain is relieved and the stored energy is released.   **6.43** (a) Alcohol (b) amine, alkene (c) ether (d) ketone, alkene (e) aldehyde (f) carboxylic acid, alkyne   **6.45** (a) Propionaldehyde (or propanal):

(b) ethylmethyl ether:

6.46 (a)

(b)

$$CH_3CH_2CH_2CH_2\overset{\overset{\displaystyle O}{\|}}{C}-OH$$

(c)

or

$$CH_3CH_2CH_2CH_2CH_2CH_2CH_2\overset{\overset{\displaystyle CH_3}{|}}{C}H-\overset{\overset{\displaystyle Cl}{|}}{C}-\overset{\overset{\displaystyle O}{\|}}{C}-OH$$

6.48

(a) $CH_3CH_2O-\overset{\overset{\displaystyle O}{\|}}{C}-$⬡

Ethylbenzoate

(b) $CH_3\overset{\overset{\displaystyle H}{|}}{N}-\overset{\overset{\displaystyle O}{\|}}{C}CH_3$

N-methylethanamide or
N-methylacetamide

(c) ⬡$-O-\overset{\overset{\displaystyle O}{\|}}{C}CH_3$

Phenylacetate

6.50

(a) $CH_3CH_2\overset{\overset{\displaystyle O}{\|}}{C}-O-CH_3 + NaOH \longrightarrow \left[CH_3CH_2C\overset{\displaystyle O}{\underset{\displaystyle O}{\diagdown}} \right]^-$

$+ Na^+ + CH_3OH$

(b) $CH_3\overset{\overset{\displaystyle O}{\|}}{C}-O-$⬡$+ NaOH \longrightarrow \left[CH_3C\overset{\displaystyle O}{\underset{\displaystyle O}{\diagdown}} \right]^- + Na^+$

$+$ ⬡$-OH$

6.52 The presence of both —OH and —C=O groups in pure acetic acid leads us to conclude that it will be a strongly hydrogen-bonded substance. That the melting and boiling points of pure acetic acid are both higher than those of water, a substance we know to be strongly hydrogen-bonded, supports this conclusion.

6.54 (a) $CH_3CH_2CH_2CH(OH)CH_3$ (b) $CH_3CH(OH)CH_2OH$

(c)

$$CH_3\overset{\overset{\displaystyle O}{\|}}{C}OCH_2CH_3$$

(d)

⬡$-\overset{\overset{\displaystyle O}{\|}}{C}-$⬡

(e) $CH_3OCH_2CH_3$

6.56

$$H-\overset{\overset{\displaystyle H}{|}}{\underset{\underset{\displaystyle H}{|}}{C}}-\overset{\overset{\displaystyle H}{|}}{\underset{\underset{\displaystyle H}{|}}{C}}-\overset{\overset{\displaystyle CH_3}{|}}{\underset{\underset{\displaystyle H}{|}}{C^*}}-\overset{\overset{\displaystyle Br}{|}}{\underset{\underset{\displaystyle Cl}{|}}{C^*}}-\overset{\overset{\displaystyle H}{|}}{\underset{\underset{\displaystyle H}{|}}{C}}-H \quad \text{*chiral C atoms}$$

6.58

$$H_2C=\overset{\overset{\displaystyle H}{|}}{C}-\overset{\overset{\displaystyle O}{\|}}{C}-H$$

$$H-\overset{H}{\underset{H}{\triangle}}\overset{}{C}-OH$$

6.60

$$\overset{\displaystyle H}{\underset{\displaystyle CH_3}{}}C=C\overset{\displaystyle H}{\underset{\displaystyle CH_2CH_3}{}}$$

cis

$$\overset{\displaystyle CH_3}{\underset{\displaystyle H}{}}C=C\overset{\displaystyle H}{\underset{\displaystyle CH_2CH_3}{}}$$

trans

Cyclopentene does not show cis-trans isomerism because the existence of the ring demands that the C—C bonds be cis to one another. **6.63** (a) Aldehyde, trans-alkene, cis-alkene (b) ether, alcohol, alkene, amine (two of these, one aliphatic and one aromatic) (c) ketone (two of these), amine (two of these) (d) amide, alcohol (aromatic) **6.65** In a carboxylic acid, the electronegative carbonyl oxygen withdraws electron density from the O—H bond, rendering the bond more polar and the H more ionizable. And carboxylate anion is stabilized by resonance and encourages ionization of the carboxylic acid. In an alcohol no electronegative atoms are bound to the carbon that holds the —OH group, and the H is tightly bound to the O. **6.68** In both cases, stronger intermolecular forces lead to the higher boiling point. Ethanol contains O—H bonds, which form strong intermolecular hydrogen bonds, while dimethyl ether experiences only weak dipole–dipole and dispersion forces. The heavier and polar CH_2F_2 experiences dipole–dipole and stronger dispersion forces, while CH_4 experiences only weaker dispersion forces.

6.70

$$CH_3\overset{\overset{\displaystyle O}{\|}}{C}CH_2CH_3$$

CHAPTER 7

7.2 We expect linear polymer (a), with ordered regions, to be denser and have a higher melting point than branched polymer (b). **7.7** In molecular solids, relatively weak intermolecular forces bind the molecules in the lattice, so relatively little energy is required to disrupt these forces. In covalent-network solids, covalent bonds join atoms into an extended network. Melting or deforming a covalent-network solid means breaking covalent bonds, which requires a large amount of energy. **7.6** (a) Hydrogen bonding, dipole-dipole forces, London dispersion forces (b) covalent chemical bonds (c) ionic bonds (d) metallic bonds **7.8** (a) Ionic (b) metallic (c) covalent-network (It could also be characterized as ionic with some covalent character to the bonds.) (d) molecular (e) molecular (f) molecular **7.10** Because of its relatively high melting point and properties as a conducting solution, the solid must be ionic. **7.12** (a) False (b) true **7.14** (a) Ionic solids are much more likely to dissolve in water. (b) Covalent-network solids can become electrical conductors via chemical substitution. **7.16** (a) CdS (b) GaN (c) GaAs **7.18** Ge or Si (Ge is closer to Ga in bonding atomic radius.) **7.20** (a) A 1.1 eV photon corresponds to a wavelength of 1.1×10^{-6} m. (b) According to the figure, Si can absorb a portion of the visible light that comes from the sun. **7.22** $\lambda = 560$ nm **7.24** The band gap is approximately 1.85 eV, which corresponds to a wavelength of 672 nm. **7.26** Monomers are small molecules with low molecular mass that are joined together to form polymers. Three monomers mentioned in this chapter are

| Propylene (propene) | Styrene (phenyl ethene) | Isoprene (2-methyl-1,3-butadiene) |

7.28

Acetic acid   Ethanol

Ethyl acetate

If a dicarboxylic acid and a dialcohol are combined, there is the potential for propagation of the polymer chain at both ends of both monomers.

7.30 (a)

(b)

(c)

7.32

and

7.34 Flexibility of molecular chains causes flexibility of the bulk polymer. Flexibility is enhanced by molecular features that inhibit order, such as branching, and diminished by features that encourage order, such as cross-linking or delocalized π electron density. Cross-linking, the formation of chemical bonds between polymer chains, reduces flexibility of the molecular chains, increases the hardness of the material, and decreases the chemical reactivity of the polymer. **7.36** No. The function of the polymer determines whether high molecular mass and high degree of crystallinity are desirable properties. If the polymer will be used as a flexible wrapping or fiber, rigidity that is due to high

molecular mass is an undesirable property. **7.38** If a solid has nanoscale dimensions of 1–10 nm, there may not be enough atoms contributing atomic orbitals to produce continuous energy bands of molecular orbitals. **7.40** (a) False. As particle size decreases, the band gap increases. (b) False. As particle size decreases, wavelength decreases. **7.42** 2.47×10^5 Au atoms **7.44**

Teflon™ is formed by addition polymerization.

CHAPTER 8

8.1 It would be much easier to drink from a straw on Mars. When a straw is placed in a glass of liquid, the atmosphere exerts equal pressure inside and outside the straw. When we drink through a straw, we withdraw air, thereby reducing the pressure on the liquid inside. If only 0.007 atm is exerted on the liquid in the glass, a very small reduction in pressure inside the straw will cause the liquid to rise. **8.4** (a) As the reaction proceeds at constant temperature and pressure, the number of particles decreases and the container volume decreases. (b) As the reaction proceeds at constant volume and temperature, the number of particles decreases and pressure decreases. **8.7** (a) $P_{red} < P_{yellow} < P_{blue}$ (b) $P_{red} = 0.28$ atm ; $P_{yellow} = 0.42$ atm; $P_{blue} = 0.70$ atm **8.10** (a) $P(ii) < P(i) = P(iii)$ (b) $P_{He}(iii) < P_{He}(ii) < P_{He}(i)$ (c) $d(ii) < d(i)$ $d(iii)$ (d) The average kinetic energies of the particles in the three containers are equal. **8.13** (a) A gas is much less dense than a liquid. (b) A gas is much more compressible than a liquid. (c) All mixtures of gases are homogenous. Similar liquid molecules form homogeneous mixtures, while very dissimilar molecules form heterogeneous mixtures. (d) Both gases and liquids conform to the shape of their container. A gas also adopts the volume of its container, while a liquid maintains its own volume. **8.15** (a) 1.8×10^3 kPa (b) 18 atm (c) 2.6×10^2 lb/in.^{2} **8.17** (a) 8.3 m (b) 2.1 atm **8.19** (a) The tube can have any cross-sectional area. (b) At equilibrium the force of gravity per unit area acting on the mercury column is not equal to the force of gravity per unit area acting on the atmosphere. (c) The column of mercury is held up by the pressure of the atmosphere applied to the exterior pool of mercury. (d) If you took the mercury barometer with you on a trip from the beach to high mountains, the height of the mercury column would decrease with elevation. **8.21** (a) 0.349 atm (b) 265 mm Hg (c) 3.53×10^4 Pa (d) 0.353 bar (e) 5.13 psi **8.23** (a) $P = 773.4$ torr (b) $P = 1.018$ atm (c) The pressure in Chicago is greater than standard atmospheric pressure, and so it makes sense to classify this weather system as a "high-pressure system." **8.25** (i) 0.31 atm (ii) 1.88 atm (iii) 0.136 atm **8.27** (a) If V decreases by a factor of 4, P increases by a factor of 4. (b) If T decreases by a factor of 2, P decreases by a factor of 2. (c) If n decreases by a factor of 4, P decreases by a factor of 4. **8.29** (a) If equal volumes of gases at the same temperature and pressure contain equal numbers of molecules and molecules react in the ratios of small whole numbers, it follows that the volumes of reacting gases are in the ratios of small whole numbers. (b) Since the two gases are at the same temperature and pressure, the ratio of the numbers of atoms is the same as the ratio of volumes. There are 1.5 times as many Xe atoms as Ne atoms. (c) Yes. By definition, one mole of an ideal gas contains Avogadro's number of particles. At a given temperature and pressure, equal numbers of particles occupy the same volume, so one mole of an ideal gas will always occupy the same volume at the given temperature and pressure. **8.31** (a) An ideal gas exhibits pressure, volume, and temperature relationships described by the equation $PV = nRT$. (b) Boyle's law, $V = $ constant$/P$; Charles's

law, V = constant $\times$ T; Avogadro's law, V = constant $\times$ n. Collect all the equalities: V = (constant $\times$ T $\times$ n)/P. Call the constant R and multiply both sides of the equation by P, PV = nRT. (c) PV = nRT; P in atmospheres, V in liters, n in moles, T in kelvins. (d) R = 0.08315 L-bar/mol-K. **8.33** Flask A contains the gas with M = 30 g/mol, and flask B contains the gas with M = 60 g/mol.
8.35

P	V	n	T
2.00 atm	1.00 L	0.500 mol	48.7 K
0.300 atm	0.250 L	3.05×10^{-3} mol	27 °C
650 torr	11.2 L	0.333 mol	350 K
10.3 atm	585 mL	0.250 mol	295 K

8.37 8.2×10^2 kg He **8.39** (a) 5.15×10^{22} molecules (b) 6.5 kg air **8.41** (a) 91 atm (b) 2.3×10^2 L **8.43** (a) 29.8 g Cl_2 (b) 9.42 L (c) 501 K (d) 2.28 atm **8.45** (a) n = 2×10^{-4} mol O_2 (b) The roach needs 8×10^{-3} mol O_2 in 48 h, approximately 100% of the O_2 in the jar. **8.47** (a) 1.32×10^7 L (b) 5.1×10^8 mol Hg **8.49** For gas samples at the same conditions, molar mass determines density. Of the three gases listed, (c) Cl_2 has the largest molar mass. **8.51** (c) Because the helium atoms are of lower mass than the average air molecule, the helium gas is less dense than air. The balloon thus weighs less than the air displaced by its volume. **8.53** (a) d = 1.77 g/L (b) M = 80.1 g/mol **8.55** M = 89.4 g/mol **8.57** 4.1×10^{-9} g Mg **8.59** (a) 21.4 L CO_2 (b) 40.7 L O_2 **8.61** 0.402 g Zn **8.63** (a) When the stopcock is opened, the volume occupied by $N_2(g)$ increases from 2.0 L to 5.0 L. P_{N_2} = 0.40 atm (b) When the gases mix, the volume of $O_2(g)$ increases from 3.0 L to 5.0 L. P_{O_2} = 1.2 atm (c) P_t = 1.6 atm **8.65** (a) P_{He} = 1.87 atm, P_{Ne} = 0.807 atm, P_{Ar} = 0.269 atm, (b) P_t = 2.95 atm **8.67** χ_{CO_2} = 0.00039 **8.69** P_{CO_2} = 0.305 atm, P_t = 1.232 atm **8.71** P_{N_2} = 1.3 atm, P_{O_2} = 0.54 atm, P_{CO_2} = 0.27 atm **8.73** 2.5 mole % O_2 **8.75** P_t = 2.47 atm **8.77** (a) Increase in temperature at constant volume or decrease in volume or increase in pressure (b) decrease in temperature (c) increase in volume, decrease in pressure (d) increase in temperature **8.79** The fact that gases are readily compressible supports the assumption that most of the volume of a gas sample is empty space. **8.81** Average speed is the sum of the speeds of all particles divided by the total number of particles. The root mean square speed is the speed of a molecule with the same kinetic energy as the average kinetic energy of the sample. The root mean square speed is larger for a given gas sample at a fixed temperature, but the difference between the two is small. **8.83** (a) Average kinetic energy of the molecules increases. (b) Root mean square speed of the molecules increases. (c) Strength of an average impact with the container walls increases. (d) Total collisions of molecules with walls per second increases. **8.85** (a) In order of increasing speed and decreasing molar mass: HBr < NF_3 < SO_2 < CO < Ne (b) u_{NF_3} = 324 m/s (c) The most probable speed of an ozone molecule in the stratosphere is 306 m/s. **8.87** Effusion is the escape of gas molecules through a tiny hole. Diffusion is the distribution of a gas throughout space or throughout another substance. **8.89** The order of increasing rate of effusion is $^2H^{37}Cl$ < $^1H^{37}Cl$ < $^2H^{35}Cl$ < $^1H^{35}Cl$. **8.91** As_4S_6 **8.93** (a) Non-ideal-gas behavior is observed at very high pressures and low temperatures. (b) The real volumes of gas molecules and attractive intermolecular forces between molecules cause gases to behave nonideally. (c) According to the ideal-gas law, the ratio PV/RT should be constant for a given gas sample at all combinations of pressure, volume, and temperature. If this ratio changes with increasing pressure, the gas sample is not behaving ideally. **8.95** Ar (a = 1.34, b = 0.0322) will behave more like an ideal gas than CO_2 (a = 3.59, b = 0.427) at high pressures. **8.97** (a) P = 4.89 atm (b) P = 4.69 atm (c) Qualitatively, molecular attractions are more important as the amount of free space decreases and the number of molecular collisions increases. Molecular volume is a larger part of the total volume as the container volume decreases. **8.99** From the value of b for Xe, the nonbonding radius is 2.72 Å. From Figure 7.6, the bonding atomic radius of Xe is 1.30 Å. We expect the bonding radius of an atom to be smaller than its non-

bonding radius, but this difference is quite large. **8.101** V = 3.1 mm^3 **8.105** (a) 13.4 mol $C_3H_8(g)$ (b) 1.47×10^3 mol $C_3H_8(l)$ (c) The ratio of moles liquid to moles gas is 110. Many more molecules and moles of liquid fit in a container of fixed volume because there is much less space between molecules in the liquid phase. **8.108** P_t = 5.3×10^2 torr **8.111** 42.2 g O_2 **8.115** T_2 = 687 °C **8.120** (a) P(ideal) =177 atm (b) P(van der Waals) = 187.4 atm (c) Under the conditions of this problem (large number of moles of gas), the correction for the real volume of molecules dominates. **8.123** (a) 44.58% C, 6.596% H, 16.44% Cl, 32.38% N (b) $C_8H_{14}N_5Cl$ (c) Molar mass of the compound is required in order to determine molecular formula when the empirical formula is known. **8.128** (a) 5.02×10^8 L $CH_3OH(l)$ (b) $CH_4(g) + 2\,O_2(g) \longrightarrow CO_2(g) + 2\,H_2O(l)$, $\Delta H°$ = -890.4 kJ; ΔH for combustion of the methane is -1.10×10^{13} kJ. $CH_3OH(l) + 3/2\,O_2(g) \longrightarrow CO_2(g) + 2\,H_2O(l)$, $\Delta H°$ = -726.6 kJ; ΔH for combustion of the methanol is -9.00×10^{12} kJ. (c) The enthalpy change upon combustion of 1.00 L of $CH_4(l)$ is -2.59×10^4 kJ and for 1.00 L of $CH_3OH(l)$, -1.79×10^4 kJ. Clearly $CH_4(l)$ has the higher enthalpy of combustion per unit volume.

CHAPTER 9

9.1 (a) A greater volume than 22.4 L (b) The gas will occupy more volume at 85 km than at 50 km. (c) We expect gases to behave most ideally in the thermosphere, around the stratopause and in the troposphere at low altitude. **9.6** *Salt water* contains high concentrations of dissolved salts and solids. It includes the world ocean (97.2% of all water, approximately 35,000 ppm of dissolved salts) and brackish or salty water (0.1% of all water). *Freshwater* (0.6% of all water on earth) refers to natural waters that have low concentrations (less than 500 ppm) of dissolved salts and solids. It includes the waters of lakes, rivers, ponds, and streams. *Groundwater* is freshwater that resides in the soil. It resides in aquifers, porous rock that holds water, and composes 20% of the world's freshwater. **9.10** (a) Its temperature profile (b) troposphere, 0 to 12 km; stratosphere, 12 to 50 km; mesosphere, 50 to 85 km; thermosphere, 85 to 110 km **9.12** (a) The partial pressure of O_3 is 3.0×10^{-7} atm (2.2×10^{-4} torr). (b) 7.3×10^{15} O_3 molecules/1.0 L air **9.14** 8.6×10^{16} CO molecules/1.0 L air **9.16** (a) 570 nm (b) visible electromagnetic radiation **9.18** (a) *Photodissociation* is cleavage of a bond such that two neutral species are produced. *Photoionization* is absorption of a photon with sufficient energy to eject an electron, producing an ion and the ejected electron. (b) Photoionization of O_2 requires 1205 kJ/mol. Photodissociation requires only 495 kJ/mol. At lower elevations, high-energy short-wavelength solar radiation has already been absorbed. Below 90 km, the increased concentration of O_2 and the availability of longer-wavelength radiation cause the photodissociation process to dominate. **9.20** Ozone depletion reactions, which involve only O_3, O_2, or O (oxidation state = 0), do not involve a change in oxidation state for oxygen atoms. Reactions involving ClO and one of the oxygen species with a zero oxidation state do involve a change in the oxidation state of oxygen atoms. **9.22** (a) A chlorofluorocarbon is a compound that contains chlorine, fluorine, and carbon, while a hydrofluorocarbon is a compound that contains hydrogen, fluorine, and carbon. An HFC contains hydrogen in place of the chlorine present in a CFC. (b) HFCs are potentially less harmful than CFCs because their photodissociation does not produce Cl atoms, which catalyze the destruction of ozone. **9.24** (a) The C—F bond requires more energy for dissociation than the C—Cl bond and is not readily cleaved by the available wavelengths of UV light. (b) Chlorine is present as chlorine atoms and chlorine oxide molecules, Cl and ClO, respectively. **9.26** (a) Methane, CH_4, arises from decomposition of organic matter by certain microorganisms; it also escapes from underground gas deposits. (b) SO_2 is released in volcanic gases and also is produced by bacterial action on decomposing vegetable and animal matter. (c) Nitric oxide, NO, results from oxidation of decomposing organic matter and is formed in lightning flashes. **9.28** (a) $H_2SO_4(aq) + CaCO_3(s) \longrightarrow CaSO_4(s) + H_2O(l) + CO_2(g)$ (b) The $CaSO_4(s)$ would be much less reactive with acidic solution, since it would require a strongly acidic solution to shift the relevant equilibrium to the right: $CaSO_4(s) + 2H^+(aq) \rightleftharpoons Ca^{2+}(aq) + 2HSO_4^-(aq)$. $CaSO_4$ would protect $CaCO_3$ from attack by acid rain, but it would not provide the structural strength of limestone. **9.30** (a) Ultraviolet (b) 357 kJ/mol (c) The average C—H bond energy from Table 8.4 is 413 kJ/mol. The C—H bond energy in CH_2O, 357 kJ/mol, is less than the "average" C—H bond energy.

(d)

$$\overset{:O:}{\underset{\|}{H-C-H}} + h\nu \longrightarrow \overset{:O:}{\underset{\|}{H-C\cdot}} + H\cdot$$

9.32 Incoming and outgoing energies are in different regions of the electromagnetic spectrum. CO_2 is transparent to incoming visible radiation but absorbs outgoing infrared radiation. **9.34** 0.099 M Na^+ **9.36** (a) 3.22×10^3 g H_2O (b) The final temperature is 43.4 °C. **9.38** 4.361×10^5 g CaO **9.40** (a) *Groundwater* is freshwater (less than 500 ppm total salt content) that is under the soil; it composes 20% of the world's freshwater. (b) An *aquifer* is a layer of porous rock that holds groundwater. **9.42** The minimum pressure required to initiate reverse osmosis is greater than 5.1 atm. **9.44** (a) $CO_2(g)$, HCO_3^-, $H_2O(l)$, SO_4^{2-}, NO_3^-, HPO_4^{2-}, $H_2PO_4^-$ (b) $CH_4(g)$, $H_2S(g)$, $NH_3(g)$, $PH_3(g)$ **9.46** 25.1 g O_2 **9.48** $Mg^{2+}(aq) + Ca(OH)_2(s) \longrightarrow Mg(OH)_2(s) + Ca^{2+}(aq)$ **9.50** 0.42 mol $Ca(OH)_2$, 0.18 mol Na_2CO_3 **9.52** $4FeSO_4(aq) + O_2(aq) + 2H_2O(l) \longrightarrow 4Fe^{3+}(aq) + 4OH^-(aq) + 4SO_4^{2-}(aq)$; $Fe^{3+}(aq) + 3HCO_3^-(aq) \longrightarrow Fe(OH)_3(s) + 3CO_2(g)$ **9.54** (a) *Trihalomethanes* are the by-products of water chlorination; they contain one central carbon atom bound to one hydrogen and three halogen atoms.
(b)

$$\underset{Cl}{\overset{H}{\underset{|}{\overset{|}{Cl-C-Cl}}}} \qquad \underset{Cl}{\overset{H}{\underset{|}{\overset{|}{Cl-C-Br}}}}$$

9.59 Multiply Equation 9.7 by a factor of 2; then add it to Equation 9.9. 2 $Cl(g)$ and 2 $ClO(g)$ cancel from each side of the resulting equation to produce Equation 9.10. **9.62** Although HFCs have long lifetimes in the stratosphere, it is infrequent that light with energy sufficient to dissociate a C—F bond will reach an HFC molecule. F atoms, the bad actors in ozone destruction, are much less likely than Cl atoms to be produced by photodissociation in the stratosphere. **9.64** The formation of $NO(g)$ is endothermic, so K increases with increasing temperature. The oxidation of $NO(g)$ to $NO_2(g)$ is exothermic, so the value of K decreases with increasing temperature. **9.68** 7.1×10^8 m^2 **9.70** (a) CO_3^{2-} is a relatively strong Brønsted–Lowry base and produces OH^- in aqueous solution. If $[OH^-(aq)]$ is sufficient for the reaction quotient to exceed K_{sp} for $Mg(OH)_2$, the solid will precipitate. (b) At these ion concentrations, $Q > K_{sp}$ and $Mg(OH)_2$ will precipitate. **9.74** (a) 2.5×10^7 ton CO_2, 4.2×10^5 ton SO_2 (b) 4.3×10^5 ton $CaSO_3$ **9.77** (a)

$$H-\ddot{O}-H \longrightarrow H\cdot + \cdot\ddot{O}-H$$

(b) 258 nm (c) The overall reaction is $O_3(g) + O(g) \longrightarrow 2O_2(g)$. $OH(g)$ is the catalyst in the overall reaction because it is consumed and then reproduced. **9.79** The enthalpy change for the first step is −141 kJ, for the second step, −249 kJ, for the overall reaction, −390 kJ. **9.83** (a) Rate $= k[O_3][H]$ (b) $k_{avg} = 1.13 \times 10^{44}$ M^{-1} s^{-1}

CHAPTER 10

10.1 (a) As the book falls, potential energy decreases and kinetic energy increases. (b) 71 J, assuming no transfer of energy as heat (c) A heavier book falling from the same shelf has greater kinetic energy when it hits the floor. **10.5** (a) No. The distance traveled to the top of a mountain depends on the path taken by the hiker. Distance is a path function, not a state function. (b) Yes. Change in elevation depends only on the location of the base camp and the height of the mountain, not on the path to the top. Change in elevation is a state function, not a path function. **10.8** (a) The sign of w is (+). (b) The internal energy of the system increases during the change; the sign of ΔE is (+). **10.11** (a) $\Delta H_A = \Delta H_B + \Delta H_C$. The diagram and equation both show that the net enthalpy change for a process is independent of path, that ΔH is a state function. (b) $\Delta H_Z = \Delta H_X + \Delta H_Y$. (c) Hess's law states that the enthalpy change for net reaction Z is the sum of the enthalpy changes for steps X and Y, regardless of whether the reaction actually occurs via this path. The diagrams are a visual statement of Hess's law. **10.13** An object can possess energy by virtue of its motion or position. Kinetic energy depends on the mass of the object and its velocity. Potential energy depends on the position of the object relative to the body with which it interacts. **10.15** (a) 1.9×10^5 J (b) 4.6×10^4 cal (c) As the automobile brakes to a stop, its speed (and hence its kinetic energy) drops to zero. The kinetic energy of the automobile is primarily transferred to friction between brakes and wheels and somewhat to deformation of the tire and friction between the tire and road. **10.17** 1 Btu $= 1054$ J **10.19** (a) The *system* is the well-defined part of the universe whose energy changes are being studied. (b) A *closed system* can exchange heat but not mass with its surroundings. (c) Any part of the universe not part of the system is called the surroundings. **10.21** (a) Work is a force applied over a distance. (b) The amount of work done is the magnitude of the force times the distance over which it is applied. $w = F \times d$. **10.23** (a) Gravity; work is done because the force of gravity is opposed and the pencil is lifted. (b) Mechanical force; work is done because the force of the coiled spring is opposed as the spring is compressed over a distance. **10.25** (a) In any chemical or physical change, energy can be neither created nor destroyed; energy is conserved. (b) The *internal energy (E)* of a system is the sum of all the kinetic and potential energies of the system components. (c) Internal energy of a closed system increases when work is done on the system and when heat is transferred to the system. **10.27** (a) $\Delta E = -0.077$ kJ, endothermic (b) $\Delta E = -22.1$ kJ, exothermic (c) $\Delta E = 7.25$ kJ, endothermic **10.29** (a) Since no work is done by the system in case (2), the gas will absorb most of the energy as heat; the case (2) gas will have the higher temperature. (b) In case (2) $w = 0$ and $q = 100$ J. In case (1) energy will be used to do work on the surroundings ($-w$), but some will be absorbed as heat ($+q$). (c) ΔE is greater for case (2) because the entire 100 J increases the internal energy of the system rather than a part of the energy doing work on the surroundings. **10.31** (a) A *state function* is a property that depends only on the physical state (pressure, temperature, etc.) of the system, not on the route used to get to the current state. (b) Internal energy is a state function; heat is not a state function. (c) Volume is a state function. The volume of a system depends only on conditions (pressure, temperature, amount of substance), not the route or method used to establish that volume. **10.33** (a) ΔH is usually easier to measure than ΔE because at constant pressure, $\Delta H = q_p$. The heat flow associated with a process at constant pressure can easily be measured as a change in temperature, while measuring ΔE requires a means to measure both q and w. (b) H is a static quantity that depends only on the specific conditions of the system. q is an energy *change* that, in the general case, does depend on how the change occurs. We can equate change in enthalpy, ΔH, with heat, q_p, only for the specific conditions of constant pressure and exclusively P-V work. (c) The process is endothermic. **10.35** At constant pressure, $\Delta E = \Delta H - P\Delta V$. The values of either P and ΔV or T and Δn must be known to calculate ΔE from ΔH. **10.37** $\Delta E = 1.47$ kJ; $\Delta H = 0.824$ kJ **10.39** (a) $C_2H_5OH(l) + 3O_2(g) \longrightarrow 3H_2O + 2CO_2(g)$, $\Delta H = -1235$ kJ

(b) $C_2H_5OH(l) + 3 O_2(g)$

$$\Delta H = -1235 \text{ kJ}$$

$3 H_2O(g) + 2 CO_2(g)$

5.41 (a) $\Delta H = -142.3$ kJ/mol $O_3(g)$ (b) $2 O_3(g)$ has the higher enthalpy. **5.43** (a) Exothermic (b) -87.9 kJ heat transferred (c) 15.7 g MgO produced (d) 602 kJ heat absorbed **5.45** (a) -29.5 kJ (b) -4.11 kJ (c) 60.6 J **5.47** (a) $\Delta H = 726.5$ kJ (b) $\Delta H = -1453$ kJ (c) The exothermic forward reaction is more likely to be thermodynamically favored. (d) Vaporization is endothermic. If the product were $H_2O(g)$, the reaction would be more endothermic and would have a less negative ΔH. **5.49** (a) J/mol-°C or J/mol-K (b) J/g-°C or J/g-K (c) To calculate heat capacity from specific heat, the mass of the particular piece of copper pipe must be known. **5.51** (a) 4.184 J/g-K (b) 75.40 J/mol-°C (c) 774 J/°C (d) 904 kJ **5.53** (a) 2.66×10^3 J (b) It will require more heat to increase the temperature of one mole of octane, $C_8H_{18}(l)$, by a certain amount than to increase the temperature of one mole of water, $H_2O(l)$, by the same amount. **5.55** $\Delta H = -44.4$ kJ/mol NaOH **5.57** $\Delta H_{rxn} = -25.5$ kJ/g $C_6H_4O_2$ or -2.75×10^3 kJ/mol $C_6H_4O_2$ **5.59** (a) Heat capacity of the complete calorimeter $= 14.4$ kJ/°C (b) 7.56 °C **5.61** Hess's law is a consequence of the fact that enthalpy is a state function. Since ΔH is independent of path, we can describe a process by any series of steps that adds up to the overall process. ΔH for the process is the sum of ΔH values for the steps. **5.63** $\Delta H = -1300.0$ kJ **5.65** $\Delta H = -2.49 \times 10^3$ kJ **5.67** (a) *Standard conditions* for enthalpy changes are $P = 1$ atm and some common temperature, usually 298 K. (b) *Enthalpy of formation* is the enthalpy change that occurs when a compound is formed from its component elements. (c) *Standard enthalpy of formation* ΔH_f° is the enthalpy change that accompanies formation of one mole of a substance from elements in their standard states. **5.69** (a) $\frac{1}{2}N_2(g) + O_2(g) \longrightarrow NO_2(g)$, $\Delta H_f^\circ = 33.84$ kJ (b) $S(s) + 3/2 O_2(g) \longrightarrow SO_3(g)$, $\Delta H_f^\circ = -395.2$ kJ (c) $Na(s) + \frac{1}{2}Br_2(l) \longrightarrow NaBr(s)$, $\Delta H_f^\circ = -361.4$ kJ (d) $Pb(s) + N_2(g) + 3 O_2(g) \longrightarrow Pb(NO_3)_2(s)$, $\Delta H_f^\circ = -451.9$ kJ **5.71** $\Delta H_{rxn}^\circ = -847.6$ kJ **5.73** (a) $\Delta H_{rxn}^\circ = -196.6$ kJ (b) $\Delta H_{rxn}^\circ = 37.1$ kJ (c) $\Delta H_{rxn}^\circ = -976.94$ kJ (d) $\Delta H_{rxn}^\circ = -68.3$ kJ **5.75** $\Delta H_f^\circ = -248$ kJ **5.77** (a) $C_8H_{18}(l) + \frac{25}{2}O_2(g) \longrightarrow 8 CO_2(g) + 9 H_2O(g)$, $\Delta H = -5064.9$ kJ (b) $8 C(s, \text{graphite}) + 9 H_2(g) \longrightarrow C_8H_{18}(l)$ (c) $\Delta H_f^\circ = -259.5$ kJ **5.79** (a) $C_2H_5OH(l) + 3 O_2(g) \longrightarrow 2 CO_2(g) + 3 H_2O(g)$ (b) $\Delta H_{rxn}^\circ = -1234.8$ kJ (c) 2.11×10^4 kJ/L heat produced (d) 0.071284 g CO_2/kJ heat emitted **5.81** (a) *Fuel value* is the amount of energy produced when 1 g of a substance (fuel) is combusted. (b) 5 g of fat (c) These products of metabolism are expelled as waste via the alimentary tract, $H_2O(l)$ primarily in urine and feces, and $CO_2(g)$ as gas. **5.83** 108 or 1×10^2 Cal/serving (b) Sodium does not contribute to the calorie content of the food because it is not metabolized by the body. **5.85** 59.7 Cal **5.87** (a) $\Delta H_{comb} = -1850$ kJ/mol C_3H_4, -1926 kJ/mol C_3H_6, -2044 kJ/mol C_3H_8 (b) $\Delta H_{comb} = -4.616 \times 10^4$ kJ/kg C_3H_4, -4.578×10^4 kJ/kg C_3H_6, -4.635×10^4 kJ/kg C_3H_8 (c) These three substances yield nearly identical quantities of heat per unit mass, but propane is marginally higher than the other two. **5.89** 1×10^{12} kg $C_6H_{12}O_6$/yr **5.91** (a) 469.4 m/s (b) 5.124×10^{-21} J (c) 3.086 kJ/mol **5.93** The spontaneous air bag reaction is probably exothermic, with $-\Delta H$ and thus $-q$. When the bag inflates, work is done by the system, so the sign of w is also negative. **5.97** $\Delta H = 38.95$ kJ; $\Delta E = 36.48$ kJ **5.102** (a) $\Delta H_{rxn}^\circ = -353.0$ kJ (b) 1.2 g Mg needed **5.106** (a) $\Delta H^\circ = -631.3$ kJ (b) 3 mol of acetylene gas has greater enthalpy. (c) Fuel values are 50 kJ/g $C_2H_2(g)$, 42 kJ/g $C_6H_6(l)$. **5.109** If all work is used to increase the man's potential energy, the stair climbing uses 58 Cal and will not compensate for the extra order of 245 Cal fries. (More than 58 Cal will be required to climb the stairs because some

energy is used to move limbs and some will be lost as heat.) **10.112** (a) 1.479×10^{-18} J/molecule (b) 1×10^{-15} J/photon. The X-ray has approximately 1000 times more energy than is produced by the combustion of 1 molecule of $CH_4(g)$. **10.114** (a) ΔH° for neutralization of the acids is HNO_3, -55.8 kJ; HCl, -56.1 kJ; NH_4^+, -4.1 kJ. (b) $H^+(aq) + OH^-(aq) \longrightarrow H_2O(l)$ is the net ionic equation for the first two reactions. $NH_4^+(aq) + OH^-(aq) \longrightarrow NH_3(aq) + H_2O(l)$ (c) The ΔH° values for the first two reactions are nearly identical, -55.8 kJ and -56.1 kJ. Since spectator ions do not change during a reaction and these two reactions have the same net ionic equation, it is not surprising that they have the same ΔH°. (d) Strong acids are more likely than weak acids to donate H^+. Neutralization of the two strong acids is energetically favorable, while the third reaction is barely so. NH_4^+ is likely a weak acid. **10.116** (a) $\Delta H^\circ = -65.7$ kJ (b) ΔH° for the complete molecular equation will be the same as ΔH° for the net ionic equation. Since the overall enthalpy change is the enthalpy of products minus the enthalpy of reactants, the contributions of spectator ions cancel. (c) ΔH_f° for $AgNO_3(aq)$ is -100.4 kJ/mol.

CHAPTER 11

11.2 (a) In its final state, methane is a gas at 185 °C. **11.3** (a) 385 mm Hg (b) 22 °C (c) 47 °C **11.4** The stronger the intermolecular forces, the higher the boiling point of a liquid. Propanol, $CH_3CH_2CH_2OH$, has hydrogen bonding and the higher boiling point. **11.5** (a) Normal boiling point, 360 K; normal freezing point, 260 K (b) (i) gas (ii) solid (iii) liquid (c) The triple point is approximately 185 K at 0.45 atm. **11.6** (a) As temperature increases, the number of molecules with sufficient kinetic energy to overcome intermolecular attractive forces increases, and viscosity and surface tension decrease. (b) The same attractive forces that cause surface molecules to be difficult to separate (high surface tension) cause molecules elsewhere in the sample to resist movement relative to each other (high viscosity). **11.8** (a) $CHBr_3$ has a higher molar mass, is more polarizable, and has stronger dispersion forces, so the surface tension is greater. (b) As temperature increases, the viscosity of the oil decreases because the average kinetic energy of the molecules increases. (c) Adhesive forces between polar water and nonpolar car wax are weak, so the large surface tension of water draws the liquid into the shape with the smallest surface area, a sphere. (d) Adhesive forces between nonpolar oil and nonpolar car wax are similar to cohesive forces in oil, so the oil drops spread out on the waxed car hood. **11.10** (a) The three molecules have similar structures and experience the same types of intermolecular forces. As molar mass increases, the strength of dispersion forces increases and the boiling points, surface tension, and viscosities all increase. (b) Ethylene glycol has an —OH group at both ends of the molecule. This greatly increases the possibilities for hydrogen bonding; the overall intermolecular attractive forces are greater and the viscosity of ethylene glycol is much greater. (c) Water has the highest surface tension but lowest viscosity because it is the smallest molecule in the series. There is no hydrocarbon chain to inhibit their strong attraction to molecules in the interior of the drop, resulting in high surface tension. The absence of an alkyl chain also means the molecules can move around each other easily, resulting in the low viscosity. **11.12** (a) Melting, endothermic (b) evaporation, endothermic (c) deposition, exothermic (d) condensation, exothermic **11.14** Melting does not require separation of molecules, so the energy requirement is smaller than for vaporization, where molecules must be separated. **11.16** 2.3×10^3 g H_2O **11.18** (a) 39.3 kJ (b) 60 kJ **11.20** (a) The critical pressure is the pressure required to cause liquefaction at the critical temperature. (b) As the force of attraction between molecules increases, the critical temperature of the compound increases. (c) All the gases in Table 11.5 can be liquefied at the temperature of liquid nitrogen, given sufficient pressure. **11.22** (a) No effect (b) no effect (c) Vapor pressure decreases with increasing intermolecular attractive forces because fewer molecules have sufficient kinetic energy to overcome attractive forces and escape to the vapor phase. (d) Vapor pressure increases with increasing temperature because average kinetic energies of molecules increase. (e) Vapor pressure decreases with increasing density because attractive intermolecular forces increase. **11.24** (a) $CBr_4 < CHBr_3 < CH_2Br_2 < CH_2Cl_2 < CH_3Cl < CH_4$. The trend is dominated by dispersion forces even though four of the molecules are polar. The order of increasing volatility is the order of increasing vapor pressure, decreasing molar mass, and decreasing strength of dispersion forces. (b) Boiling point increases as the strength of intermolecular forces increases; this is the order of decreasing volatility and the reverse of the order in part (a). $CH_4 < CH_3Cl < CH_2Cl_2 < CH_2Br_2 < CHBr_3 < CBr_4$ **11.26** (a) The temperature of the water in the two pans is the same. (b) Vapor pressure does not depend on either volume or surface area of the liquid. At the same temperature, the vapor pressures of water in the two containers are the same. **11.28** (a) Approximately 48 °C (b) approximately 340 torr (c) approximately 17 °C (d) approximately 1000 torr **11.30** (a) The critical point is the temperature and pressure beyond which the gas and liquid phases are indistinguishable. (b) The line that separates the gas and liquid phases ends at the critical point because at conditions beyond the critical temperature and pressure, there is no distinction between gas and liquid. In experimental terms a gas cannot be liquefied at temperatures higher than the critical temperature, regardless of pressure. **11.32** (a) $H_2O(g)$ will condense to $H_2O(s)$ at approximately 4 torr; at a higher pressure, perhaps 5 atm or so, $H_2O(s)$ will melt to form $H_2O(l)$. (b) At 100 °C and 0.50 atm, water is in the vapor phase. As it cools, water vapor condenses to the liquid at approximately 82 °C, the temperature where the vapor pressure of liquid water is 0.50 atm. Further cooling results in freezing at approximately 0 °C. The freezing point of water increases with decreasing pressure, so at 0.50 atm the freezing temperature is very slightly above 0 °C. **11.34** (a) 24 K (b) Neon sublimes at pressures less than the triple point pressure, 0.43 atm. (c) No **11.36** (a) Methane on the surface of Titan is likely to exist in both solid and liquid forms. (b) As pressure decreases upon moving away from the surface of Titan, $CH_4(l)$ (at −178 °C) will vaporize to $CH_4(g)$, and $CH_4(s)$ (at temperatures below −180 °C) will sublime to $CH_4(g)$. **11.38** (a) Evaporation is an endothermic process. The heat required to vaporize sweat is absorbed from your body, helping to keep it cool. (b) The vacuum pump reduces the pressure of the atmosphere above the water until atmospheric pressure equals the vapor pressure of water and the water boils. Boiling is an endothermic process, and the temperature drops if the system is not able to absorb heat from the surroundings fast enough. As the temperature of the water decreases, the water freezes. **11.44**

(i) $\mathcal{M} = 44$ (ii) $\mathcal{M} = 72$ (iii) $\mathcal{M} = 123$

(iv) $\mathcal{M} = 58$ (v) $\mathcal{M} = 123$ (vi) $\mathcal{M} = 60$

(a) Molar mass: Compounds (i) and (ii) have similar rodlike structures. The longer chain in (ii) leads to greater molar mass, stronger London dispersion forces, and higher heat of vaporization. (b) Molecular shape: Compounds (iii) and (v) have the same chemical formula and molar mass but different molecular shapes. The more rodlike shape of (v) leads to more contact between molecules, stronger dispersion forces, and higher heat of vaporization. (c) Molecular polarity: Compound (iv) has a smaller molar mass than (ii) but a larger heat of vaporization, which must be due to the presence of dipole–dipole forces. (d) Hydrogen bonding interactions: Molecules (v) and (vi) have similar structures. Even though (v) has larger molar mass and disper-

sion forces, hydrogen bonding causes (vi) to have the higher heat of vaporization. **11.47** P(benzene vapor) = 98.7 torr

CHAPTER 12

12.1 $k_f > k_r$ (b) The equilibrium constant is greater than 1. **12.7** From the smallest to the largest equilibrium constant, (c) < (b) < (a). **12.11** K_c decreases as T increases, so the reaction is exothermic. **12.13** (a) $K_p = K_c = 8.1 \times 10^{-3}$. (b) Since $k_f < k_r$, in order for the two rates to be equal, [A] must be greater than [B], and the partial pressure of A is greater than the partial pressure of B. **12.15** (a) $K_c = [N_2O][NO_2]/[NO]^3$; homogeneous (b) $K_c = [CS_2][H_2]^4/[CH_4][H_2S]^2$; homogeneous (c) $K_c = [CO]^4/[Ni(CO)_4]$; heterogeneous (d) $K_c = [H^+][F^-]/[HF]$; homogeneous (e) $K_c = [Ag^+]^2/[Zn^{2+}]$; heterogeneous (f) $K_c = [H^+][OH^-]$; homogeneous (g) $K_c = [H^+][OH^-]$; homogeneous **12.17** (a) Mostly reactants (b) mostly products **12.19** No, the equilibrium constant can never be a negative number. The equilibrium constant is a ratio of rate constants (or a ratio of concentrations), which are never negative. **12.21** $K_p = 1.0 \times 10^{-3}$ **12.23** (a) The equilibrium favors NO and Br_2 at this temperature. (b) $K_c = 77$ (c) $K_c = 8.8$ **12.25** (a) $K_p = 0.541$ (b) $K_p = 3.42$ (c) $K_c = 281$ **12.27** $K_c = 0.14$ **12.29** Pure solids and liquids are normally excluded from equilibrium-constant expressions because their concentrations, the ratio of moles of a substance to volume occupied by the substance, are constant. **12.31** (a) $K_p = P_{O_2}$ (b) $K_c = [Hg(solv)]^4[O_2(solv)]$ **12.33** $K_c = 10.5$ **12.35** (a) $K_p = 51$ (b) $K_c = 2.1 \times 10^3$ **12.37** (a) $[H_2] = 0.012\,M$, $[N_2] = 0.019\,M$, $[H_2O] = 0.138\,M$ (b) $K_c = 653.7 = 7 \times 10^2$ **12.39** (a) $P_{CO_2} = 4.10$ atm, $P_{H_2} = 2.05$ atm, $P_{H_2O} = 3.28$ atm (b) $P_{CO_2} = 3.87$ atm, $P_{H_2} = 1.82$ atm, $P_{CO} = 0.23$ atm (c) $K_p = 0.11$ **12.41** $K_c = 2.0 \times 10^4$ **12.43** (a) A reaction quotient is the result of a general set of concentrations whereas the equilibrium constant requires equilibrium concentrations. (b) to the right (c) The concentrations used to calculate Q must be equilibrium concentrations. **12.45** (a) $Q = 1.1 \times 10^{-8}$, the reaction will proceed to the left. (b) $Q = 5.5 \times 10^{-12}$, the reaction will proceed to the right. (c) $Q = 2.19 \times 10^{-10}$, the mixture is at equilibrium. **12.47** $P_{Cl_2} = 5.0$ atm **12.49** (a) $[Br_2] = 0.00767\,M$, $[Br] = 0.00282\,M$, 0.0451 g Br(g) (b) $[H_2] = 0.014\,M$, $[I_2] = 0.00859\,M$, $[HI] = 0.081\,M$, 21 g HI **12.51** $[NO] = 0.002\,M$, $[N_2] = [O_2] = 0.087\,M$ **12.53** The equilibrium pressure of $Br_2(g)$ is 0.416 atm. **12.55** (a) $[Ca^{2+}] = [SO_4^{2-}] = 4.9 \times 10^{-3}\,M$ (b) A bit more than 1.0 g $CaSO_4$ is needed in order to have some undissolved $CaSO_4(s)$ in equilibrium with 1.4 L of saturated solution. **12.57** $[IBr] = 0.223\,M$, $[I_2] = [Br_2] = 0.0133\,M$ **12.59** (a) $P_{CH_3I} = P_{HI} = 0.422$ torr, $P_{CH_4} = 104.7$ torr, $P_{I_2} = 7.54$ torr **12.61** (a) Shift equilibrium to the right (b) decrease the value of K (c) shift equilibrium to the left (d) no effect (e) no effect (f) shift equilibrium to the right **12.63** (a) No effect (b) no effect (c) no effect (d) increase equilibrium constant (e) no effect **12.65** (a) $\Delta H° = -155.7$ kJ (b) The reaction is exothermic, so the equilibrium constant will decrease with increasing temperature. (c) Δn does not equal zero, so a change in volume at constant temperature will affect the fraction of products in the equilibrium mixture. **12.67** An increase in pressure favors formation of ozone. **12.71** $K_p = 24.7$; $K_c = 3.67 \times 10^{-3}$ **12.74** (a) $P_{Br_2} = 1.61$ atm, $P_{NO} = 0.628$ atm, $P_{NOBr} = 0.179$ atm; $K_c = 0.0643$ (b) $P_t = 0.968$ atm (c) 10.49 g NOBr **12.77** At equilibrium, $P_{IBr} = 0.21$ atm, $P_{I_2} = P_{Br_2} = 1.9 \times 10^{-3}$ atm **12.80** $K_p = 4.33$, $K_c = 0.0480$ **12.83** $[CO_2] = [H_2] = 0.264\,M$, $[CO] = [H_2O] = 0.236\,M$ **12.87** (a) 26% of the CCl_4 is converted to C and Cl_2. (b) $P_{CCl_4} = 1.47$ atm, $P_{Cl_2} = 1.06$ atm **12.91** $Q = 8 \times 10^{-6}$. $Q > K_p$, so the system is not at equilibrium; it will shift left to attain equilibrium. A catalyst that speeds up the reaction and thereby promotes the attainment of equilibrium would decrease the CO concentration in the exhaust. **12.93** At equilibrium, $[H_6IO_4^-] = 0.0015\,M$ **12.97** At 850 °C, $K_p = 14.1$; at 950 °C, $K_p = 73.8$; at 1050 °C, $K_p = 2.7 \times 10^2$;

at 1200 °C, $K_p = 1.7 \times 10^3$. Because K increases with increasing temperature, the reaction is endothermic.

CHAPTER 13

13.1 (a)

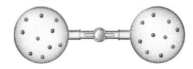

(b) $\Delta H = 0$ for mixing ideal gases. ΔS is positive because the disorder of the system increases. (c) The process is spontaneous and therefore irreversible. (d) Since $\Delta H = 0$, the process does not affect the entropy of the surroundings. **13.4** ΔS is positive. **13.7** (a) At 300 K, $\Delta G = 0$, and the system is at equilibrium. (b) The reaction is spontaneous at temperatures above 300 K. **13.10** (a) The minimum in the plot is the equilibrium position of the reaction. (b) The quantity x is $\Delta G°$. **13.11** Spontaneous: a, b, c, d; nonspontaneous: e **13.13** (a) $NH_4NO_3(s)$ dissolves in water, as in a chemical cold pack. Naphthalene (moth balls) sublimes at room temperature. (b) Melting of a solid is spontaneous above its melting point but nonspontaneous below its melting point. **13.15** (a) Endothermic (b) above 100 °C (c) below 100 °C (d) at 100 °C **13.17** (a) For a *reversible* process, the forward and reverse changes occur by the same path. In a reversible process, both the system and the surroundings are restored to their original condition by exactly reversing the change. A reversible change produces the maximum amount of work. (b) There is no net change in the surroundings. (c) The vaporization of water to steam is reversible if it occurs at the boiling temperature of water for a specified external (atmospheric) pressure and if the required heat is added infinitely slowly. (d) No. Natural processes are spontaneous in the direction they occur and nonspontaneous in the opposite direction. By definition they are irreversible. **13.19** (a) If the ideal gas is contained in a closed system at constant volume, a decrease in external temperature leads to a decrease in both temperature and pressure of the gas. (b) If the ideal gas is contained in a closed system at constant pressure, a decrease in external temperature leads to a decrease in both temperature and volume of the gas. (c) No. ΔE is a state function. $\Delta E = q + w$; q and w are not state functions. Their values do depend on path, but their sum, ΔE, does not. **13.21** (a) An ice cube can melt reversibly at the conditions of temperature and pressure where the solid and liquid are in equilibrium. (b) We know that melting is a process that increases the energy of the system even though there is no change in temperature. ΔE is not zero for the process. **13.23** (a) At constant temperature, $\Delta S = q_{rev}/T$, where q_{rev} is the heat that would be transferred if the process were reversible. (b) No. ΔS is a state function, so it is independent of path. **13.25** (a) Entropy increases. (b) 89.2 J/K **13.27** (a) For a spontaneous process, the entropy of the universe increases; for a reversible process, the entropy of the universe does not change. (b) For a reversible process, if the entropy of the system increases, the entropy of the surroundings must decrease by the same amount. (c) For a spontaneous process, the entropy of the universe must increase, so the entropy of the surroundings must decrease by less than 42 J/K. **13.29** (a) Positive ΔS (b) $\Delta S = 1.02$ J/K (c) Temperature need not be specified to calculate ΔS, as long as the expansion is isothermal. **13.31** (a) Yes, the expansion is spontaneous. (b) As the ideal gas expands into the vacuum, there is nothing for it to "push back," so no work is done. Mathematically, $w = -P_{ext}\Delta V$. Since the gas expands into a vacuum, $P_{ext} = 0$ and $w = 0$. (c) The "driving force" for the expansion of the gas is the increase in entropy. **13.33** (a) An increase in temperature produces more available microstates for a system. (b) A decrease in volume produces fewer available microstates for a system. (c) Going from liquid to gas, the number of available microstates increases. **13.35** (a) ΔS is positive. (b) S of the system clearly increases in 13.11 (b) and (e); it clearly decreases in 13.9 (c). The entropy change is difficult to judge in 13.9 (a) and definition of the system

in (d) is problematic. **13.37** S increases in (a) and (c); S decreases in (b). **13.39** (a) The entropy of a pure crystalline substance at absolute zero is zero. (b) In translational motion the entire molecule moves in a single direction; in rotational motion the molecule rotates or spins around a fixed axis. In vibrational motion the bonds within a molecule stretch and bend, but the average position of the atoms does not change.

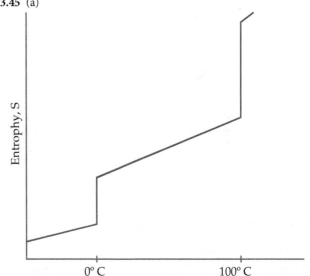

13.41 (a) $Ar(g)$ (b) $He(g)$ at 1.5 atm (c) 1 mol of $Ne(g)$ in 15.0 L (d) $CO_2(g)$ **13.43** (a) $\Delta S < 0$ (b) $\Delta S > 0$ (c) $\Delta S < 0$ (d) $\Delta S \approx 0$ **13.45** (a)

(b) Boiling water, at 100 °C, has a much larger entropy change than melting ice at 0 °C. **13.47** (a) $C_2H_6(g)$ (b) $CO_2(g)$ **13.49** (a) $Sc(s)$, 34.6 J/mol-K; $Sc(g)$, 174.7 J/mol-K. In general, the gas phase of a substance has a larger $S°$ than the solid phase because of the greater volume and motional freedom of the molecules. (b) $NH_3(g)$, 192.5 J/mol-K; $NH_3(aq)$, 111.3 J/mol-K. Molecules in the gas phase have more motional freedom than molecules in solution. (c) 1 mol of $P_4(g)$, 280 J/K; 2 mol of $P_2(g)$, 2(218.1) = 436.2 J/K. More particles have a greater motional energy (more available microstates). (d) C (diamond), 2.43 J/mol-K; C (graphite), 5.69 J/mol-K. The internal entropy in graphite is greater because there is translational freedom among planar sheets of C atoms, while there is very little freedom within the covalent-network diamond lattice. **13.51** For elements with similar structures, the heavier the atoms, the lower the vibrational frequencies at a given temperature. This means that more vibrations can be accessed at a particular temperature, resulting in greater absolute entropy for the heavier elements. **13.53** (a) $\Delta S° = -120.5$ J/K. $\Delta S°$ is negative because there are fewer moles of gas in the products. (b) $\Delta S° = +176.6$ J/K. $\Delta S°$ is positive because there are more moles of gas in the products. (c) $\Delta S° = +152.39$ J/K. $\Delta S°$ is positive because the product contains more total particles and more moles of gas. (d) $\Delta S° = +92.3$ J/K. $\Delta S°$ is positive because there are more moles of gas in the products. **13.55** (a) $\Delta G = \Delta H - T\Delta S$ (b) If ΔG is positive, the process is nonspontaneous, but the reverse process is spontaneous. (c) There is no relationship between ΔG and rate of reaction. **13.57** (a) Exothermic (b) $\Delta S°$ is negative; the reaction leads to a decrease in disorder. (c) $\Delta G° = -9.9$ kJ (d) If all reactants and products are present in their standard states, the reaction is spontaneous in the forward direction at this temperature. **13.59** (a) $\Delta H° = -537.22$ kJ, $\Delta S° = 13.7$ J/K, $\Delta G° = -541.40$ kJ, $\Delta G° = \Delta H° - T\Delta S° = -541.31$ kJ

(b) $\Delta H° = -106.7$ kJ, $\Delta S° = -142.2$ kJ, $\Delta G° = -64.0$ kJ, $\Delta G° = \Delta H° - T\Delta S° = -64.3$ kJ (c) $\Delta H° = -508.3$ kJ, $\Delta S° = -178$ kJ, $\Delta G° = -465.8$ kJ, $\Delta G° = \Delta H° - T\Delta S° = -455.1$ kJ. The discrepancy in $\Delta G°$ values is due to experimental uncertainties in the tabulated thermodynamic data. (d) $\Delta H° = -165.9$ kJ, $\Delta S° = 1.4$ kJ, $\Delta G° = -166.2$ kJ, $\Delta G° = \Delta H° - T\Delta S° = -166.3$ kJ **13.61** (a) $\Delta G° = -140.0$ kJ, spontaneous (b) $\Delta G° = +104.70$ kJ, nonspontaneous (c) $\Delta G° = +146$ kJ, nonspontaneous (d) $\Delta G° = -156.7$ kJ, spontaneous **13.63** (a) $2C_8H_{18}(l) + 25O_2(g) \longrightarrow 16CO_2(g) + 18H_2O(l)$ (b) Because $\Delta S°$ is positive, $\Delta G°$ is more negative than $\Delta H°$. **13.65** (a) The forward reaction is spontaneous at low temperatures but becomes nonspontaneous at higher temperatures. (b) The reaction is nonspontaneous in the forward direction at all temperatures. (c) The forward reaction is nonspontaneous at low temperatures but becomes spontaneous at higher temperatures. **13.67** $\Delta S > 60.8$ J/K **13.69** (a) $T = 330$ K (b) nonspontaneous **13.71** (a) $\Delta H° = 155.7$ kJ, $\Delta S° = 171.4$ kJ. Since $\Delta S°$ is positive, $\Delta G°$ becomes more negative with increasing temperature. (b) $\Delta G° = 19$ kJ. The reaction is not spontaneous under standard conditions at 800 K (c) $\Delta G° = -15.7$ kJ. The reaction is spontaneous under standard conditions at 1000 K. **13.73** (a) $T_b = 79$ °C (b) From the *Handbook of Chemistry and Physics*, 74th Edition, $T_b = 80.1$ °C. The values are remarkably close; the small difference is due to deviation from ideal behavior by $C_6H_6(g)$ and experimental uncertainty in the boiling point measurement and the thermodynamic data. **13.75** (a) $C_2H_2(g) + \frac{5}{2}O_2(g) \longrightarrow 2CO_2(g) + H_2O(l)$ (b) -1299.5 kJ of heat produced/mol C_2H_2 burned (c) $w_{max} = -1235.1$ kJ/mol C_2H_2 **13.77** (a) ΔG becomes more negative. (b) ΔG becomes more positive. (c) ΔG becomes more positive. **13.79** (a) $\Delta G° = -5.40$ kJ (b) $\Delta G = 0.30$ kJ **13.81** (a) $\Delta G° = -16.77$ kJ, $K = 870$ (b) $\Delta G° = 8.0$ kJ, $K = 0.039$ (c) $\Delta G° = -497.9$ kJ, $K = 2 \times 10^{87}$ **13.83** $\Delta H° = 269.3$ kJ, $\Delta S° = 0.1719$ kJ/K (a) $P_{CO_2} = 6.0 \times 10^{-39}$ atm (b) $P_{CO_2} = 1.6 \times 10^{-4}$ atm **13.85** (a) $HNO_2(aq) \rightleftharpoons H^+(aq) + NO_2^-(aq)$ (b) $\Delta G° = 19.1$ kJ (c) $\Delta G = 0$ at equilibrium (d) $\Delta G = -2.7$ kJ **13.87** (a) The thermodynamic quantities T, E, and S are state functions. (b) The quantities q and w depend on the path taken. (c) There is only one *reversible* path between states. (d) $\Delta E = q_{rev} + w_{max}$, $\Delta S = q_{rev}/T$. **13.91** (a) 16 arrangements (b) 1 arrangement (c) The gas will spontaneously adopt the state with the most possible arrangements for the molecules, the state with maximum disorder. **13.96** (a) For all three compounds listed, there are fewer moles of gaseous products than reactants in the formation reaction, so we expect $\Delta S_f°$ to be negative. If $\Delta G_f° = \Delta H_f° - T\Delta S_f°$ and $\Delta S_f°$ is negative, $-T\Delta S_f°$ is positive and $\Delta G_f°$ is more positive than $\Delta H_f°$. (b) In this reaction, there are more moles of gas in products, $\Delta S_f°$ is positive, $-T\Delta S_f°$ is negative and $\Delta G_f°$ is more negative than $\Delta H_f°$. **13.100** (a) $K = 4 \times 10^{15}$ (b) An increase in temperature will decrease the mole fraction of CH_3COOH at equilibrium. Elevated temperatures must be used to increase the speed of the reaction. (c) $K = 1$ at 836 K or 563 °C. **13.104** (a) $\Delta G = 8.77$ kJ (b) $w_{min} = 8.77$ kJ. In practice, a larger than minimum amount of work is required. **13.108** (a) Acetone, $\Delta S_{vap}° = 88.4$ J/mol-K; dimethyl ether, $\Delta S_{vap}° = 86.6$ J/mol-K; ethanol, $\Delta S_{vap}° = 110$ J/mol-K; octane, $\Delta S_{vap}° = 86.3$ J/mol-K; pyridine, $\Delta S_{vap}° = 90.4$ J/mol-K. Ethanol does not obey Trouton's rule. (b) Hydrogen bonding (in ethanol and other liquids) leads to more ordering in the liquid state and a greater than usual increase in entropy upon vaporization. Liquids that experience hydrogen bonding are probably exceptions to Trouton's rule. (c) Owing to strong hydrogen bonding interactions, water probably does not obey Trouton's rule. $\Delta S_{vap}° = 109.0$ J/mol-K. (d) ΔH_{vap} for $C_6H_5Cl \approx 36$ kJ/mol **13.113** (a) For any given total pressure, the condition of equal moles of the two gases can be achieved at some temperature. For individual gas pressures of 1 atm and a total pressure of 2 atm, the mixture is at equilibrium at 328.5 K or 55.5 °C. (b) 333.0 K or 60 °C (c) 374.2 K or 101.2 °C (d) The reaction is endothermic, so an increase in the value of K as calculated in parts (a)–(c) should be accompanied by an increase in T.

CHAPTER 14

14.1 Vessel 2 **14.3** Equation (d) **14.9** (1) Total potential energy of the reactants (2) E_a, activation energy of the reaction (3) ΔE, net energy change for the reaction (4) total potential energy of the products **14.12** (a) $NO_2 + F_2 \longrightarrow NO_2F + F$; $NO_2 + F \longrightarrow NO_2F$ (b) $2NO_2 + F_2 \longrightarrow 2NO_2F$ (c) F (atomic fluorine) is the intermediate (d) rate $= k[NO_2][F_2]$)

14.16

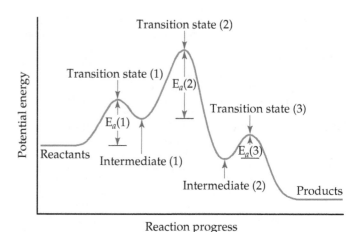

14.17 (a) *Reaction rate* is the change in the amount of products or reactants in a given amount of time. (b) Rates depend on concentration of reactants, surface area of reactants, temperature, and presence of catalyst. (c) The stoichiometry of the reaction (mole ratios of reactants and products) must be known to relate rate of disappearance of reactants to rate of appearance of products.

14.19

Time (min)	(a) Mol A	Mol B	[A] (mol/L)	Δ[A] (mol/L)	(b) Rate (M/s)
0	0.065	0.000	0.65		
10	0.051	0.014	0.51	−0.14	2.3×10^{-4}
20	0.042	0.023	0.42	−0.09	1.5×10^{-4}
30	0.036	0.029	0.36	−0.06	1.0×10^{-4}
40	0.031	0.034	0.31	−0.05	0.8×10^{-4}

(c) $\Delta[B]_{avg}/\Delta t = 1.3 \times 10^{-4}$ M/s
14.21 (a)

Time (s)	Time Interval (s)	Concentration (M)	ΔM	Rate (M/s)
0		0.0165		
2,000	2,000	0.0110	−0.0055	28×10^{-7}
5,000	3,000	0.00591	−0.0051	17×10^{-7}
8,000	3,000	0.00314	−0.00277	9.23×10^{-7}
12,000	4,000	0.00137	−0.00177	4.43×10^{-7}
15,000	3,000	0.00074	−0.00063	2.1×10^{-7}

(b) The average rate of reaction is 1.05×10^{-6} M/s. (c) From the slopes of the tangents to the graph, the rates are 12×10^{-7} M/s at 5000 s, 5.8×10^{-7} M/s at 8000 s.

14.23
(a) $-\Delta[H_2O_2]/\Delta t = \Delta[H_2]/\Delta t = \Delta[O_2]/\Delta t$
(b) $-\frac{1}{2}\Delta[N_2O]/\Delta t = \frac{1}{2}\Delta[N_2]/\Delta t = \Delta[O_2]/\Delta t$
(c) $-\Delta[N_2]/\Delta t = -1/3\Delta[H_2]/\Delta t = -1/2\Delta[NH_3]/2\Delta t$
(d) $-\Delta[C_2H_5NH_2]/\Delta t = \Delta[C_2H_4]/\Delta t = \Delta[NH_3]/\Delta t$

14.25 (a) $-\Delta[O_2]/\Delta t = 0.24 \text{ mol/s}$; $\Delta[H_2O]/\Delta t = 0.48 \text{ mol/s}$ (b) P_{total} decreases by 28 torr/min. **14.27** (a) If [A] doubles, there is no change in the rate or the rate constant. The overall rate is unchanged because [A] does not appear in the rate law; the rate constant changes only with a change in temperature. (b) The reaction is zero order in A, second order in B, and second order overall. (c) units of $k = M^{-1}\text{s}^{-1}$ **14.29** (a) Rate $= k[N_2O_5]$ (b) Rate $= 1.16 \times 10^{-4} M/s$ (c) When the concentration of N_2O_5 doubles, the rate doubles. (d) When the concentration of N_2O_5 is halved, the rate doubles. **14.31** (a, b) $k = 1.7 \times 10^2 M^{-1}\text{s}^{-1}$ (c) If $[OH^-]$ is tripled, the rate triples. (d) If $[OH^-]$ and $[CH_3Br]$ both triple, the rate increases by a factor of 9. **14.33** (a) Rate $= k[OCl^-][I^-]$ (b) $k = 60 M^{-1}\text{s}^{-1}$ (c) Rate $= 6.0 \times 10^{-5} M/s$ **14.35** (a) Rate $= k[BF_3][NH_3]$ (b) The reaction is second order overall. (c) $k_{avg} = 3.41 M^{-1}\text{s}^{-1}$ (d) $0.170 M/s$ **14.37** (a) Rate $= k[NO]^2[Br_2]$ (b) $k_{avg} = 1.2 \times 10^4 M^{-2}\text{s}^{-1}$ (c) $\frac{1}{2}\Delta[NOBr]/\Delta t = -\Delta[Br_2]/\Delta t$ (d) $-\Delta[Br_2]/\Delta t = 8.4 M/s$ **14.39** (a) $[A]_0$ is the molar concentration of reactant A at time zero. $[A]_t$ is the molar concentration of reactant A at time t. $t_{1/2}$ is the time required to reduce $[A]_0$ by a factor of 2. k is the rate constant for a particular reaction. (b) A graph of ln[A] versus time yields a straight line for a first-order reaction. (c) On a graph of ln[A] versus time, the rate constant is the (–slope) of the straight line. **14.41** Plot [A] versus time. **14.43** (a) $k = 3.0 \times 10^{-6}\text{s}^{-1}$ (b) $t_{1/2} = 3.2 \times 10^4\text{s}$ **14.45** (a) $P = 30$ torr (b) $t = 51$ s **14.47** Plot $(\ln P_{SO_2Cl_2})$ versus time, $k = -\text{slope} = 2.19 \times 10^{-5}\text{s}^{-1}$ **14.49** (a) The plot of $1/[A]$ versus time is linear, so the reaction is second order in [A]. (b) $k = 0.040 M^{-1}\text{min}^{-1}$ (c) $t_{1/2} = 38$ min **14.51** (a) The plot of $1/[NO_2]$ versus time is linear, so the reaction is second order in NO_2. (b) $k = \text{slope} = 10 M^{-1}\text{s}^{-1}$ (c) rate at $0.200 M = 0.400 M/s$; rate at $0.100 M = 0.100 M/s$; rate at $0.050 M = 0.025 M/s$ **14.53** (a) The energy of the collision and the orientation of the molecules when they collide determine whether a reaction will occur. (b) At a higher temperature, there are more total collisions and each collision is more energetic. (c) The rate constant usually increases with an increase in reaction temperature. **14.55** $f = 4.94 \times 10^{-2}$. At 400 K approximately 1 out of 20 molecules has this kinetic energy.

14.57 (a)

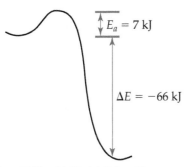

(b) E_a (reverse) $= 73$ kJ **14.59** (a) False. If you compare two reactions with similar collision factors, the one with the larger activation energy will be slower. (b) False. A reaction that has a small rate constant will have either a small frequency factor, a large activation energy, or both. (c) True. **14.61** Reaction (b) is fastest and reaction (c) is slowest. **14.63** (a) $k = 1.1 \text{ s}^{-1}$ (b) $k = 13 \text{ s}^{-1}$ (c) The method in parts (a) and (b) assumes that the collision model and thus the Arrhenious equation describe the kinetics of the reactions. That is, activation energy is constant over the temperature range under consideration. **14.65** A plot of ln k versus $1/T$ has a slope of -5.71×10^3; $E_a = -R(\text{slope}) = 47.5 \text{ kJ/mol}$. **14.67** The reaction will occur 88 times faster at 50 °C, assuming equal initial concentrations. **14.69** (a) An *elementary reaction* is a process that occurs in a single event; the order is given by the coefficients in the balanced equation for the reaction. (b) A *unimolecular* elementary reaction involves only one reactant molecule; a *bimolecular* elementary reaction involves two reactant molecules. (c) A *reaction mechanism* is a series of elementary reactions that describes how an overall reaction occurs and explains the

experimentally determined rate law. **14.71** A transition state is a high-energy complex formed when one or more reactants collide and distort in a way that can lead to formation of product(s). An intermediate is the product of an early elementary reaction in a multistep reaction mechanism. **14.73** (a) Unimolecular, rate $= k[Cl_2]$ (b) bimo- lecular, rate $= k[OCl^-][H_2O]$ (c) bimolecular, rate $= k[NO][Cl_2]$ **14.75** (a) Two intermediates, B and C. (b) three transition states (c) C $\longrightarrow$ D is fastest. (d) endothermic **14.77** (a) $H_2(g) + 2 \text{ICl}(g) \longrightarrow I_2(g) + 2 \text{HCl}(g)$ (b) HI is the intermediate. (c) If the first step is slow, the observed rate law is rate $= k[H_2][\text{ICl}]$. **14.79** The graph of $1/[NO]$ versus time is linear with positive slope, indicating that the reaction is second order in [NO]. The rate law obtained by assuming the second step is rate determining is rate $= [NO]^2[Cl_2]$. The two-step mechanism is consistent with the data. **14.81** (a) A catalyst is a substance that changes (usually increases) the speed of a chemical reaction without undergoing a permanent chemical change itself. (b) A homogeneous catalyst is in the same phase as the reactants, while a heterogeneous catalyst is in a different phase. (c) A catalyst has no effect on the overall enthalpy change for a reaction, but it does affect activation energy. It can also affect the frequency factor. **14.83** (a) 270 Pt atoms in a 2.0-nm sphere (b) 200 Pt atoms on the surface of a 2.0-nm sphere (c) 74% Pt atoms on the surface (d) 4300 Pt atoms in a 5.0-nm sphere; 1300 Pt atoms on the surface; 30% Pt atoms on the surface (e) The 2-nm sphere will definitely be more catalytically active because it has a much greater percentage of its atoms on the surface where they can participate in the chemical reaction. **14.85** (a) Multiply the coefficients in the first reaction by 2 and sum. (b) $NO_2(g)$ is a catalyst because it is consumed and then reproduced in the reaction sequence. (c) This is a homogeneous catalysis. **14.87** (a) Use of chemically stable supports makes it possible to obtain very large surface areas per unit mass of the precious metal catalyst because the metal can be deposited in a very thin, even monomolecular, layer on the surface of the support. (b) The greater the surface area of the catalyst, the more reaction sites, the greater the rate of the catalyzed reaction. **14.89** To put two D atoms on a single carbon, it is necessary that one of the already existing C—H bonds in ethylene be broken while the molecule is adsorbed, so that the H atom moves off as an adsorbed atom and is replaced by a D atom. This requires a larger activation energy than simply adsorbing C_2H_4 and adding one D atom to each carbon. **14.91** (a) Living organisms operate efficiently in a very narrow temperature range; the role of enzymes as homogeneous catalysts that speed up desirable reactions, without heating and undesirable side effects, is crucial for biological systems. (b) catalase: $2 H_2O_2 \longrightarrow 2 H_2O + O_2$; nitrogenase: $N_2 \longrightarrow 2 NH_3$ (nitrogen fixation) (c) This model assumes that the rate of the bound substrate being chemically transformed into bound product is slow and rate determining. **14.93** Carbonic anyhdrase lowers the activation energy of the reaction by 42 kJ. **14.95** (a) The catalyzed reaction is approximately 10,000,000 times faster at 25 °C. (b) The catalyzed reaction is 180,000 times faster at 125 °C. **14.99** (a) Rate $= 4.7 \times 10^{-5} M/s$ (b, c) $k = 0.84 M^{-2}\text{s}^{-1}$ (d) If the [NO] is increased by a factor of 1.8, the rate would increase by a factor of 3.2. **14.101** The reaction is second order in NO_2. If $[NO_2]_0 = 0.100 M$ and $[NO_2]_t = 0.025 M$, use the integrated form of the second-order rate equation to solve for t. $t = 48$ s **14.105** (a) The half-life of ^{241}Am is 4.3×10^2 yr, that of ^{125}I is 63 days (b) ^{125}I decays at a much faster rate. (c) 0.13 mg of each isotope remains after 3 half-lives. (d) The amount of ^{241}Am remaining after 4 days is 1.00 mg. The amount of ^{125}I remaining after 4 days is 0.957 grams. **14.109** The plot of $1/[C_5H_6]$ versus time is linear and the reaction is second order. $k = 0.167 M^{-1}\text{s}^{-1}$ **14.112** (a) When the two elementary reactions are added, $N_2O_2(g)$ appears on both sides and cancels, resulting in the overall reaction. $2NO(g) + H_2(g) \longrightarrow N_2O(g) + H_2O(g)$ (b) First reaction, $-[NO]/\Delta t = k[NO]^2$; second reaction, $-[H_2]/\Delta t = k[H_2][N_2O_2]$ (c) N_2O_2 is the intermediate. (d) Since [H_2] appears in the rate law, the second step must be slow relative to the first. **14.115** (a) $Cl_2(g) + CHCl_3(g) \longrightarrow HCl(g) + CCl_4(g)$ (b) $Cl(g)$, $CCl_3(g)$ (c) reaction 1, unimolecular; reaction 2, bimolecular; reaction 3, bimolecular (d) Reaction 2 is rate determining. (e) Rate $= k[CHCl_3][Cl_2]^{1/2}$.   **14.122** (a) $k = 8 \times 10^7 \, M^{-1} \, s^{-1}$

(b) :N̈=Ö:

:Ö=N̈—F̈: ⟷ (:Ö̈—N̈=F̈)

(c) NOF is bent with a bond angle of approximately 120°.

(d)
$$\left[\begin{array}{c} O{=}N \\ \quad \diagdown \\ \quad F{\diagdown} F \end{array} \right]$$

(e) The electron-deficient NO molecule is attracted to electron-rich F_2, so the driving force for formation of the transition state is greater than simple random collisions.

CHAPTER 1

page 6 No. Both visible light and X-rays are forms of electromagnetic radiation. They therefore both travel at the speed of light, *c*. Their differing ability to penetrate skin is due to their different energies, which we will discuss in the next section.

page 7 $E = h\nu = (6.63 \times 10^{-34}\,\text{J-s})(5 \times 10^{-3}\,\text{s}^{-1}) = 3 \times 10^{-30}\,\text{J}$; this radiation cannot produce a burst of $5 \times 10^{-36}\,\text{J}$ because it can only produce energy in multiples of $3 \times 10^{-30}\,\text{J}$.

page 8 Ultraviolet. Figure 1.4 shows that a photon in the ultraviolet region of the electromagnetic spectrum has a higher frequency and therefore a greater energy than a photon in the infrared region.

page 10 According to the third postulate, photons of only certain allowed frequencies can be absorbed or emitted as the electron changes energy state. The lines in the spectrum correspond to the allowed frequencies.

page 11 Absorb, because it is moving from a lower-energy state ($n = 3$) to a higher-energy state ($n = 7$)

page 13 Yes, all moving objects produce matter waves, but the wavelengths associated with macroscopic objects, such as the baseball, are too small to allow for any way of observing them.

page 15 The small size and mass of subatomic particles. The term $h/4\pi$ in the uncertainty principle is a very small number that becomes important only when considering extremely small objects, such as electrons.

page 16 Bohr proposed that the electron in the hydrogen atom moves in a well-defined circular path around the nucleus (an orbit). In the quantum-mechanical model, no effort is made to describe the motion of the electron. An orbital is a wave function related to the probability of finding the electron at any point in space.

page 17 The energy of an electron in the hydrogen atom is proportional to $-1/n^2$, as seen in Equation 1.5. The difference between $-1/(2)^2$ and $-1/(1)^2$ is much greater than the difference between $-1/(3)^2$ and $-1/(2)^2$.

page 22 (a) There is one $3s$ orbital, three $3p$ orbitals, and ten $3d$ orbitals, for a total of 14 orbitals. (b) $3s < 3p < 3d$.

page 28 The $6s$ orbital, which starts to hold electrons at element 55, Cs

page 33 We can't conclude anything! Each of the three elements has a different valence electron configuration for its $(n - 1)d$ and ns subshells: For Ni, $3d^8 4s^2$; for Pd, $4d^{10}$; and for Pt, $5d^9 6s^1$.

CHAPTER 2

page 47 Atomic number is governed by the number of protons in the nucleus, but atomic weight is governed by both the number of protons and neutrons in the nucleus (electrons are too light to worry about). Co/Ni, Cu/Zn, and Te/I are other pairs of elements whose atomic weights are "off" compared to their atomic numbers.

page 50 The $2p$ electron in a Ne atom would experience a larger Z_{eff} than the $3s$ electron in Na, due to the better shielding by all the $2s$ and $2p$ electrons for Na's $3s$ electron.

page 52 These trends work against each other: Z_{eff} increasing would imply that the valence electrons are pulled tighter in to make the atom smaller, while orbital size "increasing" would imply that atomic size would also increase. The orbital size effect is larger: As you go down a column in the periodic table, atomic size generally increases.

page 55 It is harder to remove another electron from Na^+, so the process in Equation 2.3 would require more energy and, hence, shorter-wavelength light (see Sections 1.1 and 1.2).

page 56 Since Z_{eff} increases as you go from boron to carbon, we would expect that the first ionization energy would be larger for carbon. Therefore, I_2 for C is even greater.

page 58 The same

page 60 The numbers are the same; the signs are opposite.

CHAPTER 3

page 70 No. Cl has seven valence electrons. The first and second Lewis symbols are both correct—they both show seven valence electrons, and it doesn't matter which of the four sides has the single electron. The third symbol shows only five electrons and is incorrect.

page 72 CaF_2 is an ionic compound consisting of Ca^{2+} and F^- ions. When Ca and F_2 react to form CaF_2, each Ca atom loses two electrons to form a Ca^{2+} ion and each fluorine atom in F_2 takes up an electron, forming two F^- ions. Thus, we can say that each Ca atom transfers one electron to each of two fluorine atoms.

page 72 No. Figure 2.9 shows that the alkali metal with the smallest first ionization energy is Cs with a value of $+376\,\text{kJ/mol}$. Figure 2.11 shows that the halogen with the largest electron affinity is Cl with a value of $-349\,\text{kJ/mol}$. The sum of the two energies gives a positive energy (endothermic). Therefore, all other combinations of alkali metals with halogens will also have positive values.

page 76 Rhodium, Rh

page 77 Weaker. In both H_2 and H_2^+ the two H atoms are principally held together by the electrostatic attractions between the nuclei and the electron(s) concentrated between them. H_2^+ has only one electron between the nuclei whereas H_2 has two and this results in the H—H bond in H_2 being stronger.

page 78 Triple bond. CO_2 has two C—O double bonds. Because the C—O bond in carbon monoxide is shorter, it is likely to be a triple bond.

page 79 Electron affinity measures the energy released when an isolated atom gains an electron to form a 1− ion. The electronegativity measures the ability of the atom to hold on to its own electrons and attract electrons from other atoms in compounds.

page 80 Polar covalent. The difference in electronegativity between S and O is $3.5 - 2.5 = 1.0$. Based on the examples of F_2, HF, and LiF, the difference in electronegativity is great enough to introduce some polarity to the bond but not sufficient to cause a complete electron transfer from one atom to the other.

page 82 IF. Because the difference in electronegativity between I and F is greater than that between Cl and F, the magnitude of Q should be greater for IF. In addition, because I has a larger atomic radius than Cl, the bond length in IF is longer than that in ClF. Thus, both Q and r are larger for IF and, therefore, $\mu = Qr$ will be larger for IF.

page 83 Smaller dipole moment for C—H. The magnitude of Q should be similar for C—H and H—I bonds because the difference in electronegativity for each bond is 0.4. The C—H bond length is 1.1 Å and the H—I bond length is 1.6 Å. Therefore $\mu = Qr$ will be greater for H—I because it has a longer bond (larger r).

page 84 OsO_4. The data suggest that the yellow substance is a molecular species with its low melting and boiling points. Os in OsO_4 has an oxidation number of $+8$ and Cr in Cr_2O_3 has an oxidation number of $+3$. In Section 3.4, we learn that a compound with a metal in a high oxidation state should show a high degree of covalence and OsO_4 fits this situation.

page 88 There is probably a better choice of Lewis structure than the one chosen. Because the formal charges must add up to 0 and the formal charge on the F atom is +1, there must be an atom that has a formal charge of −1. Because F is the most electronegative element, we don't expect it to carry a positive formal charge.

page 90 Yes. There are two resonance structures for ozone that each contribute equally to the overall description of the molecule. Each O—O bond is therefore an average of a single bond and a double bond, which is a "one-and-a-half" bond.

page 90 As "one-and-a-third" bonds. There are three resonance structures, and each of the three N—O bonds is single in two of those structures and double in the third. Each bond in the actual ion is an average of these: $(1 + 1 + 2)/3 = 1\frac{1}{3}$.

page 92 No, it will not have multiple resonance structures. We can't "move" the double bonds, as we did in benzene, because the positions of the hydrogen atoms dictate specific positions for the double bonds. We can't write any other reasonable Lewis structures for the molecule.

page 92 The formal charge of each atom is shown here:

$$\overset{\cdot\cdot}{N}=\overset{\cdot\cdot}{\overset{\cdot\cdot}{O}} \qquad \overset{\cdot\cdot}{\overset{\cdot\cdot}{N}}=\overset{\cdot\cdot}{\overset{\cdot}{O}}$$
$$\text{F.C.} \quad 0 \quad\quad 0 \qquad\quad -1 \quad +1$$

The first structure shows each atom with a zero formal charge and therefore it is the dominant Lewis structure. The second one shows a positive formal charge for an oxygen atom, which is a highly electronegative atom, and this is not a favorable situation.

page 95 The atomization of ethane produces $2\ C(g) + 6\ H(g)$. In this process, six C—H bonds and one C—C bond are broken. We can use $6D(\text{C—H})$ to estimate the amount of enthalpy needed to break the six C—H bonds. The difference between that number and the enthalpy of atomization is an estimate of the bond enthalpy of the C—C bond, $D(\text{C—C})$.

page 95 H_2O_2. From Table 3.4, the bond enthalpy of the O—O single bond in H_2O_2 (146 kJ/mol) is much lower than that of the O=O bond in O_2 (495 kJ/mol). The weaker bond in H_2O_2 is expected to make it more reactive than O_2.

CHAPTER 4

page 114 Octahedral. Removing two atoms that are opposite each other leads to a square-planar geometry.

page 115 The molecule does not follow the octet rule because it has ten electrons around the central A atom. There are four electron domains around A: two single bonds, one double bond, and one nonbonding pair.

page 116 Each of the three represents a single electron domain in the VSEPR model.

page 119 Yes. Based on one resonance structure, we might expect the electron domain that is due to the double bond to "push" the domains that are due to the single bonds, leading to angles slightly different from 120°. However, we must remember that there are two other equivalent resonance structures—each of the three O atoms has a double bond to N in one of the three resonance structures (Section 3.6). Because of resonance, all three O atoms are equivalent, and they will experience the same amount of repulsion, which leads to bond angles equal to 120°.

page 119 A tetrahedral arrangement of electron domains is preferred because the bond angles are 109.5° compared to 90°. bond angles in a square-planar arrangement of electron domains. The larger bond angles result in smaller repulsions among electron domains and a more stable structure.

page 123 Yes. The C—O and C—S bond dipoles exactly oppose each other, like in CO_2, but because O and S have different electronegativities, the magnitudes of the bond dipoles will be different. As a

consequence, the bond dipoles will not cancel each other and the OCS molecule has a nonzero dipole moment.

page 128 Both p orbitals are perpendicular to the Be—F bond axes.

page 128 (bottom) The unhybridized p orbital is oriented perpendicular to the plane defined by the three sp^2 hybrids (trigonal-planar array of lobes) with one lobe on each side of the plane.

page 133 The molecule should not be linear. Because there are three electron domains around each N atom, we expect sp^2 hybridization and H—N—N angles of approximately 120°. The molecule is expected to be planar; the unhybridized $2p$ orbitals on the N atoms can form a π bond only if all four atoms lie in the same plane. You might notice that there are two ways in which the H atoms can be arranged: They can be both on the same side of the N=N bond or on opposite sides of the N=N bond.

page 138 The σ bond component is formed from sp hybrid orbitals.

page 140 The molecule would fall apart. With one electron in the bonding MO and one in the antibonding MO, there is no net stabilization of the electrons relative to two separate H atoms.

page 144 (a) Gold, Au. Tungsten, W, lies near the middle of the transition metal series where the bands arising from the d orbitals and the s orbital are approximately half-filled. This electron count should fill the bonding orbitals and leave the antibonding orbitals mostly empty. (b) Because both elements have similar numbers of electrons in the bonding orbitals but tungsten has fewer electrons in antibonding orbitals, it will have a higher melting point.

CHAPTER 5

page 160 $CH_4 < CCl_4 < CBr_4$. Because all three molecules are nonpolar, the strength of dispersion forces determines the relative boiling points. Polarizability increases in order of increasing molecular size and molecular weight, $CH_4 < CCl_4 < CBr_4$; hence, the dispersion forces and boiling points increase in the same order.

page 164 $Ca(NO_3)_2$ in water, because calcium nitrate is a strong electrolyte that forms ions and water is a polar molecule with a dipole moment. Ion–dipole forces cannot be present in a CH_3OH/H_2O mixture because CH_3OH does not form ions.

CHAPTER 6

page 179 C=N, because it is a polar double bond. C—H and C—C bonds are relatively unreactive.

page 181 Two C—H bonds and two C—C bonds

page 182 The isomers have different properties, as seen in Table 6.3.

page 187 Only two of the four possible C=C bond sites are distinctly different in the linear chain of five carbon atoms with one double bond.

page 193

page 197

page 201 All four groups must be different from one another.

CHAPTER 7

page 219 A condensation polymer. The presence of both —COOH and —NH$_2$ groups allow molecules to react with one another forming C—N bonds and splitting out H$_2$O.

page 220 As the vinyl acetate content increases more side chain branching occurs which inhibits the formation of crystalline regions thereby lowering the melting point.

page 223 No. The emitted photons have energies that are similar in energy to the band gap of the semiconductor. If the size of the crystals is reduced into the nanometer range, the band gap will increase. However, because 340-nm light falls in the UV region of the electromagnetic spectrum, increasing the energy of the band gap will only shift the light deeper into the UV.

CHAPTER 8

page 234 Small

page 235 1470 lb

page 239 It would be halved.

page 240 No—you have to convert T to Kelvin to calculate this properly.

page 242 Avogadro's number, 6.022×10^{23}

page 246 Less dense

page 249 The pressure due to N$_2$ would be the same, but the total pressure would increase.

page 254 HCl (slowest) $<$ O$_2$ $<$ H$_2$ (fastest)

page 256 3/2

page 259 (a) Decrease, (b) No change

page 260 (b) 100 K and 5 atm

page 261 They do have intermolecular attractions for each other, and they do take up space.

CHAPTER 9

page 280 Photoionization is a process in which a molecule breaks into ions upon illumination with light; photodissociation is a process in which molecules break up upon illumination with light but the products bear no charge.

page 281 Because those molecules do not absorb light at those wavelengths

page 283 Yes—Cl is neither a product nor a reactant in the overall reaction, and its presence does speed the reaction up.

page 286 SO$_2$ in the atmosphere reacts with oxygen to form SO$_3$. SO$_3$ in the atmosphere reacts with water in the atmosphere to form H$_2$SO$_4$, sulfuric acid. The sulfuric acid dissolves in water droplets that fall to Earth, causing "acid rain" that has a pH of 4 or so.

page 287 NO$_2$ photodissociates to NO and O; the O atoms react with O$_2$ in the atmosphere to form ozone, which is a key ingredient in photochemical smog.

page 289 Higher humidity means there is more water in the air. Water absorbs infrared light, which we feel as heat. After sundown, the ground that has been warmed earlier in the day reradiates heat out. In locations with higher humidity, this energy is absorbed somewhat by the water and in turn is reradiated to some extent back to the Earth, resulting in warmer temperatures compared to a low-humidity location.

page 290 We need to be below water's critical point. Therefore, to sublime water we need to be below 0.006 atm. A wide range of temperatures will work for sublimation at this pressure—the most environmentally relevant ones are -50 °C to 100 °C.

page 294 The pollutants are capable of being oxidized (either directly by reaction with dissolved oxygen or indirectly by the action of organisms such as bacteria).

page 298 The 0.20-m solution is hypotonic with respect to the 0.5-m solution. (A hypotonic solution will have a lower concentration and hence a lower osmotic pressure.)

page 300 They would have the same osmotic pressure because they have the same concentration of particles. (Both are strong electrolytes that are 0.20 M in total ions.)

CHAPTER 10

page 312 No. The potential energy is lower at the bottom of the hill. (b) Once the bike comes to a stop, its kinetic energy is zero, just as it was at the top of the hill.

page 313 Open system. Humans exchange matter and energy with their surroundings.

page 317 Endothermic

page 319 The balance (current state) does not depend on the ways the money may have been transferred into the account or on the particular expenditures made in withdrawing money from the account. It depends only on the net total of all the transactions.

page 319 Because E, P, and V are state functions that don't depend on path, $H = E + PV$ must also be a state function.

page 320 No. If ΔV is zero, then the expression $w = -P\Delta V$ is also zero.

page 321 A thermometer to measure temperature changes

page 323 No. Because only half as much matter is involved, the value of ΔH would be $\frac{1}{2}(-483.6 \text{ kJ}) = -241.8$ kJ.

page 326 Hg(l). Rearranging Equation 5.22 gives $\Delta T = \dfrac{q}{C_s \times m}$. When q and m are constant for a series of substances, then $\Delta T = \dfrac{\text{constant}}{C_s}$. Therefore, the element with the smallest C_s in Table 5.2 has the largest ΔT, Hg(l).

page 331 (a) The sign of ΔH changes. (b) The magnitude of ΔH doubles.

page 334 No. Because O$_3$(g) is not the most stable form of oxygen at 25 °C, 1 atm [O$_2$(g) is], ΔH_f° for O$_3$(g) is not necessarily zero. In Appendix C we see that it is 142.3 kJ/mol.

page 339 Fats, because they have the largest fuel value of the three

page 341 Combustion of H$_2$(g) produces only H$_2$O(g). No CO$_2$(g) or other gases that might contribute to climate change issues are produced.

CHAPTER 11

page 359 (a) Both viscosity and surface tension decrease with increasing temperature because of the increased molecular motion. (b) Both properties increase as the strength of intermolecular forces increases.

page 361 Melting (or fusion), endothermic

page 364 CCl$_4$. Both compounds are nonpolar; therefore, only dispersion forces exist between the molecules. Because dispersion forces are stronger for the larger, heavier CBr$_4$, it has a lower vapor pressure than CCl$_4$. The substance with the larger vapor pressure at a given temperature is more volatile.

CHAPTER 12

page 380 (a) The rates of the forward and reverse reactions. (b) Greater than 1

page 380 When the concentrations of reactants and products are no longer changing

page 383 It does not depend on starting concentrations.

page 383 Units of moles/L are used to calculate K_c; units of partial pressure are used to calculate K_p.

page 384 0.00140

page 387 It is cubed.

page 389 $K_p = P_{H_2O}$

page 391 $K_c = [NH_4^+][OH^-]/[NH_3]$

page 399 (a) It shifts to the right. (b) It shifts to the left.

page 399 (bottom) It will shift to the left, the side with a larger number of moles of gas.

page 402 As the temperature increases, a larger fraction of molecules in the liquid phase have enough energy to overcome their intermolecular attractions and go into the vapor; the evaporation process is endothermic.

page 404 No

CHAPTER 13

page 419 No, nonspontaneous processes can occur so long as they receive some continuous outside assistance. Examples of nonspontaneous processes with which we may be familiar include the building of a brick wall and the electrolysis of water to form hydrogen gas and oxygen gas.

page 421 No. Just because the system is restored to its original condition doesn't mean that the surroundings have likewise been restored to their original condition, so it is not necessarily reversible.

page 423 ΔS depends not merely on q but on q_{rev}. Although there are many possible paths that could take a system from its initial to final state, there is always only one reversible isothermal path between two states. Thus, ΔS has only one particular value regardless of the path taken between states.

page 425 Because rusting is a spontaneous process, ΔS_{univ} must be positive. Therefore, the entropy of the surroundings must increase, and that increase must be larger than the entropy decrease of the system.

page 427 $S = 0$, based on Equation 19.5 and the fact that $\ln 1 = 0$.

page 428 A molecule can vibrate (atoms moving relative to one another) and rotate (tumble), whereas a single atom cannot undergo these motions.

page 431 It must be a perfect crystal at 0 K (third law of thermodynamics), which means it has only a single accessible microstate.

page 435 ΔS_{surr} always increases. For simplicity, assume that the process is isothermal. The change in entropy of the surroundings in an isothermal process is $\Delta S_{surr} = \dfrac{-q_{sys}}{T}$. Because the reaction is exothermic, $-q_{sys}$ is a positive number. Thus, ΔS_{surr} is a positive number and the entropy of the surroundings increases.

page 437 (a) In any spontaneous process the entropy of the universe increases. (b) In any spontaneous process operating at constant temperature, the free energy of the system decreases.

page 438 It indicates that the process to which the thermodynamic quantity refers has taken place under standard conditions, as summarized in Table 13.2.

page 442 Above the boiling point, vaporization is spontaneous, and $\Delta G < 0$. Therefore, $\Delta H - T\Delta S < 0$, and $\Delta H < T\Delta S$.

CHAPTER 14

page 461 The rate will increase.

page 464 Average rate is for a large time interval; instantaneous rate is for an "instant" in time. Yes, they can have the same numeric value, especially if a plot of concentration versus time is linear.

page 467 (top) Reaction rate is what we measure as a reaction proceeds—change in concentration in time for one or more of the components in the mixture. Reaction rate always has units of concentration per time, usually M/s. A rate constant is what we calculate from reaction rate data, and its magnitude is proportional to the reaction rate, but its units depend on the reaction order. The rate law of a reaction is an equation that relates reaction rate to the rate constant: Rate $= k[A]^m[B]^n$, for components A and B in the reaction.

page 467 No. Rate is always change in concentration per time; rate constant has units that depend on the form of the rate law.

page 468 (a) The reaction is second order in NO, first order in H_2, and third order overall. (b) No. Doubling NO concentration will quadruple the rate, but doubling H_2 concentration will merely double the rate.

page 469 No reaction will take place.

page 475 1.25 g

page 477 The half-life will increase.

page 480 No—transition states are by definition not stable.

page 480 The collision may not have occurred with enough energy for reaction to occur, and/or the collision may not have occurred with the proper orientation of reactant molecules to favor product formation.

page 483 Bimolecular

page 487 Most reactions occur in elementary steps; the rate law is governed by the elementary steps, not by their sum (which is the overall balanced equation).

page 489 The odds of three molecules colliding with each other properly to react is very low.

page 492 By lowering the activation energy for the reaction or by increasing the frequency factor

page 493 A homogeneous catalyst will be harder to separate from the reaction mixture than a heterogeneous one.

page 495 People do say this, but we have to be careful. An enzyme-catalyzed reaction will have a lower transition state energy than the uncatalyzed reaction, but the nature of the transition state is probably different than the uncatalyzed version.

CHAPTER 1

Figure 1.3 The wavelength of (a) is twice that of (b) and the frequency of (a) is consequently half that of (b). Thus, the wavelength of (b) is 0.50 m and its frequency is 6.0×10^8 cycles/s.

Figure 1.4 The X-ray has a shorter wavelength and, consequently, higher frequency than the red light.

Figure 1.5 The hottest area is the white or yellowish white area in the center.

Figure 1.7 If the tube is not evacuated, the electrons that are freed from the metal surface will strike gas molecules near that surface. As a result, they will become attached to the gas molecules and never arrive at the positive terminal.

Figure 1.12 The $n = 2$ to $n = 1$ transition involves a larger energy change than the $n = 3$ to $n = 2$ transition. (Compare the space differences between the states in the figure.) If the $n = 2$ to $n = 1$ transition produces visible light, the $n = 3$ to $n = 2$ transition must produce radiation of lower energy. The infrared radiation has lower frequency and, hence, lower energy than visible light, whereas the ultraviolet has greater frequency and greater energy. Thus, the $n = 2$ to $n = 1$ transition will produce ultraviolet radiation.

Figure 1.16 The region of highest electron density is where the density of dots is highest, which is near the nucleus.

Figure 1.17 The fourth shell ($n = 4$) would contain four subshells, labeled 4s, 4p, 4d, and 4f.

Figure 1.18 There would be four maxima and three nodes.

Figure 1.22 (a) The intensity of the color indicates that the probability of finding the electron is greater at the interior of the lobes than on the edges. (b) $2p_x$.

Figure 1.24 The 4d and 4f subshells are not shown.

CHAPTER 2

Figure 2.1 Row 7—these elements are generally radioactive and not stable.

Figure 2.3 2s

Figure 2.6 Bottom and left

Figure 2.7 They get larger, just like the atoms do.

Figure 2.9 Ar; it has a larger Z_{eff}.

Figure 2.10 There is more electron–electron repulsion in the case of oxygen because two electrons have to occupy the same orbital.

Figure 2.11 The halogens (group 7A); it does make sense because we know that they are very stable as anions.

Figure 2.12 Ionization energy—lower ionization energy is correlated with increasing metallic character.

Figure 2.14 Anions are above the lines; cations are below the line.

Figure 2.22 Lilac

CHAPTER 3

Figure 3.1 Covalent

Figure 3.2 Yes, the same sort of reaction should occur between any of the alkali metals and any of the elemental halogens.

Figure 3.3 Cations have a smaller radius than their neutral atoms and anions have a larger radius. Because Na and Cl are in the same row of the periodic table, we would expect Na^+ to have a smaller radius than Cl^-, so we would guess that the larger green spheres represent Cl^-.

Figure 3.4 The distance between ions in KF should be larger than that in NaF and smaller than that in KCl. We would thus expect the lattice energy of KF to be between 701 and 910 kJ/mol.

Figure 3.6 The repulsions between the nuclei would decrease, the attractions between the nuclei and the electrons would decrease, and the repulsions between the electrons would be unaffected.

Figure 3.7 The electronegativity decreases with increasing atomic number.

Figure 3.9 μ will decrease

Figure 3.10 The bonds are not polar enough to cause enough excess electron density on the halogen atom to lead to a red shading.

Figure 3.12 The lengths of the bonds of the outer O atoms to the inner O atom are the same.

Figure 3.13 Yes. The electron densities on the left and right parts of the molecule are the same, indicating that resonance has made the two O—O bonds equivalent to one another.

Figure 3.14 The dashed bonds represent the "half bonds" that result when the two resonance structures are averaged.

Figure 3.15 Exothermic

Figure 3.17 As the bond gets longer, it gets weaker. We would therefore expect a plot of bond enthalpy versus bond length to have a negative slope.

CHAPTER 4

Figure 4.1 The atomic radii (Figure 2.7)

Figure 4.3 Octahedral

Figure 4.7 The electron pair in the bonding domain is attracted toward two nuclear centers, whereas the nonbonding pair is attracted toward just one.

Figure 4.8 90°

Figure 4.9 The nonbonding electron pairs exert a greater repulsive force than the bonding electron pairs.

Figure 4.10 The heads of the arrows point toward regions of highest electron density, as indicated by the red color.

Figure 4.14 As the internuclear distance decreases, nucleus–nucleus repulsion becomes a dominant component of the potential energy.

Figure 4.16 The small lobes of the sp hybrid orbitals are very much smaller in spatial extent and, therefore, provide very little overlap with the F orbitals.

Figure 4.17 Three: one s and two p orbitals

Figure 4.23 The two p orbitals that form the π bond must align, and each of them is perpendicular to the plane of the sp^2 hybrid orbitals.

Figure 4.24 Acetylene, because it has two C—C π bonds, whereas ethylene has one π bond

Figure 4.26 C—H and C—C

Figure 4.33 The σ_{1s}^*

Figure 4.34 The two electrons in the σ_{1s} MO

Figure 4.35 By drawing Lewis structures you can show that there are three (chlorine), two (sulfur), one (phosphorus), and zero (silicon) nonbonding electron pairs per atom.

Figure 4.36 In the fourth period, vanadium and chromium have very similar melting points. Molybdenum and tungsten have the highest melting points in the fifth and sixth periods, respectively. All of these elements are located near the middle of the period where the bonding orbitals are mostly filled and the antibonding orbitals mostly empty.

Figure 4.37 The molecular orbitals become more closely spaced in energy.

Figure 4.38 Potassium has only one valence electron per atom. If we fill the 4s band halfway probably a small amount of electron density will leak over and start to fill the 3d orbitals as well. The 4p orbitals should be empty.

CHAPTER 5

Figure 5.2 The density in a liquid is much closer to a solid than it is to a gas.

Figure 5.9 Both compounds are nonpolar and incapable of forming hydrogen bonds. Therefore, the boiling point is determined by the dispersion forces, which are stronger for the larger, heavier SnH_4.

Figure 5.10 The non-hydrogen atom must possess a nonbonding electron pair.

Figure 5.11 There are four electron pairs surrounding oxygen in a water molecule. Two of the electron pairs are used to make covalent bonds to hydrogen within the H_2O molecule, while the other two are available to make hydrogen bonds to neighboring molecules. Because the electron-pair geometry is tetrahedral (four electron domains around the central atom), the $H—O\cdots H$ bond angle is approximately $109°$.

CHAPTER 6

Figure 6.1 Tetrahedral

Figure 6.2 The OH group is polar whereas the CH_3 group is nonpolar. Hence, adding CH_3 will (a) reduce the substance's solubility in polar solvents and (b) increase its solubility in nonpolar solvents.

Figure 6.5 C_nH_{2n}, because there are no CH_3 groups, each carbon has two hydrogens.

Figure 6.7 Just one

Figure 6.9 Intermediates are minima and transition states are maxima on energy profiles.

Figure 6.14 Both lactic acid and citric acid

Figure 6.15 No, because there are not four different groups around any carbon

Figure 6.18 Those labeled "basic amino acids," which have basic side groups that are protonated at pH 7

Figure 6.25 The long hydrocarbon chains, which are nonpolar

Figure 6.27 The polar parts of the phospholipids seek to interact with water whereas the nonpolar parts seek to interact with other nonpolar substances and to avoid water.

Figure 6.29 Negative charge because of charge on phosphate groups

Figure 6.31 GC because each base has three hydrogen bonding sites, whereas there are only two in AT

CHAPTER 7

Figure 7.2 The intermolecular forces are stronger in toluene, as shown by its higher boiling point. The molecules pack more efficiently in benzene, which explains its higher melting point, even though the intermolecular forces are weaker.

Figure 7.17 Decrease. As the quantum dots get smaller, the band gap increases and the emitted light shifts to shorter wavelength.

Figure 7.20 Each carbon atom in C_{60} is bonded to three neighboring carbon atoms through covalent bonds. Thus, the bonding is more like graphite, where carbon atoms also bond to three neighbors, than diamond, where carbon atoms bond to four neighbors.

CHAPTER 8

Figure 8.2 It will increase.

Figure 8.5 Decrease

Figure 8.6 1520 torr

Figure 8.7 Linear

Figure 8.10 one

Figure 8.11 It is small and inert.

Figure 8.17 About a third

Figure 8.18 Higher speeds are correlated with smaller molar masses (assuming constant T).

Figure 8.20 n, moles of gas

Figure 8.22 Not really—CO_2 is least ideal and does have the largest molar mass, but H_2, the lightest gas, deviates more from the ideal line than the heavier N_2.

Figure 8.23 True

Figure 8.25 It would increase.

CHAPTER 9

Figure 9.1 About 85 km

Figure 9.3 The atmosphere absorbs a significant fraction of solar radiation.

Figure 9.4 The peak value is about 5×10^{12} molecules per cm^3. If we use Avogadro's number to convert molecules to moles, and the conversion factor of $1000\ cm^3 = 1000\ mL = 1\ L$, we find that the concentration of ozone at the peak is 8×10^{-9} mole/L.

Figure 9.16 This is ambiguous; both temperature and salinity vary with density in similar ways; but temperature seems to parallel density better. Temperature decreases down to 1000 m, then remains relatively constant; density increases down to 1000 m, and then remains relatively constant.

Figure 9.17 The depth of the aquifer; the nature of the intervening layers (how porous or dense they are)

Figure 9.19 Water is the chemical species that is crossing the membrane, not the ions.

Figure 9.24 The water will move through the semipermeable membrane toward the more concentrated solution. Thus, the liquid level in the left arm will increase.

Figure 9.25 Water will move toward the more concentrated solute solution, which is inside the red blood cells, causing them to undergo hemolysis.

CHAPTER 10

Figure 10.1 In the act of throwing, the pitcher transfers energy to the ball, which then becomes kinetic energy of the ball. For a given amount of energy E transferred to the ball, Equation 10.1 tells us that the speed of the ball is $v = \sqrt{2E/m}$ where m is the mass of the ball. Because a baseball has less mass than a bowling bowl, it will have a higher speed for a given amount of energy transferred.

Figure 10.2 When she starts going uphill, kinetic energy is converted to potential energy and her speed decreases.

Figure 10.3 The electrostatic potential energy of two oppositely charged particles is negative (Equation 10.2). As the particles become closer, the electrostatic potential energy becomes even more negative—that is, it decreases.

Figure 10.4 Yes, the system is still closed—matter can't escape the system to the surroundings unless the piston is pulled completely out of the cylinder.

Figure 10.5 If $E_{final} = E_{initial}$, then $\Delta E = 0$.

Figure 10.6

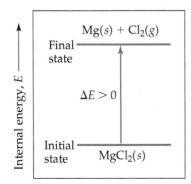

Figure 10.7 No. The sign on w is positive and the sign on q is negative. We need to know the magnitudes of q and w to determine whether $\Delta E = q + w$ is positive or negative.

Figure 10.10 The battery is doing work on the surroundings, so $w < 0$.

Figure 10.11 We need to know whether $Zn(s)$ or $HCl(aq)$ is the limiting reagent of the reaction. If it is $Zn(s)$, then the addition of more Zn will lead to the generation of more $H_2(g)$ and more work will be done.

Figure 10.17 Endothermic—heat is being added to the system to raise the temperature of the water.

Figure 10.18 Two cups provide more thermal insulation so less heat will escape the system.

Figure 10.19 The stirrer ensures that all of the water in the bomb is at the same temperature.

Figure 10.21 The condensation of $2\ H_2O(g)$ to $2\ H_2O(l)$

Figure 10.22 Yes, ΔH_3 would remain the same as it is the enthalpy change for the process $CO(g) + \frac{1}{2}O_2(g) \longrightarrow CO_2(g)$.

Figure 10.24 Grams of fat

CHAPTER 11

Figure 11.3 Wax is a hydrocarbon that cannot form hydrogen bonds. Therefore, coating the inside of tube with wax will dramatically decrease the adhesive forces between water and the tube and change the shape of the water meniscus to an inverted U-shape. Neither wax nor glass can form metallic bonds with mercury so the shape of the mercury meniscus will be qualitatively the same, an inverted U-shape.

Figure 11.5 Because we are dealing with a state function, the energy of going straight from a solid to a gas must be the same as going from a solid to a gas through an intermediate liquid state. Therefore, the heat of sublimation must be equal to the sum of the heat of fusion and the heat of vaporization: $\Delta H_{sub} = \Delta H_{fus} + \Delta H_{vap}$.

Figure 11.8 Increases, because the molecules have more kinetic energy as the temperature increases and can escape more easily

Figure 11.9 All liquids including ethylene glycol reach their normal boiling point when their vapor pressure is equal to atmospheric pressure, 760 torr.

Figure 11.11 Freezing, because for most substances the solid phase is denser than the liquid phase and increasing the pressure will eventually drive a phase transition from the liquid to the solid state (provided the temperature is below the critical temperature)

CHAPTER 12

Figure 12.1 The color in the tube stops changing.

Figure 12.2 No

Figure 12.6 The boxes would be approximately the same size.

Figure 12.7 It will be lower; some CO_2 has to react with CaO to make some $CaCO_3$.

Figure 12.9 500 atm and 400 °C

Figure 12.10 Nitrogen (and some of the added hydrogen) is converted into ammonia.

Figure 12.14 About two to three times faster, based on the graph

Figure 12.15 About 5×10^{-4}

CHAPTER 13

Figure 13.1 Yes, the potential energy of the eggs decreases as they fall.

Figure 13.2 Because the final volume would be less than twice the volume of Flask A, the final pressure would be greater than 0.5 atm.

Figure 13.3 The freezing of liquid water to ice is exothermic.

Figure 13.4 To be truly reversible, the temperature change δT must be infinitesimally small.

Figure 13.8 There are two other independent rotational motions of the H_2O molecule:

Figure 13.9 Ice, because it is the phase in which the molecules are held most rigidly

Figure 13.11 The decrease in the number of molecules due to the formation of new bonds.

Figure 13.13 During a phase change, the temperature remains constant but the entropy change can be large.

Figure 13.14 Based on the three molecules shown, the addition of each C increases $S°$ by 40–45 J/mol-K. Based on this observation, we would predict that $S°(C_4H_{10})$ would 310–315 J/mol-K. Appendix C confirms that this is a good prediction: $S°(C_4H_{10})$ = 310.0 J/mol-K.

Figure 13.16 Spontaneous

Figure 13.17 If we plot progress of the reaction versus free energy, equilibrium is at a minimum point in free energy, as shown in the figure. In that sense, the reaction runs "downhill" until it reaches that minimum point.

CHAPTER 14

Figure 14.3 B

Figure 14.4 It decreases.

Figure 14.8 The reaction is first order in CH_3NC.

Figure 14.10 At early times in the reaction; both graphs look linear close to $t = 0$.

Figure 14.17 The energy needed to overcome the energy barrier (the activation energy) looks about twice as large as the overall energy change for the reaction.

Figure 14.23 For the blue curve: The transition states are at the top of the peaks (2) and the intermediate is in the "valley" between the two peaks. For the red curve: The top of the peak is the transition state; no intermediates are shown.

Figure 14.27 Substrate; if products bound tightly, they would not leave and the active site would not be free.

absolute zero The lowest attainable temperature; 0 K on the Kelvin scale and −273.15 °C on the Celsius scale.

absorption spectrum A pattern of variation in the amount of light absorbed by a sample as a function of wavelength.

accuracy A measure of how closely individual measurements agree with the correct value.

acid A substance that is able to donate a H^+ ion (a proton) and, hence, increases the concentration of $H^+(aq)$ when it dissolves in water.

acid rain Rainwater that has become excessively acidic because of absorption of pollutant oxides, notably SO_3, produced by human activities.

actinide element Element in which the $5f$ orbitals are only partially occupied.

activated complex (transition state) The particular arrangement of atoms found at the top of the potential-energy barrier as a reaction proceeds from reactants to products.

activation energy (E_a) The minimum energy needed for reaction; the height of the energy barrier to formation of products.

active site Specific site on a heterogeneous catalyst or an enzyme where catalysis occurs.

activity The decay rate of a radioactive material, generally expressed as the number of disintegrations per unit time.

activity series A list of metals in order of decreasing ease of oxidation.

addition polymerization Polymerization that occurs through coupling of monomers with one another, with no other products formed in the reaction.

addition reaction A reaction in which a reagent adds to the two carbon atoms of a carbon–carbon multiple bond.

adsorption The binding of molecules to a surface.

alcohol An organic compound obtained by substituting a hydroxyl group (—OH) for a hydrogen on a hydrocarbon.

aldehyde An organic compound that contains a carbonyl group (C=O) to which at least one hydrogen atom is attached.

alkali metals Members of group 1A in the periodic table.

alkaline earth metals Members of group 2A in the periodic table.

alkanes Compounds of carbon and hydrogen containing only carbon–carbon single bonds.

alkenes Hydrocarbons containing one or more carbon–carbon double bonds.

alkyl group A group that is formed by removing a hydrogen atom from an alkane.

alkynes Hydrocarbons containing one or more carbon–carbon triple bonds.

alloy A substance that has the characteristic properties of a metal and contains more than one element. Often there is one principal metallic component, with other elements present in smaller amounts. Alloys may be homogeneous or heterogeneous.

amide An organic compound that has an NR_2 group attached to a carbonyl.

amine A compound that has the general formula R_3N, where R may be H or a hydrocarbon group.

amino acid A carboxylic acid that contains an amino (—NH_2) group attached to the carbon atom adjacent to the carboxylic acid (—COOH) functional group.

angstrom A common non-SI unit of length, denoted Å, that is used to measure atomic dimensions: $1 Å = 10^{-10}$ m.

anion A negatively charged ion.

anode An electrode at which oxidation occurs.

antibonding molecular orbital A molecular orbital in which electron density is concentrated outside the region between the two nuclei of bonded atoms. Such orbitals, designated as $\sigma^\star$ or $\pi^\star$, are less stable (of higher energy) than bonding molecular orbitals.

aqueous solution A solution in which water is the solvent.

aromatic hydrocarbons Hydrocarbon compounds that contain a planar, cyclic arrangement of carbon atoms linked by both σ and delocalized π bonds.

Arrhenius equation An equation that relates the rate constant for a reaction to the frequency factor, A, the activation energy, E_a, and the temperature, T: $k = Ae^{-E_a/RT}$. In its logarithmic form it is written $\ln k = -E_a/RT + \ln A$.

atmosphere (atm) A unit of pressure equal to 760 torr; 1 atm = 101.325 kPa.

atom The smallest representative particle of an element.

atomic mass unit (amu) A unit based on the value of exactly 12 amu for the mass of the isotope of carbon that has six protons and six neutrons in the nucleus.

atomic number The number of protons in the nucleus of an atom of an element.

atomic radius An estimate of the size of an atom. See **bonding atomic radius**.

atomic weight The average mass of the atoms of an element in atomic mass units (amu); it is numerically equal to the mass in grams of one mole of the element.

Avogadro's hypothesis A statement that equal volumes of gases at the same temperature and pressure contain equal numbers of molecules.

Avogadro's law A statement that the volume of a gas maintained at constant temperature and pressure is directly proportional to the number of moles of the gas.

Avogadro's number (N_A) The number of ^{12}C atoms in exactly 12 g of ^{12}C; it equals 6.022×10^{23} mol^{-1}.

band An array of closely spaced molecular orbitals occupying a discrete range of energy.

band gap The energy gap between a fully occupied band called a valence band and an empty band called the conduction band.

band structure The electronic structure of a solid, defining the allowed ranges of energy for electrons in a solid.

bar A unit of pressure equal to 10^5 Pa.

base A substance that is an H^+ acceptor; a base produces an excess of $OH^-(aq)$ ions when it dissolves in water.

battery A self-contained electrochemical power source that contains one or more voltaic cells.

Beer's law The light absorbed by a substance (A) equals the product of its extinction coefficient (ε), the path length through which the light passes (b), and the molar concentration of the substance (c): $A = \varepsilon bc$.

bimolecular reaction An elementary reaction that involves two molecules.

biochemistry The study of the chemistry of living systems.

biodegradable Organic material that bacteria are able to oxidize.

bomb calorimeter A device for measuring the heat evolved in the combustion of a substance under constant-volume conditions.

bond angles The angles made by the lines joining the nuclei of the atoms in a molecule.

bond dipole The dipole moment that is due to unequal electron sharing between two atoms in a covalent bond.

bond enthalpy The enthalpy change, ΔH, required to break a particular bond when the substance is in the gas phase.

bonding atomic radius The radius of an atom as defined by the distances separating it from other atoms to which it is chemically bonded.

bonding molecular orbital A molecular orbital in which the electron density is concentrated in the internuclear region. The energy of a bonding molecular orbital is lower than the energy of the separate atomic orbitals from which it forms.

bonding pair In a Lewis structure a pair of electrons that is shared by two atoms.

bond length The distance between the centers of two bonded atoms.

bond order The number of bonding electron pairs shared between two atoms, minus the number of antibonding electron pairs: bond order = (number of bonding electrons − number of antibonding electrons)/2.

bond polarity A measure of the degree to which the electrons are shared unequally between two atoms in a chemical bond.

Born–Haber cycle A thermodynamic cycle based on Hess's law that relates the lattice energy of an ionic substance to its enthalpy of formation and to other measurable quantities.

Boyle's law A law stating that at constant temperature, the product of the volume and pressure of a given amount of gas is a constant.

calorie A unit of energy, it is the amount of energy needed to raise the temperature of 1 g of water by 1 °C from 14.5 °C to 15.5 °C. A related unit is the joule: 1 cal = 4.184 J.

calorimeter An apparatus that measures the heat released or absorbed in a chemical or physical process.

calorimetry The experimental measurement of heat produced in chemical and physical processes.

capillary action The process by which a liquid rises in a tube because of a combination of adhesion to the walls of the tube and cohesion between liquid particles.

carbide A binary compound of carbon with a metal or metalloid.

carbohydrates A class of substances formed from polyhydroxy aldehydes or ketones.

carbonyl group The C=O double bond, a characteristic feature of several organic functional groups, such as ketones and aldehydes.

carboxylic acid A compound that contains the —COOH functional group.

catalyst A substance that changes the speed of a chemical reaction without itself undergoing a permanent chemical change in the process.

cathode An electrode at which reduction occurs.

cathode rays Streams of electrons that are produced when a high voltage is applied to electrodes in an evacuated tube.

cation A positively charged ion.

cellulose A polysaccharide of glucose; it is the major structural element in plant matter.

chain reaction A series of reactions in which one reaction initiates the next.

changes of state Transformations of matter from one state to a different one, for example, from a gas to a liquid.

charcoal A form of carbon produced when wood is heated strongly in a deficiency of air.

Charles's law A law stating that at constant pressure, the volume of a given quantity of gas is proportional to absolute temperature.

chemical bond A strong attractive force that exists between atoms in a molecule.

chemical changes Processes in which one or more substances are converted into other substances; also called **chemical reactions**.

chemical equation A representation of a chemical reaction using the chemical formulas of the reactants and products; a balanced chemical equation contains equal numbers of atoms of each element on both sides of the equation.

chemical equilibrium A state of dynamic balance in which the rate of formation of the products of a reaction from the reactants equals the rate of formation of the reactants from the products; at equilibrium the concentrations of the reactants and products remain constant.

chemical formula A notation that uses chemical symbols with numerical subscripts to convey the relative proportions of atoms of the different elements in a substance.

chemical kinetics The area of chemistry concerned with the speeds, or rates, at which chemical reactions occur.

chemical properties Properties that describe a substance's composition and its reactivity; how the substance reacts or changes into other substances.

chemical reactions Processes in which one or more substances are converted into other substances; also called **chemical changes**.

chemistry The scientific discipline that studies the composition, properties, and transformations of matter.

chiral A term describing a molecule or an ion that cannot be superimposed on its mirror image.

chlorofluorocarbons Compounds composed entirely of chlorine, fluorine, and carbon.

cholesteric liquid crystalline phase A liquid crystal formed from flat, disc-shaped molecules that align through a stacking of the molecular discs.

coal A naturally occurring solid containing hydrocarbons of high molecular weight, as well as compounds containing sulfur, oxygen, and nitrogen.

colligative property A property of a solvent (vapor-pressure lowering, freezing-point lowering, boiling-point elevation, osmotic pressure) that depends on the total concentration of solute particles present.

collision model A model of reaction rates based on the idea that molecules must collide to react; it explains the factors influencing reaction rates in terms of the frequency of collisions, the number of collisions with energies exceeding the activation energy, and the probability that the collisions occur with suitable orientations.

combustion reaction A chemical reaction that proceeds with evolution of heat and usually also a flame; most combustion involves reaction with oxygen, as in the burning of a match.

complementary colors Colors that, when mixed in proper proportions, appear white or colorless.

compound A substance composed of two or more elements united chemically in definite proportions.

compound semiconductor A semiconducting material formed from two or more elements.

concentration The quantity of solute present in a given quantity of solvent or solution.

condensation polymerization Polymerization in which molecules are joined together through condensation reactions.

condensation reaction A chemical reaction in which a small molecule (such as a molecule of water) is split out from between two reacting molecules.

conduction band A band of molecular orbitals lying higher in energy than the occupied valence band and distinctly separated from it.

continuous spectrum A spectrum that contains radiation distributed over all wavelengths.

conversion factor A ratio relating the same quantity in two systems of units that is used to convert the units of measurement.

copolymer A complex polymer resulting from the polymerization of two or more chemically different monomers.

core electrons The electrons that are not in the outermost shell of an atom.

corrosion The process by which a metal is oxidized by substances in its environment.

covalent bond A bond formed between two or more atoms by a sharing of electrons.

covalent-network solids Solids in which the units that make up the three-dimensional network are joined by covalent bonds.

critical pressure The pressure at which a gas at its critical temperature is converted to a liquid state.

critical temperature The highest temperature at which it is possible to convert the gaseous form of a substance to a liquid. The critical temperature increases with an increase in the magnitude of intermolecular forces.

crystal lattice An imaginary network of points on which the repeating motif of a solid may be imagined to be laid down so that the structure of the crystal is obtained. The motif may be a single atom or a group of atoms. Each lattice point represents an identical environment in the crystal.

crystalline solid (crystal) A solid whose internal arrangement of atoms, molecules, or ions possesses a regularly repeating pattern in any direction through the solid.

cycloalkanes Saturated hydrocarbons of general formula C_nH_{2n} in which the carbon atoms form a closed ring.

Dalton's law of partial pressures A law stating that the total pressure of a mixture of gases is the sum of the pressures that each gas would exert if it were present alone.

decomposition reaction A chemical reaction in which a single compound reacts to give two or more products.

degenerate A situation in which two or more orbitals have the same energy.

density The ratio of an object's mass to its volume.

desalination The removal of salts from seawater, brine, or brackish water to make it fit for human consumption.

deuterium The isotope of hydrogen whose nucleus contains a proton and a neutron: ^2_1H.

diatomic molecule A molecule composed of only two atoms.

diffusion The spreading of one substance through a space occupied by one or more other substances.

dimensional analysis A method of problem solving in which units are carried through all calculations. Dimensional analysis ensures that the final answer of a calculation has the desired units.

dipole A molecule with one end having a partial negative charge and the other end having a partial positive charge; a polar molecule.

dipole–dipole force A force that becomes significant when polar molecules come in close contact with one another. The force is attractive when the positive end of one polar molecule approaches the negative end of another.

dipole moment A measure of the separation and magnitude of the positive and negative charges in polar molecules.

dispersion forces Intermolecular forces resulting from attractions between induced dipoles. Also called London dispersion forces.

doping Incorporation of a hetero atom into a solid to change its electrical properties. For example, incorporation of P into Si.

double bond A covalent bond involving two electron pairs.

double helix The structure for DNA that involves the winding of two DNA polynucleotide chains together in a helical arrangement. The two strands of the double helix are complementary in that the organic bases on the two strands are paired for optimal hydrogen bond interaction.

dynamic equilibrium A state of balance in which opposing processes occur at the same rate.

effective nuclear charge The net positive charge experienced by an electron in a many-electron atom; this charge is not the full nuclear charge because there is some shielding of the nucleus by the other electrons in the atom.

effusion The escape of a gas through an orifice or hole.

elastomer A material that can undergo a substantial change in shape via stretching, bending, or compression and return to its original shape upon release of the distorting force.

electrolyte A solute that produces ions in solution; an electrolytic solution conducts an electric current.

electrolytic cell A device in which a nonspontaneous oxidation-reduction reaction is caused to occur by passage of current under a sufficient external electrical potential.

electromagnetic radiation (radiant energy) A form of energy that has wave characteristics and that propagates through a vacuum at the characteristic speed of 3.00×10^8 m/s.

electron A negatively charged subatomic particle found outside the atomic nucleus; it is a part of all atoms. An electron has a mass 1/1836 times that of a proton.

electron affinity The energy change that occurs when an electron is added to a gaseous atom or ion.

electron configuration The arrangement of electrons in the orbitals of an atom or molecule.

electron density The probability of finding an electron at any particular point in an atom; this probability is equal to ψ^2, the square of the wave function. Also called the probability density.

electron domain In the VSEPR model, a region about a central atom in which an electron pair is concentrated.

electron-domain geometry The three-dimensional arrangement of the electron domains around an atom according to the VSEPR model.

electronegativity A measure of the ability of an atom that is bonded to another atom to attract electrons to itself.

electronic charge The negative charge carried by an electron; it has a magnitude of 1.602×10^{-19} C.

electronic structure The arrangement of electrons in an atom or molecule.

electron-sea model A model for the behavior of electrons in metals.

electron shell A collection of orbitals that have the same value of n. For example, the orbitals with

$n = 3$ (the $3s$, $3p$, and $3d$ orbitals) comprise the third shell.

electron spin A property of the electron that makes it behave as though it were a tiny magnet. The electron behaves as if it were spinning on its axis; electron spin is quantized.

element A substance consisting of atoms of the same atomic number. Historically defined as a substance that cannot be separated into simpler substances by chemical means.

elemental semiconductor A semiconducting material composed of just one element.

elementary reaction A process in a chemical reaction that occurs in a single event or step. An overall chemical reaction consists of one or more elementary reactions or steps.

empirical formula A chemical formula that shows the kinds of atoms and their relative numbers in a substance in the smallest possible whole-number ratios.

enantiomers Two mirror-image molecules of a chiral substance. The enantiomers are nonsuperimposable.

endothermic process A process in which a system absorbs heat from its surroundings.

energy The capacity to do work or to transfer heat.

energy-level diagram A diagram that shows the energies of molecular orbitals relative to the atomic orbitals from which they are derived. Also called a **molecular-orbital diagram**.

enthalpy A quantity defined by the relationship $H = E + PV$; the enthalpy change, ΔH, for a reaction that occurs at constant pressure is the heat evolved or absorbed in the reaction: $\Delta H = q_p$.

enthalpy of formation The enthalpy change that accompanies the formation of a substance from the most stable forms of its component elements.

enthalpy of reaction The enthalpy change associated with a chemical reaction.

entropy A thermodynamic function associated with the number of different equivalent energy states or spatial arrangements in which a system may be found. It is a thermodynamic state function, which means that once we specify the conditions for a system—that is, the temperature, pressure, and so on—the entropy is defined.

enzyme A protein molecule that acts to catalyze specific biochemical reactions.

equilibrium constant The numerical value of the equilibrium-constant expression for a system at equilibrium. The equilibrium constant is most usually denoted by K_p for gas-phase systems or K_c for solution-phase systems.

equilibrium-constant expression The expression that describes the relationship among the concentrations (or partial pressures) of the substances present in a system at equilibrium. The numerator is obtained by multiplying the concentrations of the substances on the product side of the equation, each raised to a power equal to its coefficient in the chemical equation. The denominator similarly contains the concentrations of the substances on the reactant side of the equation.

ester An organic compound that has an OR group attached to a carbonyl; it is the product of a reaction between a carboxylic acid and an alcohol.

ether A compound in which two hydrocarbon groups are bonded to one oxygen.

excited state A higher energy state than the ground state.

exothermic process A process in which a system releases heat to its surroundings.

extensive property A property that depends on the amount of material considered; for example, mass or volume.

face-centered lattice A crystal lattice in which the lattice points are located at the faces and corners of each unit cell.

f-block metals Lanthanide and actinide elements in which the $4f$ or $5f$ orbitals are partially occupied.

first law of thermodynamics A statement that energy is conserved in any process. One way to express the law is that the change in internal energy, ΔE, of a system in any process is equal to the heat, q, added to the system, plus the work, w, done on the system by its surroundings: $\Delta E = q + w$.

first-order reaction A reaction in which the reaction rate is proportional to the concentration of a single reactant, raised to the first power.

folding The process by which a protein adopts its biologically active shape.

force A push or a pull.

formal charge The number of valence electrons in an isolated atom minus the number of electrons assigned to the atom in the Lewis structure.

fossil fuels Coal, oil, and natural gas, which are presently our major sources of energy.

free energy (Gibbs free energy, G) A thermodynamic state function that gives a criterion for spontaneous change in terms of enthalpy and entropy: $G = H - TS$.

frequency The number of times per second that one complete wavelength passes a given point.

frequency factor (A) A term in the Arrhenius equation that is related to the frequency of collision and the probability that the collisions are favorably oriented for reaction.

fuel cell A voltaic cell that utilizes the oxidation of a conventional fuel, such as H_2 or CH_4, in the cell reaction.

fuel value The energy released when 1 g of a substance is combusted.

functional group An atom or group of atoms that imparts characteristic chemical properties to an organic compound.

fusion The joining of two light nuclei to form a more massive one.

gas Matter that has no fixed volume or shape; it conforms to the volume and shape of its container.

gas constant (R) The constant of proportionality in the ideal-gas equation.

geometric isomerism A form of isomerism in which compounds with the same type and number of atoms and the same chemical bonds have different spatial arrangements of these atoms and bonds.

Gibbs free energy A thermodynamic state function that combines enthalpy and entropy, in the form $G = H - TS$. For a change occurring at constant temperature and pressure, the change in free energy is $\Delta G = \Delta H - T\Delta S$.

glass An amorphous solid formed by fusion of SiO_2, CaO, and Na_2O. Other oxides may also be used to form glasses with differing characteristics.

glucose A polyhydroxy aldehyde whose formula is $CH_2OH(CHOH)_4CHO$; it is the most important of the monosaccharides.

Graham's law A law stating that the rate of effusion of a gas is inversely proportional to the square root of its molecular weight.

gray (Gy) The SI unit for radiation dose corresponding to the absorption of 1 J of energy per kilogram of biological material; 1 Gy = 100 rads.

green chemistry Chemistry that promotes the design and application of chemical products and processes that are compatible with human health and that preserve the environment.

greenhouse gases Gases in an atmosphere that absorb and emit infrared radiation (radiant heat), "trapping" heat in the atmosphere.

ground state The lowest-energy, or most stable, state.

group Elements that are in the same column of the periodic table; elements within the same group or family exhibit similarities in their chemical behavior.

Haber process The catalyst system and conditions of temperature and pressure developed by Fritz Haber and coworkers for the formation of NH_3 from H_2 and N_2.

half-life The time required for the concentration of a reactant substance to decrease to half its initial value; the time required for half of a sample of a particular radioisotope to decay.

halogens Members of group 7A in the periodic table.

hard water Water that contains appreciable concentrations of Ca^{2+} and Mg^{2+}; these ions react with soaps to form an insoluble material.

heat The flow of energy from a body at higher temperature to one at lower temperature when they are placed in thermal contact.

heat capacity The quantity of heat required to raise the temperature of a sample of matter by 1 °C (or 1 K).

heat of fusion The enthalpy change, ΔH, for melting a solid.

heat of sublimation The enthalpy change, ΔH, for vaporization of a solid.

heat of vaporization The enthalpy change, ΔH, for vaporization of a liquid.

Henry's law A law stating that the concentration of a gas in a solution, S_g, is proportional to the pressure of gas over the solution: $S_g = kP_g$.

Hess's law The heat evolved in a given process can be expressed as the sum of the heats of several processes that, when added, yield the process of interest.

heterogeneous catalyst A catalyst that is in a different phase from that of the reactant substances.

heterogeneous equilibrium The equilibrium established between substances in two or more different phases, for example, between a gas and a solid or between a solid and a liquid.

hole A vacancy in the valence band of a semiconductor, created by doping.

homogeneous catalyst A catalyst that is in the same phase as the reactant substances.

Hund's rule A rule stating that electrons occupy degenerate orbitals in such a way as to maximize the number of electrons with the same spin. In other words, each orbital has one electron placed in it before pairing of electrons in orbitals occurs.

hybridization The mixing of different types of atomic orbitals to produce a set of equivalent hybrid orbitals.

hybrid orbital An orbital that results from the mixing of different kinds of atomic orbitals on the same atom. For example, an sp^3 hybrid results from the mixing, or hybridizing, of one s orbital and three p orbitals.

hydration Solvation when the solvent is water.

hydride ion An ion formed by the addition of an electron to a hydrogen atom: H^-.

hydrocarbons Compounds composed of only carbon and hydrogen.

hydrogen bonding Bonding that results from intermolecular attractions between molecules containing hydrogen bonded to an electronegative element. The most important examples involve OH, NH, and HF.

hydrolysis A reaction with water. When a cation or anion reacts with water, it changes the pH.

hydrophobic Water repelling. The term is often used to describe a type of colloid.

hypothesis A tentative explanation of a series of observations or of a natural law.

ideal gas A hypothetical gas whose pressure, volume, and temperature behavior is completely described by the ideal-gas equation.

ideal-gas equation An equation of state for gases that embodies Boyle's law, Charles's law, and Avogadro's hypothesis in the form $PV = nRT$.

indicator A substance added to a solution that changes color when the added solute has reacted with all the solute present in solution. The most common type of indicator is an acid–base indicator whose color changes as a function of pH.

instantaneous rate The reaction rate at a particular time as opposed to the average rate over an interval of time.

intermediate A substance formed in one elementary step of a multistep mechanism and consumed in another; it is neither a reactant nor an ultimate product of the overall reaction.

intermolecular forces The short-range attractive forces operating between the particles that make up the units of a liquid or solid substance. These same forces also cause gases to liquefy or solidify at low temperatures and high pressures.

internal energy The total energy possessed by a system. When a system undergoes a change, the change in internal energy, ΔE, is defined as the heat, q, added to the system, plus the work, w, done on the system by its surroundings: $\Delta E = q + w$.

ion Electrically charged atom or group of atoms (polyatomic ion); ions can be positively or negatively charged, depending on whether electrons are lost (positive) or gained (negative) by the atoms.

ion–dipole force The force that exists between an ion and a neutral polar molecule that possesses a permanent dipole moment.

ion exchange A process by which ions in solution are exchanged for other ions held on the surface of an ion-exchange resin; the exchange of a hard-water cation such as Ca^{2+} for a soft-water cation such as Na^+ is used to soften water.

ionic bond A bond between oppositely charged ions. The ions are formed from atoms by transfer of one or more electrons.

ionic compound A compound composed of cations and anions.

ionic hydrides Compounds formed when hydrogen reacts with alkali metals and also the heavier alkaline earths (Ca, Sr, and Ba); these compounds contain the hydride ion, H^-.

ionic solids Solids that are composed of ions.

ionization energy The energy required to remove an electron from a gaseous atom when the atom is in its ground state.

ion-product constant For water, K_w is the product of the aquated hydrogen ion and hydroxide ion concentrations: $[H^+][OH^-] = K_w = 1.0 \times 10^{-14}$ at 25 °C.

irreversible process A process that cannot be reversed to restore both the system and its surroundings to their original states. Any spontaneous process is irreversible.

isoelectronic series A series of atoms, ions, or molecules having the same number of electrons.

isomers Compounds whose molecules have the same overall composition but different structures.

isothermal process One that occurs at constant temperature.

isotopes Atoms of the same element containing different numbers of neutrons and therefore having different masses.

joule (J) The SI unit of energy, 1 kg-m^2/s^2. A related unit is the calorie: 4.184 J = 1 cal.

Kelvin scale The absolute temperature scale; the SI unit for temperature is the kelvin. Zero on the Kelvin scale corresponds to −273.15 °C.

ketone A compound in which the carbonyl group (C=O) occurs at the interior of a carbon chain and is therefore flanked by carbon atoms.

kinetic energy The energy that an object possesses by virtue of its motion.

kinetic-molecular theory A set of assumptions about the nature of gases. These assumptions, when translated into mathematical form, yield the ideal-gas equation.

lanthanide (rare earth) element Element in which the $4f$ subshell is only partially occupied.

lattice energy The energy required to separate completely the ions in an ionic solid.

law of mass action The rules by which the equilibrium constant is expressed in terms of the concentrations of reactants and products, in accordance with the balanced chemical equation for the reaction.

Le Châtelier's principle A principle stating that when we disturb a system at chemical equilibrium, the relative concentrations of reactants and products shift so as to partially undo the effects of the disturbance.

Lewis structure A representation of covalent bonding in a molecule that is drawn using Lewis symbols. Shared electron pairs are shown as lines, and unshared electron pairs are shown as pairs of dots. Only the valence-shell electrons are shown.

Lewis symbol (electron-dot symbol) The chemical symbol for an element, with a dot for each valence electron.

lime-soda process A method used in large-scale water treatment to reduce water hardness by removing Mg^{2+} and Ca^{2+}. The substances added to the water are lime, CaO [or slaked lime, $Ca(OH)_2$], and soda ash, Na_2CO_3, in amounts determined by the concentrations of the undesired ions.

line spectrum A spectrum that contains radiation at only certain specific wavelengths.

liquid Matter that has a distinct volume but no specific shape.

liquid crystal A substance that exhibits one or more partially ordered liquid phases above the melting point of the solid form. By contrast, in nonliquid crystalline substances the liquid phase that forms upon melting is completely unordered.

lock-and-key model A model of enzyme action in which the substrate molecule is pictured as fitting rather specifically into the active site on the enzyme. It is assumed that in being bound to the active site, the substrate is somehow activated for reaction.

main-group elements Elements in the s and p blocks of the periodic table.

mass A measure of the amount of material in an object. It measures the resistance of an object to being moved. In SI units, mass is measured in kilograms.

mass percentage The number of grams of solute in each 100 g of solution.

mass spectrometer An instrument used to measure the precise masses and relative amounts of atomic and molecular ions.

matter Anything that occupies space and has mass; the physical material of the universe.

matter waves The term used to describe the wave characteristics of a moving particle.

mean free path The average distance traveled by a gas molecule between collisions.

metallic bond Bonding, usually in solid metals, in which the bonding electrons are relatively free to move throughout the three-dimensional structure.

metallic elements (metals) Elements that are usually solids at room temperature, exhibit high electrical and heat conductivity, and appear lustrous. Most of the elements in the periodic table are metals.

metallic solids Solids that are composed of metal atoms.

metalloids Elements that lie along the diagonal line separating the metals from the nonmetals in the periodic table; the properties of metalloids are intermediate between those of metals and nonmetals.

metric system A system of measurement used in science and in most countries. The meter and the gram are examples of metric units.

microstate The state of a system at a particular instant; one of many possible energetically equivalent ways to arrange the components of a system to achieve a particular state.

mineral A solid, inorganic substance occurring in nature, such as calcium carbonate, which occurs as calcite.

mixture A combination of two or more substances in which each substance retains its own chemical identity.

molar heat capacity The heat required to raise the temperature of one mole of a substance by 1 °C.

molarity The concentration of a solution expressed as moles of solute per liter of solution; abbreviated M.

molar mass The mass of one mole of a substance in grams; it is numerically equal to the formula weight in atomic mass units.

mole A collection of Avogadro's number (6.022×10^{23}) of objects; for example, a mole of H_2O is 6.022×10^{23} H_2O molecules.

molecular compound A compound that consists of molecules.

molecular equation A chemical equation in which the formula for each substance is written without regard for whether it is an electrolyte or a nonelectrolyte.

molecular formula A chemical formula that indicates the actual number of atoms of each element in one molecule of a substance.

molecular geometry The arrangement in space of the atoms of a molecule.

molecularity The number of molecules that participate as reactants in an elementary reaction.

molecular orbital (MO) An allowed state for an electron in a molecule. According to molecular-orbital theory, a molecular orbital is entirely analogous to an atomic orbital, which is an allowed state for an electron in an atom. Most bonding molecular orbitals can be classified as σ or π, depending on the disposition of electron density with respect to the internuclear axis.

molecular-orbital diagram A diagram that shows the energies of molecular orbitals relative to the atomic orbitals from which they are derived; also called an **energy-level diagram**.

molecular-orbital theory A theory that accounts for the allowed states for electrons in molecules.

molecular solids Solids that are composed of molecules.

molecular weight The mass of the collection of atoms represented by the chemical formula for a molecule.

molecule A chemical combination of two or more atoms.

mole fraction The ratio of the number of moles of one component of a mixture to the total moles of all components; abbreviated X, with a subscript to identify the component.

momentum The product of the mass, m, and velocity, v, of an object.

monomers Molecules with low molecular weights, which can be joined together (polymerized) to form a polymer.

nanomaterial A solid whose dimensions range from 1 to 100 nm and whose properties differ from those of a bulk material with the same composition.

natural gas A naturally occurring mixture of gaseous hydrocarbon compounds composed of hydrogen and carbon.

nematic liquid crystalline phase A liquid crystal in which the molecules are aligned in the same general direction, along their long axes, but in which the ends of the molecules are not aligned.

net ionic equation A chemical equation for a solution reaction in which soluble strong electrolytes are written as ions and spectator ions are omitted.

neutralization reaction A reaction in which an acid and a base react in stoichiometrically equivalent amounts; the neutralization reaction between an acid and a metal hydroxide produces water and a salt.

neutron An electrically neutral particle found in the nucleus of an atom; it has approximately the same mass as a proton.

noble gases Members of group 8A in the periodic table.

node Points in an atom at which the electron density is zero. For example, the node in a $2s$ orbital is a spherical surface.

nonbonding pair In a Lewis structure a pair of electrons assigned completely to one atom; also called a lone pair.

nonelectrolyte A substance that does not ionize in water and consequently gives a nonconducting solution.

nonmetallic elements (nonmetals) Elements in the upper right corner of the periodic table; nonmetals differ from metals in their physical and chemical properties.

nonpolar covalent bond A covalent bond in which the electrons are shared equally.

normal boiling point The boiling point at 1 atm pressure.

normal melting point The melting point at 1 atm pressure.

nuclear model Model of the atom with a nucleus containing protons and neutrons and with electrons in the space outside the nucleus.

nucleic acids Polymers of high molecular weight that carry genetic information and control protein synthesis.

nucleon A particle found in the nucleus of an atom.

nucleus The very small, very dense, positively charged portion of an atom; it is composed of protons and neutrons.

octet rule A rule stating that bonded atoms tend to possess or share a total of eight valence-shell electrons.

orbital An allowed energy state of an electron in the quantum mechanical model of the atom; the term *orbital* is also used to describe the spatial distribution of the electron. An orbital is defined by the values of three quantum numbers: n, l, and m_l.

organic chemistry The study of carbon-containing compounds, typically containing carbon–carbon bonds.

osmosis The net movement of solvent through a semipermeable membrane toward the solution with greater solute concentration.

osmotic pressure The pressure that must be applied to a solution to stop osmosis from pure solvent into the solution.

overall reaction order The sum of the reaction orders of all the reactants appearing in the rate expression when the rate can be expressed as rate $= k[A]^a[B]^b \ldots$.

overlap The extent to which atomic orbitals on different atoms share the same region of space. When the overlap between two orbitals is large, a strong bond may be formed.

oxidation A process in which a substance loses one or more electrons.

oxidation number (oxidation state) A positive or negative whole number assigned to an element in a molecule or ion on the basis of a set of formal rules; to some degree it reflects the positive or negative character of that atom.

oxidation-reduction (redox) reaction A chemical reaction in which the oxidation states of certain atoms change.

oxidizing agent, or oxidant The substance that is reduced and thereby causes the oxidation of some other substance in an oxidation-reduction reaction.

oxyanion A polyatomic anion that contains one or more oxygen atoms.

ozone The name given to O_3, an allotrope of oxygen.

partial pressure The pressure exerted by a particular gas in a mixture.

parts per billion (ppb) The concentration of a solution in grams of solute per 10^9 (billion) grams of solution; equals micrograms of solute per liter of solution for aqueous solutions.

parts per million (ppm) The concentration of a solution in grams of solute per 10^6 (million) grams of solution; equals milligrams of solute per liter of solution for aqueous solutions.

pascal (Pa) The SI unit of pressure: 1 Pa $=$ 1 N/m^2.

Pauli exclusion principle A rule stating that no two electrons in an atom may have the same four quantum numbers (n, l, m_l, and m_s). As a reflection of this principle, there can be no more than two electrons in any one atomic orbital.

period The row of elements that lie in a horizontal row in the periodic table.

periodic table The arrangement of elements in order of increasing atomic number, with elements having similar properties placed in vertical columns.

petroleum A naturally occurring combustible liquid composed of hundreds of hydrocarbons and other organic compounds.

phase change The conversion of a substance from one state of matter to another. The phase changes we consider are melting and freezing (solid $\rightleftharpoons$ liquid), sublimation and deposition, and vaporization and condensation (liquid $\rightleftharpoons$ gas).

phase diagram A graphic representation of the equilibria among the solid, liquid, and gaseous phases of a substance as a function of temperature and pressure.

photochemical smog A complex mixture of undesirable substances produced by the action of sunlight on an urban atmosphere polluted with automobile emissions. The major starting ingredients are nitrogen oxides and organic substances, notably olefins and aldehydes.

photodissociation The breaking of a molecule into two or more neutral fragments as a result of absorption of light.

photoelectric effect The emission of electrons from a metal surface induced by light.

photoionization The removal of an electron from an atom or molecule by absorption of light.

photon The smallest increment (a quantum) of radiant energy; a photon of light with frequency ν has an energy equal to $h\nu$.

pi (π) bond A covalent bond in which electron density is concentrated above and below the internuclear axis.

Planck's constant (h) The constant that relates the energy and frequency of a photon, $E = h\nu$. Its value is 6.626×10^{-34} J-s.

plastic A material that can be formed into particular shapes by application of heat and pressure.

polar covalent bond A covalent bond in which the electrons are not shared equally.

polarizability The ease with which the electron cloud of an atom or a molecule is distorted by an outside influence, thereby inducing a dipole moment.

polar molecule A molecule that possesses a nonzero dipole moment.

polymer A large molecule of high molecular mass, formed by the joining together, or polymerization, of a large number of molecules of low molecular mass. The individual molecules forming the polymer are called monomers.

potential energy The energy that an object possesses as a result of its composition or its position with respect to another object.

pressure A measure of the force exerted on a unit area. In chemistry, pressure is often expressed in units of atmospheres (atm) or torr: 760 torr $=$ 1 atm; in SI units pressure is expressed in pascals (Pa).

probability density (ψ^2) A value that represents the probability that an electron will be found at a given point in space. Also called **electron density**.

protein A biopolymer formed from amino acids.

quantum The smallest increment of radiant energy that may be absorbed or emitted; the magnitude of radiant energy is $h\nu$.

radial probability function The probability that the electron will be found at a certain distance from the nucleus.

rare earth element See **lanthanide element**.

rate constant A constant of proportionality between the reaction rate and the concentrations of reactants that appear in the rate law.

rate-determining step The slowest elementary step in a reaction mechanism.

rate law An equation that relates the reaction rate to the concentrations of reactants (and sometimes of products also).

reaction mechanism A detailed picture, or model, of how the reaction occurs; that is, the order in which bonds are broken and formed and the changes in relative positions of the atoms as the reaction proceeds.

reaction order The power to which the concentration of a reactant is raised in a rate law.

reaction quotient (Q) The value that is obtained when concentrations of reactants and products are inserted into the equilibrium expression. If the concentrations are equilibrium concentrations, $Q = K$; otherwise, $Q \neq K$.

reaction rate A measure of the decrease in concentration of a reactant or the increase in concentration of a product with time.

reduction A process in which a substance gains one or more electrons.

renewable energy sources Energy such as solar energy, wind energy, and hydroelectric energy derived from essentially inexhaustible sources.

resonance structures (resonance forms) Individual Lewis structures in cases where two or more Lewis structures are equally good descriptions of a single molecule. The resonance structures in such an instance are "averaged" to give a more accurate description of the real molecule.

reverse osmosis The process by which water molecules move under high pressure through a semipermeable membrane from the more concentrated to the less concentrated solution.

reversible process A process that can go back and forth between states along exactly the same path; a system at equilibrium is reversible if equilibrium can be shifted by an infinitesimal modification of a variable such as temperature.

root-mean-square (rms) speed (μ) The square root of the average of the squared speeds of the gas molecules in a gas sample.

rotational motion Movement of a molecule as though it is spinning like a top.

salinity A measure of the salt content of seawater, brine, or brackish water. It is equal to the mass in grams of dissolved salts present in 1 kg of seawater.

saponification Hydrolysis of an ester in the presence of a base.

second law of thermodynamics A statement of our experience that there is a direction to the way events occur in nature. When a process occurs spontaneously in one direction, it is nonspontaneous in the reverse direction. It is possible to state the second law in many different forms, but they all relate back to the same idea about spontaneity. One of the most common statements found in chemical contexts is that in any spontaneous process the entropy of the universe increases.

second-order reaction A reaction in which the overall reaction order (the sum of the concentration-term exponents) in the rate law is 2.

sigma (σ) bond A covalent bond in which electron density is concentrated along the internuclear axis.

sigma (σ) molecular orbital A molecular orbital that centers the electron density about an imaginary line passing through two nuclei.

single bond A covalent bond involving one electron pair.

smectic liquid crystalline phase A liquid crystal in which the molecules are aligned along their long axes and arranged in sheets, with the ends of the molecules aligned. There are several different kinds of smectic phases.

specific heat (C_s) The heat capacity of 1 g of a substance; the heat required to raise the temperature of 1 g of a substance by 1 °C.

spectrum The distribution among various wavelengths of the radiant energy emitted or absorbed by an object.

spin magnetic quantum number (m_s) A quantum number associated with the electron spin; it may have values of $+\frac{1}{2}$ or $-\frac{1}{2}$.

spontaneous process A process that is capable of proceeding in a given direction, as written or described, without needing to be driven by an outside source of energy. A process may be spontaneous even though it is very slow.

standard atmospheric pressure Defined as 760 torr or, in SI units, 101.325 kPa.

standard enthalpy change ($\Delta H°$) The change in enthalpy in a process when all reactants and products are in their stable forms at 1 atm pressure and a specified temperature, commonly 25 °C.

standard enthalpy of formation ($\Delta H_f°$) The change in enthalpy that accompanies the formation of one mole of a substance from its elements, with all substances in their standard states.

standard free energy of formation ($\Delta G_f°$) The change in free energy associated with the formation of a substance from its elements under standard conditions.

standard molar entropy ($S°$) The entropy value for a mole of a substance in its standard state.

standard solution A solution of known concentration.

standard temperature and pressure (STP) Defined as 0 °C and 1 atm pressure; frequently used as reference conditions for a gas.

starch The general name given to a group of polysaccharides that acts as energy-storage substances in plants.

state function A property of a system that is determined by its state or condition and not by how it got to that state; its value is fixed when temperature, pressure, composition, and physical form are specified; P, V, T, E, and H are state functions.

stratosphere The region of the atmosphere directly above the troposphere.

structural formula A formula that shows not only the number and kinds of atoms in the molecule but also the arrangement (connections) of the atoms.

structural isomers Compounds possessing the same formula but differing in the bonding arrangements of the atoms.

subshell One or more orbitals with the same set of quantum numbers n and l. For example, we speak of the $2p$ subshell ($n = 2$, $l = 1$), which is composed of three orbitals ($2p_x$, $2p_y$, and $2p_z$).

substitution reactions Reactions in which one atom (or group of atoms) replaces another atom (or group) within a molecule; substitution reactions are typical for alkanes and aromatic hydrocarbons.

substrate A substance that undergoes a reaction at the active site in an enzyme.

surface tension The intermolecular, cohesive attraction that causes a liquid to minimize its surface area.

surroundings In thermodynamics, everything that lies outside the system that we study.

system In thermodynamics, the portion of the universe that we single out for study. We must be careful to state exactly what the system contains and what transfers of energy it may have with its surroundings.

termolecular reaction An elementary reaction that involves three molecules. Termolecular reactions are rare.

tertiary structure The overall shape of a large protein, specifically, the manner in which sections of the protein fold back upon themselves or intertwine.

thermochemistry The relationship between chemical reactions and energy changes.

thermodynamics The study of energy and its transformation.

thermoplastic A polymeric material that can be readily reshaped by application of heat and pressure.

thermosetting plastic A plastic that, once formed in a particular mold, is not readily reshaped by application of heat and pressure.

third law of thermodynamics A law stating that the entropy of a pure, crystalline solid at absolute zero temperature is zero: $S(0 \text{ K}) = 0$.

torr A unit of pressure (1 torr = 1 mm Hg).

transition elements (transition metals) Elements in which the d orbitals are partially occupied.

transition state (activated complex) The particular arrangement of reactant and product molecules at the point of maximum energy in the rate-determining step of a reaction.

translational motion Movement in which an entire molecule moves in a definite direction.

triple bond A covalent bond involving three electron pairs.

troposphere The region of Earth's atmosphere extending from the surface to about 12 km altitude.

uncertainty principle A principle stating there is an inherent uncertainty in the precision with which we can simultaneously specify the position and momentum of a particle. This uncertainty is significant only for particles of extremely small mass, such as electrons.

unimolecular reaction An elementary reaction that involves a single molecule.

unit cell The smallest portion of a crystal that reproduces the structure of the entire crystal when repeated in different directions in space. It is the repeating unit or building block of the crystal lattice.

valence band A band of closely spaced molecular orbitals that is essentially fully occupied by electrons.

valence-bond theory A model of chemical bonding in which an electron-pair bond is formed between two atoms by the overlap of orbitals on the two atoms.

valence electrons The outermost electrons of an atom; those that occupy orbitals not occupied in the nearest noble-gas element of lower atomic number. The valence electrons are the ones the atom uses in bonding.

valence orbitals Orbitals that contain the outer-shell electrons of an atom.

valence-shell electron-pair repulsion (VSEPR) model A model that accounts for the geometric arrangements of shared and unshared electron pairs around a central atom in terms of the repulsions between electron pairs.

van der Waals equation An equation of state for nonideal gases that is based on adding corrections to the ideal-gas equation. The correction terms account for intermolecular forces of attraction and for the volumes occupied by the gas molecules themselves.

vapor Gaseous state of any substance that normally exists as a liquid or solid.

vapor pressure The pressure exerted by a vapor in equilibrium with its liquid or solid phase.

vibrational motion Movement of the atoms within a molecule in which they move periodically toward and away from one another.

viscosity A measure of the resistance of fluids to flow.

volatile Tending to evaporate readily.

vulcanization The process of cross-linking polymer chains in rubber.

wave function A mathematical description of an allowed energy state (an orbital) for an electron in the quantum mechanical model of the atom; it is usually symbolized by the Greek letter ψ.

wavelength The distance between identical points on successive waves.

work The movement of an object against some force.

PHOTO AND ART CREDITS

INDEX

Useful Conversion Factors and Relationships

Length
SI unit: meter (m)

$$1 \text{ km} = 0.62137 \text{ mi}$$
$$1 \text{ mi} = 5280 \text{ ft}$$
$$= 1.6093 \text{ km}$$
$$1 \text{ m} = 1.0936 \text{ yd}$$
$$1 \text{ in.} = 2.54 \text{ cm (exactly)}$$
$$1 \text{ cm} = 0.39370 \text{ in.}$$
$$1 \text{ Å} = 10^{-10} \text{ m}$$

Mass
SI unit: kilogram (kg)

$$1 \text{ kg} = 2.2046 \text{ lb}$$
$$1 \text{ lb} = 453.59 \text{ g}$$
$$= 16 \text{ oz}$$
$$1 \text{ amu} = 1.660538782 \times 10^{-24} \text{ g}$$

Temperature
SI unit: Kelvin (K)

$$0 \text{ K} = -273.15 \text{ °C}$$
$$= -459.67 \text{ °F}$$
$$\text{K} = \text{°C} + 273.15$$
$$\text{°C} = \tfrac{5}{9}(\text{°F} - 32°)$$
$$\text{°F} = \tfrac{9}{5}\text{°C} + 32°$$

Energy (derived)
SI unit: Joule (J)

$$1 \text{ J} = 1 \text{ kg-m}^2/\text{s}^2$$
$$= 0.2390 \text{ cal}$$
$$= 1 \text{ C-V}$$
$$1 \text{ cal} = 4.184 \text{ J}$$
$$1 \text{ eV} = 1.602 \times 10^{-19} \text{ J}$$

Pressure (derived)
SI unit: Pascal (Pa)

$$1 \text{ Pa} = 1 \text{ N/m}^2$$
$$= 1 \text{ kg/m-s}^2$$
$$1 \text{ atm} = 1.01325 \times 10^5 \text{ Pa}$$
$$= 760 \text{ torr}$$
$$= 14.70 \text{ lb/in}^2$$
$$1 \text{ bar} = 10^5 \text{ Pa}$$
$$1 \text{ torr} = 1 \text{ mm Hg}$$

Volume (derived)
SI unit: cubic meter (m³)

$$1 \text{ L} = 10^{-3} \text{ m}^3$$
$$= 1 \text{ dm}^3$$
$$= 10^3 \text{ cm}^3$$
$$= 1.0567 \text{ qt}$$
$$1 \text{ gal} = 4 \text{ qt}$$
$$= 3.7854 \text{ L}$$
$$1 \text{ cm}^3 = 1 \text{ mL}$$
$$1 \text{ in}^3 = 16.4 \text{ cm}^3$$

Color Chart for Common Elements

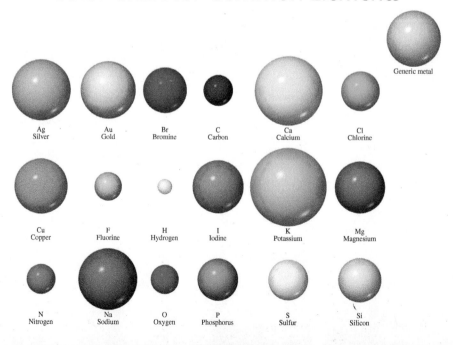